Photonic Crystals and Light Localization in the 21st Century

NATO Science Series

A Series presenting the results of activities sponsored by the NATO Science Committee. The Series is published by IOS Press and Kluwer Academic Publishers, in conjunction with the NATO Scientific Affairs Division.

A. Life Sciences	IOS Press
B. Physics	Kluwer Academic Publishers
C. Mathematical and Physical Sciences	Kluwer Academic Publishers
D. Behavioural and Social Sciences	Kluwer Academic Publishers
E. Applied Sciences	Kluwer Academic Publishers
F. Computer and Systems Sciences	IOS Press
1. Disarmament Technologies	Kluwer Academic Publishers
2. Environmental Security	Kluwer Academic Publishers
3. High Technology	Kluwer Academic Publishers
4. Science and Technology Policy	IOS Press
5. Computer Networking	IOS Press

NATO-PCO-DATA BASE

The NATO Science Series continues the series of books published formerly in the NATO ASI Series. An electronic index to the NATO ASI Series provides full bibliographical references (with keywords and/or abstracts) to more than 50000 contributions from international scientists published in all sections of the NATO ASI Series.
Access to the NATO-PCO-DATA BASE is possible via CD-ROM "NATO-PCO-DATA BASE" with user-friendly retrieval software in English, French and German (WTV GmbH and DATAWARE Technologies Inc. 1989).

The CD-ROM of the NATO ASI Series can be ordered from: PCO, Overijse, Belgium

Series C: Mathematical and Physical Sciences – Vol. 563

Photonic Crystals and Light Localization in the 21st Century

edited by

Costas M. Soukoulis
Ames Laboratory and Department of Physics and Astronomy,
Iowa State University,
Ames, Iowa, U.S.A.

Kluwer Academic Publishers
Dordrecht / Boston / London

Published in cooperation with NATO Scientific Affairs Division

Proceedings of the NATO Advanced Study Institute on
Photonic Crystals and Light Localization
Crete, Greece
June 18–30, 2000

A C.I.P. Catalogue record for this book is available from the Library of Congress.

ISBN 0-7923-6947-5

Published by Kluwer Academic Publishers,
P.O. Box 17, 3300 AA Dordrecht, The Netherlands.

Sold and distributed in North, Central and South America
by Kluwer Academic Publishers,
101 Philip Drive, Norwell, MA 02061, U.S.A.

In all other countries, sold and distributed
by Kluwer Academic Publishers,
P.O. Box 322, 3300 AH Dordrecht, The Netherlands.

Printed on acid-free paper

Printed in the Netherlands.

TABLE OF CONTENTS

RANDOM LASERS

LOCALIZATION OF LIGHT

PHOTONIC CRYSTALS AND NONLINEARITIES

PREFACE

This volume contains papers presented at the NATO Advanced Study Institute (ASI) *Photonic Crystals and Light Localization* held at the Creta Maris Hotel in Limin Hersonissou, Crete, June 18-30, 2000.

Photonic crystals offer unique ways to tailor light and the propagation of electromagnetic waves (EM). In analogy to electrons in a crystal, EM waves propagating in a structure with a periodically modulated dielectric constant are organized into photonic bands, separated by gaps where propagating states are forbidden. There have been proposals for novel applications of these photonic band gap (PBG) crystals, with operating frequencies ranging from microwave to the optical regime, that include zero-threshold lasers, low-loss resonators and cavities, and efficient microwave antennas. Spontaneous emission, suppressed for photons in the photonic band gap, offers novel approaches to manipulate the EM field and create high-efficiency light-emitting structures. Innovative ways to manipulate light can have a profound influence on science and technology.

The objectives of this NATO-ASI were (i) to assess the state-of-the-art in experimental and theoretical studies of photonic crystals, light localization, and random lasers; (ii) to discuss how such structures can be fabricated to improve technologies in different areas of physics and engineering; and (iii) to identify problems and set goals for further research. This was accomplished by the excellent presentations given by the lecturers and invited speakers, who paid special attention to the tutorial aspects of their contributions. The location of the NATO-ASI was a perfect and idyllic setting, which allowed the participants to develop scientific interactions and friendships. All objectives were met in the ASI and three areas within the field of photonic crystals were identified as the most promising and hope to receive considerable attention within the next few years.

The first area of effort is in materials fabrication. This involves the creation of high quality, low loss, periodic dielectric structures either in 3D or 2D, especially on the optical scale. However, optical photonic crystals may be best fabricated from self-organizing materials and techniques, than with conventional techniques used in the semiconductor industry.

The second area of consideration is applications and spin offs, which may have technological and economic importance. Several contributors presented possible applications of PBGs in microwave and optical regimes. Microwave mirrors, directional antennas, resonators (especially for the 2 GHz region), filters, switches, waveguides, Y splitters, and resonant microcavities were discussed. It was also pointed out that 2D photonic crystals, with a waveguide confinement in the perpendicular direction, might yield much richer structures and designs for optical applications.

Finally, the third area is the studies of fundamentally new physical phenomena in condensed matter physics and quantum optics associated with localization, random lasers, and photonic band gaps.

This book compiles the lectures presented at the *Photonic Crystals and Light Localization* NATO ASI meeting and presents an excellent review of the recent developments of this rapidly expanding field. The lectures cover theoretical, experimental, and the application aspects of photonic crystals, light localization, and random lasers. This collection of papers is roughly balanced between theory and experiment. It contains chapters that present the latest research results appropriate of an advanced research workshop, as well as results that review a particular field, with the goal of providing the reader with a sufficient overview and extensive references for a more detailed study.

The book is divided into eight chapters representing the various topics discussed at the ASI. Chapter I gives a historical overview of the PBG field, including acoustic and elastic PBGs. Chapter II provides a detailed experimental review of all the different techniques in fabricating photonic crystals in the infrared and optical wavelengths. Some applications to optoelectronic devices are presented in this chapter. Chapter III provides an up-to-date review of the experimental efforts in fabricating photonic crystals by self-organization. Chapter IV provides a detailed review of the potential application of photonic crystals, with specific examples in both the millimeter and optical regime. Chapter V covers the theoretical and experimental developments of metallic photonic crystal structures. Left-handed materials are discussed in this chapter. Chapter VI provides a detailed review of random lasers, which are disordered systems that both scatter and amplify light. Chapter VII provides an excellent review of the localization of light field. Finally, Chapter VIII covers some extra work on photonic crystals and non-linearities. We hope this book will not only prove interesting and stimulating to researchers active in the PBG field, but also serve as a useful reference to non-specialists, because of the introductory lectures.

The advanced study institute was made possible through the generous support of the NATO Scientific Affairs Division, Brussels, Belgium and the Ames Laboratory, operated by the U.S. Department of Energy by Iowa State University under Contract No. W-7405-Eng-82. Support from University of Crete, FORTH, Greek General Secretariat of Research and Technology, the European Office of the U.S. Army Research Office, and NSF is also acknowledged. I would like to thank the organizing committee, E. N. Economou, S. John, and A. Lagendijk for their valuable help on the organization of the program and the workshop. I would like to express my appreciation to Rebecca Shivvers, who prepared the conference materials and edited the manuscripts for this book. Finally, I wish to express my deepest appreciation to all the participants for making this a lively and enjoyable conference.

C. M. Soukoulis
Physics and Astronomy Department
Ames Laboratory
Iowa State University
Ames, Iowa 50011 U.S.A.

NOVELTIES OF LIGHT WITH PHOTONIC CRYSTALS

J. D. Joannopoulos, S. Fan, A. Mekis, and S. G. Johnson

Department of Physics and Center for Materials Science and Engineering
Massachusetts Institute of Technology
Cambridge, MA 02139–4307, USA

Abstract

Within the past several years "photonic crystals" have emerged as a new class of materials providing capabilities along new dimensions for the control and manipulation of light. These materials are viewed ideally as a composite of a periodic array of macroscopic dielectric or metallic scatterers in a homogeneous dielectric matrix. A photonic crystal affects the properties of a photon in much the same way that a semiconductor affects the properties of an electron. Consequently, photons in photonic crystals can have band structures, localized defect modes, surface modes, etc. This new ability to mold and guide light leads naturally to many novel phenomena associated with light — phenomena that have not been possible with traditional materials.

INTRODUCTION

For the past 50 years, semiconductor physics has played a vital role in almost every aspect of modern technology. Advances in this field have allowed scientists to tailor the conducting properties of certain materials and have initiated the transistor revolution in electronics. New research suggests that we may now be able to tailor the properties of light. The key in achieving this goal lies in the use of a new class of materials called photonic crystals [1]. The underlying concept behind these materials stems from the pioneering work of Yablonovitch [2] and John [3]. The basic idea consists in designing materials that can affect the properties of photons in much the same way that ordinary

C.M. Soukoulis (ed.), Photonic Crystals and Light Localization in the 21st Century, 1–24.

semiconductor crystals affect the properties of electrons. This is achieved by constructing a crystal consisting of a periodic array of macroscopic uniform dielectric (or possibly metallic) "atoms." In this crystal photons can be described in terms of a bandstructure, as in the case of electrons. Of particular interest is a photonic crystal whose bandstructure possesses a complete photonic band gap (PBG). A PBG defines a range of frequencies for which light is forbidden to exist inside the crystal. Forbidden, that is, unless there is a defect in the otherwise perfect crystal. A defect could lead to localized photonic states in the gap, whose shapes and properties would be dictated by the nature of the defect. Moreover, a very significant and attractive difference between photonic crystals and electronic semiconductor crystals is the former's inherent ability to provide complete tunability. A defect in a photonic crystal could, in principle, be designed to be of any size, shape or form and could be chosen to have any of a wide variety of dielectric constants. Thus, defect states in the gap could be tuned to any frequency and spatial extent of design interest. In addition to tuning the frequency, one also has control over the symmetry of the localized photonic state. All of these capabilities provide a new "dimension" in our ability to "mold" or control the properties of light. In this sense defects are *good* things in photonic crystals and therein lies the exciting potential of photonic crystals. Photonic crystals should allow us to manipulate light in ways that have not been possible before. The purpose of this paper is to highlight some of these novel possibilities.

Experimentalists have begun exploring the possibilities of fabricating such periodic structures with semiconductor-based, insulator-based, and metallodielectric-based materials at micrometer and submicrometer lengthscales. Exciting recent examples of fabricated two- and three-dimensionally periodic structures are presented elsewhere in these proceedings. In this paper we shall introduce concepts and properties that are valid, in general, in three-dimensional photonic crystals, but for the sake of simplicity and ease of visualization all our examples will involve two-dimensional photonic crystals. For definiteness, we consider a perfect array of infinitely long dielectric rods located on a square lattice of lattice constant a and investigate the propagation of light in the plane normal to the rods. The rods have a radius of $0.20a$, and a refractive index of 3.4 (which corresponds to GaAs at a wavelength of 1.55 micron). Such a structure possesses a complete gap between the first and the second transverse magnetic (TM) modes. (For TM modes, the electric field is parallel to the rods). Once we have a band gap, we can introduce a defect inside the crystal to trap or localize light. In particular, we shall investigate defects and defect-complexes that can correspond to specific components and devices such as waveguides, waveguide bends, microcavities, waveguide-crossings, waveguide-splitters, channel-drop filters, and input/output couplers. Finally, we shall conclude this paper, with a brief discussion of some of the interesting properties that are associated with *radiation losses* when one is dealing with photonic crystal systems that do *not* possess a complete photonic band gap.

PHOTONIC CRYSTAL WAVEGUIDES

By making a line defect, we can create an extended mode that can be used to guide light. Using photonic crystals to guide light constitutes a novel mechanism. Traditionally, waveguiding is achieved in dielectric structures, such as optical fibers, by total internal reflection. When the fibers are bent very tightly, however, the angle of incidence becomes too large for total internal reflection to occur, and light escapes at the bend. Photonic crystals can be designed to continue to confine light even around tight corners.

To illustrate this point, we remove a row of dielectric rods from the photonic crystal described above. This has the effect of introducing a single guided-mode band inside the gap. The field associated with the guided mode is strongly confined in the vicinity of the defect and decays exponentially into the crystal. An intriguing aspect of photonic crystal waveguides is that they provide a unique way to guide optical light, tractably and efficiently, through narrow channels of air. Once light is introduced inside the waveguide, it really has nowhere else to go. The only source of loss is reflection from the waveguide input. This suggests that we may use photonic crystals to guide light around tight corners. This is shown in Fig. 1. Although the radius of curvature of the bend is less than the wavelength of the light, nearly all the light is transmitted through the bend over a wide range of frequencies through the gap. The small fraction of light that is not transmitted is reflected. For specific frequencies, 100% transmission can be achieved [4]. Note that a critical and necessary condition for 100% transmission efficiency is that the photonic crystal waveguide be *single-mode* in the frequency range of interest.

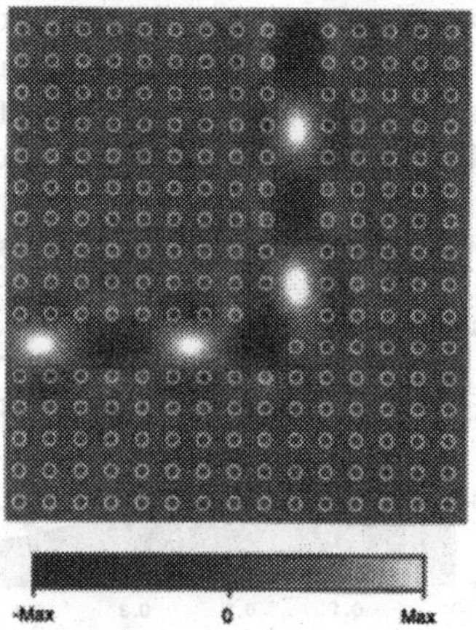

Figure 1: Electric field pattern in the vicinity of the sharp 90-degree bend. The electric field is polarized along the axis of the dielectric rods. The white circles indicate the position of the rods. Note that unlike the mechanism of total internal reflection, a photonic crystal may allow light to be guided in air.

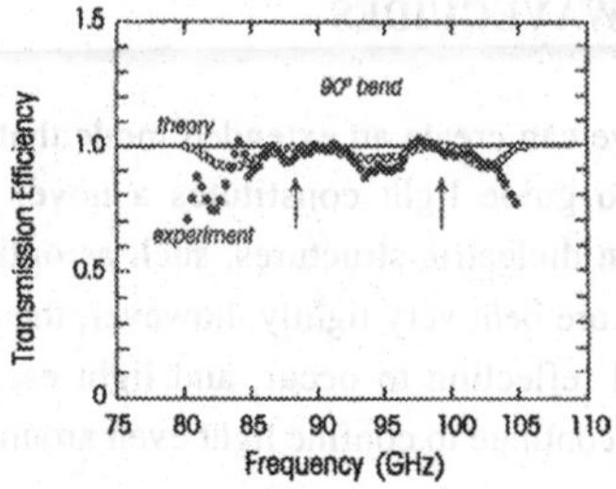

Figure 2: Transmission efficiency around a sharp 90-degree bend for a waveguide "carved out" of a square lattice of alumina rods in air. The filled circles are experimental measurements and the open circles are the theoretical prediction.

A recent experimental verification of 100% transmission efficiency at very sharp bends is illustrated in Fig. 2. These are results from S. Y. Lin *et al.* [5] who performed experiments at microwave lengthscales for a series of waveguide bends (similar to the configuration in Fig. 1) using an appropriately scaled square lattice of alumina rods in air. The filled circles are experimental measurements and the open circles are the theoretical prediction. Good agreement is obtained over a wide range of frequencies.

BOUND STATES AT WAVEGUIDE BENDS AND CONSTRICTIONS

Bound states in waveguides, and especially in waveguide bends, have recently been the subject of widespread theoretical and experimental investigation. Jaffe and Goldstone [6] proved that bends, which behave like local bulges in the guide, always support bound states in constant cross-section quantum waveguides under the condition that the wavefunction vanishes on the boundary. Photonic crystals, however, provide a new

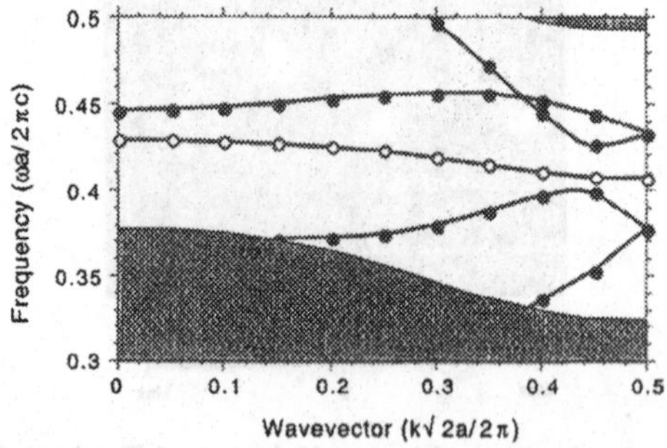

Figure 3. Superimposed dispersion relations for the two guides in Fig. 4. Open circles are for the narrow waveguide and filled circles are for the wide waveguide.

mechanism for the appearance of bound states in waveguides [7]. In particular, photonic crystal waveguides can be designed to possess mode gaps in their spectrum. These mode gaps make it possible for bound states to exist in bends, bulges, and even constrictions, both above and below the cutoff frequency for guided modes. As an example, consider the guided-mode bands plotted along the (1,1) direction as shown in Fig. 3. These are a superposition of the bands for a (1,1) waveguide with one missing-row (open circles) and for a (1,1) waveguide with three missing-rows (filled circles). Note that the guided-mode band of the narrower waveguide falls completely within the mode gap of the wider waveguide. This suggests that a constriction in the wider waveguide could then lead to a bound state within the constriction. This is exactly what happens as shown in Fig. 4

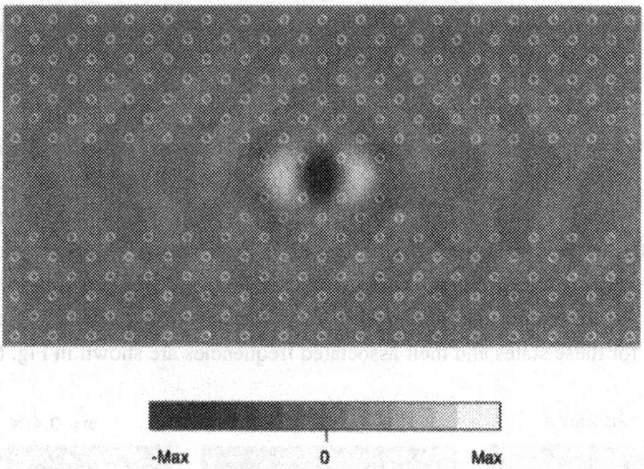

Figure 4. Electric field for the bound state at ω=0.411($2\pi c/a$) in a constriction of length 3a. Most of the field pattern is concentrated in the constriction itself.

By choosing a configuration such that the constriction has length $3\sqrt{2}a$, we indeed find a bound state at ω=0.411($2\pi c/a$). The electric field of the mode is mostly confined to the inside of the narrow guide section. Since the mode is close in frequency to the mode gap edge, the decay constant is small and the electric field decays slowly in the semi-infinite section. Nevertheless, it is a *bona fide* bound state whose counterpart would be impossible to obtain in conventional waveguides.

Let us now turn our attention to bends in photonic crystal waveguides. Like straight waveguides with a bulge or constriction, bent waveguides can also be viewed as one finite and two semi-infinite waveguide sections of different wave vectors and dispersion relations joined together [4]. By analogy to the straight waveguide, we can create a bound state in a bend by joining three sections, the two semi-infinite section having a mode gap and the finite section having a guided mode in that mode gap. In order to investigate further the mechanism for the appearance of bound states in bends, we need a configuration that allows for a number of bound states to exist. Such a configuration preferably would consist of a finite section, whose guided mode covers most of the bulk

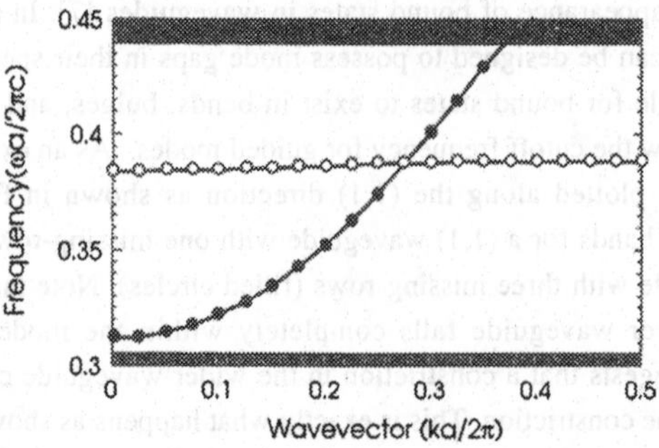

Figure 5. Superimposed dispersion relations for the two waveguides each of which is formed by removing a single row of atoms. Open circles are for the waveguide along (1,1) and the filled circles are for the waveguide along (1,0).

gap, and of two semi-infinite sections, each possessing a guided mode band with a narrow bandwidth. We create one such configuration by removing one row of rods from the square array in the (10) and the (11) directions, respectively. The band structures for these guides are shown in Fig. 5 superimposed with one another. The dispersion relations indeed satisfy our requirements. For a bend section along (1,0) of length $3a$, we find three bound states, two even and one odd with respect to the mirror plane of symmetry. The electric field for these states and their associated frequencies are shown in Fig. 6.

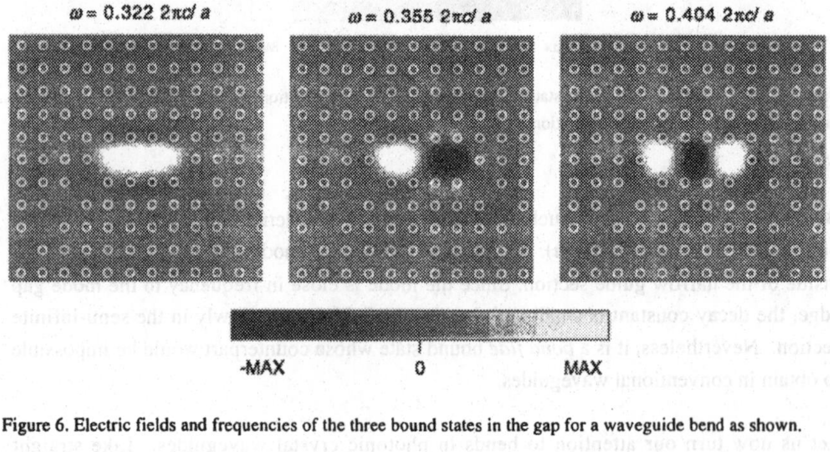

Figure 6. Electric fields and frequencies of the three bound states in the gap for a waveguide bend as shown.

Note that the highest frequency mode is above the upper cutoff frequency of the guided mode of the infinite guide section. Such a mode would not exist in analogous conventional waveguide structures, where there can only be a lower cutoff.

Finally, these bound states clearly resemble what one would have expected from simple cavity modes. Indeed, after removing the semi-infinite guide sections on both sides of the bend, we obtain similar eigenmodes at frequencies almost identical to the bound state frequencies. The subject of cavity modes is discussed more fully in the next section.

PHOTONIC CRYSTAL MICROCAVITIES

In addition to making line defects, we can also create local imperfections that trap light at a point within the crystal. As a simple example, let us choose a single rod and form a defect by changing its radius. Figure 7 shows the defect-state frequencies for several values of the defect radius. Let us begin with the perfect crystal — where every rod has a radius of 0.20*a* — and gradually reduce the radius of a single rod. Initially, the perturbation is too small to

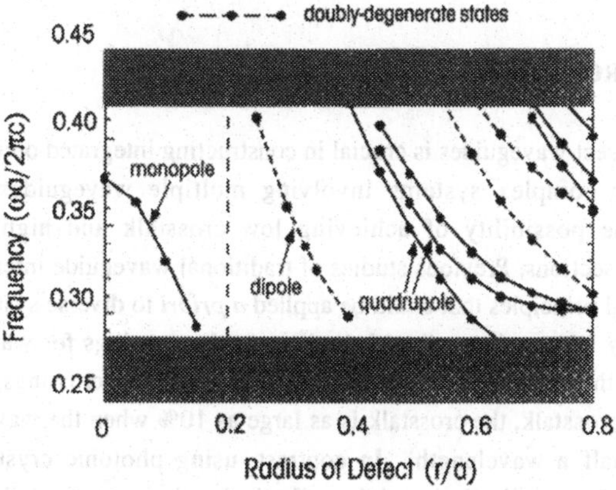

Figure 7. Defect states introduced into the gap by changing the radius of a single rod in an otherwise perfect square lattice of dielectric rods in air. When the radius is 0.2*a* there is no defect and when the radius is zero the rod has been completely removed. The shaded regions indicate the edges of the band gap.

localize a state inside the crystal. When the radius reaches 0.15*a*, a singly-degenerate symmetric localized state appears in the vicinity of the defect. Since the defect involves removing dielectric material in the crystal, the state appears at a frequency close to the lower edge of the band gap. As the radius of the rod is further reduced, the frequency of the defect state sweeps upward across the gap.

Instead of reducing the size of a rod, we also could have made it larger. Starting again with a perfect crystal, we gradually increase the radius of a rod. When the radius reaches 0.25*a*, two doubly-degenerate modes appear at the top of the gap. Since the defect involves adding material, the modes sweep downward across the gap as we increase the radius. They eventually disappear into the continuum (below the gap) when the radius becomes larger than 0.40*a*. The electric fields of these modes have two nodes in the plane and are thus dipolar in symmetry. If we keep increasing the radius, a large number of localized modes can be created in the vicinity of the defect. Several modes appear at the top of the gap: first a quadrupole, then another (non-degenerate) quadrupole, followed by a second-order monopole and two doubly-degenerate hexapoles. We see that both the frequency and symmetry of the resonant mode can be tuned simply by adjusting the size of the rod. One important aspect of a finite-sized microcavity is its quality factor Q, defined as $\lambda/\delta\lambda$ where $\delta\lambda$ is the width of the cavity resonance. It is a measure of the optical energy stored in the microcavity over the cycle-average power radiated out of the cavity. P. Villeneuve *et al.* [8] have studied a finite-sized crystal made of dielectric rods where a single rod has been removed. They find that value of Q increases exponentially with the number of rods and reaches a value close to 10^4 with as little as four rods on either side of the defect. Also note that these cavities possess small modal volumes on the order of $(\lambda/2n)^3$. The combination of large quality factor with small modal volume offers a unique capability of maximally enhancing spontaneous emission.

WAVEGUIDE CROSSINGS

The ability to intersect waveguides is crucial in constructing integrated optical circuits, due to the desire for complex systems involving multiple waveguides. Of particular importance, is the possibility of achieving low crosstalk and high throughput in perpendicular intersections. Previous studies of traditional waveguide intersections [9, 10] have lacked general principles that could be applied *a priori* to diverse systems. Moreover, they have typically been concerned with shallow-angle crossings for wavelengths many times smaller than the waveguide width. Although perpendicular crossings in such systems exhibit negligible crosstalk, the crosstalk is as large as 10% when the waveguide width is on the order of half a wavelength. In contrast, using photonic crystal waveguides, perpendicular crossings can be designed that effectively eliminate crosstalk, even when the waveguide width is small, permitting single-mode waveguides with optimal miniaturization. Simulations of such structures show peak throughputs of nearly unity while crosstalk falls as low as 10^{-9} [11].

The fundamental idea is to consider coupling of the four branches, or ports, of the intersection in terms of a resonant cavity at the center. If the resonant modes excited from the input port can be prevented by symmetry from decaying into the transverse ports, then crosstalk is eliminated and the system reduces to the well-known phenomenon of resonant tunneling through a cavity. This situation can be achieved by means of the following conditions:

(1) Each waveguide must have a mirror symmetry plane through its axis and perpendicular to the other waveguide, and have a single guided mode in the frequency range of interest. This mode will be either even or odd with respect to the mirror plane.

(2) The center of the intersection must be occupied by a resonant cavity that respects the mirror planes of both waveguides.

(3) Two resonant modes must exist in the cavity, each of which is even with respect to one waveguide's mirror plane and odd with respect to the other. These should be the only resonant modes in the frequency range of interest.

If these requirements are satisfied, then each resonant state will couple to modes in just one waveguide and be orthogonal to modes in the other waveguide. An example of such a configuration is illustrated shematically in Fig. 8. (For simplicity, we depict a lowest-order even waveguide mode.) Therefore, under the approximation that the ports only

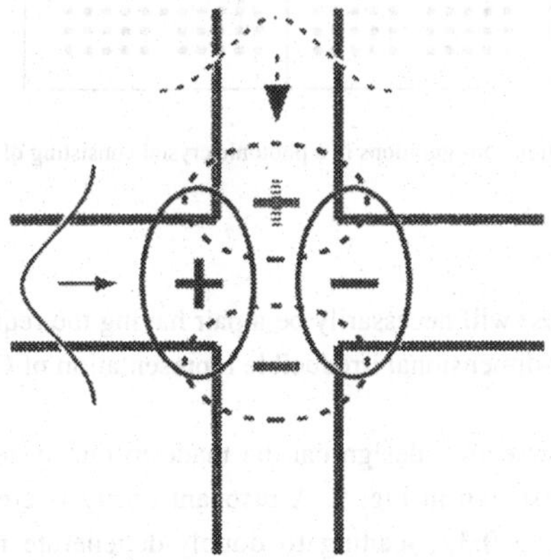

Figure 8. Abstarct diagram of symmetry requirements for waveguide crossing, showing waveguide mode profiles and resonant-cavity mode contours. By symmetry the solid-line modes cannot couple with the dashed-line modes and vice versa.

couple to one another through the resonant cavity, crosstalk will be prohibited. The transmission to the output port is described by resonant tunneling, and one can use coupled-mode theory [12] to show that the throughput spectrum will be a Lorentzian peaked at unity on resonance. The width of the Lorentzian is given by the inverse of the cavity's quality factor Q, which is proportional to the lifetime of the resonance mode.

Perfect throughput will not be attained, however, due to the effect of direct coupling of the input port with the transverse ports, resulting in crosstalk — this can be decreased arbitrarily, but at the expense of the throughput bandwidth. Direct coupling is reduced by making the cavity larger, since this increases the distance between the localized waveguide modes. The drawback to increased cavity size is that it can either create extraneous resonance modes or, as in the case of the photonic crystal cavities below, increase the Q of the resonance.

The required parity of the cavity modes is easy to achieve in practice, due to the fact that a perpendicular intersection of identical waveguides typically has C_{4v} point symmetry (the symmetry group of the square). In this case, any non-accidental degenerate modes (such as

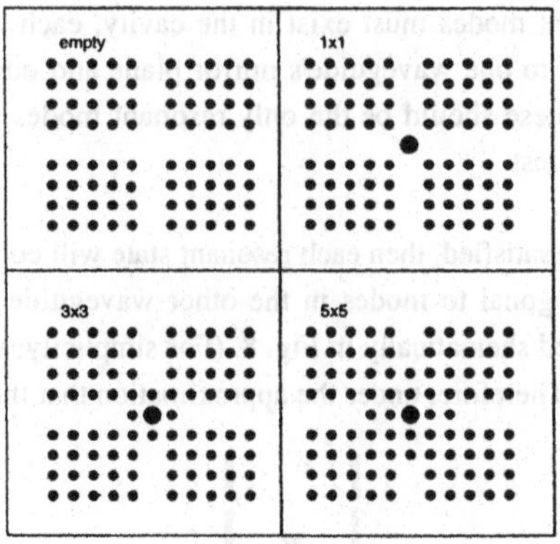

Figure 9. Waveguide intersection configurations in a photonic crystal consisting of a square lattice of dieletric rods in air.

many higher-order modes) will necessarily be a pair having the requisite symmetry of Fig. 8, as that is the only two-dimensional irreducible representation of C_{4v}.

A realization of the intersection design can be made in our system of square lattice of dielectric rods in air as shown in Fig. 9. A resonant cavity is created by increasing the radius of a single rod to 0.3*a*, leading to doubly-degenerate modes of the requisite symmetry with a frequency of 0.36 ($2\pi c/a$) (see also Fig. 7) [8]. The properties of the resonant modes can also be varied by increasing the thickness of the "walls" of the cavity as illustrated. To determine the performance of these waveguide-crossing configurations, we study the effects of sending a broad-spectrum propagation Gaussian pulse to the input port (left). The fractional power transmission is then evaluated as a function of frequency for the output port (right) and one of the transverse ports (top), yielding the throughput and crosstalk, respectively. We find that both the throughput and the crosstalk for the empty intersection lie in the 20–40% range. This is because the empty intersection does not support resonant states of the correct symmetry. In contrast, the 1×1 intersection reaches nearly 100% throughput with a crosstalk at the same frequency of 1.8%. As the "walls" of the cavity get thicker as for intersections 3×3 and 5×5, the crosstalk falls precipitously to values of 5×10^{-10} and 4×10^{-10} respectively. The steady-state electric field distribution for the case of 5×5 at a frequency of 0.36 ($2\pi c/a$) is shown in Fig. 10.

Finally, we note that both the crosstalk and the resonance Q derive from the exponential decay of light through the bulk photonic crystal. Because the crosstalk must tunnel through twice as many crystal layers as the resonance decay, the crosstalk tends to be approximately Q^{-2}.

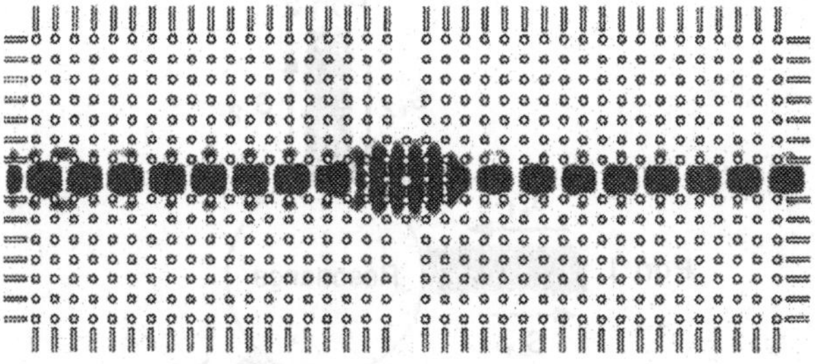

Figure 10. Steady-state electric field distribution for the case of the 5×5 waveguide intersection. Essentially all the power is transported through the junction with negligible crosstalk in the transverse waveguides.

WAVEGUIDE BRANCHES

Waveguide branches also play an important role in integrated photonic circuits. Ideally, such a device splits the input power into the two output waveguides without significant reflection or radiation losses. Motivated by the goal of miniaturizing photonic components and circuits, there have been many efforts to construct wide-angle branches [13-17]. Despite such efforts, the splitting angles are still limited to a few degrees for conventional structures, due to the inherent radiation loss at the branching region. Moreover, while such loss can be substantially reduced by increasing the index contrast between the guide and the surrounding media [18], it can not be completely suppressed. Photonic crystals offer a way to completely eliminate radiation losses, and thereby open the possibility of designing wide-angle branches with high performance. Very recently, estimates of the transmission characteristics of a 120° Y-branch in a photonic crystal with hexagonal symmetry have been presented by Yonekura *et al.* [19]. However, direct and accurate numerical characterizations of the transmission and reflection properties through a single waveguide branch have not been previously performed. Moreover, to our knowledge, a general criterion for ideal performance of waveguide branches in a photonic crystal has yet to be developed in the literature. In this section, we present a brief theoretical description [20] of the necessary considerations for optimal construction of a waveguide branch in a photonic crystal. We find that structures with 120° rotational symmetry, including the configuration considered by Yonekura *et al.* [19], do not completely eliminate reflection. Based upon our analysis, we introduce designs of photonic crystal waveguide branches with 180° branching angle that display near-zero reflection and almost-complete transmission.

In order to obtain a qualitative understanding of waveguide branches in a photonic crystal, we consider the theoretical model shown in Fig. 11. The branching region is treated as a cavity that couples to the input and output waveguides. The resonance in the cavity then determines the transport properties of the branch.

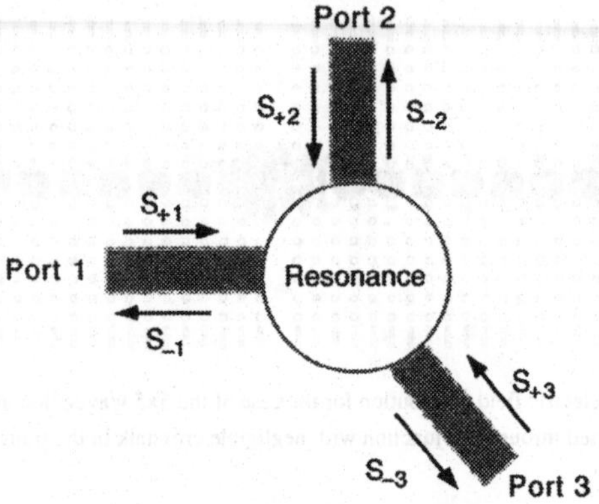

Figure 11. Schematic of a theoretical model for waveguide branches. The gray regions represent the waveguides, and the circle represents a resonator. S_{+j} and S_{-j} are the input and output wave amplitudes at the j'th port, respectively.

The transmission and reflection properties of such a model can be calculated using coupled-mode theory [12], which relates the incoming and outgoing wave amplitudes S_{+j} and S_{-j} at port j, to the amplitude of the resonant mode A, as follows:

$$\frac{dA}{dt} = i\omega_0 A - A\sum_j \frac{1}{\tau_j} + \sum_j (S_{+j}\sqrt{2/\tau_j}) \tag{1}$$

$$S_{-j} = -S_{+j} + A\sqrt{2/\tau_j} \tag{2}$$

Here, ω_0 is the resonant frequency, and $1/\tau_j$ is the amplitude decay rate of the resonance into the j-th port. Also, for simplicity we have assumed a single-mode cavity. When the electromagnetic wave at a frequency ω is incident upon the system from port 1, *i.e.* $S_{+2} = S_{+3} = 0$, it can be shown [20] that the reflection coefficient R is given by:

$$R = \left|\frac{S_{-1}}{S_{+1}}\right|^2 = \left|\frac{-i(\omega-\omega_0) + \frac{1}{\tau_1} - \frac{1}{\tau_2} - \frac{1}{\tau_3}}{i(\omega-\omega_0) + \frac{1}{\tau_1} + \frac{1}{\tau_2} + \frac{1}{\tau_3}}\right|^2 \tag{3}$$

From Eq. (3), it immediately follows that *zero* reflection can be achieved at the resonant frequency ω_0 if the rate-matching condition:

$$\frac{1}{\tau_1} = \frac{1}{\tau_2} + \frac{1}{\tau_3} \tag{4}$$

is satisfied. Furthermore, one can show that the power will be split evenly between port 2 and port 3 in a symmetric configuration when $1/\tau_2 = 1/\tau_3$.

Let us now consider a structure with C_{3v} symmetry *(i.e.,* the symmetry group of a equilateral triangle). In the case where the resonance is singly degenerate, the decay rates into the three ports are equal, *i.e.,* $\tau_1 = \tau_2 = \tau_3$ which leads to a transmission coefficient of 4/9 (instead of the optimal 1/2) at resonance. While the coupled-mode analysis is approximate, this case in fact provides the exact upper limit of transmission for *any* structure with 120° rotational symmetry.

Arbitrarily high transmission, however, can be achieved in a structure *without* three-fold rotational symmetry. Based on the analysis presented above, we performed numerical simulations of T-shaped waveguide branches (*i.e.* waveguide branches with 180° branching angle). The waveguides are introduced by removing one partial row and one full column of rods in our basic system of square lattice of dielectric rods in air. To characterize the transmission and reflection properties of the branches, we excite a Gaussian pulse in the input waveguide, and analyze the field amplitude at a point deep inside an output waveguide. For the case of a perfect empty T-junction we find that the transmission coefficient remains higher than 40% for a wide range of frequencies, with a peak of 46% at the frequency $\omega_0 = 0.38\ (2\pi c/a)$.

We can qualitatively explain these results using the coupled-mode theory arguments presented above. Suppose we approximate the cavity region by a point defect formed by removing one rod from the perfect crystal. Such a defect creates a localized state that possesses the full symmetry of the lattice (*i.e.* a monopole as in Fig. 7). The localized state therefore should couple to all the input and output waveguides with substantially the same strength, resulting in a peak transmission of 44.4%, in qualitative agreement with the simulation.

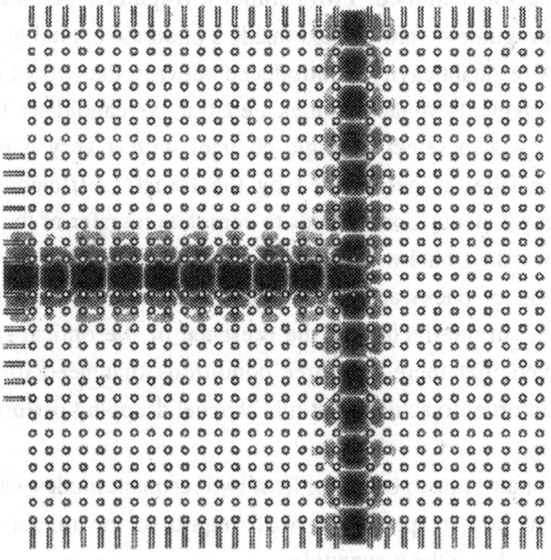

Figure 12. Electric field pattern in the vicinity of a waveguide T-branch in a photonic crystal. Note the presence of two extra rods near the junction (lying within the verical waveguide), that are needed in order to satisfy the optimal rate-matching condition as explained in the text.

In order to improve the transmission, we therefore need to reduce (slightly) the coupling between the resonance and the output waveguides, in order to satisfy the rate-matching condition of Eq. (4). This is achieved by placing extra rods between the input and output waveguides as illustrated in Fig. 12. The radius of these extra rods can then be varied for performance optimization. As the radius is increased from zero, the transmission is significantly improved and approaches the optimal value of 50% at a radius near $0.1a$. Further increasing the radius, however, results in a deviation from the rate-matching condition, and therefore leads to a decrease in transmission.

In Fig. 12, we plot the steady state field distribution at $\omega_0 = 0.39\ (2\pi c/a)$ for the structure with extra rods of radius $0.1a$. The fields are completely confined within the waveguide regions and split equally into the output waveguides.

CHANNEL DROP FILTERS

One of the most prominent devices in the telecommunications industry is the channel drop filter. This prominence is a consequence of both its importance and its size (~10cm×10cm)! Channel dropping filters are devices that are necessary for the manipulation of Wavelength Division Multiplexed (WDM) optical communications, whereby one channel is dropped at one carrier wavelength, leaving all other channels unaffected. Photonic crystals present a unique opportunity to investigate the possibilities of miniaturizing such a device to the scale of the wavelength of interest — 1.55 microns. We now combine line defects and point defects to make a novel photonic crystal channel-drop filter that gives access to one channel of a wavelength division multiplexed signal while leaving other channels undisturbed. Two parallel waveguides — a main transmission line and a secondary waveguide — are created inside a photonic crystal by removing two rows of dielectric rods. A resonant cavity is introduced between the two waveguides by creating one or more local defects. Resonant cavities are attractive candidates for channel dropping since they can be used to select a single channel with a very narrow linewidth. The performance of the filter is determined by the transfer efficiency between the two waveguides. Perfect efficiency corresponds to complete transfer of the selected channel — into either the forward or backward direction in the secondary waveguide — with no forward transmission or backward reflection in the main transmission line. All other channels should remain unaffected by the presence of the optical resonator. Fan *et al.* [21–23] have proved that there are three conditions that need to be satisfied by the coupling resonator in order to achieve optimal channel dropping performance:

(1) The resonator must possess at least two resonant modes, each of which must be even and odd, respectively, with regard to the mirror plane of symmetry perpendicular to the waveguides.
(2) The modes must be degenerate (or nearly so). Note that the intrinsic symmetry of the system does not support degeneracies, consequently one must force an accidental degeneracy!
(3) The modes must have an equal Q (or nearly so).

All three conditions are necessary in order to achieve complete transfer. The reflected amplitude in the transmission line originates solely from the decay of the localized states. The reflection therefore will not be cancelled if the optical resonator supports only a single mode. To ensure the cancellation of the reflected signal, the structure must possess a plane of mirror symmetry perpendicular to both waveguides, and support two localized states with different symmetry with respect to the mirror plane, one even and one odd. Since the states have different symmetries, tunneling through each one constitutes an independent process. The even state decays with the same phase along both the forward and backward directions while the odd state decays with opposite phase. When the two tunneling processes are combined, because of the phase difference, the decaying amplitudes cancel along the backward direction of the transmission line. In order for cancellation to occur, the lineshapes of the two resonances must overlap. Since each resonance possesses a Lorentzian lineshape, both resonances must have substantially the same center frequency and the same width. When such degeneracy occurs, the incoming wave interferes destructively with the decaying amplitude along the forward direction in the transmission line, leaving all the power to be transferred into the secondary waveguide at the resonant frequency.

A photonic crystal system provides precisely the control necessary in order to satisfy all three conditions. An example of a photonic crystal channel-drop filter is shown in Fig. 13. The cavity consists of a single point defect with a radius $0.60a$. As we have already seen in Fig. 7, this defect supports a doubly-degenerate hexapole state near $\omega_0 = 0.39$ $(2\pi c/a)$ with the required symmetry. However, the presence of the waveguides next to the cavity breaks the degeneracy of the hexapoles. To restore the degeneracy, we change the dielectric constant (or equivalently the size) of two rods adjacent to the defect. By properly changing the rods, we can affect the modes in different ways and force an accidental degeneracy in frequency. An approximate degeneracy in width exists between the states since the hexapoles possess large enough orbital angular momentum to ensure roughly equal decay

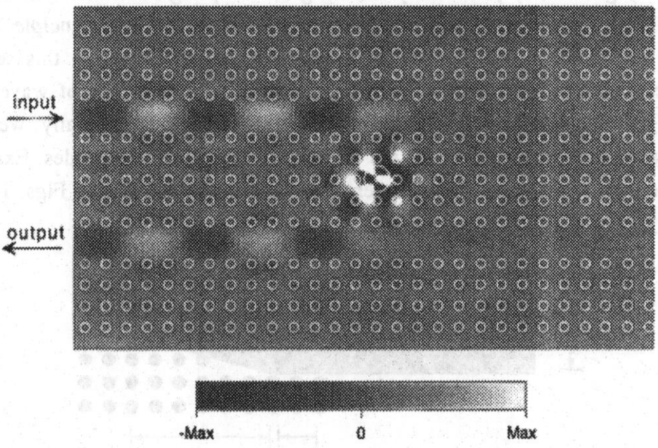

Figure 13: Steady-state field distribution of the photonic crystal channel drop filter at resonance. Note that the size of this device is on the order of the wavelength of the light in air.

of the even and odd modes into the waveguides. We simulate the filter response of the structure shown in Fig. 13 by sending a pulse through the upper waveguide. The transmission in the main line is close to 100% for every channel, except at the resonant frequency, where the transmission drops to 0% and the transfer efficiency approaches 100%. The quality factor is larger than 6,000. Since the even state (even with respect to the mirror plane perpendicular to the waveguides) is odd with respect to the mirror plane parallel to the waveguides, the transfer occurs along the backward direction in the secondary waveguide, as shown in Fig. 13. Finally, although the lineshape of the current resonant modes is Lorentzian, it can be modified to be of the preferred "square-wave" shape by introducing complexes of coupled resonant modes as discussed in detail in Ref. [23].

INPUT/OUTPUT COUPLING

From a practical point of view, in order to employ photonic crystal waveguides in integrated optical circuits, light must be efficiently coupled from traditional dielectric waveguides and fibers into and out of the various defects in photonic band gap materials. Because of the different underlying physics of traditional index guiding and PBG guiding, coupling of light into and out of photonic crystal waveguides is not a trivial problem. Results from microwave experiments with alumina photonic crystals demonstrate that there are large insertion losses when electromagnetic waves are coupled into and out of photonic crystal waveguides [5]. This results in substantial reflection and scattering from photonic crystal waveguide ends, which adversely affects the outcome of transmission measurements. To overcome this limitation, we need an efficient waveguide interconnect design.

One way to achieve coupling is to use a resonant mode to couple the modes in the two types of waveguides. By judiciously choosing the coupling coefficients of the guided modes to the resonance, very high transmission can be achieved in principle. However, limits are set on the useful bandwidth by the resonance width. In this section we investigate a non-resonant way of coupling between the two types of waveguides to achieve high transmission for a large frequency range [24]. Specifically, we consider *tapered* waveguide terminations for the traditional dielectric waveguides. Examples of input and output tapered waveguide interconnections are illustrated in Figs. 14 and 15, respectively.

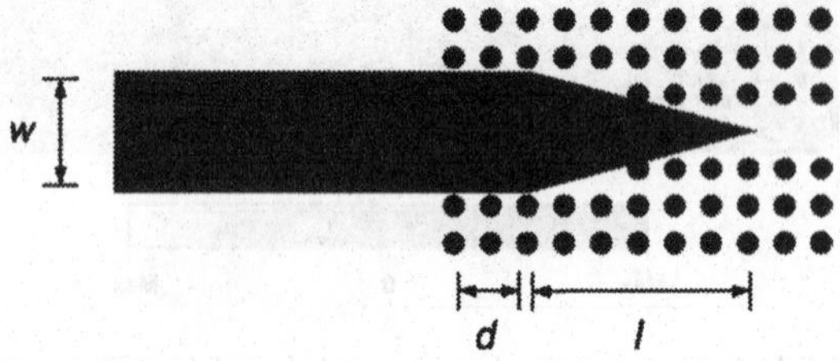

Figure 14: Tapered coupler for coupling *into* a photonic crystal waveguide.

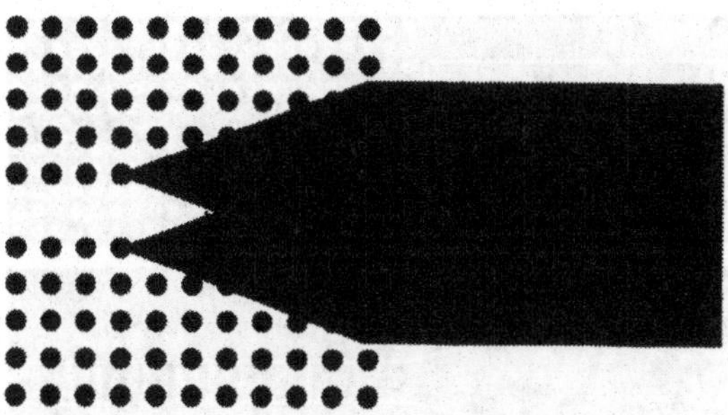

Figure 15: Coupler with an outer and an inverse inner taper for coupling light *out of* a photonic crystal waveguide.

We calculate the transmission through the interconnect junctions by sending a Gaussian pulse through the system with center frequency $\omega_0 = 0.36$ $(2\pi c/a)$ and width of about 0.04 $(2\pi c/a)$. As the pulse traverses the coupler, part of the power is transmitted into the output coupler, some of it is reflected, and the rest is lost to radiation modes. Since we do not rely on resonant coupling, we expect the efficiency of the coupler will not vary greatly within the frequency range covered by the pulse.

The results of some of our calculations are presented in Fig. 16. If we simply terminate a wide dielectric waveguide (say of width $6a$) and place it next to the photonic crystal waveguide, coupling is very inefficient. We calculate the transmission in the vicinity of the frequency ω_o, to be only 22% of the incident power. One of the reasons for this is the poor mode profile-matching between the fundamental modes of the wide dielectric and of the much narrower PC waveguide.

A taper can reduce the dielectric waveguide cross-section adiabatically in a relatively short distance while still retaining almost perfect throughput. For instance, with a taper of length $10a$ one can join a waveguide of width $6a$ to one with width $2a$ with 100% transmission within numerical accuracy of the calculations as shown in the second panel of Fig. 16. So we can focus our attention on input coupling from dielectric waveguides with a width that is on the order of the lattice constant. For input coupling we employ the tapered coupler of Fig. 14. The width of the dielectric waveguide is w, the taper length is l, and the taper begins at distance d from the line defined by the centers of the posts comprising the photonic crystal edge. Since the taper intrudes into the photonic crystal itself, some posts comprising the crystal may touch the dielectric guide coupler, adding roughness to the taper. In general, the measured transmission values improved by only about 1% when the posts were removed. For the set of parameters $w = 2a$, $l = 10a$, and $d = 5a$, we obtain a major improvement of transmission to 91% as shown in the third panel of Fig. 16.

An important parameter in this set is w. With $w = 1.5a$ or $2.5a$ one can obtain 94% transmission, and with $w = 0.5a$, 96%. On the other hand, $w = 1.0a$ yields only 76% transmission. The explanation of these results involves mode-gap creation upon folding-in

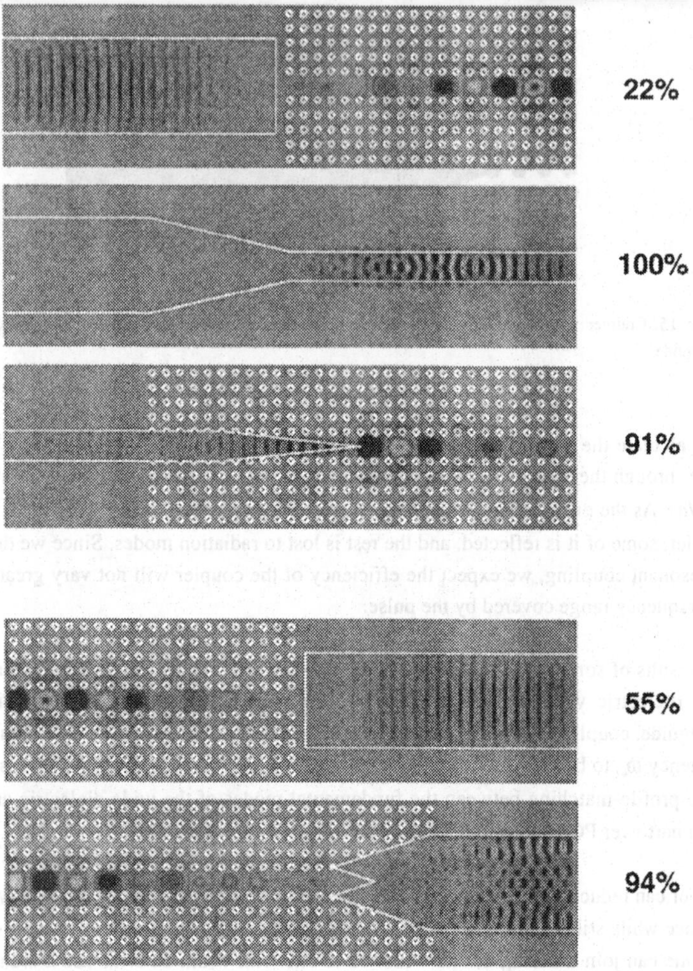

Figure 16: Electric field patterns and associated transmission coefficients for various interconnect coupler configurations. In all cases a pulse is travelling from left to right.

of the dielectric waveguide modes into the Brillouin zone of the photonic crystal waveguide [24]. Typically, for a given w, the transmission will increase with l, and flatten out at about $l = 4a$. The cross-over happens at l approximately equal to the wavelength of the light in air. This underscores that the taper works efficiently because it changes the width of the dielectric waveguide to zero cross-section adiabatically, that is, on a length-scale larger than the light wavelength. As we have seen, the parameter d denotes the distance of the beginning of the taper from the photonic crystal edge. According to our calculations, the efficiency of the coupler is not a strong function of d, however, for $d = 0$ there can be radiation losses to free space modes. As clearly evident in the third panel of Fig. 16, it is the last section of the taper where most of the coupling action occurs, so as long as d is such that this last section is inside the photonic crystal, no radiation losses are suffered and transmission remains high.

Let us now consider the out-coupling from the photonic crystal waveguide mode to the dielectric waveguide. For a benchmark test, we calculate the throughput to a dielectric waveguide that is terminated flat as shown in the fourth panel of Fig. 16. The measured transmission is 55%. Actually, the result is also 55% for the case of a different dielectric waveguide with $w = 2a$. This result agrees with what we expect from a k-matching argument. Transmission through an interface between two different dielectric materials at normal incidence can be given in terms of the propagation constants k and q on the two sides of the interface as

$$T = 4kq/(k+q)^2 \tag{5}$$

At the pulse frequency ω_o, the wavevector in the photonic crystal guide is $k = 0.23\ (2\pi/a)$ and in the dielectric waveguide with $w = 2a$ it is $k = 1.20\ (2\pi/a)$. The simple model yields $T = 0.54$, very close to the value obtained from the numerical simulations. The width w of the guide does not change the transmission greatly even when $w = 6a$ because for waveguide widths $w \gg \lambda/2n$ the fundamental mode wavevector k is roughly $k = \omega_o n/c = 1.224\ (2\pi/a)$, where $n = 3.4$ is the dielectric constant of the traditional waveguide.

We expect the efficiency of the tapered coupler described in Fig. 14 to remain fairly high even for coupling *out of* the photonic crystal waveguide because of the time-reversibility of Maxwell's equations. Radiation losses in our simulations are usually under 1%. Nevertheless, since the dielectric waveguides we use are mostly *multimode*, we do not expect exactly the same transmission efficiency. We measure the transmission out of such a coupler to be 85%. However, one can improve on this value by using an inverse taper, that is a taper with $l < 0$. This is equivalent to "tapering" the air photonic crystal waveguide. For the same waveguide width, and $d = 7a$ and $l = -10a$, transmission increases to 89%. A smoother type of inverse taper with both an outer and inner taper is shown in Fig. 15. The results for this case are shown in the bottom panel of Fig. 16 with a transmission of 94%.

The width of the waveguide w still remains an important parameter. As w decreases, our calculations show that the coupling efficiency drops as well. If we decrease the width of the waveguide in Fig. 15 to $w = 2a$, ending up with an inverse taper with $l = -4a$, transmission is only 83%. As the output waveguide width decreases, so does the number of modes in the waveguide at the pulse frequency. Since the number of available channels that the mode in the photonic crystal waveguide can couple into decreases, transmission efficiency decreases as well. In contrast, in the case of coupling *into* the photonic crystal waveguide, a very wide dielectric waveguide has a low efficiency, because in this case there are many channels to which a reflected wave from the junction can couple. For example, for a waveguide of width $w = 7a$ the transmission we measure is only 64% even with a large taper length $l = 10a$.

RADIATION LOSSES

All of the systems and principles discussed in all of the previous sections remain at once valid in 3 dimensions, as long as one is dealing with 3D photonic crystal systems possessing an omnidirectional photonic band gap. When this does not obtain, as in the case of a 3D photonic crystal with a partial gap, or a two-dimensionally periodic photonic cystal slab in 3D, or a one-dimensionally periodic bar in 3D, coupling to radiation modes can occur, resulting in "leaky" behavior of the photon fields. Clearly, it would be extremely helpful to develop an understanding of this coupling and to identify regimes where the coupling could be minimized. Recently, we have performed analytical and computational studies of defects in bar and slab photonic crystal geometries that reveal at least two distinct mechanisms for reducing radiation losses (or equivalently, *increasing* the radiation Q) [25]. For simplicity, let us focus entirely on the radiation losses associated with a single-rod defect in an otherwise one-dimensionally periodic row (*i.e.* a bar) of dielectric rods ($r = 0.2a$) in air in 2D. Without the presence of the defect, there are guided-mode bands lying below the light-cone and a mode gap ranging from 0.264 ($2\pi c/a$) to 0.448 ($2\pi c/a$) at the Brillouin zone edge [26]. Although these guided modes are degenerate with radiation modes above the light line, they are *bona-fide* eigenstates of the system and consequently are orthogonal to, and do not couple with, the radiation modes. The presence of a point-defect, however, has two important consequences. Firstly, it can mix the various guided modes to create a defect state that can be exponentially localized along the bar-axis.

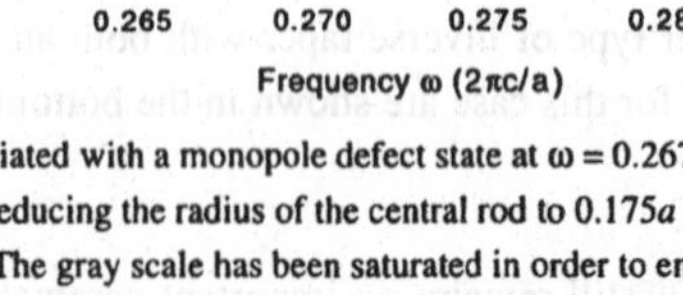

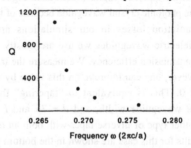

Figure 17. Electric field associated with a monopole defect state at $\omega = 0.267$ ($2\pi c/a$) with radiation Q = 570. The defect is formed by reducing the radius of the central rod to $0.175a$ in an otherwise perfect array of dielectric rods of radius $0.2a$. The gray scale has been saturated in order to emphasize the "far-field" radiation pattern.

Secondly, it can scatter the guided modes into the radiation modes and consequently lead to resonant (or leaky) mode behavior away from the bar-axis. It is this scattering that leads to an intrinsically *finite* value for the radiation Q.

So what are the principles that one can follow in order to configure the system for high values of radiation Q? One approach is simply to delocalize the defect state resonance. This can be accomplished by either delocalizing *along* the direction of periodicity, or *perpendicular* to the periodicity, or both. Delocalizing the defect state involves reducing the effect of the defect perturbation and consequently the scattering of the guided mode states into the radiation manifold. Very recently, Benisty *et al.* [27] argued that high radiation Q's in a two-dimensionally periodic photonic crystal "slab" geometry could be achieved by employing low-index contrast films in order to delocalize *perpendicular* to the slab (or plane of periodicity). Turning back to our simple example involving a bar, we shall now illustrate this effect by delocalizing *along* the bar (or the direction of periodicity). If we make our defect rod smaller in radius than the photonic crystal rods ($r = 0.2a$) we can obtain a monopole (or s-like) defect state as shown in Fig. 17. This is the electric field associated with a defect-state at $\omega = 0.267$ $(2\pi c/a)$ created using a defect rod of radius $0.175a$. (Note that the gray scale has been saturated in order to emphasize the far-field radiation pattern.) As the properties of the defect rod are perturbed further, the defect state moves further away from the lower band edge into the gap. As it does this, it becomes more localized, accumulating more and more k-components, leading to stronger coupling with the radiation modes. A calculation of the radiation Q for the defect state as a function of frequency is shown in Fig. 18. The radiation Q is clearly highest when the frequency of the defect state is near the lower band edge at $\omega_l = 0.264$ $(2\pi c/a)$ where it is most delocalized. As the defect state moves away from the band edge, its localization increases typically as $(\omega - \omega_l)^{1/2}$ leading to a Q that falls off as $(\omega - \omega_l)^{3/2}$ [25].

Another approach is to exploit the symmetry properties of the defect-state in order to introduce nodes in the far-field pattern that could lead to weak coupling with the radiation manifold [25]. This is a rather subtle mechanism that depends sensitively on the structural

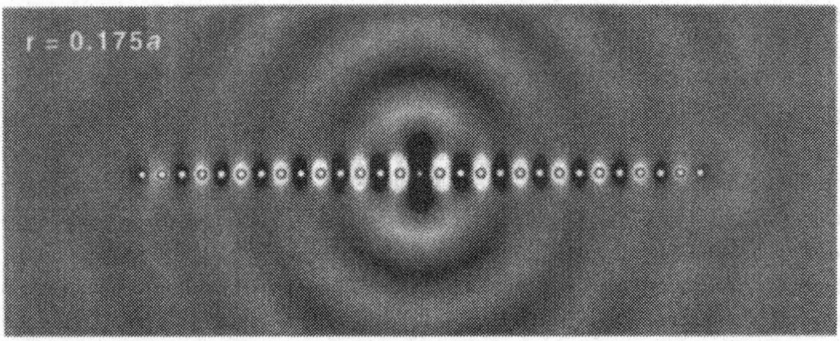

Figure 18. Radiation Q as a function of the position in frequency of the defect state. The defect state has its highest Q near the lower band edge where it is most delocalized.

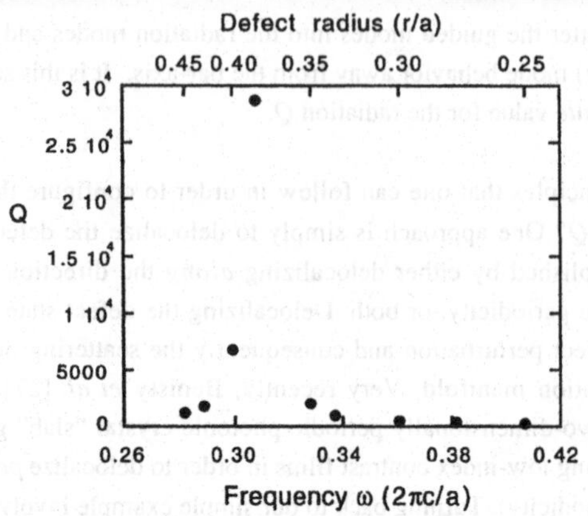

Figure 19. Radiation Q as a function of frequency and radius of the defect state. Note that in contrast to Fig. 18, the defect state attains its maximum Q within the band gap region.

parameters of the defect and typically leads to maximum Q for defect frequencies *within* the mode gap. We believe that the very high Q resonance calculated near mid-gap by Painter *et al.* [28] for a dielectric-defect in a two-dimensionally periodic photonic crystal slab geometry can be explained precisely by this mechanism. To illustrate the idea, consider the nature of the defect states that can emerge from the lower and upper band-edge states in our simple working example. As we have seen, making the defect-rod smaller draws a monopole (s-like) state from the lower band-edge into the gap. Using a Green-function formalism it can be shown [25] that the far-field pattern for these two types of defect-state is proportional to a term:

$$f(\theta) = \int_{-\infty}^{\infty} dz\, \varepsilon_{eff}(z) e^{-\kappa|z|} e^{-i\frac{\omega}{c} z\cos\theta} \left(e^{ikz} \pm e^{-ikz}\right) \tag{6}$$

where z is along the axis of periodicity, $\varepsilon_{eff}(z)$ is an effective dielectric function for the system, κ is the inverse localization length of the defect-stae, θ is an angle defined with respect to the z-axis, and k is the propagation constant $\sim\pi/a$. The plus and minus signs refer to the monopole and dipole states, respectively.

Now it is clear from Eq. (6) that the presence of the minus-sign for the dipole-state could be exploited to try and cancel the contributions of opposite sign. Indeed, one might expect that by tuning the structural parameters of the defect [*i.e.* changing $\varepsilon_{eff}(z)$] one could achieve $f(\theta) = 0$ (*i.e.* add nodal planes) for several values of θ. The presence of such extra nodal planes could greatly reduce the coupling to the radiation manifold leading to high values of Q. Of course, one would expect this cancellation to work well only over a narrow range of parameter space. In Fig. 19 we plot the calculated values of radiation Q for the dipole-state, obtained by increasing the radius of the defect rod in our example. Note that the highest Q (~30,000) is now obtained for a defect frequency deep within the mode gap region. Note also that the Q of the defect-state is a very sensitive function of the structural parameters of the defect, reaching its maximum for a defect radius of $0.375a$. The electric field patterns for the defect-states corresponding to defect radii $r = 0.40a$, $r = 0.375a$, and $r = 0.35a$ are shown in Fig. 20. The field pattern for $r = 0.375$a is clearly distinct from the others, revealing extra nodal planes along the diagonals. The ability to introduce extra nodal planes is at the heart of this new mechanism for achieving very large values of Q. For the monopole state of Figs. 17 and 18, this is not possible.

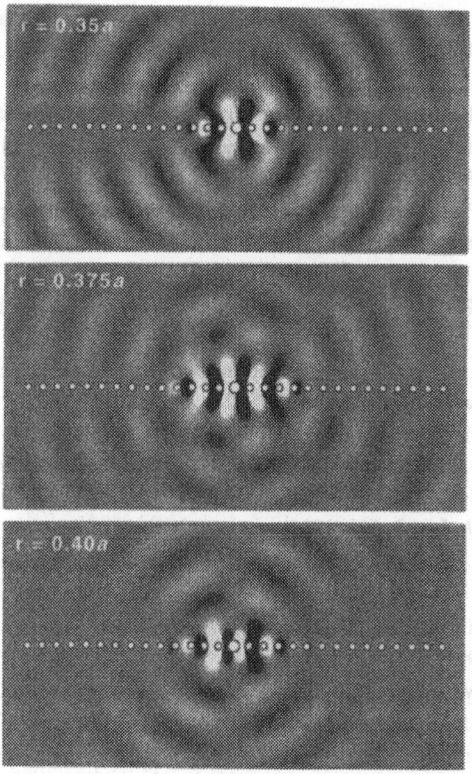

Figure 20. Electric fields associated with dipole defect states corresponding to defect radii $r = 0.40a$, $r = 0.375a$ and $r = 0.35a$. The extra nodal planes along the diagonals that are distinct for $r = 0.375a$ lead to a very high Q (~30,000) for this state.

ACKNOWLEDGEMENT

This work is supported in part by the MRSEC program of the NSF under award number DMR-9400334.

REFERENCES

[1] J. D. Joannopoulos, R. D. Meade, and J. N. Winn, *Photonic Crystals* (Princeton, New York, 1995).

[2] E. Yablonovitch, *Phys. Rev. Lett.* **58**, 2509 (1987).

[3] S. John, *Phys. Rev. Lett.* **58**, 2486 (1987).

[4] A. Mekis, J. C. Chen, I. Kurland, S. Fan, P. R. Villeneuve, and J. D. Joannopoulos, *Phys. Rev. Lett.* **77**, 3787 (1996).

[5] S. Y. Lin, E. Chow, V. Hietch, P. R. Villeneuve, and J. D. Joannopoulos, *Science* **282**, 274 (1998).

[6] J. Goldstone and R.L. Jaffe, *Phys. Rev. B* **45**, 100 (1992).

[7] A. Mekis, S. Fan, and J. D. Joannopoulos, *Phys. Rev. B* **58**, 4809 (1998).

[8] P. R. Villeneuve, S. Fan, and J. D. Joannopoulos, *Phys. Rev. B* **54**, 7837 (1996).

[9] K. Aretz, H. Beu1ow, *Electronics Letters* **25**, no. 11, p. 730 (May 1989).

[10] M. G. Daly, P. E. Jessop, D. Yevick, *J. Lightwave Technol.* **14**, pp. 1695 (1996).

[11] S. G. Johnson, C. Manolatou, S. Fan, P. R. Villeneuve, J. D. Joannopoulos, and H. A. Haus, Optics Letters **23**, 1855 (1998).

[12] H. A. Haus, *Waves and Fields in Optoelectronics* (Prentice-Hall, Englewood Cliffs, NJ, 1984).

[13] M. Rangaraj, M. Minakata, and S. Kawakami, *J. Lightwave Technol.* **7**, 753 (1989).

[14] H. Hatami-Hanza, M. J. Lederer, P. L. Chu, and I. M. Skinner, *J. Lightwave Technol.* **12**, 208(1994).

[15] A. Klekaump, P. Kersten, and W. Rehm, *J. Lightwave Technol.* **14**, 2684 (1996).

[16] M. H. Hu, J. Z. Huang, R. Scanrmozzino, M. Levy, and R. M. Osgood, *IEEE Photonic Tech. Lett.* **9**, 203 (1997).

[17] H. -B. Lin, J. -Y. Su, R. -S. Cheng, and W. -S. Wan, *IEEE J. Quantum Electron.* **35**, 1092 (1999).

[18] J. S. Foresi, D. R. Lim, L. Liao, A. M. Agarwal, and L. C. Kimerling, *Proc. SPIE* **3007**, 112 (1997).

[19] J Yonekura, M. Ikeda, and T. Baba, *J. Lightwave Technol.* **17**, 1500 (1999).

[20] S. Fan, S. G. Johnson, J. D. Joannopoulos, C. Manolatou, and H. A. Haus, submitted for publication (2000).

[21] S. Fan, P. R. Villeneuve, J. D. Joannopoulos, and H. A. Haus, *Phys. Rev. Lett.* **80**, 960 (1998).

[22] S. Fan, P. R. Villeneuve, J. D. Joannopoulos, and H. A. Haus, *Opt. Express* **3**, 4 (1998).

[23] S. Fan, P. R. Villeneuve, J. D. Joannopoulos, M. J. Khan, C. Manolatou, and H. A. Haus, *Phys. Rev. B* **59**, 15882 (1999).

[24] A. Mekis and J. D. Joannopoulos, *Optics Letters*, in press (2000).

[25] S. G. Johnson, S. Fan, A. Mekis, and J.D. Joannopoulos, unpublished.

[26] S. Fan, J. Winn, A. Devenyi, J. Chen, R. Meade, and J. D. Joannopoulos, *J. Opt. Soc. Am. B* **12**, 1267 (1995).

[27] H. Benisty, D. Labilloy, C. Weisbuch, C. J. M. Smith, T. F. Krauss, D. Cassagne, A. Béraud, and C. Jouanin, *App. Phys. Lett.* **76**, 532 (2000).

[28] O. Painter, J. Vuckovic, and A. Scherer, *J. Opt. Soc. Am. B* **16**, 275 (1999).

3D PHOTONIC CRYSTALS: FROM MICROWAVES TO OPTICAL FREQUENCIES

C. M. SOUKOULIS
Ames Laboratory and Department of Physics and Astronomy, Iowa State University, Ames, IA 50011

Abstract. An overview of the theoretical and experimental efforts in obtaining a photonic band gap, a frequency band in three-dimensional dielectric structures in which electromagnetic waves are forbidden, is presented.

1. INTRODUCTION AND HISTORY

Electron waves traveling in the periodic potential of a crystal are arranged into energy bands separated by gaps in which propagating states are prohibited [1]. It is interesting to see if analogous band gaps exist when electromagnetic (EM) waves propagate in a periodic dielectric structure (e.g., a periodic lattice of dielectric spheres of dielectric constant ϵ_a embedded in a uniform dielectric background ϵ_b). If such a band gap or frequency gap exists, EM waves with frequencies inside the gap cannot propagate in any direction inside the material. These frequency gaps are referred to as "photonic band gaps."

Photonic band gaps can have a profound impact on many areas in pure and applied physics [2,3]. Due to the absence of optical modes in the gap, spontaneous emission is suppressed for photons with frequencies in the forbidden region [4,5]. It has been suggested that, by tuning the photonic band gap to overlap with the electronic band edge, the electron-hole recombination process can be controlled in a photonic band gap material, leading to enhanced efficiency and reduced noise in the operation of semiconductor lasers and other solid state devices [3,5]. The suppression of spontaneous emission can also be used to prolong the lifetime of selected chemical species in catalytic processes [6]. Photonic band gap materials can also find applications in frequency-selective mirrors, band-pass filters, and resonators. Besides technical applications in various areas, scientists are interested in

C.M. Soukoulis (ed.), Photonic Crystals and Light Localization in the 21st Century, 25–40.

the possibility of observing the localization of EM waves by the introduction of defects and disorder in a photonic band gap material [7-9]. This will be an ideal realization of the phenomenon of localization uncomplicated by many-body effects present in the case of electron localization. Another interesting effect is that, zero-point fluctuations, which are present even in vacuum, are absent for frequencies inside a photonic gap. Electromagnetic interaction governs many properties of atoms, molecules, and solids. The absence of EM modes and zero point fluctuations inside the photonic gap can lead to unusual physical phenomena [7-12]. For example, atoms or molecules embedded in such a material can be locked in excited states if the photons emitted to release the excess energy have frequency within the forbidden gap. All the aforementioned ideas [2,3] about new physics and new technology hinge upon the assumption of the existence of material with photonic gaps.

To search for the appropriate structures, scientists at Bellcore employed a "cut-and-try" approach in which various periodic dielectric structures were fabricated in the microwave regime and the dispersion of EM waves were measured to see if a frequency gap existed [13]. The process was time consuming and not very successful. After attempting dozens of structures over a period of two years, Yablonovitch and Gmitter identified [13] only one structure with a photonic band gap. This structure consists of a periodic array of overlapping spherical holes inside a dielectric block. The centers of the holes are arranged in a face-centered-cubic (fcc) lattice and the holes occupy 86% of the volume of the block.

Stimulated by the experimental work, theorists became interested in the solution of the photonic band problem and in the search for structures with photonic band gaps. Early work in this area employed the "scalar wave approximation" which assumed the two polarizations of the EM waves can be treated separately, thus decoupling the problem into the solution of two scalar wave equations. When we first became involved with the photon band problem, calculations had already been completed for the experimental structure in the scalar wave approximation [14,15]. The results showed the existence of a gap but the position and size of the gap were not in quantitative agreement with the experiment, indicating the need for a full vector wave treatment. It turned out from subsequent calculations that the errors made in neglecting the vector nature of the EM wave were more serious than initially anticipated, and the scalar wave calculations actually gave qualitatively wrong results.

The vector wave solution of Maxwell's equations for a periodic dielectric system was carried out independently by several groups shortly after the appearance of the scalar wave results [16-18]. All of the methods employ a plane wave expansion of the electromagnetic fields and use Bloch's theorem to reduce the problem to the solution of a set of linear equations.

When the photon band structure for the experimental fcc structure [13] of 86% air spheres in a dielectric matrix, was calculated [18], it showed that the experimental fcc structure does not have a complete photonic band gap for the lowest-lying bands. A very large depletion of DOS is found, called a "pseudo-gap." Actually, this result was also obtained earlier by two other groups [16,17], although at that time we were not aware of their results. At this point, the existence of photonic gap materials was seriously doubted [19]. However, since we found that the plane wave expansion method [16-18] can solve the photon band problem efficiently and much faster than the experimental "cut-and-try" method, we used it to investigate whether other structures could succeed where the fcc air sphere structure failed.

2. PHOTONIC BAND GAP STRUCTURES WITH THE DIAMOND LATTICE SYMMETRY

Ho, Chan, and Soukoulis were the first to give a prescription for a periodic dielectric structure [18] that possesses a full photonic band gap rather than a pseudogap. This proposed structure is a periodic arrangement of dielectric spheres in a diamond-like structure. A systematic examination [18] of the photonic band structures for dielectric spheres and air spheres on a diamond lattice, as a function of the refractive index contrasts and filling ratios, was made. It was found that photonic band gaps exist over a wide region of filling ratios for both dielectric spheres and air spheres for refractive-index contracts as low as 2. However, this diamond dielectric structure is not easy to fabricate, especially in the micron and submicron length scales for infrared or optical devices. However, after we communicated our findings about the diamond structure, Yablonovitch very quickly devised [20] an ingenious way of constructing a diamond lattice. He noted that the diamond lattice is a very open structure characterized by open channels along the [110] directions. Thus, by drilling cylindrical holes through a dielectric block, a structure with the symmetry of the diamond structure can be created. Since there are 6 sets of equivalent [110] directions in the lattice, there are 6 sets of holes drilled. If the crystal is oriented such that the [111] surface is exposed, then three sets of these holes will be slanted at angles of 35.26° with respect to the normal [111] direction. The remaining three sets of holes have their axes parallel to the [111] surface and are harder to make on a thin film oriented in the [111] direction. Thus, in the end, the experimentalists decided to abandon the second three sets of holes and construct a structure with only the first three sets of holes which became the first experimental structure that demonstrates the existence of a

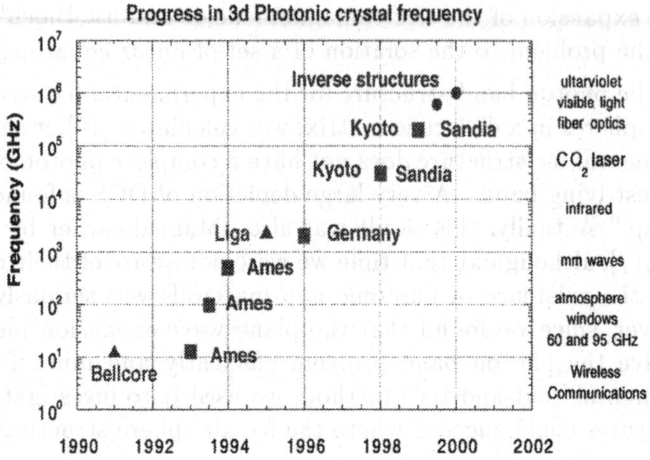

Figure 1. The frequency of the midgap in GHz of 3d photonic crystals versus the year that were fabricated. The triangle symbol is the "3-cylinder" structure suggested by Yablonovitch, the square symbol is the layer-by-layer structure of Ames laboratory at Iowa State University and the circural symbol are inverse closed-packed structures.

photonic band gap, in agreement with the predictions [21] of the theoretical calculations. This is a successful example where the theory was used to design dielectric structures with desired properties. In Fig. 1, we present the historical progress of the midgap frequency of 3D photonic crystals. Notice that the first 3D photonic crystal was fabricated in 1991 by Yablonovitch, while he was still at Bellcore.

We repeated our calculations for several variations on the diamond lattice [21]. One calculation uses the diamond lattice generated by 6 sets of air cylinders or dielectric cylinders in the six [110] directions. The other calculation uses a diamond rod lattice in which, instead of putting spheres at the lattice sites, we joined them together by nearest-neighbor rods. We also tested the effects on the photon band gap when 3 sets of cylinders are omitted in the 6-cylinder diamond structure. All of these structures exhibit photonic band gaps, with the best performance coming from a diamond rod lattice, which achieves a maximum gap of 30% for a refractive index contrast of 3.6.

Very narrow photonic band gaps have also been found [22] in a simple cubic geometry. For 2D systems, theoretical studies have shown [23-26] that a triangular lattice of air columns in a dielectric background [23-25] and a graphite lattice [26] of dielectric rods in air background are the best overall 2D structure, which gives the largest photonic gap with the smallest retroactive index contrast. In addition, it was demonstrated [27-30] that lattice imperfections in a 2D and/or 3D periodic arrays of a dielectric material can give rise to fully localized EM wave functions. The main challenge in

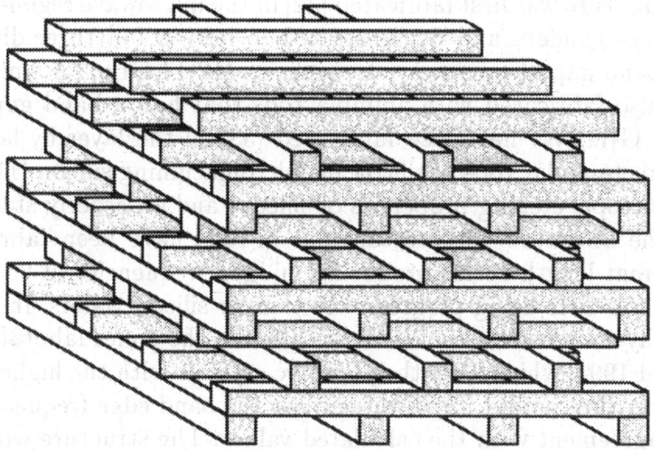

Figure 2. The new layer-by-layer structure producing full three-dimensional photonic band gaps. The structure is constructed by an orderly stacking of dielectric rods, with a simple one-dimensional pattern of rods in each layer. Although rods of rectangular cross-section are shown here, the rods may also have cylindrical or elliptical cross sections.

the photonic band gap field is the discovery of a 3D dielectric structure that exhibits a photonic gap but, in addition, can be built by microfabrication techniques on the scale of optical wavelengths.

3. LAYER-BY-LAYER PHOTONIC BAND GAP STRUCTURES

The search for simplifying the structure and reducing the dimensionality of the structural building blocks continued. The Iowa State group has designed [31] a novel three-dimensional layer-by-layer structure that has a full three-dimensional photonic band gap over a wide range of structural parameters. The new structure (Fig. 2) consists of layers of one-dimensional rods with a stacking sequence that repeats every fourth layer with a repeat distance of c. Within each layer the rods are arranged in a simple one-dimensional pattern and are separated by a distance a, a significant simplification from the two-dimensional grid found earlier. The rods in the next layer are rotated by an angle θ has the value of 90° but in general could vary from 90° to 60° but still have a full three-dimensional photonic band gap. The rods in the second neighbor plane are shifted by half the spacing, a, relative to rods in the first plane in a direction perpendicular to the rods. The rods in every alternate layer are parallel (Fig. 2). This structure has the symmetry of a face centered tetragonal (fct) lattice. For the special case of $c/a = \sqrt{2}$, the lattice can be derived from a fcc unit cell with a basis of two rods. This layered structure can be derived from diamond by replacing the 110 chains of atoms with the rods.

This structure was first fabricated [32] in the microwave regime by stacking alumina cylinders and demonstrated to have a full three-dimensional photonic band gap at microwave frequencies (12-14 GHz). A similar structure was also fabricated with alumina rods that had a band gap between 18 and 24 GHz. We have also fabricated [33-35] the layer-by-layer structure with rectangular rods of silicon by micromachining silicon [110] wafers, using anisotropic etching properties of silicons and an orderly stacking procedure. The structure with rectangular Si-rods have been fabricated for three different length scales producing midgap frequencies of 95 GHz, 140 GHz, and 450 GHz using progressively thinner silicon wafers. In Fig. 2, we show the layer-by-layer structure fabricated by the Ames laboratory group in 1993 and 1994, which were the photonic crystals with the highest midgap frequency at that period. In all three cases the band edge frequencies are in excellent agreement with the calculated values. The structure with midgap at 94 GHz has also been fabricated by laser machining alumina wafers, illustrating the usefulness of our layer-by-layer structure. This performance puts the new structure in the frequency range where a number of millimeter and submillimeter wave applications have been proposed, including efficient mm wave antennas, filters, sources, and waveguides. However, most of these applications are based on the presence of defect or cavity modes, which are obtained by locally disturbing the periodicity of the photonic crystal. The frequency of these modes lie within the forbidden band gap of the pure crystal, and the associated fields are localized around the defect. We have demonstrated [36,37] the existence of such cavity structures built around the layer-by-layer PBG crystal. The defects are formed by either adding or removing dielectric material to or from the crystal. We have observed [36,37] localized defect modes with peak and high Q values. The measurements are in good agreement with theoretical calculations.

An interesting class of photonic crystals is the A7-family of structures [38]. These structures have rhombohedral symmetry and can be generated by connecting lattice points of the A7 structure by cylinders. The A7 class of structures can be described a two structural parameters - an internal displacement u and a shear angle α- that can be varied to optimize the gap. For special values of the parameters the structure reduces to simple cubic, diamond, and the Yablonovitch 3-cylinder structure. Gaps as large as 50% are found [38] in the A7 class of structures for well optimized values of the structural parameters and fabrication of these structures would be most interesting. It is worth noting that the fcc structure *does* have [39,40] a true photonic band gap between the eight and the ninth bands (see Fig. 3). The fcc lattice does *not* have [16-18] a PBG between the lowest bands (bands 2 and 3).

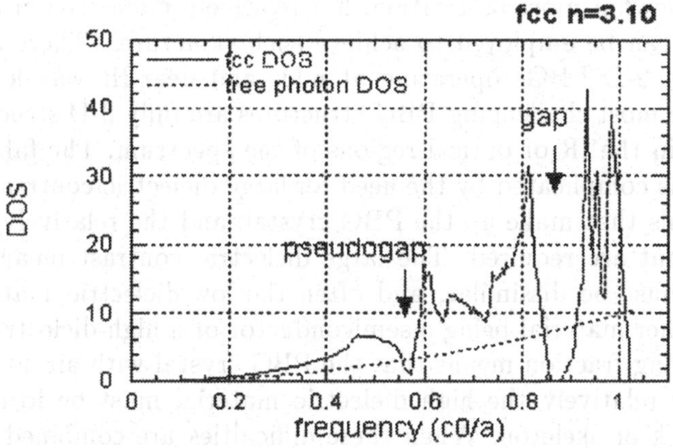

Figure 3. Density of states for the fcc system of low dielectric spheres (filling ratio 0.74) in a high dielectric background, with a refractive index contrast of 3.1, displaying the full gap between the 8 and 9 bands and the weaker pseudogap between bands 2 and 3. Frequencies are in dimensionless units where c0 is the speed of light (in the dielectric background) and a the lattice constant.

4. FABRICATION OF PHOTONIC BAND GAP STRUCTURES

There have been intensive efforts to build and test photonic band gap structures, dating back to the original efforts of Yablonovitch [13] shortly after his first proposal for PBG crystals. Fabrication can be either easy or extremely difficult, depending upon the desired wavelength of the band gap and the level of dimensionality. Since the wavelength of the band gap scales directly with the lattice constant of the photonic crystal, lower frequency structures that require larger dimensions will be easier to fabricate. At microwave frequencies, where the wavelength is on the order of one centimeter, the photonic crystals are decidedly macroscopic, and simple machining techniques or rapid prototyping methods can be employed in building the crystals. At the other extreme, optical wavelength PBGs require crystal lattice constants less than one micron. Building PBGs in the optical regime requires methods that push current state-of-the art micro- or nano-fabrication techniques. In a similar manner, the dimensionality of the PBG has a big impact on the ease or difficulty of fabrication. Since one-dimensional PBGs require periodic variation of the dielectric constant in only one direction, they are relatively easy to build at all length scales. One-dimensional PBG mirrors (more commonly known as distributed Bragg reflectors) have used in building optical and near-infrared photonic devices for many years. Two common examples of devices using 1-D PBGs are distributed feedback lasers and vertical-cavity surface-emitting lasers. Two-dimensional PBGs require somewhat more fabrication, but relatively main-stream fabrication techniques can be employed to achieve such structures. There are several examples of 2-D PBGs operating at mid- and near-IR wavelengths [26]. Clearly, the most challenging PBG structures are fully 3-D structures with band gaps in the IR or optical regions of the spectrum. The fabrication of 3-D PBGs is complicated by the need for large dielectric contrasts between the materials that make up the PBG crystal, and the relatively low filling fractions that are required. The large dielectric contrast means that the materials must be dissimilar, and often the low-dielectric material is air with the other material being a semiconductor or a high-dielectric ceramic. The low filling fraction means that the PBG crystal with air as one dielectric will be relatively the high dielectric material must be formed into a thin network or skeleton. When these difficulties are combined with need for micron or sub-micron dimensions to reach into the optical region, the fabrication becomes very difficult, indeed. This area of PBG research has been one of the most active, and perhaps most frustrating, in recent years.

An alternative layer-by-layer structure has been proposed by Fan et al. [41] to fabricate PBGs at optical frequencies. This consists of a layered structure of two dielectric materials in which a series of air columns is drilled into the top surface. The structural parameters have been optimized to yield 3D photonic gap to midgap ratios of 14% using Si, SiO_2 and air, to 23% using Si and air (i.e., the SiO_2 layers are replaced by air.

As we have discussed above, the first successful PBG crystal was fabricated by Yablonovitch [20] at the millimeter-wave region of the spectrum. Since 1991, both Yablonovitch and Scherer have been working towards reducing the size of the structure to micrometer length scales [42]. However, it is very difficult to drill uniform holes of appreciable depth with micron diameters. So Scherer's efforts were partially successful in producing a PBG crystal with a gap at optical frequencies. This is the reason that is not included in Fig. 1.

Another approach was undertaken by a group at the Institute of Microtechnology in Mainz, Germany in collaboration with the Research Center of Crete and Iowa State University. They fabricated PBG structures using deep x-ray lithography [43]. PMMA resist layers with thickness of 500 microns were irradiated to form a "three-cylinder" structure. In Fig. 4 a photonic crystal with a lattice constant of $114\mu m$ made from negative tone resist is shown. Since the dielectric constant of the PMMA is not large enough for the formation of a PBG, the holes in the PMMA structure were filled with a ceramic material. After the evaporation of the solvent, the samples were heat treated at 1100°C, and a lattice of ceramic rods corresponding to the holes in the PMMA structure remained. A few layers of this structure were fabricated with a measured band gap centered at 2.5

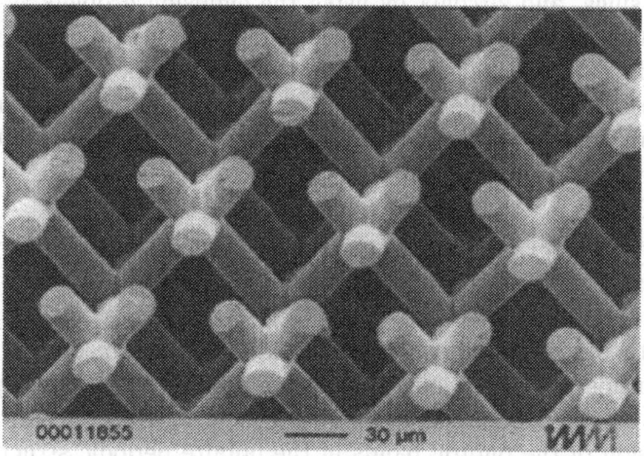

Figure 4. The "three-cylinder" photonic crystal made from negative tone resist.

THz. This frequency and the year that was achieved are shown in Fig. 1, with the name of Liga. Recent experiments are currently trying to fill the PMMA holes with metal.

The layer-by-layer structure shown in Fig. 2 were fabricated [44] by laser rapid prototyping using laser-induced direct-write deposition from the gas phase. The PBG structure consisted of oxide rods and the measured photonic band gap was centered at 2 THz. This frequency and the year that was fabricated are shown in Fig. 1, with the name of Germany. However, our calculations were unable to confirm those measurements. More experiments on this promising direction are needed.

Very recent work in Sandia Labs by Lin [45], as well as in Kyoto University by Noda [46] have been able to grow up to five layers, of the layer-by-layer structure of Iowa State University shown in Fig. 2, at both the 10 micron and 1.5 micron wavelength. This is really a spectacular achievement. They're measured transmittance shows a band gap centered at 30 THz and 200 THz respectively. They were able to overcome very difficult technological challenges, in planarization, orientation, and 3-D growth at micrometer length scales.

Finally, colloidal suspensions [47-49] have the ability to spontaneously form bulk 3D crystals with lattice parameters on the order of 1-1000 nm. Also, 3D dielectric lattices have been developed [50] from a solution of artificially grown monodisperse spherical SiO_2 particles. However, both these procedures give structures with quite small dielectric contrast ratio (less than 2), which is not enough to give a full band gap. A lot of effort is going into finding new methods in increasing the dielectric contrast ratio. Several groups [51-58] are trying to produce ordered macroporous materials of titania, silica, and zirconia by using the emulsion droplets as templates around which material is deposited through a sol-gel process. Subsequent drying and heat treatment yields solid materials with spherical pores left behind the emulsion droplets. Another very promising technique in fabricating photonic crystals at optical wavelengths is 3D holographic lithography [59].

5. THEORETICAL TECHNIQUES AND TRANSFER MATRIX RESULTS

All of the theoretical results discussed above were obtained with the plane-wave expansion technique [16-18], which is now very well developed. However, most of the theoretical techniques concentrate on the calculation of the dispersion of the photon bands in the infinite periodic structure, while experimental investigations focus mainly on the transmission of EM waves through a finite slab of the photonic band gap patterned in the required periodic structure. Even with the knowledge of the photon band structure, it is still a non-trivial task to obtain the transmission coefficient for comparison with experiment. Another important quantity for the photonic band gap experiments and devices is the attenuation length for incident EM waves inside the photonic band gap. Another topic of interest is the behavior of impurity modes associated with the introduction of defects into the photonic band gap structure. While this problem can be tackled within a plane wave approach using the supercell method [27,28] in which a simple defect is placed within each supercell of an artificially periodic system, the calculations require a lot of computer time and memory. Recently, Pendry and MacKinnon [60] introduced a complimentary technique for studying photonic band gap structures which is called the transfer-matrix method. In the transfer matrix method (TMM), the total volume of the system is divided into small cells and the fields in each cell are coupled to those in the neighboring cells. Then the transfer matrix is defined by relating the incident fields on one side of the PBG structure with the outgoing fields on the other side. Using the TMM, the band structure of an infinite periodic system can be calculated. The main advantage of this method is the calculation of the transmission and reflection coefficients for EM waves of various frequencies incident on a finite thickness slab of the PBG material. In this case, the material is assumed to be periodic in the directions parallel to the interfaces.

We want to stress that this technique can also be applied to cases where the plane-wave method fails or becomes too time consuming. For example, when the dielectric constant is frequency dependent, or has a non-zero imaginary part, and when defects are present in an otherwise periodic sys-

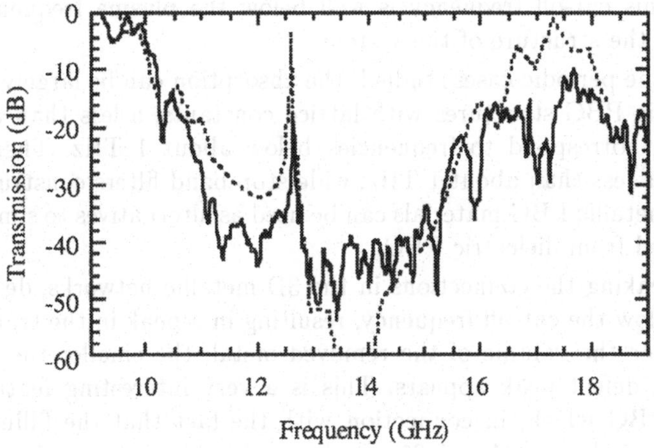

Figure 5. Theoretical (dashed line) and experimental (solid line) transmission characteristics of a defect structure.

tem, this technique works well. The TMM has previously been applied in studies of defects in 2D PBG structures [61], of PBG materials in which the dielectric constants are complex and frequency dependent [62], of 3D layer-by-layer PBG materials [34], of 2D metallic PBG structures [62,63] and 3D metallic structures [62]. In all these examples, the agreement between theoretical predictions and experimental measurements is very good, as can be seen in Fig. 5.

In particular, for 2D systems consisting of metallic cylinders [56], there is considerable difference between the two polarizations. For p-polarized waves, the results are qualitatively similar to the dielectric PBG systems. Propagating modes are interrupted by band gaps appearing close to the edges of the Brillouin zone. On the other hand, for s-polarized waves, there is a cut-off frequency ν_c. There are no propagating modes for frequencies between zero and ν_c, so the transmission has a very sharp drop in this frequency range. Above ν_c, there is the usual behavior of bands interrupted by gaps.

For 3D metallic PBG structures [64], the results are very sensitive on the topology of the structure. Systems with isolated metallic scatterers (cermet topology) exhibit similar behavior to the dielectric PBG materials. But, for metallic scatterers forming a continuous network (network topology), there are no propagating modes for frequencies smaller than a cut-off frequency for both polarizations and for any incident angle. Note that for dielectric PBG materials, there is no cut-off frequency for both types of the topology. We have shown this behavior, in both 2D and 3D cases, can be explained using a simple waveguide model where the ν_c is predicted with good accuracy. This cut-off frequency is well below the plasma frequency and is related to the structure of the system.

In all the periodic cases studied, the absorption can be largely neglected for metallic PBG structures with lattice constants, a less than about 100 μm which correspond to frequencies below about 1 THz. Therefore, for frequencies less than about 1 THz, wide stop-band filters constructed from periodic metallic PBG materials can be used as alternatives to similar filters constructed from dielectric PBG.

By breaking the connections in the 3D metallic networks, defect states appear below the cut-off frequency, resulting in a peak in the transmission. The smaller the volume of the removed metal, the smaller the frequency where the defect peak appears. This is a very interesting feature of the metallic PBG which, in connection with the fact that the filling ratio of the metal can be less than 0.01, can be used in the construction of narrow band-pass filters smaller in size than those constructed from dielectric PBG. By increasing the lattice constant, the Q factor and the transmission at the defect peak increase by order of magnitudes, while the dimensionless defect frequency remains almost constant. The absorption at the frequency where the defect peak appears increases as the lattice constant increases, an effect which may create problems in some of the possible applications. An important advantage of metallic PBG structures is they could be smaller in size and lighter than the corresponding dielectric PBG materials.

6. EFFECTS OF ABSORPTION AND DISORDER

We have studied how the absorption affects [62] the structural gaps and the possible difficulties of their experimental investigation. We have found that for absorbing cases, the transmission becomes thickness dependent for every frequency. For non-absorbing cases, the transmission is basically thickness independent, except for frequencies inside the structural gaps. This thickness dependence increases as the frequency increases. As a consequence, for a very thick absorbing system, the transmission in the upper edge of a structural gap could become so small that it can be impossible to find the recovery of the transmission at the upper edge of the gap, since, experimentally, there is always a lower bound for a transmission measurement (noise level). Thus, for absorbing PBG materials, the thicker slab is not necessarily better in contrast with what is commonly accepted for non-absorbing PBG materials.

We have also studied 2D disordered systems [65] which are periodic on the average. The corresponding periodic systems consist of cylinders forming a square lattice and embedded in a different dielectric medium. By introducing disorder in these periodic systems, the higher gaps, which are narrow, disappear quickly and the logarithmic average of the transmission, $< ln(T) >$, or the localization length, ℓ, becomes almost constant at relatively high frequencies (ω higher than about c/a). These high frequency values of the localization length depend upon the filling ratio and can be as small as 5.2a (a is the lattice constant of the unperturbed periodic system) for the cases that we have studied. On the other hand, for low frequencies, $< ln(T) >$ is not affected by the disorder and it is close to zero which corresponds to very high localization lengths. At intermediate frequencies, there are large drops in the $< ln(T) >$ which correspond to the lowest gaps of the periodic cases. The wider the gaps of the periodic cases, the higher the amount of disorder needed to close these gaps. The gaps of the s-polarized waves are generally wider and survive a high amount of disorder, in contrast with the gaps of the p-polarized waves which are destroyed easily by the disorder. A systematic study of the optimum conditions for the appearance of the gaps has shown these conditions are fulfilled for cylinders of high dielectric material with filling ratio around 0.25 for the s-polarized waves. In these cases, the gaps are wider and they survive even a high amount of disorder, resulting to localization lengths smaller than 5a.

Finally, we have also studied 3D disordered systems [66] which are periodic on the average. Preliminary results show that for structures with network topology, the gaps disappear easily by breaking the network. In contrast, introducing positional disorder but keeping the network topology, the gaps survive a high amount of of disorder and the corresponding localization length at frequencies close to the gap can be small.

Yan et al. [67] have also considered many types of fabrication related disorders, from the variation of the layer thickness and channel depth, to the misalignment of channels between successive layers. They also found that the band gap suffered little change. They argued that the apparent insensitivity of the photonic band gap arises from the fact that the wavelength of the light is much larger than the length scale of the disorder. Finally, Chutinan and Noda [68] have theoretically calculated the effects of disorder in the layer-by-layer structure, shown in Fig. 2, and found that indeed the bandgap is robust to misalignments of the cylinders forming the structure.

7. CONCLUSIONS

In summary, we have reviewed the theoretical and experimental efforts in obtaining 2D and 3D dielectric structures that possess a full photonic band gap. The plane-wave method results of Ho, Chan, and Soukoulis suggested the first structure to exhibit a true photonic band gap, and the Yablonovitch "3-cylinder" structure of diamond symmetry was the first experimental structure with a photonic band gap. We have demonstrated that a systematic search for the structures that possess optimal photonic gaps can be conducted via theoretical calculations. We find that the photonic band gap depends crucially on i) the local connectivity or geometry, ii) the refractive index contrast and iii) the filling ratio of a structure. Multiply-connected geometries produce larger gaps than simply connected structures.

We have designed a new layer-by-layer structure that has a full three-dimensional photonic band gap. Each layer consists of a set of one-dimensional pattern of parallel dielectric rods. The rods were rotated by 90° between neighboring layers and shifted by half the distance a between second neighbor layers. This stacking procedure led to a unit cell of four layers. This structure has been fabricated by stacking alumina rods producing full 3-dimensional photonic band gaps between 12 and 14 GHz. The structure has been fabricated by micromachining silicon wafers and stacking the wafers in an orderly fashion producing millimeter wave photonic band gap structures at progressively smaller length scales. The Iowa State group has achieved these photonic band gap structures with midgap frequencies of 100 and 500 GHz. A number of applications of the microwave and millimeter wave PBG crystals may be realized with the structures we have already fabricated. This layer-by-layer structure has been proven to be the structure for the extension of photonic band crystals into the infrared and optical regimes an area that will surely lead to new areas in basic physics together with novel applications. Both the Sandia and the Kyoto University groups has been able to fabricate photonic crystals at the 1.5 micron, which is the wavelength that most of the telecommunications take place. We are excited about the future applications of photonic band gaps and the prospects of using our calculational techniques to design and help the fabrication of these photonic band gap materials.

8. ACKNOWLEDGMENTS

This work was done in collaboration K.-M. Ho, C. T. Chan, M. Sigalas, and R. Biswas. Ames Laboratory is operated by the U.S. Department of Energy by Iowa State University under Contract No. W-7405-Eng-82. This work was supported by the Director for Energy Research, Office of Basic Energy Sciences and Advanced Energy Projects, by a NATO Grant No. CRG 972102 and a NSF international grant.

References

1. See e.g., C. Kittel, *Introduction of Solid State Physics*, (5th Edition, Wiley, 1976) Ch. 7.
2. See the proceedings of the NATO ARW, *Photonic Band Gaps and Localization*, ed.

by C. M. Soukoulis, (Plenum, N.Y., 1993); *Photonic Band Gap Materials*, ed. by C. M. Soukoulis, NATO ASI, Series E, vol. 315.

3. For a recent review see the special issue of J. of Lightwave Technology **17**, 1928-2207 (1999); and J. D. Joannopoulos, R. D. Mead, and J. N. Winn *Photonic Crystals*, (Princeton, 1995).
4. E. M. Purcell, *Phys. Rev.* **69**, 681 (1946).
5. E. Yablonovitch, *Phys. Rev. Lett.* **58**, 2059 (1987).
6. N. Lawandy, in *Photonic Band Gaps and Localization,* ed. by C. M. Soukoulis (Plenum Publ., N.Y., 1993), p. 355
7. S. John, *Phys. Rev. Lett.* **58**, 2486 (1987); S. John, *Comments Cond. Matt. Phys.* **14**, 193 (1988); S. John, *Physics Today* **32**, 33 (1991).
8. *Scattering and Localization of Classical Waves in Random Media,* ed. by P. Sheng (World Scientific, Singapore, 1990).
9. J. M. Drake and A. Z. Genack, *Phys. Rev. Lett.* **63**, 259 (1989).
10. C. A. Condat and T. R. Kirkpatrick, *Phys. Rev. B* **36**, 6783 (1987).
11. J. Martorell and N. M. Lawandy, *Phys. Rev. Lett.* **65**, 1877 (1990).
12. G. Kurizki and A. Z. Genack, *Phys. Rev. Lett.* **66**, 1850 (1991).
13. E. Yablonovitch and T. J. Gmitter, *Phys. Rev. Lett.* **63**, 1950 (1989).
14. S. Satpathy, Z. Zhang, and M. R. Salehpour, *Phys. Rev. Lett.* **64**, 1239 (1990).
15. K. M. Leung and Y. F. Liu, *Phys. Rev. B* **41**, 10188 (1990).
16. K. M. Leung and Y. F. Liu, *Phys. Rev. Lett.* **65**, 2646 (1990).
17. Z. Zhang and S. Satpathy, *Phys. Rev. Lett.* **65**, 2650 (1990).
18. K. M. Ho, C. T. Chan, and C. M. Soukoulis, *Phys. Rev. Lett.* **65**, 3152 (1990).
19. J. Maddox, *Nature* **348**, 481 (1990).
20. E. Yablonovitch, T. J. Gmitter, and K. M. Leung, *Phys. Rev. Lett.* **67**, 2295 (1991); E. Yablonovitch and K. M. Leung, *Nature* **351**, 278 (1991).
21. C. T. Chan, K. M. Ho, and C. M. Soukoulis, *Europhys. Lett.* **16**, 563 (1991).
22. H. S. Sözuer and J. W. Haus, *J. Opt. Soc. Am. B* **10**, 296 (1993) and references therein.
23. P. R. Villeneuve and M. Piche, *Phys. Rev. B* **46**, 4964 (1992); ibid **46**, 4973 (1992).
24. R. D. Meade, K. D. Brommer, A. M. Rappe, and J. D. Joannopoulos, *Appl. Phys. Lett.* **61**, 495 (1992).
25. M. Plihal, A. Shambrook, A. A. Maradudin, and P. Sheng, *Opt. Commun.* **80**, 199 (1991); M. Plihal and A. A. Maradudin, *Phys. Rev. B* **44**, 8565 (1991).
26. A. Barra, D. Cassagne, and C. Uonanin, *Appl. Phys. Lett.* **72**, 627 (1998) and references therein.
27. E. Yablonovitch, T. J. Gmitter, R. D. Meade, A. M. Rappe, K. D. Brommer, and J. D. Joannopoulos, *Phys. Rev. Lett.* **67**, 3380 (1991).
28. R. D. Meade, K. D. Brommer, A. M. Rappe, and J. D. Joannopoulos, *Phys. Rev. B* **44**, 13772 (1991).
29. S. L. McCall, P. M. Platzman, R. Dalichaouch, D. Smith and S. Schultz, *Phys. Rev. Lett.* **67**, 2017 (1991).
30. W. Robertson, G. Arjavalingan, R. D. Meade, K. D. Brommer, A. M. Rappe and J. D. Joannopoulos, *Phys. Rev. Lett.* **68**, 2023 (1992).
31. K. M. Ho, C. T. Chan, C. M. Soukoulis, R. Biswas, and M. Sigalas, *Solid State Comm.* **89**, 413 (1994).
32. E. Ozbay, A. Abeyta, G. Tuttle, M. C. Tringides, R. Biswas, M. Sigalas, C. M. Soukoulis, C. T. Chan, and K. M. Ho, *Phys. Rev. B* **50**, 1945 (1994).
33. E. Ozbay, G. Tuttle, R. Biswas, M. Sigalas, and K. M. Ho, *Appl. Phys. Lett.* **64**, 2059 (1994).
34. E. Ozbay, E. Michel, G. Tuttle, R. Biswas, K. M. Ho, J. Bostak, and D. M. Bloom, *Optics Lett.* **19**, 1155 (1994).
35. E. Ozbay, G. Tuttle, R. Biswas, K. M. Ho, J. Bostak, and D. M. Bloom, *Appl. Phys. Lett.* **65**, 1617 (1994).
36. E. Ozbay, G. Tuttle, J. S. McCalmont, M. Sigalas, R. Biswas, C. M. Soukoulis, and

K. M. Ho, *Appl. Phys. Lett.* **67**, 1969 (1995).
37. Ozbay, G. Tuttle, M. Sigalas, C. M. Soukoulis, and K. M. Ho, *Phys. Rev. B* **51**, 13961 (1995).
38. C. T. Chan, S. Datta, K. M. Ho, and C. M. Soukoulis, *Phys. Rev. B* **49**, 1988 (1994).
39. H. S. Sozuer, J. W. Haus, and R. Inguva, *Phys. Rev. B* **45**, 13962 (1992).
40. T. Suzuki and P. Yu, *J. Opt. Soc. of Am. B* **12**, 571 (1995).
41. S. Fan, P. Villeneuve, P. Meade, and J. Joannopoulos, *Appl. Phys. Lett.* **65**, 1466 (1994).
42. C. Cheng and A. Scherer, *J. Vac. Sci. Tech. B* **13**, 2696 (1995); C. Cheng et. al. *Physica Scripta* **T68**, 17 (1996).
43. G. Feiertag et al. in *Photonic Band Gap Materials* ed. by C. M. Soukoulis (Kluwer, Dordrecht, 1996), p. 63; G. Feiertag et. al., *Appl. Phys. Lett.* **71**, 1441 (1997).
44. M. C. Wanke, O. Lehmann, K. Muller, Q. Wen, and M. Stuke, *Science* **275**, 1284 (1997).
45. S. Y. Lin et. al., *Nature* **394** 251 (1998); J. G. Fleming and S. Y. Lin, *Opt. Lett.* **24**, 49 (1999)
46. N. Yamamoto, S. Noda and A. Chutinan, *Jpn. J. Appl. Phys.* **37** L1052 (1998); S. Noda et. al., *Appl. Phys. Lett.* **75**, 905 (1999); S. Noda et. al., *Science* **289**, 604 (2000).
47. R. J. Hunter, *Foundations of Colloidal Science* (Clarendon, Oxford, 1993).
48. I. Tarhan and G. H. Watson, *Phys. Rev. Lett.* **76**, 315 (1996); in *Photonic Band Gap Materials* ed. by C. M. Soukoulis (Kluwer, Dordrecht, 1996), p. 93.
49. W. L. Vos, R. Sprik, A. van Blaaderen, A. Imhof, A. Lagendijk, G. H. G. H. Wegdam, *Phys. Rev. B* **54**, 16231 (1996).
50. Yu A. Vlasov et al., *Appl. Phys. Lett.* **71**, 1616 (1997) and references therein.
51. J.E.G.J. Wijnhoven and W. L. Vos, *Science* **281**, 802 (1998).
52. A. Imhof and D. J. Pine, *Nature* **389**, 948 (1997).
53. B. T. Holland et. al., *Science* **281**, 538 (1998).
54. A. A. Zakhidov et. al., *Science* **282**, 897 (1998).
55. G. Subramania et. al.,*Appl. Phys. Lett.* **74**, 3933 (1999).
56. A. Velev et.al., *Nature* **389**, 448 (1997).
57. A. Blanco et. al., *Nature* **405**, 437 (2000).
58. O. D. Velev and E. Kaler, *Adv. Mater.* **12**, 531 (2000), and references therein.
59. M. Campbell et al., *Nature* **404**, 53 (2000).
60. J. B. Pendry and A. MacKinnon, *Phys. Rev. Lett.* **69**, 2772 (1992).
61. M. M. Sigalas, C. M. Soukoulis, E. N. Economou, C. T. Chan, and K. M. Ho, *Phys. Rev. B* **48**, 14121 (1993).
62. M. M. Sigalas, C. M. Soukoulis, C. T. Chan, and K. M. Ho, *Phys. Rev. B* **49**, 11080 (1994).
63. D. R. Smith, S. Shultz, N. Kroll, M. M. Sigalas, K. M. Ho, and C. M. Soukoulis, *Appl. Phys. Lett.* **65**, 645 (1994).
64. M. M. Sigalas, C. T. Chan, K. M. Ho, and C. M. Soukoulis, *Phys. Rev. B* **52**, 11744 (1995).
65. M. M. Sigalas, C. M. Soukoulis, C. T. Chan, and D. Turner, *Phys. Rev. B* **54**, 8340 (1996); E. Lidorikis et. al., *Phys. Rev. B.* **61**, 13458 (2000).
66. M. Sigalas, C. M. Soukoulis, C. T. Chan, and K. M. Ho in *Photonic Band Gap Materials*, ed. by C. M. Soukoulis (Kluwer, Dordrecht, 1996), p.173; M. M. Sigalas et. al., *Phys. Rev. B.* **59**, 12767 (1999).
67. S. Fan, P. R. Villeneuve and J. D. Joannopoulos, *Appl. Phys.* **78**, 1415 (1995).
68. A. Chutinan and S. Noda, *J Opt. Soc. Am. B* **16**, 240 (1999).

TUNABLE PHOTONIC CRYSTALS

KURT BUSCH
Institut für Theorie der Kondensierten Materie
Universität Karlsruhe
P.O. Box 6980, 76128 Karlsruhe, Germany

AND

SAJEEV JOHN
Department of Physics
University of Toronto
60 St. George Street, Toronto, Ontario, Canada M5S 1A7

1. Introduction

In semiconductor materials electron waves propagate in a periodic potential, which originates from the atomic lattice. This modifies the dispersion relation of free electrons: A complicated bandstructure with a band gap is formed. A judicious incorporation of defects (doping) facilitates the manipulation of the electronic properties of these materials. For many decades now, it has been possible to tailor semiconductors to almost any need. The results are well-known: Almost all modern electronic devices are based on these materials, mainly on silicon. For about a decade now, the optical analogues to electronic semiconductors, the so-called Photonic Crystals (PCs), are the subject of intense international research efforts [1, 2]. PCs are materials with a periodically varying index of refraction, that facilitates the control over both propagation of light and - in case they exhibit a complete photonic band gap (PBG) - the inhibition of spontaneous emission of light from atoms and molecules. By analogy with electronic semiconductors, the periodicity of the underlying lattice of a PC should be of the same order of magnitude as the wavelength of the electromagnetic radiation.

Despite the far-reaching analogies between electronic waves in semiconductors and electromagnetic waves in PCs, there are pronounced differences between the two as can be seen from the corresponding equations of motion. Electrons are described by a scalar wavefield. The electromagnetic field, however, is vectorial by nature. Furthermore, the time-independent

C.M. Soukoulis (ed.), Photonic Crystals and Light Localization in the 21st Century, 41–57.

Schrödinger equation allows solutions with negative energy eigenvalues, whereas the corresponding wave equation in electrodynamics contains only the square of the eigenfrequencies; hence, negative eigenvalues are excluded from the outset. That these differences have a disadvantageous effect on the likelihood of the formation of PBGs may be inferred from the few PCs that appear in nature in contrast to ubiquitous semiconductor materials. From the multitude of the optical phenomena only the colorful speckles of opals and some crystallites on the wings of butter flies can be attributed to PC effects. Due to the extreme requirements of miniaturization, substantial progress in nanotechnology has allowed one only recently to condsider the artificial manufacturing of PCs for optical frequencies in a controlled way. It is, however, conceivable that PCs will play a key role in the realization of novel optical devices. Besides important technological aspects, through their potential in controlling electromagnetic waves, PCs provide entirely new avenues of basic research, in particular in the field of Quantum Optics. For instance, unlike microdisk or microsphere cavity resonators which perturb the local density of states (LDOS) of the electromagnetic vacuum, a PC that exhibits a complete PBG can completely supress the total photon density of states (DOS). Accordingly, the trapping of light in localized (defect) modes of a PBG material is far more robust than the resonance trapping of light in conventional microcavity modes. Moreover, it is possible to engineer an arbitrary number of individual localized states which may interact weakly with each other inside a large scale PBG material, but which maintain their immunity from vacuum modes outside the PBG material. This facilitates the development of large scale integrated optical circuits within a PBG in which the nature of radiative dynamics is controlled by the LDOS of photons within the PC rather than the free space DOS outside the PC.

In this work, we demonstrate how the photonic band structure and corresponding LDOS may actively be modified through the control of optical anisotropies in the materials that make up the PC. Consider, for instance, the director field $\hat{n}$ of a nematic liquid crystalline material that is (possibly through infiltration of certain void regions) an integral part of the PC. The orientation of the director $\hat{n}$ may be externally controlled through DC electric or magnetic fields. If the director $\hat{n}$ is continously rotated with respect to the isotropic PC backbone which itself has only discrete rotational symmetries, the stop gap structure of the isotropic backbone may be dramatically modified: Along certain high symmetry directions, a larger index contrast between the backbone material and the nematic liquid crystalline material will develop and, hence, increase the stop gap as well as shift its center frequency. Along certain other high symmetry directions the opposite effect will occur. Clearly, other types of optical anisotropies, such as Faraday-, Pockels- and natural optical activity may be utilized in a similar fashion. Therefore, active band structure modification through electro- or magneto-optically accessible anisotropies will enable the design of novel photonic devices such as switches, routers and modulators. Under suitable circumstances, the above-mentioned effects may conspire, resulting in a fully tunable photonic bandgap [4], leading to complete control of spontaneous emission.

2. Photonic Bandstructure and Density of States

The simplest way to calculate photonic band structures is to apply the methods of electronic band structure calculations. However, various adjustments are necessary in order to take into account the specific differences between photonic and electronic crystals. In what follow we want to outline how the widely used plane wave method (PWM) [3] may be applied to the problem of photonic band structure computation. We consider the wave equation for a magnetic field with harmonic time dependence for a three-dimensional periodic array of scatterers. If the materials differ only in the dielectric but not in the magnetic permeability, by combining Maxwell's equations we obtain the following wave equation

$$\nabla \times \left(\epsilon^{-1}(\vec{r})\nabla \times \vec{H}(\vec{r})\right) - \frac{\omega^2}{c^2}\vec{H}(\vec{r}) = 0 \ . \tag{1}$$

Information about the structure of the Photonic Crystal is fully contained in the dielectric tensor $\epsilon(\vec{r}) = \epsilon(\vec{r} + \vec{R})$ which is periodic with respect to the set $\mathcal{R} = \{n_1\vec{a}_1 + n_2\vec{a}_2 + n_3\vec{a}_3; (n_1, n_2, n_3) \in \mathcal{Z}^3\}$ of lattice vectors $\vec{R}$ that are generated by the primitive translations $\vec{a}_i$, $i = 1, 2, 3$. We discuss from the outset the general case of the anisotropic tensor. The special case of an isotropic medium can be obtained by replacing the dielectric tensor by a scalar times the unit tensor.

The photonic dispersion relation can be obtained straightforwardly by considering the wave equation (1) in reciprocal space, i.e., the dual description of the crystal lattice. To this end, the periodic inverse dielectric tensor is expanded in a Fourier series on $\mathcal{G}$ the reciprocal (dual) lattice corresponding to $\mathcal{R}$:

$$\epsilon^{-1}(\vec{r}) = \sum_{\vec{G}\in\mathcal{G}} \epsilon_{\vec{G}}^{-1}\, e^{i\vec{G}\vec{r}} \quad , \tag{2}$$

where the Fourier coefficients $\epsilon_{\vec{G}}^{-1} = \frac{1}{V}\int_V d^3r\, \epsilon^{-1}(\vec{r})\, e^{-i\vec{G}\vec{r}}$ are obtained through an integration over the Wigner-Seitz cell (WSC) whose volume we have designated by V. Using the Bloch-Flouquet theorem, the magnetic field may be expanded as

$$\vec{H}(\vec{r}) \equiv \vec{H}_{\vec{k}}(\vec{r}) = \sum_{\vec{G}\in\mathcal{G}} \sum_{\lambda=1}^{2} h_{\vec{G}}^{\lambda}\, \hat{e}_{\vec{G}}^{\lambda}\, e^{i(\vec{k}+\vec{G})\vec{r}} \quad . \tag{3}$$

Here, we utilized the fact that $\nabla \cdot \vec{H}(\vec{r}) = 0$, so that λ labels the two transverse polarizations for any plane wave $\vec{G}$ such that $\hat{e}^{\lambda=1,2}$ form an orthogonal triad. Due to the discrete translational symmetry of the lattice, the wave vector $\vec{k}$ labeling the solution may be restricted to lie in the first Brillouin zone (BZ). As a consequence, the dispersion relation in the infinitely extended momentum space is folded back onto the first BZ, introducing a discrete band index n. However, care must be exercised in identifying the irreducible part of the Brillouin zone (IBZ): The dielectric tensor in (1) may have less rotational symmetries than the underlying lattice and consequently, the IBZ for a photonic crystal containing anisotropic materials may be considerably larger than the IBZ for the corresponding isotropic crystal. Rather than dealing with an IBZ that changes from problem to problem, one can choose to work with the standard IBZ for the isotropic material and solve (1) for all inequivalent transformations of the given dielectric tensor with respect to the rotational symmetries of the underlying lattice [4].

Inserting (2) and (3) into (1) results in an infinite matrix eigenvalue problem

$$\sum_{\vec{G}'\in\mathcal{G}} \sum_{\lambda'=1}^{2} M_{\vec{G}\vec{G}'}^{\lambda\lambda'}\, h_{\vec{G}'}^{\lambda'} = \frac{\omega^2}{c^2}\, h_{\vec{G}}^{\lambda} \quad , \tag{4}$$

where the matrix elements $M_{\vec{G}\vec{G}'}^{\lambda\lambda'}$ are given by

$$M_{\vec{G}\vec{G}'}^{\lambda\lambda'} = |\vec{k}+\vec{G}|(\hat{e}_{\vec{G}}^{\lambda} \cdot \epsilon_{\vec{G}-\vec{G}'}^{-1} \cdot \hat{e}_{\vec{G}'}^{\lambda'})|\vec{k}+\vec{G}'| \quad . \tag{5}$$

In order to obtain the photonic band and mode structure, (4) has to be solved for both eigenvalues and eigenvectors which, for a given wave vector $\vec{k}$, are labeled by the band index n. Then, the electric field corresponding to a given eigenfrequency $\omega_n(\vec{k})$, can be computed from Maxwell's equation

$$\vec{E}_{n\vec{k}}(\vec{r}) = -i\frac{c}{\omega_n(\vec{k})}\, \epsilon^{-1}(\vec{r})\, \nabla \times \vec{H}_{n\vec{k}}(\vec{r}) \quad . \tag{6}$$

The photonic dispersion relation gives rise to a photonic density of states (DOS), which plays a fundamental role in the understanding of the properties of a PC. The photonic DOS $N(\omega)$ is defined by "counting" all allowed states of the PC with a given frequency ω, i.e., by the sum of all bands and the integral over the first BZ of a Dirac-δ function

$$N(\omega) = \sum_n \int_{BZ} d^3k \; \delta(\omega - \omega_n(\vec{k})). \tag{7}$$

For applications to quantum optical experiments in photonic crystals it is, however, necessary to invesitgate not only the (overall) availability of modes with frequency ω but also the local coupling between the electromagnetic environment provided by the photonic crystal at the location of, say, an excited atom that wants to emit a photon with frequency ω [5]. Consequently, it is the overlap matrix element of the atomic dipole moment to the photons in this mode that is determining quantum optical properties such as decay rates, etc. This may be combined in the local, DOS (LDOS) $N(\vec{r}, \omega)$, defined as

$$N(\vec{r}, \omega) = \sum_n \int_{BZ} d^3k \; |\vec{E}_{n\vec{k}}(\vec{r})|^2 \, \delta(\omega - \omega_n(\vec{k})). \tag{8}$$

As shown, for. instance in [6], the LDOS may be profoundly different from location to location within the Wigner-Seitz cell as well as from the total DOS indicating that the emission properties of active material placed inside a photonic crystal may be strongly dependent on its location within the Wigner-Seitz cell. For an actual calculation, the integrals in (7) and (8) must be suitably discretized and we may again revert to the methods of electronic band structure calculations, which are described in detail, for instance, in [6] and [7].

When implementing the details of the above-mentioned procedure, care must be exercised. For numerical purposes, Eq. (4) is truncated by retaining only a finite number of reciprocal lattice vectors [3, 6]. In the case of birefringent or biaxial dielectric materials, the dielectric tensor $\epsilon(\vec{r})$ in Eq. (2) is real and symmetric. For materials with inversion symmetry, $\epsilon(\vec{r}) = \epsilon(-\vec{r})$, Eq. (4) is likewise a standard real symmetric eigenvalue problem. The main numerical problem in obtaining the eigenvalues from Eq. (4) is the evaluation of the Fourier coefficients of the inverse dielectric tensor in Eq. (2). As in the case of isotropic dielectric materials [6], this can be done in two different ways. One can calculate the inverse dielectric tensor in real space and then compute its Fourier coeffcients. We refer to this as the direct method. Alternatively, one can calculate the matrix of Fourier coeffcients of the real space tensor and then take its inverse to obtain the required Fourier coefficients. The latter method was shown by Ho, Chan, and Soukoulis (HCS) [3] to be more efficient than the direct method for the isotropic dielectric tensor. Since both Fourier transformation and matrix inversion are linear operations, for a complete set of plane waves the eigenvalue spectrum obtained by the direct method and for the HCS method must coincide exactly. However, we are numerically restricted to operate on a finite dimensional subspace of the full reciprocal space. This leads to dramatically different rates of convergence of the two methods as the dimension of the subspace (number of plane waves) is increased. Just as in the case of isotropic dielectric materials, for birefringent PCs, we find that the HCS method converges substantially faster than the direct method (see section IV.B).

3. Inverse Opals

The single greatest obstacle to realizing the potential of PBG materials has been the lack of an inexpensive and reliable means of microfabricating large scale three-dimensional materials with sizeable gaps at near-visible frequencies. In this paper we discuss in detail the possibility of overcoming this obstacle using self-assembling three-dimensional structures based on "inverse opals" [8, 9, 10].

3.1. FULLY INFILTRATED INVERSE OPAL

Starting from a close-packed face centered cubic lattice of SiO_2 spheres (opal) with diameter on the scale of a micron, PBG materials with gaps in the range of 5-15 % of the center frequency may be realized by infiltration of the opal with high refractive index materials such as Si or Ge, and subsequent removal of. the SiO_2 by chemical etching, leaving behind a connected network of high dielectric material with filling ratios around $f = 0.26$ ("swiss cheese structures"). The etching out of the SiO_2 enhances the dielectric contrast, which, in turn, leads to larger gaps. Moreover, the presence of air voids rather than solid SiO_2 will greatly ease the injection of atomic vapors with which quantum optical experiments can be carried out and also facilitates the infiltration by active materials such as conducting polymers and dyes for laser applications or the infiltration by liquid crystalline materials in order to enable electro-optical tuning effects discussed below. In Figs. 1 and 2 we present the bandstructure and corresponding total DOS of an inverted fcc structure consisting of close-packed air spheres in a silicon matrix with the dielectric constant $\epsilon_b \approx 11.9$. We observe that the fcc structure possesses a pseudo-gap between the 4th and 5th band around the dimensionless frequency $\tilde{\omega} = \omega a/2\pi c \approx 0.524$ and a complete 4.25 % band gap between the 8th and 9th band with a center frequency of $\tilde{\omega} \approx 0.794$.

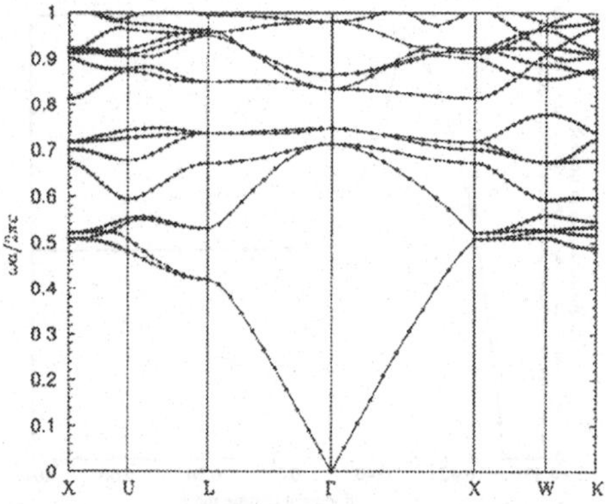

Figure 1. Bandstructure for a close-packed fcc lattice of air spheres in silicon ($\epsilon \approx 11.9$), the inverse opal.

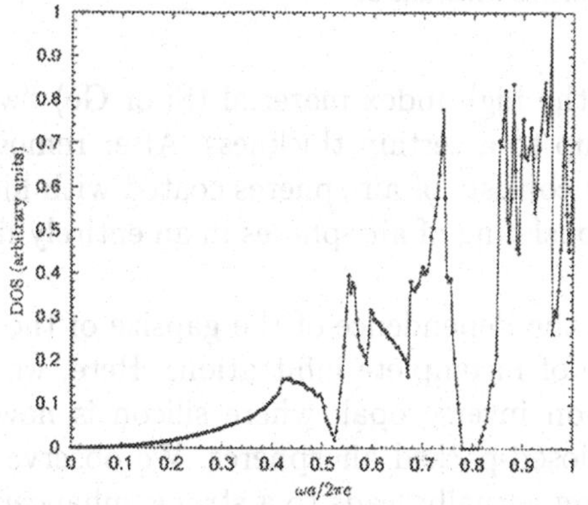

Figure 2. DOS for a close-packed fcc lattice of air spheres in silicon ($\epsilon \approx 11.9$), the inverse opal.

3.2. EFFECT OF INCOMPLETE INFILTRATION

The manufacturing process of infiltrated opals itself suggests two possible approaches to enlarging the PBG: (i) Sintering the artificial opal prior to infiltration improves the stability of the structure and makes it easier to handle. With sintering, the formerly touching spheres are now bonded by a tube-like connection. Infiltrating this sintered structure will result in an inverted structure with a slightly smaller filling ratio of high dielectric material. (ii) In practice [8, 9, 10], the infiltration of a close-packed opal structure may lead only to an incomplete occupation of the void regions between the SiO_2 spheres. The size of the remaining void may thus be viewed as a parameter with which the microscopic Mie resonances of neighboring spheres may be fine-tuned with respect to the macroscopic Bragg-resonances of the fcc lattice in order to find a maximal synergy-effect. We model this

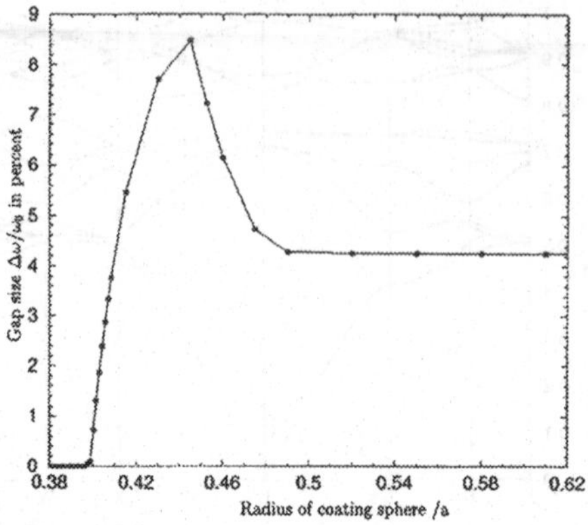

Figure 3. **Dependence of the gap size as a function of radius of coating for a close-packed fcc lattice of air spheres coated with silicon ($\epsilon \approx 11.9$). The coating radius is measured in units of the cubic lattice constant a.**

by assuming that the high index material (Si or Ge) "wets" the surface of the SiO_2 spheres up to a certain thickness. After removal of the SiO_2 the resulting structure consists of air spheres coated with high dielectric material, rather than consisting of air spheres in an entirely filled high dielectric matrix.

Fig. 3 displays the dependence of the gapsize of the inverted fcc structure on the degree of incomplete infiltration. Here, we choose to plot the results of the silicon inverse opal, where silicon is now assumed to form a coating of the closed-packed air spheres. We observe that a slightly incomplete infiltration actually leads to a strong enhancement of the gapsize compared to the completely infiltrated structure. *For a coating radius of $R_c \approx 0.445a$ (corresponding to about 24.5% total volume fraction of silicon) the gap size of the incompletely infiltrated structure is doubled compared to the fully infiltrated one.* As the infiltration becomes more and more incomplete, the band gap eventually disappears altogether as there is not enough high dielectric material to sustain a band gap. Similar enhancements of the gapsize are observed for the case of sintering the opal prior to infiltration [6].

Recently, Blanco et al. succeeded in manufacturing and characterizing the first silicon-based inverse opal [10]. An analysis of the reflection spectrum from their sample, together with a subsequent comparison of the measured data to numerical values from bandstructure computations, revealed that the structure exhibits a complete 5% PBG centered around $1.5\mu m$, consistent with a filling fraction of 23% (by volume) of silicon. Therefore, their structure represents the first very-large-scale, easy-to-manufacture photonic crystal that exhibits a complete PBG at the lower of the two telecommunication windows at near-IR frequencies.

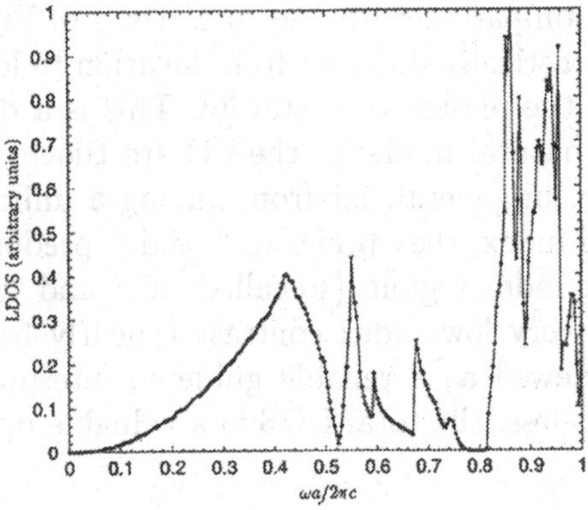

Figure 4. LDOS for a close-packed fcc lattice of air spheres in silicon ($\epsilon \approx 11.9$) at the center of the air spheres.

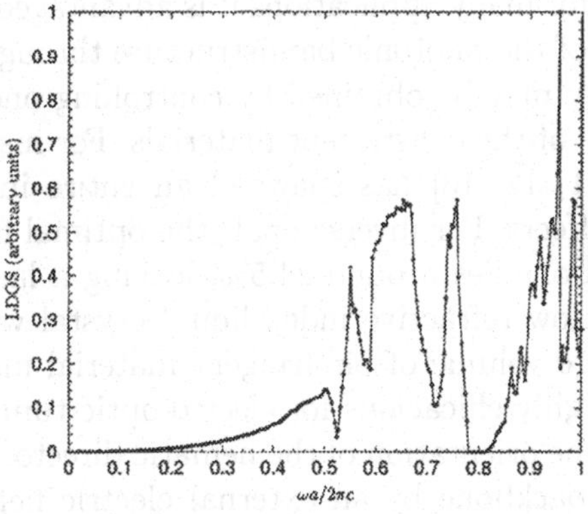

Figure 5. LDOS for a close-packed fcc lattice of air spheres in silicon ($\epsilon \approx 11.9$) at the position inside the dielectric backbone that is furthest away from the center of the air spheres.

3.3. LOCAL DENSITY OF STATES

To complete the investigation of the properties of inverse opals, we turn our attention to the local density of states: As discussed in section II, the spontaneous emission dynamics of active media in photonic crystals is determined by the LDOS, $N(\omega, \bar{r})$, rather than the total DOS, $N(\omega)$ [5]. It is, therefore, imperative to have detailed knowledge about the LDOS in order to understand and predict the outcome of fluorescence experiments. In Figs. 4 and 5 we show the LDOS for the fully infiltrated inverse opal made of silicon for two different locations within the Wigner-Seitz cell of the photonic crystal (the corresponding total DOS is shown in Fig. 2). Figure 4 displays the LDOS at the center of the air spheres, whereas Fig. 5 shows the LDOS inside the dielectric backbone, furthest away from the center of the air spheres. Comparing with the total DOS of Fig. 2, we find that the LDOS may be drastically different from location to location within the Wigner-Seitz cell of the photonic crystal [6]. This is a direct consequence of the fact that the natural modes of the PC are Bloch waves rather than plane waves and are, in general, far from having a uniform modulus. Depending on the band index, they prefer to "reside" predominantly in either low or high dielectric index regions (so-called "air" and "dielectric" bands). Only in the case of very low index contrast ("nearly free photons") may the total DOS be viewed as a reliable guide to interpreting fluorescence phenomena. Nevertheless, the total DOS ia a valuable upper bound on the LDOS.

4. The fully tunable PBG

As discussed above, for many applications it is advantageous to obtain some degree of tunability of the photonic bandstructure through electro-optic effects. Such tunability may be obtained by controlling one or several forms of optical anisotropy of the constituent materials. For instance, the science of liquid crystals [11, 12, 13] has spawned an entire industry related to these electro-optic effects. For inverse opals the optimal filling ratios of the high dielectric backbone lies around 24.5%, leaving a large empty volume for infiltration by a low refractive index liquid crystal with strong optical anisotropy. This large volume of birefringent material makes the resulting composite system highly efficacious for electro-optic tuning effects. In particular, a change in the orientation of the nematic director field with respect to the inverse opal backbone by an external electric field can completely open or close the full, three-dimensional PBG [4].

We now evaluate the tunable bandstructure of the optimized inverse opal [6], described above, made of silicon. This structure, which consists of about 24.5% silicon by volume, has a 8.6% bandgap between bands 8 and 9. Next, we partially infiltrate the nearly 75% void regions with the nematic liquid crystal BEHA [13] such that it wets the inner surface of the air spheres. The principal indices of refraction for BEHA are $n_{LC}^{\parallel} = 1.6$ and $n_{LC}^{\perp} = 1.4$. We choose $R_i = 0.2812a$ so that roughly half the void volume is filled with BEHA and the total volume fraction of BEHA is 36.8%. In Fig. 6 we show the total photon density of states (DOS) when the nematic director $\hat{n}$ is oriented along the (0,0,1) axis of the fcc backbone. The complete 8.6% photonic band gap of the inverse opal backbone (see Fig. 1) is destroyed upon infiltration of the liquid crystal but a pronounced pseudo-gap with a low DOS remains. The closing of the band gap between bands 8 and 9 for $\hat{n} = (0, 0, 1)$ occurs first at the W-points of the full Brillouin zone which experience a strong anisotropy. If $\hat{n}$ is rotated away from the

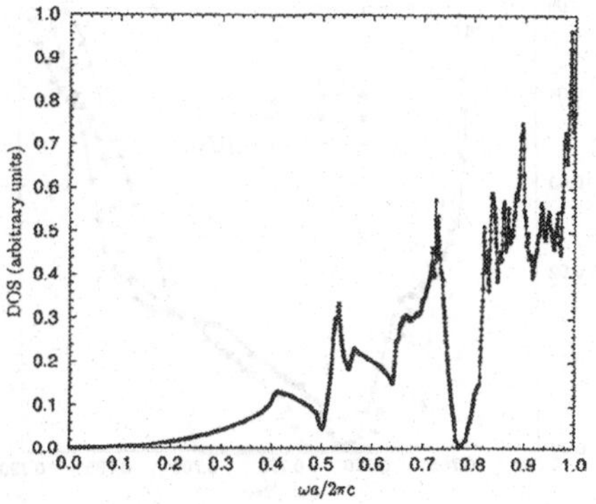

Figure 6. Total DOS for an inverse opal which is infiltrated with a nematic liquid crystal. The nematic director is orientated along the (0,0,1) axis of the inverse opal backbone. The inverse opal backbone is made of silicon (24.5% by volume) which is partially infiltrated with the liquid crystal BEHA (36.8% by volume). The isotropic refractive index of silicon is $n_{Si} = 3.45$ and the principal refractive indices of BEHA are $n_{LC}^{\parallel} = 1.6$ and $n_{LC}^{\perp} = 1.4$.

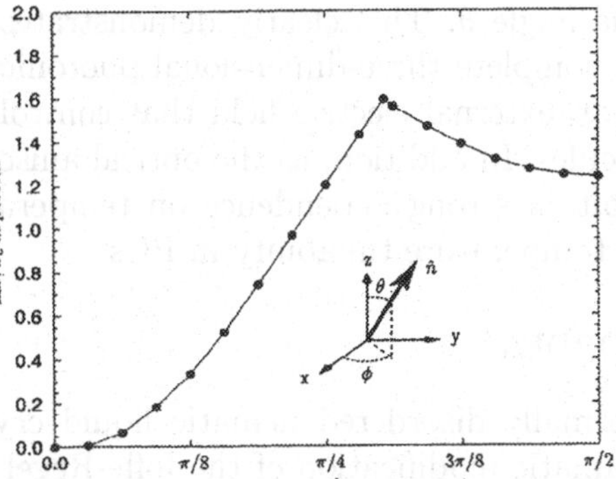

Figure 7. Dependence of the photonic band gap size for a silicon inverse opal infiltrated with the nematic liquid crystal (BEHA) on the orientation of the nematic director $\hat{n}(\phi, \theta)$ for fixed angle $\phi = \pi/4$. The volume fractions are the same as in Fig. 6.

(0,0,1) direction, different high symmetry points in the Brillouin zone will be affected differently. Most notably, the anisotropy seen by the W-points is reduced. In Fig. 7 we display the dependence of the gap size between band 8 and 9 as $\hat{n}$ rotates from (0,0,1) through (1,1,1) to the (1,1,0) direction. In terms of spherical coordinates, $\phi = \pi/4$ and θ ranges from 0 to $\pi/2$. For the liquid crystal PBG material, this leads to an opening of a complete photonic band gap. The PBG reaches a maximum value of 1.6%, when $\hat{n}$ points along the (1,1,1) axis, direction for which the anisotropy as seen by the W-point is at a minimum. The effect of re-orienting $\hat{n}$ on the photon density of states is further illustrated in Fig. 8, where, for fixed $\phi = \pi/4$, we consider

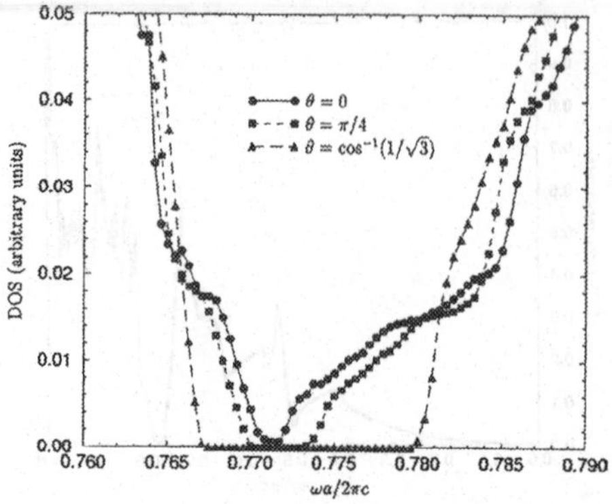

Figure 8. Total photon DOS for a silicon inverse opal which is infiltrated with the nematic liquid crystal (BEHA) for various orientations of the nematic director $\hat{n}(\phi, \theta)$. The angle $\phi = \pi/4$ is fixed and the volume fractions are the same as in Figure 6. The PBG is closed for $\theta = 0$ but reaches a maximum value $\Delta\omega/\omega_c \simeq 1.6\%$ relative to its center frequency ω_c for $\hat{n} = (1,1,1)/\sqrt{3}$.

various values of the angle θ. This clearly demonstrates an electro-optic shutter effect to the complete three-dimensional photonic band gap which may be realized by an external electric field that controls the orientation of the nematic molecules. In addition, as the optical anisotropy of nematic liquid crystals exhibits a strong dependence on temperature, it becomes possible to realize a temperature tunability in PCs.

4.1. TUNABLE DISORDER

Moreover, for a thermally disordered nematic liquid crystal (no applied external field), a dramatic modification of the Ioffe-Regel criterion [14] for localization may be realized. Light localization in a disordered dielectric medium is expected [15, 16, 17] when:

$$\pi^2 c\,\rho(\omega)\;(\ell^*)^2 \simeq 1 \;. \tag{9}$$

Here, c is the speed of light in vacuum, $\rho(\omega)$ is the photon density of states at frequency ω, and ℓ^* is the transport mean free path for photons, determined by the extent of disorder in the medium. For photons in ordinary vacuum ($\omega = ck$), $\rho(\omega) = \omega^2/(\pi^2 c^3)$ and this condition reduces to the Ioffe-Regel condition, $\ell^*\,(\omega/c) \simeq 1$. However, in the liquid crystal PBG material, ℓ^* represents the transport mean free path for optical Bloch waves arising from the deviations of the medium from perfect periodicity. The very low DOS (depending on the orientation of $\hat{n}$) at the bottom of the pseudo-gap or near the complete band gap, provides a very favorable scenario for the photon localization according to criterion (9) even when $\ell^*\,(\omega/c) \gg 1$.

As discussed in section II, the convergence of the PWM critically relies on the usage of the HCS method [3], generalized to the current situation of PCs with anisotropic constituents. If the direct method is used instead, a relative error of at least 10% for the eigenfrequencies persists even for very large numbers of plane waves. As an illustration of the above, we computed the eigenfrequencies for bands 8 and 9 at one of the W-points, i.e., at W= $2\pi/a(1, 1/2, 0)$ for the case of the fully tunable PC described above. The nematic director field was oriented along the (1,1,1) direction. In Tab. 1 we display the results for 113, 339, 531, 749, 965, and 1219 plane waves for both the HCS and the direct method, respectively. Table 1 clearly

TABLE 1. Dependence of the eigenfrequencies of band 8 and 9, i.e., ω_8 and ω_9 at the W-point W= $2\pi/a(1, 1/2, 0)$ on the number of plane waves for the HCS and direct method.

	HCS method		Direct method	
N_g	ω_8	ω_9	ω_8	ω_9
113	0.773238	0.781674	0.892353	1.013902
339	0.767281	0.780931	0.873415	0.921519
531	0.766699	0.780624	0.865101	0.886800
749	0.766669	0.780531	0.858867	0.868011
965	0.766673	0.780621	0.854983	0.856984
1219	0.766643	0.780618	0.844537	0.851014

shows the very much different convergence properties of the two methods: While the HCS results are numerically converged beyond 531 plane waves, the direct method is nowhere near convergence, even for as many as 1219 plane waves. For even larger numbers of plane waves the two method finally converge to the same result which is the HCS result.

5. Optical switching and routing applications

If the air voids of a silicon inverse opal are fully infiltrated with the nematic liquid crystal BEHA, the reduced index contrast prevents the system from exhibiting a complete PBG. Nevertheless, this structure may have important applications as an all-optical switch or router by virtue of the large tuning effects of the stop gaps along certain high symmetry directions. In Fig. 9 we display the photonic bandstructure for a piece of the IBZ with

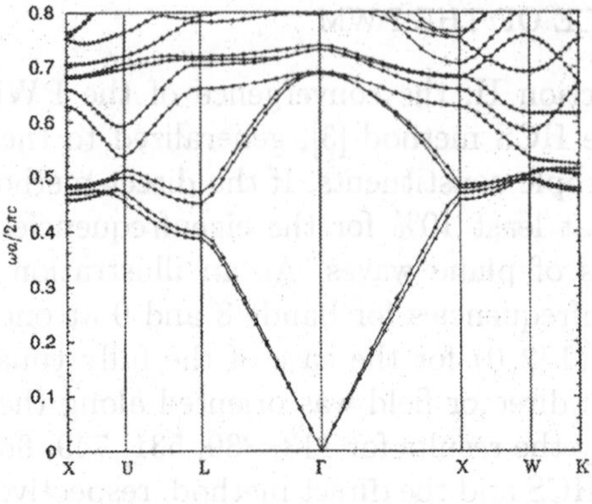

Figure 9. **Photonic band structure of a silicon inverse opal which has been fully infiltrated with the nematic liquid crystal BEHA. The nematic director is orientated along the (0,0,1) axis of the inverse opal backbone. The inverse opal backbone is made of silicon (24.5% by volume). The isotropic refractive index of silicon is $n_{Si} = 3.45$ and the principal refractive indices of BEHA are $n_{LC}^{\parallel} = 1.6$ and $n_{LC}^{\perp} = 1.4$. The coordinates of the high symmetry points given by X = $2\pi/a(1,0,0)$, U = $2\pi/a(1,1/4,1/4)$, L = $2\pi/a(1/2,1/2,1/2)$, W = $2\pi/a(1,1/2,0)$, and K = $2\pi/a(3/4,3/4,0)$.**

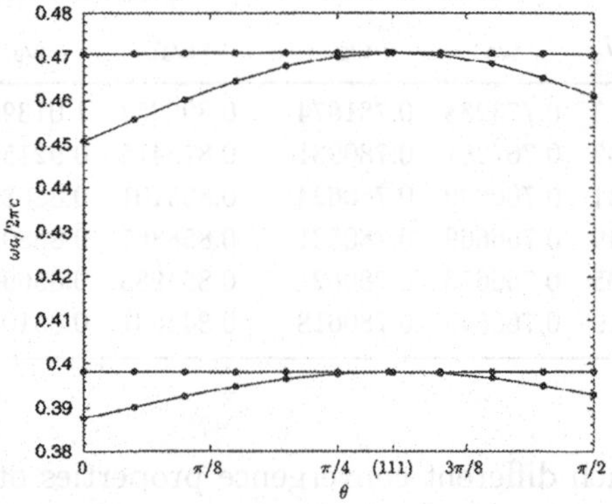

Figure 10. **Variation of bands 1 to 4 at the L-point L=$2\pi/a(1/2,1/2,1/2)$ for a silicon inverse opal which has been fully infiltrated with the nematic liquid crystal BEHA. The nematic director $\hat{n}(\phi,\theta)$ is rotated (for fixed angle $\phi = \pi/4$). The material parameters are the same as in Fig. 9.**

the coordinates of the high symmetry points given by: X = $2\pi/a(1,0,0)$, U = $2\pi/a(1,1/4,1/4)$, L = $2\pi/a(1/2,1/2,1/2)$, W = $2\pi/a(1,1/2,0)$, and K = $2\pi/a(3/4,3/4,0)$. The orientation of the nematic director $\hat{n}$ is along the cubic (0,0,1) axis. There exists a large stop gap between bands 2 and 3 in Γ-L direction. Figure 10 illustrates how this stop bandedge is modified when the director $\hat{n}$ is -as above- re-oriented to angles $\phi = \pi/4$ (fixed) between x- and y-axis and angle θ away from the z-axis: At the L-point, the 3rd band is shifted from $\omega a/2\pi c = 0.45$ to $\omega a/2\pi c = 0.47$ as the nematics director is rotated from the (0,0,1) z-direction to the (1,1,1) direction. If, for instance, the lattice constant is chosen such that the dimensionless frequency $\omega a/2\pi c = 0.45$ corresponds to a vacuum wavelength of 1.5 μm, then the photon dispersion curve near the L-point is shifted over a band of more than 60 nm in width as the nematic director is rotated. Similar results may be found for other high symmetry directions, such as Γ-X or Γ-W. This illustrates the super-electro-optic modulation effect provided by the silicon inverse opal infiltrated with liquid crystalline material. For instance, it has previously been suggested [18] that two-dimensional PC could be utilized for "superprism" effects or wavelength dependent angular beam steering. In a tunable PC, the steering of light can be modulated over a large range of angles by simply applying an external voltage. As a consequence, an electro-actively tunable PC can be used as a tunable mirror or diffraction grating that selectively routes telecommunication signals in all-optical networks without having to take recourse to complicated electronic controls that physically rotate a mirror.

6. Tunability of two-dimensional Photonic Crystals

Similar results for tuning the photonic bandstructure through electro-optic or thermal effects may be realized in two-dimensional PCs such as macroporous silicon [19] as well. For instance, in a recent proof-of-principle experiment, the liquid crystal E7, known for its large nematic temperature range and large optical anisotropy of $\Delta n = 0.2$, was infiltrated into the air pores of a PC with a triangular lattice pitch of 1.58 μm and a band gap wavelength range of 3.3 - 5.9 μm. The refractive index for the H-polarized field propagating perpendicular to the pore axis depends on the alignment of the liquid crystal director field inside the pores. This may be modeled by an axial alignment, in which the liquid crystal director is parallel to the pore axis. After infiltration, the band gap for the H polarized field shifted dramatically and the high frequency band edge was tuned over a range of 80 nm as the liquid crystal was heated from the nematic to the isotropic phase. The measured high frequency band edge wavelength shift is plotted as a function of temperature and compared with theoretical calculations in Fig. 11. As the temperature is increased, the photonic band edge wavelength is redshifted until the phase transition from the nematic to the isotropic phase. The fact that the experimental and theoretical shifts are in the same direction indicates that the actual alignment is largely axial. However, the lack of evidence of a complete axial shift in the experimental data suggests a more complicated director field. In fact, an escaped-radial configuration appears to fully account for the deviations between experiment and theory [20]. In this case, the H-polarized light experiences the spatially averaged

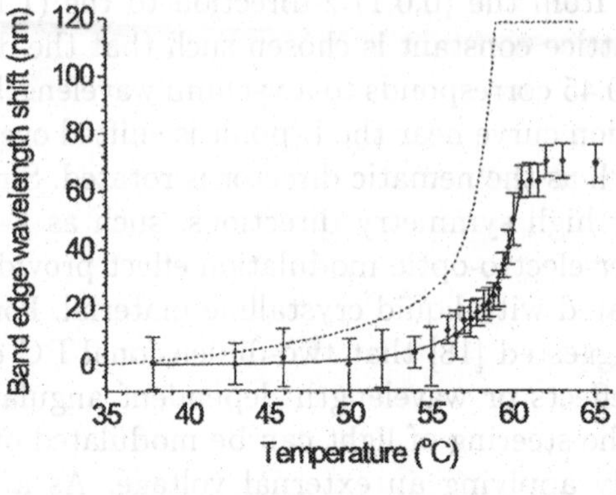

Figure 11. Dependence of the wavelength shift of the air band edge on temperature for two-dimensional photonic crystal made from macroporous silicon that has been infiltrated by the nematic liquid crystal E7. For a detailed description see [20]. Solid line: fit to data. Dashed line: calculations based on axial director alignment.

refractive index within the pore which is larger than in the fully aligned case and increases with temperature until the nematic-isotropic phase transition occurs.

In addition, theoretical calculations for an electro-optical alignment of the nematic director in the plane perpendicular to the pore axis suggest that, for the above discussed two-dimensional PC infiltrated with the liquid crystal E7, the photonic band edge may be shifted by as much as 120 nm when the nematic director is re-oriented in the plane of periodicity. [21].

7. Conclusions

In summary, opal templates infiltrated with high index refractive index semiconductors such as Si [10], Ge, GaAs, or GaP provide a clear route to the realization of large scale three-dimensional PBG materials with gaps in the visible or near visible spectrum. Using this approach PBG materials exhibiting nearly perfect periodicity over several hundred lattice constants may be achieved. By fine tuning the materials synthesis, it is possible to double the size of the PBG. This involves careful sintering of the template spheres and careful control of the infiltration process. An increase in gap size is expected when the template is infiltrated over the range of 80-100%. The maximum gap occurs, when the partial infiltration is approximately 90%.

In addition, we have demonstrated the complete electro-active tunability of a three-dimensional PBG by partially infiltrating an inverse opal PBG material with a nematic liquid crystal. Similarly, inverse opal based PCs that do not exhibit a complete PBG still provide a hightly efficient system for super-electro-optical modulation effects. The resulting tunability of spontaneous emission, wave-guiding effects such as switching and routing, and light localization may considerably enhance the technological utility of liquid crystal-PC materials over and above that of the simpler non-tunable systems.

Recently, the first tunable photonic band gap using liquid crystals infiltrated into a two-dimensional macroporous silicon PC has been demonstrated [20]. The resulting structure exhibits a bandgap that could be continously temperature-tuned over a wavelength range of 80 nm. This clearly demonstrated the soundness of the concept of electro-active tunability of both two- and three-dimensional PC and shows that optical steering effects within the framework of an integrated photonics may be easily realized in two-dimensional PCs.

8. Acknowledgments

This work has been supported by Photonics Research Ontario. KB would like to acknowledge the financial support by the Deutsche Forschungsgemeinschaft (DFG) under Grant No. Bu 1107/2-1.

References

1. C.M. Soukoulis (Ed.), *Photonic Band Gap Materials*, Kluwer Academic Publishers, Dordrecht (1996)
2. IEEE (Ed.) *special issue on Photonic Crystals IEEE Journal of Lightwave Technology* **17**(11), (1999)
3. K.-M. Ho, C.T. Chan, and C.M. Soukoulis, *Phys. Rev. Lett.* **65**, 3152 (1990)
4. K. Busch and S. John, *Phys. Rev. Lett.* **83**, 967 (1999)
5. K. Busch, N. Vats, S. John, and B.C. Sanders, *Phys. Rev. E*, in press (2000)
6. K. Busch and S. John, *Phys. Rev. E* **58**, 3896 (1998)
7. J. Hama, M. Watanabe, and T. Kato, *J. Phys.: Condensed Matter* **2**, 7445 (1990)
8. J. E. G. J. Wijnhoven and W. L. Vos, *Science* **281**, 802 (1998)
9. A.A. Zakhidov et al., *Science* **282**, 897(1998)
10. A. Blanco et al., *Nature (London)* **405**, 437 (2000)
11. P.G. de Gennes, and J. Prost, *The Physics of Liquid Crystals*, Clarendon Press, Oxford (1993)
12. S. Chandrasekhar, *Liquid Crystals*, Cambridge University Press (1992)
13. L.M. Blinov, and V.G. Chigrinov, *Electro-Optic Effects in Liquid Crystal Materials*, Springer, New York (1994)
14. A.I Ioffe, and A.R. Regel, *Prog. Semicond.* **4**, 237 (1960)
15. S. John, *Phys. Rev. Lett.* **58**, 2486 (1987)
16. S. John, *Phys. Rev. Lett.* **53**, 2169 (1984)
17. S. John, and R. Rangarajan, *Phys. Rev. B* **38**, 10101 (1988)
18. H. Kosaka et al., *Appl. Phys. Lett.* **74**, 1370 (1999)
19. A. Birner, U. Grüning, S. Ottow, A. Schneider, F. Müller, V. Lehmann, H. Föll, and U. Gösele, *Phys. Stat. Sol. (a)* **165**, 111 (1998)
20. S.W. Leonard, J.P. Mondia, H.M. van Driel, O. Toader, S. John, K. Busch, A. Birner, U. Gösele, and V. Lehmann, *Phys. Rev. B* **61**, R2389 (2000)
21. T. Gnielka and K. Busch, unpublished

ACOUSTIC BAND GAP MATERIALS

J.H. PAGE, A.L. GOERTZEN*, SUXIA YANG
Department of Physics and Astronomy, University of Manitoba
University of Manitoba, Winnipeg MB Canada R3T 2N2

ZHENGYOU LIU
Department of Physics, South China University of Technology
Guangzhou 510640 China

C.T. CHAN AND PING SHENG
Department of Physics, Hong Kong University of Science and Technology,
Clear Water Bay, Kowloon, Hong Kong, China

1. Introduction

In recent years, there has been a growing interest in the propagation of acoustic and elastic waves in periodic composite materials. Such materials are the acoustic or elastic analogue of photonic crystals, and in both cases, much of the interest has focused on theoretical and experimental studies of spectral gaps due to the periodicity of the underlying structure [1-11]. For sound, these are often referred to as phononic band gaps, by analogy with photonic band gaps for light and electronic band gaps for metals. Motivation for studying materials with phononic band gaps is driven in part from potential applications, examples being their role in sound filters, transducer design and acoustic mirrors. Of possibly greater interest from the fundamental scientific perspective is the rich physics of acoustic and elastic systems, where scattering contrast is affected by both density and velocity differences, and the waves can have a mixed longitudinal and transverse vector character, leading to the possibility of novel propagation phenomena. These features of phononic band gap materials may also make them interesting candidates for studies of wave localization.

Although the theory of acoustic and elastic band gap materials is now quite well developed, there have been relatively few experimental studies of these materials [7-11]. Most of these experiments have focused on two-dimensional structures, where the experimental realization of a complete spectral gap has been demonstrated. In this paper, we turn to three-dimensional materials and present recent pulsed ultrasonic transmission measurements on hexagonal close packed (hcp) arrays of monodisperse stainless steel beads immersed in water. We use this system to illustrate how ultrasonic techniques provide a powerful experimental tool for studying classical wave propagation in periodic composite media. Some of the advantages of these techniques include the ability to measure the wave field directly and the relative ease with which pulsed techniques can be used over a wide range of frequencies. By measuring the ultrasonic wave field transmitted through slab-shaped samples of different thicknesses, we determine both the dispersion curve and amplitude transmission coefficient. Because the field is pulsed, we can also

C.M. Soukoulis (ed.), Photonic Crystals and Light Localization in the 21st Century, 59–68.

measure the group velocity and investigate the dynamics of the wave fields [12] in phononic crystals. We interpret our experimental results by comparing them with theoretical calculations based on a multiple scattering theory (MST) for acoustic and elastic waves [5, 6], which is ideally suited to the spherical scatterer geometry of the present experiments. We show that this theoretical approach gives a good description of the low-frequency band structure and transmission coefficient measured in our experiments.

2. Experiment

The phononic crystals used in our experiments were constructed from monodisperse spherical steel beads surrounded by a continuous matrix of water. This choice of materials provides high scattering contrast in our ultrasonic experiments, because of the large difference in both density and velocity of the two constituent media (for the steel beads, the longitudinal and shear velocities are $v_L = 6.01$ km/s and $v_S = 3.23$ km/s, and the density is $\rho = 7.67\times10^3$ kg/m^3, while for water $v_L = 1.49$ km/s and $\rho = 1.0\times10^3$ kg/m^3). The steel bead diameter was 0.8014 ± 0.0006 mm, so that the variation in diameter from bead to bead was less than 0.15%, with the deviation from spherical shape of an individual bead being even less at 0.08%. The beads were assembled into a hexagonal close packed (hcp) array by placing the beads very carefully by hand in an acrylite cell. To ensure a defect-free crystal, the cell consisted of a flat bottom plate with hexagonal side walls, which were accurately positioned to constrain the bottom layer of beads into a close-packed triangular lattice. This template allowed subsequent layers to be added in an ABABAB... sequence of triangular arrays to form an hcp lattice with *c*-axis perpendicular to the layers. Although painstaking to carry out, this procedure allowed very high quality crystals to be assembled, thanks to the excellent monodispersity of the beads. Two crystals in the shape of hexagonal slabs were assembled, each with dimensions in the *ab* plane much greater than along the *c*-axis, so that edge effects at the side walls could be neglected. The thickness of the two crystals was 3.41 and 6.69 mm, corresponding to 5 and 10 layers, respectively.

To measure the ultrasonic field transmitted though the phononic crystals, the samples were placed horizontally in a water tank, which provided a convenient coupling medium between the ultrasonic transducers and the sample cell. We used a pulsed technique, in which planar immersion broadband transducers were placed on each side of the sample; the transducers were oriented so that the pulsed ultrasonic beam traveled upwards from the generating transducer through the sample to the receiving transducer, as shown by the schematic diagram in Fig. 1. This orientation allowed the beads to be held in place by gravity, avoiding the need for a top wall, which would have complicated the boundary conditions on the sample cell. The bottom supporting wall was made sufficiently thick that no multiple reflections in the wall could arrive at the bottom face of the sample until after the initial transmitted pulse through the sample had decayed to below the detection noise threshold. A small-diameter transducer was used to generate the pulses, and the distance between the transducer and sample was chosen to be large enough so that the sample was well into the far field of the transducer, where the input pulse was an excellent approximation to a plane wave over the cross section of the sample. The detecting transducer had a larger diameter (25 mm) allowing it to selectively measure the spatially and temporally coherent component of the field transmitted along the c-axis of the crystal. The transmitted field detected by the top transducer was amplified with a low-noise high-gain receiving amplifier, signal averaged using a digital oscilloscope, and then downloaded

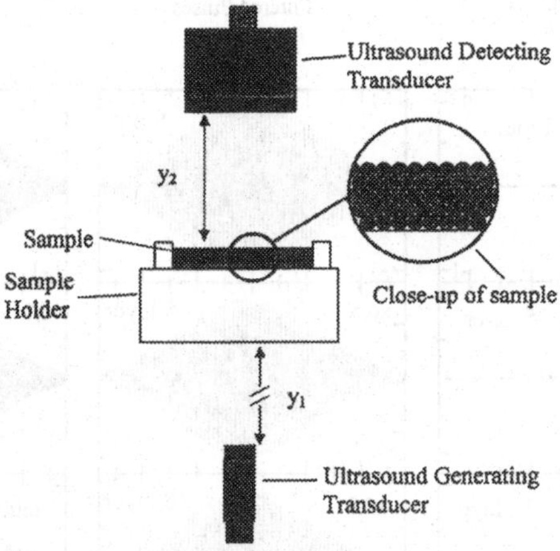

Figure 1. Schematic diagram of the experimental setup.

to a computer for subsequent analysis. To permit the effects of the support wall at the bottom of the cell to be taken into account, the transmitted field was first measured without the sample and support wall in place, then through the support wall only, and finally through the crystal sample placed on top of its supporting wall.

Our pulse propagation experiments allow us to measure the phase velocity, the group velocity and the attenuation of the ultrasonic waves as a function of frequency, thus fully characterizing wave transport through the phononic crystal and enabling the bandstructure and amplitude transmission coefficient to be measured. In the left column of Fig. 2, we compare a typical short input pulse that is incident at the support wall/sample interface with the corresponding pulses that are transmitted through the 5-layer and 10-layer samples. One advantage of using a short input pulse is that it allows the transmitted field to be measured over a wide frequency range, determined by the bandwidth of the transducers (typically ± 50% of the central frequency) in a single measurement. Short input pulses also allow the interference effects due to Bragg scattering in the crystal to be observed in real time, as indicated by the considerable broadening and modulation of the pulses transmitted through the samples that is shown in the two lower figures in the left column of Fig. 2. However, because of this pulse distortion, the velocities at which the waves travel though the crystal cannot be determined directly in the time-domain from such short pulses. Instead, we digitally filter the transmitted waveforms using a narrow-band Gaussian filter centered at frequency $f = \omega / 2\pi$, using a sufficiently narrow filter bandwidth that the filtered pulses extend over a range of times long enough to incorporate the contributions to the net phase from all multiply reflected waves in the sample. To determine the frequency dependence of the velocities, the process is repeated over the entire frequency range spanned by the transducers. Two examples of such digitally filtered pulses are shown in the middle and right columns of Fig. 2, for central frequencies of 0.5 MHz and 1.0 MHz, respectively. In both cases, the bandwidth is 0.01 MHz, sufficiently narrow to give excellent Gaussian pulses for both the input and transmitted, waves with minimal distortion and broadening due to dispersive effects. For these digitally filtered pulses, the phase delay between the filtered input and transmitted pulses is well defined, allowing the phase

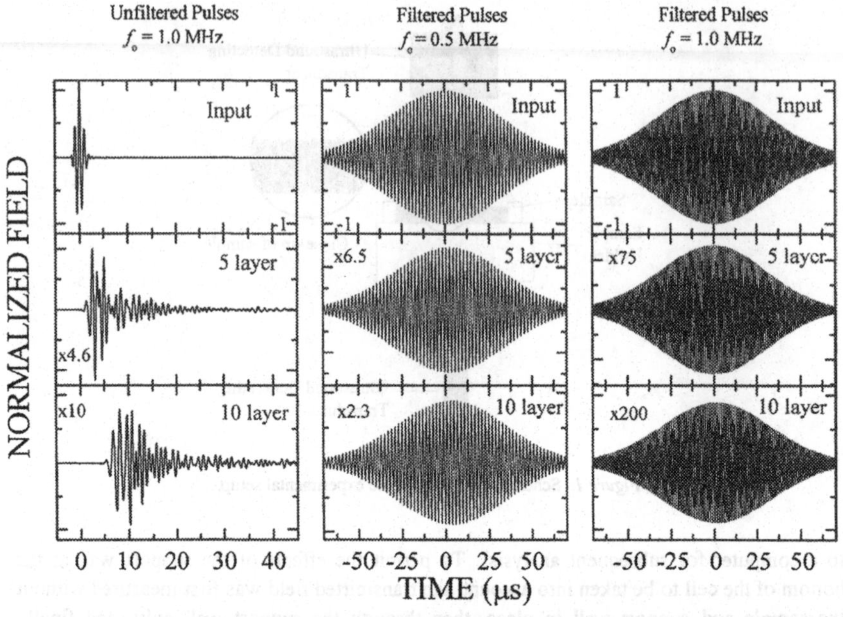

Figure 2. **Input and transmitted pulses through the 5 and 10 layer samples (left) compared with digitally filtered pulses at a bandwidth of 0.01 MHz (middle and right columns).**

velocity v_p to be determined, at the central frequency of the pulse, from the ratio of the sample thickness to the measured phase delay. The measurements are performed down to low enough frequencies that uncertainties in the phase shift of multiples of 2π could be unambiguously eliminated, as there was then only one possible value that gave physically realistic velocities. The correct value of the phase delay is also confirmed by the consistency of the measurements made at the two sample thicknesses. This method of determining the phase delay is equivalent to measuring the phase difference directly from the fast Fourier transforms of the input and transmitted pulses [13]. However, one advantage of our digital filtering method is that it also allows the group velocity to be measured directly from the pulse propagation time. By visual inspection of Fig. 2, it is clear that the group velocity is faster at 1.0 MHz than it is at 0.5 MHz. To measure the group velocity quantitatively, we determine the envelopes of the transmitted pulses and measure the group velocity from the ratio of the sample thickness to the time interval between the peaks of the pulses, the latter being obtained accurately using a least squares fitting routine. The filtered pulses in Fig. 2 also give information of the amplitude transmission coefficient, which is given at the central frequency of the pulses by the ratio of the peak heights of the transmitted and input pulses. In practice, it is simpler to measure the frequency dependence of the amplitude transmission coefficient directly from the ratio of the fast Fourier transforms of the unfiltered transmitted and input pulses, thus obtaining the frequency dependence over the entire bandwidth of the transducers in one step.

3. Theory

We have recently developed a multiple scattering theory (MST) for elastic waves that is ideally suited to calculating the band-structure of phononic crystals containing solid spherical scatterers embedded in a fluid matrix [6]. A similar model for acoustic waves has also been formulated recently by Kafesaki and Economou [5]. For this type of phononic material, the more common plane wave method has been shown to be unable to give accurate results [5]. By contrast, the MST, which is based on the same approach as the Korringa-Kohn-Roskoker (KKR) theory for electronic band-structure calculations, exhibits advantages in handling specialized geometries such as the spherical scatters in the present work. In the MST for elastic waves, the band-structure is determined by calculating the elastic Mie scattering of the waves incident on a single scatter from all the other scatterers in the crystal, and solving the resulting secular equation for the eigenfrequencies. Details of the calculation are given elsewhere [6]. Here we show the predictions of the MST for the phononic band-structure of our steel bead/water hcp crystal in Fig. 3. For this high contrast hcp crystal, the lowest gap in the spectrum is large along the *c*-axis, although it shrinks and becomes very narrow between the M and K points, so that only a very small complete phononic band gap in this material exists.

We have also extended the multiple scattering theory to describe the reflection and transmission of elastic waves by finite slabs of periodically arranged scatterers [6]. These reflection and transmission calculations are based on a double-layer scheme, in which the reflection and transmission matrix elements for a multilayer slab are obtained from those of a single layer. The advantage of this approach is that it allows a direct comparison of theory with experiments on finite systems, where it is important to account for the effects of the boundary conditions. Examples of the predictions of this theory are given in the next section where the experimental results are discussed.

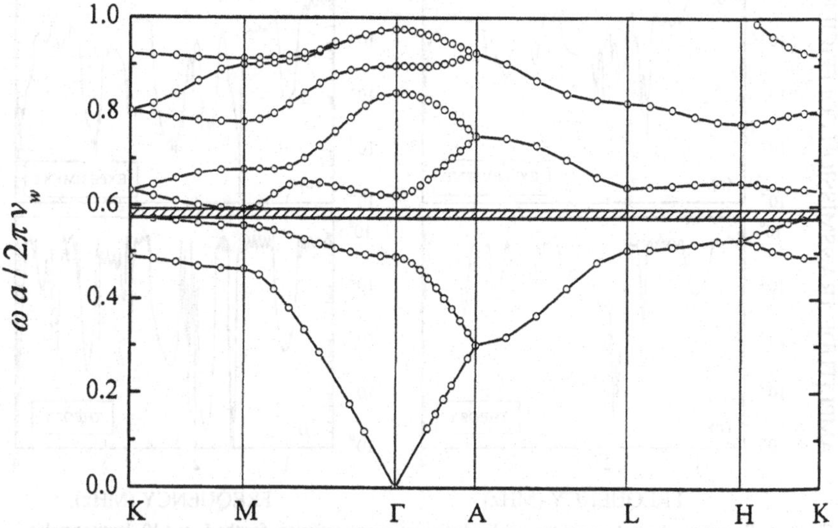

Figure 3. Band structure of an hcp crystal of stainless steel spheres in water. Here a is the lattice constant in the basal plane and v_w is the sound velocity in water.

4. Results and Discussion

Using the experimental and theoretical techniques described in the previous two sections, we have investigated the ultrasonic transmission, pulse propagation and band-structure along the *c*-axis of our hcp steel/water crystals. In Fig. 4, we plot the amplitude transmission coefficient as a function of frequency for both the 5- and 10-layer samples, with the experimental results in the upper panels and the theory in the lower ones. The deep minima in the transmission indicate the frequencies at which gaps occur in the dispersion curve along the *c*-axis, these minima becoming wider and deeper as the sample thickness increases and the spectral gaps become better defined. Considering the finite thickness of the crystals, the depth of some of the minima is remarkably large, with the transmitted intensity dropping by 2 to 6 orders of magnitude depending on the gap location. Note that the frequencies at which these minima occur in the upper panels are in very good agreement with those in the lower panels of Fig. 4, indicating excellent correspondence between the multiple scattering theory and experiment. In addition to the large maxima and minima, there are smaller regular oscillations in the transmitted amplitude that become more closely spaced as the sample thickness increases. This behaviour is consistent with the interference of multiple reflections from the top and bottom surfaces of the crystal, as was confirmed by calculating the positions of the oscillation peaks using measured data for the phase velocity in the sample. Figure 4 shows that theoretical calculations give a good description of the overall structure of the measured transmission coefficient, although the theoretical predictions are consistently higher in magnitude. This difference becomes greater at higher frequencies and may be attributed to ultrasonic absorption in the sample,

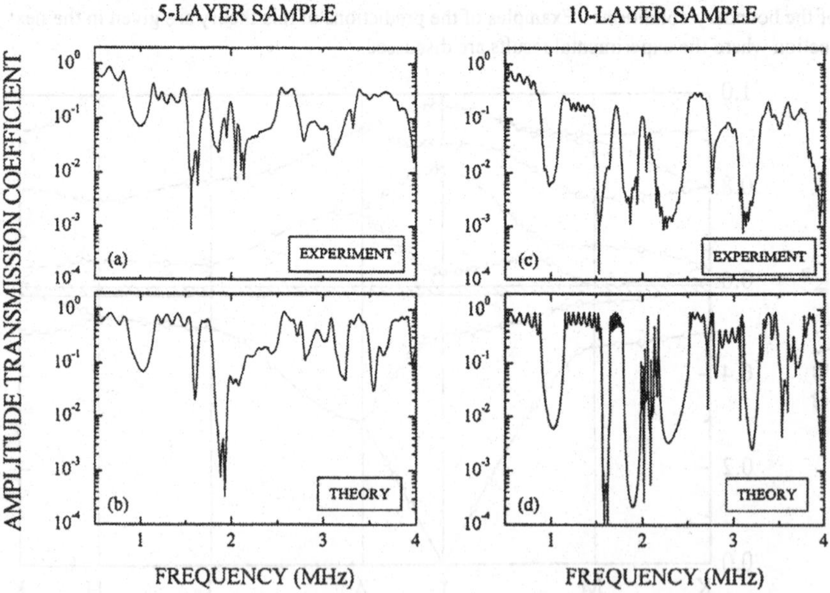

Figure 4. **Frequency dependence of the amplitude transmission coefficient for the 5- and 10- layer samples (left and right panels, respectively).**

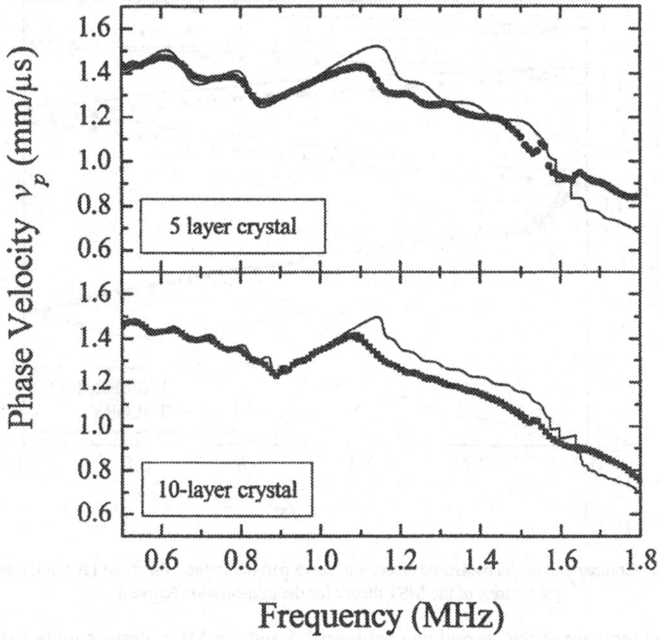

Figure 5. **Frequency dependence of the phase velocity. The symbols and curves represent experiment and theory, respectively.**

an effect that has not been included in the present calculations.

The frequency dependence of the phase velocity is plotted in Fig. 5, where we focus on the behavior for frequencies below 2 MHz, the range over which the phase velocity changes most significantly. The experimental results (solid symbols) are compared with the theoretical predictions of the MST (solid curves), determined from the phase of the complex transmission coefficient. At the lowest frequencies, the phase velocity is close to the value for pure water but drops off markedly as the frequency increases, eventually reaching values less than half the phase velocity in water as the higher frequency energy bands flatten out. There is also considerable structure in the frequency dependence of v_p over this range. The same interference effect (due to boundary reflections) that modulates the transmission also causes the net phase to oscillate, leading to periodic variations in the phase velocity that are especially pronounced (and more widely spaced) for the thinner sample. Since the spacing of the oscillations is $\Delta f = v_p/2L$, their presence can be used to confirm that the cumulative phase, from which the phase velocity is determined, has been correctly unwrapped. Note the generally excellent agreement between theory and experiment for the positions of the oscillations, the one exception being the results for the 5-layer sample above 1.2 MHz, where there is an offset. Also, the magnitude of the oscillations is less in the experimental data, another manifestation of the absorption present in the sample. Of greater interest is the variation in the phase velocity associated with the band gaps. In the lowest gap centered at 1 MHz, the velocity increases with frequency as expected, although the experimental data show a narrower gap than the theory. Perhaps more surprising is the fact that neither the theory nor experiment for v_p show a very

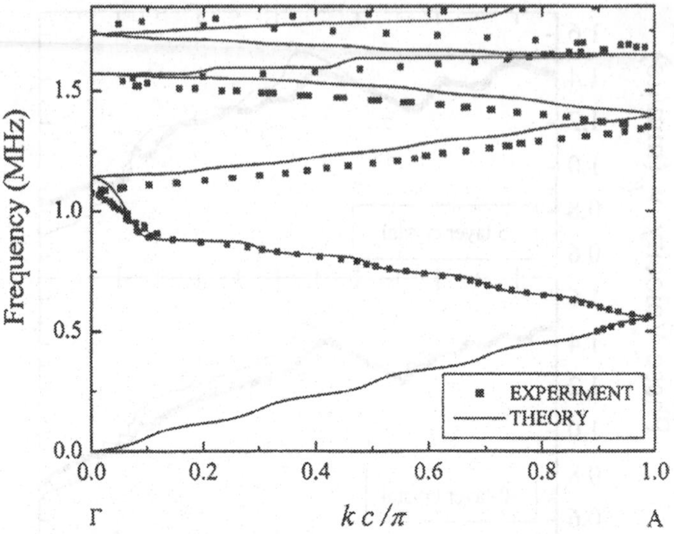

Figure 6. Comparison of the measured dispersion curve parallel to the *c* direction (symbols) with the predictions of the MST theory for the transmission (curves).

pronounced increase at the second gap between 1.5 and 1.6 MHz, despite quite sharp drops in the transmission (Fig. 4), as well as a clear gap in the infinite-crystal band structure (c.f. Fig. 3), in this frequency range.

These measurements of the phase velocity can also be used to determine the dispersion curve parallel to the *c* direction, either directly in the extended zone scheme, or in the more commonly used reduced zone scheme. The reduced zone scheme dispersion curve for the 10-layer sample is shown in Fig. 6; it was obtained in the usual way by subtracting multiples of the reciprocal lattice vector $G_{001} = 2\pi/c$ from k and making use of the symmetry of the dispersion curve about $\pm k$. In Fig. 6, our experimental results (solid symbols) are compared with the theoretical predictions of the MST theory for the transmission (solid curves). As for the plot of the phase velocity, the overall agreement between theory and experiment is very good over this range of frequencies. However, at higher frequencies the agreement is worse, possibly due to small imperfections in the crystal that have a greater effect at shorter wavelengths.

To gain a more complete picture of wave propagation through phononic crystals, we investigate the frequency dependence of the group velocity. We are not aware of any previous measurements of the group velocity in phononic crystals, although there have been several reports of optical pulse propagation in both 1D and 3D photonic crystals [12, 14-16]. Our results in the frequency range between 0.5 and 1.5 MHz are shown in Fig. 7, where again we compare experiment with MST theory, using solid symbols and curves respectively, for the two sample thicknesses. We find a very large variation in v_g over this frequency range, with the experimental data varying by about one order of magnitude, and even larger structure being exhibited in the theory, obtained by differentiating the MST dispersion curve. As with the transmission coefficient and the phase velocity, the larger variation seen in the theory can be attributed to the effects of absorption, which cuts off the long multiple scattering paths. Note the marked decrease (by about a factor of 3 relative to

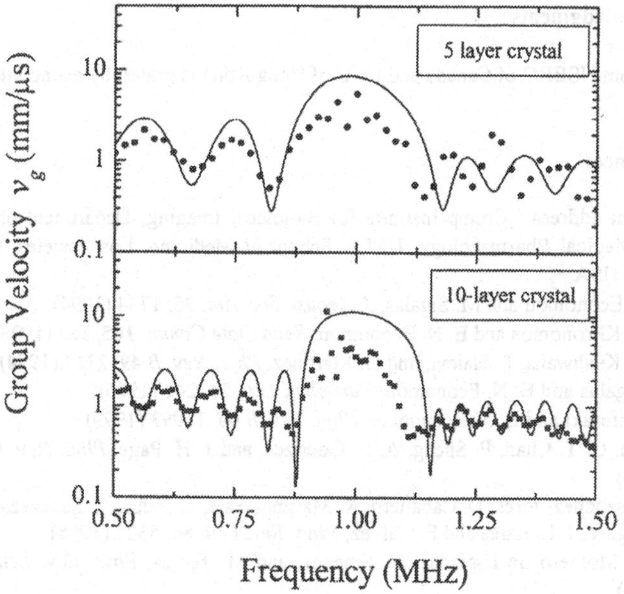

Figure 7. Frequency dependence of the group velocity. The symbols and curves represent experiment and theory, respectively.

the values near 0.5 MHz) in the group velocity as the band gap at 1 MHz is approached from either side, with even smaller values of v_g, comparable to the velocity of sound in air, being reached in the fourth pass band at the upper end of the frequency range shown. Inside the lowest band gap, there is considerable scatter in the experimental data, as the transit time becomes quite short compared with the pulse width; none-the-less, a significant increase in v_g is seen, rising to values between those of pure water and steel. By analogy with previous optical measurements in 1D photonic crystals [14, 15], we ascribe the mechanism underlying these large values of v_g to be ultrasonic pulse tunneling through the gap. These measurements thus give a direct measure of the tunneling time, the first time that this has been measured for ultrasonic waves in a phononic crystal.

5. Conclusions

We have presented experimental and theoretical results for ultrasonic wave propagation in a hcp phononic crystal made from stainless steel beads immersed in water. Our pulsed experiments measure the frequency dependence of the phase and group velocities, as well as the attenuation of the ultrasonic waves, giving new information on the band structure and transmission in this phononic crystal. Our data are interpreted using a multiple scattering theory, which gives good overall agreement with the experiments, especially at low frequencies where the absorption is less pronounced. We are currently working on extending the MST for elastic waves to include the effects of absorption, by including viscous losses at the interfaces between the water and the solid spheres.

6. Acknowledgments

Support from NSERC of Canada and RGC of Hong Kong is gratefully acknowledged.

7. References

* Present address: Crump Institute for Biological Imaging, Department of Molecular and Medical Pharmacology, UCLA School of Medicine, Los Angeles, CA 90095-1770, USA

1. E. N. Economou and M. Sigalas, *J. Acoust. Soc. Am.* **95**, 1734 (1994).
2. A. D. Klironomos and E. N. Economou, *Solid State Comm.* **105**, 327 (1998).
3. M. S. Kushwaha, P. Halevi, and G. Martinez, *Phys. Rev. B* **49**, 2313 (1994).
4. M. Sigalas and E. N. Economou, *Europhys. Lett.* **36**, 241 (1996).
5. M. Kafesaki and E. N. Economou, *Phys. Rev. B* **60**, 11993 (1999).
6. Z. Liu, C. T. Chan, P. Sheng, A. L. Goertzen, and J. H. Page, *Phys. Rev. B.* **62**, 2446 (2000).
7. J. V. Sanchez-Peres, D. Caballero, R. Martinez-Sala, C. Rubio, J. Sanchez-Dehesa, F. Meseguer, J. Llinares and F. Galvez, *Phys. Rev. Lett.* **80**, 5325 (1998).
8. F. R. Montero de Espinosa, E. Jimenez, and M. Torres, *Phys. Rev. Lett.* **80**, 1208 (1998).
9. J. O. Vasseur, P. A. Deymier, G. Frantziskonis, G. Hong, B. Dijafari-Rouhani, and L. Dobrzynski, *J.Phys.: Condens. Matter* **10**, 6051 (1998).
10. D. Caballero, J. Sanchez-Dehesa, C. Rubio, R. Martinez-Sala, J. V. Sanchez-Perez, F. Meseguer, and J. Llinares, *Phys. Rev. E* **60**, R6316 (1999).
11. R. E. Vines and J. P. Wolfe, *Physica B* **263-264**, 567 (1999).
12. A. Imhof, W. L. Vos, R. Sprik, and A. Lagendijk, *Phys. Rev. Lett.* **83**, 2942 (1999).
13. W. M. Robertson, G. Arjavalingam, R. D. Meade, K. D. Brommer, A. M. Ragge, and J. D. Joannopoulos, *Phys. Rev. Lett.* **68**, 2023 (1992).
14. A. M. Steinberg, P. G. Kwist, and R. Y. Chiao, *Phys. Rev. Lett.* 71, 708 (1993).
15. C. Spielmann, R. Szipocs, A. Stingl, and F. Krausz, *Phys. Rev. Lett.* **73**, 2308 (1994).
16. M. Scalora, R. J. Flynn, S. B. Reinhardt, R. L. Fork, M. J. Bloemer, M. D. Tocci, C. M. Bowden, H. S. Ledbetter, J. M. Bendickson, R. P. Leavitt, *Phys. Rev. E* **54**, R1078 (1996).

THE FINITE DIFFERENCE TIME DOMAIN METHOD FOR THE STUDY OF TWO-DIMENSIONAL ACOUSTIC AND ELASTIC BAND GAP MATERIALS

M. KAFESAKI[1], M. M. SIGALAS[1,2] AND N. GARCIA[1]
[1] *Laboratorio de Física de Sistemas Pequeños y Nanotecnología, Consejo Superior de Investigaciones Científicas, Serrano 144, 28006 Madrid, Spain.*
[2] *Agilent Laboratories, 3500 Deer Creek Rd., Palo Alto, CA 94304.*

Abstract. The finite difference time domain (FDTD) method has been proved recently an excellent tool for the study of classical wave propagation in periodic and random composite systems. Here we present in detail the method as it is applied in the case of *acoustic* and *elastic* wave propagation in *two-dimensional* composites. Also, we present some representative results of the method and we discuss its advantages.

1. Introduction

The propagation of acoustic (AC) and elastic (EL) waves in periodic media has been recently a problem of considerable interest [1–16]. This interest stems mainly from the fact that acoustic and elastic periodic media (phononic crystals) were found to exhibit, in a lot of cases, wide spectral gaps in their spectrum, gaps much lager than those observed in photonic crystals. This possibility of creating large gaps, which is given mainly by the variety of parameters controlling the AC and EL wave propagation in a composite system (densities, velocities), makes them very useful for the study of general question related with the wave propagation, such as the disorder induced localization of the waves. Additional reasons for the interest on the AC and EL wave propagation study are a) the possible applications of the AC and EL band gap materials (e.g. in filter and transducer technology); b) the rich physics of the AC and EL waves which stems from the variety of parameters controlling their propagation, the full vector

C.M. Soukoulis (ed.), Photonic Crystals and Light Localization in the 21st Century, 69–82.

character of the elastic waves and their scattering induced mode conversion (transformation of longitudinal wave to transverse and vice versa); and c) the ease in the fabrication of the AC and EL band gap structures. This ease is due to the fact that the characteristic structure lengths for gaps in the ultrasound regime are of the order of mm.

Among the methods which have been developed for the study of the AC and EL wave propagation in *periodic composites* the most widely used is the so called Plane Wave (PW) method [2–11]. PW is based on the expansion of the periodic coefficients in the wave equation and the periodic field amplitude in Fourier sums. The method, which can calculate very easily the band structure of infinite periodic systems and (in combination with a supercell scheme) in systems with isolated defects, has been used in most of the existing theoretical studies on AC and EL wave propagation. PW, however, presents some inefficiencies in the study of propagation in composites consisting of components with different phase (fluids in solids or solids in fluids) or composites with strong contrast in the elastic parameters of their components (the finite Fourier sums that approximate the elastic parameters in these composites do not succeed to describe functions with large discontinuities). Recently, a multiple scattering (MS) method [17] based in the electronic Korringa-Kohn-Rostoker theory came to cover some of the inefficiencies of the PW. MS method can calculate the band structure of infinite periodic systems and also the transmission of waves through small samples of a periodic or random composite. The method however has been applied until now [17, 16] only in fluid composites because, due to its heavy formalism, it is not easy to be extended to the case of full vector waves. Thus, for the study of the full elastic wave propagation in small finite samples the existing methods present certain inefficiencies, something that brings the necessity for a new method.

The FDTD method which we present here is based on the discretization of the full elastic time dependent wave equation through a finite difference scheme. Both the time and the space derivatives are approximated by finite differences and the field at a given time point is calculated through the field at the previous points. Thus one can obtain the field as a function of time at any point of a slab. The frequency dependence of the field is obtained by fast Fourier transform of the time results.

The FDTD method, while is well known in the acoustics community [18, 19, 20] and the seismology, had not been applied until recently in the study of the phononic crystals. Here the most important advantages of the method are that: a) it can give the field at any point inside and outside a sample, every time; b) it can give the field in both frequency and time domain; c) the FDTD results can be directly compared with the experiments since the method calculates the transmission through finite samples; d) it can be applied in systems with arbitrary material combination (e.g. solids in fluids or fluids in solids); e) it can be applied in periodic systems as well as in systems with arbitrary configuration of the scatterers, giving thus the possibility to study defect states, waveguides, random systems etc.

These important advantages of the method have been already exploited extensively in the field of EM wave band gap materials (photonic crystals) [21–25]. For AC and EL waves the study through the FDTD is still in the beginning [12, 26] while there is the lack of an extensive presentation of the method.

In what follows we present first the FDTD method as it is applied in two-dimensional (2D) systems, i.e. systems consisted of cylinders embedded in a homogeneous host. Then we present some characteristic FDTD results concerning propagation in a) periodic systems (in comparison with experimental and PW results), b) systems with isolated defects and c) systems with linear defects which can act as waveguides for waves with frequency in the regime of the gap.

2. Method

The starting point for the FDTD method is the elastic wave equation in isotropic inhomogeneous media [27],

$$\frac{\partial^2 u_i}{\partial t^2} = \frac{1}{\rho}\frac{\partial T_{ij}}{\partial x_j}, \tag{1}$$

where $T_{ij} = \lambda(\mathbf{r})u_{ll}\delta_{ij} + 2\mu(\mathbf{r})u_{ij}$ and $u_{ij} = (\partial u_i/\partial x_j + \partial u_j/\partial x_i)/2$ (in cartesian coordinates). In the above expressions u_i is the ith component of the displacement vector $\mathbf{u}(\mathbf{r})$, T_{ij} is the stress tensor and u_{ij} the strain tensor. Also $\lambda(\mathbf{r})$ and $\mu(\mathbf{r})$ are the so-called Lamé coefficients of the medium [27] and $\rho(\mathbf{r})$ is the mass density. The λ, μ and ρ are connected with the wave velocities in a medium through the relations $\mu = \rho c_t^2$ and $\lambda = \rho c_l^2 - 2\rho c_t^2$, where c_l and c_t are, respectively, the velocity of the longitudinal and the transverse component of the wave. In a multicomponent system the λ, μ and ρ are discontinuous functions of the position, $\mathbf{r}$.

As is mentioned above, here we study systems consisted of cylinders embedded in a homogeneous material. A cross section of such a system (periodic) is shown in Fig. 1. We consider the z axis parallel to the axis of the cylinders and propagation on the x-y plane. For such a system the parameters $\lambda(\mathbf{r})$, $\mu(\mathbf{r})$ and $\rho(\mathbf{r})$ do not depend on the coordinate z and the wave equation for the z component is decoupled from the equations for the x and the y component. The equations for the x and the y component can be written as

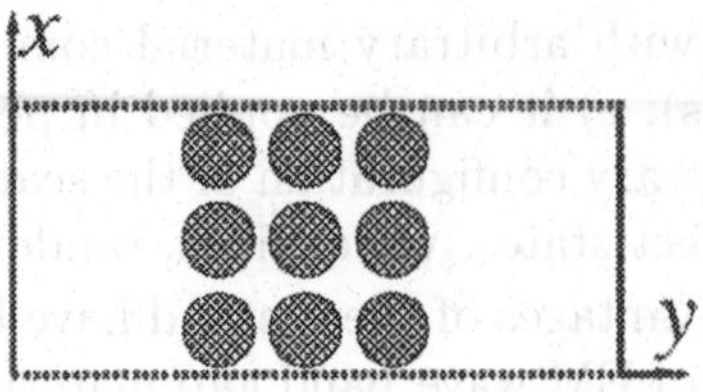

Figure 1. The computational cell.

$$\frac{\partial^2 u_x}{\partial t^2} = \frac{1}{\rho}\left(\frac{\partial T_{xx}}{\partial x} + \frac{\partial T_{xy}}{\partial y}\right), \tag{2}$$

$$\frac{\partial^2 u_y}{\partial t^2} = \frac{1}{\rho}\left(\frac{\partial T_{xy}}{\partial x} + \frac{\partial T_{yy}}{\partial y}\right), \tag{3}$$

where

$$T_{xx} = (\lambda + 2\mu)\frac{\partial u_x}{\partial x} + \lambda\frac{\partial u_y}{\partial y}, \quad T_{yy} = (\lambda + 2\mu)\frac{\partial u_y}{\partial y} + \lambda\frac{\partial u_x}{\partial x}, \tag{4}$$

$$T_{xy} = \mu\left(\frac{\partial u_x}{\partial y} + \frac{\partial u_y}{\partial x}\right). \tag{5}$$

The above equations consist the basis for the implementation of the FDTD in 2D systems. The computational domain for the calculations presented here is a rectangular area which contains a slab of the composite system in its central part (see Fig. 1). The sample is placed in a reservoir of the same material as the matrix material of the composite.

For the implementation of the FDTD method we divide the computational domain in $i_{\max} \times j_{\max}$ subdomains (grids) with dimensions $\Delta x, \Delta y$, and we define

$$u_\ell(i,j,k) = u_\ell(i\Delta x - \Delta x/2, j\Delta y - \Delta y/2, k\Delta t), \qquad \ell = x, y, \tag{6}$$

with $1 \leq i \leq i_{\max}$, $1 \leq j \leq j_{\max}$ and $k \geq 0$.

In the Eqs (2) - (5) we approximate the derivatives in both space and time with finite differences [21]. For the space derivatives we use central differences:

$$\begin{aligned} \frac{\partial u_\ell}{\partial x}\Big|_{i,j,k} &\approx D_0^x u_\ell(i,j,k) = [u_\ell(i+1/2,j,k) - u_\ell(i-1/2,j,k)]/\Delta x, \\ \frac{\partial u_\ell}{\partial y}\Big|_{i,j,k} &\approx D_0^y u_\ell(i,j,k) = [u_\ell(i,j+1/2,k) - u_\ell(i,j-1/2,k)]/\Delta y. \end{aligned} \tag{7}$$

For the time derivatives we use a combination of forward and backward differences:

$$\frac{\partial^2 u_\ell}{\partial t^2}|_{i,j,k} \approx D_+^t D_-^t u_\ell(i,j,k), \tag{8}$$

where

$$\begin{aligned} D_+^t u_\ell(i,j,k) &= [u_\ell(i,j,k+1) - u_\ell(i,j,k)]/\Delta t, \\ D_-^t u_\ell(i,j,k) &= [u_\ell(i,j,k) - u_\ell(i,j,k-1)]/\Delta t, \quad \ell = x, y. \end{aligned}$$

For Eq. (2), using expansion at (i,j,k) and following the procedure described above, we obtain

$$\begin{gathered} u_x(i,j,k+1) = 2u_x(i,j,k) - u_x(i,j,k-1) + \\ \frac{\Delta_t^2}{\rho(i,j)\Delta_x}[T_{xx}(i+1/2,j,k) - T_{xx}(i-1/2,j,k)] + \\ \frac{\Delta_t^2}{\rho(i,j)\Delta_y}[T_{xy}(i,j+1/2,k) - T_{xy}(i,j-1/2,k)]. \end{gathered} \tag{9}$$

For Eq. (3), expanding at $(i+1/2, j+1/2, k)$,

$$\begin{gathered} u_y(i+1/2,j+1/2,k+1) = \\ 2u_y(i+1/2,j+1/2,k) - u_y(i+1/2,j+1/2,k-1) + \\ \frac{\Delta_t^2}{\rho(i+1/2,j+1/2)\Delta_x}[T_{xy}(i+1,j+1/2,k) - T_{xy}(i,j+1/2,k)] + \\ \frac{\Delta_t^2}{\rho(i+1/2,j+1/2)\Delta_y}[T_{yy}(i+1/2,j+1,k) - T_{yy}(i+1/2,j,k)]. \end{gathered} \tag{10}$$

The T_{xx}, T_{xy}, T_{yy} are functions of the field components at the time $k\Delta t$, which are used for the updating of the fields for the next time. They are also discretized through Eqs (7) and their expressions after the discretization are given in the appendix A.

It has to be mentioned that the above way of discretization of the equations insures second order accurate central difference for the space derivatives. This has as a result, however, the field components u_x and u_y to be centered in different space points. To calculate, e.g., the field components $u_x(i+1/2, j+1/2, k)$, which are not stored in the computational memory, we use

$$\begin{aligned} u_x(i+1/2,j+1/2,k) &= [u_x(i+1,j+1,k) + u_x(i+1,j,k) + \\ &\quad u_x(i,j+1,k) + u_x(i,j,k)+]/4. \end{aligned} \tag{11}$$

Using the above procedure the components u_x and u_y at the time step $k+1$ are calculated through their values at the step k. For insuring stability of the calculations we use the stability criterion [21]

$$\Delta t \leq 0.5/c\sqrt{1/\Delta x^2 + 1/\Delta y^2}, \tag{12}$$

where the velocity c is the highest among the sound velocities of the components of the composite.

The Δx and Δy are usually chosen as the 1/40 of the lattice constant (for periodic systems) with very big accuracy for waves with wavelength compared to the scatterers size.

In order to close the computational cell in the x-direction, for periodic or symmetric along the y-direction systems, we use periodic boundary conditions $[u(\mathbf{r}+\mathbf{R}) = \exp(i\mathbf{k}\cdot\mathbf{R})u(\mathbf{r})$ ($\mathbf{R}$: lattice vector)] along the y axis at $i=1$ and $i=i_{\max}$ (see dotted lines in Fig. 1). These conditions, here, can be expressed as

$$\mathbf{u}(i_{\max}+1, j, k) = \mathbf{u}(1, j, k), \tag{13}$$

$$\mathbf{u}(0, j, k) = \mathbf{u}(i_{\max}, j, k). \tag{14}$$

For closing the cell in the y-direction we use absorbing boundary conditions. In most of the cases the first order absorbing boundary conditions introduced by Zhou et. al. [20] have been used. These conditions are obtained by the requirement the reflection at the boundaries to be zero for two angles of incidence (θ_1, θ_2), and can be written in the form

$$A\frac{\partial \bar{\mathbf{u}}}{\partial x} + B\frac{\partial \bar{\mathbf{u}}}{\partial y} + I\frac{\partial \bar{\mathbf{u}}}{\partial t} = 0. \tag{15}$$

In Eq. (15) I is the identity 2×2 matrix, $\bar{\mathbf{u}}$ is the 2×1 matrix $[u_x, u_y]^T$ (T denotes the transpose of a matrix), and A, B are 2×2 matrices. For the boundary $j = j_{\max}$ the matrices A and B can be expressed as

$$A(\theta_1,\theta_2) = \frac{\eta_1}{\eta_1\xi_2 - \eta_2\xi_1}Q_2 - \frac{\eta_2}{\eta_1\xi_2 - \eta_2\xi_1}Q_1, \tag{16}$$

$$B(\theta_1,\theta_2) = \frac{\xi_2}{\eta_1\xi_2 - \eta_2\xi_1}Q_1 - \frac{\xi_1}{\eta_1\xi_2 - \eta_2\xi_1}Q_2, \tag{17}$$

with

$$Q_1 = \begin{bmatrix} c_{lo}\xi_1^2 + c_{to}\eta_1^2 & (c_{lo}-c_{to})\xi_1\eta_1 \\ (c_{lo}-c_{to})\xi_1\eta_1 & c_{lo}\eta_1^2 + c_{to}\xi_1^2 \end{bmatrix}, \tag{18}$$

$$Q_2 = \begin{bmatrix} c_{lo}\xi_2^2 + c_{to}\eta_2^2 & (c_{lo}-c_{to})\xi_2\eta_2 \\ (c_{lo}-c_{to})\xi_2\eta_2 & c_{lo}\eta_2^2 + c_{to}\xi_2^2 \end{bmatrix}, \tag{19}$$

and $\xi_i = \sin\theta_i$, $\eta_i = \cos\theta_i$ $(i = 1, 2)$. c_{lo} and c_{to} are, respectively, the longitudinal and the transverse wave velocity in the host material of the composite. For the boundary $j = j_{\min}$ the expressions of A and B are obtained from Eqs (16) and (17) by replacing θ_i by $\theta_i + \pi$ $(i = 1, 2)$. For the implementation of the condition (15) we require complete absorption for $\theta_1 = 0$ and $\theta_2 = \pi/4$.

The condition (15) is discretized using central differences in space and forward differences in time:

$$\frac{\partial}{\partial t} \approx D_+^t, \quad \frac{\partial}{\partial x} \approx D_0^x \quad , \frac{\partial}{\partial y} \approx D_0^y. \tag{20}$$

For calculating the transmission we consider as incident wave a pulse with a Gaussian envelop in space. The pulse is formed at $t = 0$ in the left side of the composite and propagates along the y-direction. A longitudinal pulse like that has the form

$$u_y = \alpha \sin(\omega t - y/c_{lo}) \exp[-\beta(\omega t - y/c_{lo})^2], \tag{21}$$

while for a transverse one u_y is replaced by u_x and c_{lo} by c_{to}. The incident pulse is narrow enough in space as to permit the excitation of a wide range of frequencies.

The components of the displacement vector as a function of time are collected at various detection points depending on the structure of interest. They are converted into the frequency domain using fast Fourier transform. The transmission coefficient (T) is calculated either by normalizing the (frequency dependent) transmitted field amplitude $[(u_x^2+u_y^2)^{1/2}]$ by the incident field amplitude or through the energy flux vector $\mathbf{J}$ ($J_i = T_{ij} du_j/dt$). In the second case the transmitted flux vector is also normalized by the incident wave flux.

Concerning the case of pure acoustic waves (waves in fluid composites) the application of the FDTD starts again from the Eqs (2) - (5), but omitting the terms which include the Lamé coefficient μ. The equations are discretized through the same procedure as for the full elastic case. The boundary conditions coefficients are calculated again through the equations (16) - (19) where the velocity c_{to} must be replaced by c_{lo} (this replacement is essential in all the cases where the host material is fluid).

3. Results

In the present section we present results of the FDTD method for periodic systems and for systems with defects.

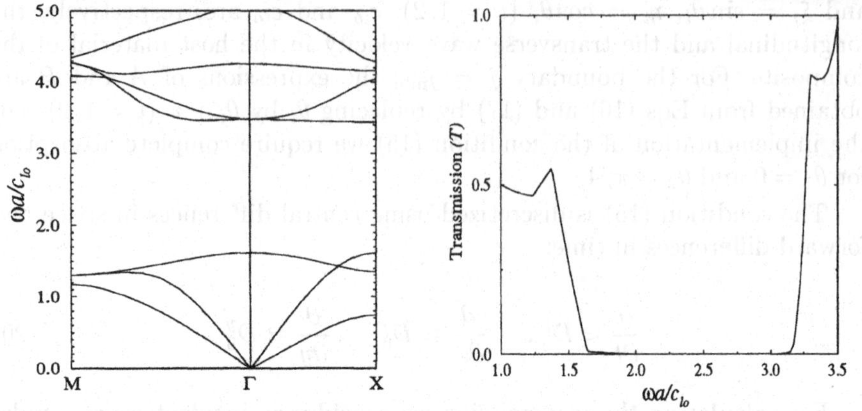

Figure 2. **Left: Band structure along the MΓX direction for a periodic system of Cu cylinders in PMMA, in a square arrangement, with cylinder radius over lattice constant $r_c/a = 0.35$. The band structure is calculated through the PW method. c_{l_o} is the longitudinal sound velocity in PMMA. Right: Transmission coefficient vs frequency for the system of the left panel. The incident wave is longitudinal propagating in the < 10 > direction.**

3.1. PERIODIC SYSTEMS

Using the FDTD method one can examine the existence of band gaps in a periodic composite system. This can be done by calculating the transmission coefficient through finite slabs of the system. Calculations like that provide a good test for the method as one can compare its results with corresponding results of other methods, where available. Here we calculate the transmission through a periodic composite consisting of Cu cylinders in PMMA host. We consider a 3×3 cylinders slab of the composite where the cylinders are placed within a square arrangement and the ratio of cylinder radius, r_c, over lattice constant, a, is 0.35. The result, which is shown in the right panel of Fig. 2, is compared with a corresponding result obtained through the PW method (see Fig. 2 - left panel). As one can see in Fig. 2, the agreement between the two methods is very good. Comparisons like that demonstrate the ability of the FDTD method to study the propagation in elastic multicomponent systems. It has to be mentioned, however, that the FDTD method is also able to calculate band structure (see Ref. [22] for such a calculation for EM waves), although through a more complicated procedure than that of the PW.

In Fig. 3 we compare FDTD results with results of a recent experimental study [11]. Fig. 3 shows the transmission coefficient for a periodic composite consisting of duraluminum cylinders in epoxy, in a square array,

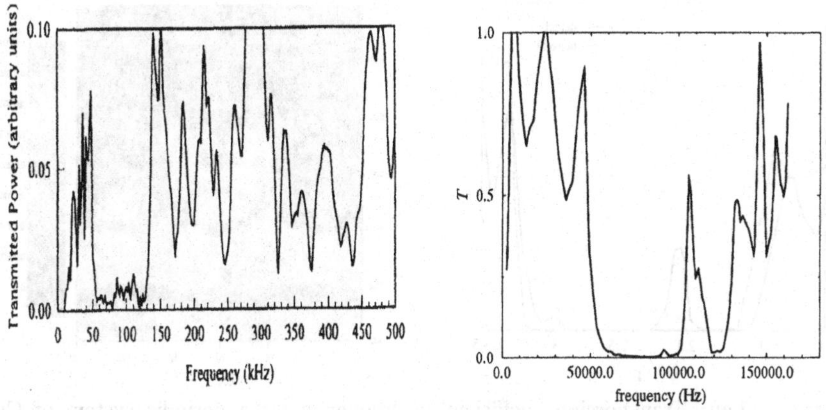

Figure 3. **Left: Experimental transmission coefficient vs frequency for a system of duraluminum cylinders in epoxy (see Ref. [11]), in a square lattice, with cylinders radius over lattice constant $r_c/a = 0.4$. Right: Transmission coefficient, calculated trough the FDTD method, for the system of the left panel.**

with $r_c/a = 0.4$. The left panel shows the experimental result and the right panel the corresponding FDTD result. The agreement between theory and experiment in the position and the width of the gaps is very good. The difference in the relative height of the peaks is due to the different size of the systems and due to the relatively high absorptivity of the epoxy, which has not been taken into account in the calculations.

3.2. DEFECTS

As we mentioned above, the FDTD method is ideal for the study of disorder induced phenomena. Here we exhibit this ability of the method by presenting results concerning systems with isolated defects.

We create an isolated defect by removing one cylinder from a periodic slab of the Cu in PMMA composite which was discussed in connection with Fig. 2. By removing one cylinder from a 3×3 cylinders slab of the composite and by calculating the transmission coefficient we obtain what is shown in the left panel of Fig. 4 - solid line (the dashed line shows the transmission for the periodic system). The transmission peak close to the midgap of the periodic system shows the formation of a defect state in this regime. Sending a monochromatic plane wave with the frequency of the defect state and examining the field over the sample we obtain the picture shown in the right panel of Fig. 4. The defect creates an s-like state, localized around the missing cylinder.

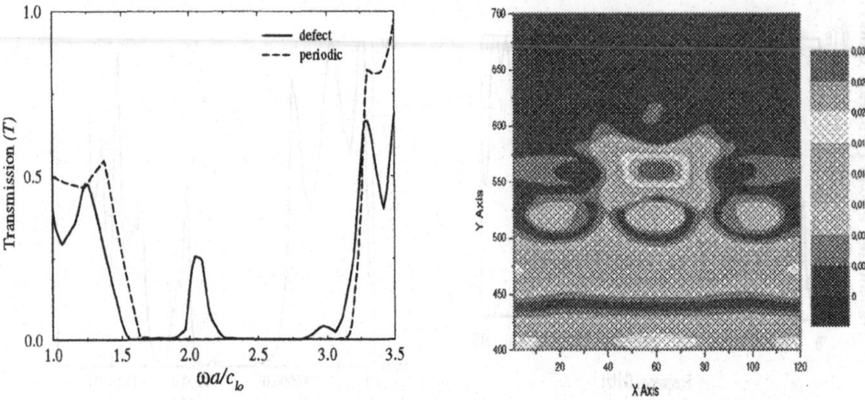

Figure 4. Left: Transmission coefficient vs frequency for a periodic system of Cu cylinders in PMMA, in a square arrangement, with cylinder radius over lattice constant $r_c/a = 0.35$, and with one missing cylinder (solid line) or without missing cylinder (dashed line). Right: The field over the sample for the system with the missing cylinder which discussed in the left panel. The incident wave is a a monochromatic plane wave with the frequency of the defect state.

3.3. WAVE GUIDES IN ELASTIC CRYSTALS

By removing a line of cylinders from a periodic composite instead of removing one single cylinder, one can create a linear defect. For electromagnetic wave propagation it has been shown [23, 24, 25] that such a defect can act as a waveguide for waves in the frequency regime of the gap as it consists the only channel of propagation for these waves. Recently, this guiding of waves through linear defects in periodic crystals was also shown for the case of the elastic waves [12, 26]. Using the FDTD method it was found that guides created as linear defects in elastic band gap materials can lead to total transmission of waves with frequency in the regime of the gap. The high transmitivity through such type of guides is demonstrated in the left panel of Fig. 5 (solid line). The results presented in Fig. 5 concern a 7×8 cylinders slab of a Cu in PMMA composite similar to the one of Fig. 2, from which we remove one row of cylinders. As one can see in Fig. 5, the transmission coefficient is close to one for almost all the gap regime of the periodic system. Sending monochromatic waves with frequencies in this regime ($T \approx 1$) one can see a great guiding of the waves through the defect state. This guiding is demonstrated in the right panel of Fig. 5, where it is shown the field created by a longitudinal incident plane wave with frequency the midgap frequency.

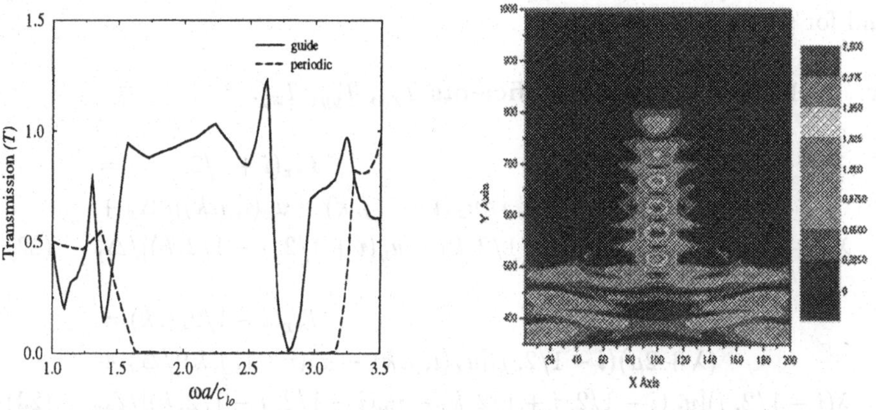

Figure 5. Left: Transmission coefficient vs frequency for a 7×8 cylinders slab of the Cu in PMMA composite discussed in Fig. 2, with one row of missing cylinders (solid line) or without missing cylinder (dashed line). Right: The field over the sample for the system of the left panel. The incident wave is a monochromatic plane wave at the midgap frequency.

Examining Fig. 5, however, one can see a pronounced dip in the transmission coefficient through the guide. Detailed examination of the origin of this dip (through band structure calculations) has shown that responsible for the dip is a gap in the propagation of the guided waves. The existence of gaps in the guided wave propagation (mini-gaps) is not something unexpected if one takes into account the periodic form of the guide "boundaries". These periodic "boundaries" impose a periodic potential in the guided wave propagation which, as the guided wave propagation is almost 1D, can easily lead to formation of gaps. The same "mini-gaps" possibly exist also for EM wave propagation through guides formed in photonic crystals, although such an existence has not been reported yet. The dips in the transmitivity of the guides formed as defects in elastic crystals is one of the main achievement of the FDTD in the field of elastic wave propagation in binary composites. Examination of the position of these dips showed that it depends on the material parameters of the components of the composites and mainly on the density and the velocities contrasts between scatterers and host.

4. Conclusions

We presented the FDTD method for 2D acoustic and elastic binary composites. The ability of the method to describe the wave propagation in these composites was demonstrated by presenting representative FDTD results for periodic systems (in comparison with PW and experimental results) and for single and line defects.

A. Calculation of the coefficients T_{xx}, T_{yy}, T_{xy}.

$$T_{xx}(i+1/2,j,k) = (\lambda+2\mu)(i+1/2,j)[u_x(i+1,j,k)-u_x(i,j,k)]/\Delta_x + \lambda(i+1/2,j)[u_y(i+1/2,j+1/2,k)-u_y(i+1/2,j-1/2,k)]/\Delta_y \tag{22}$$

$$T_{xx}(i-1/2,j,k) = (\lambda+2\mu)(i-1/2,j)[u_x(i,j,k)-u_x(i-1,j,k)]/\Delta_x + \lambda(i-1/2,j)[u_y(i-1/2,j+1/2,k)-u_y(i-1/2,j-1/2,k)]/\Delta_y \tag{23}$$

$$T_{xy}(i,j+1/2,k) = \mu(i,j+1/2)[u_x(i,j+1,k)-u_x(i,j,k)]/\Delta_y + \mu(i,j+1/2)[u_z(i+1/2,j+1/2,k)-u_y(i-1/2,j+1/2,k)]/\Delta_x \tag{24}$$

$$T_{xy}(i,j-1/2,k) = \mu(i,j-1/2)[u_x(i,j,k)-u_x(i,j-1,k)]/\Delta_z + \mu(i,j-1/2)[u_y(i+1/2,j-1/2,k)-u_y(i-1/2,j-1/2,k)]/\Delta_x \tag{25}$$

$$T_{xy}(i+1,j+1/2,k) = \mu(i+1,j+1/2)[u_x(i+1,j+1,k)-u_x(i+1,j,k)]/\Delta_y + \mu(i+1,j+1/2)[u_y(i+3/2,j+1/2,k)-u_y(i+1/2,j+1/2,k)]/\Delta_x \tag{26}$$

$$T_{xy}(i,j+1/2,k) = \mu(i,j+1/2)[u_x(i,j+1,k)-u_x(i,j,k)]/\Delta_y + \mu(i,j+1/2)[u_y(i+1/2,j+1/2,k)-u_y(i-1/2,j+1/2,k)]/\Delta_x \tag{27}$$

$$T_{yy}(i+1/2,j+1,k) = (\lambda+2\mu)(i+1/2,j+1)[u_y(i+1/2,j+3/2,k) - u_y(i+1/2,j+1/2,k)]/\Delta_y + \lambda(i+1/2,j+1)[u_x(i+1,j+1,k)-u_x(i,j+1,k)]/\Delta_x \tag{28}$$

$$
\begin{aligned}
T_{yy}(i+1/2,j,k) = \\
(\lambda+2\mu)(i+1/2,j)[u_y(i+1/2,j+1/2,k) - \\
u_y(i+1/2,j-1/2,k)]/\Delta_y + \\
\lambda(i+1/2,j)[u_x(i+1,j,k) - u_x(i,j,k)]/\Delta_x
\end{aligned}
\qquad (29)
$$

References

1. Soukoulis, C. M., ed. (1996) *Photonic Band Gap Materials,* Kluwer Academic Publishers.
2. Sigalas, M. M. & Economou, E. N. (1992) *J. Sound Vibration* **158**, 377; (1993) *Solid State Commun.* **86**, 141; (1994) *J. Applied Phys.* **75**, 2845; (1996) *Europhysics Lett.* **36**, 241.
3. Kushwaha, M. S., Halevi, P., Dobrzynski, L. & Djafari-Rouhani, B. (1993) *Phys. Rev. Lett.* **71**, 2022.
4. Economou, E. N. & Sigalas, M. M., in *Photonic Band Gaps and Localization* ed. by Soukoulis, C. M. (1993) Plenum Press, New York, pp. 317-338.
5. Economou, E. N. & Sigalas, M. M. (1993) *Phys. Rev.* B **48**, 13434; (1994) *J. Acoust. Soc. Am.* **95**, 1734.
6. Sigalas, M. M., Economou, E. N. & Kafesaki, M. (1994) *Phys. Rev. B* **50**, 3393.
7. Kafesaki, M., Sigalas, M. M. & Economou, E. N. (1995) *Solid State Commun.* **96**, 285.
8. Kushwaha, M. S. & Halevi, P. (1994) *Appl. Phys. Lett.* **64**, 1085; Kushwaha, M. S., Halevi, P, Martinez, G., Dobrzynski, L. & Djafari-Rouhani, B. (1994) *Phys. Rev.* B **49**, 2313.
9. Vasseur, J. O., Djafari-Rohani, B., Dobrzynski, L., Kushwaha, M. S. & Halevi, P. (1994) *J. Phys.:Condens. Matter* **6**, 8759.
10. Kushwaha, M. S. (1997) *Appl. Phys. Lett.* **70**, 3218.
11. Vasseur, J. O., Deymier, P. A., Frantziskonis, G., Hong, G., Djafari-Rohani, B., Dobrzynski, L. (1998) *J. Phys.:Condens. Matter* **10**, 6051.
12. Garcia-Pablos, D., Sigalas, M. M., Montero de Espinosa, F. R., Torres, M., Kafesaki, M. & Garcia, N. (2000) *Phys. Rev. Lett.* **84**, 4349.
13. Torres, M., Montero de Espinosa, F. R., Garcia-Pablos, D. & Garcia, N. (1998) *Phys. Rev. Lett.* **82**, 3054.
14. Montero de Espinosa, F. R., Jimenez, E. & Torres, M. (1998) *Phys. Rev. Lett.* **80**, 1208.
15. Martinez-Sala, R., Sancho, J., Sanchez, J. V., Gomez, V., Llinares, J. & Meseguer, F. (1995) *Nature* **378**, 241.
16. Kafesaki, M., Penciu, R. & Economou, E. N. (2000) *Phys. Rev. Lett.* **84**, 6050.
17. Kafesaki, M. & Economou, E. N. (1999) *Phys. Rev.* B **60**, 11993.
18. Smith, G.D., *Numerical Solution of Partial Differential Equations: Finite Difference Methods*, Claredon Press, Oxford.
19. Clayton, R. & Engquist, B. (1977) *Bull. Seism. Soc. Am.* **67**, 1529.
20. Zhou, J. & Saffari, N. (1996) *Proceedings of the Royal Society London*, Part A, **452**, 1609; (1997) *Bulletin of the Seismological Soc. of America* **87**, 1324.
21. Taflove, Allen (1995) *Computational Electrodynamics*, Artech House; Kunz, K. S. & Luebbers, R. J. (1993) *The finite difference time domain method for electromagnetics, CRC Press*; Jones, D. S. (1994) *Methods in electromagnetic wave propagation*, Oxford University Press.
22. Chan, C. T., Datta, S., Yu, Q. L., Sigalas, M. M., Ho, K. M. & Soukoulis, C. M. (1994) *Physica* **A211**, 411; Chan, C. T., Yu, Q. L. & Ho, K. M. (1995) *Phys. Rev.* B **51**, 16635.
23. Fan, S., Villeneuve, P. R. & Joannopoulos, J. D. (1996) *Phys. Rev.* B **54**, 11245.

24. Mekis, A., Chen, J. C., Kurland, I., Fan, S., Villeneuve, P. R. & Joannopoulos, J. D. (1996) *Phys. Rev. Lett.* **77**, 3787.
25. Sigalas, M. M., Biswas, R., Ho, K. M., Soukoulis, C. M. & Crouch, D. D. (1999) *Phys. Rev.* B **60**, 4426.
26. Kafesaki, M., Sigalas, M. M. & Garcia, N. (2000) to appear in *Phys. Rev. Lett.*
27. Landau, L. D. & Lifshitz, E. M. (1959) *Theory of Elasticity*, Pergamon.

Micro-fabrication and Nano-fabrication of Photonic Crystals

S.Y. Lin, J.G. Fleming, E. Chow

Sandia National Laboratories, P.O. Box 5800, Albuquerque, NM 87185

1. INTRODUCTION

For the past decade, the operating wavelength λ of photonic crystal structures has progressed rapidly from millimeter waves to infrared and even to optical wavelengths of λ= 400nm – 1,500 nm [1-8]. The fabrication methos has also evolved dramatically. It started from the early mechanical drilling of dielectric holes to the most recent micro- and nano-fabrication of dielectric materials using either lithographical [8-9] or chemical methods [10-11]. In this article, I intend to give an overview of photonic crystal structures created using advanced semiconductor processing techniques.

In the first part, the fabrication of 3D photonic crystals using silicon processing will be discussed. The operating λ of the crystal ranges from 1-10 μm. In the second part, we describe the creation of 2D photonic crystal slab operating at λ=1.55 μm communication wavelength. At the final part, a summary will be given, comparing various aspects of 3D and 2D photonic crystals.

2. MICRO-FABRICATION OF 3D PHOTONIC CRYSTALS

The 3D photonic crystal has a diamond crystal symmetry and was fabricated using an advanced silicon processing [7]. The crystal consists of layers of one-dimensional silicon rods with a stacking sequence that repeats itself every four layers, repeating distance c. Within each layer, the axes of the rods are parallel to each other with a pitch of d. The orientation of the axes is rotated by 90° between adjacent layers. Between every other layer, the rods are shifted relative to each other by 0.5 d. The resulting structure has a face-center-tetragonal lattice symmetry. For the special case of c/d = 1.414, the lattice can be derived from a face-centered-cubic unit cell with a basis of two rods, i.e. the diamond lattice. The optimum filling fraction of the high dielectric silicon material is 28%. At this filling fraction, the 3D crystal has a large photonic band gap centered at a frequency of 0.5 c_o/a.

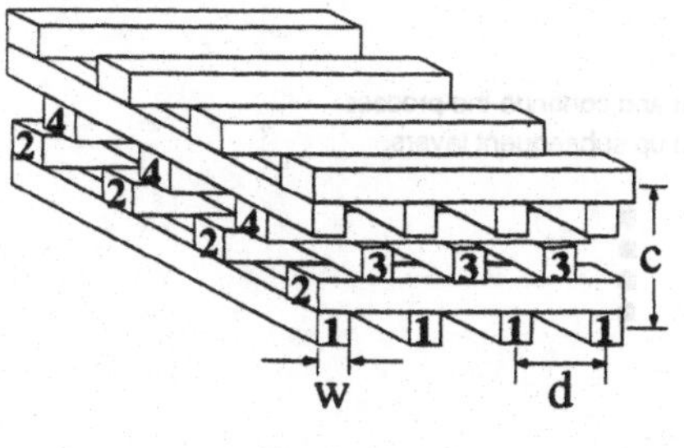

Fig. 1(a)

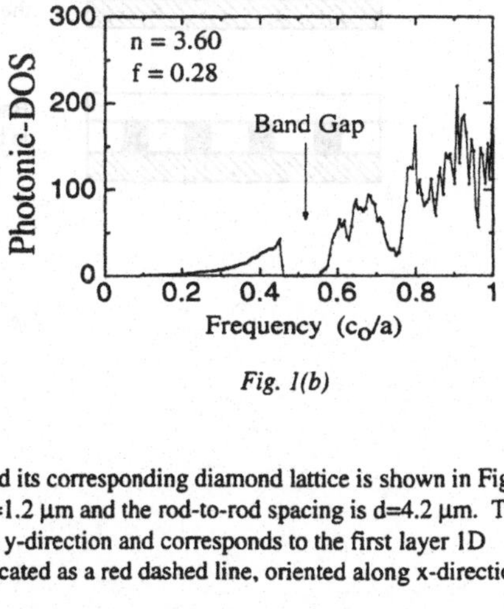

Fig. 1(b)

An SEM image of a miro-fabricated 3D structures and its corresponding diamond lattice is shown in Fig. 2(a) and (b), respectively. The width of the rod is W=1.2 μm and the rod-to-rod spacing is d=4.2 μm. The bottom atom-chain, in Fig. 2(b), is oriented along the y-direction and corresponds to the first layer 1D rods in Fig. 2(a). The next layer of atom-chain is indicated as a red dashed line, oriented along x-direction

C.M. Soukoulis (ed.), Photonic Crystals and Light Localization in the 21st Century, 83–91.

and corresponds to the second layer 1D rods in Fig. 2(a). The third- and fourth layers are also indicated in blue and red, respectively. In short, the fabricated 3D photonic crystal is a real crystal with the diamond crystal symmetry.

2

Fig. 2(a)

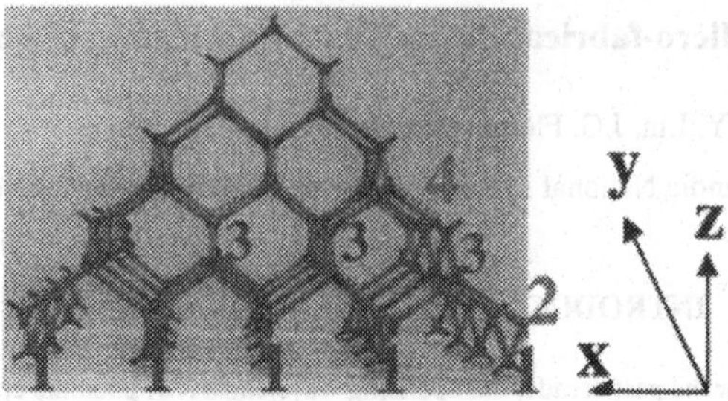
4
3
2
1
y
z
x

Fig. 2(b)

As the first and second steps of the fabrication process (see Fig. 3), a layer of SiO_2 is deposited and lithographically patterned into 1D rods. At the third steps, a polysilicon layer is deposited to cover the patterned trench structure. The fourth step of the process is to use chemical-mechanical-polishing (CMP) to planarize the poly-silicon surface. This completes the process for making a one-unit cell. The process may be continued to build more unit-cells. The oxide may also be removed by using a HF etch.

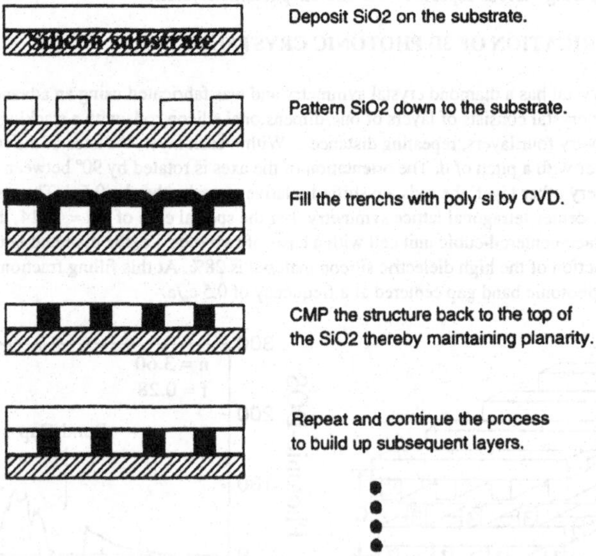
Silicon substrate
Deposit SiO2 on the substrate.
Pattern SiO2 down to the substrate.
Fill the trenchs with poly si by CVD.
CMP the structure back to the top of the SiO2 thereby maintaining planarity.
Repeat and continue the process to build up subsequent layers.

Fig. 3

By repeating this fabrication sequence, as many as ten-layers of 3D silicon photonic crystal has been built. The transmission spectrum for light propagating along the stacking direction, i.e. <001>, is shown in Fig.4(a). It has a large photonic bandgap, with a gap to mid-gap ration of 36%. The minimum transmission of T ~ 0.0003 occurs at λ=5.5 μm, corresponding to an attenuation of 35dB. This attenuation strength is sufficiently large for most opto-electronic applications, including the construction of low-loss waveguides, bends, beam splitters and high-Q micro-cavities.

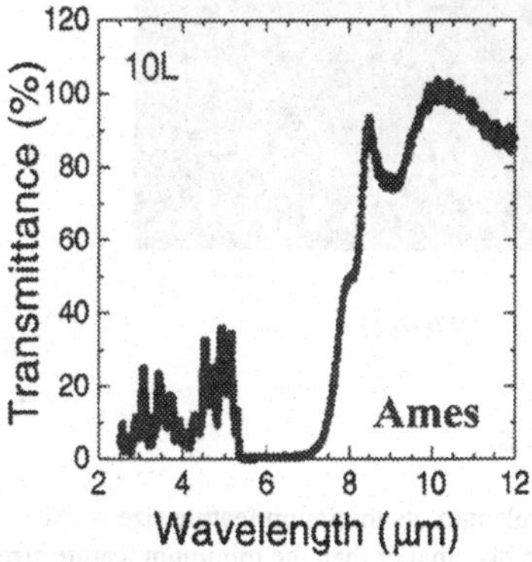

Fig.4(a)

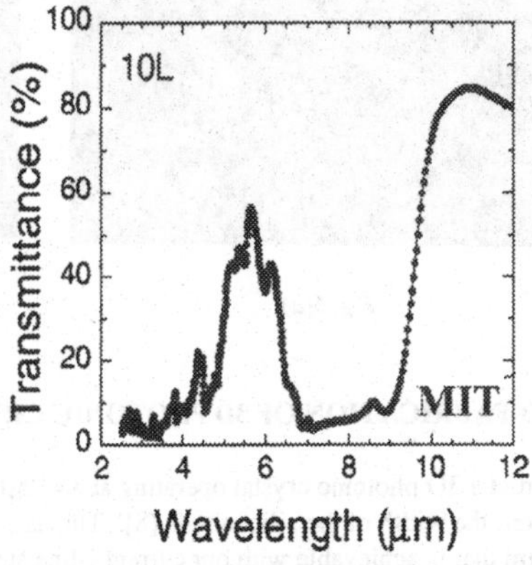

Fig.4(b)

Using this approach, many different types of photonic crystals may be fabricated on the same six-inch silicon wafer. For example, a different 3D photonic crystal structure designed at MIT [12] was fabricated at the same time. The 3D photonic crystal also has a large photonic band gap. The fine peak at λ ~ 8.7 μm, Fig. 4(b), may be due to the presence of an unintentional defect, introduced during processing. The weaker attenuation can be readily improved by using a more optimized structural parameters and is not intrinsic to the MIT design itself.

To further illustrate the power of this technique, a SEM image of 3D crystals designed by Ames lab and MIT is shown in Fig. 5(a) and (b), respectively. The basic building block for both designs is continuous 1D lines. Ames-design uses straight lines and MIT-design uses curved lines.

Fig. 5(a)

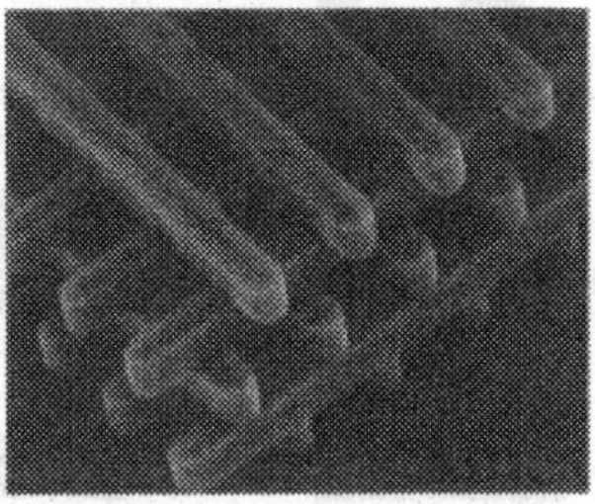

Fig. 5(b)

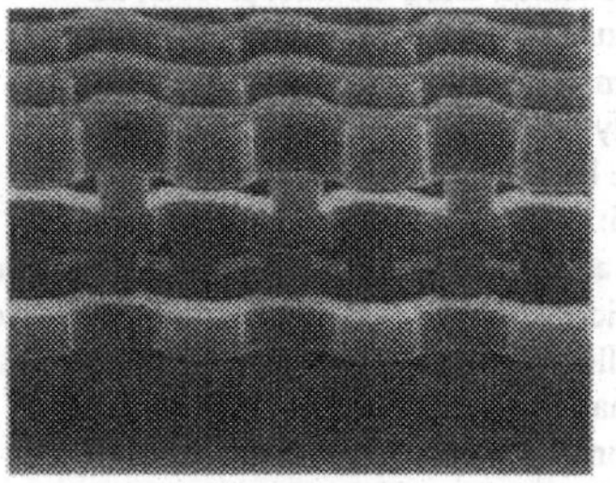

However, other design alternatives also exist. For example, new designs may be implemented using localized sections (or closed contours) as the basic building block. Examples of fabricated structures using either circular rings or star-shapes are shown in Fig.6 (a) and (b), respectively. Both structures have the faced-center-cubic (FCC) crystal symmetry. Although design may varied, the structures can all be built on the same wafer using advanced silicon processing.

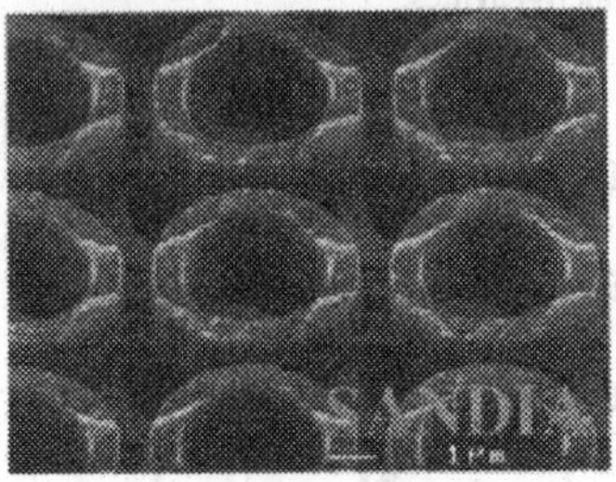

Fig. 6(a)

Fig. 6(b)

3. NANO-FABRICATION OF 3D PHOTONIC CRYSTALS

To construct a 3D photonic crystal operating at λ=1.5μm wavelength, its minimum feature size is 180 nano-meter, the width of the silicon rods [8]. This is considerably smaller than the minimum feature size of ~0.5 μm that is achievable with our current I-line stepper systems. We achieved this dimension by using the fillet processing. This approach relies on the fact that when a thin film of material is deposited over a step and then subjected to anisotropic reactive-ion-etching, a thin sliver of material remains along the sides of the step. If the step height is several times greater than the thickness of the thin film that is deposited, then the width of the fillet will be identical or at least propotional to the film thickness.

In the first step of the process, Fig. 7(a), a thin film of polysilicon is deposited having the thickness of the desired final height of the line, 0.22 μm. The polysilicon is then capped with a thin film of silicon nitride which acts as a combination etch and CMP (Chemical Mechanical Polish) stop. The sacrificial step material, SiO2, is then deposited and photopatterned, Fig.7(b). Since the minimum dimension is attained using the fillet process, the minimum feature size is now that of the pitch of the array, 0.65 μm. After photopatterning, the oxide is anisotropically etched to just above the level of the silicon nitride layer. A 30-second wet etch in a room temperature 6:1 mixture (Ammonium fluoride: Hydrofluoric acid) is then used to isotropically remove ~90 nm of silicon dioxide, Fig.7(c). Polysilicon is used to form the fillet, Fig.7(d), and is etched in a high density plasma source system, Fig.7(e). Following fillet formation, the sacrifical oxide is stripped, Fig.7(f). The fillet is then used as a mask for the etch of both the underlying silicon nitride and silicon dioxide

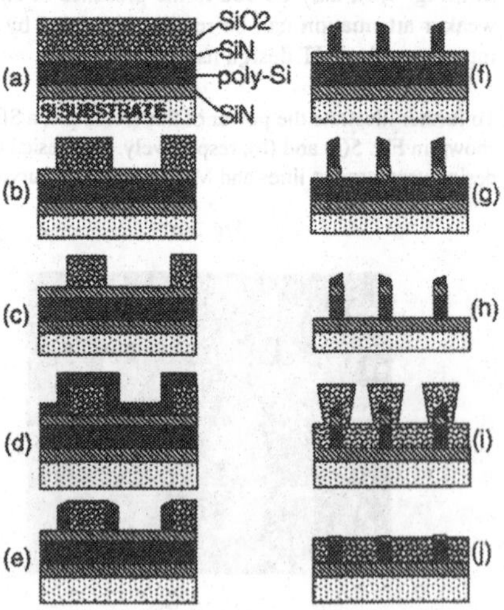

Fig.7

layers, Fig.7(g)-(h). Since the height of the poly silicon fillet is greater than that of the layer being etched, the fillet itself serves as the mask.

The next critical step involves the use of CMP to maintain planarity throughout the process. The first step is to fill the gaps between the lines of polysilicon with a 0.3 μm deposition of silicon dioxide, Fig. 1(i). The wafers are then planarized back to the silicon nitride stopping layer using CMP, Fig.1(j). At this point the entire process is repeated to form the subsequent layers of the structure.

A SEM image of the fabricated four layer 3D photonic crystal are shown in Fig.8. Its corresponding transmission spectra taken from a 3-layer and a 4-layer 3D crystal, respectively, are shown in Fig. 9(a). A strong transmittance dip is observed at $\lambda = 1.35$ to 1.95 μm, providing convincing evidence for the existence of a photonic band gap in the optical wavelength. The bandwidth of our 3D crystal is large, $\Delta\lambda = 600$ nm. Additionally, the allowed band transmission at $\lambda > 2.5$ μm is near 100%. This indicates little, if any, absorption or unwanted scattering loss exists in our 3D crystal. The transmission plot taken from an infrared crystal is shown in Fig. 9(b) for comparison purpose. The design of the optical and infrared is identical, except that their respective dimensions are different by a ratio of 6.6 :1. The vertical axis is shifted by 10dB for ease of comparison.

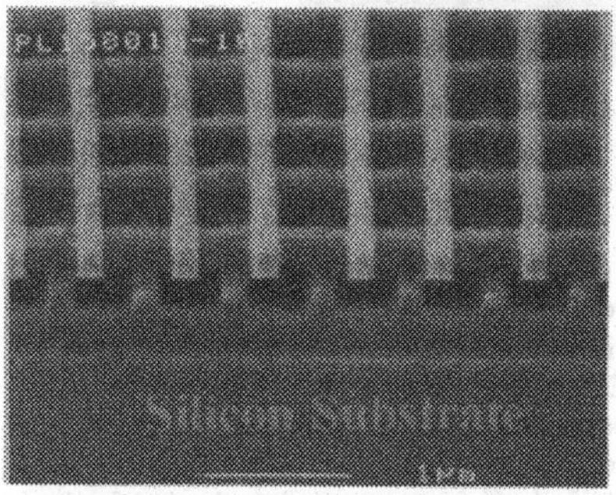

Fig.8

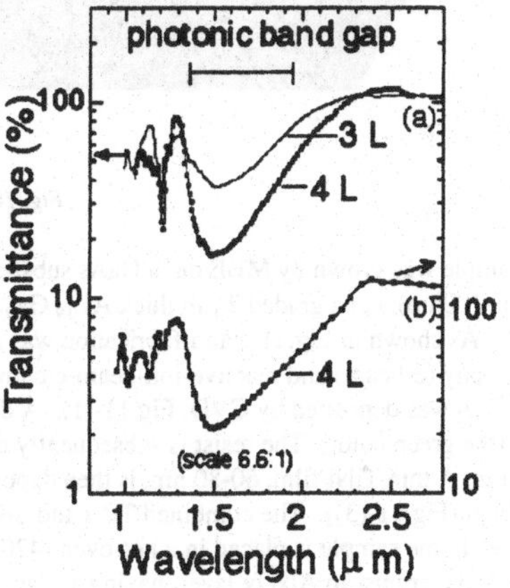

Fig. 9

4. NANO-FABRICATION OF 2D PHOTONIC CRYSTAL SLAB

A two-dimensional (2D) photonic crystal is an attractive alternative and complimentary to its 3D counterpart, due to fabrication simplicity. A 2D crystal, however, confines light only in the 2D plane, but not in the third direction, the z-direction. Earlier experiments show that such an ideal 2D system can exist [13-19]. Nonetheless, the usefulness of such 2D crystals is limited because they are less capable of guiding and controlling light in z-direction, which leads to diffraction loss.

Here, we describe a successful nano-fabrication of a waveguide-coupled 2D photonic crystal slab [20-21]. The crystal slab is found to have a strong 2D photonic band gap at $\lambda \sim 1.5$ μm. More importantly, the crystal slab is

shown to be capable of controlling light fully in all three-dimensions, a pre-requisite for realizing novel photonic-crystal devices such as thresholdless lasers.

The basic design is shown schematically in Fig.10. In the x-y plane (the 2D plane), it is a simple 2D periodic dielectric array. Notably, in the z-direction, it has a layered design. This sample has two important features. One is that the index contrast ΔN between the waveguiding layer (red color, n ~ 3.5) and the cladding layer (green color, n ~ 1.5) is large ΔN~2.0 [22-23]. Secondly, the thickness of the high index slab is thin, about half of the nearest hole-to-hole spacing a_0. The conventional waveguides, connected to 2D hole-array, are used for ease of input and output coupling. The use of the underlying oxide has an added benefit of keeping the structure vertically integrated.

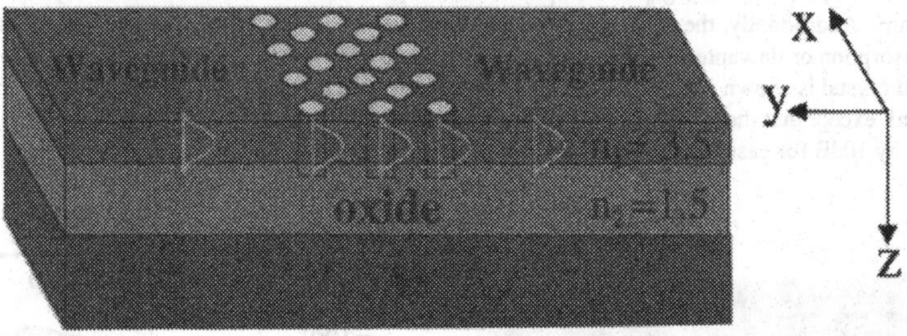

Fig. 10

The sample was grown by MBE on a GaAs substrate. The growth sequence was: (1)a thin GaAs buffer layer (~100nm), (2) a graded 2 µm thick $Al_{0.9}Ga_{0.1}As$ layer and finally (3) a ~200 nm thin layer of GaAs. As shown in Fig.11, nano-fabrication was accomplished using a combination of electron-beam-lithography (e-beam) and reactive-ion-beam-etching (RIBE). As the first step of the process, a 200nm thick SiO_2 was deposited by CVD, Fig.11-(1). A direct e-beam write was then performed on a PMMA resist (the green color). The resist is subsequently developed, Fig.11-(2), yielding a 2D hole diameter of ~200 nm. A thin TiNi film, 60-80 nm, is then deposited and lifted-off, forming a mask (red color) for the SiO_2 etch (Fig.11-(3)). The combined TiNi and SiO_2 layers serve as the final mask for RIBE-etch. After RIBE etch, the sample is placed in a hot-oven (420 C) for 20-30 minutes. This process converts the $Al_{0.9}Ga_{0.1}As$ layer into an AlxOy layer, having a low index.

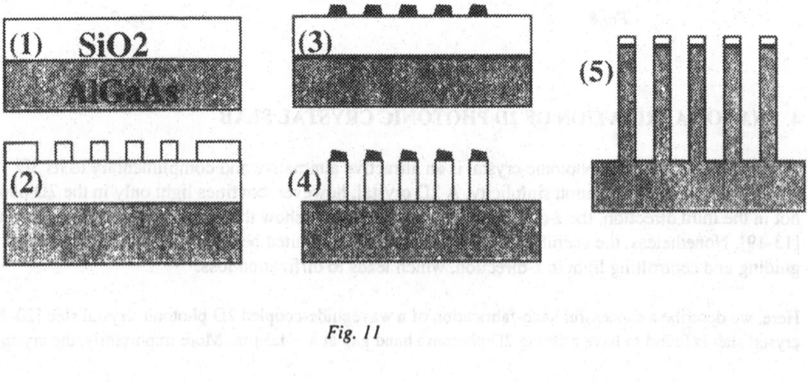

Fig. 11

A SEM cross-section image of the fabricated sample is shown in Fig. 12. For this particular sample, the GaAs thickness t = 200 nm, lattice constant a_o=400nm and hole diameter is d=240nm. The fabrication is near perfect, having a periodic 2D triangular array and very straight etched-holes. The 2D hole array section is designed to be a few rows wider than the waveguide to reduce the amount of light leaking around the side edges of photonic-crystal slab.

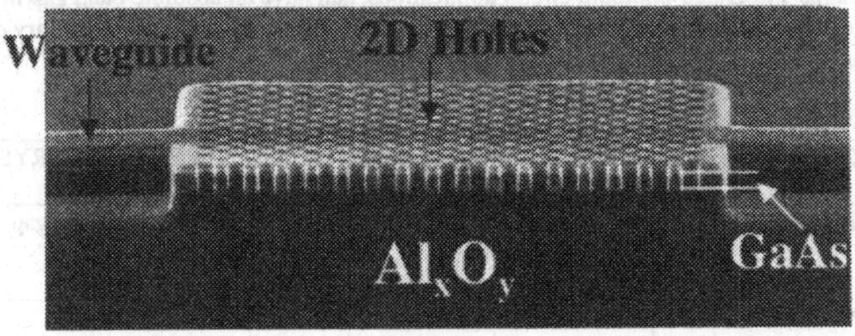

Fig. 12

To find absolute intrinsic transmittance of a 2D crystal, a reference transmission is taken from an identical waveguide with no 2D crystal built in the middle section. By rationing transmission signals, taken with and without a 2D crystal, intrinsic transmittance is obtained. This procedure eliminates external uncertainties associated with reflection at waveguide-crystal interfaces and free space-to-waveguide coupling efficiency and allows for an absolute determination of intrinsic transmittance of a 2D crystal slab.

In Fig.13, the measured and computed TE transmission spectrum is plotted in a semi-log scale as open dots and a solid line, respectively. The frequency is expressed in a reduced unit (a_o/λ). Here, ω is varied by tuning λ through three samples with different a = 400 nm (red dots), 430 nm (green dots) and 460 nm (blue dots), respectively. The observed band gap is slightly larger than the predicted value, ~8%, and may be due to small uncertainties in the fabricated hole size and lattice constant. In the band gap, $\omega \sim 0.27$, transmittance as low as $\sim 2 \times 10^{-4}$ is observed. At the lower band edge, $\omega \sim 0.25$, transmittance increases from 2×10^{-4} to unity over a small $\Delta\omega \sim 0.02$, a four order of magnitude rise. The upper and lower TE band edges occur at $\omega_1 \sim 0.34$ and $\omega_2 \sim 0.25$, respectively, yielding a large gap-to-midgap ratio, 30%.

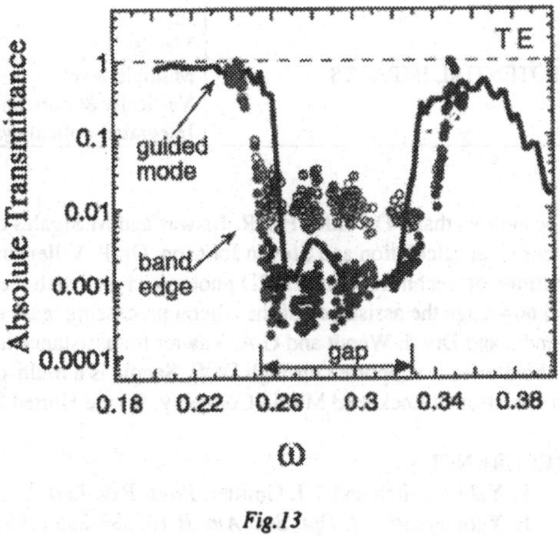

Fig.13

5. SUMMARY

In summary, a 3D photonic crystal fabricated using silicon processing has many distinctive properties such as having a large absolute photonic band gap in all directions, and the ease of introducing line defects and points defects for guiding and trapping of light. The 2D crystal slab, on the other hand, is relatively easier to build, suitable for planar-integrated-photonic-circuit applications, can have an absolute band gap in 2D as well as a weakly index confinement in the third direction. The table below gives a short summary of our 2D and 3D crystals created using semiconductor lithographic processing.

OPTICAL PROPERTIES	3D PHOTONIC CRYSTAL	2D PHOTONIC CRYSTAL SLAB
DEGREE OF LIGHT CONFINEMENT	All 3Ds; Both polarizations	2D photonic band gap; 1D "index guiding"
SIZE OF PHOTONICBANDGAP gap-to-mid gap ratio)	~ (20-30) %	~ (20-30) %
BANDWIDTH OF WAVEGUIDE (bandwidth / gap size)	~ (80-100) %	~ (20-30) %
HIGHEST ACHIEVABLE CAVITY-Q	> 1,000 – 100,000	> 500 – 10,000
BENDING RADIUS	~ 1 λ	~ 1 λ
NANO-FABRICATION COMPLEXITY	High	Medium
MATERIALS	Silicon; III-V; Metals	Silicon; III-V
POTENTIAL IMPACTS	Multiple-level, Vertically & horizontally coupled, Integrated-optical-systems	Single level (planar) Horizontally coupled, Integrated-optical-systems

The authors thank Dr. K.M. Ho, R. Biswas and M.Sigalas of Ames laboratory for the 3D photonic crystal theoretical calculation and Steven Johnson, Dr. P. Villeneuve and Prof. J.D. Joannopoulos at Massachusetts Institute of Technology for the 2D photonic crystal slab theoretical calculation. The authors also acknowledge the assistance of the silicon processing team at Microelectronics Development Laboratory of Sandia and Drs. J. Wendt and G.A. Vawter for assistance in nano-fabrication. The work at Sandia National Laboratories is supported through DOE. Sandia is a multi-program laboratory operated by Sandia Corporation, a Lockheed Martin Company, for the United States Department of Energy.

REFERENCES

1. E. Yablonovitch and T.J. Gmitter, ***Phys. Rev. Lett.*** 63, 1950 (1989).
2. E. Yablonovitch, ***J. Opt. Soc. Am. B*** 10, 283-295 (1993).
3. C.M. Soukoulis, "Photonic band gaps and localizations", NATO ASI series B, volume 308, Plenum Press, New York (1993).
4. E. Ozbay et al., ***Phys. Rev. B*** 50, 1945 (1994).
5. M.C. Wanke et al., ***Science***, vol. 275, p. 1284 (1997).
6. C.C. Cheng et al., ***Physica Scripta***, Vol. T68, 17 (1996).
7. S.Y. Lin et al., ***Nature***, Vol. 394, 251 (1998).

8. J.G. Fleming and S.Y. Lin, ***Optics Letters, 24***, p. 49 (1999).
9. S. Noda et al., Jap. J. Appl. Phys., part 2-Letters, v.35, p. L909-L912 (1996).
10. A. Blanco et al., ***Nature***, v. 405, p. 437-440 (2000).
11. W.L. Vos et al., ***Phys. Rev. B***, V. 53, p. 16231-16235 (1996).
12. S. Fan et al., Appl. Phys. Lett., v.65, p.1466-1468 (1994).
13. S.Y. Lin, et al., ***J. Modern Optics***. Vol. 41, 385-393 (1994).
14. U. Gruning, and V. Lehmann, ***Thin Solid Films***, Vol. 276, 151-154 (1996).
15. A. Rosenberg. et al., ***Optics Lett***., Vol. 21, 830-832 (1996).
16. T.F. Krauss et al, ***Nature***, Vol. 383, 699-702 (1996).
17. D. Labilloy et al., ***Phys. Rev. Lett***. 79, 4147-4150 (1997).
18. H. Benisty et al., ***IEEE J. Light Wave Tech***. 17, 2063-2077 (1999).
19. M. Kanskar,et al., ***Appl. Phys. Lett***. 70, 1438-1440 (1997).
20. E. Chow et al., ***Nature***, 407, p.983-986, 2000.
21. S.Y. Lin et al., ***Optics Letters***, vol. 25, 1297 (2000).
22. P.R. Villeneuve et al., ***IEE Proc. Optoelec.,*** vol. 145, 384-390 (1998).
23. S.G. Johnson et al., ***Phys. Rev. B*** 60 5751-5758 (1999).

SEMICONDUCTOR PHOTONIC CRYSTALS

SUSUMU NODA,[1] MASAHIRO IMADA,[1] ALONGKARN CHUTINAN,[1] AND NORITSUGU YAMAMOTO[2]

[1]*Department of Electronic Science and Engineering, Kyoto University, Kyoto 606-8501, Japan*

[2]*Electrotechnical Laboratory, Agency of Industrial Science and Technology (AIST), Ministry of International Trade and Industry (MITI), 1-1-4, Umezono, Tsukuba, Ibaraki, 305-8568, Japan*

1. INTRODUCTION

Much interest has been drawn to photonic crystals, optical materials in which the refractive index changes periodically.[1,2] A photonic band gap is formed in the crystals, and the propagation of electromagnetic waves is prohibited for all wave vectors. Various important scientific and engineering applications such as a control of spontaneous emission, a zero-threshold laser, a very sharp bending of light, and so on, are expected by utilizing the photonic band gap and the artificially introduced defect states and/or light-emitters.[1-4]

In this paper, the present status of III-V based 3D and 2D photonic crystals is reviewed by emphasizing the works performed in Kyoto University. The complete control of light and ultra-small optical integrated circuits can be expected by utilizing 3D photonic crystals. On the other hand, important devices with specific functions can be expected by utilizing 2D photonic crystals, even though the control of light is limited two-dimensionally.

2. 3D PHOTONIC CRYSTALS

Figure 1 shows one of the goals of photonic crystals,[5] where ultra-small optical integrated circuits are illustrated. In the figure, zero-threshold laser arrays with different oscillation frequencies, very sharp bend waveguides, an optical modulator, and wavelength selectors, and so on are integrated in a very small area ($<100\times100\mu m^2$) only by introducing appropriate artificial defects and/or light-emitters inside the crystal. To develop such an ultimate optical integrated circuit by photonic crystals, the following requirements should be satisfied: (i) a three-dimensional (3D) photonic crystal with a full photonic band gap is constructed in optical wavelength region, (ii) the introduction of an arbitrary defect state

C.M. Soukoulis (ed.), Photonic Crystals and Light Localization in the 21st Century, 93–103.

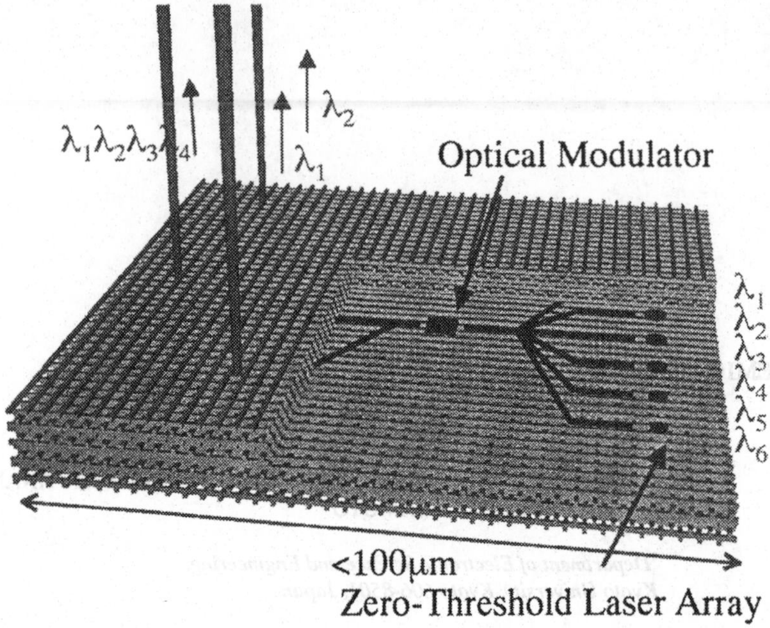

Figure 1. **Example of the future very compact quantum optical integrated circuits, where zero-threshold laser arrays with different oscillation frequencies, an optical modulator, wavelength selectors, and a very sharp bend waveguide are integrated in a very small area only by introducing appropriate artificial defects inside the crystal.**

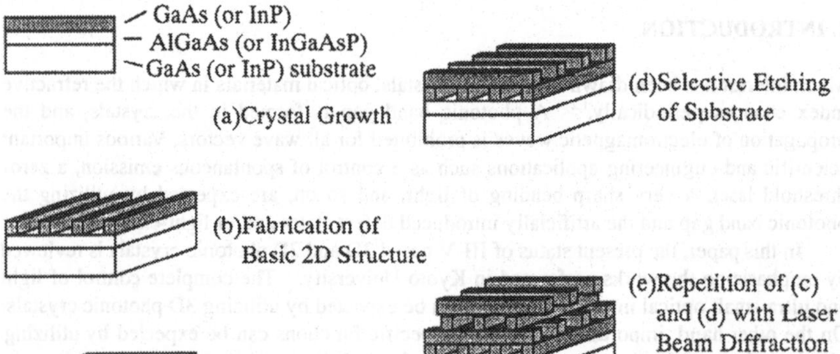

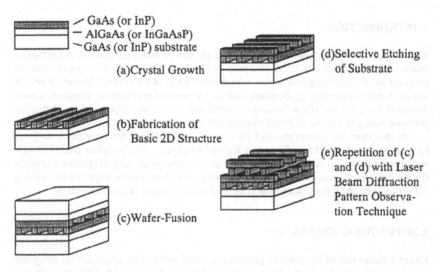

Figure 2. **Schematic drawing to show the proposed fabrication procedure of the 3D photonic crystal.**

into the crystal is possible at an arbitrary position, (iii) the introduction of an efficient light-emitting element is also possible, and (iv) the electronically conductive crystal is desirable for the actual device application. Although various important approaches such as a self-assembled colloidal crystal,[6] a GaAs based three-axis dry-etching crystal,[7] and a silicon based layer-by-layer crystal[8] with so-called woodpile structure[9] have been proposed and investigated to construct the 3D photonic crystals, it is considered difficult for these methods to satisfy the above requirements simultaneously.

2-1. Development of 3D Photonic Crystals with Desired Requirements

To fulfill the above requirements, we proposed a new realization method of the 3D photonic crystal as shown in Fig. 2,[10] where GaAs (or InP) stripes are stacked by a wafer fusion to construct the woodpile structure, which has basically a diamond structure. The four-stacked layers correspond to the one-unit of the structure, and it is theoretically confirmed that the crystal has a complete photonic band gap for all wave vectors. The important point for the construction of the photonic crystal is to make a precise alignment between the first and third stripes (and between the second and fourth stripes), where individual stripes should be shifted by half a period to construct the structure. The alignment is performed by observing an intensity change of the diffraction spots of a laser beam incident normally on the stacked stripes, where the ±1st order diffraction spots become minimal when the relative position between the parallel stripes is shifted by just half a period.[11] Here, since the crystal is constructed with III-V semiconductors which are widely utilized for optoelectronic devices, the requirement (iii) described above is satisfied. Moreover, since the wafer-fusion technique enables us to construct an arbitrary structure and to form an electronically active interface, the above requirements (i)-(iv) will be satisfied.

We at first developed the photonic crystals at infrared wavelengths,[12,13] which was followed by successful fabrication of photonic crystals at near-infrared wavelengths.[5,14,15] Figure 3 shows the top view of a crystal which we constructed recently, where the stripe period, width, and depth are 0.70, 0.19, and 0.20, respectively, and the band gap wavelength is designed to be at the near-infrared wavelengths. It is seen in Fig. 3 that a very beautiful structure is successfully constructed, and the alignment accuracy is as good as less than 30nm. The normal incident transmission and reflection spectra of the crystal are shown in Fig. 4. The clear attenuation of the transmission is seen at 1.0-1.6μm wavelength region with the maximum attenuation of -23dB at 1.2μm (more than 99% attenuation), and the reflectance is found to be ~100% at maximum in the same wavelength region. This is the record largest band gap effect and the shortest wavelength ever reported. The transmission spectra were measured also for various incident angles, and it has been shown that the structure has complete photonic band gap at 1.3 to 1.55μm wavelengths, which are very important for optical communication fields. We have also succeeded in the fabrication of the crystal with 8 stacked (2-unit) layers, which shows the maximum band gap effect of more than 40dB.

2-2. Toward Ultra-small Optical Integrated Circuits – 3D Photonic Crystal Waveguide with Sharp Bend –

Based on the results described above, we may now proceed to the development of the 3D photonic crystal circuits as shown in Fig. 1. However, before doing that, we should design each component of the circuit, since very few design rules on the 3D photonic crystal circuits have been reported until recently. For example, it has not been clear how we can design the 3D sharp bend waveguide. Thus, the 3D photonic crystal waveguide is investigated as follows.[16]

We can imagine various types of waveguides. This means that the various types of

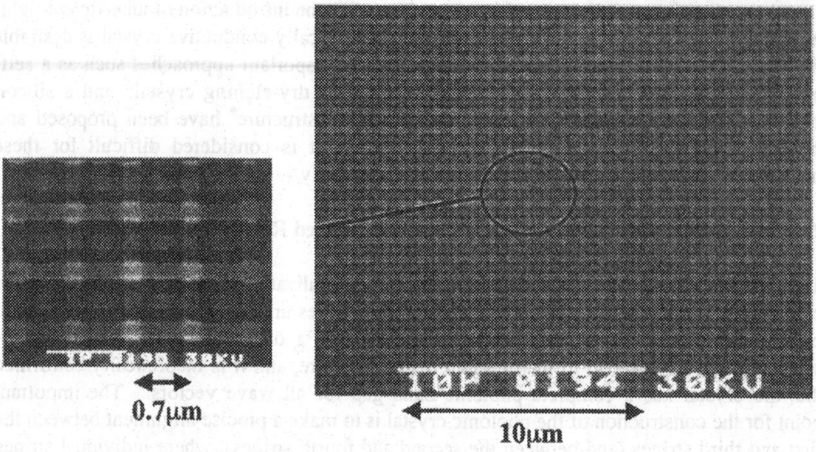

Figure 3. **SEM Top view of a crystal which we constructed recently, where the stripe period, width, and depth are 0.70, 0.19, and 0.20μm, respectively, and the band gap wavelength is designed to be at the near-infrared wavelengths.**

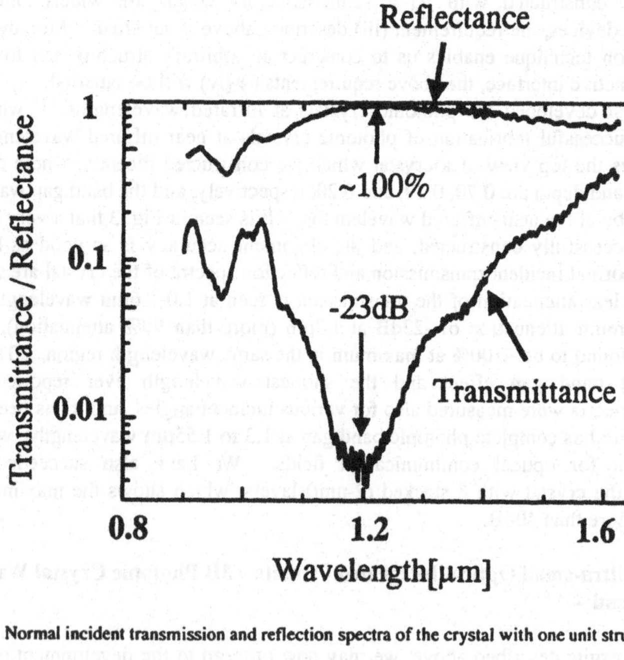

Figure 4. **Normal incident transmission and reflection spectra of the crystal with one unit structure.**

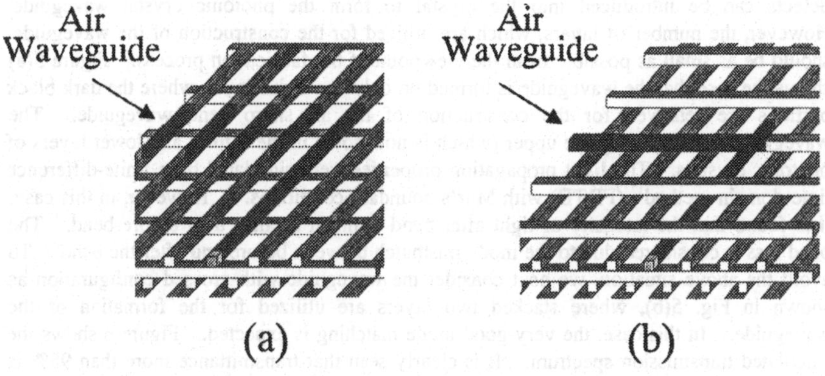

Figure 5. **3D Waveguide structure. The waveguide is formed in one striped layer (a) and in two striped layers (b).**

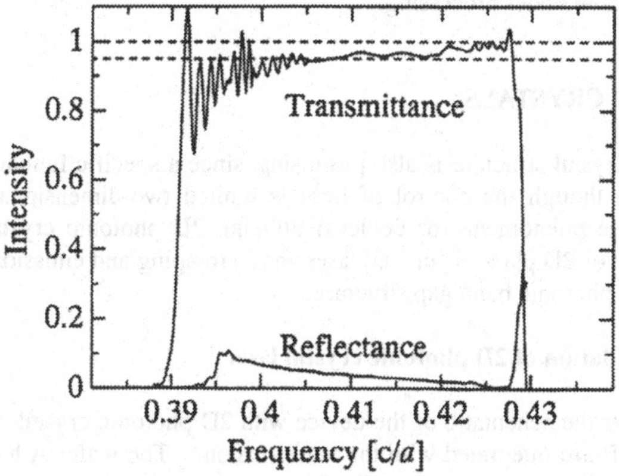

Figure 6. **Transmission spectrum of the bend waveguide shown in Fig. 5(b).**

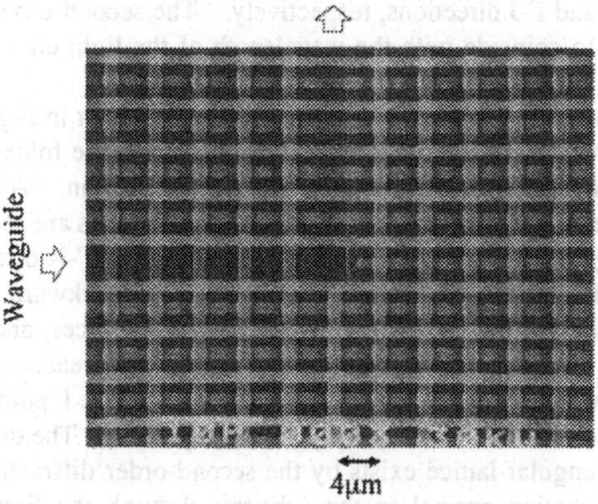

Figure 7. **SEM top view of the three-dimensional photonic crystal waveguide with a sharp bend at infrared wavelengths.**

defects can be introduced into the crystal to form the photonic crystal waveguide. However, the number of layers, which are utilized for the construction of the waveguide, should be as small as possible from the viewpoint of the fabrication process. Figure 5(a) shows the case that the waveguide is formed on only one stripe layer, where the dark black portions are removed for the construction of the air sharp bend waveguide. The waveguide is confined by the upper (which is not shown in the figure) and lower layers of photonic crystals. The light propagation properties were simulated by a finite-difference time-domain method[17] (FDTD) with Mur's boundary conditions.[18] However, in this case, it is found that the intensity of light after bend is much smaller than before bend. The bend loss is considered due to the mode mismatch between before and after the bend. To avoid the above situation, we next consider the waveguide with crossed configuration as shown in Fig. 5(b), where stacked two layers are utilized for the formation of the waveguide. In this case, the very good mode matching is expected. Figure 6 shows the calculated transmission spectrum. It is clearly seen that transmittance more than 95% is obtained in a very wide frequency region. The result provides us very important guidelines for designing of the 3D photonic crystal circuit. Very recently, we have succeeded in the fabrication of 3D photonic crystals as shown in Fig. 7, and the characterization is now under processing.

3. 2D PHOTONIC CRYSTALS

2D photonic crystal structure is also promising, since a specific functional device can be fabricated even though the control of light is limited two-dimensionally. Here, we describe two unique phenomena (or devices) utilizing 2D photonic crystal structure: 1) coherent oscillation of 2D photonic crystal laser and 2) trapping and emission of photons by single defect in 2D photonic band gap structure.

3-1. Coherent oscillation of 2D photonic crystal laser

Figure 8 shows the schematic of the device with 2D photonic crystal structure, where two wafers A and B are integrated with the wafer-fusion. The wafer A has InGaAsP/InP multiple quantum well active layer (λ=1.3μm) grown on a p-InP substrate. The wafer B has a triangular-lattice structure on an n-InP substrate. The inset shows the photograph of the fabricated triangular-lattice structure. The lattice constant is a=0.462μm, and two arrows show the Γ-X and Γ-J directions, respectively. The second-order period of the Γ-X direction is designed to coincide with the wavelength of the light emitted from the active layer.

The band diagram of the triangular-lattice structure is shown in Fig. 9. As described above, the wavelength of the active layer is designed to match the folded Γ point indicated by the broken circle, which is basically related to the Γ-X direction. As can be seen in the expanded figure of the folded Γ point, the complicated band edges are seen. This is due to the coupling of the light waves propagating in the six equivalent Γ-X directions. The light propagating in each Γ-X direction is diffracted not only to backward (180°) but also to other four Γ-X directions (±60°, ±120°) with the triangular lattices, and consequently the light propagating in individual Γ-X directions couples with each other. The lasing oscillation is considered to occur at either of the band-edges of the Γ point.

A lasing oscillation has been successfully achieved at RT.[19] The device oscillates in a plane in which the triangular-lattice exists by the second-order diffraction, but the light is coupled out to the direction normal to the substrate through the first-order diffraction. Figure 10 shows the near field pattern of the device above threshold current and the lasing spectra at individual positions. It is seen that the single mode and uniform oscillation

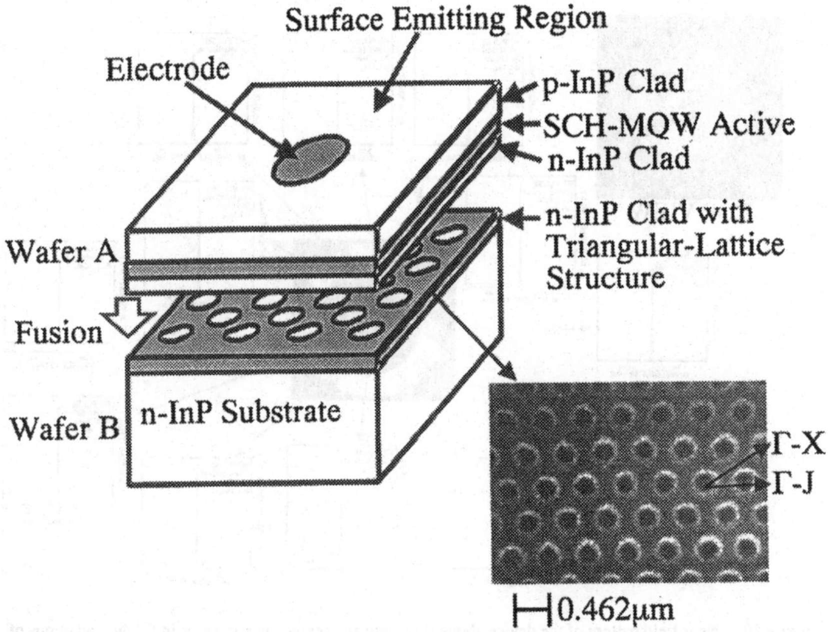

Figure 8. **Schematic structure of surface-emitting laser with 2D photonic crystal structure.**

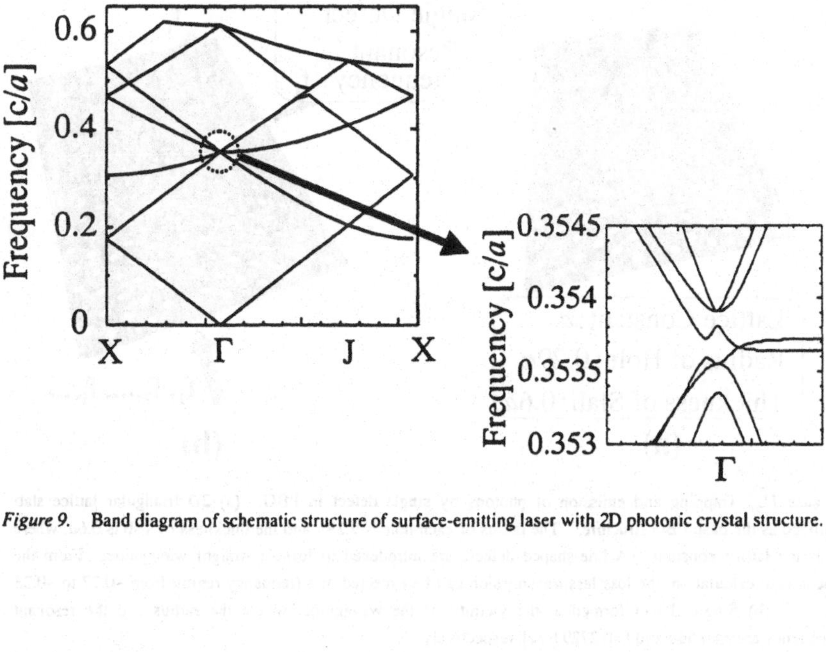

Figure 9. **Band diagram of schematic structure of surface-emitting laser with 2D photonic crystal structure.**

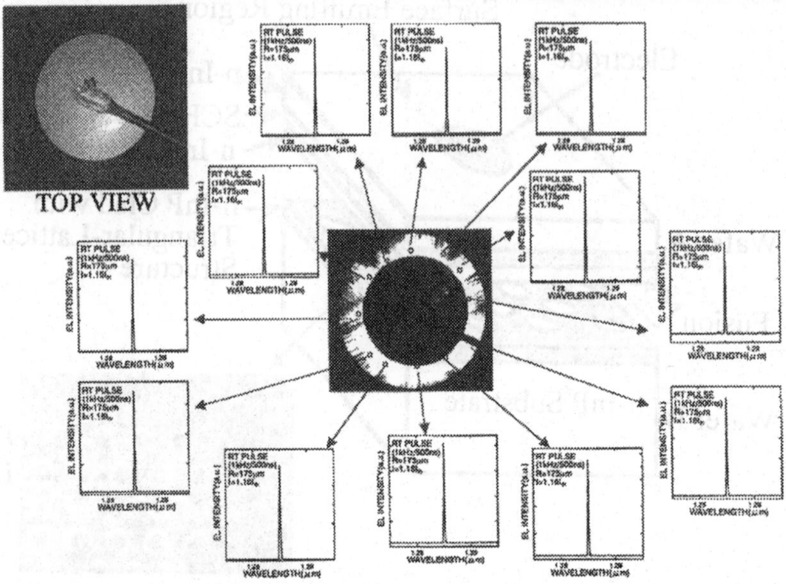

Figure 10. Near field pattern of the device above threshold and the lasing spectra at individual positions of the device. As shown in left-upper figure, center black portion is the electrode and the light emission is obtained from the periphery of it.

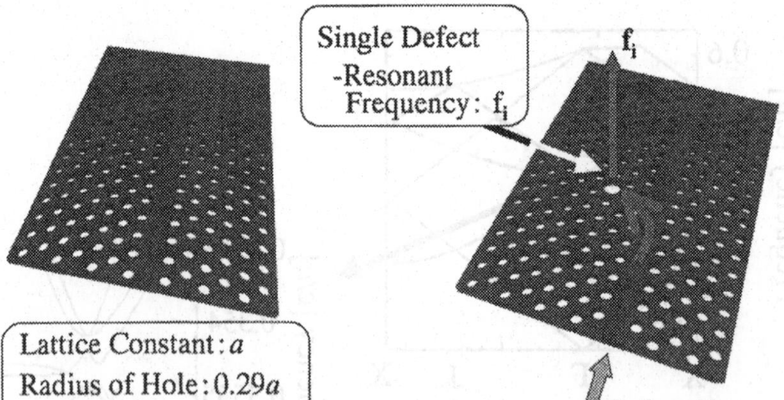

Figure 11. Trapping and emission of photons by single defect in PBG. (a) 2D triangular lattice slab utilized as the base PBG structure. The radius of each hole is $0.29a$ and the thickness of slab is $0.6a$, where a is the lattice constant. A line-shaped defects are introduced to form a straight waveguide. From the theoretical calculation, the loss-less transmission can be expected in a frequency region from ~0.27 to ~0.28 [c/a]. (b) Single defect formed at the vicinity of the waveguide, where the radius and the resonant frequency are r_i=$0.56a$ and f_i=0.2729 [c/a], respectively.

occurs two-dimensionally (coherently), which means that the lasing oscillations along the six Γ-X directions are coupled with each other as described above. The lasing mode was investigated in detail, and currently we have succeeded in finding which mode of the band edges of Fig. 6 corresponds to the experimental results. The details will be reported elsewhere.[20]

3-2. Trapping and emission of photons by a single defect (Add-Drop Device)

We describe here a very interesting phenomenon of trapping photons by a single defect introduced artificially inside the 2D photonic band gap structure. The defect traps the photons which propagate through a waveguide formed in 2D photonic crystal structure and emits them to vacuum field.

The structure considered here is 2D photonic band gap slab[21] with triangular-lattice structure as shown in Fig. 11(a). The structure makes use of the effect of 2D PBG to confine the light in the in-plane direction (for TE-like mode), and the large refractive index contrast to confine the light in the vertical direction. The radius of each hole and the thickness of the slab are chosen to be 0.29*a* and 0.6*a*, respectively, where *a* is the lattice constant of the 2D structure. In Fig. 11(a), line-shaped defects are introduced to form a straight waveguide. We calculated the transmission property of the waveguide by 3D FDTD method and confirmed that the loss-less transmission can be possible in a wide frequency region from ~0.27 [c/*a*] to ~0.28 [c/*a*],[22] where c is the light velocity. Here, we consider introducing a single defect at the vicinity of the waveguide as shown in Fig. 11(b), where the radius of the defect and the distance between the defect and waveguide are 0.56*a* and 3*a*, respectively. In this case, the frequency f_i and the quality factor Q of the defect as the optical resonator can be calculated to be 0.2729 and ~500, respectively. The Q is determined by the following two quality factors: Q_{in} for in-plane direction and Q_v for vertical direction. Q_{in} is determined dominantly by the distance between the defect and waveguide, and it becomes larger with increasing the distance. On the other hand, Q_v is determined by the effective refractive index contrast between the defect portion and the surrounding air in vertical direction, and it can be tuned variously by changing for example the thickness of the slab.[21] In the present geometry (Fig. 1(b)), Q_{in} and Q_v are almost equal.

The photon numbers, which are trapped from the waveguide and emitted to vacuum field by the single defect, was calculated by 3D FDTD method, and the result is shown in Fig. 12. The spectrum indicates only a peak of the eigenfrequency of the defect. It is clearly seen that the photons are indeed emitted to the vacuum field via the single defect for the resonant frequency of f_i =0.2729 [c/*a*]. From the detailed theoretical consideration, we have found that half of the photons which propagate through the waveguide can be trapped and emitted to the vacuum field, when the values of Q_{in} and Q_v are equal. When the large mismatch between the values of Q_{in} and Q_v is present, the emitted photon numbers becomes smaller. These phenomena can be understood from the analogy of the impedance matching condition in electronic circuit, where when the output-impedance of the electronic circuit is equal to the impedance of the load, the energy transfer from the circuit to the load becomes maximal.

Since it has been shown that trapping and emission of photons by single defect are indeed possible, we next considered introducing the additional defect as shown in Fig. 13(a). The spectra indicate only peaks of the eigenfrequencies of the defects. The radius of the additional defect is assumed to be 0.58*a*, which is ~3.5% larger than that of the defect described above, and its resonant frequency f_j is 0.2769. As can be seen in the calculated result of Fig. 13(b), photons with different frequencies f_i and f_j are trapped and emitted to vacuum fields by the corresponding defects. The result clearly shows that the drop (or add) function of photons can be realized by introducing multiple defects with different resonant frequencies at the vicinity of the waveguide.

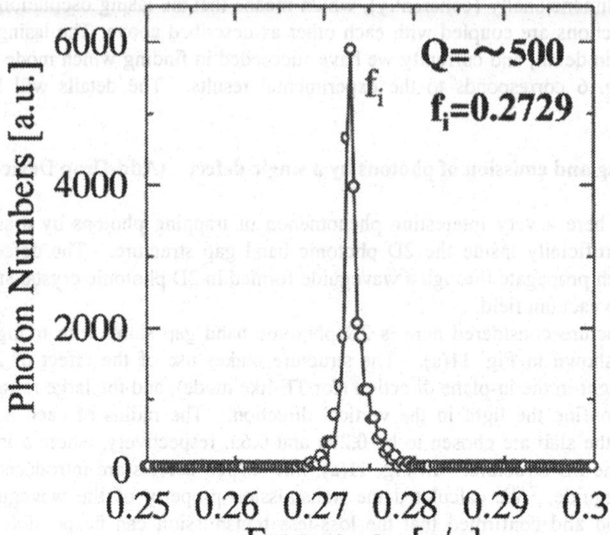

Figure 12. **Calculated photon number that are trapped from the waveguide and emitted to vacuum field by the single defect. The spectrum indicates only a peak of the eigenfrequency of the defect.**

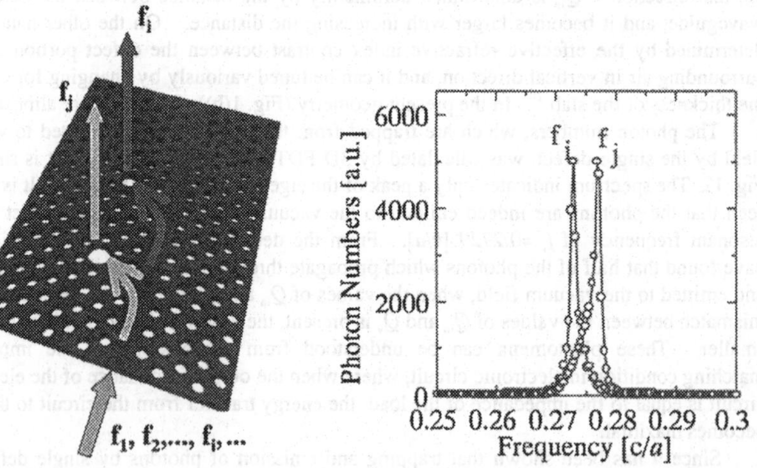

Figure 13. **Trapping and emission of photons by two isolated defects. (a) A new defect with the radius of r_j=0.58*a* and the resonant frequency of f_j=0.2769[*c/a*] is added to the defect described in Fig. 11(b). (b) Calculated photon number emitted by two defects. The spectra indicate only peaks of the eigenfrequencies of defects. Photons with different frequencies of f_i and f_j are trapped and emitted to vacuum fields by the corresponding defects. In the calculation, the mutual interaction between two defects is not considered.**

We have also succeeded in demonstration of the phenomena experimentally, and the details are reported elsewhere.[23] The phenomenon is very promising for the actual application to an ultra-small optical device with a function of dropping (or adding) photons with various energies into optical communication traffic (fiber). Such a very compact add-drop device is strongly required for wavelength division multiplex (WDM) optical communication field.

4. SUMMARY

Present status of photonic crystals based on III-V semiconductors has been explained by emphasizing the works of Kyoto University. On the 3D photonic crystals, the development of complete photonic crystals at optical wavelengths and their applications to ultra-small optical circuits have been demonstrated. On the 2D photonic crystals, a coherent lasing action due to coupling of six equivalent light-waves, and a trapping and emission of photons by single defect have been demonstrated.

REFERENCES

1. E. Yablonovitch, *Phys. Rev. Lett.* **58**, 2059 (1987).
2. S. John, *Phys. Rev. Lett.* **58**, 2486 (1987).
3. J. D. Joannopoulos, P. R. Villeneuve, and S. Fan, *Nature* **386**, 143 (1997).
4. A. Mekis, J. C. Chen, S. Fan, P. R. Villeneuve, and J. D. Joannopoulos, *Phys. Rev. Lett.* **77**, 3787 (1996).
5. S. Noda, N. Yamamoto, M. Imada, H. Kobayashi, and M. Okano, *J. Lightwave Technol.* **17**, 1948 (1999).
6. V. N. Astratov *et al.*, *Nuovo Cimento D* **17D**, 1349 (1995).
7. V. Arbet-Engels, E. Yablonovitch, C. C. Cheng, and A. Scherer, in *Micro-Cavities and Photonic Bandgaps : physics and applications.*, edited by J. Rarity and C. Weisbuch, (Kluwer Academic, Boston, 1996), p.125.
8. S. Lin *et al.*, Nature **394**, 251 (1998).
9. K. M. Ho, C. T. Chan, C. M. Soukoulis, R. Biswas, and M. Sigalas, *Solid State Commun.* **89**, 413 (1994).
10. S. Noda, N. Yamamoto, and A. Sasaki, *Jpn. J. Appl. Phys.* **35**, L909 (1996).
11. N. Yamamoto and S. Noda, *Jpn. J. Appl. Phys.* **37**, 3334 (1998).
12. N. Yamamoto and S. Noda, *Proceedings of the Tenth International Conference on Indium Phosphide and Related Materials* FB2-2, Tsukuba, Japan, 11-15 May, 1998 (IEEE Catalog #98H36129).
13. N. Yamamoto, S. Noda, and A. Chutinan, *Jpn. J. Appl. Phys.* **37**, L1052 (1998).
14. S. Noda, N. Yamamoto, H. Kobayashi, M. Okano, and K. Tomoda, *Appl. Phys. Lett.* **75**, 905 (1999).
15. S. Noda, K. Tomoda, N. Yamamoto, and A. Chutinan, *Science* **289**, 604 (2000).
16. A. Chutinan and S. Noda, *Appl. Phys. Lett.* **75**, 3739 (1999).
17. K. S. Yee, *IEEE Trans. Antennas Propagat.* **AP-14**, 302 (1966).
18. G. Mur, *IEEE Trans. Electromagn. Compat.* **EMC-23**, 377 (1981).
19. M. Imada, S. Noda, A. Chutinan, T. Tokuda, M. Murata, and G. Sasaki, *Appl. Phys. Lett.* **75**, 316 (1999).
20. M. Imada, S. Noda, A. Chutinan, M. Mochizuki, M. Okano, M. Murata, and G. Sasaki (in preparation).
21. O. J. Painter, J. Vuckovic, and A. Scherer, *J. Opt. Soc. Am. B* **16**, 275 (1999).
22. A. Chutinan and S. Noda, *Phys. Rev. B* **62**, 4488 (2000).
23. S. Noda, A. Chutinan, and M. Imada, *Nature* **407**, 608 (2000).

LIGHT PROPAGATION CHARACTERISTICS OF DEFECT WAVEGUIDES IN A PHOTONIC CRYSTAL SLAB

Toshihiko Baba and Naoyuki Fukaya

Yokohama National University
Division of Electrical and Computer Engineering
79-5 Tokiwadai, Hodogayaku, Yokohama 240-8501, Japan

1. Introduction

A channel waveguide composed of a series of defects in a uniform photonic crystal (PC) is an attractive device, in which two important properties of PCs, i.e., *photonic bandgaps* (PBGs) and *defect states*, are applied[1]. In conventional index-type waveguides, the guided light suffers large radiation loss at steep bends due to the weak optical confinement. It strongly restricts the flexibility of the optical wiring and makes photonic circuits so large as to be of the cm^2 order. The PC waveguide has the potential for eliminating this restriction. It allows low-loss steep bends, Y-blanches, and short couplers owing to the strong optical confinement of PC claddings[2-4].

Such waveguides can be demonstrated relatively easily with large PCs operating at microwave frequencies[5,6]. However, the demonstration at lightwave frequencies is a challenge due to the technical difficulty in fabricating submicron fine and deep structures of PCs. Recently, we reported the light propagation through PC waveguides for the first time[7]. In that study, we employed a two-dimensional (2-D) PC composed of airholes in a high refractive index slab bonded on a low refractive index host substrate. Such a structure is sometimes called the *PC slab*. We successfully observed the light propagation through channel waveguides composed of a series of missing airholes in the PC slab.

In this paper, we present the detail of light propagation characteristics in that experiment, which could not

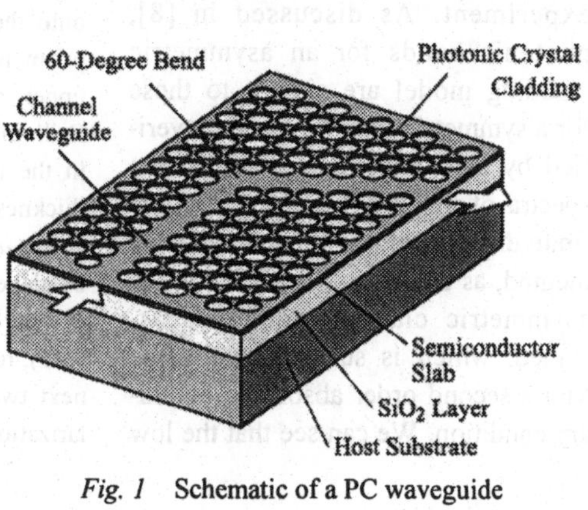

Fig. 1 Schematic of a PC waveguide

C.M. Soukoulis (ed.), Photonic Crystals and Light Localization in the 21st Century, 105–116.

be included in the first report. We investigate the correspondence of the experimental results to photonic bands and presume some key phenomena that dominates the light propagation characteristics in the PC waveguides. Then, we describe a simplified fabrication process by the use of a silicon-on-insulator (SOI) wafer, and further verify the presumption with the quantitative measurement of propagation loss.

2. PC Slab

Figure 1 shows the schematic of the PC waveguide. The slab core is made of a high refractive index medium such as a semiconductor film, and slab claddings are made of lower index media such as SiO_2, air, etc. The PC is composed of triangular lattice airholes in the slab, and waveguide channels are composed of missing airholes. The channels include straight parts and 60° bends.

We calculated the photonic band diagram of the PC slab by the supercell method, as shown in Fig. 2. Here, a is the pitch between airholes and λ is the wavelength of light. A symmetric model with air slab claddings is assumed for simple calculation. Therefore, photonic bands can be distinguished with respect to a primary polarization such as transverse electric (TE) like and transverse magnetic (TM) like. The dark shadow denotes the air light cone, which means the leaky condition of light toward the air claddings[1]. Outside the air light cone, a wide PBG lies at $a/\lambda = 0.31 - 0.47$ for the TE like polarization, while no significant PBGs exist for the TM like polarization. Structural parameters assumed in Fig. 2 are very similar to those in the experiment described in Sections 3 - 5 except that lower slab cladding was not air but SiO_2 in the experiment. As discussed in [8], photonic bands for an asymmetric cladding model are similar to those for a symmetric one. This can be verified by simulating light transmission spectra of the PC slab using the 3-D finite difference time domain (FDTD) method, as shown in Fig. 3. Here, the asymmetric cladding model is assumed, which is surrounded by the Mur's second order absorbing boundary condition. We can see that the low

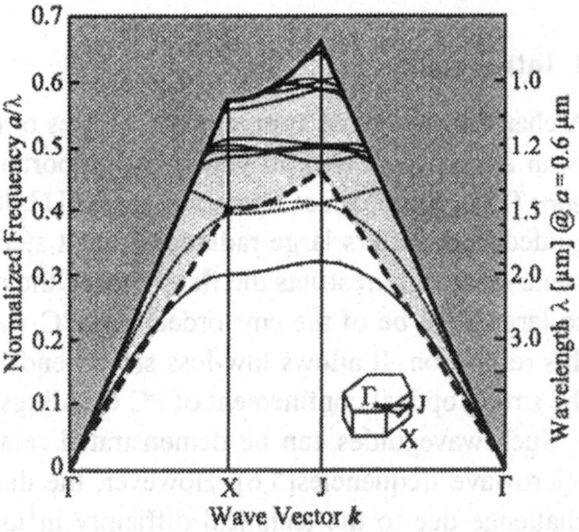

Fig. 2 Photonic bands of a PC slab projected onto the 2-D plane. The unit cell is a hexagonal prism including triangular lattice airholes and air upper and lower claddings. The corresponding Brillouin zone is also a hexagonal prism, as shown in the inset. Diameter of airholes is $0.833a$, and thickness of the slab (index n = 3.5) is $0.533a$, where a is the pitch between airholes. The number of plane waves is 1475. Dark and bright shadows denote light cones of air (n = 1.0) and SiO_2 (n = 1.45), respectively. The lowest band is TE-like and next two bands (dotted curves) are TM-like. Polarizations are intermixed at higher bands.

transmission range simulated against the TE excitation almost agrees with the PBG for the symmetric cladding model in Fig. 2. However, there are two important differences between the symmetric and asymmetric models, i.e., 1) the rigorous distinction of modes by a primary polarization is no longer possible, and 2) the light cone issue is dominated by that of SiO_2. Concerning the first point, we can still determine a primary polarization of lower frequency bands. To discuss the second issue later, the SiO_2 light cone is added in Fig. 2 for reference. It is seen that the SiO_2 light line (edge of the light cone) locates at $a/\lambda \sim 0.40$ and at X point of the Brillouin zone.

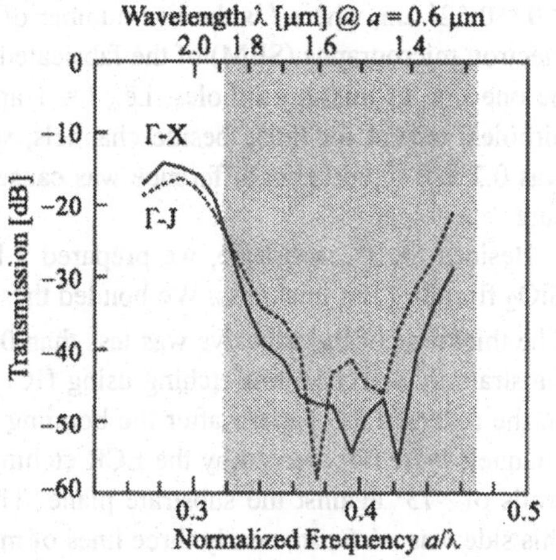

Fig. 3 Transmission spectra in a finite size PC slab, which are simulated by the 3-D FDTD method. The PC is composed of airholes of 5 periods in length and 8 periods in width. The diameter of airholes and the thickness of slab are the same as those for Fig. 2. Upper and lower claddings are air and SiO_2, respectively. The size of cubic Yee cell is $(0.055a)^3$. The excitation is TE. The gray shadow denotes the PBG obtained in Fig. 2.

3. Fabrication by Bonding Process

In the first experiment, we prepared an InP wafer with an undoped GaInAsP film of 0.35 μm thickness and 1.28 μm electronic bandgap wavelength, which was epitaxially grown by metalorganic vapor phase epitaxy. We fabricated the PC into the epitaxial film by standard electron beam (EB) lithography and electron cyclotron resonance (ECR) plasma etching with $CH_4/H_2/Ar$ gases. The designed diameter of airholes $2r$ and pitch a were 0.5 μm and 0.6 μm, respectively, for target wavelengths λ of ~1.5 μm ($a/\lambda \sim 0.4$). The width of the waveguide channel w was

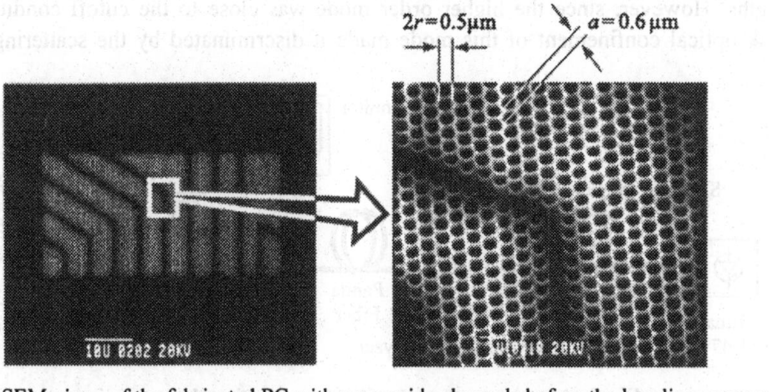

Fig. 4 SEM views of the fabricated PC with waveguide channels before the bonding process

0.02+0.52*l* μm, where *l* is the line number of missing airholes. Figure 4 shows scanning electron micrographs (SEM) of the fabricated PC. A waveguide channel was intended to be one line of missing airholes, i.e., *l* = 1 and *w* = 0.54 μm. Actually, the diameter of airholes, except for those beside channels, was 0.45 ± 0.05 μm. That beside channels was 0.3 ± 0.1 μm. This difference was caused by the proximity effect in the EB exposure.

Besides the PC substrate, we prepared a host InP substrate coated with a sputtered SiO_2 film of 3 μm thickness. We bonded these substrates face-to-face using an adhesive. The thickness of the adhesive was less than 0.2 μm. Then, we removed the epitaxial InP substrate by selective wet etching using HCl solution. Thus, we fabricated the PC slab. In the reversed PC pattern after the bonding process, we found that the airholes beside channels were not pierced by the ECR etching due to the small diameter and tilted sidewalls of ~75° against the substrate plane. Therefore, the channel width observed from this side was ~1.6 μm, nearly three lines of missing airholes. We also found some cracks and warps in the GaInAsP film, which were formed during the curing process of the adhesive.

4. Observation of Light Propagation

Figure 5 illustrates the measurement setup. A tunable laser (λ = 1.47 – 1.60 μm) was used as a light source. The polarization of light was selected by a λ/4 plate, two λ/2 plates, polarization analyzers, and a polarization maintaining fiber (Panda fiber) inserted between the laser and the sample. The light from the Panda fiber was focused on the cleaved input facet of the sample by a couple of achromatic lenses. The near field pattern (NFP) of light was observed from the top and the side by an infrared TV camera.

For the slab without airholes, light propagation in both the GaInAsP slab core and the SiO_2 lower cladding were observed at the output facet. To avoid the mixture of these two lights, we slightly rotated the sample inside the substrate plane. The oblique incidence of light separated two light paths by different refraction angles at the input facet. The light scattering in the slab was very weak except at the cracks and the warps. Theoretically, the 0.35-μm-thick GaInAsP allows two guided modes at the light source wavelengths. However, since the higher order mode was close to the cutoff condition, the weak optical confinement of this mode made it discriminated by the scattering at im-

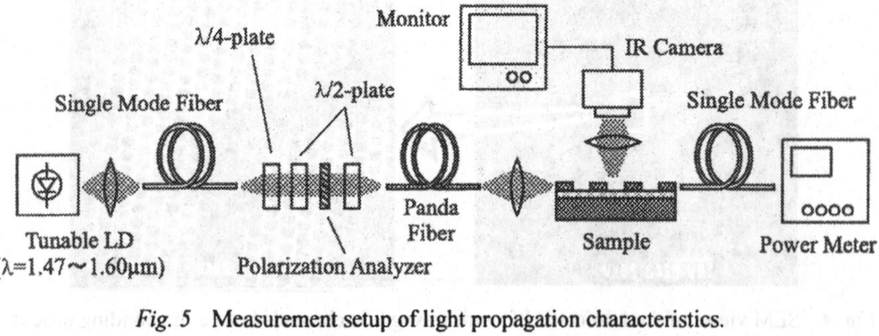

Fig. 5 Measurement setup of light propagation characteristics.

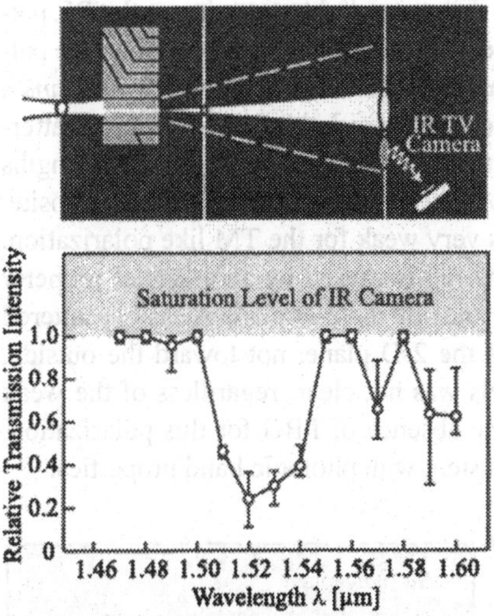

Fig. 6 Observation of the PBG from the scattered light at a crack of the slab film.

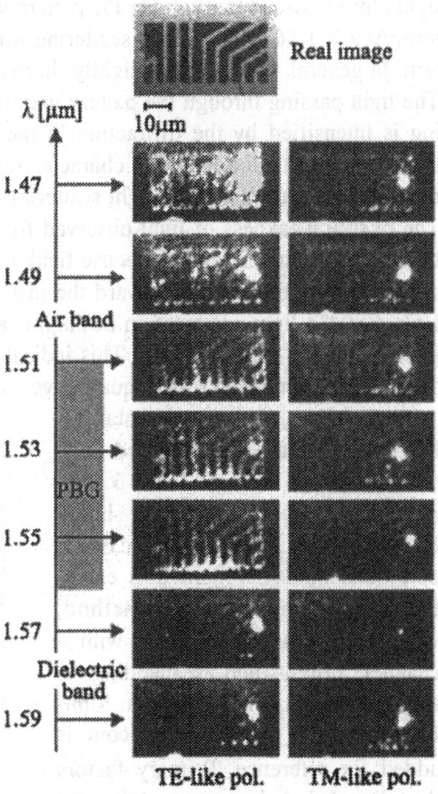

Fig. 7 Optical microscope image of the PC pattern after the bonding process and NFPs observed for various wavelengths and polarizations.

perfect interfaces. Thus, the slab showed the quasi-single mode.

For the slab with airholes, we evaluated the light transmission spectrum from the intensity of the scattered light at the crack, as illustrated in Fig. 6. At λ < 1.51 μm, the intensity reached the saturation level of the TV camera used for evaluation and was almost constant. A clear decay in the intensity was observed at λ = 1.51 – 1.56 μm. Although the decay level was difficult to estimate precisely due to the saturation, it was at least higher than 5 dB. Thus, it was thought to be a PBG.

Figure 7 summarizes the wavelength and polarization dependence of the NFP. They were observed from the top without changing the condition of the observation. In this case, the cleaved piece of the sample had a distance of ~50 μm from the cleaved facet to the PC pattern. Therefore, the light was laterally diffracted in the slab and reached the PC pattern almost uniformly. The light power that reached the pattern was kept almost constant in all the measurements. It was confirmed from the constant light spot seen in the right lower side of each figure, which was caused by a warp in the slab. At λ = 1.51 – 1.56 μm, the propagation of the TE like polarized light through the channels was clearly observed. The propagation was still clear beyond 60° bends. Besides this, we found some light spots at a crack very close to the ends of bent channels. From these results, we confirmed the light propagation in the bent channels. At λ <1.51 μm, the light almost passed through the PC pattern with the strong light scattering at the PC pattern. At $\lambda > 1.56$ μm, the light scattering was weak, but the light passed through the pattern. In general, wavelengths slightly shorter than a PBG are characterized by *air bands*. The light passing through the pattern mainly localizes in airholes, thus the light scattering is intensified by the diffraction in the vertical direction in airholes. Wavelengths slightly longer than a PBG are characterized by *dielectric bands*; the result is opposite. Figure 7 also shows that the light scattering was very weak for the TM like polarization. The overall weakness of light observed from the top is caused by an essential property that the TM light having the electric field vector outside the 2-D plane is easily scattered at the edge of the airholes toward the inside of the 2-D plane, not toward the outside. However, the light propagation through channels was not clear, regardless of the weak intensity of the scattered light. This indicates the absence of PBG for this polarization. Thus, the experimental results qualitatively consistent with photonic band properties.

Nevertheless, the experimental TE PBG is too narrow compared with calculated ones in Figs. 2 and 3. The more precise correspondence should be investigated against photonic bands of guided modes. Figure 8 is calculated using the supercell method, where a symmetric unit cell with a channel, airholes and air claddings is assumed, as shown in the inset. Similarly to Fig. 2, the SiO_2 light cone is added for reference. Primary factors that disturb low loss propagation are the light cones and slab mode conditions[1]. The former causes the leakage loss toward upper and lower claddings, and the latter, toward lateral PC claddings. As indicated in [9], the pure guided mode condition is severely restricted by the SiO_2 light cone compared with the case of the air light cone. It is seen in Fig. 8 that the pure guided mode region, which escapes the light cones and slab mode regions, exists only at $a/\lambda = 0.30 - 0.34$ (existence of guided modes is further restricted). On the other hand, experimental wavelengths $\lambda = 1.51 - 1.56$ μm correspond to $a/\lambda = 0.375 - 0.40$. Therefore, the light essentially

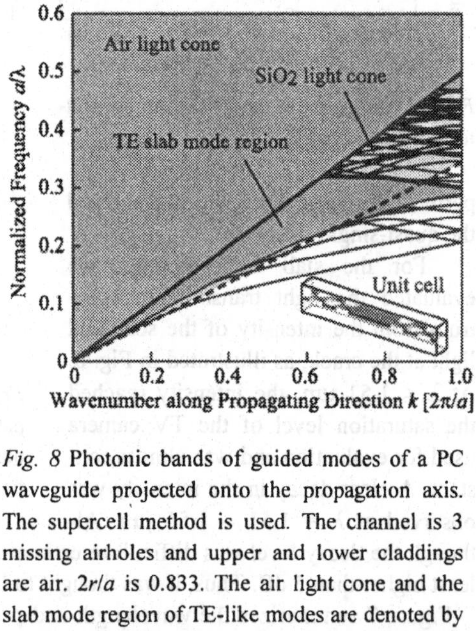

Fig. 8 Photonic bands of guided modes of a PC waveguide projected onto the propagation axis. The supercell method is used. The channel is 3 missing airholes and upper and lower claddings are air. $2r/a$ is 0.833. The air light cone and the slab mode region of TE-like modes are denoted by shadows. The SiO_2 light line is denoted by the dashed line for reference. Since the number of plane waves is limited to 2145, the convergence of bands around the PBG is not enough. In addition, so many modes in the PBG are not only caused by the wide channel and the zone folding of the PC waveguide but also by the splitting of degenerate modes due to the limited size of the supercell. Thus, only qualitative discussion will be possible with this figure.

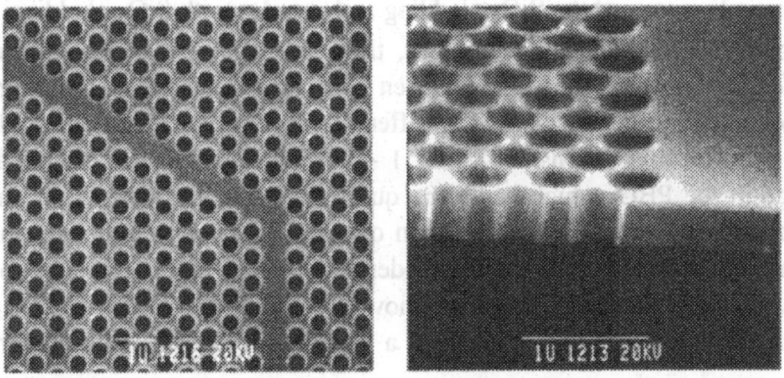

Fig. 9 Top (left figure) and side (right figure) views of a fabricated PC waveguide on an SOI substrate.

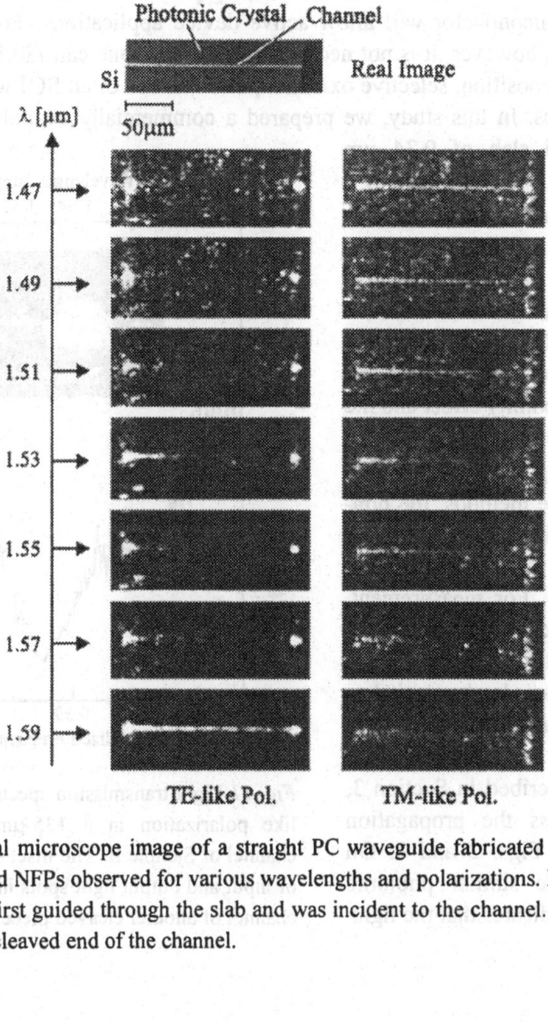

Fig. 10 Optical microscope image of a straight PC waveguide fabricated on an SOI substrate (Sample B) and NFPs observed for various wavelengths and polarizations. In this cleaved piece, the light was first guided through the slab and was incident to the channel. The output spot was observed at a cleaved end of the channel.

suffers leakage loss toward the SiO_2 cladding and couples with SiO_2 cladding modes. In the PBG between two slab mode regions, there are photonic bands indicating such *quasi-guided* modes. Anti-crossings between each two bands mean the coupling of a guided mode with another mode having different order and/or polarization[10]. Therefore, it is not reasonable to consider $\lambda = 1.51 - 1.56$ μm as a simple PBG but as a wavelength range in the PBG, which has some quasi-guided modes that suffer small influences of mode couplings. The transmission of the TE-like polarized light through the channels, as shown in Fig. 7, is a clear evidence of PBG, but the transmission through the PC at $\lambda < 1.51$ μm and > 1.56 μm, as shown in Figs. 6 and 7, seems to be caused by the coupling of a quasi-guided mode with a TM-like polarized mode and/or cladding modes.

5. PC Waveguides on SOI Substrate

In the experiment in Section 3, we used the bonding process of GaInAsP film. Such a direct-transition semiconductor will allow active device applications. For waveguides and passive devices, however, it is not necessarily required. One can fabricate a similar structure by using deposition, selective oxidation, etc. The use of an SOI wafer is one of the simplest methods. In this study, we prepared a commercially available SOI wafer with a p-doped Si slab of 0.34 μm thickness and SiO_2 lower cladding of 1 μm thickness, which were directly bonded on a Si substrate. The design and the fabrication process of the PC were almost the same as those described in Section 3. Differences were the modulation EB exposure for the compensation of the proximity effect and the use of the CF_4 inductively coupled plasma (ICP) etching for the fabrication of airholes. By these methods, the non-uniformity of the airholes was reduced to < 4 %. Figure 9 shows SEM images of a PC waveguide. For measurement, we used two samples with diameter $2r$ of 0.50 μm (Sample A) and 0.35 μm (Sample B). Both samples have pitch a = 0.6 μm and channel width l = 3. Therefore, Sample A has a similar structure to that described in Section 3, and we can discuss the propagation characteristics with Figs. 2 and 8. On the other hand, the similar photonic band calculations indicates that the light

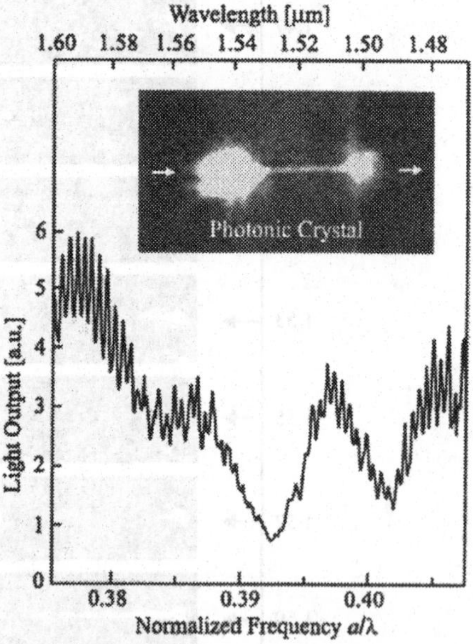

Fig. 11 Light transmission spectrum for the TE like polarization in a 135-μm-long straight channel of Sample B. The inset shows the NFP of input and output light spots in a 52-μm-long channel of another cleaved piece.

source wavelengths in the experiment overlaps with the slab mode region for Sample B due to the smaller filling factor of airholes, which leads the overall shift of photonic bands to lower frequencies. Figure 10 shows the NFP observed from the top of a straight channel of Sample B. The light spot at the output end of the channel is clearly observed for all wavelengths and polarizations. However, the laterally spreading light beside the output spot is also observed at shorter wavelengths for the TE- like polarization and at all wavelengths for the TM-like polarization. It implies the imperfect lateral confinement of light caused by the slab mode condition. Figure 11 shows a light transmission spectrum of TE-like polarized light for Sample B. The waveguide length L was 135 μm. In this cleaved piece, both channel ends were cleaved facets. The incident light power was kept constant and the output light was directly detected by a single mode fiber. In Fig. 11, a fast oscillation modulated by a slow envelope function is observed. The output intensity is nearly corresponding to the brightness of the light path in Fig. 10. The fast oscillation exhibited a nearly constant peak-to-peak interval, which was dependent on the waveguide length. This indicates that the Fabry-Perot resonance occured between the two facets. The propagation loss of the waveguide α_g is related to the finesse F of the resonance as

$$\alpha = \alpha_g + (1/L)\ln(1/R), \quad F = \frac{\pi \exp(-\alpha L/2)}{1-\exp(-\alpha L)} = \frac{\pi}{2}\sqrt{\frac{I_{max}}{I_{min}} - 1},$$

where R is the modal reflectivity at facets, and I_{max} and I_{min} are maximum and minimum

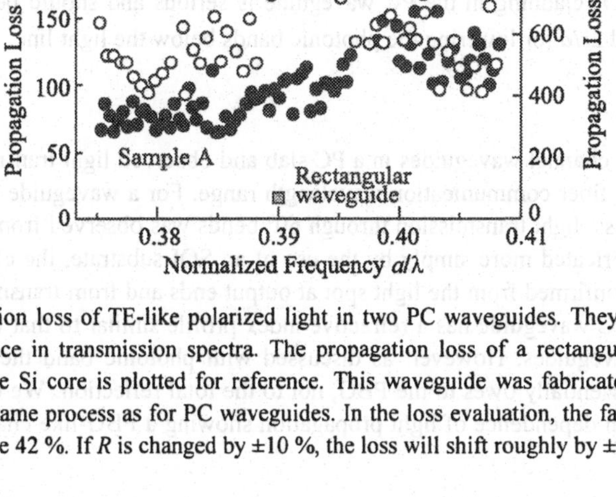

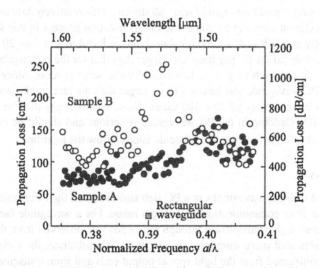

Fig. 12 Propagation loss of TE-like polarized light in two PC waveguides. They are evaluated from the resonance in transmission spectra. The propagation loss of a rectangular waveguide with 0.5 μm wide Si core is plotted for reference. This waveguide was fabricated on the SOI substrate by the same process as for PC waveguides. In the loss evaluation, the facet reflectivity R is assumed to be 42 %. If R is changed by ±10 %, the loss will shift roughly by ±100 dB/cm.

intensities of a resonance, respectively. We know that the modal reflectivity R of a waveguide grating has some dependence on the grating phase at cleaved positions[11]. However, for simplicity, we assume R as that of a simple SiO_2/Si/air slab. By the FDTD method, R is calculated to be 42 % at $\lambda = 1.55$ μm against the TE excitation. Propagation loss spectra are obtained, as shown in Fig. 12. There are large increases in propagation loss at $a/\lambda \sim 0.401$ and 0.392 for Sample A and B, respectively. As discussed in Section 4, one explanation for these increases is the mode couplings. Except these a/λ, α_g is ~300 and ~500 dB/cm for Sample A and B, respectively. The difference should be coming from the slab mode region of Sample B, which overlaps with a/λ of the light source in this experiment.

The evaluated propagation loss is anyway much larger than that of a conventional waveguide. For example, a typical propagation loss of a silica-based waveguide connectable to a single mode fiber is of 10^{-2} dB/cm order. In general, the propagation loss caused by the light scattering at rough boundaries in index-type single mode waveguide is proportional to $\sigma^2\Delta^{2.5}$, where σ is the roughness amplitude and Δ is the relative refractive index difference defined as $(n_1^2 - n_2^2)/2n_1^2$ for the core index n_1 and the cladding index n_2[12]. Let us consider a Si rectangular waveguide surrounded by air claddings. For this waveguide, Δ is 45 % and nearly 150 times as large as that for a silica waveguide. Applying the above dependence to it, the propagation loss expected for the Si/air waveguide is of the 10^3 dB/cm order. To verify this, we fabricated such a waveguide on the SOI substrate and evaluated the propagation loss by the same methods as described in this section. A result is also plotted in Fig. 12[13]. The loss of a 0.5-μm-wide single mode waveguide was ~90 dB/cm. This relatively low loss compared with the expectation seems to be due to the fine fabrication process in this study. By the EB lithography and ICP etching, the roughness was reduced to less than 20 nm. The PC waveguides exhibited the propagation loss larger than that for the rectangular waveguide by factor 3 – 7, although they were fabricated by the same process. Since the channel width of the PC waveguide was nearly 3 times larger than the rectangular waveguide, the effective loss increase may be 10 – 100 times. These results imply that the leakage loss toward the SiO_2 cladding in the PC waveguide is serious and should be eliminated by reducing a and $2r/a$ for lowering the photonic bands below the light line.

6. Conclusion

We fabricated channel waveguides in a PC slab and observed light transmission characteristics in the fiber communication wavelength range. For a waveguide fabricated by a bonding process, light transmission through 60° bends was observed from the top. For a waveguide fabricated more simply by the use of an SOI substrate, the clear light transmission was confirmed from the light spot at output ends and from transmission spectra. This type of PC waveguide has a refractive index profile similar to that in conventional index-type waveguides. However, as discussed with photonic band theories, the light propagation essentially owes to the PBG, not to the total reflection. We observed peculiar wavelength dependence of light propagation showing a PBG-like characteristic. We expected to explain the result simply by the PBG. However, it seems more reasonable to explain by a mixed characteristic of PBG and various modes coupled with each other by the zone folding effect.

The propagation loss of the PC waveguide was quantitatively evaluated by the Fabry-Perot method to be 300 – 500 dB/cm. Main origins of this large loss are the leakage toward the SiO_2 lower cladding characterized by the SiO_2 light cone and that toward the PC cladding characterized by the slab mode condition. Concerning these issues, many discussions are now going on[9,14,15]. In another experiment of rectangular waveguides on an SOI substrate, we confirmed that, if we eliminate these leakages by optimizing the structure, the loss will be reduced to at least 10 dB/cm order. In this case, the limiting factor is the roughness at boundaries. The roughness of Si sidewalls obtained by the EB lithography and the ICP etching is ~20 nm. Further low loss of the 1 dB/cm order will be possible by reducing the roughness to 1 nm order, which has already been achieved against III-V semiconductors[16].

Acknowledgments

The authors would like to thank Professor Y. Kokubun of Yokohama National University, and Professor K. Iga, Professor F. Koyama and Associate Professor T. Miyamoto of Tokyo Institute of Technology for their encouragement. This work was partly supported by a Grant-in-Aid #10210203 from the Ministry of Education, Science, Sports and Culture.

References

1. Meade, R. D., Devenyi, A., Joannopoulos, J. D., Alerhand, O. L., Smith, D. A., and Kash, K., "Novel applications of photonic band gap materials: low-loss bends and high Q cavities", *Appl. Phys. Lett.* 75, 4753-4755 (1994).
2. Mekis, A., Chen, J. C., Kurand, I., Fan, S., Villeneuve, P. R., and Joannopoulos, J. D., "High transmission through sharp bends in photonic crystal waveguides", *Phys. Rev. Lett.* **77**, 3787-3790 (1996).
3. Yonekura, J., Ikeda, M., and Baba, T. "Analysis of finite 2-D photonic crystals of columns and lightwave devices using the scattering matrix method", *J. Lightwave Technol.* **17**, 1500-1508 (1999).
4. Chutinan, A., and Noda, S., "Design for waveguides in three-dimensional photonic crystals", *Jpn. J. Appl. Phys.* **39**, 2353-2356 (2000).
5. Lin, S. Y., Chow, E., Hietara, V., Villeneuve, P. R., and Joannopoulos, J. D., "Experimental demonstration of guiding and bending of electromagnetic waves in a photonic crystal", *Science* **282**, 274-276 (1998).
6. Temelkuran, B., and Ozbay, E., "Experimental demonstration of photonic crystal based waveguides", *Appl. Phys. Lett.* **74**, 486-488 (1999).
7. Baba, T., Fukaya, N., and Yonekura, J., "Observation of light transmission in photonic crystal waveguides with bends", *Electron. Lett.* **27**, 654-655 (1999).
8. Johnson, S. G., Fan, S., Villeneuve, P. R., and Joannopoulos, J. D., "Guided modes in photonic crystal slabs", *Phys. Rev. B* **60**, 5751-5758 (1999).

9. Chutinan, A, and Noda, A., "Waveguides and waveguide bends in two-dimensional photonic crystal slabs", *Phys. Rev. B* **62**, 4488-4492 (2000).
10. Smith, C. J. M., Benisty, H., Rattier, M., Olivier, S., Krauss, T. F., De La Rue, R. M., Houdre, R., Oesterle, U. and Weisbuch, C., "Quantitative and qualitative analysis of 2D photonic crystal waveguides", *Dig. Int. Workshop on Photonic and Electromagnetic Crystal Structures*, F3-3 (2000).
11. Matsuoka, T., Yoshikuni, Y., and Nagai, H., "Verification of the light phase effect at the facet on DFB laser properties", *IEEE J. Quantum Electron.* **QE-21**, 1880-1866 (1985).
12. Suematsu, Y., and Furuya, K., "Scattering loss in thin film waveguides", *Oyobutsuri* **42**, 938-942 (1973, in Japanese).
13. Sakai, A., Hara, G., and Baba, T., "Sharply bent optical waveguide on silicon-on-insulator substrate", *Proc. SPIE Physics and Simulation of Optoelectronic Devices*, OE09-562 (2001).
14. Shinya, A., Notomi, M. and Yokohama, I., "3D-FDTD calculations for 2D photonic crystal with finite thickness", *Dig. Int. Workshop on Photonic and Electromagnetic Crystal Structures*, T4-8 (2000).
15. Benisty, H., Rattier, M., Weisbuch, C., Krauss, T. K., Smith, C. J. M., De La Rue, R. M., Cassagne, D., Beraud, A. and Jouanin, C., "Photonic crystals for integrated optics: can we use conventional semiconductor waveguides?", *Dig. Int. Workshop on Photonic and Electromagnetic Crystal Structures*, F3-2 (2000).
16. Fujita, M., Sakai, A., and Baba, T., "Ultra-small and ultra-low threshold microdisk injection laser – design, fabrication, lasing characteristics and spontaneous emission factor", *IEEE J. Sel. Top. Quantum Electron.* **5**, 673-681 (1999).

APPLICATIONS OF TWO-DIMENSIONAL PHOTONIC CRYSTALS TO SEMICONDUCTOR OPTOELECTRONIC DEVICES

H. BENISTY, S. OLIVIER, M. RATTIER, C. WEISBUCH
Laboratoire de Physique de la Matière Condensée, Ecole Polytechnique, F-91128 Palaiseau cedex

Abstract : After a brief review of the role of optics in semiconductor optoelectronic devices, we show which kinds of two-dimensional photonic crystal might find their way to the applications, taking into account feasibility and optical properties. We attempt to knit a description of the optical and confinement properties of this class of photonic crystals with the discussion of the possible pro's and con's they offer for basic and less basic applications. Two phenomena play a simple but crucial role in this field : diffraction and the out-of-plane losses. Their assessment is presented and their impact is discussed.

1. INTRODUCTION

Semiconductors hold an important place in the optoelectronic industry. It is the purpose of this contribution to enlighten the possible use of photonic crystals into this broad class of devices. The basic optical functions used in these devices can be classified as emitters, detectors, modulators, while some more advanced functions needed to route optical signals borrow much to classical optical devices, interferometers, spectrometers, combined with the extra semiconductor possibilities such as amplification.

In this contribution, we will discuss a class of two-dimensional photonic crystals (2D-PC) that lends itself best to the existing technology, namely arrays of holes etched through a conventional semiconductor waveguide such as a laser-like AlGaAs heterostructure. The assessment of these crystals is by itself a good example of how growth capabilities can be ease physical measurements, but conversely, we will discuss how the measured properties impact the implementation of such crystals for precise optical functions. In section 2, we first discuss briefly the role of optics in optoelectronics. In section 3, we introduce the features brought to the basic 2D PC picture by the particular implementation considered here, the vertical index-confining waveguide and the role of diffraction for guided waves impinging on such crystals

We then describe, in section 4, the role of these two phenomena first for mirror applications, especially in emitters. In section 5, we discuss them with regard to spectral applications, e.g. for selecting signals of given frequencies. Finally, in section 6, we briefly discuss their role for guiding and coupling. We do not consider here modulation, amplification, but we mention in passing that these may also have benefits from 2D-PC systems.

C.M. Soukoulis (ed.), Photonic Crystals and Light Localization in the 21st Century, 117–128.

2. BASICS OF OPTICS IN SEMICONDUCTOR OPTOELECTRONICS

Semiconductors

Semiconductors have been a favourite ground for optoelectronic devices because of their many combined properties. They support interband and intraband spontaneous emission and absorption, in a way that can be tailored through "bandgap engineering" in epitaxial heterostructures, starting with quantum wells (QWs), superlattices, junctions, etc, and reaching wavelengths λ from 0.4 μm to 20 μm. Controlled electron transport was of course the key to their success and is underlying most "active" devices(emitters and detectors in particular). They have a number of electro-optical (EO) properties, albeit with strong spectral dispersion of the EO coefficients, but on which the lever of bandgap engineering is also effective.[1,2]

Less mentioned but equally interesting is their alloy-dependent index of refraction in epitaxial heterostructures. The average index n of semiconductors, typically around 3–3.5, is a sever penalty to the light extraction at a planar face : with an internal critical angle θ_{crit} of less than 20°, only a fraction $1/4n^2$ (≈2%) of the internally emitted light may be extracted in air, putting a stringent limit to the external yield of electroluminescent light-emitting-diodes (LEDs), in spite of their good internal quantum efficiency(often >50%).[3]

Basic Index Structures In Optoelectronics

The planar monomode waveguide (Fig.1a) is the basic index structure, with index steps $\Delta n = n_2 - n_1$ in the range 0.1–0.5 typically, giving rise to modal width of the order of $\lambda/n \leq 0.5\mu m$. This is much smaller than the modal width of glass fibres, based on the minute index step of doped silica/silica materials, being thus many λ's, typically 5–10 μm in a monomode fibre.

The Bragg mirror, a multilayer alternate stack, is a 1D photonic crystal. For stacks of equal optical thickness ("$\lambda/4$" stacks), the stop-band width (high reflection band) Δk_o, at normal incidence, is given by the index step Δn according to $\Delta k_o/k_o = (2/\pi)(\Delta n/n)$ where $n = (n_2 + n_1)/2$ and $k_o = \omega/c$ is the central wavevector (ω,c : usual meaning). They are distributed mirrors (DBR= distributed Bragg reflector) in the gap with a penetration depth of $n/\Delta n$ periods (in the small Δn limit). Their spectral and angular dependence is basically given by $k(\theta) = k(\theta=0)/\cos\theta$, meaning that e.g. the stop-band shifts to shorter wavelengths at oblique incidence $\theta \neq 0$.

Cavities

With two such basic DBR mirrors spaced by a cavity (Fig.1b) with an epitaxially grown gain medium, one can produce lasers (VCSELs). As the active medium has a gain

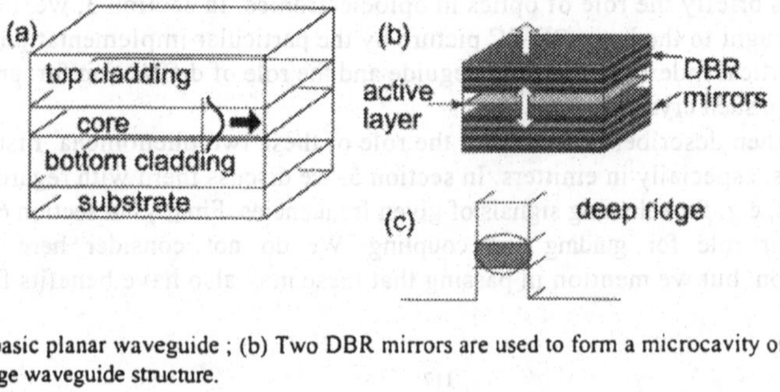

Fig.1 (a) The basic planar waveguide ; (b) Two DBR mirrors are used to form a microcavity or a VCSEL ; (c) the deep ridge waveguide structure.

saturating at some 1000 cm^{-1} and is limited to < 1 μm thickness (to limit heating, growth time, threshold current), the gain per pass is less than, say, 0.01, implying that the DBRs have to feature reflectivities $R \geq 0.99$ to reach lasing at all.

The two-DBR scheme can also be used to shape the spontaneous emission by interference efects that are constructive in the escape cone ($\theta < \theta_{crit}$) and, ideally, destructive elsewhere. This is the micro-cavity LED (MCLED, see lectures by T. Krauss) for which the requirement is much less in terms of reflectivities because in the interferometric phenomena, most of the way to emission shaping is achieved with 80% *amplitude* reflectivities, hence $R = 0.64$ only. MCLED are now a commercial product for 650 nm plastic optical fibre (POF) application (sold by Mitel), due to their superior brightness: the front area of the MCLED emits more photon than the same area of a conventional cavity-less LED. Light not extracted by the front and escaping from the sides of he conventional LED is more difficult to redirect into the POF, hence the advantage of he MCLED.

More Sophisticated Structures

Beyond vertical guiding, in-plane guiding is a vast area of physics and engineering. Only the deep-ridge structure (Fig.1c) allows to some extent sharp bends, but suffers from much more roughness scattering than softer guiding solutions (buried ridge, dielectric load,...). For these latter, however, bend radii are limited by radiation losses to 100's of μm in semiconductors, even more on SiO_2 platforms, inflicting a severe penalty to miniaturised devices.

The DBR can be implemented onto a straight waveguide, by means of lithographically defined corrugations giving rise to a slight index or gain periodicity. The resulting sharp spectral behaviour is used to achieve monomode edge-emitting lasers (DFB lasers), tunable multi-section lasers (all derived from the DBR lasers), etc. The coupling of two guides with propagation constants β_1 and β_2 by a corrugation bringing just the extra momentum $\pm K = \Delta\beta$, is also a well-documented scheme, used for example when two guides are stacked, to couple light out from the top corrugated guide into the buried one.

Evanescent coupling between adjacent guides is also very much used and is the basis of many couplers, themselves building-blocks to build splitters, multiplexers, and in particular interferometers. In their branches, one can include amplifiers (SOA) monolithically, which gives a nice way to make optical switches and related devices.

In the framework of the WDM (Wavelength Division Multiplexing) scheme for telecom transmissions, one needs elements that split the basic fibre+amplificator) bandwidth, 30 nm around 1545 nm into, say, 32 channels. To fix the ideas, a Fabry-Perot resonator with a free spectral range (FSR) of 30 nm and finesse F=100 can achieve this task (FSR=interval between modes, finesse=FSR/peak width). One now famous configuration to deal with the WDM scheme is the Array Waveguide Grating (AWG or phasar),[4] invented around 1990, which can be viewed as a generalised prism or grating. The versatility of this structure makes it a good point of comparison : if photonic crystals can result in better AWGs or alternatives to it, they will certainly be useful.

3. TWO-DIMENSIONAL PHOTONIC CRYSTALS IN A WAVEGUIDE

The basic design tool for 2D photonic crystal is the plot of Fig. 2, whose abcissa is the air fill-factor f and ordinate the normalised frequency $u = a/\lambda = \omega a/2\pi c$. Here, we have the particular case of the triangular lattice of cylindrical air holes in a medium of dielectric constant $\varepsilon = 11.3$. This lattice and this "atom" shape are best suited to the obtainment of large gaps at moderate air fill-factors $f > 0.15$ in the TE polarisation (magnetic field H along

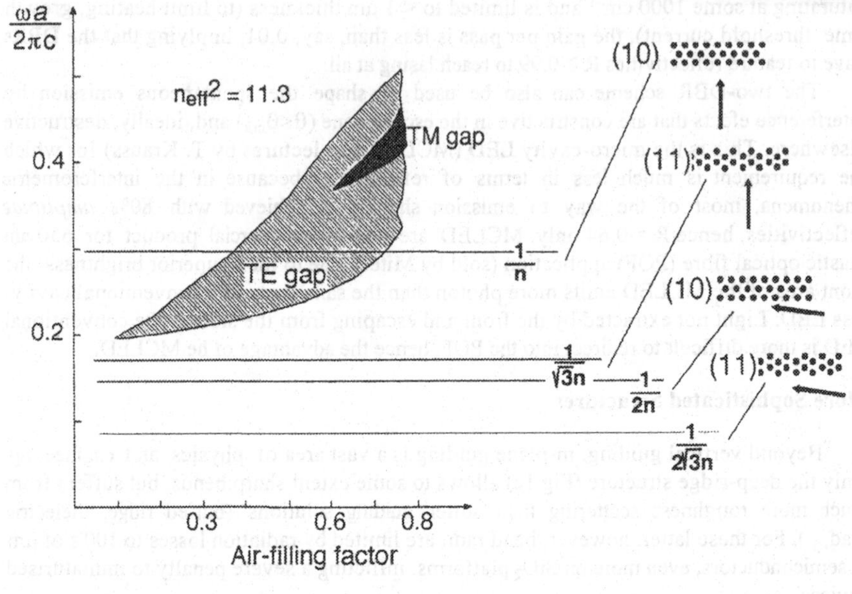

Fig. 2 Positions of the TE and TM in-plane forbidden bands as a function of the air-filling factor for a triangular lattice of cylindrical holes in a dielectric medium. Cut-off for diffractions on crystals with (10) and (11) rows, at normal or grazing incidence, are denoted by horizontal lines.

the holes). But one requires, typically, $f > 0.65$ to give rise to a common TE and TM photonic gap.

For applications to optoelectronis devices, let us now turn to the implementation of such a PC in the form of finite-depth holes drilled through a planar dielectric monomode waveguide or a membrane. To use Fig. 2, it is natural to take for the dielectric constant $\varepsilon_{eff}=n_{eff}^2$, the squared effective index of the guided mode. Note that this implementation breaks the "self-similarity" scaling of the 2D crystal, i.e., the fact that the gap is a function of only a/λ : now, for different wavelengths, n_{eff} is different (modal dispersion) even in the absence of any material dispersion. Another consequence of this geometry is the possibility that radiation losses (RLs) occur in the third dimension. This depends on the cladding indices and on all the PC parameters. For many conventional claddings, the index step is modest and we have to consider that RLs cannot be ignored (see lectures on the existence of modes of slabs "below the light line"[5]). Another reason for that is the fact that in any useful device, periodicity is simply absent, due to bends, etc.

The other simple parameter is the air fill-factor. It has been proposed that small air fill-factors would help retaining the guiding properties.[6-9] This restricts the photonic gap to TE polarisation only but hopefully ensures a minimal harm from RLs. We will detail later the kind of limitation brought by radiation losses (RLs) to particular optical figures of merits. Needless to say, this is of course a key point for applications. One distinction has to be mentioned before we are too much advanced: even with infinitely deep holes, RLs that occur in the particular device under consideration will set the ultimate limits to its performances. Conversely, the insufficient hole depth may seriously degrade expected optical features. In the first case one has to re-think the whole scheme of the device. In the second case, there is some hope of improvement through the optimisation of etching parameters and/or a different choice for the guided mode profile.

Our own approach to RLs has been detailed in Ref.10. It is based on a separable approximation of the system, from which a perturbation approach was found to be most

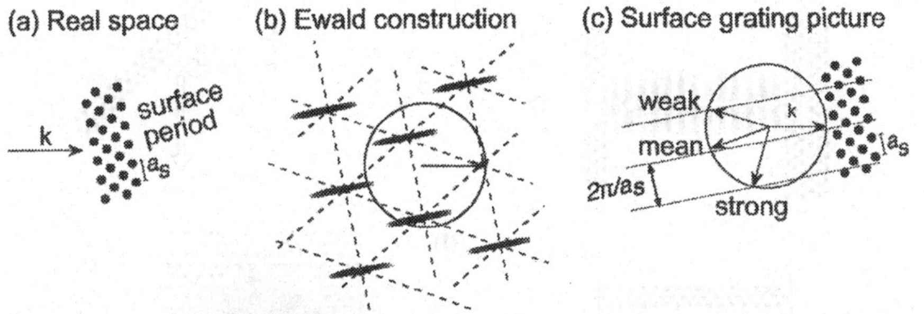

Fig. 3 : Diffraction from a plane wave impinging on a 2D PC ; (a) real space configuration ; (b) Ewald construction in reciprocal space (circle of radius k), with some relaxation of the Bragg condition due to the finite interaction region ; (c) resulting picture interpreted in terms of usual grating diffraction : the intensity is very variable in the different allowed orders.

feasible, albeit with drastic approximations such as the neglect of Bragg coherence among scatterers (holes) and the use of a scalar electromagnetic calculation. Nevertheless, it highlighted the basic trends of RLs, and in particular the fact that they tend to diminish for a smaller index step, provided the etching is deep enough to well overlap the guided mode profile. This approach also accounted for the strong modulation of RLs at the band edges: since the holes act more or less as the scatterers, the "air band" edge (high frequency side of the gap) has the largest losses because the field of Bloch waves samples much more the holes at this edge. A last useful idea introduced in this work was the possibility to introduce 3D out-of-plane losses into a purely 2D calculation by means of an adequate imaginary index n" in the air holes (air discs in 2D). This scheme is of course an approximation, but may be quite useful to tackle the losses of complex PC-based structures, e.g., those sought for integrated optics.

After this first incursion in 3D world, let us come back to 2D and have a look at the interaction between a PC and a "plane wave" (a guided wave vertically, but free in the x,y directions, Fig. 3a). Let us emphasise that even if the crystal has the simple terminations of those sketched in Fig. 2, reflection and transmission of a "plane wave" are not the only phenomena. Diffraction is also possible.[8,11] This is at variance with microwave-type pillar-based PC systems because in the semiconductor case, the outside medium of the incoming wave has a ***higher*** index than the PC average index, hence allowing larger k values at a given frequency. Unlike classical X-ray-like kinematic diffraction on crystal planes, the face of termination of the PC plays an important role here because one row of PC already achieves a large interaction strength.

The situation is then more that of thin gratings for which the diffraction rule is simple: denoting $k_{//}$ the wavevector projection on the "surface" of the crystal, one requires $k_{//inc} - k_{//diff} = pK_S$ (Fig. 3c), where p is the integer diffraction order and K the basic wavevector brought by the periodicity of the "surface" row of the crystal. We consider here the two denser faces, (10) for which $a_s = a$, and (11) for which $a_s = \sqrt{3}a$, see Fig. 2. Expressing $k_{//}$ as $\sin\theta\, n_{eff}\, 2\pi/\lambda$ and K_S as $2\pi/a_s$ and considering the two particular cases $\theta_{inc} = 0°$ and $90°$, one finds using similarly θ_{diff} to characterise the diffracted angle that this law reduces to :

$$n_{eff}\,(\{0 \text{ or } 1\} - \sin\theta_{diff})(\{1 \text{ or } \sqrt{3}\}a/\lambda) = p.$$

It is straightforward to deduce the minimal normalised frequencies allowing diffraction, say in order p = +1 or −1, called also diffraction cut-offs: they read $\{1 \text{ or } \sqrt{3}\}/\{1 \text{ or } 2\}n_{eff}$. according to the horizontal lines that have been indicated in Fig. 2.

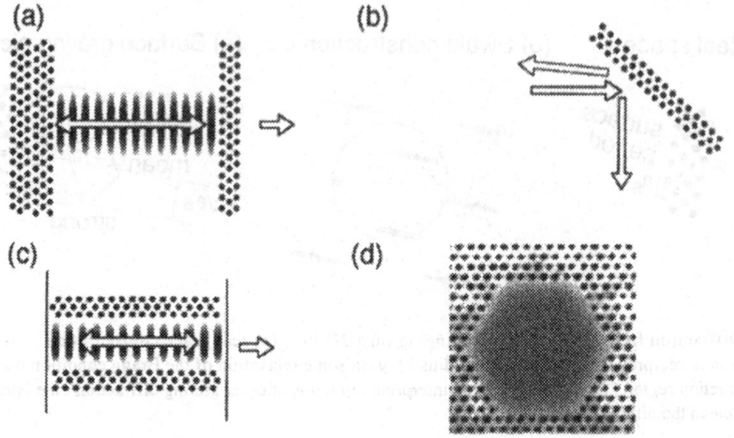

Fig. 4 : PC mirrors used (a) to define longitudinally a lasing mode ; (b) as 90° corner mirrors (the shaded arrow indicates possible diffraction) ; (c) to limit laterally a laser mode ; (d) to define a hexagonal resonator.

It is seen that diffraction at normal incidence can be really suppressed in the photonic gap (at $u < 1/n_{eff} = 0.29$) only for the dense (10) face. Diffraction will however exist for lower and lower frequencies if more oblique incidences are considered, so that for grazing incidence, diffraction is rule, not the exception. On the less dense (11) face, even normal incidence gives rise to diffraction in the photonic gap.

Once diffraction is allowed, it is a more complex task to predict its strength in a given order.[8,11] This is because the interaction takes place on much more than one row, even tens of them if one hits a photonic window (such as TM, ΓM around u=0.30 for example[12]). Exact calculations of course exist (Ref. 13, Transfer Matrix Method, see e.g., Ref. 14) but a naive view can still be elaborated as follow : Starting from kinematic diffraction, for which the presence of the reciprocal lattice vectors on the Ewald "sphere" is the basic condition to interfere constructively in the Bragg-diffracted direction (Fig. 3b), one has to introduce more relaxed conditions related to the various restrictions imposed on the geometry of the wave/crystal interaction: depletion of the impinging beam, especially in the gap, finite extent of the probed crystal. One can thenthink of replacing reciprocal nodes by a fuzzy cloud at the extremity of reciprocal lattice wavevectors, Fig. 3b, with a shape that takes into account the extent of the inetraction region in the various directions . This results in variable diffraction efficiencies according to the overlap of the fuzzy cloud with the Ewald circle (Fig. 3c).

4. PHOTONIC CRYSTALS FOR MIRROR APPLICATIONS AND IN EMITTERS

A general specification for a mirror can comprise the exact specification of R and T as a function of wavelength, angle of incidence and polarisation. Let us start with the directionality, and let us assume we are in the photonic gap. Then, in the photonic crystal we have selected, it is impossible to achieve specular reflection for all angles of incidence at any frequency in the bandgap, as the diffraction cut-off for arbitrary θ_{inc} lies around u=0.18, below the TE gap.

If one wishes to build Fabry-Pérot resonators from these PC, in order to define a lasing mode between them, this will be possible insofar as this mode has small enough transverse components (small equivalent θ_{inc}). This is an interesting configuration to avoid cleavage of edge-emitting lasers (Fig. 4a).

But if one wishes to implement, e.g.,corner mirrors for 90° deflection (Fig. 4b), these will suffer from diffraction when using the present PC crystals. Such phenomena will still more occur if one attempts to limit laterally a laser mode with them (Fig. 4c): then the waves will sample the mirror at grazing incidence (see guide behaviour below). One can even generalise the conclusion regarding 2D confinement at mesoscopic scale (say 10 wavelengths), e.g. in hexagonal cavities (Fig. 4d) : even if the boundaries have the smallest possible local period, eigenmodes of such cavities automatically take into account this phenomenon. This means that most modes will have a complex behaviour even at a straight section of the cavity boundary, as the local field is the sum of (at least) two standing waves, coupled by the local periodicity (for an eigenmode, the local incident and diffracted beams are undistinguishable). Only modes that feature straight wavefronts parallel to the boundary, corresponding to local normal " incidence," have a simple field pattern at the local scale (see below).

The other important feature of mirrors is their maximum reflectivity R_{max}, or with some more generality their losses L=1-R-T, which are equal to $1-R_{max}$ when T=0 , in the thick mirror limit. Interestingly enough, there is no satisfying published electromagnetic approach to-date determining the losses of our kind of PC. The limit case of infinite air holes could give a reflectivity still improved compared to the existing performances under the plausible assumption that these performances are still limited by the etched depth ; in our group, we have set up a perturbational approach to tackle this issue,[10] for which assessment would be welcome.

Strong reflectivities are sought for lasers whose active medium features a weak gain, in order to fold the photon path sufficiently to reach threshold. Media such as quantum dot layers indeed have weak gain and the availability of efficient low loss mirrors in the range R>95% could help keeping the length of these devices in reasonable bounds. Note that nonradiative recombinations arise in the vicinity of the etched PC surfaces and may seriously hamper the efficiency in micron-sized active devices.

The inhibition or enhancement of spontaneous emission by the Purcell effect is a phenomena investigated to speed up the maximum speed of LEDs. It also requires high-Q cavities and therefore strongly reflecting mirrors. A more fundamental modification of light-matter interaction, the so-called strong coupling regime, occurs when the dipole of the emitter ensures a large enough coupling to a single mode of the cavity. A strongly resonant "cold" cavity mode is also advantageous in this case.

5. PC FOR SPECTRALLY SELECTIVE APPLICATIONS

Spectrally Selective Elements

Spectral selectivity is of course an important feature in view of wavelength division multiplexing (WDM) in all-optical fibre networks. When considering a Fabry-Perot laser, especially a short one that can easily be monomode, it is clear that the selected frequency depends on the cavity spacing but is not inherent to the mirror. Even in the extreme case of a VCSEL featuring a very narrow cavity between DBR mirrors with a sizeable penetration depth, the mirrors determine the frequency of laser oscillation through the local slope of their phase behaviour inside their large stopband, and they are not the frequency selective elements. Conversely, for DFB laser, with a weak index (or gain) modulation along the guide, the stopband is much narrower than the gain curve so that the grating of the distributed reflector operates as a frequency selective element.

The ideal frequency selective element should be furthermore tuneable on a large range and at high speed and its frequency of operation should be deterministic from the sole

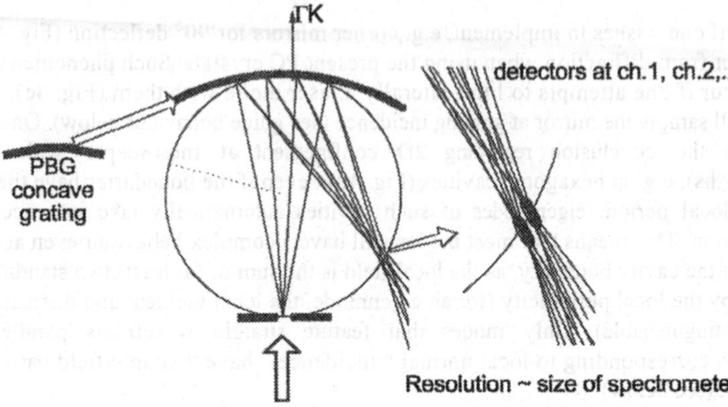

Fig. 5 : A Rowland-design-based spectrometer using a PC grating: light impinges from the bottom and the various channels are separated on the side.

fabrication parameters and not determined from posterior measurements. In the special case of the WDM comb of frequencies, the spacing between channels should be very accurate and the rejection of all other channels should be as large as possible. Of course, in the real life, not all such requirements are met. Hence, there is still room for improvement, and there will still be as long as the signal bandwidth grows.

Fabry-Perot Resonators

Symmetric Fabry-Perot resonators are simple elements made of two parallel mirrors that feature peaked transmission at a spacing-dependent frequency. To isolate a single channel around λ= 1550 nm from its thirty neighbours or so, each spaced by 0.8 nm (100 GHz), the maximum cavity order m is about 50 (the distance between peaks, i.e. the free spectral range FSR, is about λ/m and should exceed 30 nm). A finesse F of 63 is the minimum to start distinguishing a single channel (F is the ratio of peak width to FSR and is given by $\pi/(1-R)$; the quality factor is $Q = mF = 3150$, the peaks are 0.5 nm wide). This means that a reflectivity of 95% is sufficient to work in this kind of applications.

For this type of configuration, the guided beam is assumed to be well collimated and no diffraction occurs at normal incidence. Then the only limiting factor are the out-of-plane losses : if the required reflectivity is achieved, they will determine the value of the peak transmission according to $T_{peak}=T/(1-R)$. For 2.5% losses and R = 95% one has T = 2.5%, and peak transmissions of 50% are obtained. Hence losses smaller than, say, 3% and R > 95% are required to envision this precise class of applications. The exact placement of

For some other applications, e.g., filtering out 1.3 µm and 1.55 µm signals, the requirements are much more modest and can be fulfilled with the smallest cavities and a small number of rows.[15] Also, a deterministic device can be easily made as the requirement on size accuracy may be more than 10 nm, easily achieved by the e-beam writer.

Diffraction on Photonic Crystals

We have stated that diffraction was to be avoided in FP cavities. On the contrary, one can make use of it to build an integrated spectrometer (Fig. 5), with a curved surface so as to relieve the need for extra focussing elements. The large first-order diffraction efficiency for incidence on (11) rows along ΓK, especially close to the dielectric band edge[11] (low frequency), can certainly be applied to this configuration. Such applications have already

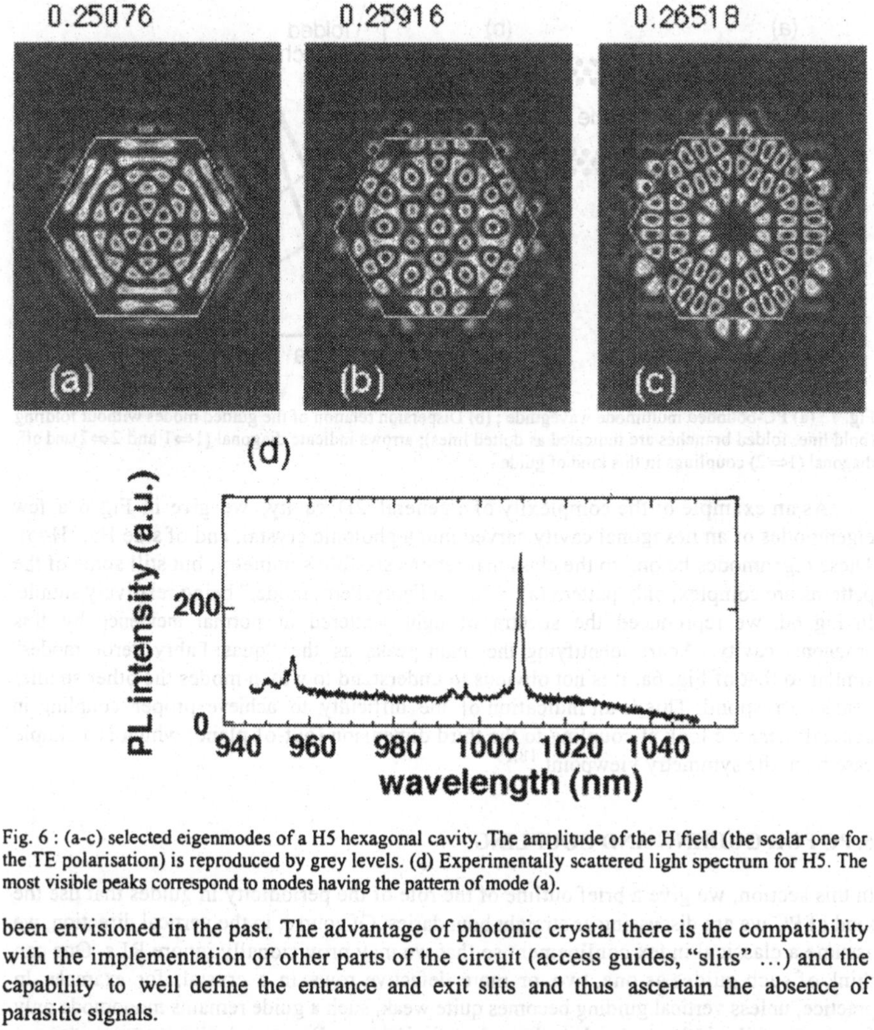

Fig. 6 : (a-c) selected eigenmodes of a H5 hexagonal cavity. The amplitude of the H field (the scalar one for the TE polarisation) is reproduced by grey levels. (d) Experimentally scattered light spectrum for H5. The most visible peaks correspond to modes having the pattern of mode (a).

been envisioned in the past. The advantage of photonic crystal there is the compatibility with the implementation of other parts of the circuit (access guides, "slits"...) and the capability to well define the entrance and exit slits and thus ascertain the absence of parasitic signals.

The selectivity of well-designed (diffraction limited) classical grating spectrometers is essentially a linear function of its size. It sets for example the number N of grating teeth, the same number which comes into the textbook diffraction function $\sin(N\varphi/2)/\sin(\varphi/2)$. The only way to gain space is to fold the beam. This goes some way towards the FP interferometer! The waveguide array is another attractive alternative in which the guide imposes the light path, and the spectrometer can thus be made much more compact.

Two-dimensional Resonators

Building up a two-dimensional cavity defines, ideally, a set of discrete frequencies and their eigenmodes. The interest and the difficulty with respect to the FP solution is that there is no obvious way to couple in general such cavity modes to modes of guides or to plane waves in free guide. Forgetting temporarily about PCs, a circular ring resonator is an interesting case: the modes have almost the same profile in the section of the ring and only different frequencies associated to azimuthal numbers m (the round-trip phase is $2m\pi$).[16] Whispering Gallery Modes (WGM) of disks feature somewhat similar properties.[17]

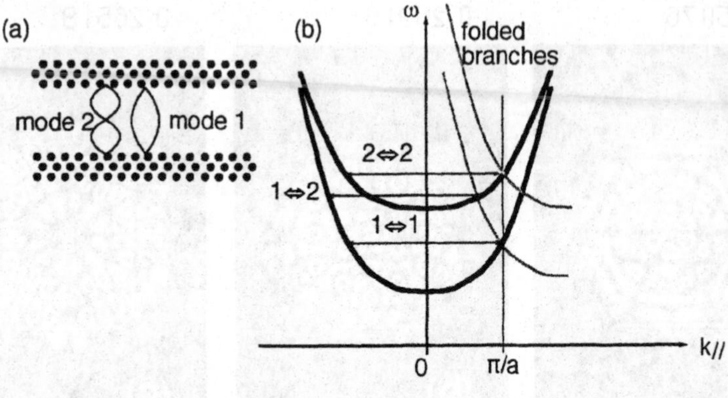

Fig. 7 : (a) PC-bounded multimode waveguide ; (b) Dispersion relation of the guided modes without foldfing (bold line, folded branches are indicated as dotted lines); arrows indicate diagonal (1⇔1 and 2⇔2)and off-diagonal (1⇔2) couplings in this kind of guide.

As an example of the complexity of a general 2D cavity, we give in Fig. 6 a few eigenmodes of an hexagonal cavity carved into a photonic crystal, and of side Ha, (H=5). These eigenmodes belong to the class that retains six-fold symmetry, but still some of the patterns are complex, only pattern (a), a "quasi Fabry-Perot mode," being relatively simple. In Fig. 6d, we reproduced the spectra of light scattered at normal incidence by this hexagonal cavity. Apart identifying the main peaks as the "quasi Fabry-Perot modes" similar to that of Fig. 6a, it is not obvious to understand to which modes the other smaller peaks correspond. This is an indication of the difficulty to achieve proper coupling in general: here we look at coupling to the third dimension (out-of-plane) which is a simple case from the symmetry viewpoint.[18,19]

6. PC FOR GUIDING AND COUPLING

In this section, we give a brief outline of the role of the periodicity in guides that use the kind of PC we are discussing as straight boundaries. Of course, in the vertical direction, we assume a classical index confinement so that we may provisionally ignore RLs. One can think of such guides as one, two or more defective rows in a crystal, for example. In practice, unless vertical guiding becomes quite weak, such a guide remains monomode only for very small widths, rather less then one missing row. Because such narrow guides are unpractical to couple to, we found it interesting to investigate multimodewaveguides of widths above 0.5 μm, typically more than 2 missing rows.

Then, one can imagine that these modes are made of rays of given angles. It may happen that two different modes correspond to rays which impinge at such a pair of incidences that the diffraction condition is perfectly fulfilled for the frequency of interest. In other words, if we now describe these modes with their wavevectors k_1, k_2 (1,2, ... = branch index), this means that the periodicity-induced wavevector $K=2\pi/a$ is able to couple two distinct branches i,j of the dispersion relation when $k_i-k_j = \pm K$ (see the scheme of Fig. 7). This is an "off-diagonal" coupling that occurs anywhere in the zone boundary, unlike the more classical counterpropagative "diagonal" coupling of DFB/DBR systems which occurs at the zone boundary and Bragg-scatters light back without changing its mode profile.

These off-diagonal couplings apply particulary to the fundamental mode and then give rise to mini stopbands on the transmission of this mode. This is of great importance for the application of PC to waveguides since it dictates their operating windows. Conversely, one may take advantage of this phenomenon for some kind of spectral selection. The exact arrangement of the PC boundaries, and its exact symmetry, play a fundamental role in determining the selection rules and coupling strength. We note also that the more the diffraction is allowed on a given kind of PC boundary, (e.g., more on (11) surface than on (10) surface), the more the couplings of guided modes using the same PC surfaces as boundaries are likely: this means that a smaller K is involved, and that more folding of the modes occur at the frequency of the bandgap. As an example of possible consequences, let us look at what happens when implementing a 90° bend in a triangular PC-based multimode channel guide : if before the bend, the boundary was of (10) type, then, after the bend, it is along (11). This means that the proper operation of the whole bend requires to find a common window between the two kind of guides. Fortunately, the mini stopbands have modest spectral extent (typically 0.5-3%), so that such a common window should still be sizeable.

Finally, the diffraction phenomenon may be used to ease the coupling between two modes of different elements, namely a cavity and a straight guide.[20] We have demonstrated such an effect in the case of a hexagonal cavity coupled to a straight waveguide. Most modes of the hexagonal cavity (of side 7a, a being the PC basic period) tend to have momentum rather normal to the common wall that separates the cavity and the guide. This means that energy launched across the wall tends to bump back into the cavity. However, there is a frequency region for which the momentum k carried by this light may fulfill the diffraction condition towards the guided mode. Of course the finite size of the system breaks a strict selection rule on momentum, but still, we have observed a clear coupling of cavity modes to the guide only in the 2%-wide spectral region for which an off-diagonal coupling takes place between the fundamental mode and a higher order mode.

7. CONCLUSIONS

To conclude these short notes, we have outlined the role of diffraction phenomena when using 2D photonic crystals into semiconductor optoelectronic devices. These phenomena arise in the bandgap because we choose a high index medium outside the PCs to preserve the existing vertical index-confinement schemes. This phenomenon can be seen at various levels: in the structure of cavity modes, in the spectral shape of the transmission of a channel waveguide bounded with PC, or when coupling is attempted between a "mesoscopic" cavity and a guide. The ways to minimize RLs, which are inherent to PCs based on index confinement in the vertical direction, will require also many studies. We have given our approach on this matter in Ref. 10 in detail. We gave only an outline in this contribution, noting that modest index contrast of the confining waveguide was a positive point, making it possible to use conventional InP-base and GaAs-based systems, provided the etching is deep enough to well overlap the guided mode profile.

References

1. C. Weisbuch, B. Vinter, *Quantum Semiconductor Structures: Fundamentals and applications.* (Academic Press, Boston, 1991).

2. L. A. Coldren, S. W. Corzine, *Diode Lasers and Photonic Integrated Circuits* (Wiley, New-York, 1995).

3. G. B. Stringfellow, M. G. Craford, Eds., *High-Brightness Light-Emitting Diodes*, (Academic Press, San Diego, 1997).

4. M. K. Smit, C. v. Dam, PHASAR-Based WDM Devices, Principles, Design,and Applications, *IEEE J. Sel. Topics in Quantum Electronics* **2**, 236 (1996).

5. S. G. Johnson, S. Fan, P. R. Villeneuve, J. D. Joannopoulos, L. A. Kolodziejski, Guided modes in photonic crystal slabs, *Phys. Rev. B* **60**, 5751 (1999).

6. T. F. Krauss, R. M. De La Rue, S. Brand, Two-dimensional photonic-bandgap structures operating at near-infrared wavelengths, *Nature* **383**, 699 (1996).

7. T. F. Krauss, R. M. De La Rue, in *Photonic Band Gap Materials* C. M. Soukoulis, Ed. (Kluwer, Dordrecht, 1996) pp. 427.

8. D. Labilloy, et al., Quantitative measurement of transmission, reflection and diffraction of two-dimensional photonic bandgap structures at near-infrared wavelengths, *Phys. Rev. Lett.* **79**, 4147 (1997).

9. D. Labilloy, H. Benisty, C. Weisbuch, C. J. M. Smith, T. F. Krauss, R. Houdré, U. Oesterle, Finely resolved transmission spectra and band structure of two-dimensional photonic crystals using InAs quantum dots emission, *Phys Rev.* **B59**, 1649 (1999).

10. H. Benisty, D. Labilloy, C. Weisbuch, C. J. M. Smith, T. F. Krauss, A. Béraud, D. Cassagne, C. Jouanin, Radiation losses of waveguide-based two-dimensional photonic crystals : positive role of the substrate, *Appl. Phys. Lett.* **76**, 532 (2000).

11. D. Labilloy, H. Benisty, C. Weisbuch, T. F. Krauss, D. Cassagne, C. Jouanin, R. Houdré, U. Oesterle, V. Bardinal, Diffraction efficiency and guided light control by two-dimensional photonic-band-gap lattices, *IEEE J. Quantum Electron.* **35**, 1045 (1999).

12. H. Benisty, et al., Optical and confinement properties of two-dimensional photonic crystals, *J. Lightwave Techn.* **17**, 2063 (1999).

13. K. Sakoda, Transmittance and Bragg reflectivity of two-dimensional photonic lattices, *Phys. Rev. B* **52**, 8992 (1995).

14. J. B. Pendry, in *Photonic Band Gap Materials* C. M. Soukoulis, Ed. (Kluwer, Dordrecht, 1996) pp. 203.

15. C. J. M. Smith, T. F. Krauss, R. M. De La Rue, D. Labilloy, H. Benisty, C. Weisbuch, U. Oesterle, R. Houdré, In-plane microcavity resonators with two-dimensional photonic bandgap mirrors, *IEE-Proc.-Optoelectron.* **145**, 337 (1998).

16. J. Zhang, D. Y. Chu, S. L. Wu, S. T. Ho, W. G. Bi, W. Tu, R. C. Tiberio, Photonic wire laser, *Phys. Rev. Lett.* **75**, 2678 (1995).

17. T. Baba, Photonic Crystals and microdisk cavities based on GaInAsP-InP system, *IEEE J. Sel. Topics in Quantum Electronics* **3**, 808–830 (1997).

18. J. M. Gérard, D. Barrier, J.-Y. Marzin, R. Kuszelewicz, L. Manin, E. Costard, V. Thierry-Mieg, T. Rivera, Quantum boxes as active probes for photonic microstructures : the pillar microcavity case, *Appl. Phys. Lett.* **69**, 449 (1996).

19. B. Gayral, J.-M. Gérard, B. Legrand, E. Costard, V. Thierry-Mieg, Optical study of GaAs/AlAs pillar microcavities with elliptical cross section, *Appl. Phys. Lett.* **72**, 1421 (1998).

20. H. Benisty, S. Olivier, M. Rattier, C. Weisbuch, C. J. M. Smith, T. F. Krauss, R. M. D. L. Rue, R. Houdré, U. Oesterle, All-photonic-crystal coupled cavity and guide, QELS/CLEO, San Francisco, May 8-11 (2000).

PATTERNED PHOTONIC CRYSTAL WAVEGUIDES

THOMAS F. KRAUSS
School of Physics and Astronomy
University of St. Andrews
St. Andrews, Fife, KY16 9SS
Scotland, U.K.

Abstract. Some of the fundamentals of 2-D photonic crystals are discussed in view of the constraints and opportunities offered by the waveguide configuration. The possibilities, limitations and future applications in light emitting devices and in integrated optics are explored.

1. Introduction

One of the arguments used by the pioneers of planar photonic crystals was that yes, they would like to have 3-D crystals, but no, they were not able to fabricate them – so why not try 2-D instead ? Fortunately, fabrication is only one of the many arguments for planar photonic crystals and many more reasons for using the 2-D platform have since evolved [1].

Using a "classical" waveguide geometry to confine light in the third (i.e. the vertical) dimension has been the key to success of planar photonic crystals. It has enabled rapid progress in mapping out the more fundamental properties of photonic crystals, i.e. their transmission, reflection and diffraction behaviour [2,3], has lead to the first device applications [4-7] and underlies the tremendous current interest in photonic crystals for integrated optics applications [8,9].

2. Design considerations

The confinement in the third dimension is typically provided by a "classical" waveguide based on total internal reflection. This configuration has obvious advantages, such as growth of layered structures by established epitaxial methods and compatibility with other planar optoelectronic elements. There are, however, major problems that need to be adressed when designing the structure.

The naive point of view is as follows (fig. 1): A high refractive index contrast is typically achieved by etching, so the structure is separated into areas of high-index material, typically semiconductor (with the in-built waveguide structure) and air. Light is then only guided in the semiconductor and not while travelling through the air, so diffraction loss and scattering out of the plane of the waveguide is inevitable. This loss can be minimised by increasing the fill-fraction of semiconductor, for example by

C.M. Soukoulis (ed.), Photonic Crystals and Light Localization in the 21st Century, 129–142.

designing a lattice of pillars with narrow air-gaps or a semiconductor honeycomb structure with small air-holes.

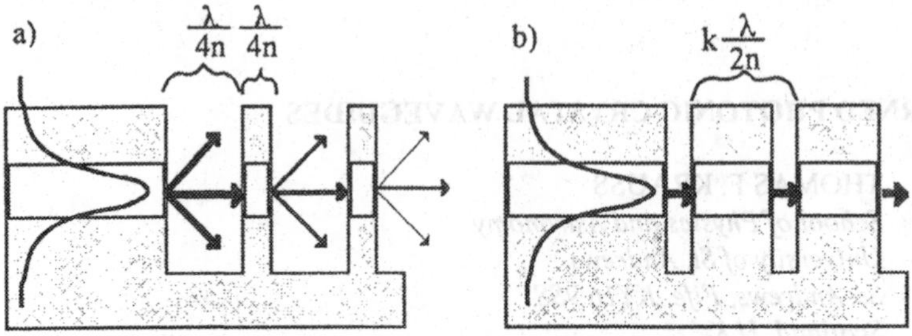

Figure 1 1a) A deeply etched waveguide, designed according to "conventional wisdom" for maximum reflectivity with the high and low index layers _/4n thick. This configuration suffers from diffraction losses, because light is not guided in the low index region and diffracts out of the waveguide plane. b) If the air-gaps, i.e. the etched holes or slots, are small enough, there is very little loss. The fundamental criterion for obtaining photonic bandgap effects, i.e. the Bragg condition, can still be fulfilled by designing the optical length of the structure as an integer multiple of half-wavelengths.

The principle of this approach is that light can "hop" across the narrow gaps without suffering excessive loss, whilst still experiencing the full refractive index contrast between semiconductor and air. This solution compromises the highest achievable bandgap and is in direct contrast to the "λ/4" condition used in multilayer mirrors that requires the optical path in both the low and the high index regions to be a quarter wavelength long for maximum interaction. Our approach, however, has so far shown the most convincing PBG effects in semiconductor waveguide structures, allowing the observation of a variety of PBG effects, including high transmission, reflection and very sharp filtering characteristics [4, 10].

The next question is, what vertical structure to use ? The two main alternatives are low or high vertical index, e.g. semiconductor ("laser-like") heterostructure vs. high index membrane, including GaAs on AlOx [11], and silicon on insulator (SOI) [12]. The membrane approach is the theoretician's favourite since it predicts well-confined modes, void of losses, in principle [13,5], and a variety of impressive results have been achieved with this approach, e.g. lasing from a single defect [14].

The low index contrast approach, however, keeps defying its critics and has proven remarkably successful, allowing, for example, the demonstration of high Q microcavities [15]. Comparative analyses have even shown that ultimately, very low losses [16,17] can be achieved in low-index structures. Also, keeping the substrate, e.g. in a semiconductor heterostructure, has the great advantage of allowing current injection and providing heat dissipation, issues of significant practical importance.

3. Fabrication

The impressive progress and volume of work produced in planar photonic crystals is a direct consequence of the fabrication technology, most notably high resolution lithography and anisotropic dry etching techniques, being adopted from the silicon microelectronics industry. The deterministic pattern generation, i.e. the ability to place features at any desired point in the lattice, is a great advantage over the self-assembly techniques and allows us to explore the richness of the photonic bandstructure to an exent that we are only beginning to explore.

3.1. LITHOGRAPHY

Considering the small size of the lattice (periodicity between 200-800 nm, with sub-100 nm control of feature size desirable), standard photolithography cannot be employed, with the exception of very recent work at NEC [12], where an I-line (λ=365 nm) stepper was used to produce patterns of 800 nm period for operation in the 1.5μm wavelength regime. Proposals have also been put forward to use Deep UV lithography (λ=193 nm) employing phase masks to explore further the opportunities offered by photolithographic techniques.

The workhorse of most planar photonic crystallographers, however, is the e-beam lithography machine, due to its unparalleled resolution and ability to exactly determine the periodic structure and its functional defects. Structures with periods down to 160 nm and features of 20 nm have been demonstrated with this technique [18], using 100kV acceleration voltage.

Holographic lithography, using multiple exposures or multiple – beam interference [19, 20], has the advantage of creating high-resolution periodic structures over large areas, but does not allow the inclusion of defects with a well-defined phase relationship; waveguides and cavities can be included using a combination of holography and photolithography, but since there is no means of high-accuracy alignment, the exact nature of the interface is dictated by chance rather than careful design.

3.2. ETCHING

In several ways, the most suitable structure for a planar photonic crystal consists of a matrix of small holes etched deeply into the material host. This requires deep and anisotropic etching with high resolution, so generally, conventional wet etching techniques cannot be used (with the exception of anodic etching, i.e. wet etching with an applied electric field).

The quality of the etching process is determined by the mask layer and by the choice of dry etching technique. The most suitable dry etching processes that result in high anisotropic etching (i.e. vertical sidewalls) feature a considerable physical component, so a "hard" dielectric or metallic mask is required. Photoresist is only of limited use, because it tends to erode under the physical impact of the etching ions.

The standard etch chemistry for GaAs/AlGaAs semiconductors is chlorine-based, typically $SiCl_4$ or Cl_2. Reactive Ion etching (RIE) with $SiCl_4$ has been used extensively [2,3,18] resulting in aspect ratios of up to 10:1 (e.g. 100 nm holes etched 1 μm deep). Ion-beam etching techniques (Chemically assisted ion beam etching, CAIBE, or reactive ion beam etching, RIBE) are arguably more suitable, with aspect ratios >20:1 achieved (120 nm holes etched ~2.5 μm deep) [21]. In CAIBE/RIBE, a collimated high-energy beam impinges on the sample, which results in the good directionality and high physical etching component required for the high aspect ratios.

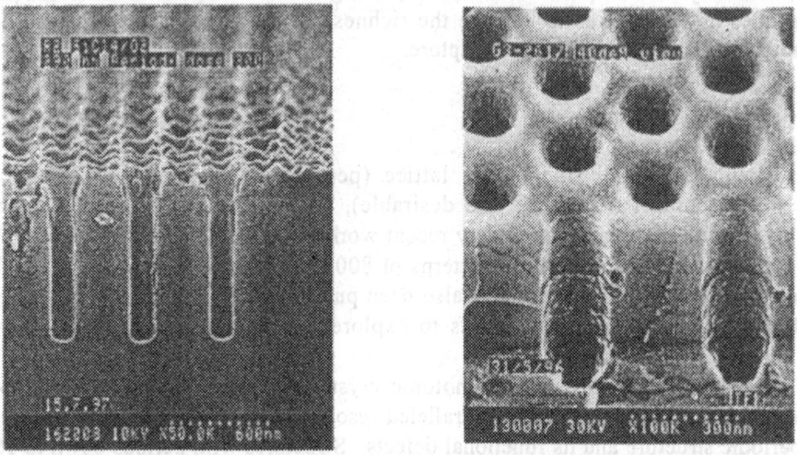

Figure 2 Two examples for 2-D photonic lattices, written by e-beam lithography and etched into a GaAs/AlGaAs waveguide structure using RIE and a dielectric mask. The lattice periods are 290 nm (left) and 260 nm (right), respectively. Left micrograph courtesy of C. Smith, University of Glasgow.

Etching InP, aimed at 1.55 μm wavelength range is not as straightforward; firstly, the etching process scales as well as the feature size, i.e. the required aspect ratio of around 10:1 and the difficulty of obtaining it does not change; generally, it is as difficult to etch 100 nm holes 1μm deep as it is to produce 200 nm holes 2μm deep. Secondly, InP dry etch chemistry is more difficult. A mixture of methane and hydrogen (CH_4/H_2) has been used succesfully, but it is problematic to achieve high aspect ratios due to the buildup of polymer during the etching process. This problem can be overcome by the use of chlorine chemistry, a solution that is not straightforward, however, because $InCl_3$, one of the main reaction products, is not volatile below 130° C - and so a heated stage is required for the process. Hot etching of InP has been demonstrated successfully in both CAIBE [22] and with a standard RIE reactor; the main problem consists of finding the (reactor dependent) balance between the chemical (temperature, reactive gas flow) and physical (DC bias or acceleration voltage) etching components.

4.Characterisation

The main problem with planar photonic crystals is that the waveguides used for vertical confinement are typically thin, on the order of λ/2n, i.e. only 100's of nm thick. Coupling light into such a small structure requires the diffraction-limited spot of a coherent source, which is inherently narrow-band and does not allow mapping out the full photonic bandgap. In order to overcome this apparent contradiction, several techniques have been developed, namely a) tunable laser [2], b) internal source (photoluminescence) [10], white light reflectivity [23] and d) "white light" from fs laser pulses [24]. A summary of these techniques listing their advantages and disadvantages is shown in the table below.

Table 1 Overview of the 4 most commonly used characterisation techniques for waveguide-based photonic crystals.

Method	Advantages	Disadvantages
Tunable laser (Ti:Sapphire or semiconductor)	Straightforward, widely available tool. High power/$\Delta\lambda$.	Sample design requires acces waveguides. Limited tuning range (10% typ.)
Internal source (PL)	Very versatile. Allows probing cavities etc. from inside.	Inherent absorption of unpumped regions. Active layer required in growth.
White light reflectivity (Tungsten lamp)	Simple and cheap.	Requires large areas because of large spot size. Cannot map out full bandstructure because of angular limitations.
Femtosecond pulses	"White" light from a coherent source.	Sample design requires acces waveguides. Expensive and specialised tool.

5. Examples for light-emitting devices using photonic microstructures

5.1. SEMICONDUCTOR LASERS WITH MICROSTRUCTURED MIRRORS

Periodic microstructures that consist of alternating layers of semiconductor material and air can be regarded as the extreme limit of the type of Bragg grating commonly used in distributed feedback (DFB) and distributed Bragg reflector (DBR) lasers. The difference is the refractive index contrast, which is typically less than 1% in a DFB/DBR laser, but as large as 3.5:1 in the case discussed here. This leads to a very much shorter interaction length of around 1 μm instead of the 100's of microns in a DFB/DBR laser and thereby opens the opportunity of creating edge-emitting laser elements with very small optical volume. This degree of compactness and the associated ability of very low threshold and high frequency operation has hitherto been reserved for vertical cavity surface emitting lasers (VCSEL's), which is why the ultrashort Bragg mirror lasers are sometimes being referred to as "horizontal VCSELs".

The best measured mirror reflectivities are around 95 % [6] and the shortest lasers of this type yet realised are 20μm long, amongst the shortest edge-emitters demonstrated to date. The key to the high reflectivity is the "narrow gap" scenario discussed above, with air – slots in the range of 80-100 nm, i.e. well below $\lambda/4$ (≈240nm). The narrow gaps place particularly high demands on the etching technology, which is the reason for redesigning the active layer of the semiconductor laser from the typical 2.5-3μm to a thickness of 1μm. Projected threshold currents are below 100μA [25] and therefore as low as that of the best VCSELs, although demonstrated threshold currents are still, somewhat disappointingly, in the mA – range [6,26].

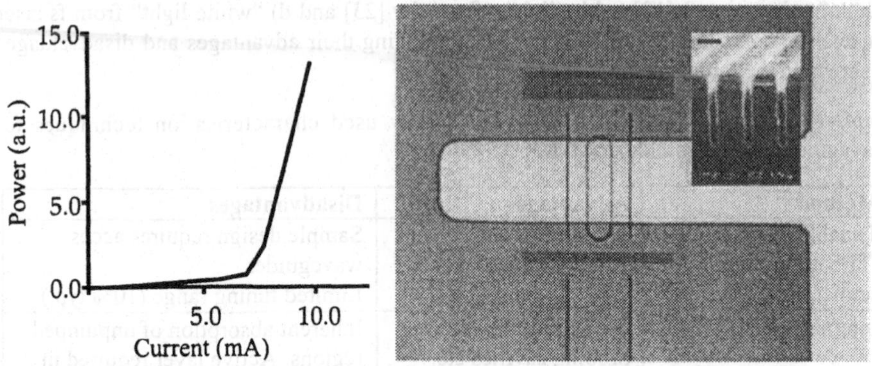

Figure 3 L-I curve and micrograph of 20 μm long semiconductor laser with microstructured mirrors, cross-section of the mirror shown in the inset.

5.2. LIGHT-EMITTING DIODES WITH HIGH EXTRACTION EFFICIENCY

Light emitting diodes are normally based on III-V semiconductors, which are the most efficient light-generating materials known, with up to 99.7 % internal quantum efficiency reported. In contrast, the extracted efficiency of an LED is typically as low as 2-4% because of the small escape cone imposed by Snell's law. One possibility to overcome this large discrepacy between generated and emitted light is to surround the active layer with a photonic crystal and use it to extract the light.

As a first exploration of this approach, we fabricated thin-film LEDs with a central unpatterned region within a 2-D photonic lattice [7] whereby the first conduction band of the lattice was designed to overlap the emission wavelength of the semiconductor. The thin film was an InP/InGaAs heterostructure produced by mounting the material on a glass slide and removing the substrate via wet etching ("substrate removal"). The film was then patterned via e-beam lithograpy and dry etching. A cross-sectional schematic of the film highlighting its operational principle are shown in Fig. 4.

The photonic lattice has the effect of a "second order grating coupler" and redirects the horizontally guided modes into vertically emitted radition. Another way of understanding the effect is to is to think of the modes as coupling to the modes of the lattice; by choosing those lattice modes that are inherently leaky (in this case, because a relatively high proportion of the modal field is in air and therefore not guided), the light scatters out of the system over a relatively short distance. By varying the lattice constant and thereby the operating point in the bandstructure, we were able to extract as much as 70% of the light generated inside the material.

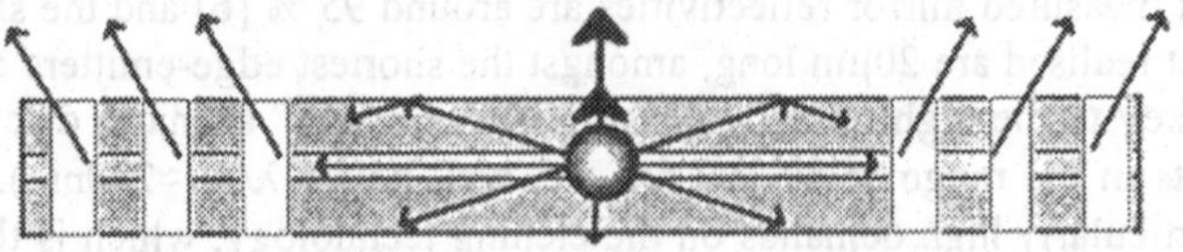

Figure 4 Operational principle of thin film LED with photonic crystal light extractor. The light is generated in the central area, and the waveguided modes are extracted via the photonic lattice.

These results were obtained via photoluminescence measurements. It is obviously of great practical importance to obtain similar results in electroluminescence and go beyond the ≈35% efficiency otherwise reported [27] for electroluminscent devices so far. In order to do this, we have made devices based on a planar microcavity design using oxidised AlGaAs (AlOx) mirrors. The thin active layer combined with the high-reflectivity mirrors yields an expected extraction efficiency of 24%.

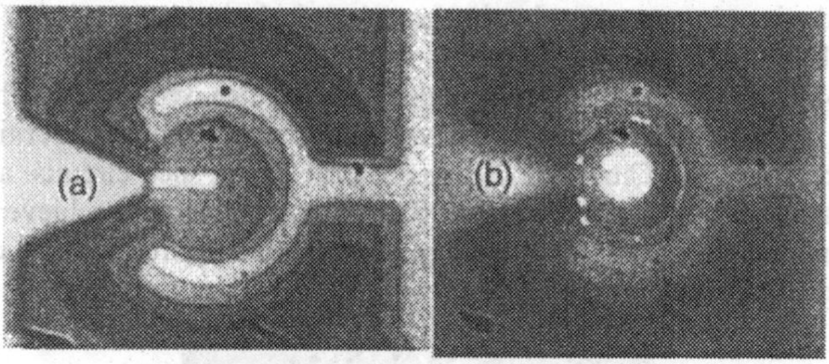

Figure 5 Top view of the microcavity LED based on oxidised Bragg mirrors. Due to the insulating nature of the mirrors, current injection has to be lateral and is provided by the finger-like (p-type) contact coming in from the left. The n-type contact is on the right of the micrograph, surrounding the central mesa. The dark outer rings are trenches etched for allowing oxidation underneath the mesa. Figure 5a) is a top view of the device to illustrate the layout, wheras figure 5b) shows the device with 0.5 mA current injected. We can clearly see current crowding around the central p-type contact, but also strong evidence of waveguided light scattering out at the edge of the mesa. By surrounding the mesa with a ring of photonic crystal, we can expect to extract most of the waveguided light and obtain efficiencies exceeding 40%.

The economic importance of high-efficiency LEDs is potentially very high. A recent report compiled by the U.S. Academy of Sciences cites lighting by LEDs as having a major impact on the economy in the next century, both in terms of lighting and energy saving. "Lighting by LEDs will have a major impact in the next century, as it represents, in the U.S., a market of $10 billion for lamps and fixtures and $ 440 billion for energy consumption, representing 19% of electricity consumption" [28].

6. Applications in integrated optics

Some of the most promising applications for waveguide-based photonic crystals are in the field of integrated optics. Here, propagation both inside and outwith the bandgap can be exploited.

6.1. PROPAGATION OF LIGHT IN THE BANDGAP

Using the photonic *bandgap* is the most obvious application for photonic crystals; obtaining bandgaps in a variety of material systems and geometries has been the subject of intense research for the last ten years after all ! In principle, the photonic crystal can be regarded as a perfect, omnidirectional mirror at bandgap frequencies, which allows one to design strongly confined waveguides, bends, cavities, and other integrated optical elements on a wavelength scale. This very property is responsible for the notion of "Photonic VLSI", i.e. the exciting prospect of a new type of integrated optics that will enable levels of integration comparable to those currently only achieved in silicon microelectronics. One only needs to compare the number of transistors on a silicon chip with the few devices in a present-day integrated optical circuit in order to realise how much potential for improvement there is.

A very important aspect of the mirror property that is often overlooked is the fact that high levels of isolation can be achieved between adjacent waveguides, a critical property in multi-channel circuits. Cross-talk is a major problem in such circuits, and isolation levels in excess of 30dB are often required. Planar photonic lattices achieve 4-10dB/unit cell, so photonic crystals can provide the good isolation required for low cross-talk in densely integrated circuits.

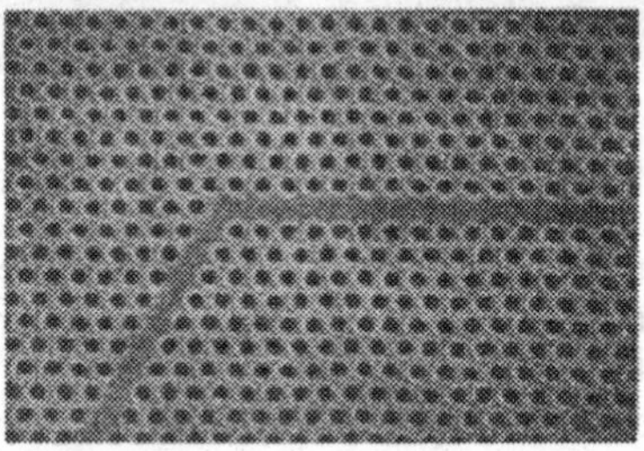

Figure 6 A photonic crystal channel waveguide, made by omitting a single set of rows. Note how the 60° bend follows the lattice symmetry. Micrograph courtesy of C. Smith, University of Glasgow.

Very compact waveguides consisting of channels in planar photonic crystals have been fabricated [29], but only a few convincing measurement results are available as yet [30].

6.2. PROPAGATION OF LIGHT OUTWITH THE BANDGAP

Whilst searching for the biggest bandgaps, it is all too easy to overlook another major aspect of these periodic structures: The richness of their bandstructure. The periodicity and strong index contrast impose severe constraints on the propagation of light, and lead to a variety of interesting effects that can be explored for their dispersive effects ("dispersion engineering"). Flat bands have low group velocities, useful for slow-wave structures and optical delay lines. The curvature of the band determines the group velocity dispersion, which can be used to compress or disperse light pulses [31]. The strong asymmetry of the bands in certain parts of the band diagram can be used to demonstrate strong spatial and spectral dispersion ("superprism", [9]) and can be understood has a special case of form birefringence, where the birefringence of the material is engineered via its microstructure.

6.2.1 The superprism effect

Beam steering and dispersion effects in periodic structures have been known for a while [32] and have been rediscovered recently with the intense interest in both photonic crystals and their application in wavelength division multiplexing systems. The superprism effect described by Kawakami and co-workers [9] is based on the asymmetry of the conduction band near the Γ-point, i.e. the fact that the wavevector changes much more dramatically with a change of frequency when moving from the Γ-point into K-direction than when moving into M-direction. They observed an angular dispersion of 50° for a change of input wavelength from 0.99 μm to 1.00 μm, which translates, when scaled to the 1.55 μm regime, into ≈2 degrees for a 50 GHz channel spacing (50 Ghz ≈ 0.4 nm @ 1.55 μm) in a typical wavelength division multiplexing (WDM) system. Assuming that the output waveguides are spaced by 5 μm, the length of crystal required to separate the different channels would be around 150 μm, which is impressively small compared to the centimetre-sized phased array waveguides commonly used.

Several aspects need to be considered when engineering such a structure:

a) The crystal strongly disperses the beam not only as a function of input wavelength, but also as a function of input angle. If a guided mode (that can be understood as a superposition of a set of plane waves propagating at different angles) impinges on the structure, the different angular components will lead to a broadening of the beam and thereby to cross-talk between the different wavelength channels. A careful choice of the operating point within the bandstructure is required to minimise this effect and maintain good beam quality.

b) The angular dispersion curve (input wavelength vs. output angle) is non-linear, i.e. different wavelengths are dispersed at different angles. The positioning of the output waveguides must therefore be adjusted in order to achieve equal wavelength separation between the different channels.

c) Operating near the Gamma-point means that the guided modes have a high k_z, i.e. a high out-of-plane component and are therefore difficult to confine. This is acceptable in the "autocloned" structure where it was first proposed [9], because the structure is three-dimensionally periodic and therefore strongly confines light in the vertical direction, but a conventional waveguide configuration would be very lossy.

6.2.2 Pulse compression/broadening

Optical pulses travelling in a dispersive medium, e.g. an optical fibre, typically suffer from broadening, because the different spectral components of the pulse travel at different speeds. This is one of the principle limitations of high-speed fibre optics telecommunications. Several methods are used to overcome this problem, including the use of dispersion shifted-fibre, where the dispersion is zero at the operating wavelength, or the use of dispersion compensating fibre, whereby two segments of fibre with opposite sign of dispersion are combined to achieve a net zero dispersion.

Periodic structures offer an a powerful and very flexible alternative, because they allow dispersion compensation irrespective of wavelength and on a very small lengthscale. Consider the following example :

A pulse travels down a fibre. The dispersion of the fibre causes the different spectral components of the pulse to travel at different speeds, with the effect that the red end of the pulse travels slower than the blue end (Dispersion can be either positive or negative, depending on the wavelength and fibre used, so blue can travel faster than red and vice versa). The pulse then enters a periodic structure, which is designed to have a band-edge near the centre frequency of the pulse.

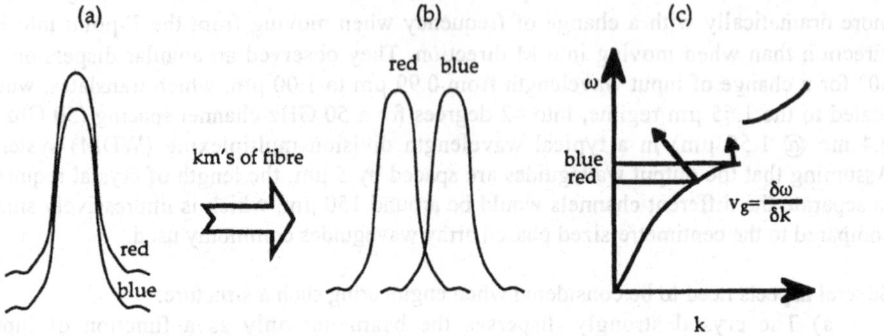

Figure 7 Dispersion in a fibre and dispersion compensation in a periodic structure.

Due to the slope of the dispersion curve near the band-edge, and the fact that the group velocity is the derivative of the ω-k diagram, the group velocity for the blue part of the pulse is much slower (represented by the shorter arrow in fig. 7 c) than the group velocity for the red part of the pulse – hence the red part travels faster and can catch up with the blue part. If the length of the periodic structure is chosen appropriately, the pulse recombines to its original shape as in fig. 7a.

This method for dispersion compensation, and pulse compression, if taken a step further, has been used in fibre gratings for several years [33] and has recently been applied to semiconductor microstructures, with pulse compression factors of up to five demonstrated [34].

6.3. COUPLED CAVITY WAVEGUIDES

A combination of confinement and dispersion effects is at the heart of the recently proposed CCWs ("coupled cavity waveguides") [35] or CROWs ("coupled resonator optical waveguides") [36] where a waveguide is formed via an array of coupled defects or cavities in a photonic lattice. Varying the type of defect and their spacing gives an element of control over the propagation of light from defect to defect, it allows tailoring of the wavelength response of the structure and of its group velocity.

Impressive experimental results, that have demonstrated light travelling with very little propagation loss, and around sharp bends have already been obtained in the microwave-regime, which turns CCWs into real competitors to the more "conventional" channel waveguides [37]. Transmission spectra of coupled cavity waveguides as a function of defect spacing are shown in fig. 8. For a 1 in 2 structure, i.e. a set of cavities consisting of a single missing hole separated by a single hole, the response is relatively broad. It sharpens up considerably for a 1 in 3, and resembles the response of an uncoupled cavity by the time the separation has reached 1 in 5.

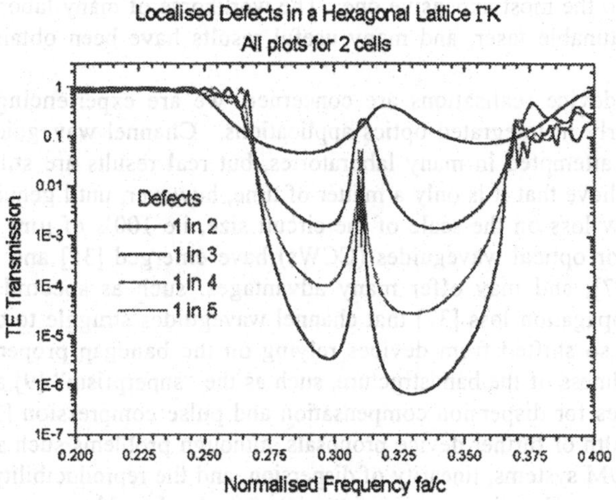

Figure 8 Evolution of the transmission through a coupled defect waveguide as a function of the spacing between defects. Courtesy of Andrew Reynolds, University of Glasgow.

7. Conclusion

Patterned photonic crystal waveguides are currently the subject of intense research in many laboratories. We believe that the key to their success is a properly designed waveguide and microstructure, where the guided mode is disturbed as little as possible while experiencing the high index contrast that gives rise to the rich bandstructure and the photonic bandgap phenomenon. The waveguide should be symmetric, to avoid polarisation coupling, the etched features should be narrow, to mainting guiding, and the depth of these features should be as deep as possible to ensure that the entire mode experiences the periodicity – any part of the mode that does not inevitably radiates away. Following these considerations, the photonic crystal consisting of a matrix of etched holes (as opposed to the structure consisting of "pillars" of high-index material) is still the most promising, which is also evidenced by the increasing number of groups using this geometry.

The fabrication of these structures is now well established, particularly in the GaAs/AlGaAs and the SiO_2/Si_3N_4 systems. The figure of merit for etching a matrix of holes is their aspect ratio, i.e. the smaller the holes and the deeper they are etched, the lower the predicted losses. Having optimised the process on a standard RIE machine, we believe that further improvement requires the use of more sophosticated techniques, such as ECR/ICP techniques that can produce denser plasmas, or the use of ion beam etching due to its higher physical etching component and lower operating pressure.

Characterisation is equally well established, and four major techniques have emerged to overcome the fundamental problem of high spectral bandwidth, to map out the entire bandgap, and the small spatial cross-section of typical structures. Of all of these techniques, continuum generation via fs pulses [Soton, Bath] seems the most powerful, but also the most expensive one. The workhorse of many laboratories in this area is still the tunable laser, and many useful results have been obtained with that technique.

As far as device realisations are concerned, we are experiencing a wealth of results, particularly in integrated optics applications. Channel waveguides and sharp bends are being attempted in many laboratories, but real results are still few and far between. We believe that it is only a matter of time, however, until genuinely low loss weaveguides (low loss on the scale of the circuit size, i.e 100's of μm) are available. Coupled resonator optical waveguides (CCWs) have emerged [35] and recently been demonstrated [37], and may offer many advantages, such as spectral control, low insertion and propagation loss [37] that channel waveguides struggle to compete with. The focus has also shifted from devices relying on the bandgap property to devices exploring the richness of the bandstructure, such as the "superprism" [9] and the use of periodic structures for dispersion compensation and pulse compression [34]. Here, we can expect a wealth of further device proposals, although problems such as the channel separation in WDM systems, linearity of dispersion, and the reproducibility of obtaining a particular target wavelength are serious issues that need to be addressed.

An area where photonic crystals have yet to convincingly demonstrate their superiority is the field of light emitting devices. Although high extraction LEDs [7, 27] and ultracompact lasers with high reflectivity PBG mirrors [6] have now been demonstrated, the ultimate dream of thresholdless lasers that motivated research in the early years of photonic crystals is still a distance away.

8. Acknowledgements

I would like to thank the Royal Society of the UK for financial support via a research fellowship, and the Nanoelectronics Research Centre at Glasgow University for ongoing technical support. Furthermore Chris Smith, Richard De La Rue, Andrews Reynolds, Maxime Rattier, Henri Benisty and Ross Stanley for invaluable discussions and some of the results presented here.

9. References

1. T.F. Krauss and R. M. De La Rue (1999) Photonic crystals at optical wavelengths - past, present and future, *Progress in Quantum Electronics* 23, 51-96.
2. T.F. Krauss, R.M. De La Rue and S. Brand (1996) Two-dimensional photonic bandgap structures operating at near-infrared wavelengths, *Nature* 383, 699-702.
3. H. Benisty, C. Weisbuch, D. Labilloy, M. Rattier, C.J.M. Smith, T.F. Krauss, R. M. De La Rue, R. Houdre, U. Oesterle, C. Jouanin and D. Cassagne (1999) Optical and confinement properties of two-dimensional photonic crystals, *Journ. Lightwave Tech.*, 17, 2063-2077.
4. T.F. Krauss, B.V. Voegele, C.R. Stanley and R.M. De La Rue (1997) Waveguide microcavity based on photonic microstructures, *IEEE Photonics Technology Letters*, 9, 176-178.

5. J.S. Foresi, P.R. Villeneuve, J. Ferrera, E.R. Thoen, G. Steinmeyer, S. Fan, J.D. Joannopoulos, L.C. Kimerling, H.I..Smith and E.P. Ippen (1997) Photonic-bandgap microcavities in optical waveguides, *Nature* 390, 143-145.
6. T. F. Krauss, O. Painter, A. Scherer, J.S. Roberts and R. M. De La Rue (1998) Photonic microstructures as laser mirrors, *Optical Engineering* 37, 1143-1148.
7. M. Boroditsky, T. Krauss, R. Coccioli, R. Vrijen, R. Bhat and E. Yablonovitch (1999) Light extraction from optically pumped light-emitting diode by thin-slab photonic crystals, *Appl. Phys. Lett.* 75 1036-1038.
8. J.D. Joannopoulos, P.R. Villeneuve, S.H. Fan (1997) Photonic crystals: Putting a new twist on light, *Nature* 386, 143-149.
9. H. Kosaka, T. Kawashima, A. Tomita, M. Notomi, T. Tamamura, T. Sato and S. Kawakami (1999) Superprism phenomena in photonic crystals: Toward microscale lightwave circuits *IEEE Journ. Lightwave Tech.* 17, 2032-2038.
10. D. Labilloy, H. Benisty, C. Weisbuch, T.F. Krauss, R.M. De La Rue, V. Bardinal, R. Houdré, U. Oesterle, D. Cassagne and C. Jouanin (1997) Quantitative measurement of transmission, reflection and diffraction of two-dimensional photonic bandgap structures at near-infrared wavelengths, *Phys. Rev. Lett.* 79, 4147-4150.
11. G.S. Petrich, P.R. Villeneuve, S. Fan, E.R. Thoen, J.D. Joannopoulos, E.P. Ippen and L. A. Kolodziejski (1999) One-dimensional Photonic bandgap microcavities for strong optical confinement in GaAs and GaAs/AlOx semiconductor waveguides, *Journ. Lightwave Tech.*, 2152-2160.
12. M. Tokushima, H. Kosaka, A. Tomita and H. Yamada (2000) Lightwave propagation through a 120 degrees sharply bent single-line-defect photonic crystal waveguide, *Appl. Phys. Lett.* 76, 952-954.
13. D.M. Atkin, P. St .J. Russell, T. A. Birks and P.J. Roberts (1996) Photonic band structure of guided Bloch modes in high index films fully etched through with periodic microstructure, *J.Mod.Optics* 43, 1035-1053.
14. O.Painter, R.K.Lee, A.Scherer, A. Yariv, J.D. O'Brien, P.D. Dapkus and I.Kim, "Two-dimensional photonic band-gap defect mode laser", Science 284, pp.1819-1821, 1999.
15. C.J.M.Smith, H. Benisty, D. Labilly, U. Oesterle, R. Houdre, T.F. Krauss, R. M. De La Rue and C. Weisbuch (1999) Near-infrared microcavities confined by two-dimensional photonic bandgap crystals, *Electronics Letters* 35 228-229.
16. H. Benisty, D. Labilloy, C. Weisbuch, C.J.M. Smith, T.F. Krauss, D. Cassagne, A. Beraud and C. Jouanin (2000) Radiation losses of waveguide-based two-dimensional photonic crystals: positive role of the substrate, *Appl. Phys. Lett.* 76, 532-534.
17. H. Benisty, P. Lalanne, S. Olivier, M. Rattier, C. Weisbuch, C.J.M. Smith, T. F. Krauss, C. Jouanin and D. Cassagne (2000) Finite-depth and intrinsic losses in vertically etched two-dimensional photonic crystals, *submitted to Optical and Quantum Electronics*.
18. T.Krauss, Y.P.Song, S.Thoms, C.D.W.Wilkinson and R.M.DelaRue (1994) Fabrication of 2-D photonic bandgap structures in GaAs/AlGaAs, *Electronics Letters* 30, 1444-1446.
19. V. Berger, O. Gauthier-Lafaye and E. Costard (1997) Photonic band gaps and holography, *J. of Appl. Phys.* 82, 60-64.

20. M. Campbell, D.N. Sharp, M.T. Harrison, R.G. Denning and A.J. Turberfield (2000) Fabrication of photonic crystals for the visible spectrum by holographic lithography, *Nature* 404, 53-56.
21. J. O'Brien, O. Painter, R. Lee, C.C. Cheng, A. Yariv and A. Scherer (1996) Lasers incorporating 2D photonic bandgap mirrors, *Electronics Letters* 32, 2243-2244.
22. C. Youtsey, R. Grundbacher, R. Panepucci, I. Adesida and C. Caneau (1994) Characterisation of chemically assisted ion beam etching of InP, *J. Vac. Sci. Tech. B* 12, 3317-3321.
23. V.N. Astratov, I.S. Culshaw, R. Mark Stevenson, D. M. Whittaker, M.S. Skolnick, T. F. Krauss and R. M. De La Rue (1999) Resonant coupling of near-infrared radiation to photonic band structure waveguides, *Journ. Lightwave Tech.*, 17, 2050-2058.
24. M.C. Netti, M.D.B. Charlton, G.J. Parker, J.J. Baumberg (2000) Visible photonic bandgap engineering in silicon nitride waveguides, *Appl. Phys. Lett.* 76, 991-993.
25. T. Baba, M. Hamasaki, N. Watanabe, P. Kaewplung, A. Matsutani, T. Mukaihara, F. Koyama and K. Iga (1996) A novel short-cavity laser with deep-grating distributed bragg reflectors, *Jap. Journ. of Appl. Phys.* 35, 1390-1394.
26. E. Höfling, F. Schäfer, J.P. Reithmaier, A. Forchel (1999) "Edge-emitting GaInAs-AlGaAs microlasers", *Photonics Technology Letters* 11, 943-945.
27. R. Windisch, C. Rooman, M. Kuijk, B. Dutta, G.H. Dohler, G. Borghs and P. Heremans (2000) Micro-lensed gigabit-per-second high-efficiency quantum-well right-emitting diodes", *Electronics Letters* 36, 351-352.
28. National Science Foundation (1998) *Harnessing Light: Optical Sciences and Engineering for the 21st Century*, National Academy Press, Washington, D.C.
29. T. Baba, N. Fukaya, J. Yonekura (1999) Observation of light propagation in photonic crystal optical waveguides with bends, *Electronics Letters* 35, 654-655.
30. H. Benisty, this volume.
31. P. Millar, R. M. De La Rue, T. F. Krauss, S. Aitchison, N.G.R. Broderick and D. J. Richardson (1999) Nonlinear propagation effects in an AlGaAs Bragg grating filter, *Opt. Lett.* 24, 685-687.
32. R. Zengerle (1987) Light propagation in singly and doubly periodic planar waveguides, *J. of Mod. Opt.*, 34, 1589-1617.
33. H. G. Winful (1984) Pulse compression in optical fibre filters, *Appl. Phys. Lett.* 46, 527-529.
34. N.G.R. Broderick, P. Millar, D.J. Richardson, J.S. Aitchison, R. De La Rue and T. F. Krauss (2000) Spectral features associated with nonlinear pulkse compression in Bragg gratings, *Opt. Lett.* 25, 740-742.
35. N. Stefanou and A.Modinos (1998) Impurity bands in photonic insulators, *Phys. Rev. B* 57, 12127-12134.
36. A.Yariv, Y. Xu, R.K.Lee and A. Scherer (1999) Coupled-resonator optical waveguide: A propoal and analysis, *Opt. Lett.* 24, 711-713.
37. M. Bayindir, B. Temelkuran and E. Ozbay (2000) Propagation of photons by hopping: A waveguiding mechanism through localized coupled cavities in three-dimensional photonic crystals, *Phys. Rev B* 61, 11855-11858.

PHOTONIC CRYSTALS FROM MACROPOROUS SILICON

R.B. WEHRSPOHN, A. BIRNER, J. SCHILLING, F. MUELLER,
R. HILLEBRAND AND U. GOESELE
Max-Planck-Institute of Microstructure Physics, Weinberg 2,
D-06120 Halle, Germany

Abstract. Regular, hexagonally-ordered macropore arrays have been obtained by photo-electrochemical etching of prepatterned silicon substrates. For typical pore diameters of about 1 μm, aspect ratios of about 100 have been achieved. Due to the high aspect ratio, the negligible surface roughness and the high dielectric constant of silicon, these macropore arrays are suitable candidates for photonic crystal devices. In this review, we present transmission spectra and the corresponding calculations of the bulk photonic crystals with a lattice constant of 1.5 μm having a complete photonic bandgap between a vacuum wavelength of 3 and 4 μm. By omitting some pores during the etching, photonic defect structures can be obtained, e.g., waveguides, beamsplitters or micro-resonators. As an example, a straight waveguide will be discussed and good agreement between theoretical calculations and experimental transmission spectra is shown. A confinement in the third dimension along the pore axis can be reached by modulating the pore diameter. This is achieved by applying a modulated current density during anodization and carefully taking into account diffusion processes in the pores. First transmission measurements along these modulated pores and the corresponding modeling are shown. The 3D photonic crystals have now in all three direction non-linear dispersion relations which can be tuned rather independently. For optoelectronic application, first macropore arrays with a lattice constant of 0.5 μm have been prepared, exhibiting a photonic bandgap around the interesting telecommunication wavelength region of 1.3μm.

1. Introduction

Photons traveling in a periodic dielectric medium show interesting new behavior. The photons behave similar to electrons moving through the periodic potential in a crystal and their movement may be described by a photonic band structure. These

C.M. Soukoulis (ed.), Photonic Crystals and Light Localization in the 21st Century, 143–154.

periodic dielectric media are called Photonic Crystals (PCs) and have attracted much interest in the last decade [1, 2, 3].

Because of fabrication deficiencies, these predictions were first demonstrated by experiments in the microwave regime [4]. However, extending the application of PCs to the near infrared or visible spectrum demands very high precision on the fabrication of the structures. Since the periodicity determines the wavelength of the photonic band gaps, these structures must be fabricated with a precision much better than the wavelength, i.e., on a sub-μm level. The translational symmetry is desired in all 3 directions of space, but already for the 2D case interesting new devices have been proposed [1, 2, 3].

Electrochemically-etched macroporous silicon exhibits pores with a diameter in the micro- to submicrometer range and a depth of up to the thickness of the silicon wafer. Because of the high uniformity, the low absorption coefficient and the high refractive index contrast, macroporous silicon can be used to fabricate two-dimensional photonic crystals with a complete band gap in the near or mid infrared spectral range [5, 6, 7].

2. 2D Photonic crystals

2.1. PREPARATION OF MACROPOROUS SILICON

A detailed description of macroporous silicon formation can be found in [8, 9]. Here, we just give a short summary. First, an n-type silicon wafer with $\langle 100 \rangle$ orientation is prepatterned by standard photo-lithography. Subsequent alkaline etching produces inverted pyramids acting as initial pores. Under anodic bias and backside illumination, the wafer is then etched in hydrofluoric acid. The electronic holes generated by the illumination near the back surface diffuse through the whole wafer and promote the dissolution of silicon mainly at the pore tips. As a result, pores grow straight along the $\langle 100 \rangle$ direction with very high aspect ratio. The arrangement of these pores can be controlled by the lithographic mask, the diameter by the illumination intensity. By controlling these parameters, variations of pore diameters both between neighboring pores and with depth can be made negligible.

Most of the samples we report about were etched on 0.5 Ωcm n-type FZ silicon substrates using a hexagonal pore arrangement. The pores have a center-to-center distance of 1.5 μm and a depth of 100 μm. The pore diameter after electrochemical etching is 0.9 μm. By subsequent oxidation/etching steps the pore diameter is increased up to 1.36 μm.

For optical investigations or applications of such structures the porous silicon has to be processed further. The two-dimensional PC has translational symmetry perpendicular to the pore axes. Therefore, analyzing the band structure requires the photons also to travel perpendicular to the pore axis. Investigations of the properties of defects demand access to the end of a waveguide and require removal of part of the porous silicon with a precision of about one pore lattice constant or

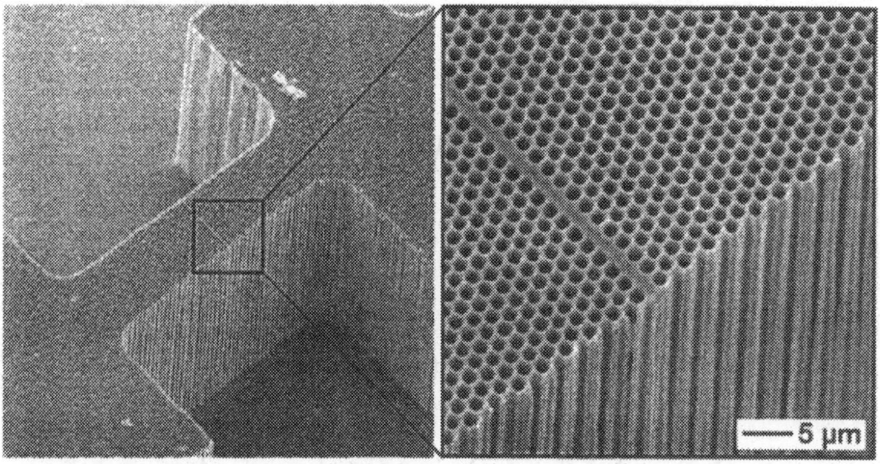

Figure 1. Laterally-structured porous silicon sample with a defect line. The H-like structure facilitates the positioning of a fiber for coupling light in and out. Pore distance is 1.5 μm, height of the porous silicon is 100 μm.

about 1 μm. A special microstructuring technique was developed to meet these specifications [10]. First, the pore walls are passivated by a thermal oxide and a CVD nitride. Afterwards, an aluminum layer is sputtered onto the porous silicon and structured by conventional photo-lithography. Although the structure sizes of this second mask are in the 10 μm range, the precision of these structures and the alignment relative to the defects is better than 1 μm. In the opened window of the aluminum mask, the passivating oxide and nitride are removed by chemical etching. In a subsequent isotropic plasma etching process the porous silicon in the areas without passivation is etched leading to the desired bar structure. The quality of this process is demonstrated in Fig. 1. A bar of porous silicon is shown with about 22 layers of pores or about 33 μm width. The microstructuring technique leads to sharp edges. The whole transition for the 100 μm deep pores is within one pore layer! Overall, we get bars of porous silicon on the silicon substrate which are 100 μm high, 2–200 μm wide and several mm long. The bars are aligned with the designed defect structures in the porous silicon.

2.2. BULK PHOTONIC CRYSTALS

The processed macroporous Si samples described above are now well suited for investigations of the optical properties for light traveling perpendicular to the pores. We have done transmission measurements on such bars for different pore diameters, polarizations, and directions. In Fig. 2 spectra are shown for the Γ-M direction, H-polarization, and two quite different diameters of a sample having 22 layers of pores and no defects. Depending on the pore diameter the center of the

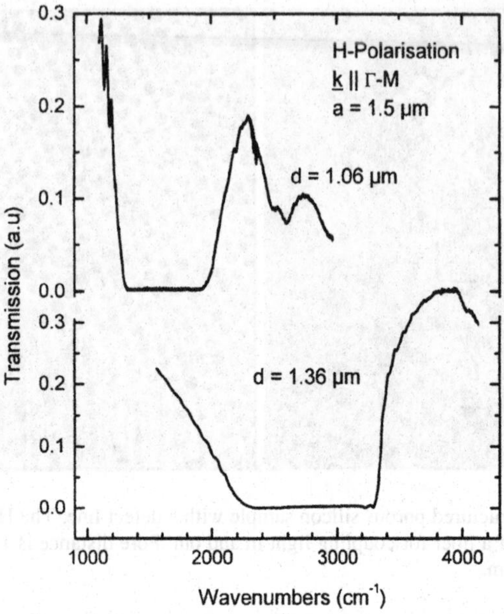

Figure 2. Transmission spectra of two samples with different pore diameter d along the $\Gamma - M$ direction, i.e., along the pore rows. Lattice constant a is 1.5 μm, the width of the porous silicon bar is 33 μm. Measurement is in H-polarisation, i.e., the magnetic field is parallel to the pore axes.

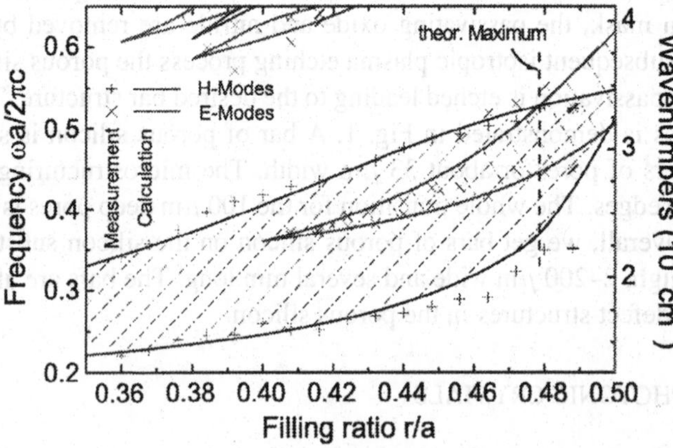

Figure 3. Dependence of the observed bandgaps on polarisation and filling factor (gap map). Theoretical (solid lines) and experimantal values (symbols) show very good agreement.

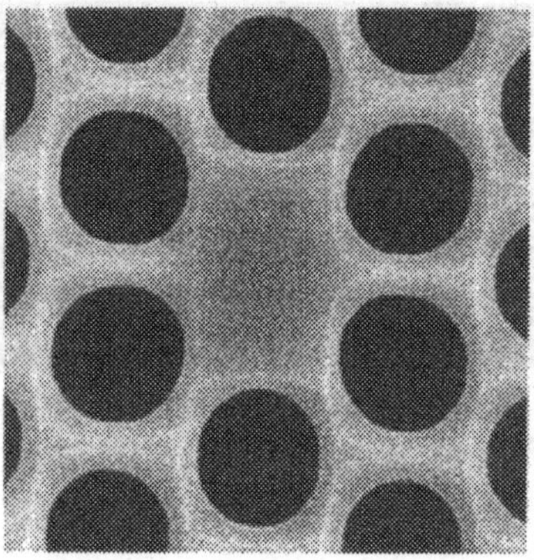

Figure 4. SEM top view of the region around a missing etch pit after electrochemical pore growth and subsequent pore widening by oxidation/etching steps. The distance between the pores is 1.5 μm, pore diameters are 1.15 μm.

stop band due to the band gap shifts from 1650 cm^{-1} (6 μm wavelength) for a pore diameter of 1.06 μm up to 2800 cm^{-1} (3.6 μm wavelength) for 1.36 μm. Repeating this measurements for other directions and E-polarization, we find a complete gap centered at 3.2 μm for 1.36 μm pore diameter and no overlap of all the different gaps for the 1.06 μm sample in good agreement with theoretical predictions for such structures.

In Fig. 3 we present the resulting bandgaps of such measurements for a whole set of samples with varying pore diameters (symbols). For comparison the theoretical predictions from a plane wave expansion method [11] are shown as solid lines. For the lower filling factors the agreement is quite perfect. Only for the very high porosities there are some slight deviations due to the difficulty in preparing and handling these very fragile samples. Small differences between the real dimensions of the samples and the values used in the calculations are, therefore, responsible for the observed discrepancies [12].

These measurements were carried out using a Bruker IFS66 FTIR spectrometer with an MCT detector element of 0.5 mm diameter. In the band gap region, transmission was reduced by more than 2 orders of magnitude. However, this value reflected the limitation of the FTIR setup and was mainly determined by the nonlinearity of the MCT detector. Recently, measurements by a tunable laser on very thin samples showed a damping of about 10 dB per pore row [13] for frequencies laying in the band gap.

2.3. WAVEGUIDES

If we omit some etch pits by using a suitable mask for the photo-lithography, the electronic holes generated at the back side by illumination are consumed by

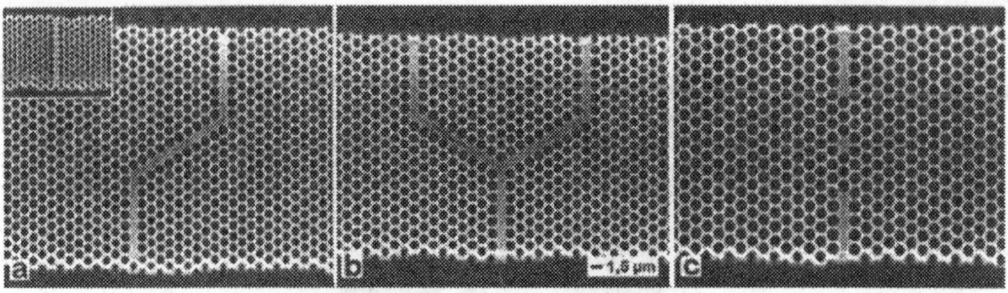

Figure 5. Different defect structures realized in macroporous silicon with 1.5 μm interpore distance.

the neighboring pores without great influence on their position. They get somewhat larger because they collect more carriers. To minimize this effect, pores are grown with a small diameter and afterwards widened by pure chemical etching or by several oxidation/etching steps. The result of this procedure is a quite perfect structure with some missing pores at predefined positions, as shown in Fig. 4 for a single missing pore. These missing pores disturb the translational symmetry and for proper conditions lead to localized states in the forbidden spectral region. Arranging such defects in a line creates defect modes with transmission bands inside the bandgap. As propagation is forbidden in the surrounding medium, waveguides with very sharp bends should be possible according to theory. We have analyzed in the past different defect structures: linear and bent waveguide [14], Y-branch and microresonator [12] (Fig. 5). Here, we will discuss the impact of the linear defect onto the optical properties in more detail [14].

Bandstructure calculations show additional states all over the bandgap localized at the defect line. As we are experimentally coupling in from a plane wave, we only couple to the even symmetry states. The theoretical transmission spectrum is depicted in the upper part of Fig. 6. For the lower frequencies single mode transmission is expected. At the in- and the out-coupling facets the waveguide modes are partially reflected leading to Fabry-Perot resonances. At higher frequencies a small gap is expected where no even states are available. Above the gap there are again states available, but the density of these states is so high, that the resonances can no longer be resolved. The measured spectrum which is shown in the lower part of Fig. 6 shows a remarkable good agreement with these predictions. For the lower frequencies the expected single mode resonances are observed. There is a well pronounced stop band and a broad transmission band at higher frequencies. Again, the observed small discrepancies in finesse and stop band frequency can be well explained by the strong influence of small deviations in the real dimensions of our structures.

The observed high finesse results from the low coupling efficiency between the strongly localized waveguide modes and the external plane waves. In a real device the waveguide facets could be avoided by connecting other optical ele-

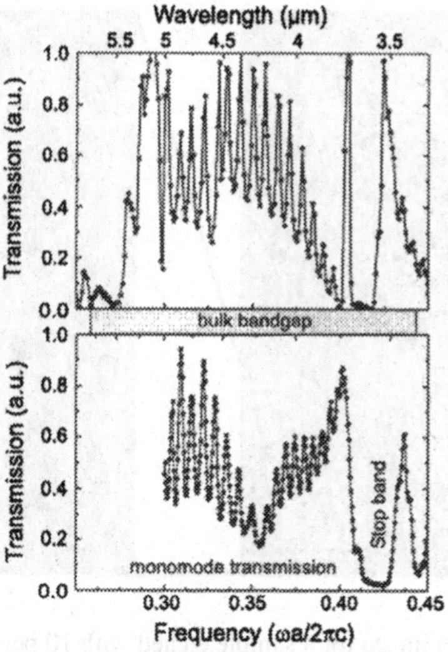

Figure 6. Experimental transmission spectrum (bottom) of a linear waveguide structure compared to theoretical predictions (top) [14]. The measurement was carried out for similar structure as in Fig. 1 with a thickness of 18a with a = 1.5 μ and for H-polarization. The bulk bandgap is marked by a gray bar.

ments directly. These linear defects act then as quite ideal waveguides where the light is very well confined within a few pore rows.

2.4. 3D CRYSTALS

According to the established growth model of Lehmann [7, 9], the current density at the pore tips is always equal to the critical current density j_{ps}. The porosity p is therefore determined by the ratio of the total current density to the critical current density, or for regular arrangements, where all pores have the same area A_{pore} the porosity is $p = A_{pore}/A_{cell} = j/j_{ps}$.

The total current is controlled by the illumination intensity. Therefore, variations of the pore diameter with depth can be achieved by controlling the light source. This concept has proven its validity in the past for compensating the variation of other growth parameters like temperature or the dilution of HF with increasing pore depth. For the application of macroporous silicon as 2D photonic crystals, this compensation is well established to get homogeneous pore diameters for pores several 100 μm deep [6, 15].

Samples were prepared from 5 Ωcm substrates with a photolithographically defined hexagonal pattern of 4.2 μm pitch. A circular area with a diameter of 20 mm was exposed to the 6 wt-% HF at 10°C. The samples reported here were etched using a sawtooth-like current density.

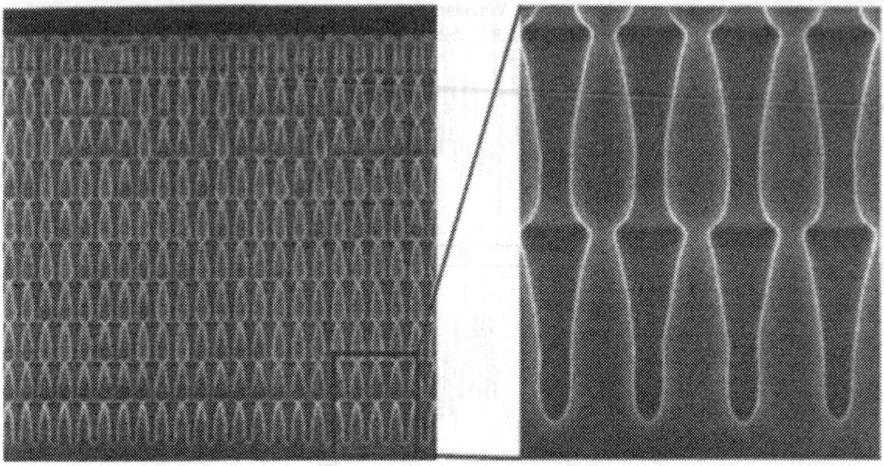

Figure 7. SEM cross-section image for a sample etched with 10 periods of modulated light.

The SEM cross-section image in Fig. 7 demonstrates the quality of this etching process. The resulting samples have the expected strong asymmetrically varying pore shapes as defined by the current profile. The sample is laterally homogeneously etched over the whole exposed area without noticeable defects. With increasing pore depth, the HF concentration at the pore tips and therefore also the critical current density j_{ps} and the etching speed v are reduced. If the sawtooth-like current density is applied on a linear time scale, this leads to a strong variation of about 30% in the length of a period from top to bottom for a 100 μm deep porous film. Using the reduction of growth speed from the homogeneous model [9] improves this effect quite remarkably. Up to 25 periods could be etched without noticeable deviation of the linear fit leading to a total thickness of over 200 μm [16].

In Fig. 8 the transmission spectrum in growth direction of the pores for a sample with a period of $l_z = 7.2$ μm is shown. Two strong stop bands can be observed near 320 cm^{-1} and near 610 cm^{-1}. As the lateral period is significantly smaller than the period in the growth direction, a first approximation of the optical behavior can be obtained by using an effective medium model. From the pore diameter, as measured from the SEM cross section images, we determined the depth-dependence of the porosity and then the effective refractive index using the Bruggeman formalism [17]. The calculated transmission spectrum for a multilayer model [18] using 10 slabs for each period and 8 periods in total is shown as a dotted line in Fig. 8. The positions of the stop bands are very well reproduced by this simple approximation. The Fabry-Perot interferences from the reflections at the front and back surfaces, which are very strong in the calculated spectrum, were

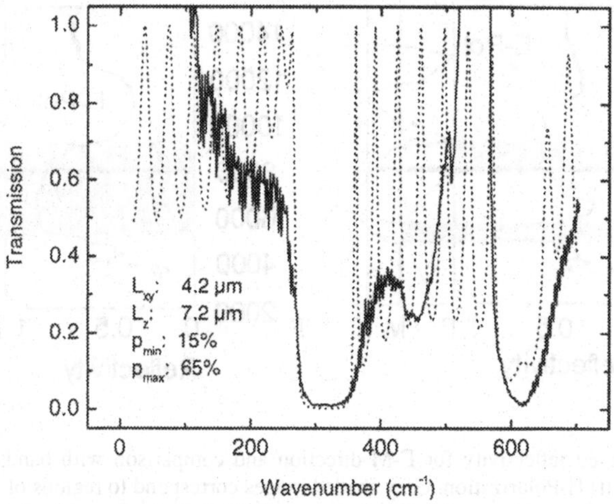

Figure 8. Transmission spectrum for light travelling parallel to the pores axes (straight line) together with the calculated spectrum from a 1D Bruggeman approximation (dotted line). The lattice constant l_{xy} in the xy-plane is 4.2 μm, in z-direction $l_z = 7.2$ μm. Porosity varies from $p_{\min} = 0.15$ to $p_{max} = 0.65$.

not resolved in the experiment. The high transmission around 550 cm^{-1} and below 180 cm^{-1} are artifacts due to the low background intensity of the spectrometer.

These samples very impressively demonstrate the ability to generate real 3D PCs by modulating the backside illumination. Although the structures produced so far, do not exhibit a complete bandgap, they have strongly nonlinear dispersion relations in all directions, a behavior which will be very useful in nonlinear optic experiments to fulfill phase matching conditions. Especially for applications like mixing experiments of beams with different wavelength, the freedom to design the third z-direction independently from the periodicity in the xy-plane will provide very high flexibility.

3. Outlook

To obtain bandgaps around 1.3 μm a downscaling of the above described triangular pore lattice is necessary. Therefore the pitch was adjusted to $a = 0.5$ μm. The pores fabricated had a radius $r = 0.18$ μm and a depth of 100 μm. During the process they were widened to $r = 0.215$ μm since a complete bandgap opens up at ratios $r/a \geq 0.4$. To investigate the 2D-bandgaps in the near IR reflection measurements were performed. For this purpose the samples were cleaved along the Γ-K direction to gain access to the side walls of the pores and to get a clean-cut interface. For the reflection measurements an IR microscope equipped with a polarizer and a mirror objective with an opening angle of 30 degrees was used

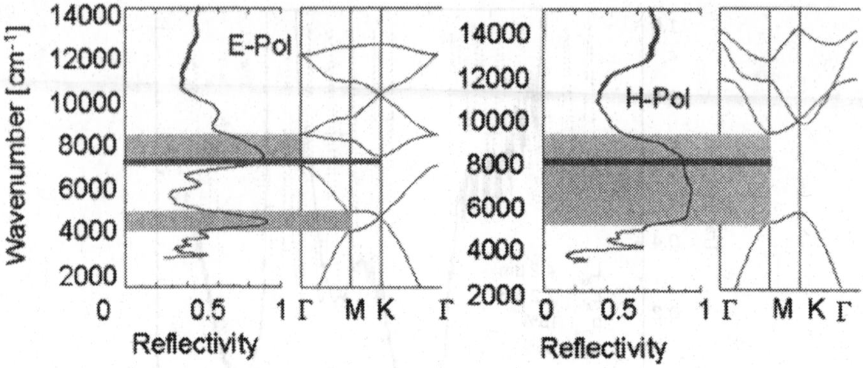

Figure 9. Measured reflectivity for Γ-M direction and comparison with bandstructure; (right) E-Polarization, (left) H-Polarization. Grey shaded ranges correspond to regions of high reflectivity. Dark shaded range shows the complete bandgap around 8000 cm^{-1} ($= 1.25\ \mu$m).

similar to Ref. [19]. The spectra were detected by a FTIR-spectrometer containing a tungsten lamp, CaF_2 -beamsplitter and a MCT-detector. The reflections for E- and H-polarisation were measured along the Γ-M direction using a gold mirror with a nominal reflectivity of 98% as reference. The resulting sample spectra are shown in Fig. 8. Due to the relatively wide opening angle the measured signal comprises contributions ranging from normal incidence reflection up to 30 off-axis and off-plane incidence reflections. The first order bandgap investigated here weakly depends on the direction of incidence [19]. Therefore bandstructure calculations performed along the wavevector path Γ-M-K-Γ can still be employed as a good approximation for the interpretation of the reflection spectra. They were computed for $r/a = 0.425$ using 967 plane waves. The shaded spectral ranges represent theoretically expected regions of high reflectivity. They mainly coincide with the bandgaps along the Γ-M direction. Figure 9 reveals good agreement between theoretical predicted ranges of total reflection and experimentally-determined high reflectivity regions. Finally, from the calculated bandstructure, a complete bandgap for E- and H-polarisation can be derived for the spectral range from 1.22 μm to 1.3 μm, thus incorporating the wavelengths of the 2nd telecommunication window.

One possible next step is towards an active device, in the simplest case an optical switch, but also an optical transistor can be envisaged. A possible realization would be the introduction of a material into the pores which changes its refractive index as a function of an applied field (electrical, magnetical, mechanical, etc.). Recently, we have shown for the first time as a proof of principle the feasibility of such an optical switch by introducing a liquid crystal into the pores and switching it thermally [20].

4. Conclusions

We have prepared two-dimensional photonic crystals based on macroporous silicon with a lattice constant of 1.5 μm exhibiting a complete gap from 3 to 4 μm wavelength. Transmission measurements show good agreement with theoretical predictions for a wide range of pore diameters. Different defects like waveguides with or without bends have been fabricated. For the linear waveguide the good agreement between theoretical calculations and measured transmission spectra is demonstrated. Periodicity in the third direction is achieved by modulated light intensity leading to real 3D photonic crystals. The possibility to grow macropores with a lattice constant of 0.5 μm has been shown. The precision of the achieved samples and the presented optical data prove the suitability of electrochemically etched macroporous silicon as a candidate for new optical devices based on PCs in the near and mid infrared spectral range.

ACKNOWLEDGMENTS

We appreciate the support for the calculations of the photonic band structure of our samples by W. Hergert from the University Halle-Wittenberg. We are grateful to K. Busch (University of Karlsruhe) and P. Villeneuve (MIT Cambridge) for calculating transmission spectra. The optical characterization by P. Kramper and V. Sandoghdar (University of Konstanz) and S. Leonard (University of Toronto) is gratefully acknowledged by the authors. Very special thanks go to S. Matthias for the technical support preparing the next-generation PCs.

References

1. *Photonic Bandgaps and Localization*, edited by C. M. Soukoulis, NATO ASI Series, Ser. B, Vol. **308**, (Plenum Press, New York 1993).
2. J. D. Joannopoulos, R. D. Meade, and J. N. Winn, *Photonic Crystals*, (Princeton University Press, New Jersey 1995).
3. *Photonic Band gap materials*, edited by C. M. Soukoulis, NATO ASI Series, Ser. E, Vol **315**, (Kluwer Academic Publishers, London 1996).
4. E. Yablonovitch, T. J. Gmitter, and K. M. Leung, *Phys. Rev. Lett.* **67**, 2295 (1991).
5. U. Grüning, V. Lehmann, S. Ottow, and K. Busch, *Appl. Phys. Lett.* **68**, 747 (1996).
6. A. Birner, U. Grüning, S. Ottow, A. Schneider, F. Müller, V. Lehmann, H. Föll, and U. Gösele, *Phys. Stat. Sol.* (a) **165**, 111 (1998).
7. V. Lehmann and U. Grüning, *Thin Solid Films* **297**, 13 (1997).
8. V. Lehmann and H. Föll, *J. Electrochem. Soc.* **137**, 653 (1990).
9. V. Lehmann, *J. Electrochem. Soc.* **140**, 2836 (1993).
10. S. Ottow, V. Lehmann, and H. Föll, *J. Electrochem. Soc.* **143**, 385 (1996).
11. K. Sakoda, *Phys. Rev. B* **51**, 4672 (1995).
12. A. Birner, A.-P. Li, F. Müller, U. Gösele, P. Kramper, V. Sandoghdar, J. Mlynek, K. Busch, V. Lehmann, to be published in *Mater. Sci. Semicon. Proces.* (2000).

13. S. W. Leonard, H. M. van Driel, K. Busch, S. John, A. Birner, A.-P. Li, F. Müller, U. Gösele,and V. Lehmann, *Appl. Phys. Lett.* **75**, 3063 (1999).
14. S. W. Leonard, H. M. van Driel, A. Birner, U. Gösele, P. R. Villeneuve, submitted to *Opt. Lett.*
15. F. Müller, A. Birner, U. Gösele, V. Lehmann, S. Ottow,and H. Föll,*J. Porous Mater.* 7, 201 (2000).
16. F. Müller, A. Birner, J. Schilling, U. Gösele, Ch. Kettner and P. Hänggi, to be published in *Phys. Stat. Sol.* (a).
17. D. A. G. Bruggeman, *Ann. Physik.*, Leipzig, **24**, 636 (1935).
18. F. Abelès, *Ann. de Physique* **5**, 596 (1950).
19. S. Rowson, A. Chenokov, C. Cuisin, J.-M. Lourtioz, *IEEE Proc.-Optoelectron.* **145**, 403 (1998).
20. S. W. Leonard, J.P. Mondia, H.M. van Driel, O. Toader, S. John, K. Busch, A. Birner, U. Gösele and V. Lehmann, *Phys. Rev. B* **61**, R2389 (2000).

CHARACTERIZATION OF A THREE-DIMENSIONAL MICROWAVE PHOTONIC BAND-GAP CRYSTAL

JAN FAGERSTRÖM[1], STIG LEIJON, NILS GUSTAFSSON, and TORLEIF MARTIN

Defence Research Establishment
Div. of Sensor Technology
P. O. Box 1165, SE-581 11 Linköping
Sweden

1 Abstract

A microwave photonic crystal has been constructed and characterized experimentally and computationally. The material has prominent electromagnetic features characteristic of a *three-dimensional photonic band structure material.* Measurements of transmission coefficients show that the material has a first band-gap (i. e., a frequency gap where extended modes are forbidden) between 10.9–13.1 GHz. The damping of transmitted amplitude is typically −40 dB in this band-gap, and close to 0 dB (with dips due to interference effects reaching down to −8 dB) within the bands (i. e., at frequencies where extended modes are allowed). Calculated transmission spectra agree qualitatively with measurements, and discrepancies are explained in terms of approximations made in the computational model. The time average Poynting vector (flow of electromagnetic power), has been calculated on a plane cut, parallell to the direction of incidence, through a model of the photonic crystal. The Poynting vector is strongly reduced at 9–12 GHz. This region corresponds well to the first band-gap. It is contemplated how a three-dimensional photonic band structure material could be utilized in radar signature managements applications.

2 Introduction

It is well known since long that electromagnetic waves can be prevented from propagation in certain directions in a multi-component material by appropriate design of the materials periodicity. This is the property on which, e. g., multilayer dielectric mirrors and Fabry-Perot interference filters are based. It has been demonstrated in the recent decade that the same phenomenon can occur for propagation in *any* direction in space, in materials with periodicity in all three

[1]To whom correspondence should be addressed. Email: fager@lin.foa.se

C.M. Soukoulis (ed.), Photonic Crystals and Light Localization in the 21st Century, 155–171.

dimensions. Such materials were for the first time claimed to exist in 1987 [1,2], and since the beginning of the 1990s, research in the field has grown enormously.

Periodic materials, in which electromagnetic waves in certain frequency bands are forbidden to propagate, are now collectively known as photonic crystals, or photonic band-gap materials. An example is given in Figure 1, which illustrates the structure and properties of a (generic) one-dimensional photonic band-gap material. The structure consists of two different materials, with relative dielectric

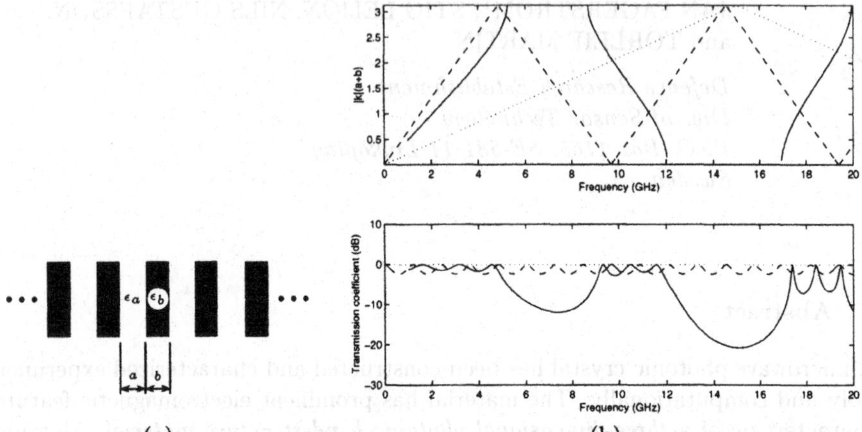

(a) (b)

Figure 1. An example of a one-dimensional photonic band-gap material. (a) Schematic representation of the geometrical structure. (b) Dispersion relation, "band structure" (top) and corresponding amplitude transmission coefficients (bottom) for a multilayer slab consisting of four unit cells [i. e., the total slab thickness is $4(a+b)$] for $\epsilon_a = 1.0$ and $\epsilon_b = 9.57$, but different values of a and b: $a = 0.01$ m and $b = 0$ m (dotted line), $a = 0$ m and $b = 0.01$ m (dashed line), $a = 0.005$ m and $b = 0.005$ m (solid line).

constants (thicknesses) ϵ_a (a) and ϵ_b (b), respectively, as illustrated in Figure 1a.

The band structures (dispersion relations) for electromagnetic wave modes, propagating along the stacking direction, are displayed in the top graph of Figure 1b. The bands are plotted for one Brillouin zone only, i. e. for $|k| \leq \frac{\pi}{a+b}$, with "folding" of the bands at the boundaries. Three different cases, with $\epsilon_a = 1.0$ and $\epsilon_b = 9.57$, are considered in Figure 1b:

I: vacuum only $a = 0.01$ m and $b = 0$ m (dotted line)

II: dielectric only $a = 0$ m and $b = 0.01$ m (dashed line)

III: vacuum and dielectric $a = 0.005$ m and $b = 0.005$ m (solid line)

Cases I and II correspond to an electromagnetic wave propagating in a homogeneous, non-periodic medium. Hence, the dotted and dashed lines at the top graph of Figure 1b are simply "light lines", $\nu(k) = c_0 k/(2\pi\sqrt{\epsilon_r})$ where ν is the frequency, c_0 the speed of light in vacuum, k is the wave vector and ϵ_r is the relative dielectric constant of the medium ($\epsilon_r = 1.0$ in case I and 9.57 in case II). The assumed periodicity of the material is obviously arbitrary in these two cases, since the thickness of one of the materials is zero. In contrast, case III corresponds to an electromagnetic wave propagating in a periodic material. In this case forbidden frequency regions, "band-gaps," appear in the band structure (solid line in Figure 1b) at the center, and at the boundaries of the Brillouin zone.

The gaps are obviously caused by the periodic variation of the dielectric constant. Note also that, as expected, the bands of case III are "intermediate" of the corresponding bands in case I and II (e. g., the first band in case III falls between the first bands in case I and II, respectively). This information will prove to be illuminating later in the present study.

The transmission properties of the materials in the three cases are illustrated in the bottom graph of Figure 1b. This graph displays the amplitude transmission coefficients $\tau = 10 \log \frac{|E_t|}{|E_i|}$ (where $|E_t|$ and $|E_i|$ are the electric field amplitudes incident at, and transmitted by the slab, respectively) for a slab with thickness $d = 4(a+b)$. The transmission is complete (0 dB) in case I (dotted line). This case corresponds to the extreme limit situation where the material consists of vacuum only. In case II (dashed line) the transmission coefficient displays a periodic interference pattern, characteristic of interference in a slab. The period can be calculated from the slab thickness d as $\Delta\nu = \frac{c_0}{2d\sqrt{\epsilon_b}}$. Finally, the most interesting case, corresponding to a photonic band-gap structure (case III) is given by the solid line. Note that the transmission is strongly reduced in the band-gap regions. There are interference patterns in the allowed band regions, similar to case II. However, in contrast to case II, the pattern is not periodic, but change with the varying slope of the bands in case III.

It is clear that most existing and potential applications of photonic band-gap materials are based on the existence of the frequency gap. However, there are cases where the properties in the allowed frequency regions, in the bands, might be exploited. One such case is low reflective materials for, e. g., signature management of military objects. One purpose of the present study is to gain experience of photonic crystals with such applications in mind. Signature management involves the design of electromagnetic properties of signature materials. A desirable feature of such materials is to have uniform transmission and reflection properties regardless of the direction of incidence. Hence, it is of great importance to study materials with relevant electromagnetic properties in all three dimensions, e. g., three-dimensional photonic crystals. To this end a crystal with three-dimensional photonic band-gap properties in the microwave region has been constructed and investigated, both experimentally and theoretically.

Section 3 describes the sample crystal under investigation. Methods used in measurements and calculations on the sample are described in Sections 4 and 5, respectively. The corresponding experimental and theoretical results are presented and discussed in Section 6. Finally, a summary and conclusions of the present work is found in Section 7.

3 "Woodpile" microwave photonic crystal

The present study is based on a microwave photonic crystal with a "woodpile" layer-by-layer structure. This layer-by-layer structure was designed by a research group at the Iowa State University [3], and was first fabricated at microwave and millimeter frequencies [4–6] by this group. (Recently, silicon processing methods have been used to fabricate similar structures in the infrared region [7].) A photograph of the sample, operating at microwave frequencies, which was used for the measurements in the present study is shown in Figure 2a. The crystal in Figure 2a

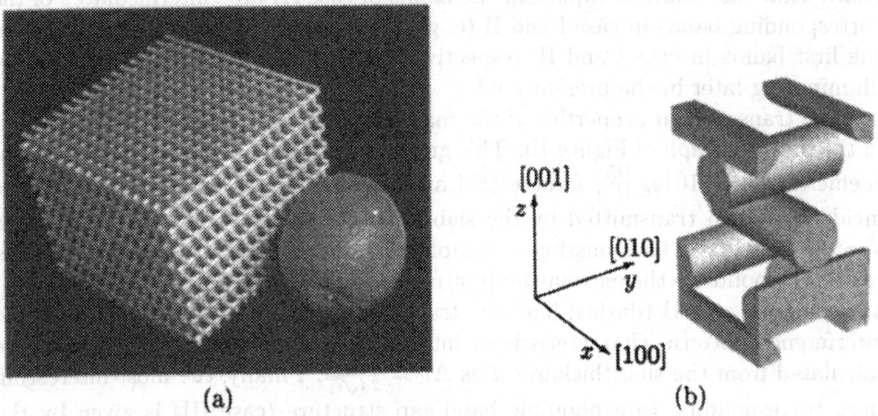

Figure 2. (a) A photograph of the "woodpile" microwave photonic crystal used in the study and (b) its tetragonal unit cell. The dimensions of the unit cell are $10\times10\times16$ mm^3.

is constructed from 512 alumina (Al_2O_3) rods, 160 mm long, with radius 2 mm. The structure was glued together, using a small drop of glue at each site where the rods touch. Technical specifications of the rods and the glue are summarized in Table 1. Each layer consists of 16 rods, which are stacked as illustrated by the unit cell in Figure 2b. The center-to-center distance between neighboring rods within each layer is 10 mm. The crystal structure thus obtained is a body centered tetragonal (bct) Bravais lattice, with a basis of two rods. The crystal structure was deliberately designed to yield (a) the first band-gap at approximately 10 GHz, and (b) a large gap-to-midgap $\Delta\nu/\nu_c$ ratio [3]. It should be mentioned that similar structures have been studied elsewhere [3–7].

A comment on notation is appropriate at this point. Throughout the paper we use crystallographic notations to denote directions and planes in the crystal. Thus, [100], [010], [001] denote directions as indicated in Figure 2b. Similarly, (100), (010), (001) denote *planes* in the crystal structure which are orthogonal to the corresponding directions. For example, (100) denotes the yz-plane in Figure 2b.

TABLE 1. Technical specifications of alumina rods and glue, used to build the microwave photonic crystal in Figure 2a.

Rods:	
Manufacturer	FRIATEC AG, Germany
Product name	FRIALIT-DEGUSSIT AL 23 (circular rods, "microwave quality")
Al_2O_3-content (by weight)	99.7 %
Length	160 ± 0.2 mm
Bending	≤ 0.2 mm
Radius	2 ± 0.2 mm
Relative dielectric constant (at 9 GHz)	9.57 ± 0.02
Electric loss tangent, $\tan\delta$	$< 3.2 \cdot 10^{-4}$
Glue:	
Manufacturer	Epoxy Technology, Inc., USA
Product name	EPO-TEC 921FL
Relative dielectric constant (at 1 MHz)	6.43

4 Measurements

Transmission measurements in the frequency range 1–20 GHz have been performed in order to characterize the electromagnetic properties of the photonic crystal. The experimental setup is displayed in Figure 3. The setup is based on a scalar network analyzer. The network analyzer is connected to two separate broad band Vivaldi horn antennas, working as transmitter and reciever (T and R in Figure 3). The measurement situation thus obtained allows the sample to be rather freely oriented in different positions in the electromagnetic field. Microwave absorbing materials are applied to the setups as indicated in Figure 3 in order to reduce noise and unwanted scattering from the background. The measurements were calibrated simply by measuring the transmitted wave with no measurement sample present.

The error limits of the transmitted electric field amplitude measurements are estimated from previous experience with the measurement methods described above. The estimated limit is ±1 dB above 3 GHz and ±3 dB below 3 GHz (where an increased noise level was observed during calibration), which includes background "clutter" and internal errors in the measurement equipment.

5 Calculations

In order to achieve a connection to the underlying physical phenomena governing the behaviour of the photonic crystal, a number of calculations have been performed. First, the amplitude transmission coefficients have been calculated for a slab of material with the same structure as the photonic crystal. Second, the time

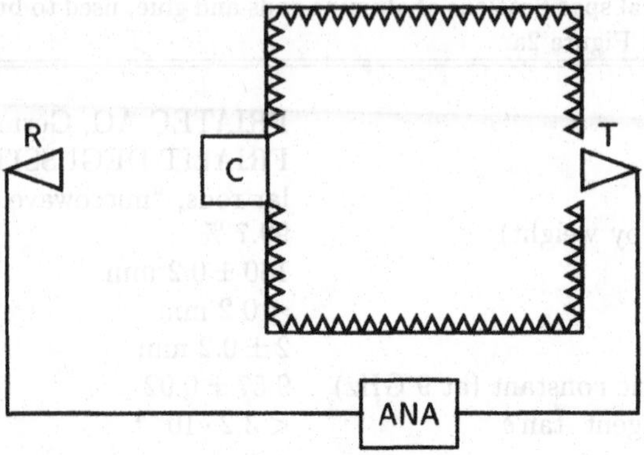

Figure 3. Schematic illustration of the experimental setup used for the measurements of electromagnetic transmission properties of the photonic crystal in the microwave region. T and R indicate transmitting and recieving antenna, respectively, C denotes the crystal, and ANA denotes the network analyzer. The dimensions of the setup is approximately 160 × 80 cm (width×height, the width measured from T to R; the shielding box is 80 × 80 cm.) Zig-zag shaped surfaces indicate microwave absorbing material.

average Poynting vector in the crystal has been calculated at different frequencies, in order to visualize the flow of electromagnetic power within the crystal. The computational models are described in turn in the following two sections.

5.1 TRANSMISSION COEFFICIENTS

The amplitude transmission coefficients were calculated using PHOTON [8], a software developed particularly for the calculation of photonic band structures, transmission- and reflection coefficients of 1D, 2D or 3D systems. The Maxwell equations are discretized in one unit cell only, using a cubic mesh. Utilizing a finite difference scheme (in the frequency domain), in combination with the Bloch theorem, the electromagnetic field is determined by solving Maxwell's equations on the mesh. This approach allows the transfer matrix of one unit cell to be determined, which has a simple relation to the transmission coefficients of a "slice" of the material, one unit cell thick. Transmission and reflection by thicker slabs (several unit cells) are obtained by repeated layer doublings, using a two-layer multiple scattering formula for each doubling. In this way, transmission and reflection can be calculated for slabs with thicknesses 1, 2, 4, 8,... etc. unit cells. For an in-depth description of the underlying theory of photonic band structures, and how it is implemented in PHOTON, please refer to the excellent presentations in References [8–10].

The calculations of the transmission coefficients presented in this study are based on the unit cell of the woodpile structure, displayed in Figure 2b. The unit cell was discretized using a cubic mesh with side length 1 mm. That is, the unit cell was divided in $10 \times 10 \times 16$ mesh cells, each $1 \times 1 \times 1$ mm^3 in size. This results in a rather coarse mesh considering the fact that the alumina rods used in the crystal have 2 mm radius. However, it turns out that qualitative features of the material is contained within this rather coarse description, as is shown in Section 6. The reason for choosing such a coarse mesh is that although the model on which PHOTON is based is generally applicable to many different types of systems, the particular implementation in PHOTON appears to suffer from numerical instabilities in some cases. (Problems of that kind are mentioned in the program documentation [8], and in the source code itself. Note also that PHOTON was originally verified for a 2D system [8], while, in the present case, the program is applied to a 3D system.) These instabilities tend to increase for finer meshes. One would normally expect an improved numerical behaviour when the mesh is refined, at least for the calculation of the electromagnetic field components. However, in the present case, the problems are probably related to the presence of evanescent states, which can cause numerical problems in the calculation of the transfer matrix. The chosen density of the mesh is a trade-off between numerical accuracy and good geometrical description. It should also be noted that the computational cost grows fast with the number of mesh cells. A computation of transmission coefficients based on a modest $10 \times 10 \times 16$ mesh takes already approximately 9 hours on a SUN Sparc Ultra-60 work station.

5.2 FIELD AND POWER DISTRIBUTIONS

In addition to transmission coefficients of slabs of the material, the electromagnetic field within the crystal has been calculated, at different frequencies. In this case the material is modelled by a piece of the crystal, with $8 \times 8 \times 4$ unit cells. The electromagnetic field within this model crystal is determined by solving Maxwell's equations using the Finite Difference method in Time Domain (FDTD) [11,12]. All FDTD calculations in the present study were performed with the TFDTD software [13]. Please refer to the references mentioned above for details on the FDTD method.

The geometrical setup of the FDTD computation is schematically displayed in Figure 4. The model crystal is enclosed in a computational volume which is discretized in space using a cubic FDTD mesh, each cube with side length $\frac{1}{3}$ mm. The computational volume extends 20 mesh cells outside the crystal in all directions. Thus, the computation includes $280 \times 280 \times 232$ ($\approx$ 18 millions) mesh cells. The structure is excited with an incident plane wave pulse in the [001] direction, with the form of a Gaussian derivative. The excitation pulse is generated on a Huygens' surface [13], which encloses the photonic crystal structure three mesh cells outside the surface of the crystal. At the boundary of the computational volume the scattered field is absorbed using absorbing boundary conditions [13].

The principle of FDTD is that the time evolution of the electromagnetic field is determined by increasing time in finite steps. For each new time step the field components are determined on a discrete spatial mesh from the field components of

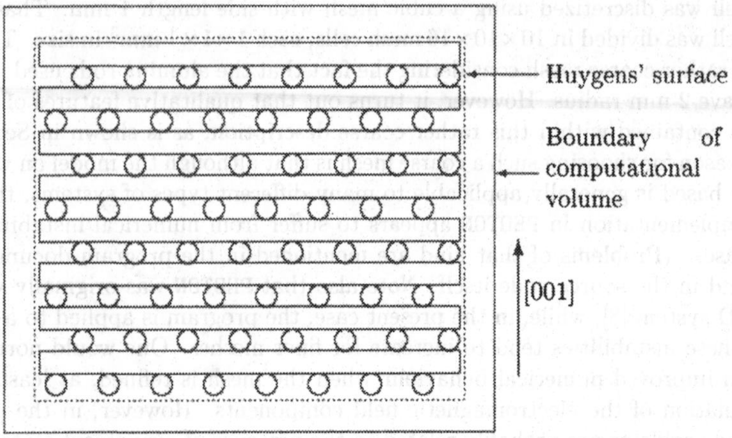

Figure 4. Geometrical setup of the FDTD calculation.

the previous time steps. When the FDTD calculation has converged, the frequency components of the field is determined by Fourier transformation of the time domain result. In this way the electromagnetic field and the time average Poynting vector $\mathbf{P} = \frac{1}{2}\mathrm{Re}[\mathbf{E} \times \mathbf{H}^*]$ was obtained on a selection of (100) plane cuts through the crystal. ($\mathbf{E}$ and $\mathbf{H}$ are the electric and magnetic field intensities, respectively, and * denotes complex conjugation.) These results are visualized and discussed in Section 6.2 for an electromagnetic pulse incident in the [001] direction.

6 Results and discussion

We now turn to a discussion of the results. Section 6.1 presents measured and calculated transmission spectra. Calculations of the time average Poynting vector within the crystal are presented in Section 6.2.

6.1 TRANSMISSION SPECTRA

Figure 5 shows the measured and calculated (using PHOTON) transmission coefficients of the microwave photonic crystal. The plots correspond to results obtained for transmission in different directions through the crystal: the [001]-direction (Figures 5a and b), which is polarization independent, and the [100]-direction (Figures 5c and d) for two perpendicular polarizations as explained in the figure caption.

Study the measurements (solid lines) in Figure 5 first. Note that the general behaviour is the same for all three cases in Figure 5: there are regions with high transmission coefficients at low and medium frequencies (up to approximately 10 GHz, and between 13–17 GHz), interrupted with band-gaps where the transmission coefficient is low. There is one broad band-gap which dominates, centered

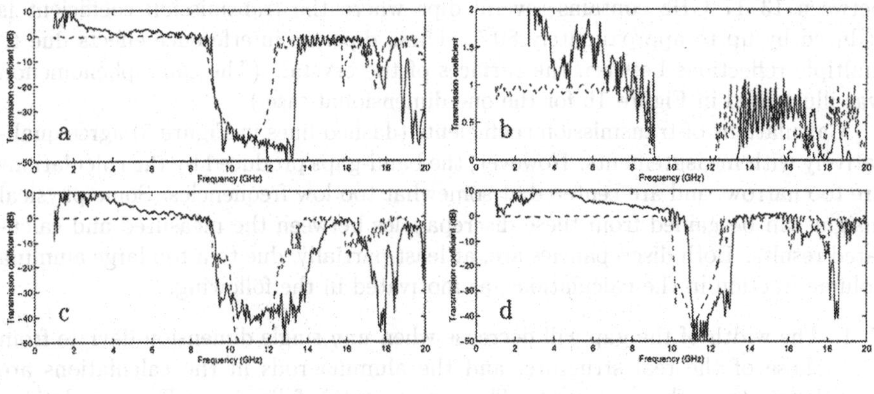

Figure 5. **Amplitude transmission coefficients of the microwave photonic crystal. Solid and dashed lines are measurements and calculations (using PHOTON), respectively. (a) Wave incident in the [001] direction (polarization independent). (b) Same as (a), but with linear scale. (c) Wave incident in the [100] direction with E-vector polarized along the rod axes (the [010] direction). (d) Wave incident in the [100] direction with E-vector polarized perpendicular to the rod axes (the [001] direction).**

at approximately 12 GHz. (This is the first band-gap of the structure, i. e., there is no other band-gap at lower frequencies.) Furthermore, at the higher frequencies above 17 GHz, there are series of dips corresponding to narrow gaps in the photonic band structure. ***The similarity of the transmission properties in all directions is the essential feature of the material under investigation.*** It has similar electromagnetic properties in all three dimensions, in contrast to, e. g., dielectric mirrors which have a photonic band-gap behaviour, but only for one particular direction of incidence.

The transmission coefficient is larger than unity at most frequencies below the band-gap, for all measurements in Figure 5. During calibration we observed noise below 3 GHz of maximum ±3 dB, which partly accounts for the large values in that region. We attribute the remaining contribution to focusing effects within the crystal. The crystal can, to some extent, be described as an effective dielectric medium at frequencies below the band-gap. The reason is that the wavelength in this region is much larger than the internal geometrical structure of the crystal. Thus, the crystal works as a dielectric lens which causes the observed focusing of the electromagnetic wave. This phenomenon is further discussed below in connection to the calculated Poynting vector in Section 6.2.

Note that the damping of the transmitted wave is very strong in the band-gap, more than −40 dB for some frequencies. This implies that the transmission coefficient spans several orders of magnitude, which makes it difficult to obtain an accurate view of the smaller variations close to unity. Therefore, as an example, Figure 5a is reproduced again in Figure 5b using a linear scale for the transmission coefficient. Note how the region with comparably high transmission coefficient between 13–17 GHz contains several dips where the transmission coefficient is reduced by up to approximately 80%. These dips are interference effects due to multiple reflections between the surfaces of the crystal. (The same phenomenon was illustrated in Figure 1b for the one-dimensional case.)

Calculations of transmission coefficients (dashed lines in Figure 5) agree qualitatively with measurements. However, the band-gaps produced by the calculations are too narrow, and are centered at somewhat too low frequencies. Some physical insight can be gained from these discrepancies between the measured and calculated results. Both discrepancies are, at least partially, due to a too large alumina volume fraction in the calculations, as motivated in the following:

1. The width of the gap will decrease when *any* single dimension deviate from those of the real structure, and the alumina rods in the calculations are larger than the real rods. The reason is the following. The calculations rely on discretization of the crystal unit cell. However, the discretization mesh used in the calculation of transmission coefficients is rather coarse, each mesh cell being $1 \times 1 \times 1$ mm^3, as explained in Section 5. As a result, the discretized rods appear very jagged, and occupy a larger volume fraction than the real, circular, rods. Since the dimensions of the rods and the unit cell are deliberately chosen to yield close to widest possible band-gap (see Section 3 and Reference [3]), the width of the gap will decrease when the volume of the rods, or any other dimension, deviate from the real structure.
2. The midgap frequency of the first band-gap will decrease, since the photonic band structure approach the band structure of homogeneous alumina as the relative volume fraction of alumina increases. This behaviour was illustrated in Figure 1b for the one dimensional case (the solid bands approach the dashed bands in Figure 1b), and is further explained in the following. Waves in a (simple) homogeneous medium are described by straight bands $\nu = \frac{c_0 k}{2\pi\sqrt{\epsilon_r}}$, where c_0 is the speed of light in vacuum, $k = \frac{2\pi}{\lambda}$ is the wave vector (λ is the wave length), and ϵ_r is the (real and frequency independent) relative dielectric constant of the medium. Taking the [001] direction of the photonic crystal (Figures 5a and b) as an example, this straight band crosses the first Brillouin zone boundary at $k_{BZ} = \frac{2\pi}{a}$ (for a body centered tetragonal, bct crystal lattice), where a is the dimension of the unit cell in the direction of propagation. In the [001] direction $a = 0.016$ m, which implies that $\nu_{BZ}^{Air} = 18.7$ GHz and $\nu_{BZ}^{Al_2O_3} = 6.1$ GHz. As expected, the first band-gap in Figures 5a and b appears between ν_{BZ}^{Air} and $\nu_{BZ}^{Al_2O_3}$. However, when the relative volume fraction of alumina increases, the frequencies at the edges of the first band-gap both decrease towards the frequency limit given by $\nu_{BZ}^{Al_2O_3}$.

At this point we would like to briefly speculate about the possibilities to obtain an omnidirectional microwave absorbing material, by modification of the material in the present study, or any other three-dimensional microwave photonic band-gap material. This is an important application, since such a material, with similar absorbing properties in all three dimensions, is desirable in the field of radar signature management. For this kind of application, the reflection properties of the material are most important, in particular low reflection coefficients and high losses within the material. It is likely that such a material would not be a photonic band material in the usual sense. The reason is that band properties appear as a result of interference, "collective" interactions within the whole material, while absorption of the wave is a local effect and would reduce this interference. Properties of photonic band-gap structures including dissipative materials have been discussed previously [14–16], focussing on dissipation as an *unwanted* feature of real photonic band structure materials. However, it would also be worthwhile to elaborate on the idea of using three-dimensional dissipative periodic structures as microwave absorbing materials. Especially since the periodicity offers an additional "construction" parameter to optimize in search for an omnidirectional microwave absorbant which is electromagnetically matched to the surrounding medium. Such materials could be investigated by extending the computational method used for transmission properties in this study.

6.2 TIME AVERAGE POYNTING VECTOR

In order to visualize the electromagnetic field penetrating the photonic crystal structure at different frequencies, the time average Poynting vector was computed on a plane cut through the center of the structure along a (100) plane, using the TFDTD software, as described in Section 5.2. The results, at frequencies in the range 5–16 GHz in steps of 1 GHz, are displayed in Figure 6. In this figure, the model photonic crystal is oriented as in Figure 4, i. e., with the (100) plane in the plane of the paper, and the [001] direction pointing upwards. The incident plane wave enters from the bottom of each picture, propagating in the [001] direction. The incident plane wave is polarized in the [100] direction (out of the plane of the paper). The frequency corresponding to each picture in Figure 6 is indicated at the bottom left.

Figure 6 displays "snapshots" of the time average Poynting vector on the (100) plane within the model crystal. The time average Poynting vector corresponds to the power per unit area transmitted in a certain direction, and is represented by a vector in three dimensions. This vector is visualized in Figure 6, in the following way. The component of the Poynting vector lying in the (100) plane is represented by arrows, and the component pointing in the [100] direction (into the paper) is represented by a gray scale. The scale used is relative to (the absolute value of) the time average Poynting vector of the incident plane wave. The number-gray scale relation is given by the color bar to the right. The number-arrow length relation is such that the distance between two neighboring grid points on the "arrow grid" represents a value of two. Note that both the arrows and the gray scale in Figure 6 have to be considered in order to obtain a correct impression of how the electromagnetic power travels through the crystal.

First of all, note that the positions of rods extending along the [100] direction in the crystal are clearly seen in most of the pictures. Rods extending in the [010] direction (along the plane of the paper) are not visible, since the plane cut is positioned right between such rod layers. One of the striking features of the series of pictures in Figures 6a–l is the strong decrease in the transmitted electromagnetic power at 9, 10, 11, and (to some extent) 12 GHz, as compared to the frequencies

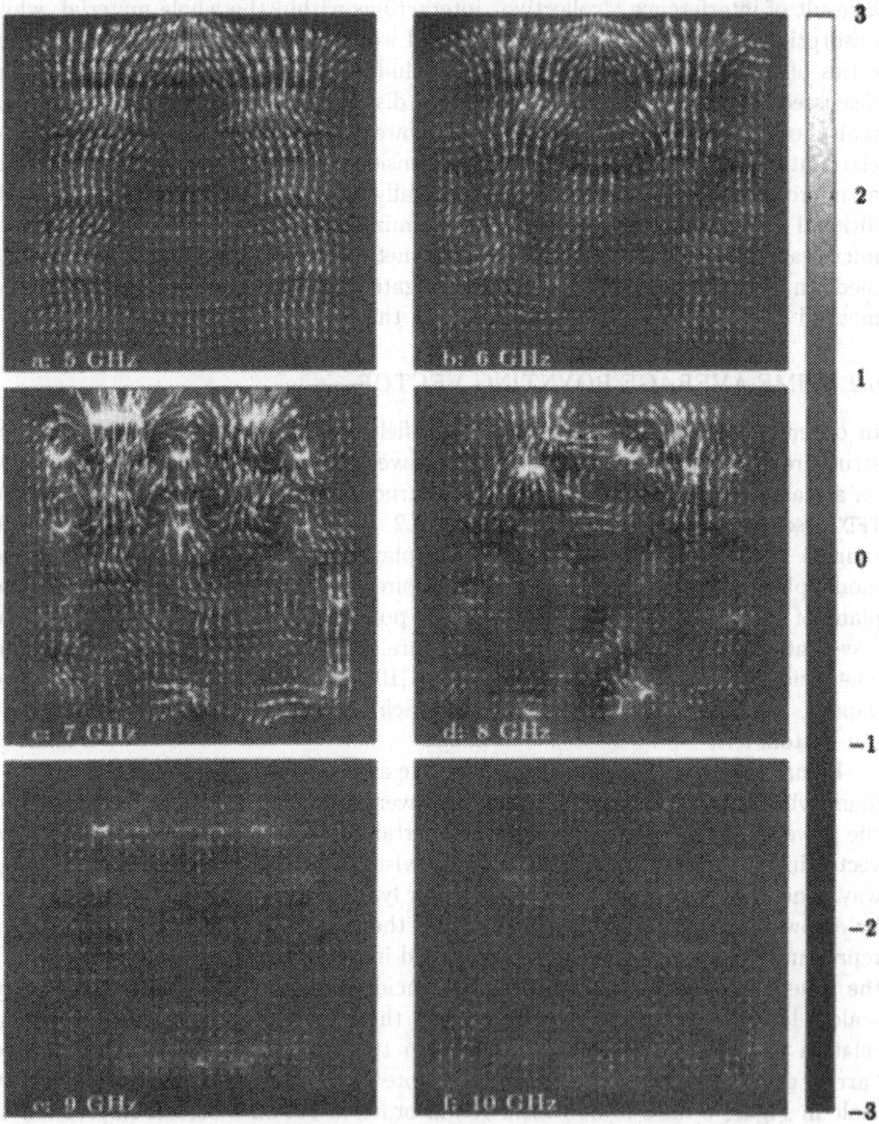

Figure 6. The time average Poynting vector at different frequencies on a (100) plane cut through the center of the model crystal as calculated with FDTD. The orientation is the same as in Figure 4. A detailed description is given in the text.

below 9 GHz and above 12 GHz. Obviously this range of reduced field intensity corresponds to the band-gap of the structure, where transmission through the structure is strongly damped. It is illuminating to compare the sequence of pictures in Figure 6 with the transmission spectrum in Figures 5a and b. No detailed

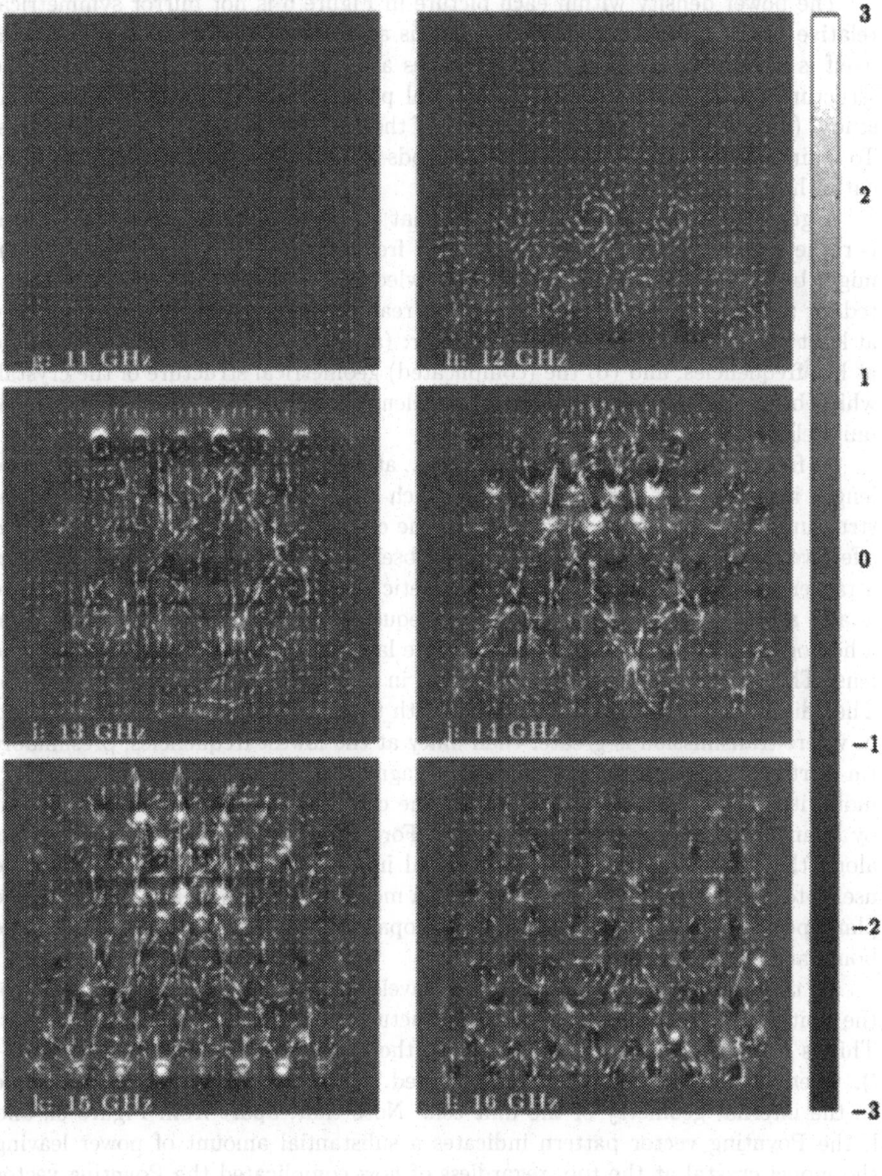

Figure 6. (Continued)

analysis of the positions of the band edges is possible from Figure 6, since the frequency step between the pictures (1 GHz) is too large, but it is clear that there is agreement between the low power density in Figures 6e–h (9–12 GHz), and the band-gap in Figures 5a and b which appears approximately between 9.1 and 13.4 GHz.

The power density within each picture in Figure 6 is not mirror symmetrical relative to the central vertical axis. This is as it should, since the model crystal itself is asymmetrical — the mirror planes are displaced from the center of the structure, in the same way as for the real photonic crystal used in the present study. (The "breaking" of the symmetry of the real crystal is for practical reasons. To maintain the mirror symmetry some rods at the boundaries would have to be cut in halves in the length direction.)

A general observation in Figure 6 is that the power flow in the model crystal is rather complicated at all but the lowest frequencies — more complicated than might be expected from the empirical knowledge that the wave is either transmitted, or almost completely reflected by the real material (see Figure 5). There are at least two explanations for this behaviour: (a) boundary effects, which dominate at low frequencies, and (b) the (complicated) geometrical structure of the crystal, which begins to be important as the wavelength approach the dimensions of the unit cell.

At frequencies below the band-gap, i. e., at 5–8 GHz (Figures 6a–d), the wavelength is larger than the unit cell, and much larger than the internal geometrical structure in the unit cell. In this region, the crystal appears to some extent as an effective dielectric medium. This can be observed particularly in Figures 6a–b as a rather smooth transport of electromagnetic power through the material. There is also a focusing effect at these lowest frequencies, which can be expected from a homogeneous piece of material with finite lateral extent, working as a dielectric lens. This was also discussed in Section 6.1 in relation to the transmission spectra. The "dielectric lens effect" is consistent with the measurements in Figures 5a and b, where transmission is greater than unity at the lowest frequencies, presumably (in part) due to focusing of the electromagnetic wave in the crystal. Furthermore, it is clear from Figures 6a–c that the calculated results are not unaffected by boundary effects of the model crystal. For example, note how the power flows along the boundaries of the model crystal in Figures 6a–c. Thus, it would be useful to perform similar calculations on a model crystal of infinite extent in the plane perpendicular to the direction of propagation, by means of, e. g., periodic boundary conditions.

As the frequency increases, and the wavelength approaches the dimensions of the unit cell, the detailed geometrical structure becomes increasingly important. This is obvious at the frequencies above the band-gap (13–16 GHz, Figure 6i–l), where the power flow has a complicated structure on the same length scale as the internal geometry of the unit cell. Note that, apart from Figure 6k and l, the Poynting vector pattern indicates a substantial amount of power leaving the model crystal at the top, regardless of how complicated the Poynting vector appears inside the material.

7 Summary and Conclusion

A microwave photonic crystal with "woodpile" layer-by-layer structure has been constructed and characterized experimentally as well as computationally. The results show that the material has prominent electromagnetic features characteristic for a ***three-dimensional photonic band structure material***, in accordance with results found in earlier studies [3–7].

Measurements of transmission and reflection coefficients show that the material has a wide, dominating band-gap between 9.1–13.4, 9.3–14.1, and 10.9–13.1 GHz, respectively, depending on the direction of propagation and polarization. In addition, there are narrow bands appearing in the frequency region between 17–20 GHz. The damping of transmitted amplitude is strong in the first band-gap, typically −40 dB, while the transmission in the bands is typically close to unity, with dips due to interference effects reaching at the most down to −8 dB. The crystal works as a dielectric lens at frequencies well below the first band-gap. The reason for this is that the material can to some extent be described as an effective dielectric medium at these wave lengths. Focusing is expected to appear in a sample with finite lateral extent consisting of such a dielectric medium.

Calculated transmission spectra agree qualitatively with measurements. However, the calculations produce spectra which are shifted towards lower frequencies and with too narrow band-gaps. These descrepancies can be understood in terms of the dimensions of the alumina rods, which are somewhat too large in the computation as compared too the rods in the real material.

It is contemplated how a three-dimensional photonic band structure material could be utilized in radar signature management applications. The band structure materials offer periodicity as an additional "construction" parameter which could be used to obtain efficient absorbing properties in three dimensions, and optimize matching of the wave impedance to the surrounding medium.

The flow of electromagnetic power represented by the time average Poynting vector, has been calculated on a plane cut, parallel to the direction of incidence, through a model "woodpile" photonic crystal. The calculations show a complicated flow of electromagnetic power within the crystal. In the frequency region 9–12 GHz the time average Poynting vector is very strongly reduced. This region corresponds nicely to the first band-gap observed in transmission and reflection spectra. Furthermore, at 5 and 6 GHz the computed time average Poynting vector indicate that focusing appear in the material, again in agreement with the measurements. The calculated power flow patterns indicate that boundary effects are important. This points at the need to further extend the geometrical size of the model crystal used in the computation, by means of, e. g., periodic boundary conditions.

8 Acknowledgments

Thanks to Lars-David Wernlund and Carl-Gustaf Ribbing for help with measurements, contacts, and discussions. Thanks to Hans Kariis for photographing the photonic crystal in Figure 2. Economical support from the innovation fund at the Defence Research Establishment is gratefully acknowledged.

References

[1] Yablonovitch, Eli, Gmitter, T. J., Meade, R. D., Rappe, A. M., Brommer, K. D., and Joannopoulos, J. D. (1987) Inhibited spontaneous emission in solid-state physics and electronics, *Phys. Rev. Lett.* **58**, 2059.

[2] John, Sajeev (1987) Strong localization of photons in certain disordered dielectric superlattices, *Phys. Rev. Lett.* **58**, 2486.

[3] Ho, K. M., Chan, C. T., Soukoulis, C. M., Biswas, R., and Sigalas, M. (1994) Photonic band gaps in three dimensions: New layer-by-layer periodic structures, *Solid State Commun.* **89**, 413.

[4] Özbay, E., Michel, E., Tuttle, G., Biswas, R., Sigalas, M., and Ho, K.-M. (1994) Micromachined millimeter-wave photonic band-gap crystals, *Appl. Phys. Lett.* **64**, 2059.

[5] Özbay, E., Abeyta, A., Tuttle, G., Tringides, M., Biswas, R., Chan, C. T., Soukoulis, C. M., and Ho, K. M. (1994) Measurement of a three-dimesional photonic band gap in a crystal structure made of dielectric rods, *Phys. Rev. B* **50**, 1945.

[6] Özbay, E. (1996) Layer-by-layer photonic crystals from microwave to far-infrared frequencies, *J. Opt. Soc. Am. B* **13**, 1945.

[7] Lin, S. Y., Fleming, J. G., Hetherington, D. L., Smith, B. K., Biswas, R., Ho, K. M., Sigalas, M. M., Zubrzycki, W., Kurtz, S. R., and Bur, Jim (1998) A three-dimensional photonic crystal operating at infrared wavelengths, *Nature* **394**, 251.

[8] Bell, P. M., Pendry, J. B., Moreno, L. Martin, and Ward, A. J. (1995) A program for calculating photonic band structures and transmission coefficients of complex structures, *Computer Phys. Commun.* **85**, 306.

[9] Pendry, J. B., and MacKinnon, A. (1992) Calculation of photon dispersion relations, *Phys. Rev. Lett.* **69**, 2772.

[10] Pendry, J. B. (1994) Photonic band structures, *J. Mod. Optics* **41**, 209.

[11] Yee, S. (1966) Numerical solution of initial boundary value problems involving Maxwell's equations in isotropic media, *IEEE Trans. Antennas Propag.* **14**, 302.

[12] Taflove, Allen (1995) *Computational Electrodynamics. The Finite-Difference Time-Domain Method*, Artech House, Boston.

[13] Martin, Torleif (1998) *Finite-difference time-domain method for electromagnetic scattering*, Licentiate Thesis LiU–TEK–LIC–1998:71, Department of Physics and Measurement Technology, Linköping University, Linköping, Sweden.

[14] Krokhin, A. A., and Halevi, P. (1996) Influence of weak dissipation on the photonic band structure of periodic composites, *Phys. Rev. B* **53**, 1205.

[15] Pendry, J. B., Holden, A. J., Stewart, W. J., and Youngs, I. (1996) Extremely low frequency plasmons in metallic mesostructures, *Phys. Rev. Lett.* **76**, 4773.

[16] Beaky, Matthew M., Burk, John B., Everitt, Henry O., Haider, Mansoor A., and Venakides, Stephanos (1999) Two-dimensional photonic crystal fabry-perot resonators with lossy dielectrics, *IEEE Trans. Microwave Theory Tech.* **47**, 2085.

ONE-DIMENSIONAL PERIODIC STRUCTURES UNDER A NEW LIGHT

D. N. CHIGRIN AND C. M. SOTOMAYOR TORRES
Institute of Materials Science and
Department of Electrical and Information Engineering
University of Wuppertal, D-42097 Wuppertal, Germany
E-mail: chigrin@uni-wuppertal.de

1. Introduction

Photonic crystals (PCs) are artificial dielectric media periodically microstructured in one, two or three spatial directions. The last decade of research efforts demonstrates that PCs are systems of strong scientific as well as industrial importance [1, 2, 3, 4]. The possibility to alter drastically the dispersion relation of photons is inherent to them. Three-dimensional (3D) PCs can exhibit energy gaps of zero density of photon states, i.e., full 3D photonic band gaps (PBGs). The control of the spontaneous emission should be possible in such periodic media [5, 6, 7]. At the same time, allowed bands of PCs display strong dispersion and spatial anisotropy, which lead to a number of new optical properties otherwise inconceivable in conventional crystals [8, 9, 10]. The strong dispersion and anisotropy of allowed bands are characteristic of any periodic structures even with a rather small refractive index contrast. This is a main difference with respect to a full PBG structure, which requires a special topology of a 3D dielectric lattice, as well as a considerably large refractive index contrast of constituents.

The subject of this paper is the simplest type of PCs, i.e., media which are periodic in one spatial direction (Fig. 1). Such structures are widely used in modern optoelectronics, ranging from Bragg mirrors for distributed-feedback lasers to narrow-band filters for dense wavelength division multiplexing systems (see e.g. [11, 12]). However, some significant improvements can be achieved if such devices are designed on the basis of photonic crystals [8, 9, 13, 14, 15, 16].

C.M. Soukoulis (ed.), Photonic Crystals and Light Localization in the 21st Century, 173–180.

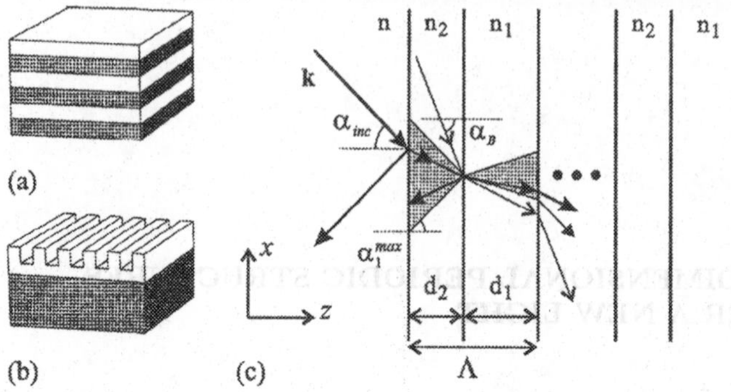

Figure 1. Two examples of 1D photonic crystals, (a) a thin-film multilayer structure and (b) a planar corrugated waveguide. (c) Schematic representation of a 1D periodic medium. The coordinate system and light rays refracting and propagating through a stack are shown. Refractive indices of alternating regions and an ambient medium are n_1, n_2 ($n_1 < n_2$) and n, respectively. Thicknesses of alternating regions are d_1 and d_2. $\Lambda = d_1 + d_2$ is a period. The full domain of incident angles α_{inc} in the range from $-\pi/2$ to $\pi/2$ is mapped onto the internal cone of half-angle $\alpha_1^{max} = \arcsin n/n_1$ (light gray area). α_B is a Brewster angle.

2. Bloch waves

Optical properties of a periodic medium are described by its permittivity, which is a periodic function of a position in space. In the case of 1D PCs the permittivity is $\varepsilon(z) = \varepsilon(z + l\Lambda)$, where z is the direction of periodicity and l is an integer. According to the Bloch-Floquet theorem (see e.g. [12]), normal electromagnetic modes of such a periodic medium are Bloch waves,

$$\mathbf{E} = \mathbf{E}_K(z) \exp(-iKz), \tag{1}$$

where $\mathbf{E}_K(z) = \mathbf{E}_K(z+l\Lambda)$ is a periodic function of period Λ. The subscript K is the Bloch wave number and indicates that the function $\mathbf{E}_K(z)$ depends on K. The dispersion relation of Bloch waves, relating the frequency of the wave, ω, with the wave vector, $\mathbf{k}$, can be derived analytically in the case of 1D PCs [12, 17]:

$$f(\omega, \mathbf{k}) = \cos(K\Lambda) - \left(\frac{1}{2}(A + D)\right) = 0. \tag{2}$$

A particular form of the functions $A(\omega, \mathbf{k}_\perp)$ and $D(\omega, \mathbf{k}_\perp)$ may be found elsewhere [12, 17], here $\mathbf{k}_\perp$ is the tangential component of the Bloch wave vector.

Properties of Bloch waves can differ drastically from those of plane waves in an homogeneous isotropic medium. A 3D photonic band structures of a homogeneous medium and a 1D PC are depicted in the figure 2.

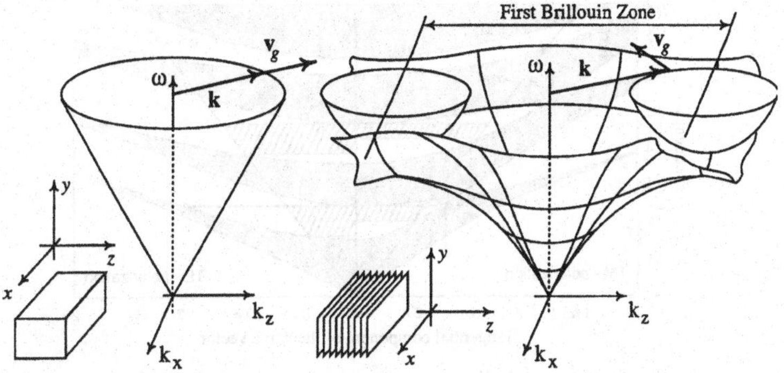

(a) Homogeneous medium (b) Photonic crystal

Figure 2. 3D photonic band structures of (a) an isotropic homogeneous nondispersive medium and (b) a 1D PC. Insets show the orientation of the media. Only 2D slices of the wave vector space are presented. The PC band structure (b) is presented only for one basic polarization.

Comparing them, the main differences can be summarized as follows [see Fig. 2(b)]: *(i) polarization states are not degenerate in a PC; (ii) photonic band gaps are developed; (iii) the energy flow does not follow the wave vector direction any more* [12].

3. Omnidirectional reflection

Probably one of the most widespread application of 1D periodic media is a Bragg mirror (Fig. 1). Mirrors come in two basic varieties: a metallic mirror with a dissipative losses of few-percent, being in fact an omnidirectional reflector and a dielectric Bragg mirror. A dielectric Bragg mirror can be made nearly loss-less, but it is highly reflecting only within a limited angular range. A structure, combining the properties of both mirror types, i.e., being omnidirectional and loss-less, is of strong interest as it is likely to find many applications in optoelectronics and all-optical systems.

Until recently, the possibility to design such a "perfect mirror" was mainly associated with 3D PCs having a full PBG. Indeed, several research groups have reported that a simple-to-fabricate Bragg mirror suffices to design a low-loss omnidirectional reflector [13, 14, 15, 16]. This demonstration can lead to various high performance optoelectronic devices employed at any desirable wavelength. Efficient antenna substrates, energy saving filters, enclosures for microcavities [18] and waveguides [19] are a few potential applications.

The properties of Bloch waves inside a Bragg mirror are governed by the dispersion relation (2). Due to the planar geometry of the problem, the

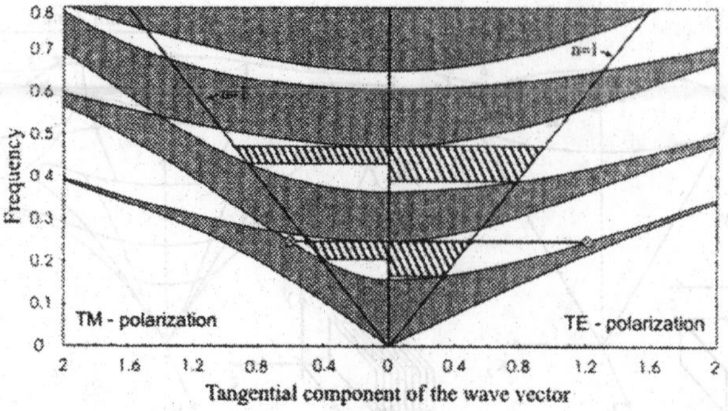

Figure 3. Projected band structure of a typical 1D PC for TE (right panel) and TM (left panel) polarizations. The frequency and the tangential component of the wave vector are defined to be normalized as $\omega\Lambda/2\pi c$ and $|\mathbf{k}_\perp|\Lambda/\pi$, respectively. The shaded areas correspond to omnidirectional reflection bands. The solid lines are the ambient-medium light-lines.

separation of the electromagnetic field into TE (transverse electric) and TM (transverse magnetic) polarization states is possible.

A projected band structure of an infinite periodic system of layers is depicted in the figure 3. The refractive indices, $n_1 = 1.4$ and $n_2 = 3.4$, are chosen close to those of SiO_2 and Si in the near IR region. Thicknesses of the layers are equal ($d_1 = d_2$). An infinite periodic structure can support both propagating and evanescent Bloch waves. In figure 3, gray areas correspond to the propagating states, whereas white areas contain the evanescent states only and are referred to as photonic band gaps.

When the frequency and the wave vector of a wave, impinging externally at an angle, α_{inc}, from a homogeneous medium of refractive index, n, onto a 1D PC [Fig. 1(c)], lies within the band gaps, an incident wave undergoes strong reflection. Pronounced high reflection bands depend strongly on frequency and angle of incidence. These can be easily understood from figure 3. Photonic band gaps *(i) rapidly move to higher frequencies with increasing incident angle, denoted by the increase of the tangential component of the wave vector* and *(ii) the TM band gaps tends to zero when approaching the Brewster light-line*, where $\omega = c|\mathbf{k}_\perp|/n_1 \sin\alpha_B$ (Fig. 3), $\alpha_B = \arctan n_2/n_1$ is the Brewster angle. These properties of the band structure restrict the angular aperture of a polarization insensitive range of high reflectance.

In essence, omni-directional reflectance can be achieved due to the limitation of the number of modes that can be excited by externally incident waves inside the Bragg mirror. Light coming from the low-index ambient medium ($n < n_1, n_2$) is funneled into the internal cone narrowed by Snell's

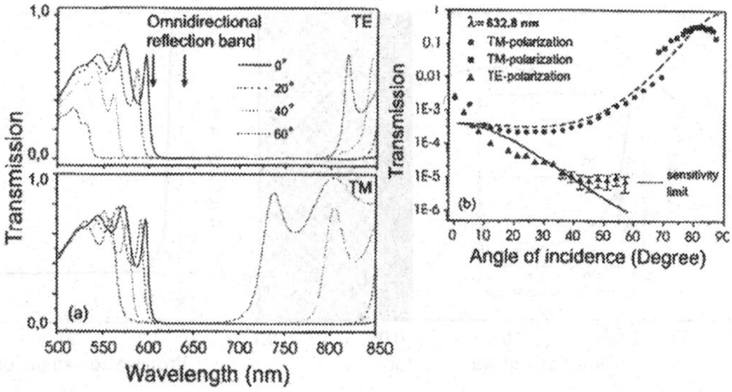

Figure 4. **(a) Transmission spectra taken from the $Na_3AlF_6/ZnSe$ 19-layers structure at different incident angles. (b) Transmission spectra of HeNe-laser light on incident angle taken from the same sample. Curves are theoretically calculated spectra.**

law [Fig. 1(c)]. In fact, *(i) a sufficiently large index contrast of PC media with respect to an ambient medium ensures that light coming from the outside will never go below the Brewster's angle inside the crystal* [Fig. 1(c)] and *(ii) a sufficiently large refractive index contrast of PC media themselves can keep the band gaps open up to the grazing angles* [13, 14, 15, 16].

A reduced region of k-space, where propagating Bloch modes of the photonic crystals PC can be excited by externally incident wave, lies above the light-line (Fig. 3), which is a 2D projection of the band structure of an ambient medium. For example, in the case of the Si/SiO_2 structure in air the first two band gaps are open for all external angles of incidence (shaded areas in figure 3). No propagating mode are allowed in the stack for any propagating mode in the ambient medium for either polarizations. This is how, total omnidirectional reflection arises.

The demonstration of an omnidirectional Bragg mirror at optical [14, 16] and IR [13] wavelengths has been reported. For optical regime, 19 layers (90 nm thick) of Na_3AlF_6 (cryolite) and *ZnSe* was fabricated by mean of standard technique [14, 16]. The transmission spectra of light coming at normal and oblique (20°, 40°, 60°) incidence are shown in figure 4(a). At $\lambda = 604.3 - 638.4nm$, a high reflectivity was observed at all incident angles for both fundamental polarizations. In figure 4(b), a transmission of HeNe-laser light ($\lambda = 632.8nm$) on incident angle is shown. Both theoretical curves and experimental data confirm omnidirectional character of high reflection band. Such a Bragg mirror can be treated as an omnidirectional high reflector [14, 16].

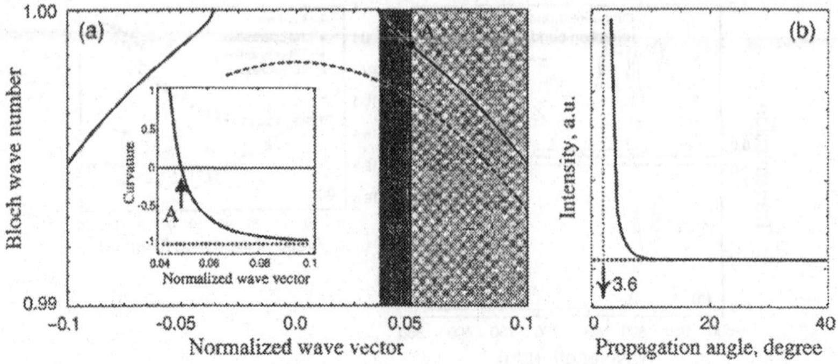

Figure 5. (a) $K - k_x$ intersection of isofrequency surfaces of a homogeneous isotropic (dashed curve) and a slightly modulated periodic (solid curve) media. Inset shows a local curvature of the isofrequency contours. The arrow marks a wave vector for which the curvature is vanishing. Concave and convex region of isofrequency contours are marked in different shades. Vertical and horizontal axes are not to scale. (b) Angular intensity distributions. Solid curve, corresponding to a PC, shows an intense peake in the direction associated to the inflection point. The dashed curve is an isotropic intensity distribution corresponding to a homogeneous medium. See text further explanations.

4. Ultra-refraction phenomena

The anisotropy of 1D periodic media in the long-wavelength regime ($\lambda \gg \Lambda$) is a well known phenomenon [12]. In this limit, isofrequency surfaces of electromagnetic modes in a PC are similar to the isofrequency surfaces of a negative uniaxial crystal. At shorter wavelengths, the anisotropy becomes stronger and isofrequency surfaces become distorted, especially near the boundaries of the Brillouin zone [Fig. 2(b)]. The energy flow inside a PC is generally not along the direction of the wave vector. The energy propagates along the direction of the group velocity ($\mathbf{v}_g = \nabla_k \omega(\mathbf{k})$), i.e., along the outward normal to the isofrequency surface. As a consequence, an isotropic distribution of wave vectors emanating from an isotropic photon source inside the crystal does not imply an isotropic distribution of energy flux.

We plot isofrequency contours of a homogeneous isotropic and a slightly modulated periodic multilayer media in figure 5(a). The refractive index of the homogeneous medium is $n = 3.4$ and a perturbation leads to a structure with indices $n_1 = 3.4$ and $n_2 = 3.41$. We further assume that layers thicknesses are equal ($d_1 = d_2$). Isofrequency contours are presented for the normalized frequency $\omega = 0.146$, which is within the first band gap of the periodic medium. Near the Brillouin zone boundary the isofrequency contour of a PC is strongly non-circular. It consists of a concave and a convex regions with positive and negative Gaussian curvatures, respectively. The curvature of a PC's isofrequency contour is depicted in the inset to figure 5(a). In contrast to the constant curvature of a homogeneous medium (dashed line in the inset) the curvature of a PC displays a strong variation. There is an inflection point where the curvature vanishes [point A in Fig. 5(a)].

In geometrical optics approximation, a vanishing curvature of the isofrequency surface leads to an infinite energy flux from a point source along the corresponding group velocity direction [20]. It assumes that the wavelength is much smaller than the source and detector sizes, and certainly much smaller than the distance between the source and the detector. Because the energy flux is inversely proportional to the curvature of the isofrequency surfaces [20], the points with zero curvature [Fig. 5(a)] will lead to sharp singularities in the energy flux, *i.e., photon-focusing caustics.* Due to the rotation invariance of a PC, the Gaussian curvature of the isofrequency surface vanishes along the circle produced by the zero curvature point A [Fig. 5(a)]. If an isotropic light source is places inside a thick slab of 1D periodic medium, sharply defined circular peaks in the intensity distribution should be detected outside the sample.

To substantiate this prediction we present a Monte Carlo simulation of an angular intensity distribution which is due to an isotropic point source inside the 1D photonic crystal. Our Monte Carlo intensity diagram construction process consists in generating a uniform random distribution of wave vectors **k** and solving equations (2) to obtain group velocities of the electromagnetic modes belonging to each value of **k**. Then the group velocity vectors are collected in all directions to form an angular plot of intensity.

The angular distribution depicted in figure 5(b) was generated with a large number (10^6) of initial wave vectors **k** and a "source" situated inside the PC. The intensity was collected by a "detector" placed on the surface of the crystal along one of the layers boundary. An intense peak appears near the direction corresponding to the inflection point with zero curvature [point A in Fig. 5(a)]. This direction corresponds to 3.6° out of the normal to the crystal boundary. Figure 5(b) shows how the light intensity diminishes rapidly with increasing angular deviation from that direction.

5. Conclusion

In conclusion, we have presented a brief review of the properties of 1D periodic structures. We have discussed an improvement of a Bragg mirror design. We have explained how to make a Bragg mirror omnidirectional. Finally we have predicted the formation of photon-focusing caustics in 1D photonic crystals. Being the simplest type of photonic crystals, thin-film interference filters, should be good laboratory structures to study photonic band gap related phenomena as well as good candidates for improvements and design of optoelectronic devices.

Acknowledgments This work was partially supported by the EU-IST project PHOBOS IST-1999-19009.

References

1. J. D. Joannopoulos, R. D. Meade, and J. N. Winn, *Photonic crystals: molding the flow of light* (Princeton University Press, Princeton NJ, 1995).
2. *Confined electron and Photon: New physics and Applications*, E. Burstein and C. Weisbuch, eds., (Plenum Press, New York, 1995).
3. *Photonic Band Gap Materials*, C. Soukoulis, ed., (Kluwer Academic, Dordrecht, 1996).
4. *Special issue on Electromagnetic crystal structures, design, synthesis, and applications*, A. Scherer, T. Doll, E. Yablonovitch, H. Everitt, and J. Higgins, eds., J. Lightwave Tech. **17,** 1928–2207 (1999).
5. V. Bykov, "Spontaneous emission in a periodic structure," Soviet Physics - JETP **35,** 269–273 (1972).
6. E. Yablonovitch, "Inhibited spontaneous emission in solid-state physics and electronics," Phys. Rev. Lett. **58,** 2059 (1987).
7. S. John, "Strong localization of photons in certain disordered dielectric superlattices," Phys. Rev. Lett. **58,** 2486–2489 (1987).
8. P. Russell, "Optics of Floquet-Block waves in dielectric gratings," Appl. Phys. B: Photophysics & Laser Chemistry **B39**, 231–246 (1986).
9. R. Zengerle, "Light propagation in singly and doubly periodic planar waveguides," J. Mod. Optics **34**, 1589–1617 (1987).
10. H. Kosaka, T. Kawashima, A. Tomita, M. Notomi, T. Tamamura, T. Sato, and S. Kawakami, "Superprism phenomena in photonic crystals: toward microscale lightwave circuits," J. Lightwave Tech. **17,** 2032–2038 (1999).
11. H. Macleod, *Thin-Film Optical Filters* (Adam Hilger, Bristol, 1986).
12. P. Yeh, *Optical Waves in Layered Media* (John Wiley and Sons, New York, 1988).
13. Y. Fink, J. N. Winn, S. Fan, C. Chen, J. Michel, J. D. Joannopoulos, and E. L. Thomas, "A dielectric omnidirectional reflector," Science **282,** 1679 (1998).
14. D. N. Chigrin, A. V. Lavrinenko, D. A. Yarotsky, and S. V. Gaponenko, "Observation of total omnidirectional reflection from a one-dimensional dielectric lattice," Appl. Phys. A: Materials Science and Processing **68,** 25–28 (1999).
15. P. S. J. Russell, S. Tredwell, and P. J. Roberts, "Full photonic bandgaps and spontaneous emission control in 1D multilayer dielectric structures," Opt. Commun. **160,** 66–71 (1999).
16. D. N. Chigrin, A. V. Lavrinenko, D. A. Yarotsky, and S. V. Gaponenko, "All-dielectric one-dimensional periodic structures for total omnidirectional reflection and partial spontaneous emission contro," J. Lightwave Tech. **17,** 2018–2024 (1999).
17. P. Russell, T. Birks, and F. Lloyd-Lucas, "Photonic Bloch waves and photonic band gaps," in Ref. [2], pp. 585–633.
18. J. A. E. Wasey and W. L. Barnes, "Efficiency of spontaneous emission from planar microcavities," J. Mod. Optics **47,** 725–741 (2000).
19. Y. Fink, D. J. Ripin, S. Fan, C. Chen, J. D. Joannopoulos, and E. L. Thomas, "Guiding optical light in air using an all-dielectric structure," J. Lightwave Tech. **17,** 2039–2041 (1999).
20. J. Wolfe, *Imaging Phonons: Acoustic Wave Propagation in Solid* (Cambridge University Press, Cambridge, 1998).

DEFECT MODES IN QUASI-ONE-DIMENSIONAL PHOTONIC WAVEGUIDES - APPLICATION TO THE RESONANT TUNNELING BETWEEN TWO CONTINUA

J. O. VASSEUR [1], M. PECQUERY [1], B. DJAFARI-ROUHANI [1], L. DOBRZYNSKI [1], A. AKJOUJ [1], J. ZEMMOURI [2], N. FETTOUHI [2], and E. H. EL BOUDOUTI [3]

[1] *Laboratoire de Dynamique et Structures des Matériaux Moléculaires, UPRESA CNRS 8024, UFR de Physique, Université de Lille I, 59655 Villeneuve d'Ascq Cédex, France*

[2] *Laboratoire de Physique des Lasers, Atomes et Molécules, Centre d'Etudes et de Recherches Lasers et Applications, UMR CNRS 8523, Université de Lille I, 59655 Villeneuve d'Ascq Cédex, France*

[3] *Laboratoire de Dynamique et d'Optique des Matériaux Département de Physique, Faculté des Sciences, Université Mohammed I 60000 Oujda, Morocco*

1. Introduction

For the last few years, we were studying quasi-one-dimensional photonic materials [1,2]. These materials are composed of an infinite one-dimensional waveguide (*the backbone*) along which stars of N' finite monomode side branches (or stubs) are grafted at N equidistant sites, N and N' being integers (see Fig. 1). This *star waveguide* is described by two structural and two compositional parameters, namely the periodicity d_1, the length d_2 of each stub, and the relative dielectric permittivity ε_i of each medium with i=1 for the backbone and i=2 for the side branches. We developed a theoretical model in order to compute the dispersion relation for an infinite number of sites ($N \rightarrow \infty$) and the transmission coefficient through the waveguide when the side branches are grafted at a finite number of nodes. In this model, electromagnetic waves only propagate in the interior of the waveguides. Two boundary conditions at the free end of the side branches were considered, namely the vanishing of either the electric field (E=0) or the magnetic field (H=0). With these conditions, the impedance at the extremity of the side branches becomes, respectively, Z=0 and $Z=\infty$. We have shown that the band structure of star waveguides may exhibit very narrow pass bands separated by large forbidden bands. These gaps originate both from the periodicity of the system and the resonance states of the grafted branches which play the role of resonators. Wide gaps/narrow bands can be obtained by an

C.M. Soukoulis (ed.), Photonic Crystals and Light Localization in the 21st Century, 181–189.

appropriate choice of the parameters, in particular the ratio between the two characteristic lengths d_1 and d_2. Increasing the number N' of side branches grafted on each node, results in larger forbidden bands. The choice of the boundary condition at the free end of the resonators plays also an important role and the condition E=0 is more favourable to the opening of large gaps. Unlike in the usual photonic crystals where the contrast in dielectric properties between the constituent materials is a critical parameter in determining the existence of gaps, relatively wide gaps exist for homogeneous star waveguides where the branches and the backbone are constituted of the same material. One would also emphasize that the width of the forbidden bands of star waveguides is, in general, much larger than the one observed in usual superlattices made of a quarter-wave stack of alternating indices of refraction [3,4].

In a recent paper [5], we have reported on the existence of localized modes inside gaps when defective branches of different length are inserted at one node of the star waveguide. Localized states appear as very narrow peaks in the transmission spectrum of comb-like waveguides composed of a finite number of grafted branches. The amplitude as well as the quality factor of these peaks are very sensitive to the length, the number, and the location of the defective branches. More specifically, larger amplitudes were obtained for defects grafted at the middle of the star waveguide.

In this paper, we consider the case of several defects grafted periodically at different nodes of the backbone. We study the effect of the interaction between these defects on the transmission of electromagnetic waves through defective star waveguides. We show that the periodic location of the defects leads to a splitting of the pass bands in several pass bands of lower width separated by gaps. We present next an application of localized modes i.e., the resonant tunneling between two monomode electromagnetic waveguides coupled by defective star waveguides. Most of the theoretical predictions are also compared with experimental results where the monomode waveguides are usual coaxial cables. Considering a complex dielectric permittivity in the calculation in order to simulate the attenuation in the coaxial cables, a good agreement between experiment and theory is observed in the hyper-frequency range.

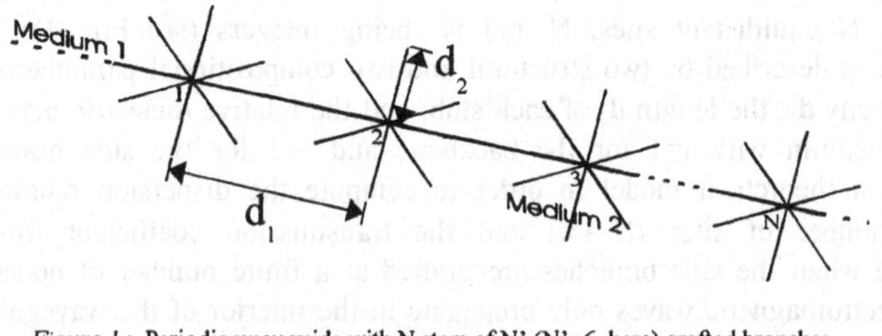

Figure 1 : Periodic waveguide with N stars of N' (N'=6, here) grafted branches.

2. Localized states in defective star waveguides

In this section, we focus on localized states associated with defective resonators grafted periodically in the star waveguide depicted in Fig. 1. The defect branches are introduced in the system by removing on each site, N'_2 resonators and replacing them by N'_3 branches of length d_3 ($\neq d_2$). We restrict our study to structures where the backbone, the side branches, and the defective resonators are constituted of the same material ($\varepsilon_1=\varepsilon_2=\varepsilon_3$ where ε_3 is the relative dielectric permittivity of the defect branches).

The analytic expressions of the dispersion relation ($N\rightarrow\infty$) for the non-defective star waveguide were obtained [2], with the help of the interface response theory [1], as

$$\cos(kd_1) = C_1 + \frac{N'}{2}\frac{F_2}{F_1}\frac{S_1 C_2}{S_2} \tag{1}$$

or

$$\cos(kd_1) = C_1 + \frac{N'}{2}\frac{F_2}{F_1}\frac{S_1 S_2}{C_2}, \tag{2}$$

where k is the modulus of the one-dimensional wave vector for propagation of electromagnetic waves in the star waveguide. In Eqs. (1) and (2), the quantities C_i, S_i and F_i (i=1,2) are defined as $C_i = \cosh(\alpha_i d_i)$, $S_i = \sinh(\alpha_i d_i)$ and $F_i = \alpha_i = j\omega\sqrt{\varepsilon_i}/c$, where ω is the wave circular frequency, c the speed of light in vacuum, and $j=\sqrt{-1}$. The dispersion relation (1) (resp. (2)) has been written with the boundary condition E=0 (resp H=0) at the free end of the resonators. The presence of defects placed periodically with the periodicity $D=(M-1)d_1$, M being integer, in the star waveguide leads to the following dispersion relation

$$\cos[(M-1)kd_1] = -\frac{C_1\left(t - t^{2M-1}\right) + t^{2M} - 1 + \chi t\left(1 - t^{2M-2}\right)}{t^{M-1} - t^{M+1}} \tag{3}$$

with

$$\chi = \frac{S_1}{F_1}\left[\left(N' - \frac{N'_2}{2}\right)\frac{F_2 C_2}{S_2} - \frac{N'_3}{2}\frac{F_3 C_3}{S_3}\right] \tag{4}$$

when the electric field vanishes at the free end of the resonators, and

$$\chi = \frac{S_1}{F_1}\left[\left(N' - \frac{N'_2}{2}\right)\frac{F_2 S_2}{C_2} - \frac{N'_3}{2}\frac{F_3 S_3}{C_3}\right] \tag{5}$$

when the boundary condition H=0 has been taken into account. In Eq. (3), $t = \exp(jkd_1)$ where k is given by either Eqs. (1) or (2). In Eqs. (4) and (5), the symbols F_3, C_3, and S_3 associated with the defects have the same meaning as above. From these dispersion relations, the interface response theory allows to determine analytically the transmission coefficient through a one-dimensional waveguide with a finite number N of sites. These analytical expressions will be published elsewhere.

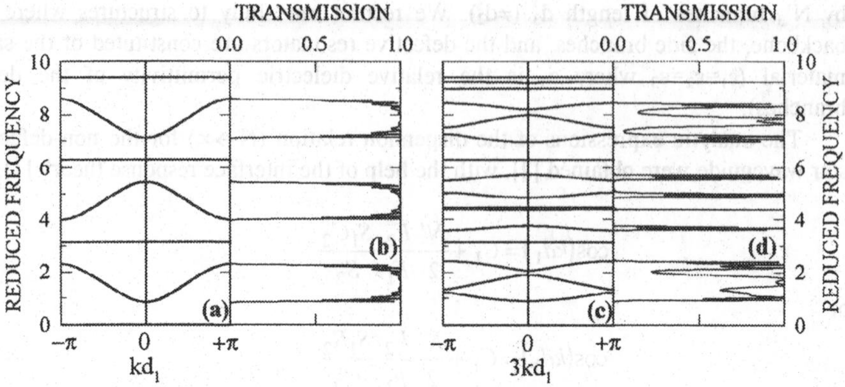

Figure 2: Left panel: (a) Dispersion curves (reduced frequency $\Omega = \omega d_1 \sqrt{\varepsilon_1} / c$ versus the dimensionless wave vector kd_1) for the one-dimensional structure depicted in Fig. 1, with N'=1, $N \to \infty$ and the boundary condition E=0. (b) Transmission coefficient through the same structure with the side branches grafted at N=11 nodes. Right panel: Same as in left panel, but with defect resonators of length $d_3=0.7d_2$ grafted with periodicity $D=3d_1$.

2.1. NUMERICAL RESULTS

In the left panel of Fig. 2, we present the band structure and the transmission coefficient of an infinite non-defective star waveguide with the same characteristic lengths, $d_1=d_2$, one resonator grafted on each node and the boundary condition E=0 at the free ends of the stubs. One notes the presence of pass bands separated by large gaps. The flat bands correspond to non-propagating modes whose eigenfunctions vanish at each node of the star waveguide and do not contribute to the transmission as shown on Fig. 2(b) [5]. The transmission was calculated for N=11 sites. In the right panel of Fig. 2, some resonators have been replaced by side branches of length $d_3=0.7d_2$, the separation between two defects being $D=3d_1$ (M=4, $N'=N'_2=N'_3=1$ in Eq. (3)). One observes in Fig. 2(c), that the periodic location of the defects induces the splitting of the pass-bands of the non-defective structure and their folding into a smaller Brillouin zone. Localized states associated with the presence of defects occur in the stop bands of the quasi-one-dimensional waveguide. Fig. 2(d) shows the transmission coefficient through the same defective star waveguide but with N=11 sites and defects located on nodes N=3, 6, and 9. The symmetrical location of the defects respective to the middle of the structure gives the larger amplitude of the peaks associated with localized states [5]. With another defect length, the position of these peaks should be shifted in frequency. A more complete study shows also that the frequency of the defect modes and the behaviour of the transmission are strongly influenced by the periodicity D.

2.2. EXPERIMENTAL RESULTS

In order to check the validity of the above theoretical predictions in a frequency range up to 500 MHz, we have performed experiments where both the one-dimensional waveguide and the side branches are standard 50Ω coaxial cables constituted of the same material. The cables were assembled together with metallic T connectors. The transmission measurements were realized by using a tracking generator coupled to a spectrum analyzer. The cross section of the cables is negligible compared to their length and the propagating modes inside the coaxial cables are T.E.M. waves. This satisfies the assumption of monomode propagation. The electromagnetic impedance at the free ends of the resonators may be adapted in order to realize the boundary condition E=0 or H=0. We have then compared the experimental measurements with the theoretical predictions. Attenuation in the coaxial cables was simulated in the computations by a complex relative dielectric permittivity, $\varepsilon = \varepsilon' - j\varepsilon''$. The imaginary part of ε was obtained from the attenuation specification data supplied by the manufacturer of the coaxial cables as a function of frequency f i.e., $\varepsilon'' = 23.41 f^{-0.47}$ with f in units of Hz.

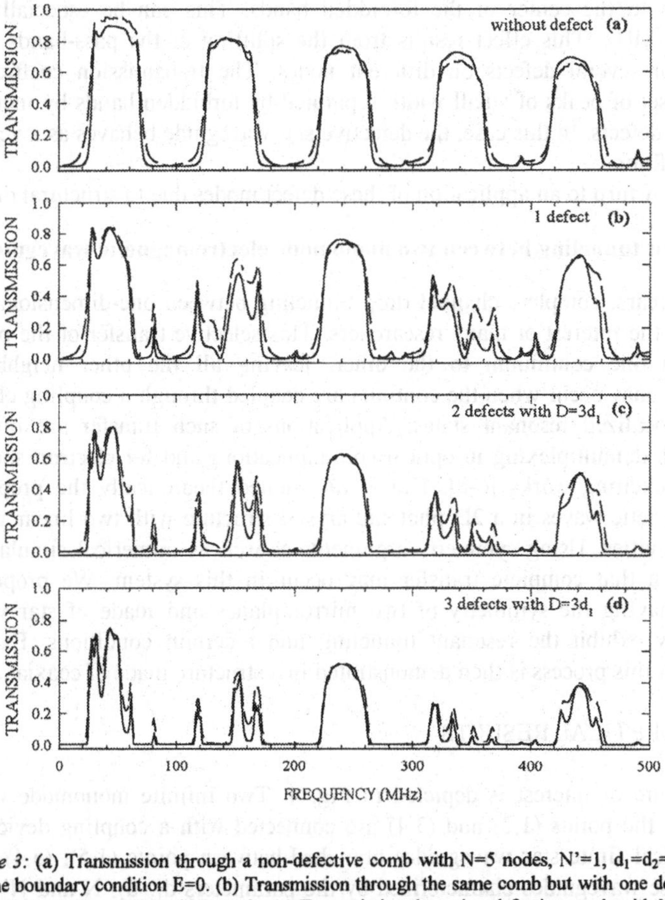

Figure 3: (a) Transmission through a non-defective comb with N=5 nodes, N'=1, $d_1=d_2=1$m, and the boundary condition E=0. (b) Transmission through the same comb but with one defect of length $d_3=1.45$m on the middle node. (c) Transmission through a defective comb with N=8, N'=1 and one defect of length $d_3=1.45$m on nodes N=3 and N=6. (d) Transmission through a defective comb with N=11, N'=1 and one defect of length $d_3=1.45$m on nodes N=3, N=6 and N=9. Solid line: Theoretical result and dashed line: experimental measurement.

The top panel of Fig. 3 presents the transmission coefficient through a non-defective waveguide with N=5 sites, N'=1 resonator on each site and $d_1=d_2=1m$. The solid curve corresponds to the computed coefficient and the dashed line represents the measured transmission. One observes a good agreement between these results. The variations of the transmission coefficient through the same structure but with one defect side branch of length $d_3=1.45m$ grafted on the middle node are shown on Fig. 3(b). One notes the presence of two localized modes of strong amplitude in the first gap around 100 MHz. These modes are well detached from the edges of the first and second pass bands. At higher frequencies, the amplitude of the localized modes is very much lower because of the stronger attenuation. The effect of the interaction between two defects is illustrated in Fig. 3(c). New localized modes appear especially in the closed vicinity of the first pass-band. The fourth band transforms into 4 independent peaks of lower amplitude. Finally, with 3 identical defects in the waveguide (see bottom panel of Fig. 3), some of the new localized modes shift from the edge of the pass bands to the center of the forbidden bands. This can be especially observed around 60 MHz. This effect results from the splitting of the pass-bands due to the presence of several defects on different nodes. The transmission coefficient could become a set of peaks of small width separated by forbidden bands by increasing the number of defects. In this case, the defective star waveguide behaves as a very efficient frequency filter.

We now turn to an application of these defect modes due to structural disorder.

3. Resonant tunneling between two monomode electromagnetic waveguides

In recent years, complete channel drop tunneling between one-dimensional continua has raised the interest of many researchers. This selective transfer of the propagating state from one continuum to the other, leaving all the other neighbour states unaffected, may occur when the continua are coupled through a coupling element that supports localized resonant states. Applications of such transfer are important in wavelength demultiplexing in optical communications and for electron spectroscopy. In recent exciting works [6-8], Fan *et al.* studied theoretically the propagation of electromagnetic waves in a 2D photonic crystal structure with two linear waveguides and two cavities. Using symmetry arguments as well as numerical simulations, they have shown that complete transfer may occur in this system. We propose here a structure having the symmetry of two mirror planes and made of star waveguides which may exhibit the resonant tunneling under certain conditions. Experimental evidence of this process is then demonstrated in a structure made of coaxial cables.

3.1. THEORETICAL RESULTS

The structure of interest is depicted in Fig. 4. Two infinite monomode waveguides passing by the points (1,2) and (3,4) are connected with a coupling device made of four identical finite star waveguides branched between points (1,5), (5,4), (2,6) and (6,3). These waveguides characterized by the parameters d_1, d_2, N and N' (N=5 and N'=2 in Fig. 4) are similar to those presented previously and present large forbidden bands. The distance d_0 between points 1 and 2 is the same as that between points 3 and

4. One wire of length $2d_3$ is fixed between points 5 and 6 with a side branch of length d_4 in its middle.

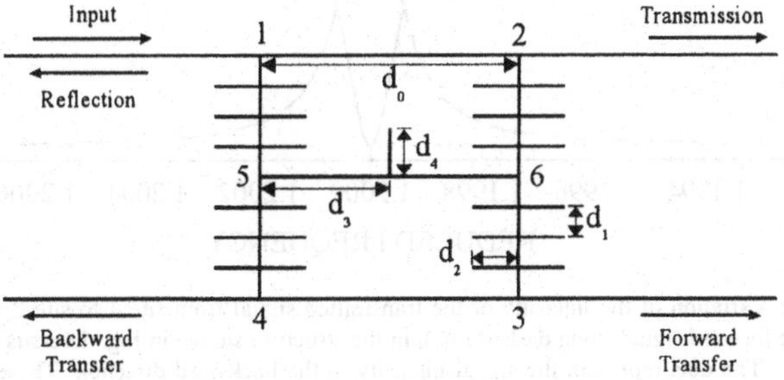

Figure 4: The structure under consideration.

The resonant tunneling between the two infinite monomode wires occurs at a specific pulsation, ω_0, if an input signal is completely transferred from point 1 to point 3 while the neighboring states continue to travel along the upper guide. Once the pulsation ω_0, the length d_1 and the integers N and N' are chosen, the other lengths d_2, d_0, d_3, and d_4 involved in the model can be calculated analytically in order to obtain this complete transfer. The relations giving strictly these lengths are demonstrated to be (see Ref. [9] for details)

$$\tan(\alpha_0 d_2) = N'\sin(\alpha_0 d_1)/\left[\left[\sin(Nkd_1)/\sin((N-1)kd_1)\right] - \cos(\alpha_0 d_1)\right], \tag{6}$$

$$\tan(\alpha_0 d_0 / 2) = 1, \tag{7}$$

$$\tan(\alpha_0 d_3) = \left[\sin(\alpha_0 d_1)\sin((N-1)kd_1)/\sin(kd_1)\right]^2, \tag{8}$$

and

$$\tan(\alpha_0 d_4) = -\tan(2\alpha_0 d_3)/2, \tag{9}$$

where $\alpha_0 = \omega_0\sqrt{\varepsilon}/c$ and k is defined by either Eq. (1) or (2). For these lengths, two resonant states of the system originating from two neighbouring localized states of the coupling device, become to merge at the pulsation ω_0. This leads to a peak of selective transmission whose width is related to the separation between the two localized states. We give in Fig. 5 the variations of the different transmission coefficients versus the reduced frequency, $\Omega = \omega\sqrt{\varepsilon}d_1/c$. We observe both the dip (solid line) in the direct transmission and the drop in the forward signal (long dashed line). The backward transfer signal represented by the dotted line, as well as the reflected signal (not shown) are almost completely absent over the entire frequency range. The quality factor of the sharp peaks is of the order of 10000 but can be improved by changing the integers N and N' as well as the different lengths. One would also specify that using loops rather than stubs as resonators in such systems avoids the difficulties for the determination of the boundary condition at the free extremity of each stub.

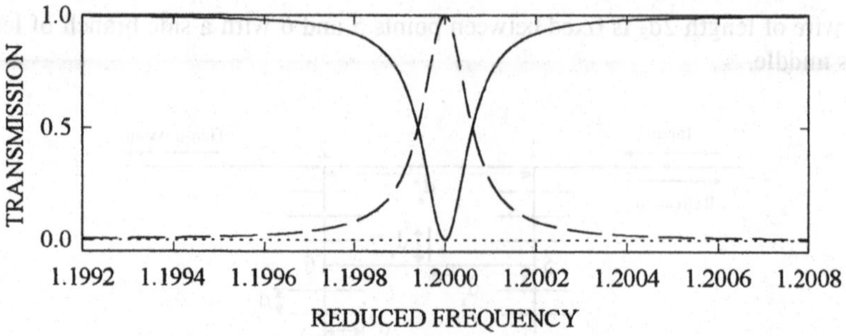

Figure 5: Variation of the intensity of the transmitted signal from site 1 to site 2 (solid line), and of the forward signal (long dashed line), in the structure shown in Fig. 4 versus the reduced frequency. The dots represent the signal intensity in the backward direction. These theoretical results were obtained for N=6, N'=1, d_0=1.3090d_1, d_2=0.3091d_1, d_3=1.3088d_1, and d_4=0.0002d_1 with the boundary condition E=0 at the free ends of all the side branches. The resonant reduced frequency is Ω_0=1.20.

3.2. EXPERIMENTAL RESULTS

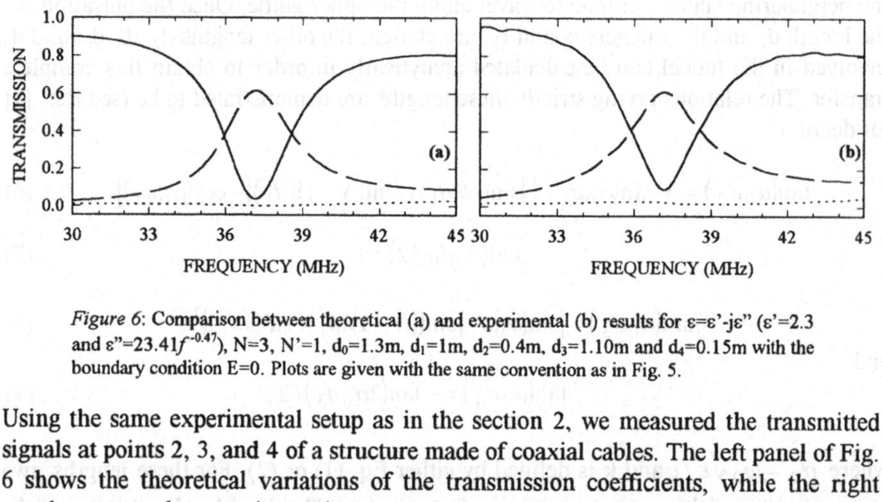

Figure 6: Comparison between theoretical (a) and experimental (b) results for $\varepsilon=\varepsilon'-j\varepsilon''$ (ε'=2.3 and $\varepsilon''=23.41f^{-0.47}$), N=3, N'=1, d_0=1.3m, d_1=1m, d_2=0.4m, d_3=1.10m and d_4=0.15m with the boundary condition E=0. Plots are given with the same convention as in Fig. 5.

Using the same experimental setup as in the section 2, we measured the transmitted signals at points 2, 3, and 4 of a structure made of coaxial cables. The left panel of Fig. 6 shows the theoretical variations of the transmission coefficients, while the right panel presents the experimental measurements. Although the radiative losses in the coaxial cables are negligible, the attenuation of the electromagnetic waves in the cables is important. Due to this absorption phenomenon, the amplitude of a narrow peak of selective transmission would become very low. Therefore, we choose the conditions of a relatively large resonant peak i.e., a structure made of a low number of coaxial cables whose lengths are of the order of the meter. In the computed transmissions coefficients, the imaginary part of the complex dielectric constant varies with frequency in the same manner as in the previous section. One observes that taking into account the attenuation in the coaxial cables, experimental measurements validate fairly well the theoretical prediction. This is, to our knowledge, the first reliable experimental observation of the existence of resonant tunneling of electromagnetic waves.

One notes also that designing a "resonant tunneling device" working at optical frequencies necessitates the manufacturing of propagation channels with a length of the order of the micrometer. The high selectivity of the device requires a precision on the lengths of the order of the nanometer. Recent technological advances in the micro-fabrication technology allow manufacturing of such channels. Moreover, in order to avoid the radiative losses, very important at optical frequencies, one may imagine designing the "resonant tunneling device" inside a 2D photonic crystal by removing rows of cylinders.

4. Conclusion

We have investigated the propagation of electromagnetic waves in defective quasi-one-dimensional waveguides. Localized states associated with defects in the structure were theoretically predicted. We have shown that resonant tunneling between two monomode infinite waveguides may occur at a specific frequency when they are connected with a coupling device constituted of star waveguides. We think that our model systems may have potential applications for making filtering or multiplexing devices.

References

1. J. O. Vasseur, P. A. Deymier, L. Dobrzynski, B. Djafari-Rouhani, and A. Akjouj, Absolute band-gaps and electromagnetic transmission in quasi-one-dimensional comb structures, *Phys. Rev. B* **55**, 10434 (1997).

2. L. Dobrzynski, A. Akjouj, B. Djafari-Rouhani, J. O. Vasseur, and J. Zemmouri, Giant gaps in photonic band structures, *Phys. Rev. B* **57**, R9388 (1998).

3. J. M. Bendickson, J. P. Dowling, and M. Scalora, Analytic expressions for electromagnetic mode density in finite, one-dimensional, photonic band-gap structures, *Phys. Rev. E* **53**, 4107 (1996).

4. R. Wang, J. Dong, and D. Y. Xing, Defect studies in a one-dimensional photonic band-gap structure, *Phys. Status Solidi A* **200**, 529 (1997).

5. J. O. Vasseur, B. Djafari-Rouhani, L. Dobrzynski, B. Djafari-Rouhani, A. Akjouj, and J. Zemmouri, Defect modes in one-dimensional comblike photonic waveguides, *Phys. Rev. B* **59**, 13446 (1999).

6. S. Fan, P. R. Villeneuve, J. D. Joannopoulos, and H. A. Haus, Channel drop tunneling through localized states, *Phys. Rev. Lett.* **80**, 960 (1998).

7. S. Fan, P. R. Villeneuve, J. D. Joannopoulos, and H. A. Haus, Channel drop filters in photonic crystals, *Opt. Express* **3**, 4 (1998).

8. S. Fan, P. R. Villeneuve, J. D. Joannopoulos, M. J. Khan, C. Monolatou, and H. A. Haus, Theoretical analysis of channel drop tunneling processes, *Phys. Rev. B* **59**, 15882 (1999).

9. L. Dobrzynski, B. Djafari-Rouhani, A. Akjouj, J. O. Vasseur, and J. Zemmouri, Resonant tunneling between two continua, *Phys. Rev. B* **30**, 10628 (1999).

EXPERIMENTAL PROBES OF THE OPTICAL PROPERTIES OF PHOTONIC CRYSTALS

Willem L. Vos[*], Henry M. van Driel[†], Mischa Megens[‡], A.Femius Koenderink, and Arnout Imhof[§]

van der Waals-Zeeman Instituut, Universiteit van Amsterdam, Valckenierstraat 65, 1018 XE Amsterdam, The Netherlands

1 INTRODUCTION

The propagation of electromagnetic radiation in three-dimensional periodic dielectric structures is strongly modified if the wavelength of the radiation is on the order of the lattice spacing.[1–5] Such structures are called photonic crystals. Their periodicity gives rise to photonic band structures in a way that is analogous to electronic band structures.[6] Much of the recent interest in photonic crystals stems from the possibility of making lattices for which there exists a range of frequencies in which waves cannot propagate in any direction in the crystal.[1–4] Such a photonic band gap occurs if the coupling between light and lattice is sufficiently strong. The coupling is conveniently gauged by the polarizability per volume of the scatters.[7] If a lattice could be constructed with a photonic band gap at optical frequencies, this would result in spectacular effects such as the inhibition of spontaneous emission,[3] and localization of light.[4]

Following the first demonstration of a photonic band gap in the microwave range by Yablonovitch *et al.*,[8] there have been many attempts to fabricate crystal that will work at optical frequencies. This requires a structure that has a lengthscale that is about a ten thousandth of the size of the microwave crystals. In 1996, teams from Siemens[9] and the University of Glasgow[10] made crystals with two-dimensional bandgaps, that is, bandgaps for light confined to a plane. Grüning *et al.*[9] electrochemically etched silicon to produce a gap at a wavelength $\lambda \sim 5\mu m$, while Krauss *et al.*[10] performed lithography on AlGaAs to obtain a gap near $\lambda = 850$ nm. In the past two years, Lin *et al.*[11] and Noda *et al.*[12] took the next logical step: using advanced techniques, several microstructured semiconductor layers were stacked to make three-dimensional crystals. They created structures with stop gaps at telecom wavelengths in the near-infrared.

Stacking, however, is not the only way to make three-dimensional crystals. An easier method is to make photonic crystal from self-organizing systems such as colloidal suspen-

[*]Author for correspondence: wvos@wins.uva.nl

[†]Permanent address: Department of Physics, University of Toronto, Toronto, Canada, M5S 1A7

[‡]Present address: Department of Physics, Princeton University, Princeton NJ 08544, U.S.A.

[§]Present address: Debye Instituut, Universiteit Utrecht, Princetonplein 1, 3584 CC Utrecht, The Netherlands

C.M. Soukoulis (ed.), Photonic Crystals and Light Localization in the 21st Century, 191–218.

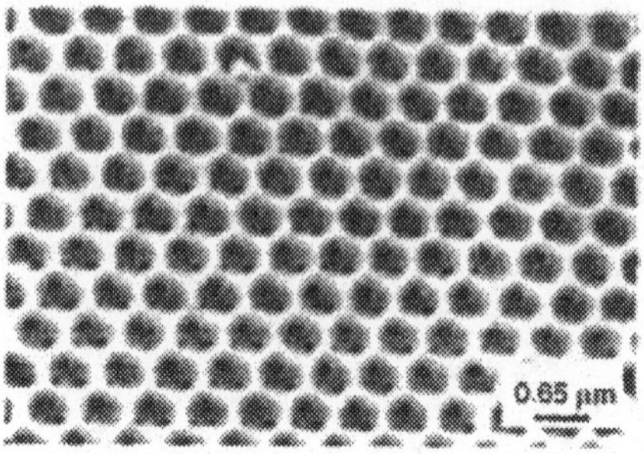

Figure 1: Scanning electron micrograph of the surface of an air-sphere crystal in titania with $a = 913 \pm 9$ nm. The scale bar is 0.65 μm long. The hexagonal arrangement of voids in this near-perfect section are an *fcc* (111) plane. From Ref. 30.

sions. These systems have naturally the right structure size for the optical range, but unfortunately only a small refractive index variation, hence a weak coupling. Recently, however, self-organizing systems have been used as templates to structured materials with high refractive (see, e.g., Ref. 13, 14). This has lead to the development of extended three-dimensional photonic crystals[15–17] that strongly interact with light.[18] The conceptual ease of making such so-called air-sphere crystals has sparked an explosion of activities in the field (see, e.g., Ref. 14, 19).

From early on, the theory of photonic crystals has been well developed.[1,2,20,21] To keep theory for three dimensions tractable, infinitely large perfect crystals are usually described. In practice, however, the physics is certainly affected by the finite size of the crystal or by inevitable disorder.[6] In this contribution, we review experiments that probe the optical properties of photonic crystals; we aim to compare experimentally measurable quantities to theoretical models.

2 EXPERIMENTAL

Our experiments are mainly concerned with systems made by self-organization. We use colloidal suspensions of particles with high size monodispersities and sharp interfaces.[22,23] Photonic crystals made from colloids are carefully grown, with a wide range of particle volume fractions (ϕ),[7,23–26] and artificial opals were made by slowly drying the crystals.[7,16] Colloidal particles with intentionally low dye content (see Ref. 27) were made to grow photonic crystals with internal light sources.[25,26,28,29] Strongly interacting crystals of air spheres in titania were developed[16](cf. Fig. 1), and carefully characterized. It appears that the air-sphere crystals possess a titania backbone with a dielectric constant of 6.3-6.5 in the IR-visible region.[30] Recently, electrochemistry has been applied as a new means to make crystals with unexpected optical properties.[31] The samples are extensively characterized by a range of techniques, such as optical microscopy and reflectivity, scanning electron microscopy, Raman scattering, x-ray diffraction. In particular, we have found that small angle x-ray scattering using synchrotron radiation (at the ESRF) is a highly valuable tool to study photonic crystals non destructively in great detail and document highly ordered crystals.[22–24,30,32]

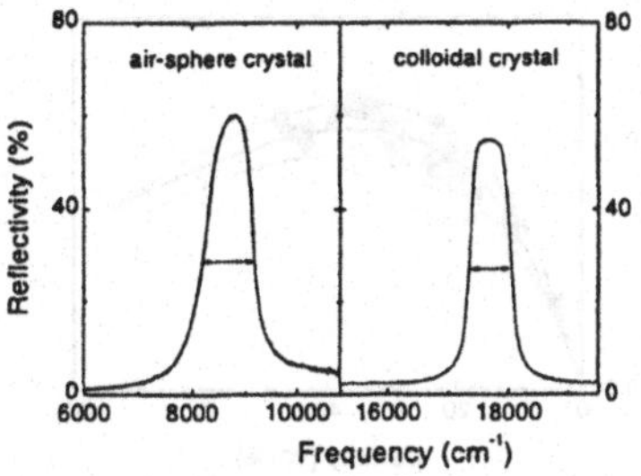

Figure 2: Reflectivity measured at normal incidence for an air-sphere crystal in TiO_2 with $a = 860$ nm (left, solid curve) and for a colloidal crystal of $R = 101$ nm polystyrene spheres in methanol with $a = 338$ nm (right, dashed curve) as a function of frequency ($\omega/2\pi c$) in wave numbers. The full widths at half maximum are indicated by the horizontal arrows.

3 BRAGG DIFFRACTION AND STOP GAPS

The interaction between radiation and photonic crystals causes the splitting of degenerate bands for wave vectors on the surface of the Brillouin zone, and the appearance of frequency gaps. Waves with frequencies within these stop gaps are Bragg diffracted and cannot propagate. Stop gaps are associated with every propagation direction with respect to a set of lattice planes. The widths of stop gaps increase with the interaction strength between light and the crystal. Since stop gaps are the precursors to a photonic band gap, the study of their optical properties is essential. Here, we will discuss several techniques to study stop gaps, notably their widths, since the center frequencies, that are determined by the lattice spacing and the average refractive index, are well understood.[7, 33] The mechanism how a photonic band gap actually develops, namely from multiple Bragg diffraction, is treated in section 7.

3.1 Reflectivity

Reflectivity is perhaps the oldest way to study Bragg diffraction of crystals.[5, 6] In essence, light with frequencies inside a stop gap is diffracted and rejected from the crystal. Figure 2 shows the reflectivity as a function of frequency for a crystal of air spheres in titania, and for a colloidal crystal of polystyrene spheres in methanol. The air-sphere crystal, with lattice parameter a = 860 nm, shows a strong Bragg peak at 8800 cm^{-1}, with a large relative width (full width at half maximum (FWHM) divided by the center frequency) of 11.3 %, and a maximum reflectivity of 60 %. The colloidal crystal shows a Bragg peak at 17600 cm^{-1}, with a relative width of 4.0 %, and a maximum reflectivity of 55 % on a flattish top. The larger width of the Bragg peak of the air-sphere crystal is due to the larger spatial variation of the refractive index, which results in stronger coupling. Several features of the experimental curves are remarkable compared to the ideal peak shape predicted by dynamical diffraction theory:[5] the experimental peaks are rounded and have maxima less than 100 %. An ideal diffraction peak has a flat top with 100 % reflectivity, that abruptly falls off at the edges. The width of the top is equal to the width of the stop gap and the FWHM is only a few percent larger. In presence of absorption, diffraction peaks become rounded and asymmetric with maxima less than 100 %, but the FWHM remains the same. We can exclude absorption as the cause for the experimental features, but extinction — that also removes energy from incident or diffracted beams — likely plays a role. Extinction may be due to various imperfections, e.g.,

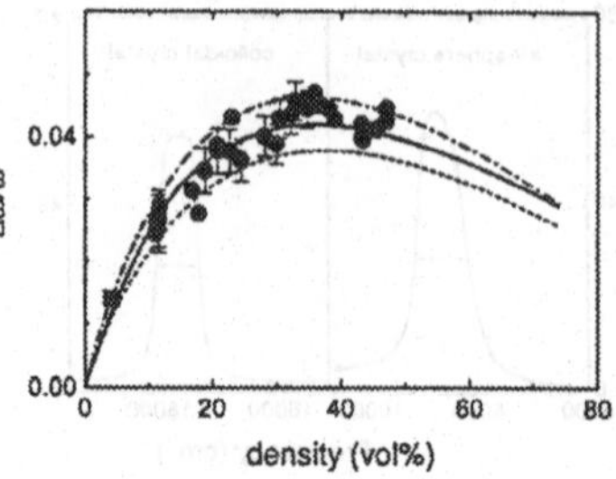

Figure 3: Relative width of Bragg peaks for crystals of polystyrene colloids, with various radii, in water or methanol as a function of the particle density, measured at normal incidence. We define $\Delta\omega$ as the full width at half maximum, and ω as the center frequency.[34] The curves are theoretical calculations using the dynamical diffraction theory (dotted curve), band structure calculations and KKR theory (both solid curve), and the E-field expansion with two bands (dashed-dotted curve).

mosaic spread that causes light to be diffracted non-specularly, grain boundaries between simultaneously illuminated crystal domains that scatter light diffusively, or non-crystalline features that sometimes occur on the surfaces of air-sphere crystals (cf. Fig. 2 of Ref. 16). At this point, we caution that for zero photonic interaction a diffraction peak may broaden due to crystal faults such as strain or finite crystal domains ("Scherrer broadening").[5] Thus, the degree of crystalline order should be checked independently from experiments that probe photonic crystal properties. Therefore, we have done extensive characterization.

From the consideration of theoretical diffraction peaks above, we propose that the FWHM of a diffraction peak is a robust measure of the width of a stop gap. In Fig. 3, we plot the relative widths for crystals of polystyrene colloids, with various radii, in water or methanol as a function of the particle density (for a preliminary account, see Ref. 34). The data were measured on many different samples that were prepared with various amounts of deionization. For each sample, we measured reflectivity as a function of height in the capillary; hence, as a function of particle density, since colloids sediment under gravity. Figure 3 shows that with increasing particle density, the relative width increases, levels off near 40 vol%, and then decreases. In earlier transmission experiments,[35] the widths were difficult to resolve and consequently suffered from a relatively large uncertainty. For comparison, we have calculated the relative widths with several theories shown in Fig. 3: *(i)* plane-wave band structure calculations,[2,20] *(ii)* plane-wave band structures in the two band approximation,[36] *(iii)* dynamical diffraction theory,[5,37] and *(iv)* KKR multiple scattering theory.[38] The experimental widths agree very well with all calculations, confirming the hypothesis that the FWHM of a diffraction peak is a good measure of the width of a stop gap. Similarly, relative peak widths of air-sphere crystals match with stop gap widths calculated for a model of close-packed air spheres in a completely infiltrated backbone[18] (with too large a filling fraction) and match very well with an appropriately optimized model.[39,40]

Using the dynamical diffraction theory, one can derive that the relative width of a stop gap is proportional to the polarizability α per volume v,[37] that is a very useful gauge for a photonic interaction parameter Ψ.[7] For (111) diffraction, the proportionality constant is equal to one, within a few percent. We conclude that it is possible to experimentally measure the interaction strength between light and photonic crystals by the relative width of a stop gaps (for fcc crystals usually the L-gap). For crystals of dielectric spheres, one can rewrite the photonic parameter as: $\Psi = 4\pi\alpha/v = 3\phi(m^2-1)/(m^2+2)g(Kr)$, where m is the ratio of the

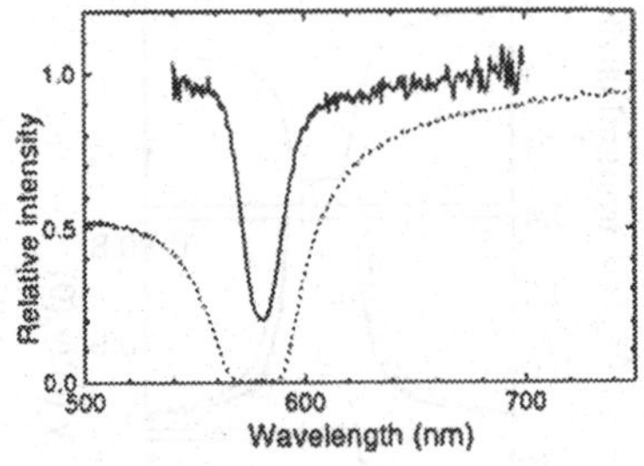

Figure 4: Transfer function for light sources inside a crystal (solid curve, relative fluorescence intensity of dye) and transmission for plane waves emitted by a light source far away outside the crystal (dotted curve). Both spectra were taken normal to the *fcc* (111) crystal planes at the same spatial spot, see Ref. 28.

refractive indices of the spheres and the surrounding medium, and $g(K r)$ is the form factor of the scatterers (here Rayleigh-Gans) as a function of sphere radius r and diffraction vector K. This reformulation allows a physical interpretation of Fig. 3: the stop gap first increases because the density of scatterers increases, but then it saturates and decreases because the particles scatter less efficiently (the form factor decreases). Apparently the polarizability of a single unit cell elegantly gauges the interaction between light and a photonic crystal.

3.2 Transmission

Transmission of plane waves incident from outside is a well-known method to study photonic gaps.[8] Examples of transmission at normal incidence ($\alpha = 0°$) to (111) lattice planes are shown in Figs. 4 and 5a for colloidal crystals of silica spheres in water[28] and polystyrene spheres in water.[41] The transmission is high at low frequencies (or long wavelengths) and at high frequencies (or short wavelengths) and decreases dramatically towards the edge of the stopgap, thereby forming a deep characteristic "notch." Idealized transmission curves through Bragg planes are expected to be equal to one minus the reflectivity (see above).[5] Hence, the transmission is expected to show a sharply bounded notch, and indeed the stop gap in Fig. 4 (linear transmission scale) decreases to zero with rather abrupt edges. It is expected that the width of the notch at zero transmission is equal to the width of the stop gap. The experimental notch, however, is about 25 nm wide, much wider than values of 11.1–11.7 nm predicted by dynamical diffraction[5, 37] or band structure theories.[20] We have observed this discrepancy in many other cases. A likely explanation for the wide transmission notches is that light samples the complete thickness of the sample, that is, more than a thousand lattice planes, including planes far from the capillary wall that may be less well aligned. In contrast, reflectivity (and emission spectra, see below) probes relatively few crystal planes that are well aligned close to the cell wall and reflectivity from misaligned planes is not detected. These observations are corroborated by results on thin crystals (up to 50 layers) whose transmission agrees well with theoretical estimates that include a significant Scherrer broadening.[42]

It is remarkable that in Figs. 4 and 5a the transmission at frequencies above the stop gap is lower than below the stop gap. This contrasts to idealized transmission curves, that have equal transmission values at low and high frequencies.[5] In experiments by many other workers, a similarly decreasing transmission with increasing frequency is observed, which has been ascribed to a Rayleigh-like scattering from crystal defects by Vlasov *et al.*[43] It is also

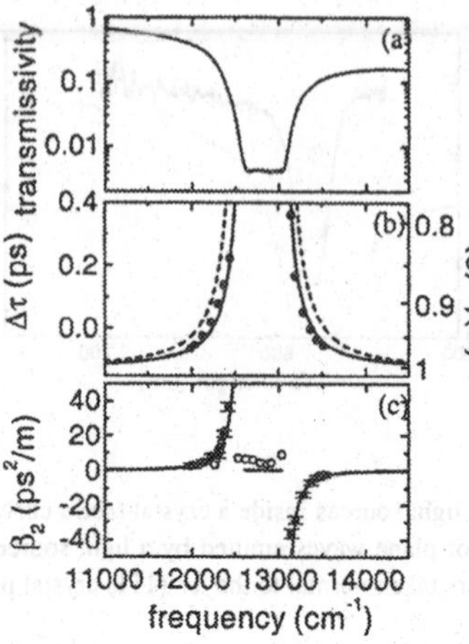

Figure 5: (a) Transmission spectrum of a colloidal photonic crystal. (b) Measured pulse delay times ($\Delta\tau$, solid circles) near the L-gap versus the central frequency of the incoming pulses. (c) Group velocity dispersion parameter (β_2), measured in transmission (solid circles) and reflection (open circles). The solid curves in (b) and (c) represent the dynamical diffraction theory[5] and the dashed curve in (b) the two-band model for the E-field.[36] From Ref. 41.

interesting that the attenuation in the middle of a stop gap that is apparent on a semilogarithmic scale as in Fig. 5(a), is much lower than theoretically expected on the basis of the number of crystal layers (see also Ref. 37). For comparison, in thin crystals studied with microwaves, with length scales for which precise machining is feasible, the attenuation in the middle of stop gaps agrees well with theoretical estimates, and the transmission below and above stop gaps are in close agreement.[44] These results taken together suggest that attenuation in a stop gap is limited by crystal imperfections (except finite crystal size).

3.3 Group Velocity

While continuous wave reflectivity and transmission are very useful to determine the presence of stop gaps, they do not provide full information on the light propagation through the crystal. Time-resolved experiments are essential to reveal the dynamics of the electromagnetic fields in the photonic crystal. In one-dimensional multilayer systems, pulsed-laser experiments have demonstrated extremely short tunneling times at in-gap frequencies,[45, 46] as well as very low group velocities at near-gap frequencies.[47] Pulse slowing was also studied in a synthetic opal.[48] We have used phase-sensitive ultrashort-pulse interferometry[49] to probe the modification of light propagation close to the band edges of a photonic crystal. This technique measures the interferometric cross correlation function of a laser pulse transmitted by the sample with the incoming pulse. In Fig. 5(b) the time delays are plotted versus the central frequency of the incoming pulse. The pulse delay time $\Delta\tau$ is the time delay introduced by the crystal plus the capillary minus an equal distance of glycerol, and can therefore be negative. For comparison, the sample transmission spectrum, measured in a spectrometer with a white light source, is shown in Fig. 5(a). The data clearly demonstrate a large decrease of the group velocity near the edges of the stop gap. The largest time delay measured corresponds to a pulse propagation speed of only about 80 % of that far from the gap. This means that the pulse experiences an increased effective path length due to multiple reflections in the crystal.

To describe the data in Fig. 5(b), we used the dynamical diffraction theory,[5] that approximates the displacement field in the crystal by the two strongest Fourier components: the incident and the diffracted waves. The theory yields a dispersion relation $\omega(k)$ that can be differentiated to obtain the group velocity. The input parameters are the refractive indices of water (1.33) and polystyrene (1.59), as well as the particle diameter (222 nm) and the lattice spacing. The (111) lattice spacing is fixed independently by requiring that the predicted location of the stop gap coincides with the center of the transmission minimum, yielding a value of 284 nm. With all parameters fixed, the time delay was calculated for a 0.4 mm crystal and an offset was added to allow for the capillary and index-matching glycerol. The result is shown in Fig. 5(b). The dynamical diffraction theory is seen to describe the data very well. It gives an average refractive index of 1.372 and a relative gap width of 0.032. As an independent check we measured the wavelength-dependent diffraction angle corrected for Snell's law. At $\lambda = 633$ nm the crystal was observed to have a diffraction angle of 54.2° degrees, from which we derive a lattice spacing of 286 nm and an average refractive index of 1.366, agreeing with the values above. It has been predicted[21] that the D-field expansion is reasonably accurate for crystals of dielectric spheres but fails badly for dielectric spheres, and the opposite holds for the E-field. Indeed, an analogous theory that keeps the two strongest components of the *electric* field[36] did not describe the data well. We note that the data of Ref. 48 do not distinguish between the expansions. Our result also agrees with a closer inspection of Fig. 3, revealing that the two band E-field model predicts the largest widths. Since measured widths are in principle upper bounds for the "photonic" width, due to possible defect-broadening, this model overestimates the stop gap widths. The dynamical diffraction theory agrees better with the experimental data.

Even though the measurements in Fig. 5(b) explore only one set of lattice planes, one-dimensional models do not describe the data as well as the 3D dynamical diffraction theory. The best mapping of the real 3D crystal onto a 1D multilayer stack was obtained with the model of Lidorikis *et al.*,[50] which also needs no adjustable parameters. This model gives a reasonable correspondence to the data, but the gap width is off by 40 %, resulting in differences with the measured delay times.

3.4 Group Velocity Dispersion

We have been able to measure the group velocity dispersion (gvd), since our interferometric technique yields phase information about pulses sent through a sample.[51] The gvd quantifies the relative phase shift of frequencies in a wave packet. The gvd can be interpreted as being inversely proportional to an effective photon mass, in analogy to electronic band structures. This property has not been measured before in photonic crystals. Pulse reshaping, that is present in dispersive systems such as photonic crystals, does not affect the gvd at all whereas it hampers an unambiguous estimation of the group velocity. The measured gvd parameter $\beta_2 = (d^2k/d\omega^2)|_{\omega_0}$, with ω_0 the center frequency of the pulse, is plotted in Fig. 5(c). If the pulse frequency comes to within a few percent of the band edges, the gvd diverges. The measured values are two to three orders of magnitude larger than well-known values for ordinary glass. At the high-frequency side of the stop gap, we find a branch of anomalous dispersion. The cubic coefficient (not shown) was found to be positive on both sides of the gap. The curve in Fig. 5(c) is β_2 calculated from the dynamical diffraction theory by taking the second derivative of k with respect to ω, using the same parameter values as before. Again, the data are described remarkably well by this theory. In analogy to electrons in semiconductors,[6] our measurements can be interpreted as large effects on the effective photon mass, which is negative below and positive above a gap.

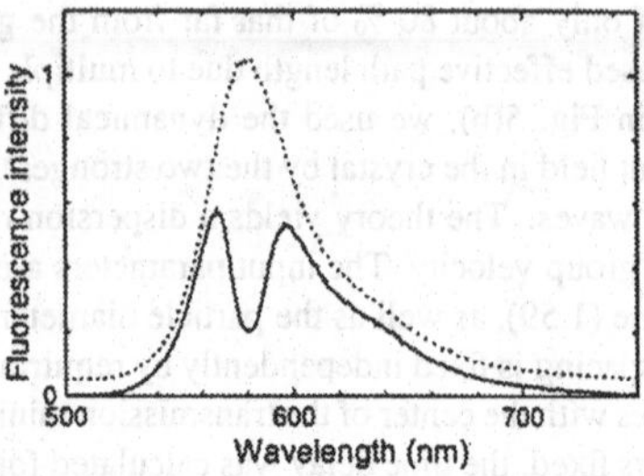

Figure 6: Fluorescence spectrum of dye in a photonic colloidal crystal (solid curve) and in a colloidal liquid of spheres (dotted curve, offset by 0.05). Bragg reflection causes a stop gap in the spectrum of the crystal.[28]

By doing the interferometry experiments in reflection, we have succeeded in studying frequencies inside the stop gap. Figure 5(c) shows the resulting data for the gvd. The data agree well with the data measured in transmission outside the stop gap. A dramatic change takes place in crossing the edge of the stop gap: inside the gap, the dispersion is very low and constant. An important conclusion from these experiments is that the gvd naturally distinguishes the edges from the inside of stop gaps. No further interpretation is necessary, in contrast to all other probes of stop gaps.

4 EMISSION BY LIGHT SOURCES INSIDE PHOTONIC CRYSTALS

In the previous section, we have seen that the periodic structure of a photonic crystal gives rise to Bragg diffraction, that is associated with stop gaps for propagation in certain directions. In the direction of a stop gap light is excluded from the material. The situation is reminiscent of atoms or molecules in one-dimensional Fabry-Perot cavities.[52, 53, 55] A Fabry-Perot cavity can modify the spontaneous emission rate of atoms or molecules inside.[52, 55] The main difference between Fabry-Perot cavities and photonic crystals is that photonic crystals act as three-dimensional cavities, thereby promising complete control over emission. We investigate the modification of the emission spectrum of light sources inside photonic crystals, and we study their dynamics. Emission spectra of internal sources have been measured before, and stop gaps in these spectra have been observed. Unexpectedly, these stop gaps differ in several respects from those encountered in conventional transmission spectra, e.g., the attenuation and the width of gaps in emission spectra are smaller than in transmission spectra. In time-resolved emission studies, there have been surprising reports of modified lifetimes, up to a factor of 2, even for weakly photonic crystals. We argue that such large changes are not of photonic origin and present a simple model that relates the luminescence lifetimes to the interaction between light and the crystals.

4.1 Emission Spectra

We have obtained fluorescence spectra of dye in many different photonic crystals composed of dyed silica spheres in water. A typical example is shown in Fig. 6 and compared to the spectrum of a dilute colloidal liquid of dyed spheres. The crystal changes the fluorescence spectrum of the dye considerably: the spectrum acquires a pronounced stop gap. The

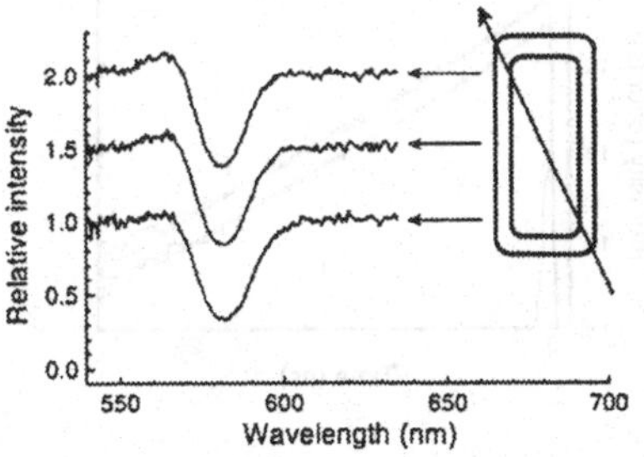

Figure 7: Internal transmission spectra (relative fluorescence intensities) for various distances from light source to sample surface. The depth of the light source varies with the depth of the light beam which excites the fluorescence (see schematic drawing). The upper curves have been offset by 0.5 and 1.0 respectively. Each curve corresponds to the position in the sample as indicated.[28]

stop gap is caused by the (111) crystal planes. The crystal planes act as Bragg mirrors for the fluorescence, preventing part of the light to leave the crystal. We observed that the central wavelength of the stop gap depends on the density of spheres in the crystal. We can vary the density and hence tune the stop gap wavelength. As an example, we have carefully tuned the stop gap on the dye emission spectrum in Fig. 6.

We have also measured the transfer functions for various emission directions.[28] Stop gaps are observed for all emission directions. Away from the normal, the central wavelength of the stop gap goes to shorter wavelengths, qualitatively resembling Bragg reflection. The shift of the central wavelength is very well explained using Bragg's law $2d \sin\theta = \lambda/n_{\mathrm{eff}}$ with an effective refractive index n_{eff}, if allowance is made for refraction at the sample interface using Snell's law. This agrees with earlier diffraction experiments.[7] We note that Bragg's law with an effective Maxwell-Garnett refractive index yields results which closely correspond with dynamical diffraction theory.[5] Emission wavelengths that are equal to the Bragg wavelength at normal incidence, can still propagate in oblique directions. For shorter emission wavelengths, the light is Bragg reflected at a certain angle, but can propagate in other directions, such as the normal one. The resulting variations in fluorescence intensity are familiar from X-ray fluorescence, where they are referred to as Kossel lines.[5]

In Fig. 4, the stop gap in the transfer function is about 20 nm wide. A width between 11.1 and 11.7 nm is predicted theoretically.[20, 5] The width of the stop gap in transmission, however, is much larger. Apparently the course of plane waves through the sample is qualitatively different from that of light generated inside.

It is striking that for the same crystal, the transfer function shows much less attenuation than the transmission of external sources, where the attenuation at the center of a stop gap is appreciable, see Figs. 4 and 6. To elucidate the origin of this difference, we have varied the position of the light source inside the sample as follows (*cf.* inset of Fig. 7); the light which excites the dye is sent at a glancing angle of 30° through the sample. Thus, the beam is close to the front surface at one edge and close to the back surface at the other edge of the sample. By imaging a specific part of the sample on the detector, we select the depth of the emitting sources. The beam waist at the sample measures only 20 μm FWHM, and the width of the imaged area is 50 μm, both much less than the 300 μm sample thickness. The resulting transfer functions are shown in Fig. 7. The outermost curves correspond to regions which are 400 μm apart on the sample. Surprisingly, the attenuation of the fluorescence stop gap does not depend on the depth of the sources. We checked that the fluorescence originates

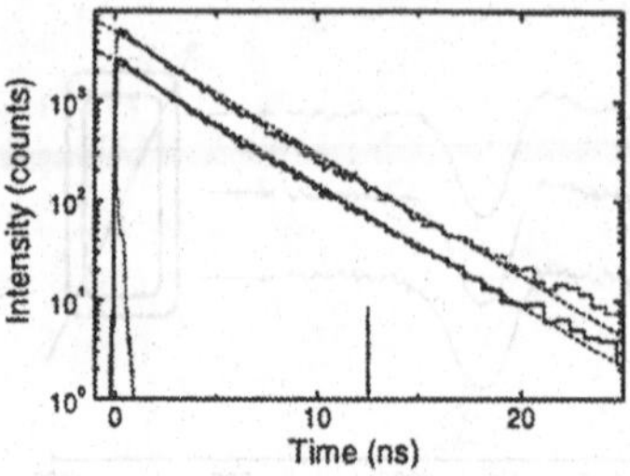

Figure 8: Time-resolved intensity for dye in a photonic crystal made of dyed silica spheres (radius 121 nm) in water at 65 vol% (solid curve), and for similar dyed colloids in a disordered dilute reference sample (dashed curve, offset by a factor of 2), at $\lambda = 577$ nm.[25, 29] The mean lifetimes of 3.54 ± 0.02 ns are indicated by straight dotted lines. The narrow spike at 0 ns is the instrument response and the weak spike at 12 ns is an afterpulse from the laser.

in the bulk of the sample by photochemically bleaching the dye close to the surface with an intense laser beam tuned to a Bragg reflection. The bleaching did not deepen the stop gap. We can also exclude the possibility that the depth dependence is washed out by a diffuse excitation beam: Fig. 4 shows that there is a large transmission of light at the excitation wavelength (488 nm). Indeed we observed a well-defined blue beam behind the sample. From the observation that the stop gap is already present for sources close to the surface, we conclude that the stop gap takes only few crystal planes to build up. It is remarkable that the attenuation in the stop gap does not increase with further increasing depth of the source. Apparently the attenuation in the stop gap in the transfer function is mostly determined close to the surface but not by the bulk of the crystal.

From the comparison between the transfer function and the transmission spectrum (see Fig. 4), it is clear that a considerable amount of fluorescence light with wavelengths in a stop gap reaches the sample surface and then leaves the crystal in the direction of a stop gap. The explanation for this phenomenon is that defects near the surface of the crystal scatter in all directions, including the direction of the stop gap. The phenomenon can be understood as follows: Light emitted in the direction of a stop gap is attenuated, but the light can propagate perfectly well in other directions (see Ref. 28 and Fig. 12). The light will be scattered by a small concentration of defects that always occur in crystals.[6] Radiation scattered by defects deep inside the crystal will experience a similar attenuation as in a plane wave experiment. If light is scattered by defects close to the surface of the crystal, this radiation will appear unattenuated outside, even in the direction of a stop gap, because the light traverses only a thin layer of photonic crystal. Thus, light appears in the direction of a stop gap. The internal sources emit light in a large solid angle of nearly 2π to the exit surface, hence an appreciable contribution is expected compared to the light that directly propagates into the 0.016π solid angle of the detector. In contrast, in a plane wave transmission spectrum the contribution of diffuse scattering is hardly noticeable. The reason is that the beam that propagates to the detector is well collimated, whereas the randomly scattered light is spread over 4π solid angle. This elucidates why the stop gap in fluorescence is shallower than the deep stop gap in plane wave transmission spectra (*cf.* Fig. 4).

Very recently, we have obtained emission spectra of dye inside air-sphere crystals.[54] The spectra appear to be strongly modified by multiple Bragg diffraction effects, see section 7.

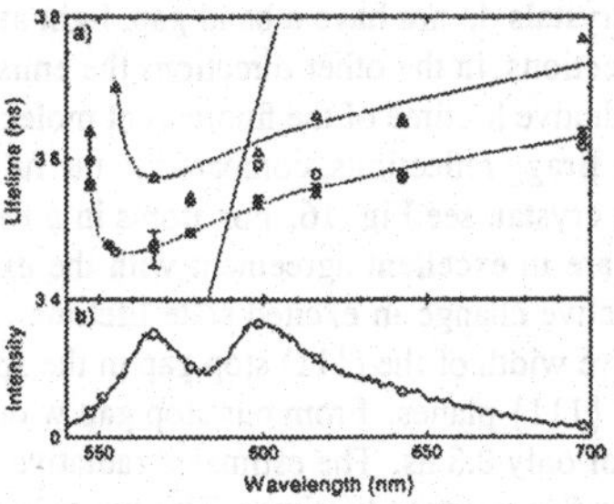

Figure 9: (a) Excited state lifetime of dye inside photonic crystals (open and solid circles, densities of 65 and 53 vol%, respectively) and in a colloidal liquid (triangles), at various wavelengths in the dye spectrum. The solid circles are an average of two measurements, indicated by error bars. The dotted curves are guides to the eye.[25] The emission spectrum of the 65 vol% crystal is shown in (b) for comparison. The open circles indicate the wavelengths at which lifetimes were measured.

4.2 Time Resolved Emission

We have studied time resolved emission of dye in photonic crystals. Our system consists of dye-doped silica spheres in water, with a dielectric contrast of 1.2. The dye is covalently attached to the silica spheres and covered by a silica layer. The chief advantage of our system is the ability to confidently compare the crystal with a reference system consisting of the same spheres in a random arrangement. Figure 8 shows two typical time-resolved fluorescence traces, one of dye in a colloidal crystal and one of dye in a colloidal liquid, measured at a wavelength of 577 nm, corresponding to the crystal's stop gap. The measured fluorescence intensities extend over three full decades. The fluorescence decay is very close to a single exponential, which indicates that unwanted non-radiative effects are effectively reduced by the low dye concentration and the protective cover layer.[27] From the fluorescence decay curves we have obtained lifetimes by calculating the average time at which a photon is detected. The lifetimes for the curves in Fig. 8 are both 3.5 ns, *i.e.*, there is hardly any difference in lifetime between a crystal and a colloidal liquid.

Figure 9 shows fluorescence lifetimes as a function of wavelength in the dye spectrum, for two photonic crystals with different densities, and for a colloidal liquid. The densities of the crystals that we have used were 65 and 53 vol%. Due to the density difference the center wavelength of the stop gaps of the crystals differ: for the low density crystal the stop gap is at 617 ± 9 nm, whereas for the high density crystal it is at 582 ± 2 nm. Since the stop gap wavelengths of the two crystals differ, the densities of optical modes of the two crystals should also display different wavelength dependencies. This difference should become visible in the measured lifetimes. However, the measured lifetimes in these crystals do not show a significant wavelength dependence. The variations in lifetime are on the order of only 0.05 ns, or 2 %. This observation shows that the influence of the photonic band structure on lifetime in these crystals is surprisingly small, considering the large changes in the spectra. Below we will resolve this seeming paradox.

We can interpret the variation in lifetimes by comparing this variation to the width of the stop gaps of the crystals. A simple model connects the lifetimes to the width of the stop gaps, and it explains why the photonic crystals under study have only a small influence on lifetimes. In the direction of a stop gap, light cannot be emitted since the zero point fluctuations are expelled from the photonic crystal by repeated reflection from the lattice planes.

Since our weakly photonic crystals do not have a band gap, light at a specific wavelength is reflected only for certain directions, in the other directions the emission persists. We expect that the relative change in radiative lifetime of the fluorescent molecules is of the order of the solid angle subtended by the Bragg reflections, compared to the full 4π solid angle which is available in the absence of a crystal, see Fig. 16. For atoms in a Fabry-Pérot interferometer the results of this approach are in excellent agreement with the experiments of Heinzen *et al.*[52] It turns out that the relative change in excited state lifetime is in good approximation equal to four times the relative width of the (111) stop gap in the spectrum;[25] the factor of 4 stems from the four pairs of $\{111\}$ planes. From our stop gap width of 2 %, we estimate a change in radiative lifetime of only 0.3 ns. The estimated radiative lifetime change provides an upper bound for changes in fluorescence lifetimes. This upper bound is consistent with the measured variations in τ of the crystals in Fig. 9. Apparently a large change in fluorescence spectrum can coincide with only a minor change in fluorescence lifetime, which resolves the paradox mentioned above.

The observed small change in lifetime contrasts with earlier results. Martorell and Lawandy found a change in lifetime by a factor 1.8 for their crystals of polystyrene spheres in water with rhodamine dye dissolved in the liquid.[56] It has been suggested that their large change in lifetime is not caused by photonic band structure but by other factors such as chemical interactions and adsorption of the dye on the sphere surfaces. Petrov *et al.*[57] have measured fluorescence of dye in a polymer-filled opal. The decay curves were fitted with a distribution of lifetimes, in which the short lifetimes were about half as long as the long lifetimes. The nonexponential decay was attributed to a modified density of optical modes while chemical or nonradiative effects were not considered. The fluorescence lifetimes were not spectrally resolved to demonstrate the anticipated variation in density of optical modes with wavelength. Surprisingly, lifetime changes were noted for wavelengths at the low frequency side of the stop gap, where the solid angle subtended by the Bragg reflections is least and our simple argument predicts no lifetime change. In both of the previous studies, the widths of the stop gaps of the samples are the same as the width of the stop gaps of our crystals, hence the change of the radiative lifetimes should in both cases be similar to the data in Figs. 8 and 9.

5 DISORDER

Disorder in photonic crystals is of fundamental interest in the study of Anderson localization of light, as witnessed by one of the first proposals for the study of photonic crystals.[4] Anderson localization[58] of light is an interference effect in random multiple scattering of light, which is commonly studied in disordered optical materials.[59, 60] Disorder, always present in any real crystal (see Ref. 6, chapter 30), gives rise to considerable random multiple scattering in photonic crystals. A convenient way to study the transport of light in a multiple scattering system is enhanced backscattering.[61–63] The intensity scattered by an object exhibits a clear maximum in the exact backscatter direction, which results from constructive interference of counterpropagating light paths. It is well established that a triangular peak superimposed on the diffuse background results.[61–63] The width of this 'enhanced backscattering cone' is inversely proportional to the transport mean free path ℓ. The transport mean free path is the length scale over which the direction of propagation of light is randomized and thus it quantifies the effect of disorder in the medium on the propagation of light. The transport mean free path limits the useful size range of photonic crystals for applications. An alternative method to obtain the transport mean free path is to measure the total transmission (*i.e.*, diffuse and coherent intensity transmitted by the sample integrated over all forward angles). A set of data as a function of sample thickness is needed to obtain the transport mean free path.

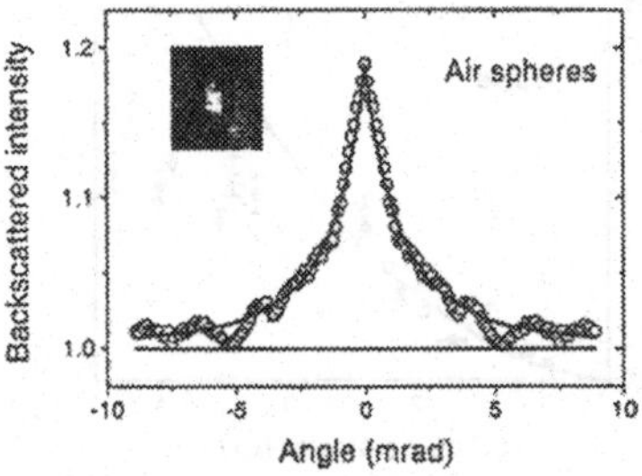

Figure 10: The backscattered intensity normalized to the diffuse background as a function of angle θ for an air-sphere crystal (λ =460 nm) with a lattice parameter 360 ± 10 nm. The curve is a least-squares fit to the data of the cone shape predicted by diffusion theory for a disordered medium. For the air spheres we find the profile as a function of $|\theta|$ by integrating over circles concentric with the peak in the two-dimensional image (inset). The points $\theta < 0$ are duplicates of $\theta > 0$.[64]

We have measured enhanced backscattering from a TiO_2 air-sphere crystal for various wavelengths by collecting the backscattered intensity on a CCD camera positioned in the focal plane of a positive collection lens. A typical backscatter cone of an air-sphere crystal with lattice parameter 360 ± 10 nm is shown in Fig. 10.[64] The inset shows the two-dimensional image obtained from averaging multiple camera exposures. The backscatter cone shows as a bright spot compared to the diffuse background. The backscattered intensity as a function of $|\theta|$ is obtained by averaging over circles concentric with the intensity peak. To facilitate visual inspection, the data are plotted both for $\theta > 0$ and $\theta < 0$. The solid line is a least squares fit to the coneshape as predicted by diffusion theory.[63] From the width of the cone we typically obtain transport mean free paths of 15 μm, which is equivalent to a distance of about 40 unit cells, or 70 lattice planes. Hence, the distance over which light becomes diffuse is so large that Bragg diffraction can easily build up. For opals of polystyrene spheres in air we find similar transport mean free paths.

The width of the cone is crucially influenced by the fact that the (111) planes are parallel to the sample surface in our experiment, resulting in L-gaps which coincide with the incident and backscatter direction. Starting from the diffusion equation for transport of light,[63,65] we observe that the cone is affected by two different mechanisms, the first of which concerns the diffuse intensity. Light paths returning to the sample surface at directions close to normal incidence suffer from internal reflection due to Bragg diffraction. Internal reflection creates longer light paths, hence the cone becomes narrower.[65] The magnitude of the internal reflection effect is determined by the total solid angle of directions which are in a stop gap. This effect is maximal at the blue edge of the L-gap, and does not depend on the orientation of the sample with respect to the incident beam.

The second effect results from the attenuation of the coherent beam due to Bragg diffraction for frequencies in the L-gap. The cone is affected because the coherent beam acts as a source for the diffuse intensity. Due to the strong attenuation of the coherent beam at wavelengths within the stopband, the backscatter cone is predominantly composed of light paths starting very close to the sample surface. Since these light paths are shorter on average,[63] this effect broadens the cone. This effect only occurs if the incident and backscatter directions are chosen to match the Bragg condition, and depends strongly on the attenuation length, which we previously noted to be much longer than predicted by, e.g., a two-band model.

We have measured enhanced backscattering as a function of frequency[64] for opals and

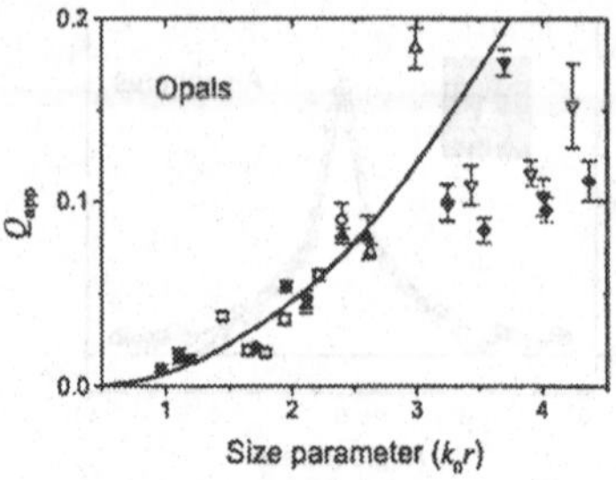

Figure 11: The apparent scattering efficiency per sphere Q_{app} as a function of the size parameter, for polystyrene opals made of particles with radii 120 (black squares), 180 (open squares), 213 (circles), 241 (open circles), 262 (black triangles), 326 (open triangles), 403 (downward black triangles), 426 (downward open triangles), 439 nm (black lozenges). The solid line is the Rayleigh-Gans scattering efficiency of a thin shell of refractive index 1 in an effective medium of refractive index 1.45.[64]

air-sphere crystals with the incident beam normal to the (111) planes. For frequencies below the L-gap, the cone width is not affected by either mechanism, since Bragg diffraction does not occur along any direction. For frequencies in the L-gap both mechanisms are relevant. Quantitatively the internal reflection effect dominates, leading to a net narrowing of the backscatter cone. For frequencies beyond the blue edge of the L-gap, the coherent beam is not Bragg diffracted, while the fraction of oblique propagation directions decreases continuously. The cone width, which is minimal at the blue edge of the L-gap, increases for increasing frequency. One may measure the attenuation effect, and hence the attenuation length, by choosing a frequency beyond the blue edge of the L-gap and recording backscatter cones as a function of incident and backscatter direction. The cone width will increase for the limited angular interval in which the incident direction matches the Bragg condition.

We have acquired enhanced backscattering cones for many opals of polystyrene spheres of different sizes for several wavelengths. Figure 11 (*cf.* Ref. 64) shows the apparent scattering efficiency $Q_{app} = 1/(n\ell\pi r^2)$ of the spheres in the opals as a function of size parameter $2\pi r/\lambda$, where r is the sphere radius, λ the wavelength, and n the number density of spheres in the opals. The apparent scattering efficiency increases with increasing sizeparameter.[32] As a simple model we propose that the scattering in the opals is mainly due to polydispersity of the spheres and small displacements from their lattice sites. The difference in refractive index profile of the displaced, slightly polydisperse Mie-spheres as compared to the ideal structure is a collection of thin shells of air and polystyrene. We have calculated the scattering efficiency[66] of spherical shells of refractive index 1 and radius r in a homogeneous medium with the effective index of refraction of the opals (1.45). As shown in figure 11, this simple shell model compares well to the data for shell thicknesses which are 5 % of the nearest neighbor distance between spheres in the crystal. This value is consistent with the small sphere polydispersity of $\sim$ 2 %, and with the estimated root mean square displacement $u_{RMS} \leq 3.5\%$.

From the discussion above we conclude that extinction of the coherent beam and the build-up of a diffuse intensity are intrinsic to photonic crystals. Especially for self-organized systems, the size randomness of the building blocks sets the length scale over which light becomes diffuse, irrespective of the degree of ordering, to be at most 40 unit cells.

Disorder in photonic crystals has an important effect on the emission spectra of internal sources.[28] We have identified that disorder considerably reduces the attenuation for internal

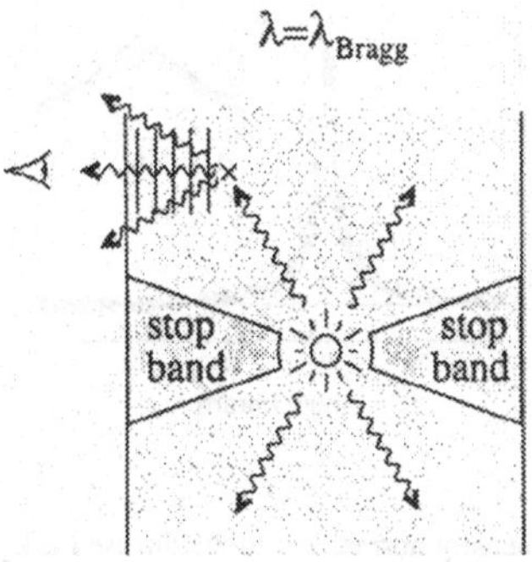

Figure 12: Schematic drawing of the trajectory of light emitted by a point source inside a photonic crystal if the light is just Bragg diffracted by the crystal planes indicated. The cross indicates a defect close to the surface of the crystal.[28]

sources in the frequency range of a stop gap (cf. Figs. 4, 6, and 7). The relevant mechanism is depicted in Fig. 12: light emitted in the direction of a stop gap is attenuated, but the light can propagate perfectly well in other directions. The light will be scattered by a small concentration of defects that always occur in any crystal. If light is scattered by defects close to the surface of the crystal, this radiation will appear unattenuated outside, even in the direction of a stopgap, because the light traverses only a thin layer of photonic crystal. Thus, light appears in the direction of a stop gap and the attenuation appears reduced.

6 ABSORPTION

Absorption is highly detrimental for photonic band gap effects. One of the main goals with photonic band gap crystals is to control excitations of atoms or molecules at time scales at least comparable with the excited state lifetime τ. If the atoms have radiative lifetimes $\tau \sim$ nsec typical of dipole oscillators with 100% quantum efficiency, then in a time τ light propagates for $\sim 10^6$ periods, or over a distance of $\sim 10^6$ wavelengths. Hence, the absorption length l_{abs} should be large: $l_{abs} > 10^6\lambda$. For rare-earth atoms, with $\tau \sim$ msec, the requirement is even more stringent by another 6 orders of magnitude. Whether one can observe a Bragg diffraction from a crystal (see for instance Zakhidov *et al.*'s beautiful shiny graphite crystals[17]) is not a very rigorous measure for absorption, because a Bragg diffraction can build up within of the order of 10 layers pathlength, i.e., 10 wavelengths (back and forth). Thus, an absorption length $l_{abs} > 10\lambda$ reveals Bragg diffraction, but will allow only a tiny effect on lifetimes.

The effect of enhanced backscattering is very sensitive to any effect that cuts off long light paths, because the top of the cone consists of contributions from very high scattering orders ($> 10^3$ scattering events, i.e., light paths of at least $10^3\ell$, of order ~cm). Both finite sample thickness and absorption result in a rounding of the backscatter cone,[67, 60] which is cusped for infinite non-absorbing media. We have recorded enhanced backscattering from polystyrene opals (see Fig. 13, Ref. 64) using the off-centered rotation technique,[68] which allows a high angular resolution of 0.3 mrad. Disregarding this finite resolution, the rounding of the cone top, shown in the inset of Fig. 13, allows us to conclude that the diffuse absorption length L_a is more than 500 μm, which exceeds the sample thickness of 300 μm. The diffuse absorption length measures the average distance between starting and ending points of a

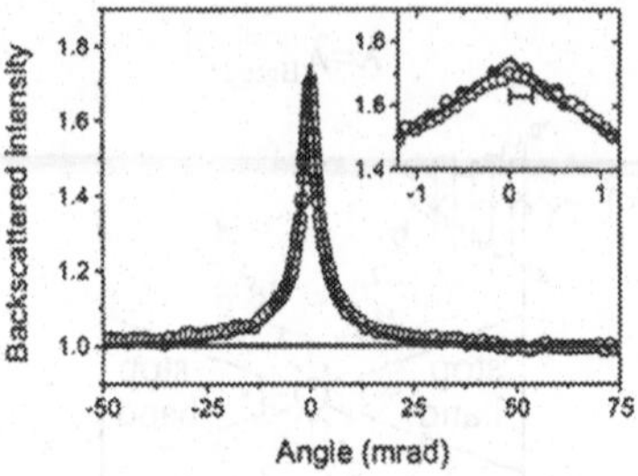

Figure 13: The backscattered intensity normalized to the diffuse background as a function of angle θ for an opal composed of polystyrene spheres of radius 180 nm measured at a wavelength of 685 nm. The curve is a least-squares fit to the data of the cone shape predicted by diffusion theory for a disordered medium. The inset shows a close up of the top. The horizontal bar indicates the high angular resolution.[64]

random light path over which the intensity decays by a factor $1/e$ as a result of absorption. Hence, the absorption length l_{abs}, *i.e.*, the average length of such a path, is at least longer than 0.5 cm. Since the rounding in the inset of Fig. 13 is clearly comparable to the finite resolution of the setup, we conclude that the value quoted above underestimates the absorption length by at least an order of magnitude. The important conclusion is that the random multiple scattering is a useful probe to show that the absorption length indeed exceeds the relevant wavelengths by six orders of magnitude in polystyrene opals.

7 STRONG INTERACTION

The previous sections have mostly dealt with weakly photonic crystals, for which the edge frequencies of a stop gap increase with angles of incidence away from the normal, following the well-known Bragg law. With increasing crystal photonic strength and increasing frequency, light can diffract from more than one set of lattice planes simultaneously and entirely new physics is revealed. Here we illustrate two profound ways in which Bragg's law breaks down for strongly photonic crystals. First, we find from reflectivity data taken as a function of angle from the normal to the (111) face that although the lowest frequency gap (associated with the L-stopgap) obeys Bragg's law for small angles, for angles starting near 35° a single reflectivity peak splits into two peaks indicating coupling of Bragg reflection processes from *two* planes, *viz.*, (111) and (200) crystal planes.[39] Second, at much higher frequencies in the vicinity of the region for which 2nd order Bragg reflection from (111) planes might occur, we observe three reflectivity peaks which do not change significantly with angle. We argue that multiple Bragg diffraction from *large numbers* of lattice planes results in band repulsions between Bloch states causing the frequencies of the edges of the stop gaps to become independent of angle of incidence.[40] One of the peaks is the precursor of a full photonic band-gap that would occur in a material of even higher dielectric contrast (> 7.8) than the titania air spheres. Multiple Bragg diffraction and low-dispersion Bloch modes have recently also been observed in emission spectra of light sources inside photonic crystals.[54]

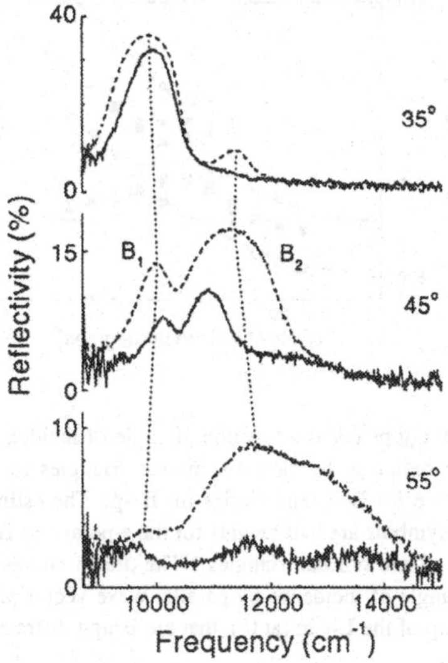

Figure 14: Bragg-reflection spectra for light incident on a crystal with a = 860 nm at angles of 35°, 45° and 55° for s- (dashed curves) and p-polarization (solid curves). The curves are offset, as shown by the left-hand scales. The vertical dotted lines are guides to the eye for the s-polarized peaks. B_1 and B_2 label the main peaks in both s- and p-polarized spectra.[39]

7.1 Coupling of Several Bragg Reflections

In the experiments designed to probe the spectral dependence of the reflectivity as a function of beam incidence angle (α), we find that for both s- and p-polarization a single peak associated with the L-stop-gap occurs at 8700 cm^{-1} for α =0°. This peak which we label as B_1 shifts to about 10000 cm^{-1} at α =30°, in agreement with simple Bragg diffraction. For angles between 35° and 55° a much more complex behavior is observed as shown in Fig. 14. The B_1 peak becomes narrower and weaker between α =35° and 55°, and even decreases in frequency at higher α. Starting at α =30°, a new peak, called B_2, appears at 11400 cm^{-1}. It first shifts down and then up in frequency, while becoming stronger and broader. There is also evidence for a weaker peak but we shall not concentrate on them here. The different polarizations show striking differences: for s-polarization, B_2 appears at a lower angle, and at α =45° this peak has a 400 cm^{-1} higher frequency, a larger width and a higher amplitude compared to p-polarization. Beyond 55°, a single broad peak occurs in the s-polarized spectra while the p-polarized peaks have disappeared. The overall decrease of the p-spectra amplitudes relative to those of the s-spectra is probably due to the air-crystal boundary conditions for the electric and magnetic fields. The fact that the peaks do not reach ideal (100 %) reflectivity is probably related to a mosaic spread as well as diffuse scattering.

Figure 15 shows the center frequencies of all peaks as a function of α and demonstrates that the frequencies of B_1 and B_2 display an avoided crossing centered near 10500 cm^{-1}. The figure also shows the full widths at half maximum of the reflection peaks, that gauge the widths of stop gaps in the dispersion relations. The large frequency separations between the peaks in the avoided crossing region is similar to the widths of the peaks, a characteristic of

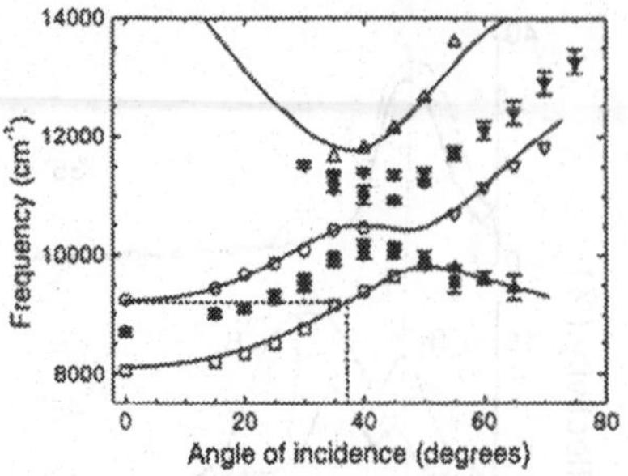

Figure 15: Frequencies of Bragg peaks as a function of angle of incidence for a crystal with $a = 860$ nm. Center frequencies are indicated by closed symbols: triangles for B_1-s polarized, squares are for B_1-p, inverted triangles are for B_2-s, and circles for B_2-p. The estimated error bars of the peak centers are indicated. Open symbols are half heights for the s-polarized B_1 peaks (squares and circles) and for the B_1 peaks (inverted and normal triangles). The drawn curves are calculated Bloch modes (s-polarized), converted to angle of incidence by parallel wave vector projection.[39] The dashed lines indicate the frequencies at top of the L-gap (at 0°), that are Bragg diffracted all the way up to 37°.[18]

coupled wave phenomena. We attribute the avoided crossing behavior to coupling of Bragg reflection events from (111) and (200) planes. This coupling also flattens the photon dispersion relations. Figure 16 shows the surface of the first Brillouin zone of the *fcc* structure, the surface associated with Bragg diffraction. For simple diffraction from real space (111) planes, the incident ($\mathbf{k}_{in}$) and reflected wave vectors ($\mathbf{k}_r$) lie on parallel (111)-type faces of the zone surface, with $\mathbf{k}_r = \mathbf{k}_{in} + \mathbf{G}$, with $\mathbf{G}$ the $hkl = 111$ reciprocal lattice vector. The angle *inside* the crystal is equal to the angle between $\mathbf{k}_r$ and Γ-L, or to the angle between $\mathbf{k}_{in}$ and a vector from Γ to L. Diffraction occurs on the surface of the 1st Brillouin zone for small angles, and moves into the 2nd zone as $\mathbf{k}_{in}$ moves beyond the U point with increasing α. If $\mathbf{k}_{in}$ passes through the U point (for intermediate α), two diffracted wave vectors appear simultaneously: $\mathbf{k}_r$ on the (111) Bragg plane and $\mathbf{k}'_r$ on the (200) plane. In multiple Bragg diffraction, the diffracted waves are coupled, hence both diffraction processes are modified compared to simple Bragg diffraction. The occurrence of two or more coupled Bragg diffraction processes accounts for our experimental observations.

We have calculated the photonic dispersion curves by solving the Maxwell equations using the well-known plane wave expansion technique. The dielectric function for the crystal is represented by $\varepsilon(\mathbf{r}) = \sum \epsilon_{\mathbf{G}} \exp(i\mathbf{G}\cdot\mathbf{r})$, where the sum extends over all reciprocal lattice vectors $\mathbf{G}$. Each of the eigenmodes for frequency ω and wave vector $\mathbf{k}$ is represented as $E^{\omega}_{\mathbf{k}}(r,t) = \exp(-i\omega t)\sum E^{\omega}_{\mathbf{k},\mathbf{G}}\exp[i(\mathbf{k}-\mathbf{G})\cdot\mathbf{r}]$. Using a variety of analytical models for $\varepsilon(\mathbf{r})$, we find that the dispersion relations of the low-frequency modes relevant to us can be computed with *only three* distinct ϵ_G, *viz.*, ϵ_0, $\epsilon_{(111)}$, and $\epsilon_{(200)}$ (along with their symmetry related equivalents). We take $\epsilon_0 = 1.41$ from the square of the effective refractive index of 1.18. The 1200 cm^{-1} width of the Bragg peak at $\alpha = 0°$ fixes $\epsilon_{(111)} = -0.18$. We have chosen $\epsilon_{(200)} = 0.1\epsilon_{(111)}$, guided by a model of close-packed air spheres, although variations of this coefficient by 50 % shift the dispersion curves less than 5 %. The calculated band-structures are converted to an external angle of incidence by parallel wave vector considerations and plotted in Fig. 15. At low angles and low frequencies, the two bands are mainly mixed (000) and (111) bands that bound the (111) Bragg diffraction. The band at high frequencies and low angles is a (200) mode. With increasing angle, the bands move together and obtain mixed character. Beyond 55°, the bands have changed character: the lowest mode is now the (200)

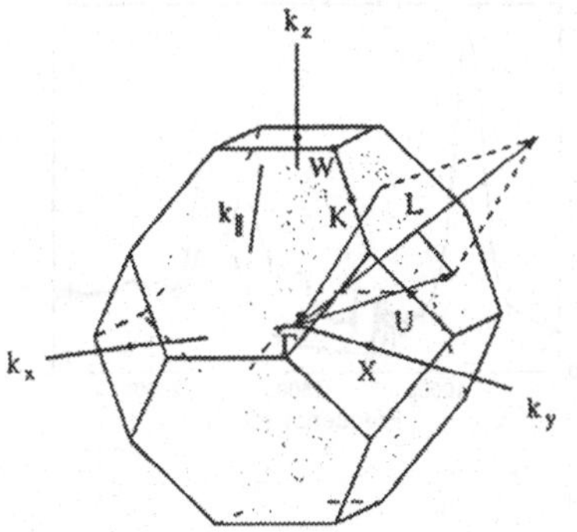

Figure 16: The first Brillouin zone of the *fcc* structure of the air-sphere crystals. Γ indicates the origin of reciprocal space, and K, L, U, and W are high symmetry points on the edge of the Brillouin zone. The arrow from the zone edge to Γ denotes the wave vector of an incident light beam, and the arrow from Γ to the zone edge indicates the wave vector of a reflected light beam. The long arrow from Γ through L is the 111 reciprocal lattice vector that is probed in the experiment. The shaded circles with radius $k_{\|} = k_L \times 0.59$ indicate the range of wave vectors for which light with a frequency at the top of the L-stop band is reflected.[18]

mode, whereas the upper two have become the mixed (000) and (111) bands. It is remarkable that the positions of the bands, that delimit the edges of stop bands, are in excellent agreement with the half heights of the reflectivity peaks. This supports the proposition from section 3.1 that FWHM are good measures of widths of stop bands, but now extended to non-zero angles of incidence.

In the present experiments, multiple Bragg diffraction is observed with a coupling band width of about 10 % and an angular range of more than 10°. For comparison, in delicate x-ray diffraction experiments on atomic crystals the characteric intensity modulations occur over an angular range of arc seconds. This difference is easily understood, since photonic interactions are 3 to 6 orders of magnitude stronger in the optical regime than in the x-ray regime. The strong interactions cause strong band repulsions and flat dispersion bands that are the basis to the formation of photonic band gaps in the optical regime. Conversely, an x-ray photonic band gap is unlikely to occur on account of the weak interactions. Of course there are other differences between optical and x-ray scattering. The former is based on macroscopic Maxwell equations and as our data above illustrate, polarization characteristics play a major role. X-ray scattering is based on the microscopic Maxwell equations, hence polarization effects are subtle.

On the Brillouin zone surface illustrated in Fig. 16, the shaded area is the region of k-space over which light at a frequency (8700 cm^{-1}) corresponding to the top of the L gap at $\alpha = 0°$ is reflected. The extent of this range can be estimated from the data in Fig. 15 which shows that the top of the reflectivity gap at $\alpha = 0°$ coincides with the bottom of the reflectivity gap near $\alpha = 37°$. Taking into account all eight (111) faces of the Brillouin zone, one finds that 2.2π solid angle of wave vectors are diffracted, i.e., light propagation is inhibited for more than 55 % of all possible directions. It has been proposed that this strongly inhibited light propagation, observed earlier for crystals with a = 480 nm,[18] leads to large changes in the optical density of states, and hence to grossly altered emission characteristics.

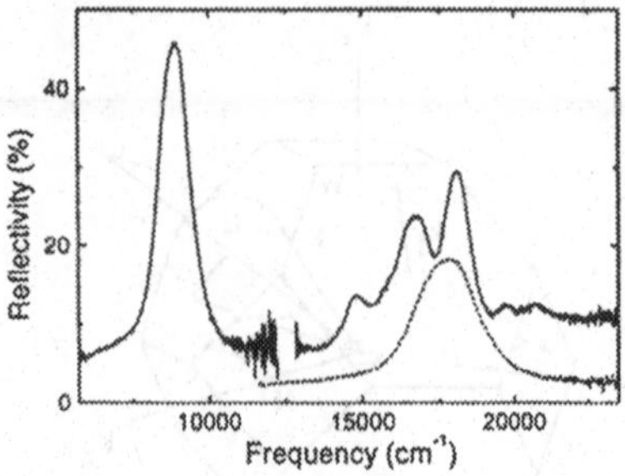

Figure 17: Reflection spectra for titania air-sphere crystals (a = 860 nm) at normal incidence as a function of frequency (solid curves). The peak at 8700 cm^{-1} is the *fcc* (111) first order Bragg reflection. The three peaks at 14830, 16760, and 18070 cm^{-1} are in the range of 2nd order diffraction. For comparison, the dashed peak at 17600 cm^{-1} is the (111) peak plotted at double the frequency (and reduced in reflectivity) as an estimate of a (222) 2nd order Bragg peak in the weak photonic limit.[40]

7.2 Coupling of Multiple Bragg Reflections: Onset of a Complete Band-gap.

At higher frequencies than those associated with the L-stop gap, one can expect that Bragg coupling in a strongly photonic crystal will become much more complex, involving scattering from many planes and the formation of Bloch states with a multitude of plane wave components. The dispersion relations for certain Bloch modes can be expected to become flat over a large volume of k-space. For a crystal with an appropriate dielectric contrast (>7.8), it has been predicted that a complete photonic gap can occur.[21,69,70] One may wonder what experimental features are characteristic of a photonic band gap or even the onset of such.

In the titania air-sphere crystals, optical reflectivity measurements at normal incidence (Fig. 17) reveal three Bragg peaks at frequencies of 14800, 16700 and 18100 cm^{-1}, beyond the (111) 1st order Bragg diffraction at 8700 cm^{-1}. It can be excluded that the triple peaks are due to disorder effects.[40] The new stop gaps occur in the frequency region where 2nd order ($22\bar{2}$) Bragg diffraction would occur in a weakly photonic crystal, and where a complete photonic band gap is expected in a strongly photonic crystal. For comparison, in Fig. 17, we also plot the (111) 1st order peak at twice its frequency to simulate a (222) 2nd order peak. Clearly there is a marked difference in the weak and strong reflectivity signatures. In a weakly photonic crystal the peak reflectivity frequency would also be expected to obey Bragg's law. Figure 18 displays the high frequency component of the spectra at 0°, 15°, 30°, and 45°. Compared to normal incidence, the peaks in the 15° spectrum have broadened and shifted down by ~500 cm^{-1}, the reflectivity is reduced, and a new component has appeared at 19200 cm^{-1}. At 30°, the overall spectrum has shifted to the blue, in qualitative agreement with Bragg behavior. The 14800 cm^{-1} and the 16000 cm^{-1} bands have disappeared, and there is a broad band centered at 17800 cm^{-1}. At 45°, there are bands at 18000, 19800, and 21000 cm^{-1}. The decrease in reflectivity amplitude with angle may be due to surface boundary conditions or multiple Bragg diffraction and grating modes that take light into non-specular directions.[71] The main observation, however, is that in strongly photonic crystals, the usual higher-order Bragg diffraction has changed to a complex coupling of many Bloch waves, that causes reflection bands to display little dispersion.

To obtain insight into our observations, we have computed the photonic band structures for our air-sphere crystals by the plane-wave expansion method for vector waves. We have used a spatially-dependent dielectric function $\varepsilon(\mathrm{r})$ that corresponds closely to the de-

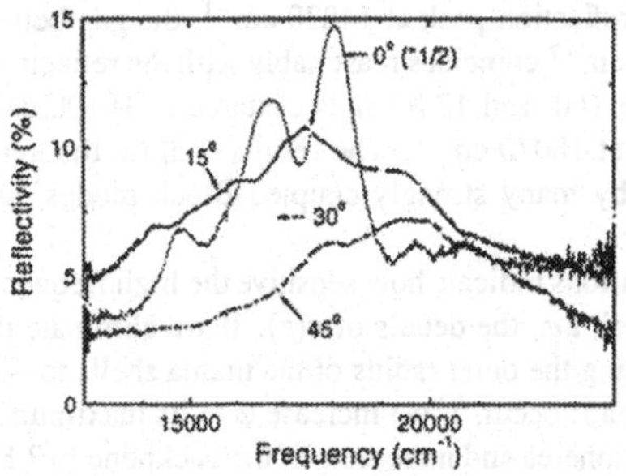

Figure 18: Reflection spectra of titania air-sphere crystals for angles of incidence of 0° (dotted curve, same as in Fig. 17 but multiplied by 0.5), 15° (solid curve), 30° (dashed curve), and 45° (dash-dotted curve).[40]

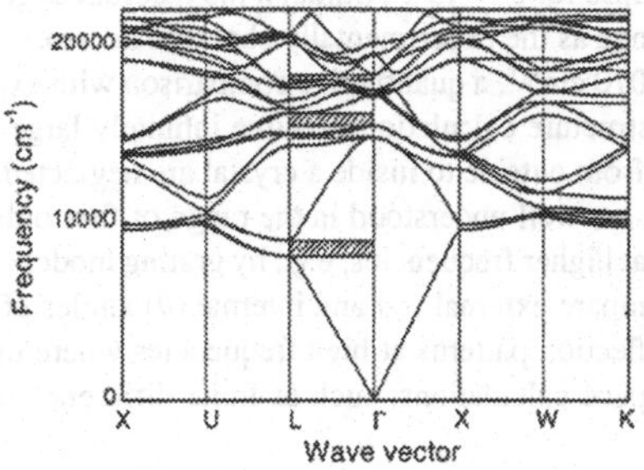

Figure 19: Photonic band structures for our titania air-sphere crystals ($a = 860$ nm), between common high-symmetry points in the Brillouin zone.[6] The results are computed with a model of dielectric shells with inner radius 1.0, outer radius 1.09, and connecting windows between the air spheres with radius 0.4. The dielectric constant of the TiO_2 is $\varepsilon = 6.5$, the lattice parameter is 860 nm, and 339 plane waves have been used. Stop gaps in the $\Gamma - L$ direction are indicated by hatched boxes.[40]

tailed structure obtained from SAXS and scanning electron microscopy experiments. The *fcc* crystals are well described by overlapping shells of dielectric material (titania), with inner radius 1.0 (touching close-packed air spheres) and outer radius 1.09 in units of the radius of close-packed spheres. This leaves the characteristic octagonal air voids seen, e.g., in SEM photographs. The air spheres inside the shells are connected to their twelve nearest neighbors by cylindrical windows with radius 0.4. The resulting TiO_2 filling fraction is $\varphi = 0.10$, the average for the samples considered. The dielectric constant of titania is taken as $\varepsilon = 6.5$, the isotropically averaged value for visible light. Bandstructures were calculated using up to 339 plane waves, although for the first 20 bands discussed here the frequencies are defined to better than 1% for as few as 120 plane waves.

Figure 19 shows the bandstructure for our crystals along high symmetry directions in the *fcc* Brillouin zone, calculated for $a = 860$ nm. We find three high frequency stop gaps beyond the 1st order stop gap (8700 cm^{-1}) between the Γ and L-points. These gaps can be directly compared to the reflectivity peaks at normal incidence, even though the peaks are somewhat asymmetrical: the gap between the 5th and the 6th bands centered at 14800 cm^{-1}

coincides well with the reflection peak at 14830 cm^{-1}, the gap between the 8th and the 9th bands centered at 15800 cm^{-1} coincides reasonably with the reflectivity peak at 16760 cm^{-1}, and the gap between the 16th and 17th bands centered at 18100 cm^{-1} coincides very well with the reflection peak at 18070 cm^{-1}. The results confirm theoretically that the observed phenomena are caused by many strongly coupled Bloch modes, associated with multiple Bragg diffraction.

Additional computations indicate how sensitive the high frequency gaps are to details of the topology of the model, *i.e.*, the details of $\varepsilon(\mathbf{r})$. If we eliminate the connecting windows altogether, while increasing the outer radius of the titania shells to ~ 1.1 to keep φ constant, no high frequency stop-gaps occur. If we increase φ to its maximum value (0.26) in a close-packed *fcc* crystal of air spheres and increase ε of the backbone to 7.84, all three gaps survive but only the one between the 8th and 9th bands develops into a complete photonic gap, in agreement with earlier work.[21,69] These results indicate that the reflectivity peak at 16700 cm^{-1} is the precursor of the photonic band gap.

Calculations of the band structure along directions at an angle θ with respect to the $\Gamma - L$ direction, toward the U-point, indicate that the lowest stop-gap collapses for $\theta \sim 10°$ while the two higher gaps collapse for $\theta \sim 15°$. Although the theoretical gaps collapse in the same angular sequence and range as the experimentally observed decrease of the reflectivity peaks at 14830, 16760, and 18070 cm^{-1}, a quantitative comparison with experiment is a challenge. Since plane wave band structure calculations assume infinitely large crystals, effects caused by coupling of the light from outside to inside a crystal are neglected. Experimentally, wave vector projection effects are well understood in the range of first order diffraction, but these effects are compounded at higher frequencies, e.g., by grating modes (see below). This makes it difficult to directly compare external (α) and internal (θ) angles of propagation. Interpretation of the complex reflection patterns at high frequencies where the photonic band gap is expected, call for real-space calculations, such as finite difference time domain or transfer matrix techniques.

If momentum conservation parallel to the crystal surface is assumed in the frequency range of the newly observed peaks, the next Brillouin zone is reached at angles of about 30°. Hence the observed bands would be dispersionless over the whole face of the relevant Brillouin zone, a characteristic that might be expected for a crystal possessing a complete band gap. On the other hand, the band structures in Fig. 19 do not reveal a photonic band gap for the *fcc* titania crystals. These facts taken together warrant a note of caution in using reflectivity (or transmission) data to define a complete gap.

8 PROBES OF A PHOTONIC BAND GAP

At this point, the question arises what is suitable probe of a photonic band gap. One may consider cw reflectivity or transmission, to obtain stop gaps that overlap for all directions. While this method has been applied to the structures used in the microwave range,[8,44] such a probe encounters challenges in the case of the promising air-sphere crystals, as we have seen in the previous section. Also, the high frequency bands relevant to fcc crystals may be "uncoupled" modes,[72,73] and thus give rise to apparent stop gaps.

The first experimental probe of photonic band gaps proposed here is the study of the emission spectrum of light sources inside a photonic crystal.[28] We have seen above that in absence of a band gap, the attenuation in the transfer function is limited by scattering off defects near the samples' surface. This channel will be shut off in case of a photonic band gap, see Fig. 20, hence it is predicted that the transfer function will experience a complete attenuation in the frequency range of the gap.

The second band gap probe proposed here is to measure the radiative dynamics of light

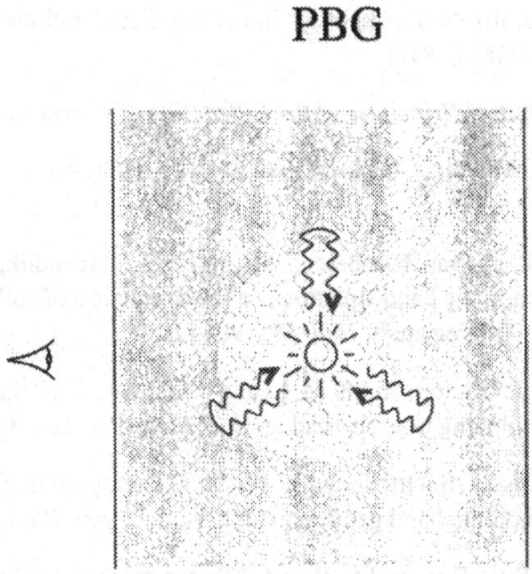

Figure 20: Schematic drawing of the trajectory of light emitted by a point source inside a photonic crystal with a photonic band gap. Locally the light can be emitted around a defect, but the light cannot propagate through the crystal. As a result, for the frequency range of the band gap, a notch is expected in the emission spectrum with a complete attenuation.[28]

sources inside photonic crystals.[3] This allows a direct access to the local density of states,[74] that will reveal a photonic band gap.[75]

Finally, a third probe is the measurement of the group velocity dispersion for all directions of propagation.[41] The gvd is an unambiguous probe of stop gaps, as it diverges at the edges of such gaps, and is very small inside of them. Thus, extensive gvd measurements allow the mapping of stop gaps for all directions, and hence, in case of overlap, a band gap.

9 ACKNOWLEDGMENTS

We are grateful to Judith Wijnhoven, Lydia Bechger, and earlier on Carlos van Kats for expert sample preparation, to Ad Lagendijk for continuous encouragements and support, to Henry Schriemer, Frank Schuurmans, Gijs van Soest, Rudolf Sprik, Michiel Thijssen, Gerard Wegdam for experimental help, discussions, and a great atmosphere, and to Theyencheri Narayanan, Peter Bösecke, and Olivier Diat for help at the ESRF. This work is part of research program of the "Stichting voor Fundamenteel Onderzoek der Materie (FOM)", which is supported by the "Nederlanse Organisatie voor Wetenschappelijk Onderzoek" (NWO).

REFERENCES

1. C.M. Soukoulis, ed., *Photonic Band Gap Materials*, Kluwer, Dordrecht (1996).

2. J.D. Joannopoulos, R.D. Meade, and J.N. Winn, *Photonic Crystals*, Princeton University Press, Princeton NJ (1995).

3. E. Yablonovitch, "Inhibited spontaneous emission in solid-state physics and electronics," *Phys. Rev. Lett.* **58**, 2059 (1987).

4. S. John, "Strong localization of photons in certain disordered dielectric superlattices," *Phys. Rev. Lett.* **58**, 2486 (1987).

5. R.W. James, *The Optical Principles of the Diffraction of X-rays*, Bell, London (1962).

6. N.W. Ashcroft and N.D. Mermin, *Solid State Physics*, Holt, Rinehart, and Winston, New York (1976).

7. W.L. Vos, R. Sprik, A. van Blaaderen, A. Imhof, A. Lagendijk, and G.H. Wegdam, "Strong effects of photonic band structures on the diffraction of colloidal crystals," *Phys. Rev. B* **53**, 16231 (1996); erratum: *Ibid.* **55**, 1903 (1997).

8. E. Yablonovitch, T.J. Gmitter, and K.M. Leung, "Photonic band structure: the face centered cubic case employing nonspherical atoms," *Phys. Rev. Lett.* **67**, 2295 (1991).

9. U. Grüning, V. Lehmann, S. Ottow, and K. Busch, "Macroporous silicon with a complete two-dimensional photonic band gap centered at 5 μm," *Appl. Phys. Lett.* **68**, 747 (1996).

10. T.F. Krauss, R.M. DeLaRue, and S. Brand, "Two-dimensional photonic bandgap structures operating at near-infrared wavelengths," *Nature* **383**, 699 (1996).

11. S.Y. Lin, J.G. Fleming, D.L. Hetherington, B.K. Smith, R. Biswas, K.M. Ho, M.M. Sigalas, W. Zubrzycki, S.R. Kurtz, and J. Bur, "A three-dimensional photonic crystal operating at infrared wavelengths," *Nature* **394**, 251 (1998).

12. N. Yamamoto, S. Noda, and A. Chutinan, "Development of one period of a three-dimensional photonic crystal in the 5-10 μm wavelength region by wafer fusion and laser beam diffraction pattern observation techniques," *Jpn. J. Appl. Phys.* **37**, L1052 (1998).

13. A. Imhof and D.J. Pine, "Ordered macroporous materials by emulsion templating," *Nature* **389**, 948 (1997).

14. O.D. Velev and E. Kaler, "Structured porous materials via colloidal crystal templating: from inorganic oxides to metals," *Adv. Mater.* **12**, 531 (2000), and references therein.

15. B.T. Holland, C.F. Blanford, and A. Stein, "Synthesis of macroporous minerals with highly ordered three-dimensional arrays of spherical voids," *Science* **281**, 538 (1998).

16. J.E.G.J. Wijnhoven and W.L. Vos, "Preparation of photonic crystals made of air spheres in titania," *Science* **281**, 802 (1998).

17. A.A. Zakhidov, R.H. Baughman, Z. Iqbal, C. Cui, I. Khayrullin, S.O. Dantas, J. Marti, and V.G. Ralchenko, "Carbon structures with three-dimensional periodicity at optical wavelengths," *Science* **282**, 897 (1998).

18. M.S. Thijssen, R. Sprik, J.E.G.J. Wijnhoven, M. Megens, T. Narayanan, A. Lagendijk, and W.L. Vos, "Inhibited light propagation and broad band reflection in photonic air-sphere crystals," *Phys. Rev. Lett.* **83**, 2730 (1999).

19. A. Blanco, E. Chomski, S. Grabtchak, M. Ibisate, S. John, S.W. Leonard, C. Lopez, F. Meseguer, H. Miguez, J.P. Mondia, G.A. Ozin, O. Toader, and H.M. van Driel, "Large scale synthesis of a silicon photonic crystal with a complete three-dimensional photonic band gap near 1.5 micrometers," *Nature* **405**, 437 (2000).

20. K.M. Ho, C.T. Chan, and C.M. Soukoulis, "Existence of a photonic gap in periodic dielectric structures," *Phys. Rev. Lett.* **65**, 3152 (1990).

21. H.S. Sözüer, J.W. Haus, and R. Inguva, "Photonic bands: convergence problems with the plane-wave method," *Phys. Rev. B* **45**, 13962 (1992).

22. M. Megens, C.M. van Kats, P. Bösecke, and W.L. Vos, "In-situ characterization of colloidal spheres by synchrotron small-angle x-ray scattering," *Langmuir* **13**, 6120 (1997).

23. M. Megens, C.M. van Kats, P. Bösecke, and W.L. Vos, "Synchrotron small angle x-ray scattering of colloids and photonic colloidal crystals," *J. Appl. Cryst.* **13**, 637 (1997).

24. W.L. Vos, M. Megens, C.M. van Kats, and P. Bösecke, "X-ray diffraction of photonic colloidal single crystals," *Langmuir* **13**, 6004 (1997).

25. M. Megens, J.E.G.J. Wijnhoven, A. Lagendijk, and W.L. Vos, "Fluorescence lifetimes and linewidths of dye in photonic crystals," *Phys. Rev. A* **59**, 4727 (1999).

26. M. Megens, Ph.D. thesis, Universiteit van Amsterdam (October 1999), available as pdf from our website.

27. A. Imhof, M. Megens, J.J. Engelberts, D.T.N. de Lang, R. Sprik, and W.L. Vos, "Spectroscopy of Fluorescein (FITC) dyed colloidal silica spheres," *J. Phys. Chem. B* **103**, 1408 (1999).

28. M. Megens, J.E.G.J. Wijnhoven, A. Lagendijk, and W.L. Vos, "Light sources inside photonic crystals," *J. Opt. Soc. Am. B* **16**, 1403 (1999).

29. M. Megens, H.P. Schriemer, A. Lagendijk, and W.L. Vos, "Comment on: Spontaneous emission of organic molecules embedded in photonic crystal," *Phys. Rev. Lett.* **83**, 5401 (1999).

30. J.E.G.J. Wijnhoven, L. Bechger, and W.L. Vos, to be published.

31. J.E.G.J. Wijnhoven, S.J.M. Zevenhuizen, M. Hendriks, D. Vanmaekelbergh, J.J. Kelly, and W.L. Vos, "Electrochemical assembly of ordered macropores in gold." *Adv. Mater.* **12**, 888 (2000).

32. M. Megens and W.L. Vos, "Excursions of particles in a colloidal crystal," *Phys. Rev. Lett.* (submitted,2000).

33. W.L. Vos, R. Sprik, A. Lagendijk, G.H. Wegdam, A. Imhof, and A. van Blaaderen, "Dispersive effects on light scattering of photonic colloidal crystals," *1994 European Quantum Electronics Conference, Postdeadline digest*, IEEE/LEOS, Piscataway NJ, (1994), paper EPD6.

34. W.L. Vos, J.E.G.J. Wijnhoven, and M. Megens, "Experimental probe of gaps in photonic crystals," *Conference on Lasers and Electro-Optics Europe*, IEEE/LEOS, Piscataway NJ, 1998), paper CFB6.

35. W.L. Vos, M. Megens, C.M. van Kats, and P. Bösecke, "Transmission and diffraction by photonic colloidal crystals," *J. Phys.: Condens. Matter* **8**, 9503 (1996).

36. K.W.K. Shung and Y.C. Tsai, "Surface effects and band measurements in photonic crystals," *Phys. Rev.B* **48**, 11265 (1993).

37. R.J. Spry and D.J. Kosan, "Theoretical analysis of the crystalline colloidal array filter," *Appl. Spectrosc.* **40**, 782 (1986).

38. A. Moroz and C. Sommers, "Photonic band gaps of three-dimensional face-centered cubic lattices," *J. Phys.: Condens. Matter* **11**, 997 (1999).

39. H.M. van Driel and W.L. Vos, "Multiple Bragg wave coupling in photonic band gap crystals," *Phys. Rev. B* **62**, 9872 (2000).

40. W.L. Vos and H.M. van Driel, "Higher order Bragg diffraction by strongly photonic fcc crystals: onset of a photonic bandgap," *Phys. Lett. A* **272**, 101 (2000).

41. A. Imhof, W.L. Vos, R. Sprik, and A. Lagendijk, "Large dispersive effects near the band edges of photonic crystals," *Phys. Rev. Lett.* **83**, 2942 (1999).

42. J.F. Bertone, P. Jiang, K.S. Hwang, D.M. Mittleman, and V.L. Colvin, "Thickness dependence of the optical properties of ordered silica-air and air-polymer photonic crystals," *Phys. Rev. Lett.* **83**, 300 (1999).

43. Yu.A. Vlasov, V.N. Astratov, O.Z. Karimov, and A.A. Kaplyanskii, "Existence of a photonic pseudogap for visible light in synthetic opal," *Phys. Rev. B* **55**, 13357 (1997).

44. E. Özbay, "Micromachined photonic band gap crystals: from microwave to far-infrared," in: C.M. Soukoulis, ed., *Photonic Band Gap Materials*, Kluwer, Dordrecht (1996), p. 41.

45. A.M. Steinberg, P.G. Kwiat, and R.Y. Chiao, "Measurement of the single-photon tunneling time," *Phys. Rev. Lett.* **71**, 708 (1993).

46. C. Spielmann, R. Szipocs, A. Stingl, and F. Krausz, "Tunneling of optical pulses through photonic band gaps," *Phys. Rev. Lett.* **73**, 2308 (1994).

47. M. Scalora, R.J. Flynn, S.B. Reinhardt, R.L. Fork, M.J. Bloemer, M.D. Tocci, C.M. Bowden, H.S. Ledbetter, J.M. Bendickson, and R.P. Leavitt, "Ultrashort pulse propagation at the photonic band edge: large tunable group delay with minimal distortion and loss," *Phys. Rev. E* **54**, R1078 (1996)

48. Yu.A. Vlasov, S. Petit, G. Klein, B. Hönerlage, and C. Hirlimann, "Femtosecond measurements of the time of flight of photons in a three-dimensional photonic crystal," *Phys. Rev. E* **60**, 1030 (1999).

49. R.H.J. Kop and R. Sprik, "Phase sensitive interferometry with ultrashort optical pulses," *Rev. Sci. Instrum.*, **66**, 5459 (1995).

50. E. Lidorikis, Q. Li, and C.M. Soukoulis, "Optical bistability in colloidal crystals," *Phys. Rev.E* **55**, 3613 (1997).

51. R.H.J. Kop, P. de Vries, R. Sprik, and A. Lagendijk, "Kramers-Kronig relations for an interferometer," *Opt. Commun.* **138**, 118 (1997).

52. D.J. Heinzen, J.J. Childs, J.E. Thomas, and M.S. Feld, "Enhanced and inhibited visible spontaneous emission by atoms in a confocal resonator," *Phys. Rev. Lett.* **58**, 1320 (1987).

53. S. Haroche, "Cavity quantum electrodynamics," in *Systèmes fondamentaux en optique quantique/Fundamental systems in quantum optics*, Eds. J. Dalibard, J.-M. Raimond, J. Zinn-Justin, North-Holland, Amsterdam (1992).

54. H.P. Schriemer, H.M. van Driel, A.F. Koenderink, and W.L. Vos, "Modified spontaneous emission spectra of laser dye in inverse opal photonic crystals," *Phys. Rev. A. Rapid Comm.* **63** (January 1, 2001).

55. F. DeMartini, G. Innocenti, G. R. Jacobovitz, and P. Mataloni, "Anomalous spontaneous emission time in a microscopic optical cavity," *Phys. Rev. Lett.* **59**, 2955 (1987).

56. J. Martorell and N. M. Lawandy, "Observation of inhibited spontaneous emission in a periodic dielectric structure," *Phys. Rev. Lett.* **65**, 1877 (1990).

57. E. P. Petrov, V. N. Bogomolov, I. I. Kalosha, and S V. Gaponenko, "Spontaneous emission of organic molecules embedded in a photonic crystal," *Phys. Rev. Lett.* **81**, 77 (1998); "Modification of the spontaneous emission of dye molecules in photonic crystals," *Acta Phys. Pol. A* **94**, 761 (1998).

58. P.W. Anderson, "Absence of diffusion in certain random lattices," *Phys. Rev.* **109**, 1492 (1958); S. John, "Electromagnetic absorption in a disordered medium near a photon mobility edge," *Phys. Rev. Lett.* **53**, 2169 (1984).

59. D.S. Wiersma, P. Bartolini, A. Lagendijk, and R. Righini, "Localization of light," *Nature* **390**, 671 (1997).

60. F.J.P. Schuurmans, M. Megens, D. Vanmaekelbergh, and A. Lagendijk, "Light scattering near the localization transition in macroporous GaP networks," *Phys. Rev. Lett.* **83**, 2183 (1999).

61. Y. Kuga and A. Ishimaru, "Retroreflectance from a dense distribution of spherical particles," *J. Opt. Soc. Am. A* **8**, 831 (1984), M. P. van Albada and A. Lagendijk, "Observation of weak localization of light in a random medium," *Phys. Rev. Lett.* **55**, 2692 (1985); P. E. Wolf and G. Maret, "Weak localization and coherent backscattering of photons in disordered media," *Phys. Rev. Lett.* **55**, 2696 (1985).

62. E. Akkermans, P. E. Wolf, and R. Maynard, "Coherent backscattering of light by disordered media: Analysis of the peak line shape," *Phys. Rev.Lett.* **56**, 1471 (1986).

63. M. B. van der Mark, M. P. van Albada, and A. Lagendijk, "Light scattering in strongly scattering media: Multiple scattering and weak localization," *Phys. Rev. B* **37**, 3575 (1988).

64. A.F. Koenderink, M. Megens, G. van Soest, W.L Vos, and A. Lagendijk, "Enhanced backscattering from photonic crystals," *Phys. Lett. A* **268**, 104 (2000).

65. A. Lagendijk, R. Vreeker, and P. de Vries, "Influence of internal reflection on diffusive transport in strongly scattering media," *Phys. Lett. A* **136**, 81 (1989).

66. H. C. van der Hulst, *Light Scattering by Small Particles*, Dover, New York (1981).

67. P. Sheng, *Introduction to Wave Scattering, Localization, and Mesoscopic Phenomena*, Academic, San Diego (1995).

68. D. S. Wiersma, M. P. van Albada, and A. Lagendijk, "An accurate technique to record the angular distribution of backscattered light," *Rev. Sci. Instrum.* **66**, 5473 (1995).

69. K. Busch and S. John, "Photonic band gap formation in certain self-organizing systems," *Phys. Rev. E* **58**, 3986 (1998).

70. R. Biswas, M.M. Sigalas, G. Subramania, C.M. Soukoulis, and K.M. Ho, "Photonic band gaps of porous solids," *Phys. Rev. B* 61, 4549 (2000).

71. D. Labilloy, H. Benisty, C. Weisbuch, T.F. Krauss, D. Cassagne, C. Jouanin, R. Houdre, U. Oesterle, and V. Bardinal, "Diffraction efficiency and guided light control by two dimensional photonic band gap lattices," *IEEE J. Quant. Electr.* 35, 1045 (1999).

72. W.M. Robertson, G. Arjavalingam, R.D. Meade, K.D. Brommer, A.M. Rappe, and J.D. Joannopoulos, "Measurement of photonic band structure in a two-dimensional periodic dielectric array," *Phys. Rev. Lett.* 68, 2023 (1992).

73. K. Sakoda, "Group-theoretical classification of eigenmodes in three-dimensional photonic lattices," *Phys. Rev. B* 55, 15345 (1997).

74. R. Sprik, B.A. van Tiggelen, and A. Lagendijk, "Optical emission in periodic dielectrics," *Europhys. Lett.* 35, 265 (1996).

75. T. Suzuki and P.K.L. Yu, "Emission power of an electric dipole in the photonic band structure of the fcc lattice," *J. Opt. Soc. Am. B* 12, 570 (1995).

INVERSE OPALS FABRICATION

H. Míguez, A. Blanco, F. García-Santamaría, M. Ibisate, C. López, F. Meseguer*
Unidad Asociada CSIC-UPV Edificio de Institutos II. Universidad Politécnica de Valencia, 46022 Valencia, Spain * email:fmese@fis.upv.es
also
Instituto de Ciencia de Materiales de Madrid (Consejo Superior de Investigaciones Científicas)
Cantoblanco, 28049 Madrid, Spain

F. López-Tejeira, J. Sánchez-Dehesa
Dep. de Física Teórica de la Materia Condensada, Facultad de Ciencias, Universidad Autónoma de Madrid, 28049 Madrid, Spain

1. Introduction

Here we report on different approaches to the fabrication, characterization, and modelling of inverse opals. We start from silica opal templates with sphere size in the range between 0.2 μm and 1.3 μm. The opal porous lattice is highly infiltrated with semiconductors (CdS, Ge) as well as polymers by several methods such as Chemical Bath Deposition, etc. Afterwards the template is removed from the composite, by a mild chemical etching method.[1] Thus, an inverse opal is obtained. The periodicity of the template can be varied to place the photonic gaps or pseudogaps in different frequency regions.

Optical properties of CdS and polymer inverse opals, as well as the comparison with theoretical calculations of the transmission and reflectance, are reported. Ge inverse opal presents a huge refractive index contrast (4/1) well above the threshold for appearance of a sizeable full band gap.

The proposal of the Photonic Band Gap (PBG) materials in 1987[2,3] has given an enormous boost to photonics. It opens the possibility to use the photon as an information carrier as the electron does in semiconductor technology. At variance with electrons, photons have no mass nor charge and therefore they are more efficient in transporting and also in the processing of information. Fibre optics is an example of the overwhelming possibilities of photonic technology. Three-dimensional (3D) PBG materials are most promising. Finding procedures to fabricate 3D PBG materials with a full gap in the visible infrared region of the EM spectrum is a real challenge. Our approach lies on the synthesis of semiconductors

C.M. Soukoulis (ed.), Photonic Crystals and Light Localization in the 21st Century, 219–227.

and insulators within the mesoporous voids of artificial opals.[4] This method is very attractive because it is easy and cheap. Here we report on the fabrication of inverse opals made of different materials as polymers,[5] CdS and Ge.[6] These opals have also been used to infiltrate Silicon.[7] Here we will give information about the different steps to achieve the inverse matrix.

This paper is organised as follows: First, we report on template fabrication. We will mainly comment on large sphere opals that allow the synthesis of inverse opals with photonic band features at frequencies below the bulk absorption edge of the materials that form the inverse matrix. Second, we report on both the various infiltration methods and the fabrication of the inverse photonic lattice. The reflectance and transmission properties of these templates can be well accounted for by calculations based on the transfer matrix algorithm and/or by an analysis of the photonic band structure.[8,9]

2. Template fabrication

The fabrication method of templates with small silica sphere size (between 0.2 and 0.6 microns) has been reported in the literature.[10,11,12] Here we have focussed on the method of fabrication of large sphere opals (between 0.6 μm and 1.3 μm) that is of paramount importance in the fabrication of the most promising semiconductor inverse opals with narrow electronic band gap materials. These templates guarantee that gaps and pseudgaps of inverted networks made of several semiconductors (as Ge and Si) appear in the transparency region. The fabrication method involves several steps: The synthesis of particles, the settlement process to order them, and finally the sintering of the resulting sample.

We have used a modified Stöber method to make the synthesis process in a suspension of smaller silica particles (around 500 nm in size) that act as seeds in the synthesis process. If needed, the synthesis process is repeated several times and the spheres homogeneously increase in size to values of 1.3 micrometers, with monodispersity better than 5%.

A settling process based on natural sedimentation does not permit to order suspensions of large particles (above 600 nm). Here we make use of two other methods that slow down the settling process and therefore favor FCC ordering. The first one, useful for particles up to 900 nm, relies on the use of electrophoretical methods.[13] In the second one, we use mixtures of water and other solvents and co-solvents as ethylene glycol.

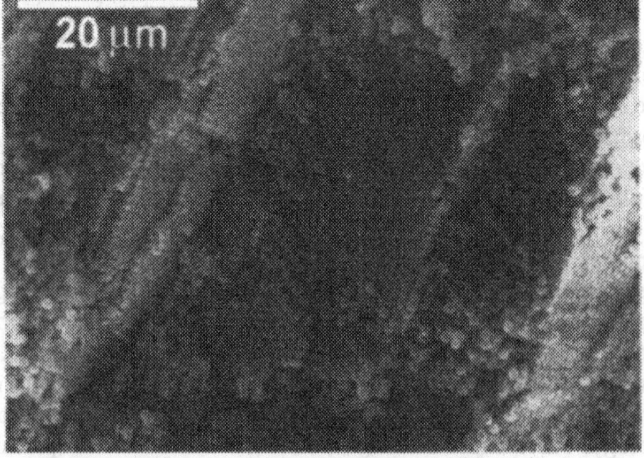

Figure 1. SEM image of the cleft edge of an bare opal with silica particles of 1.3 micrometers. One can see different terraces with (111) facets.

The sintering process, similar to that employed for small sphere templates, endows the opals with mechanical stability. The success of the inverse opal fabrication strongly depends on the connectivity between silica particles provided by the sintering process.[14] Such treatment also permits to control the opal void volume, a crucial parameter in the search of optimal semiconductor infilling and, therefore, the maximum gap value.[15] Figure 1 shows a scanning electron microscope (SEM) image of the cleft edge of a silica template of 1.3 μm silica particles. One can see different terraces with (111) facets.

Now, we will show different examples of inverse opals made of Polymer, CdS, and Ge. We also will explain the processes to achieve them as well as some of their characteristics.

3. Polymer inverse opals

The inverse polymer opal, made of epoxy resin, is achieved in a manner similar to those previously reported.[16] The template is first soaked in the monomer in which a few drops of catalyser have been added. After some hours, when the polymerization process is finished, we remove the silica through a mild etching process.

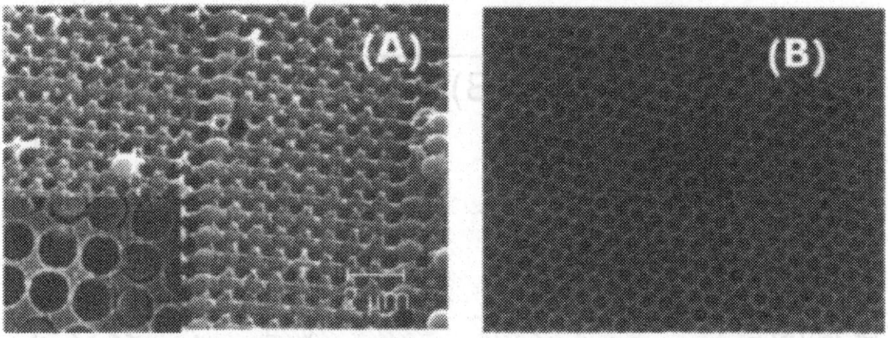

Figure 2. SEM images of cleft edges of (A) a polymer-opal composite with about 100% of polymer infilling and (B) the corresponding inverse opal: The inset in (A) shows that some silica spheres are removed which allows visualization of the small windows connecting different layers. The particle diameter of the template is 850 nm.

Figure 2 shows SEM images of the cleft edge of both a polymer-opal composite (A) and the polymer inverse opal (B) that results from an opal template of 850 nm particles. The inset of Fig. 2A shows some polymer voids where the silica spheres are removed. It allows seeing the small windows connecting different layers. The number of windows (four in the case of (100) face) gives a clue to the symmetry of the crystallographic facet. One can conclude that polymer penetrates easily throughout the void lattice and fills completely the empty space between the silica spheres. The infiltration process is such that the inverted lattice can be regarded as the negative replica of the bare opal. This is due to the fact that the specific volume change on polymerisation (<5%) allows a good replica of the template.

The study of the bare opal along with the opal-composite and the inverse opal allows us to make a comparison between different opal-like structures with the same structure and lattice constant but different refractive index contrast. Also, as the refractive index of polymer (n=1.62) is close to that of silica (n=1.45), we can compare the direct and the inverse lattices. We have performed reflectance experiments of the three systems in which the refractive index contrasts (n_{void}/n_{sphere}) are 1/1.45 (bare opal), 1.6/1.45 (polymer-silica composite) and 1.6/1 (polymer inverse opal). We have explained the experiments with photonic band calculations where we plot selected bands along ΓL and LU directions of the Brillouin zone (see Fig. 3). The photonic band structures shown in this article have been obtained using a plane wave basis in an iterative implementation[17] with a tolerance under 1_10^{-4}. We have plotted only the LU direction because photonic bands are rather isotropic around the L point. Theory and experiments are summarized in Fig. 3 for a sample of 390 nm sphere diameter. In the left panel of Fig. 3, experimental reflectance spectra are shown for the three systems (dotted line for the bare opal; solid lines for the polymer-silica composite and dashed lines for the polymer inverse opal). The centre panel plots, using the same convention, show those bands involved that lie in the ΓL direction which fairly agree with the experiment. Finally, the right-hand side panel plots the bands along the LU direction together with experimental measure of the position of reflectance peak when the sample is tilted off the (111) direction. Here squares, diamonds, and circles stand for bare opal, composite, and inverse structures respectively. The agreement theory-experiment is fairly good. Although both bare and inverse opal, have similar value for refractive index contrast inverse opals shows a much larger pseudogap than the direct opal structure.

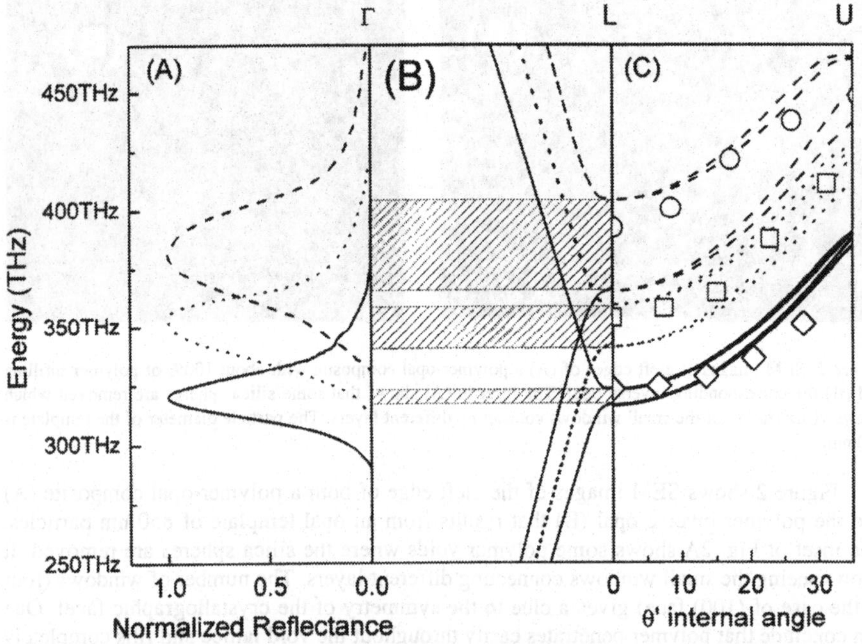

Figure 3. Experimental reflectance spectra (lines in left panel and symbols in right panel) and calculation (center and right panels) of different opal-like structures with the same periodicity (390 nm) but different refractive index contrast values (n_{void}/n_{sphere}). Bare opal (1/1.45) corresponds to dotted lines; polymer-opal composite (1.6/1.45) represented by solid lines, and polymer inverse opal (1.6/1) plotted as dashed lines. Symbols (squares, diamonds and circles for the bare opal, composite, and inverse structure, respectively) correspond to the reflectance peak position as the sample is tilted off the (111) direction.

4. CdS inverse opals

CdS has very often been infiltrated in opals due to its lucent properties in the visible range, showing very exciting results in optical gain and spontaneous emission inhibition.[18] Although CdS inverted opals do not have a full photonic band gap, their high refractive index contrast (2.5, the contrast threshold for gap opening being 2.8) should increase those interesting effects.

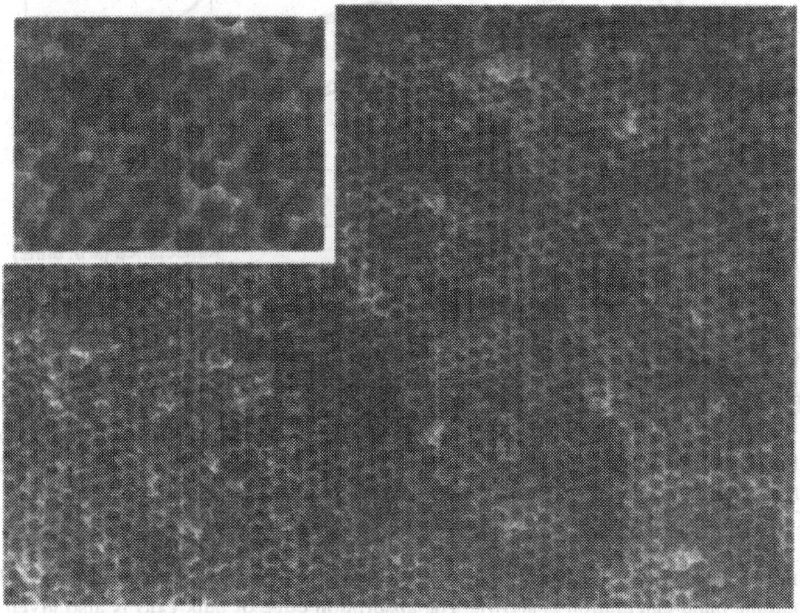

Figure 4. **SEM image of a 385 nm spheres size inverse opal of CdS. A (111) internal facet is shown. The inset is a detail of the structure where small windows connecting the removed spheres can be seen as well.**

CdS is grown by means of a chemical bath deposition (CBD) method in which the opaline sample is immersed in different solutions. The process consists of two stages which are repeated several times. During the first stage, the opal is immersed in a 2.5_10^{-2} M $CdSO_4$ aqueous solution for several minutes. After that, the opal/$CdSO_4$ is placed in a 3.5_10^{-2} M $S{=}C(NH_2)_2$ aqueous solution. The time for each stage depends on particular experimental requirements[19]. Both stages take place at 60 ºC and are catalyzed by ammonia. Employing these growth conditions, the amount of CdS inside the opal is controlled as well as the growth on the external sample surface, thus preventing the eventual blocking of the growth inside the opaline structure. The CdS amount inside the opal matrix can be followed and controlled by optical measurements. After some repeated cycles, nearly 100% CdS infilled opals can be obtained. Once the full infiltration is achieved, a soft etching process, by dipping the sample into a 1% diluted HF solution, allows to remove the silica spheres. Figure 4 shows a SEM image of the internal (111) facet of CdS inverse opal with 385 nm diameter hollow spheres. As can be directly seen in the inset of Fig. 4, CdS grows in the form of grains which cover the silica spheres occupying all the free space available, and more important, the FCC ordered structure is conserved.

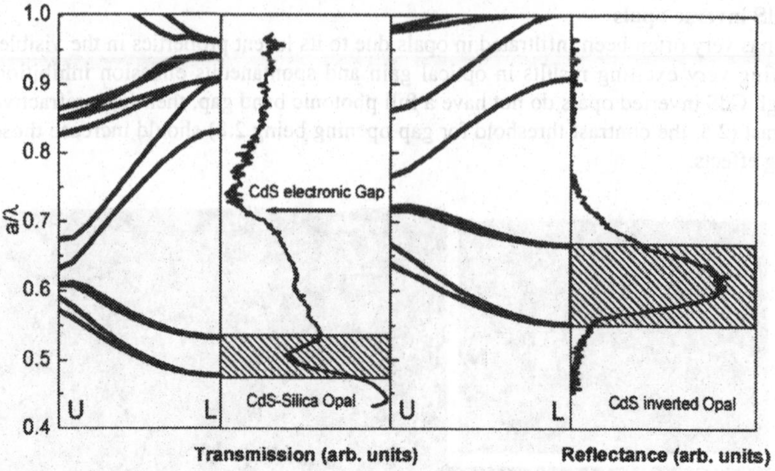

Figure 5. Left: Experimental transmission spectrum and theoretical calculations for a CdS-Silica opal made of 275 nm spheres. The CdS electronic gap is indicated with an arrow. Right: Experimental reflectance for CdS inverted opal. Notice the huge increase of the pseudogap width (shadowed areas in both spectra).

The optical properties of CdS inverse opals have been measured by means of reflectance and transmission experiments. Figure 5 shows experimental data for a 275 nm sphere CdS-opal (with about 96% of CdS infilling) before and after inversion. The sphere size is chosen to guarantee that the first pseudogap at the L point is in the transparency region of bulk CdS. Along with the experimental data, photonic band structure calculations, based on plane wave method, are also shown.

In the left panel a transmission spectrum for the opal-CdS composite system as well as the photonic band calculation is shown. The absorption edge of bulk CdS is also given. In the right panel the same is plotted for the resulting inverse opal. The frequency of the light is plotted in reduced units, a/λ, being a and λ the lattice parameter and the wavelength respectively. In both cases, theoretical calculations agree with experimental findings of the first pseudogap (at L point).

It is important to point out that the photonic properties are improved at every stage of the process. Starting from bare opal (with a refractive index contrast of 1.45), the gap to midgap ratio, for first stop band at L point, is about 5%. For the CdS-opal composite (with a refractive index contrast of 1.7), the gap ratio is 11%. Finally, in the inverted structure (with a refractive index contrast of 2.5) the gap ratio is 17.5%. Such big increase in the band gap width, could be exploited for optical applications based on this type of photonic structure such as electroluminescent photonic devices or low threshold laser systems.

5. Ge inverse opals

Ge is transparent to infrared radiation (below 0.67 eV) and it presents an extremely high refractive index contrast (n=4). This makes Ge inverse opals one of the most promising photonic band gap materials made of a semiconductor.

The process to obtain Ge inverse opals involves chemical reaction at high temperatures (above 500°C). We take advantage of the high thermal and mechanical stability of the template lattice to achieve the inverse Ge matrix. It involves several stages.[6] First, a Germanium precursor ($Ge(OCH_3)_4$) is infiltrated in the opal voids. The alkoxide is allowed to completely infill the template. Second, through a hydrolysis process we obtain GeO_2. Third,

Ge is obtained by a reduction process at 550°C. As a consequence of the different reactions and also because of the Ge aggregation process, Ge does not completely infill the opal voids. In order to increase the infiltration percentage and, also give connectivity to the Ge meso-lattice, opals are subjected to several rounds of GeO_2 and Ge formation processes as described above. After five cycles, Ge shows connectivity in ranges larger than the single crystal domain of the bare templates. Finally, Ge infiltrated opals are chemically etched to remove silica particles with the same method used for the other inverse opals. In this way, we seek to remove the SiO_2 spheres from the composite and obtain Ge inverse opals.

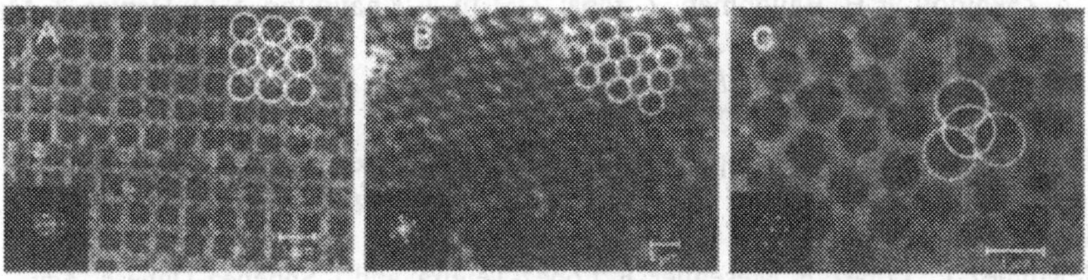

Figure 6. (A) {100}, (B) {110}, and (C) {111} front views of a 1.2 μm lattice parameter Ge inverse opal. FFTs are shown in all cases. The underlying plane can be observed through the first layer of the Ge mesh in the first two cases. The windows interconnecting the air cavities with those in the underlying plane can be seen: four in the case of {100}, five for {110}, and three for {111} faces.

Figure 6 shows examples of the three highest symmetry facets of the FCC structure from cleft edges of the Ge inverse lattice. At variance with the case of the polymer inverse opal (where polymer forms spherical shells around the air voids that are interconnected through small windows), Ge forms an interconnected grain mesh. This is very clear in the case of (100) and (110) facets, where the layer underneath can clearly be seen though the large windows of the spherical holes of the upper layer. Along with the direct SEM image Fast Fourier Transformed (FFT) images are shown to highlight the preservation of the template symmetry. As far as photonic properties is concerned, the existence of a complete PBG for a structure like this one has been theoretically predicted.[15] We have not so far obtained optical spectra that can prove the presence of such a gap because the lattice parameter of the template is smaller than required (sphere size of 850 nm). Templates made of larger spheres (above 1200 nm) will allow to place the full gap at a frequency below the absorption edge of bulk Ge ($\lambda \geq$ 1850 nm at RT).

In summary, here we have shown several examples of inverse opals for different refractive index contrast ranging from 1.6 (for the inverse polymer opal) up to 4 (for the germanium inverse opal) the largest inverse opal achieved so far. The fabrication method is easy and inexpensive because both the precursors and the chemical processes used are of customary use in chemistry.

Acknowledgments
H. Míguez thanks Comunidad Autonoma de Madrid for a graduate FPI grant. This work has been partially financed by the Fundación Ramón Areces, the Spanish CICyT project MAT97-0698-C04 and European Community project IST-1999-19009.

REFERENCES

1 A.A Zakhidov, R.H. Baughman, Z. Iqbal, C. Cui, I. Khayrullin, S.O. Dantas, J. Martí, and V.G Ralchenko. *Science 282*, 897, (1998).
2. E. Yablonovitch, *Phys. Rev. Lett.* **58**, 2059 (1987).
3. S. John, *Phys. Rev. Lett.* **58**, 2486 (1987).
4. H. Míguez, A. Blanco, C. López, F. Meseguer, H.M. Yates, M.E. Pemble, F. López-Tejeira, F. García-Vidal, and J. Sánchez-Dehesa. *J. Lightwave Technology* **17**, 1975, (1999).
5. H. Míguez, C. López, F. Meseguer, F. López-Tejeira, and J. Sánchez-Dehesa, *Adv. Mater*. to be published.
6. H. Míguez, F. Meseguer, C. López, M. Holgado, G. Andreassen, A. Mifsud, V. Fornés, *Langmuir* **16**, 4405 (2000).
7. A. Blanco E. Chomski, S. Grabtchak, M. Ibisate, S. John, S.W. Leonard, C. López, F. Meseguer, H. Míguez, J.P. Mondia, G.A. Ozin, O. Toader, and H. van Driel, *Nature* **405**, 437, (2000).
8. F. Reynolds, F. López Tejeira, D. Cassagne, F.J. García Viadal, C. Jouanin, and J. Sánchez-Dehesa, *Phys. Rev. B* **60**, 11422 (1999).
9. H.S. Sözüer, J.W. Haus, and R. Inguva, *Phys. Rev. B* **45**, 13962 (1992).
10. Yu.A Vlasov, V.N. Astratov, O.Z. Karimov, A.A. Kaplyanskii, V.N. Bogomolov, and A.V. Prokofiev, *Phys. Rev. B* **55**, 13357 (1997).
11. H. Míguez, C. López, F. Meseguer, A. Blanco, L. Vázquez, R. Mayoral, M. Ocaña, V. Fornés, and A. Mifsud, *Appl. Phys. Lett.* **71**, 1148 (1997).
12. P. Jiang, J.F. Bertone, and K.S. Hwang, V.L. Colvin, *Chem. Mater.* **11**, 2132 (1999).
13. M. Holgado, F. García-Santamaría, A. Blanco, M. Ibisate, A. Cintas, H. Míguez, C.J. Serna, C. Molpeceres, J. Requena, A. Mifsud, F. Meseguer, and C. López, *Langmuir* **15**, 4701 (1999).
14. H. Míguez, F. Meseguer, C. López, A. Blanco, J.S. Moya, J. Requena, A. Mifsud, and V. Fornés, *Adv. Mater.* **10**, 480 (1998).
15. K. Busch and S. John, *Phys. Rev. E* **58**, 3896 (1998).
16. S.H. Park, and Y. Xia, *Adv. Mater.* **10**, 1045 (1998).
17. R. Meade, A.M. Rappe, K.D. Rommer, and J.D. Joannopoulos, *Phys. Rev. B* **48**, 8434 (1993); S.G. Johnson, *Phys. Rev. E* **55**, 15942 (1997). We acknowledge MIT photonic band package for photonic band structure calculations.

18. A. Blanco, C. López, R. Mayoral, H. Míguez, F. Meseguer, A. Mifsud, and J. Herrero, *Appl. Phys. Lett.* **73**, 1781 (1998); Yu.A. Vlasov, K. Luterova, Y. Pelant, B. Hönerlage, and V. N. Astratov, *Appl. Phys. Lett.* *71*, 1616 (1997); S. Tsunekawa, Y.A. Barnakov, V.V. Poborchii, S.M. Samoilovich, A. Kasuya, and Y. Nishina, *Microporous Materials* **8**, 275 (1997).
19 A. Blanco, C. Lopez, H. Miguez, and F. Meseguer, to be published

THE COMPLETE PHOTONIC BAND GAP IN INVERTED OPALS: HOW CAN WE PROVE IT EXPERIMENTALLY?

D. J. Norris* and Yu. A. Vlasov

NEC Research Institute, Inc.
4 Independence Way
Princeton, NJ 08540 USA

Ever since a complete photonic band gap was predicted to exist in periodic structures,[1,2] experimentalists have been trying to observe this effect at optical frequencies. Much of this effort has focused on fabricating three-dimensionally periodic structures (also called photonic crystals)[3] that have the proper symmetry, lattice spacing, refractive index, etc. to obtain a complete band gap.[4] Once the correct structure is made, one might imagine that the existence of the band gap will be simple to verify. Unfortunately, this is not necessarily the case. As was shown in the microwave regime, where the photonic band gap was first demonstrated,[5,6] such measurements are far from trivial even in near-perfect millimeter-scale structures. Similar measurements in micron-scale optical photonic crystals should be even more challenging. For example, residual disorder will always be present in these structures and will complicate the analysis. Thus, it is useful to ask how one might experimentally verify a band gap in an optical photonic crystal. Here we discuss some aspects of this issue. In particular, we consider potential solutions for photonic crystals made by the so-called *self-assembly* methods.

Recently, these methods have been developed as an alternative route to obtain 3D photonic crystals. A common approach is to utilize sub-micron colloidal spheres[7] (e.g. polymer or silica), which can be induced to spontaneously order on a face-centered cubic (*fcc*) lattice. In nature, this process leads to gemstone opals.[8] In analogy, sub-micron spheres assembled in the laboratory are referred to as *synthetic opals*. Unfortunately, as prepared, synthetic opals are not particularly interesting photonic crystals. For example, silica has a relatively low refractive index (~1.4). However, since the interstitial spaces between the spheres are empty, they can be filled with other materials.[9] In this way, the opal can be used as a template. Subsequent removal of the template, either by etching or burning away the spheres, leads to so-called *inverted opals*. A variety of such structures, including carbon,[10] metal oxides,[11-15] polymers,[16-18] metals,[19-22] and semiconductors[23-26] can now be prepared using this procedure. In general, inverted opals have been studied

*email: dnorris@research.nj.nec.com; vlasov@research.nj.nec.com
URL: www.neci.nj.nec.com/homepages/dnorris; www.neci.nj.nec.com/homepages/vlasov

C.M. Soukoulis (ed.), Photonic Crystals and Light Localization in the 21st Century, 229-237.

since, in principle, they can have the proper symmetry (*fcc*), volume fraction (~20%), and refractive index contrast (>2.85), necessary to obtain a complete photonic band gap at visible or near visible wavelengths.[27] Thus, this approach has been explored as a simple method to obtain complete optical photonic band gaps.

Indeed, several groups have reported inverted opals that may nearly satisfy[13,23,24] or fully satisfy[25,26] the requirements for a complete band gap. So it has become important to probe the existence of the gap in these materials. If we follow the microwave measurements,[5,6] our approach would be to measure optical transmission spectra versus optical wavevector. In other words, we could measure the width of the transmission dips (caused by stop bands) as a function of the propagation direction. In this manner, we would attempt to confirm the gap by mapping the frequency of the band edges for all wavevectors (or at least for critical points in the Brillouin zone). In principle, if we find that a range of frequencies exists where the stop bands overlap for all directions, we have verified the complete band gap. However, in practice, one must be aware of several complications with this approach.

First, to vary the propagation direction, it is tempting to rotate the sample and change the angle of incidence. However, in a photonic crystal this can be problematic.[5,28,29] It is difficult to convert an external angle of incidence to an internal direction of propagation. Snell's law does not apply near a photonic band gap since the effective refractive index of the photonic crystal changes significantly. Furthermore, a priori, we do not know how the refractive index varies since this is related to the properties of the photonic band gap, which is exactly what we are trying to measure. To avoid these difficulties, one can instead probe the transmission at normal incidence. For each measurement, a sample surface is prepared with a different lattice direction exposed. In this way, the experimental transmission versus internal direction of propagation can be determined unambiguously.

The second complication relates to the interpretation of the transmission dips. For each direction, we wish to extract the position of the band edges. It is relatively straightforward to extract the mean position of the stop band from transmission measurements. However, it is more problematic to extract the exact position of the band edges and correspondingly the width. Experimentalists are tempted to describe the width of the transmission dip with a parameter such as the full width at half maximum (FWHM), width at 10% transmission, etc., and then relate this to the gap. Unfortunately, two problems exist with this practice. First, even in a perfect photonic crystal, such parameters can only qualitatively describe the width of the actual gap.[30] This occurs since the experimental width depends strongly on the size of the crystal, while the theoretical width is defined for an infinite structure. Second, and more importantly, any experimentally obtained value of the width will be influenced by residual disorder, present in any real photonic crystal. This disorder can cause inhomogeneous broadening in the width of the transmission dip. If this width is then used to extract the stop band, the experiment can easily overestimate the stop band and correspondingly, come to an incorrect conclusion about the existence of a complete gap, as shown in Ref. 31.

Therefore, to probe the existence of a complete band gap in inverted opals, one should first consider the presence of disorder and how its effect can be minimized. Since the structure of such samples is transferred from the synthetic opal, any disorder present in this template will be replicated in the final photonic crystal. The most common method for preparing the synthetic opal is sedimentation in which spheres are allowed to settle and self-assemble onto a flat substrate. The final sediment is then sintered to obtain a macroscopic, easy-to-handle template. While the synthetic opal is a highly ordered crystal of sub-micron spheres, local defects can be found, such as point defects, stacking faults, etc. Furthermore, due to the macroscopic size of sedimented opals, they are polycrystalline; the typical size of a single crystalline domain is ~50-100μm. Therefore, any optical measurement that probes a sample volume that is much larger than the single do-

Figure 1. Electron micrographs (top view and cross section) of a planar opal template prepared by adapting the method of Jiang *et al.* to 1μm spheres.

domain size will be inhomogeneously broadened not only by point defects, but also due to averaging over multiple domains.

To minimize such effects in optical measurements, one solution is to improve the template to reduce disorder in the final inverted opal. To achieve this, several advances in template preparation have recently been reported: a) van Blaaderen *et al.* have shown how to reduce stacking faults by forcing the opal to grow in specific lattice directions (other than the typical <111>).[32] This is achieved by patterning the substrate to influence the arrangement of the first layer of spheres in the self-assembly process. In addition to improving the template, this method is helpful in orienting the template such that specific lattice directions are perpendicular to the substrate. b) Jiang *et al.* have shown how to form thin planar opal structures by a simple "dip-coat" process.[33] This method, which extends prior work on the 2D assembly of spheres,[34] uses capillary forces to uniformly deposit a specific number of layers (e.g., 25) of close-packed spheres onto a large area substrate (e.g., cm^2). While point defects remain, these structures have the potential of being single crystals (i.e., not polycrystalline). Figure 1 shows an example of such a structure made in our laboratory using 1μm diameter silica spheres. Of course, if either of these new templates is utilized in the formation of inverted opals, the reduction of disorder will help in the examination of the band gap. Furthermore, unlike typical sedimented opals, these new templates may provide more control over the placement of the photonic crystal on the substrate, an important issue for any potential applications.

However, in addition to improving templates, it is also valuable to find optical techniques that minimize the influence of disorder in band gap measurements. Recently, we have reported a simple method that should prove extremely helpful in probing photonic properties of inverted opals (or any other optical photonic crystal).[35] As stated above, if an optical method probes a large volume, the results (e.g., the transmission dip) will be inhomogeneously broadened (see Fig. 2a). Thus, if we limit the probe volume in an optical measurement, we can reduce the effect of disorder. This can be achieved by using an optical microscope to examine a specific region of the sample at normal incidence.

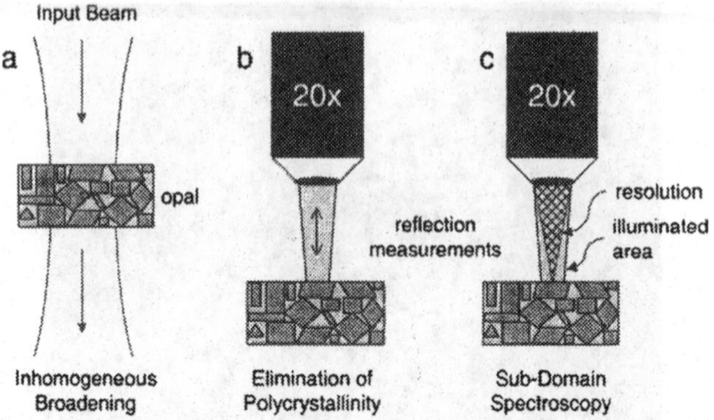

Figure 2. Illustrations to explain sub-domain spectroscopy. a) Transmission measurements on opal-based photonic crystals can easily be inhomogenesously broadened due to averaging over disorder. b) An optical microscope can be used to eliminate polycrystallinity as a source of disorder. c) Further, the optical resolution of the microscope allows one to probe within a single domain. Thus, the influence of point and surface defects can also be significantly reduced.

Obviously, the first form of disorder that can be eliminated by the microscope is the polycrystallinity often found in inverted opals. As depicted in Fig. 2b, this occurs as soon as the optical beam is slightly smaller than the single domain size. (Since inverted opals are often much thicker than the single domain size, reflection must be used instead of transmission to isolate the optical properties of a single crystallite.) However, note that the beam in Fig. 2b will still average over surface roughness and lattice defects inside the domain. To try to eliminate these additional sources of disorder, the microscope can easily go further and probe a small region within a single domain (see Fig. 2c). It is this situation, where we probe *within* a single domain, which we originally referred to as ***single domain spectroscopy***, in analogy to ***single molecule spectroscopy***, which uses a similar apparatus.[36] In hindsight, we believe this name has caused confusion as it is often misinterpreted in terms of Fig. 2b. Perhaps a better description that avoids this confusion is ***sub-domain spectroscopy*** (SDS).

Although conceptually simple, SDS has several subtle points for those unfamiliar with optical microscopy. We now briefly explain these along with the experimental setup. A standard inverted microscope (Nikon TE200) with an epifluorescence attachment is used to illuminate the surface of an opal sample with white lamp light. The incoming light is focused and the reflected light is collected by the same microscope objective (magnification of 20x). Its numerical aperture (NA=sinθ, where θ is the half-angle of the cone collected by the lens) is carefully chosen to compromise between spatial resolution ($\propto 1/NA$) and small θ. (If θ is small, the experiment closely approximates a plane wave.) Typically, the NA is 0.15, which corresponds to an external angle of 9 degrees. It is important to realize that the ability of SDS to minimize the influence of disorder does not depend on the size of the illuminated spot. In our setup, a large area of the sample is illuminated by the lamp (~1mm^2). This is necessary to create an image of the sample surface. By attaching a projection eyepiece (5x) to the output port of the microscope, a magnified, reflected image of the sample is reformed at an external image plane. Since the sample is placed at the working distance of the objective, the spatial resolution of the image is still defined by the NA of the objective (~1-2μm). As depicted in Fig. 3a, the entrance slits of an imaging spectrometer (Spex Triax 320) are placed at the external

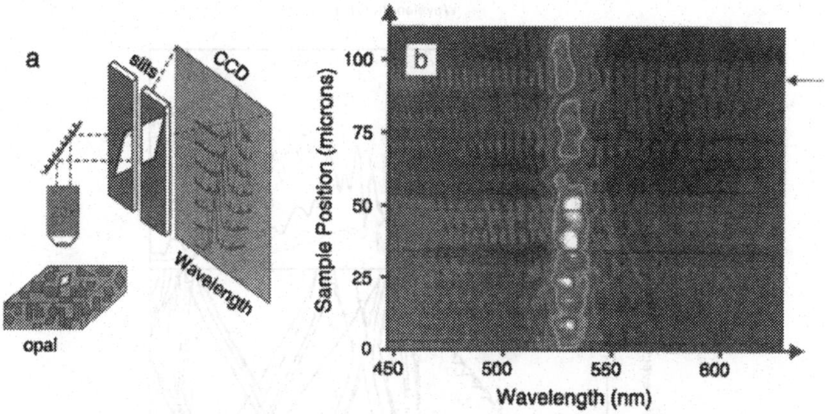

Figure 3. a) Scheme of SDS setup. b) A typical CCD image that demonstrates the final output of our setup. The image represents the intensity of the reflected light. The y-axis is the position along the sample surface. The x-axis represents the wavelength of the reflected light. A reflection peak with fringes is seen. These features move slightly along the y-axis due to disorder.

image plane to perform spectroscopy. Thus, it is the position of the slits, not the illuminated spot, that determines the area of the sample that is probed. A stripe-like portion of the image is selected by the slits, dispersed by the spectrometer grating, and then focused onto a 2D CCD array. By collecting the dispersed image with the CCD, the experiment can be highly parallel. For example, Fig. 3b shows a typical reflection image, which represents sample position (along the slit) on the y-axis versus the wavelength of reflected light on the x-axis. The sample can then be quickly scanned to explore how photonic properties depend on position. We also note that in addition to the spectrometer, the user can always examine the sample surface through the standard eyepieces of the microscope. This allows a particularly nice surface region of the sample to be selected by eye before performing the spectroscopy.

Once this simple apparatus is set up, it can be extremely versatile for probing photonic properties. As we have shown previously,[35] if we take a single line scan (e.g. at the position of the arrow in Fig. 3) the linewidth of the reflection peak is significantly narrower than results taken as in Figs. 2a or 2b. Thus, the microscope removes inhomogeneous broadening, as expected. Furthermore, an additional feature of this technique is that it allows *band edge resonances* to be observed. In any finite sized photonic crystal, the reflection peak should be accompanied by fringes on either side due to interference from the crystal boundaries (Fabry-Perot-like resonances). Since these fringes are extremely sensitive to disorder, they are rarely seen in optical photonic crystals. However, in Fig. 3, these band edge resonances are clearly observed. In addition to being a strong indication that we have dramatically reduced the influence of disorder, the observation of fringes also has important implications. Above, we mentioned that, even in a perfect crystal, it is problematic to extract the width of a stop band from the width of a transmission or reflection peak To avoid this problem, Shung and Tsai have proposed that the positions of the band edge resonances can be used to extract the width of the stop band from experimental data.[30] They also showed that by determining the positions of the band edge resonances, one can obtain the experimental photonic band diagram around the

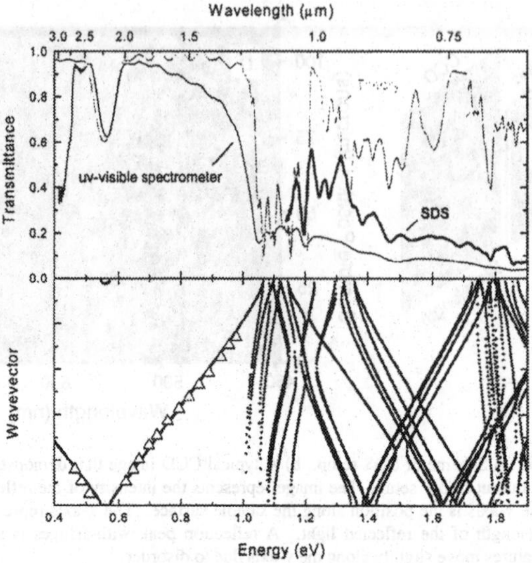

Figure 4. Top panel: experimental (thin and thick lines) and theoretical (gray line) transmission spectra obtained on the template shown in Fig. 1. See text for details. Bottom panel: the theoretical band diagram for this structure. Triangles correspond to the experimental positions of the band edge resonances.

stop band. Thus, with results such as those in Fig. 3, the band gap properties of real optical photonic crystals can be explored in detail.[35]

With these advantages, this technique should be particularly useful in the analysis of inverted opals. Such structures have been predicted to have a complete photonic band gap when the refractive index is greater than 2.85.[27] However, this gap occurs at relatively high energies in the Brillouin zone, between the eighth and ninth bands. In analogy to gratings, this gap is sometimes referred to as a *second order gap*. (In comparison, diamond structures have a *first order* complete gap between the second and third bands.) Unfortunately, higher bands are known to be much more susceptible to disorder. This can be rationalized from the fact that at higher energies the optical wavelength decreases and becomes comparable in size to even small imperfections in the lattice. Due to these issues, the question remains whether the residual disorder present in current inverted opals is small enough to observe the complete gap. In fact, it has been shown theoretically that even a 2% deviation in the lattice constant of *fcc* inverted opals can close the complete gap.[37] Other sources of disorder, such as stacking faults[31] or inhomogeneous filling of the opal template, can further restrict the ability to obtain a complete gap. Thus, it is extremely important to experimentally explore the higher order bands.

We argue that the best route to achieve this task is to combine inverted opals made from the new templates, discussed above, with the optical microscope technique. At first glance, one might believe that the microscope will not be necessary for samples obtained from the thin templates made by the dip-coat method.[33] After all, these samples can be single crystals over large areas. However, in Fig. 4 we show the usefulness of the microscope, even in this case. In this simple example, the microscope is used to measure the optical properties of a bare template, similar to the one shown in Fig. 1. Since the template is thin, both reflection and transmission can be obtained on the microscope simulta-

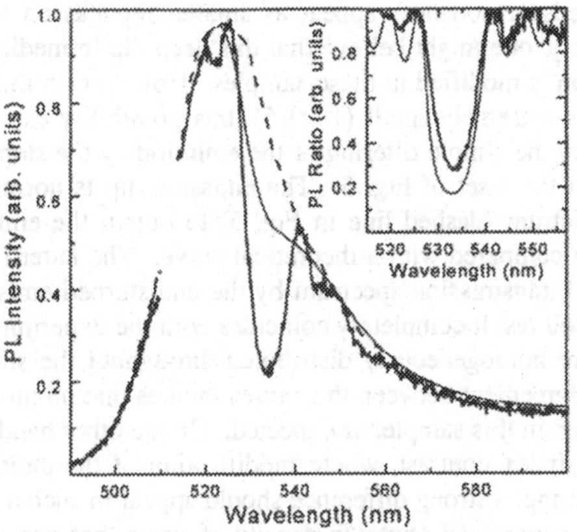

Figure 5. **Emission results obtained from an opal filled with CdSe colloidal quantum dots, excited at 514nm. On the microscope, an emission spectrum with a deep spectral dip (thick line) is observed due to the stop band of the opal. This is compared with the spectrum obtained for quantum dots outside the opal (dashed line), and one obtained according to Fig. 2a (thin line). The inset compares the experimental and calculated emission transfer function (see text).**

simultaneously. The top panel of Fig. 4 compares three transmission spectra for the <111> direction on an absolute scale. First, the transmission through the sample is measured on a standard uv-visible spectrometer with a 100μm beam (thin line). Second, a full 3D transmission calculation is shown for this structure obtained using the multiple scattering method[38] (gray line). Theory shows the first order stop band as a transmission dip at 2.2 μm. The second order gap region begins at 1.2μm. Due to the low refractive index contrast of this structure, many bands influence the transmission in the second order region. These bands are shown in the band diagram in the lower panel. The important point to notice is that the simple measurement obtained by the uv-visible spectrometer is able to reproduce the first order region fairly well, in terms of amplitude, shape, and even the observation of band edge resonances. However, in the second order region, where residual disorder becomes more important, the individual features are washed out. In contrast, when the same sample is placed on the microscope, the thick curve is obtained. Although currently limited by the spectral range of the CCD, it is clear that the microscope obtains increased resolution in the second order region. Individual features, predicted by theory, can be observed in experiment. Obviously, these types of results on high refractive index structures should prove extremely interesting.

Finally, it is important to mention that, although transmission (or reflection) measurements have been emphasized above as a method to examine the existence of the photonic band gap, an equally valid alternative would be to analyze the emission of dipoles placed inside the structure. One example is to use the spontaneous emission rate as a probe of the photonic density of states. This approach has recently been applied to opal-based structures by a number of groups.[39-41] We believe that the microscope can prove helpful for the next generation of such experiments. Figure 5 demonstrates the use of SDS to reduce the influence of disorder and obtain information about embedded dipoles. The emission from a test sample (an opal template filled with fluorescent CdSe quantum dots) is measured with the microscope. A deep emission dip is observed at 530nm due to the stop band along the <111> direction of the *fcc* lattice. As in reflection data, this dip is significantly narrower than measurements obtained as in Figs. 2a or 2b.

Furthermore, band edge resonances appear as smaller replicas on the side of the main emission dip. Naively, one might believe that this deep dip immediately implies that the spontaneous emission is modified in these samples. However, in this test sample, where the index contrast is extremely small (1.4:1.5), this possibility can easily be ruled out. Instead, it arises from the simple filtering of the emission by the stop band of the crystal. This is confirmed in the inset of Fig. 5. The emission dip is normalized by the undisturbed emission spectrum (dashed line in Fig. 5) to obtain the emission transfer function,[41] which is then compared with a theoretical curve. The latter is obtained by multiplying the calculated transmission spectrum by the undisturbed emission spectrum. We find that the calculated result completely coincides with the experiment once the fact that the quantum dots are homogeneously distributed throughout the structure is taken into account. The good agreement between the curves implies that no modification of spontaneous emission occurs in this sample, as expected. On the other hand, in an inverted opal with high refractive index contrast, where modification of the emission rate would accompany simple filtering, a strong difference should appear in such a plot. This would be an indication of the suppressed photonic density of states that occurs due to a photonic band gap. Thus, this kind of measurement on the microscope could be used to explore photonic band gaps in inverted opals.

In conclusion, we have discussed some of the issues facing researchers trying to examine the existence of complete photonic band gaps in self-assembled photonic crystals. To reduce the influence of residual disorder in these samples, we believe two approaches will be necessary. First, the latest generation of templates should be used to make high quality, single-crystalline, inverted opals. Second, optical microscopy techniques, such as SDS, should be utilized to avoid any remaining disorder. Optical measurements can include reflection, transmission, and emission from dipoles embedded inside the photonic crystal. This general strategy should be particularly important in examining the second order band gap region, where the complete band gap has been predicted to occur.

REFERENCES

1. E. Yablonovitch, Inhibited spontaneous emission in solid-state physics and electronics, *Phys. Rev. Lett.* **58**, 2059 (1987).
2. S. John, Strong localization of photons in certain disordered dielectric superlattices, *Phys. Rev. Lett.* **58**, 2486 (1987).
3. J. D. Joannopoulos, R. D. Meade, and J. N. Winn. *Photonic Crystals*, Princeton University Press, Princeton, (1995).
4. For a review see articles in this volume and in *Photonic Band Gap Materials, Vol. 315 of NATO Advanced Study Institute, Ser. E*, C. M. Soukoulis, ed., Kluwer, Dordrecht (1996).
5. E. Yablonovitch and T. J. Gmitter, Photonic band structure: The face-centered cubic case, *Phys. Rev. Lett.* **63**, 1950 (1989).
6. E. Yablonovitch, T. J. Gmitter, and K. M. Leung, Photonic band structure: The face-centered cubic case employing nonspherical atoms, *Phys. Rev. Lett.* **67**, 2295 (1991).
7. Y. Xia, B. Gates, Y. Yin, Y. Lu, Monodispersed colloidal spheres: Old materials with new applications, *Adv. Mater.* **12**, 693 (2000).
8. J. V. Sanders, Colour of precious opal, *Nature* **204**, 1151 (1964).
9. V. N. Astratov, V. N. Bogomolov, A. A. Kaplyanskii, A. V. Prokofiev, L. A. Samoilovich, S. M. Samoilovich, and Yu. A. Vlasov, Optical spectroscopy of opal matrices with CdS embedded in its pores: quantum confinement and photonic band gap effects, *Il Nuovo Cimento*, **17D**, 1349 (1995).
10. A. A. Zakhidov, R. H. Baughman, Z. Iqbal, C. Cui, I. Khayrullin, S. O. Dantas, J. Marti, and V. G. Ralchenko, Carbon structures with three-dimensional periodicity at optical wavelengths, *Science* **282**, 897 (1998).
11. O. D. Velev, T. A. Jede, R. F. Lobo, and A. M. Lenhoff, Porous silica via colloidal crystallization, *Nature* **389**, 447 (1997).
12. B. T. Holland, C. F. Blanford, and A. Stein, Synthesis of macroporous minerals with highly ordered three-dimensional arrays of spheroidal voids, *Science* **281**, 538 (1998).

13. J. E. G. J. Wijnhoven and W. L. Vos, Preparation of photonic crystals made of air spheres in titania, *Science* **281**, 802 (1998).
14. G. Subramania, K. Constant, R. Biswas, M. M. Sigalas, and K. -M. Ho, Optical photonic crystals fabricated from colloidal systems, *Appl. Phys. Lett.* **74**, 3933 (1999).
15. G. Subramanian, V. N. Manoharan, J. D. Thorne, and D. J. Pine, Ordered macroporous materials by colloidal assembly: A possible route to photonic bandgap materials, *Adv. Mater.* **11**, 1261 (1999).
16. S. H. Park and Y. Xia, Macroporous membranes with highly ordered and three-dimensionally interconnected spherical pores, *Adv. Mater.* **10**, 1045 (1998).
17. P. Jiang, K. S. Hwang, D. M. Mittleman, J. F. Bertone, and V. L. Colvin, Template directed preparation of macroporous polymers with oriented and crystalline arrays of voids, *J. Am. Chem. Soc.* **121**, 11630 (1999).
18. M. Deutsch, Yu. A. Vlasov, and D. J. Norris, Conjugated-polymer photonic crystals, *Adv. Mater.* **12**, 1176 (2000).
19. O. D. Velev, P. M. Tessier, A. M. Lenhoff, and E. W. Kaler, A class of porous metallic nanostructures, *Nature* **401**, 548 (1999).
20. K. M. Kulinowski, P. Jiang, H. Vaswani, V. L. Colvin, Porous metals from colloidal templates, *Adv. Mater.* 12, 833 (2000).
21. J. E. G. J. Wijnhoven, S. J. M. Zevenhuizen, M. A. Hendriks, D. Vanmaekelbergh, J. J. Kelly, and W. L. Vos, Electrochemical assembly of ordered macropores in gold, *Adv. Mater.* **12**, 888 (2000).
22. N. Eradat, J. D. Huang, Z. V. Vardeny, A. A. Zakhidov, and R. H. Baughman, Fabrication and optical studies of metal-infiltrated opal photonic crystals and metallic replicas, published in this volume.
23. Yu. A. Vlasov, N. Yao, and D. J. Norris, Synthesis of photonic crystals for optical wavelengths from semiconductor quantum dots, *Adv. Mater.* **11**, 165 (1999).
24. P. V. Braun and P. Wiltzius, Electrochemically grown photonic crystals, *Nature* **402**, 603 (1999).
25. H. Míguez, F. Meseguer, C. López, M. Holgado, G. Andreasen, A. Mifsud, and V. Fornés, Germanium fcc structure from a colloidal crystal template, *Langmuir* **16**, 4405 (2000).
26. A. Blanco, E. Chomski, S. Grabtchak, M. Ibisate, S. John, S. W. Leonard, C. López, F. Meseguer, H. Míguez, J. P. Mondia, G. A. Ozin, O. Toader, and H. M. van Driel, Large-scale synthesis of a silicon photonic crystal with a complete three-dimensional bandgap near 1.5μm, *Nature* **405**, 437 (2000).
27. K. Busch and S. John, Photonic band gap formation in certain self-organizing systems, *Phys. Rev. E* **58**, 3896 (1998).
28. V. N. Astratov, Yu. A. Vlasov, O. Z. Karimov, A. A. Kaplyanskii, Yu. G. Musikhin, N. A. Bert, V. N. Bogomolov, and A. V. Prokofiev, Photonic band gaps in 3D ordered fcc silica matrices, *Phys. Lett. A* **222**, 349 (1996).
29. V. Yannopapas, N. Stefanou, and A. Modinos, Theoretical analysis of the photonic band structure of face-centred cubic colloidal crystals, *J. Phys: Condens. Matter* **9**, 10261 (1997).
30. K. W.-K. Shung and Y. C. Tsai, Surface effects and band measurements in photonic crystals, *Phys. Rev. B* **48**, 11265 (1993).
31. Yu. A. Vlasov, V. N. Astratov, A. V. Baryshev, A. A. Kaplyanskii, O. Z. Karimov, and M. F. Limonov, Manifestation of intrinsic defects in optical properties of self-organized opal photonic crystals, *Phys. Rev. E* **61**, 5784 (2000).
32. A. van Blaaderen, R. Ruel, and P. Wiltzius, Template-directed colloidal crystallization, *Nature* **385**, 321 (1997).
33. P. Jiang, J. F. Bertone, K. S. Hwang, and V. L. Colvin, Single-crystal colloidal multilayers of controlled thickness, *Chem. Mater.* **11**, 2132 (1999).
34. N. D. Denkov, O. D. Velev, P. A. Kralchevsky, I. B. Ivanov, H. Yoshimura, and K. Nagayama, Two-dimensional crystallization, *Nature* **361**, 26 (1993).
35. Yu. A. Vlasov, M. Deutsch, and D. J. Norris, Single domain spectroscopy of self-assembled photonic crystals, *Appl. Phys. Lett.* **76**, 1627 (2000).
36. For example, see S. A. Empedocles, D. J. Norris, and M. G. Bawendi, Photoluminescence spectroscopy of single CdSe nanocrystallite quantum dots, *Phys. Rev. Lett.* **77**, 3873 (1996).
37. Z. -Y. Li, Z. -Q. Zhang, Fragility of photonic band gaps in inverse-opal photonic crystals, *Phys. Rev. B* **62**, 1516 (2000).
38. N. Stefanou, V. Yannopapas, and A. Modinos, Heterostructures of photonic crystals: Frequency bands and transmission coefficients, *Comp. Phys. Comm.* **113**, 49 (1998).
39. E. P. Petrov, V. N. Bogomolov, I. I. Kalosha, and S. V. Gaponenko, Spontaneous emission of organic molecules embedded in a photonic crystal, *Phys. Rev. Lett.* **81**, 77 (1998).
40. K. Yoshino, S. B. Lee, S. Tatsuhara, Y. Kawagishi, M. Ozaki, and A. A. Zakhidov, *Appl. Phys. Lett.* **73**, 3506 (1998).
41. M. Megens, J. E. G. J. Wijnhoven, A. Lagendijk, and W. L. Vos, Fluorescence lifetimes and linewidths of dye in photonic crystals. *Phys. Rev. A* **59**, 4727 (1999); Light sources inside photonic crystals, *J. Opt. Soc. Am. B* **16**, 1403 (1999).

MANIPULATING COLLOIDAL CRYSTALLIZATION FOR PHOTONIC APPLICATIONS: FROM SELF-ORGANIZATION TO DO-IT-YOURSELF ORGANIZATION

ALFONS VAN BLAADEREN,[1,2] KRASSIMIR P. VELIKOV,[1] JACOB P. HOOGENBOOM,[1,2] DIRK L. J. VOSSEN,[1,2] ANAND YETHIRAJ,[1,2] ROEL DULLENS,[1] TEUN VAN DILLEN,[2] ALBERT POLMAN[2]

[1]*Condensed Matter Dept., Debye Inst., Utrecht University, P. O. Box 80000, 3508 TA Utrecht, The Netherlands*
[2]*FOM Inst. for Atomic and Molecular Physics, P.O. Box 41883, 1009 DB Amsterdam, The Netherlands*
A.vanBlaaderen@phys.uu.nl

INTRODUCTION

Photonic crystals are regular three-dimensional (3D) structures with which the propagation and spontaneous emission of photons can be manipulated in new ways if the feature sizes are roughly half the wavelength and the coupling with the electromagnetic radiation is sufficiently strong. 'Early' speculation on these new possibilities can be found in the Refs.[1-4] A more recent overview can be found in Ref.[5] and, of course, the other chapters in this book. A useful analogy to guide thinking about the properties and the applications of photonic crystals is the propagation of electrons in a semiconductor in comparison to the propagation of photons scattered by a regular 3D dielectric material. An example is the possibility of opening up a region of energy, a photonic band gap, for which the propagation of photons is forbidden, in analogy to the electronic band gap present in semiconductors. However, there are also important differences; for instance, the scattering of photons cannot be described well by scalar wave equations because the polarization of light cannot be neglected. Most theoretical and experimental work for visible light applications have until now focused on pure dielectric structures, interestingly, recent calculations have shown that metallo-dielectric structures should also be considered as having very interesting photonic properties in the visible, including, if one neglects absorption, a complete band gap.[6-8] And even with absorption taken into account, it seems that for relatively thin photonic crystals most of the interesting optical properties remain.[8]

Because the feature sizes of photonic crystals need to be about half the wavelength of the electromagnetic radiation of interest, the actual realization of such structures for near-infrared and visible light is quite a challenge. In this paper we want to give an overview of

C.M. Soukoulis (ed.), Photonic Crystals and Light Localization in the 21st Century, 239–251.

the methods we are currently investigating to achieve well-defined 3D structures with submicron feature sizes by the manipulation of the self-organization of colloidal particles. We will focus here primarily on colloidal crystals for which the inter-particle spacing is close to the particle's size, so the structures can be dried. This will allow for a large dielectric contrast and also for the possibility to use the colloidal crystals as templates to make so-called 'inverse' structures. This last process, recently reviewed in Ref.[9], is not part of the present paper, but it requires the same high quality crystals needed for photonic crystals made directly from (metallo-)dielectric spheres. It is the present understanding that only inverse structures of the colloidal crystal lattices can be easily made (like face centered cubic, FCC) will have a complete band gap. However, the density-of-states can also be modulated quite strongly in photonic crystals of high-index-core-shell systems. Moreover, binary structures or other complex structures like 3D quasicrystals have hardly been investigated and by removing one of the sphere sizes, by heating or dissolving them, relatively low filling fractions can be obtained. In the case of metallo-dielectric spheres the situation is reversed and the 'reverse' structures do not have a complete band gap, while many crystalline symmetries of spherical particles in liquids have a complete band gap.[6-8]

Before going into specific examples of the manipulation of colloidal crystallization, we will first explain what we mean by the two terms: *colloidal* and *self-organization*. An important aspect in the definition of what should be called a colloid or colloidal particle is the fact that these particles, which can consist of macromolecules or other subunits, undergo so-called Brownian motion. This erratic motion is the direct result of the not completely averaged-out collisional effects of solvent molecules constantly hitting the particle. Brownian motion ensures that a concentrated colloidal dispersion in which many particles interact with each other can find a thermodynamically well-defined equilibrium state. If certain criteria are met, such as the concentration of particles and a high monodispersity (narrow width in the size distribution), these systems will spontaneously form regular 3D structures or colloidal crystals completely analogous to molecular crystals.[10,11] This kind of (mostly first-order) phase transition can be described by statistical mechanics and we will use the possibility of such calculations as our definition of 'pure' self-organization (SO). A self-organizing system thus organizes itself in a state of lowest free energy. Therefore, shaking a box with ball bearings, even though the balls under the right frequency and amplitude might arrange themselves on a lattice, is not considered self-organization.[12] On the other end of the extreme, one has 'do-it-yourself-organization' (DYO) where control over the kind of structures that can be made is highest, but where no minimizing principle guides the organization of matter. Most methods used in making integrated circuits, like lithography, are DYO and in most cases 3D structures need to be built up in a layer-by-layer fashion. Although DYO methods offer great control, they are generally slow, costly, and not easy to extend to many unit cells in three dimensions because errors tend to accumulate. On the other hand, pure SO leads relatively easily to larger 3D structures, but control over, e.g., crystal symmetry and orientation is harder to achieve.

After a brief experimental section, we first will describe the kind of colloidal model particles we are using, with reference to the literature on how these can be made and characterized. Subsequently, we will give typical examples of how colloidal crystallization can be manipulated. Manipulation is possible by playing with the boundary conditions, like crystallization against a corrugated wall or between two confining walls, by using strong electric fields both at low frequencies and optical frequencies, by a flow field and, even further away from equilibrium, by controlled drying. Finally, we will show how high-energy heavy ion-irradiation can be used to deform inorganic photonic crystals in a controlled way.

EXPERIMENTAL

As this paper is intended to give an 'educational' oversight of the projects being pursued to manipulate colloidal crystallization, the experimental section is relatively short and intended to give an idea on how the experiments were performed. For details we will refer as much as possible to literature.

The seeded growth of fluorescent silica *core-shell co*lloids and the particle characterization by many different techniques (e.g., scanning and transmission electronmicroscopy SEM, TEM and light scattering) is described in Refs.[13-15] Very monodisperse silica seed particles can be made by performing silica growth in a microemulsion.[16] Recently, the fluorescent core colloidal model system properties have been extended by the development of a polymethylmethacrylate (PMMA) shell layer that can both be density and index matched.[17] Other core-shell systems with nanocrystalline and metal cores are briefly described in Refs.[15,18] and references cited in that paper.

The fluorescently dyed PMMA templates used in the *colloidal epitaxy* studies were made by electron beam lithography.[19] We also used particle templates made by optical tweezers (see below).

The effects of *electric fields* of *low frequencies* were also studied using confocal microscopy on matched fluorescent core-shell colloids. The colloids were imaged through transparent tinindiumoxide electrodes, more experimental details are given in Ref.[20] The effects of a *flow field* on the structures generated in these electro-rheological fluids were studied similarly as described by Amos et al. [21]

Multiple time-shared *optical tweezers* were constructed as described by Visscher[22] using opto acoustic modulaters to manipulate a 1064 nm cw laser beam. The set-up constructed by us can be combined with confocal microscopy (Leica TCS). The positively charged cover glasses were made as described in Ref.[23] using a silane coupling agent (3-aminopropyltriethoxysilane).

Controlled drying experiments were performed as given in Ref.[24] using silica spheres dispersed in ethanol.

Deformation by ion (Xe^{4+}, 4 MeV) *irradiation* with fluences about 10^{14} ions/cm^2 is described in Ref. [25]

RESULTS AND DISCUSSION

Core Shell Colloids

The colloidal particles used all have a core-shell geometry, with cores of metal (silver, gold), a nano-crystal (e.g., ZnS or CdS), or a high index dielectric material (e.g., ZnS). The shells used are made of silica or polymethylmethacrylate (PMMA) and both can be covalently labeled with organic dyes. The advantage of using a core-shell approach is the increase in flexibility in tuning both the optical properties and the interaction potential between the colloidal particles. For instance, in the case of a high index core and a lower index shell, like ZnS covered with silica, the high index filling fraction can be optimized even when the spheres are touching and at the same time the strong Van der Waals forces that would be present between pure ZnS particles can be reduced significantly.[10] Further, the core-shell approach allows a quite natural way of random doping of the photonic crystals. An example is shown in Fig. 1 where a fluorescence scanning confocal microscopy picture is shown of a solid solution of 10% larger fluoresceine labeled silica spheres on the lattice positions of a crystal of rhodamine labeled spheres (diameter 950 nm). Although this particular example is not so interesting for photonic applications, it does illustrate a general procedure in which photonic crystals can be 'doped' in a random way by using core-shell systems. For instance, in the case of the synthesis of 'air-sphere' or 'inverted' photonic crystals where a colloidal crystal is used as template and the particles are removed after deposition of other material by oxidation and heat or by dissolving them, high dielectric material can be positioned on lattice positions (which would normally be air) by using high-index core-shell particles. Also, in the reverse situation where one would like to dope a photonic crystal of (metallo)dielectric spheres with a 'hole' (low dielectric material), one could, for instance, use a latex sphere as dopant and later burn it away, or one could make use of hollow particles as shown in Fig. 2.[15,18]

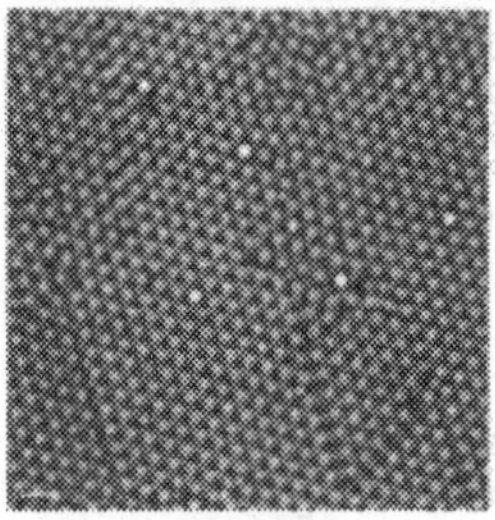

Figure 1. Confocal micrograph of a solid solution of fluoresceine labeled particles (white) on a crystalline lattice of rhodamine labeled spheres (bar 2 μm)

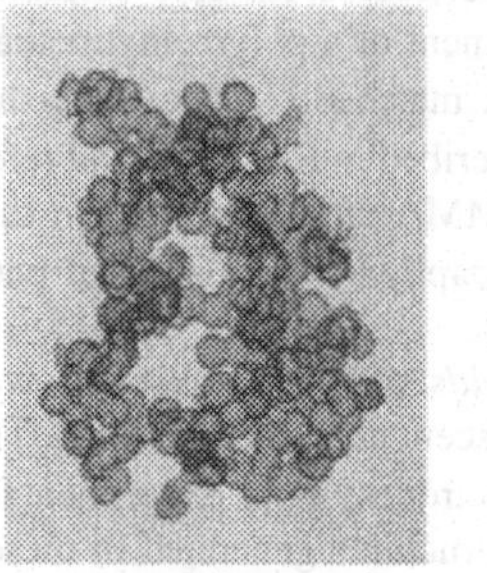

Figure 2. TEM picture of hollow silica spheres (radius 60 nm) created after dissolution of the ZnS cores.

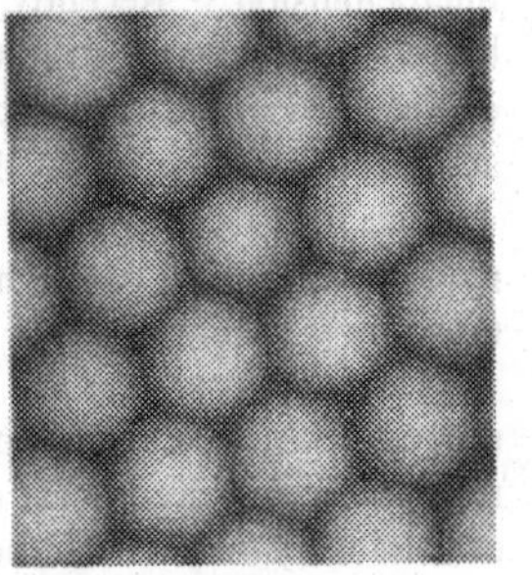

Figure 3. TEM picture of silica spheres made by seeded growth were the initial seeds were grown in a microemulsion. Radius: 35 nm, relative width of the size distribution: 2 %.

Manipulating Colloidal Crystallization: Colloidal Epitaxy

The ability to manipulate the boundaries of the container in which crystallization takes place is a powerful way to steer the crystallization process. The reason for the increased possibilities compared to the atomic world is directly related to the size of colloids. Because colloids are so much larger than atoms, truly 'atomically' smooth walls can be made easily. If the container walls are only several particle diameters away, then this distance determines the crystal structure that will optimally fit. At high volume fractions of particles the most important contribution to the free energy is the packing efficiency. Not only can the orientation of the crystals be induced, but also new structures, like buckling phases, have been found.[26]

Furthermore, making corrugations on container walls that are of the size of the colloidal building blocks is also possible. We made use of such structured walls to manipulate colloidal crystallization in ways which are very similar to epitaxial crystal growth. By having the spheres slowly fall down through sedimentation on the template and by heterogeneous nucleation at the wall, large crystals could be made. We have grown large, pure face centered cubic (FCC) crystals from particles that interacted with an almost hard-sphere potential both on non-close-packed (100) and (110) crystal faces. These crystals could be grown mm's thick (several thousand layers).[19]

Here we show the first results obtained by growing hard-sphere like colloidal crystals onto a template with the (110) crystal face of a hexagonally-close-packed (HCP) crystal (Fig. 4). The HCP colloidal crystal structure is meta-stable compared to FCC crystals for particles with a hard-sphere potential and becomes even more unfavorable in free energy for softer potentials. The free-energy difference between an FCC and HCP stacking for hard-sphere-like potentials is quite small though (on the order of ~10^{-4} *kT*/particle).[27] However, as far as we know, a pure HCP crystal has not yet been observed. These results not only open up the use of HCP colloidal crystals for photonic applications, but will also allow a systematic study of the effects of stacking errors. Hard-sphere crystals have the tendency not to crystallize in the thermodynamically most stable FCC form, but instead with a random stacking sequence of close packed layers (*ABC* stacking is FCC, while *ABA* is HCP). In the same way as this has been done with the HCP templating, it is also possible to grow any desired stacking sequence!

Electrostatic repulsion on flat walls can also be used to influence colloidal crystallization. Recently, 2D templates made with regions of opposite surface charge were shown to direct 2D colloidal crystal formation.[28] Also non-close-packed structures could be formed additionally using capillary forces in a similar way as described in the section on controlled drying.

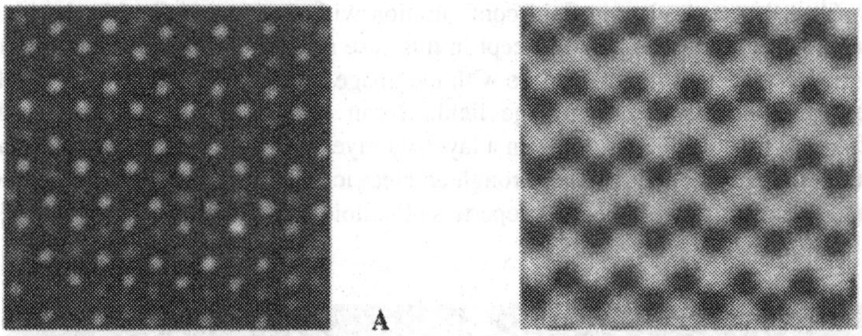

A B

Figure 4. Confocal micrographs of the first colloidal HCP crystal. a) (Dyed) PMMA template with holes in the symmetry of the (110) HCP plane. b) 8 th (and vaguely 7th) layer of the HCP crystal above the template. Sphere diameter 1.4 μm fluorescent core diameter 385 nm.

Manipulating Colloidal Crystallization: Electric Fields, Low Frequencies

Colloidal particles dispersed in a solvent with low conductivity and subjected to a relatively high electric field (~1 V/μm) are called electro-rheological fluids because the application of the field can turn the low viscosity dispersion, reversibly, into a solid with a yield stress. By application of the field, strong dipolar interactions (tens of *kT*) arise between the particles because of their dielectric mismatch (at zero frequency) with the solvent and the particles form strings spanning the container size in milliseconds. For photonic applications, far out-of-equilibrium structures where the interactions are many times *kT* are not so interesting. When structures can form that are closer to equilibrium (interactions only a few times *kT*), a lot of interesting possibilities for control are opened up. In this regime of interactions the system can reach the lowest free energy configuration. We have recently shown experimentally that this is (most likely) a body centered tetragonal (BCT) crystal.[20] An energy calculation[29] had already shown that this structure has a lower energy than an FCC crystal, and, furthermore, it has been found in computer simulations.[30] However, a full free energy calculation, including entropy, has not been done. In addition we found an interesting metastable sheet-like configuration that formed from the strings of particles and that slowly turned into the BCT crystals (see also the figures in the section on flow).[20]

In the same work we have also shown that if the initial charge stabilized dispersion is made concentrated enough that an FCC colloidal crystal is formed, it can be switched through a martensitic crystal transition from FCC into BCT. Moreover, without a field the

FCC crystal remains oriented with its (100) face parallel with the transparent electrode surface. For the photonic crystals made from metallo-dielectric spheres, this ability to switch between two different colloidal crystal structures is quite interesting (see the contribution of Moroz), even though a milliseconds switching speed is relatively slow.

Here we want to report on what happens when the electric field is not applied along the direction of gravity as described in Ref.[20], but instead in the plane perpendicular to gravity. In this case the transparent electrodes were replaced by two metal wires with a thickness of 50 μm a few mm apart. Now the electric field is in a plane perpendicular to gravity and the electric field can be used to 'anneal' the crystals that have already formed or can also influence crystallization when it takes place. In this geometry single crystals of several mm could be grown. Figure 5a shows a close packed plane of a single crystal imaged with a confocal microscope, where the electric field direction is in the imaging plane approximately from top to bottom. We chose to show a relatively defect rich plane, as in this case, the electric field direction becomes obvious from the alignment of these defects in the field.

In Figs. 5b-d the same electric field configuration with the electric field in the plane perpendicular with gravity was used. Except in this case a relatively thin colloidal crystal was imaged under different field strengths with the image plane parallel to gravity and the electric field perpendicular to the image field. It can be seen in Figs. 5b-d that the transition from FCC to BCT takes place in a layer-by-layer fashion. Clearly, the additional ability to tune the particle interactions through an electric field provides for extra degrees of freedom to switch or tailor photonic properties of colloidal crystals.

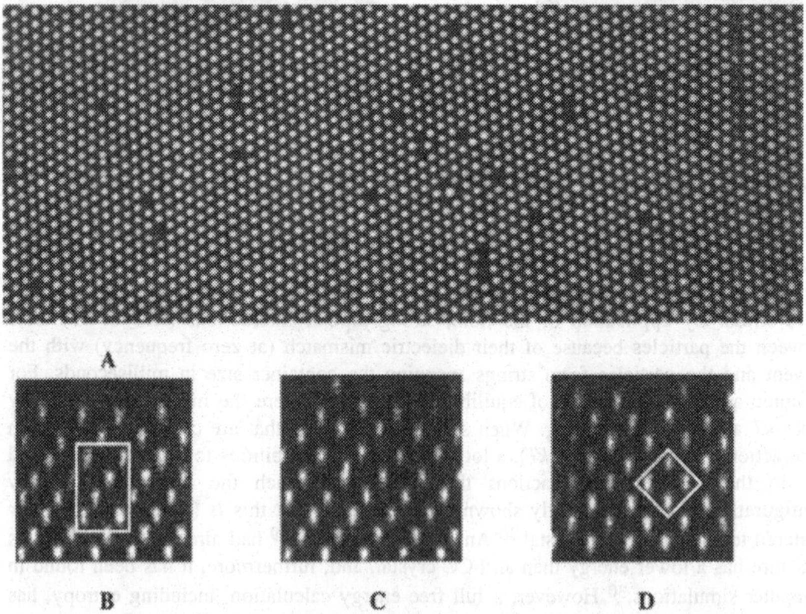

Figure 5. Confocal micrograph of: **a)** close-packed plane of a single BCT crystal created by application of an electric field (~0.5 V/μm) directed from top to bottom and the direction of gravity perpendicular to the (*x*-*y*) imaging plane. **b-d)** micrographs (*x*-*z* plane) taken at three different electric field strengths (field direction perpendicular to the imaging plane, gravity from top to bottom), showing the layer-by-layer transition from FCC to BCT crystal symmetry (0.08 V/μm, 0.1 V/μm and 0.08 V/μm resp.). Colloid diameter 1 μm, fluorescent core nm 400 nm.

Manipulating Colloidal Crystallization: Electric Fields, Optical Frequencies

If particles with a refractive index higher than the suspending liquid are placed in an inhomogeneous light field, they will experience forces pushing them toward the highest field strength. Simply focusing a laser beam of several mW with a high numerical aperture microscope objective is sufficient to trap colloidal particles (silica, latex) with sizes of several hundred nm to several μm in water. After the pioneering work of Ashkin[31,32] these optical tweezers or optical traps have become an important manipulation and force measuring tool in (micro) biology.[22] Recently, optical traps have also been used to measure interaction potentials between colloids and to create a 2D potential field to induce 2D colloidal crystallization.[33,34]

Here we show in Fig. 6a that a time shared optical trap created with opto acoustic modulators can easily place 50 particles on any desired 2D pattern. We plan to use this ability to induce and manipulate 3D crystallization with high index core-shell colloids that can be trapped in a sea of matched fluorescent core-shell colloids that can be imaged with confocal microscopy. Another example of the use of optical tweezers is shown in Fig. 6b where silica spheres have been attached one by one onto a substrate with opposite surface charge. We are extending this method of pure DYO to 3D structures and have already successfully grown 3D crystals by using the 2D structures as templates for colloidal epitaxy.

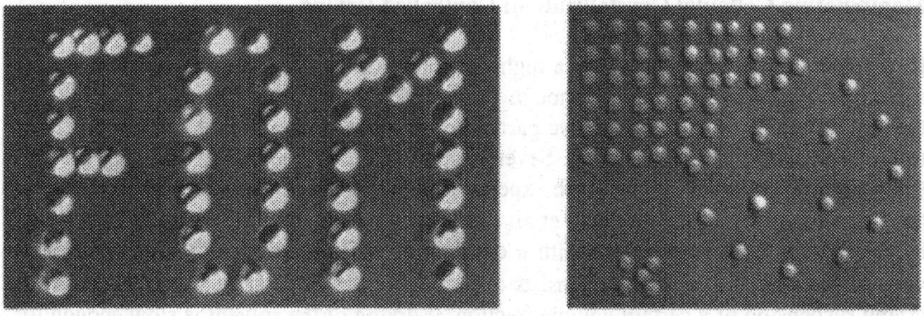

A B

Figure 6. Video microscopy picture of: a) the letters FOM formed in water using 1.4 μm diameter silica colloids and time-shared pairs of optical tweezers, distance from the cover glass ~ 5 μm, b) the same colloids that were placed one by one on a glass cover glass with opposite surface charge.

Manipulating Colloidal Crystallization: Flow Fields

Although colloidal crystals have such small elastic moduli –one of the reasons for the term 'soft condensed matter'- that they are easily melted by a flow field, they can also be manipulated in less destructive ways by flow. As recent experiments on PMMA hard-sphere colloidal model particles have shown, mm size single (twinned) FCC colloidal crystals could be obtained relatively easily by applying a simple shear field.[21] As far as we know, shear has not yet been used to make crystals for photonic applications. We plan to investigate the effects of a simple shear between two parallel glass plates in real space using a confocal microscope. The shear cell we are designing will have the ability to move both the top and bottom plate, so that the plane of zero velocity, where imaging is easy, can be moved through the sample volume. Initial experiments without a controlled shear cell, but just moving two glass plates with a spacer between two fingers already shows the organizing effects of flow on the structures that form under the influence of an electric field of low frequency (1 MHz). The metastable sheets that were described as precursors to the BCT crystals in Ref.[20] and above, are seen in Fig. 7a to be aligned by the flow. The regularity is probably due to the initial density of the colloids, however electric field induced interactions cannot be ruled out yet. After two hours the sheets started to turn into crystals but some of the initial shear induced orientation was still visible (Fig. 7b).

Not only will it be easy to combine shear alignment of colloidal crystallization with electric fields, there are also unexplored ways to use it in conjunction with templates and binary crystallization.

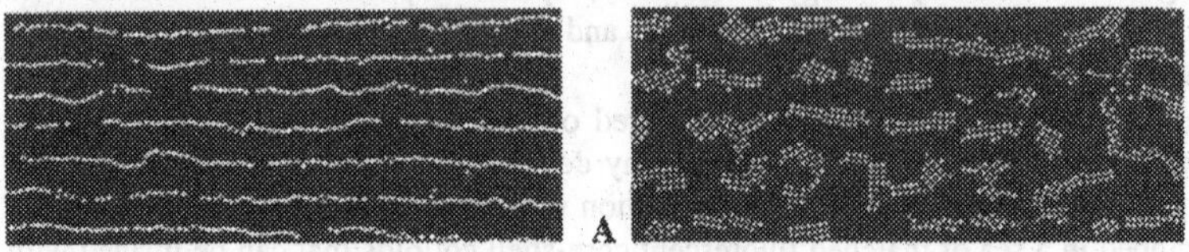

A B

Figure 7. Confocal micrographs showing structures formed in an electric field (0.5 V/μm) after application of a simple shear one minute after application of the field. Both the shear and electric field were perpendicular to the imaging plane. **a**) sheets formed after several minutes. **b**) start of BCT crystal formation after two hours. Colloid diameter 1 μm, fluorescent core nm 400 nm.

Manipulating Colloidal Crystallization: Controlled Drying

If colloidal particles are present in a high concentration in a thin liquid layer wetting the surface of a substrate that is thin enough for particles to stick through, the line tension at the liquid particle interface can drive particles together and cause close packed structures to be formed after complete drying. Several groups have explored this way of covering a substrate with colloidal crystals both experimentally and theoretically. A recent review of the subject is given in Ref.[35] Jiang et al. recently demonstrated that cm wide areas could be covered by controlled drying with a constant number of colloidal crystal layers in a very simple way.[24] The method consists of putting a (glass) substrate vertically in a slow drying suspension of a certain volume fraction. If drying of the solvent is slow enough for it to be the limiting process, the number of layers is only a function of the volume fraction (and a constant related to the particle radius and solvent properties). Fifty layers have been deposited in one try and several depositions can be performed after each other. Unfortunately, this method does not work for particles so heavy that the settling rate is larger than the reclining meniscus. For silica this is a radius of about 200 nm. We did explore the method for particles with a significantly smaller particle polydispersity (see the section on the core-shell colloids) than explored in Ref.[24] and found mm size single crystals and cm size regions with constant number of spheres (results not shown here). Moreover, the templates used for the colloidal epitaxy procedure surprisingly are also able to manipulate this kind of colloidal crystal deposition (for some initial results see Ref.[15]).

Here, however, we want to focus on the possibilities this method has to produce structures that cannot be formed (easily) by using bulk crystallization. This is because this method is a lot closer to DYO than it is to SO. Although it is likely that Brownian motion is still important to have the particles find a local 'best' packing arrangement, controlled drying is certainly not a reversible equilibrium method. However, the DYO aspect opens up a lot of ways to tune the structures. One obvious possibility is to build up the photonic crystals in a layer-by-layer fashion where some of the particles in the layers (or some layers) have different properties than other particles (or layers). For instance, the method works also for the deposition of just one single layer and it is not difficult, if particles of exactly the same size are used, to build up a close packed crystal consisting of alternating layers of silica and latex spheres. In Fig. 8a it is shown that after depositing a layer of silica spheres with a radius of 202 nm, it is possible to deposit a layer of smaller spheres (size ratio 0.60) in the hexagonal pattern of holes left by the larger spheres. These are first results that have not yet been optimized, but they do demonstrate that an AB_2 crystal that is also known to be formed in bulk colloidal crystallization[36] at this size ratio (0.60) can be built up in a layer by layer fashion. The third layer of larger spheres will be stacked right on top of the first layer, etc. What was not expected was that for a slightly different size ratio (0.49) structures like shown in Fig. 8b and Fig. 8c formed. If these structures, here only consisting of two layers are thought to repeat themselves in 3D this would lead to crystals of the form AB_1 and AB_3, respectively. Both these crystals would not form in bulk binary crystallization. Although not expected, the formation of the AB_3 packing arrangement for the size ratio 0.49 can be understood. Just for this size ratio the arrangement depicted in Fig. 8c leads to the smaller spheres just touching. The arrangement leading to AB crystals, Fig. 8b, is even more amazing. It is clear that it formed when the concentration of spheres was below the value that leads to the configuration depicted in Fig. 8a. However, it was unexpected that the small spheres would not occupy the hexagonal holes randomly but instead formed a regular pattern where the smaller spheres were never touching. The explanation for the forces organizing the small spheres has to be that the spheres minimize the surface tension of the drying film while going into the holes. Research is ongoing to determine the optimal growth conditions for the structures shown in the Fig. 8 and to see if they can indeed be extended in 3D. As these are only the first trials, it is likely that other surprises will show up at other size ratios and by a more systematic investigation using templates.

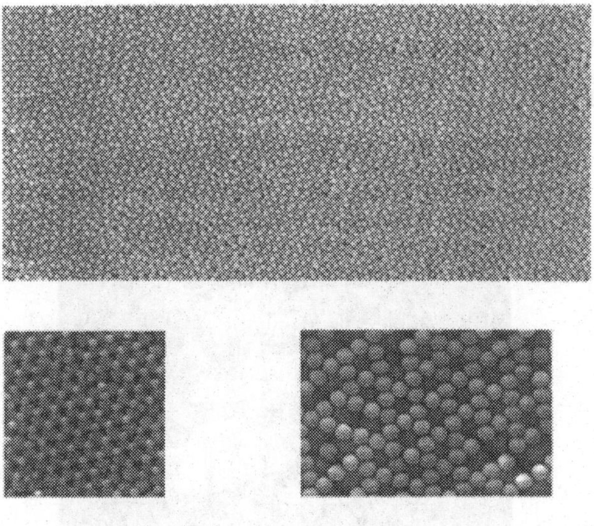

A

B C

Figure 8. SEM pictures of: **a**) two layers of particles with size ratio 0.60 (larger sphere radius 202 nm) deposited by a controlled-drying process layer-by-layer. The two layers form the start of an AB_2 crystal.
b-c) two layers with size ratio 0.49 (larger sphere radius 202 nm). The start of an AB_1 crystal (**b**) and of an AB_3 crystal (**c**).

Manipulating Colloidal Crystallization: Deformation by Ion Irradiation

Once final inorganic photonic structures using colloids have been made, be it direct by using colloids or 'inverse' structures by using crystals as templates, it would be convenient if there was a method for optical fine-tuning. For relatively thin (< 10 micron) photonic crystals, high energy ion beams of heavy atoms provide for such a method. We recently discovered that such beams of heavy atoms can linearly deform particles perpendicular to the direction of the ion's path, if the energy of the beam is large enough to go through the inorganic colloidal particle and most of its energy is delivered through electronic stopping.[25] In this way, single inorganic amorphous or polycrystalline colloidal spheres can be turned into oblate ellipsoids (Fig. 9) or by multiple irradiations from different directions into more complex shapes.[25] When the particles are part of a colloidal crystal, however, the deformation process becomes more complicated because the stress build-up induced by the deformation is anisotropic. This results in a deformation of the particles that depends on the relative orientation of the ion beam with respect to the colloidal crystal orientation. In order to demonstrate the possibilities, we deformed ZnS-core (radius 84 nm) silica-shell (total radius 130 nm), particles in a thin colloidal crystal consisting of 5 layers (Fig. 10). These core-shell particles were optimized to have the widest stop gap.[18,37] Because the crystal is relatively thin, the stop gap is not very deep and it is superimposed on a background scattering caused by defects. The fringes are due to interference between the quite flat top and bottom crystalline planes. It is clear, however, that a significant shift of 41 nm occurred in the position of the stop gap. At this time we cannot predict this shift, because it is caused both by a deformation of the particle shape *and* a change in the crystal symmetry and lattice constants, both of which are not yet known independently. Work is in progress to simulate the deformation process so that more quantitative predictions can be made. From the first results presented here, it is clear, however, that high energy ion irradiation does allow for fine tuning of both the lattice constant and/or the symmetry of inorganic thin (< 10 μm) colloidal crystals.

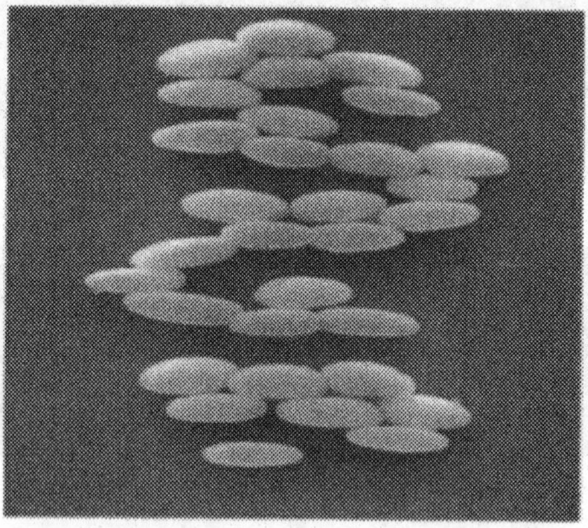

Figure 9. SEM picture of core-shell ZnS-silica (core 333 nm, total radius 350 nm) particles deformed into an oblate ellipsoidal shape by ion irradiation. Ion beam in plane (top-bottom) with respect to the image plane.

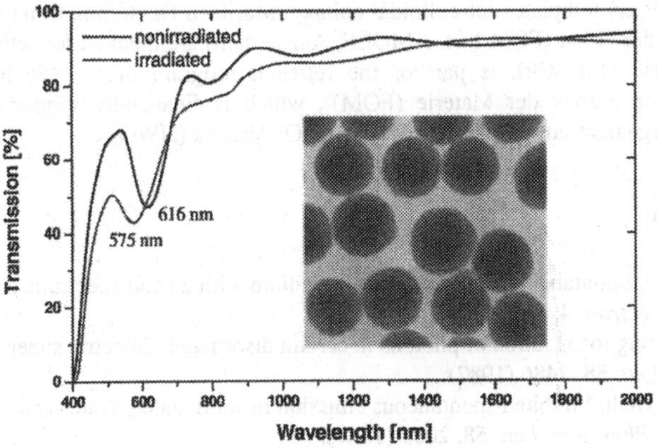

Figure 10. Transmission spectra taken of ZnS-silica core-shell colloidal crystal deformed by ion irradiation (Inset ZnS core radius 84 nm total radius 130 nm; before irradiation). The crystals were 5 layers thick and formed by controlled drying. The shift in the transmission minimum is 41 nm.

CONCLUSIONS

Shortly after the discovery of the first transistor there were researchers who wanted to stop research on the subject of semiconductors as everybody in the field was getting different results. Photonic crystal research has only just made its first 'semi conductor' for light, a structure with a (possible) complete band gap in the near infrared using silica colloidal crystals as templates.[38] It seems certainly a daunting, if not impossible, task to meet the purity and low defect levels that were required in the semi conductor industry to achieve reproducible results. For instance, this would mean the growth of a colloidal crystal the size of a km with only one dislocation in it! It is quite clear though, that such extreme levels of control will not be necessary to achieve interesting photonic applications. Certainly, an optical transistor, which would likely require very regular crystals on the one hand and great control over defects and doping on the other, is still some time away. However, we hope to have shown in this contribution that although the ways to explore colloidal crystallization and colloidal crystals for manipulating photons have only just started, it is already clear that the potential for the level of control is high. The most promising methods to arrive at useful photonic structures are a mix of pure 'self-organization' and pure 'do-it-yourself' organization. Also, most of the methods of which examples are shown can be combined to achieve new effects and several interesting directions to manipulate the properties of colloidal photonic crystals have not even been explored yet, like, the use of the anisotropic refractive index of liquid crystals to switch the photonic properties. If, as we believe, the pace of progress keeps its present fast rate, the first applications for visible and near infrared light, including possibilities for new physics, will arrive soon.

Acknowledgements

Ad Lagendijk and Willem Vos (University of Amsterdam) are thanked for discussions. We are grateful to Anja K. van Langen-Suurling and Hans Romijn (DIMES, Delft) for making the (master) templates for colloidal epitaxy. Marileen Dogterom, Cendrine Faivre and Astrid van der Horst (FOM Inst. AMOLF, Amsterdam) are thanked for setting up the optical tweezers. This work is part of the research program of the 'Stichting voor Fundamenteel onderzoek der Materie (FOM)', which is financially supported by the 'Nederlandse organization voor Wetenschappelijk Onderzoek (NWO)'.

REFERENCES

1. V. P. Bykov, Spontaneous emission from a medium with a band spectrum, *Sov. J. Quantom Electron.* **4**, 861 (1975).
2. S. John, Strong localization of photons in certain disordered dielectric superlattices, *Phys. Rev. Lett.* **58**, 2486 (1987).
3. E. Yablonovitch, Inhibited spontaneous emission in solid-state physics and electronics, *Phys. Rev. Lett.* **58**, 2059 (1987).
4. J. D. Joannopoulos, R. D. Meade, and J. N. Winn. *Photonic Crystals* ed., Princeton Univ. Press, Princeton, (1995).
5. T.F. Krauss and R.M. Delarue, Photonic Crystals in the Optical Regime - Past, Present and Future, *Progress in Quantum Electronics* **23**, 51 (1999).
6. A. Moroz, Three-dimensional complete photonic-band-gap structures in the visible, *Phys. Rev. Lett.* **83**, 5274 (1999).
7. A. Moroz, Photonic crystals of coated metallic spheres, *Europhys. Lett.* **50**, 466 (2000).
8. W. Y. Zhang, X. Y. Lei, Z. L. Wang *et al.*, Robust photonic band gap from tunable scatterers, *Phys. Rev. Lett.* **84**, 2853 (2000).
9. O. D. Velev and E. W. Kaler, Structured porous materials via colloidal crystal templating: From inorganic oxides to metals, *Adv. Mater.* **12**, 531 (2000).
10. W.B. Russel, D.A. Saville, and W.R. Schowalter. *Colloidal Dispersions* ed., Cambridge University Press, Cambridge, (1995).
11. T. Palberg, Colloidal crystallization dynamics, *Curr. Opin. Colloid Interface Sci.* **2**, 607 (1997).
12. O. Pouliquen, M. Nicolas, and P. D. Weidman, Crystallization of non-Brownian spheres under horizontal shaking, *Phys. Rev. Lett.* **79**, 3640 (1997).
13. A. van Blaaderen and A. Vrij, Synthesis and Characterization of Colloidal Dispersions of Fluorescent, Monodisperse Silica Spheres, *Langmuir* **8**, 2921 (1992).
14. N. A. M. Verhaegh and A. van Blaaderen, Dispersions of Rhodamine-Labeled Silica Spheres - Synthesis, Characterization, and Fluorescence Confocal Scanning Laser Microscopy, *Langmuir* **10**, 1427 (1994).
15. A. van Blaaderen, From the de Broglie to visible wavelengths: Manipulating electrons and photons with colloids, *MRS Bull.* **23**, 39 (1998).
16. F. J. Arriagada and K. Osseoasare, Synthesis of Nanometer-Sized Silica By Controlled Hydrolysis in Reverse Micellar Systems, in: *Colloid Chemistry of Silica*, Amer. Chemical Soc., Washington, Vol. 234, (1994).
17. W. K. Kegel and A. van Blaaderen, Direct observation of dynamical heterogeneities in colloidal hard-sphere suspensions, *Science* **287**,290 (2000).
18. K.P. Velikov and A. van Blaaderen, ZnS-core silica-shell colloids for photonic applications, *Submitted* (2000).
19. A. van Blaaderen, R. Ruel, and P. Wiltzius, Template-directed colloidal crystallization *Nature* **385**, 321 (1997).
20. U. Dassanayake, S. Fraden, and A. van Blaaderen, Structure of electrorheological fluids, *J. Chem. Phys.* **112**, 3851 (2000).

21. R. M. Amos, J. G. Rarity, P. R. Tapster *et al.*, Fabrication of large-area face-centered-cubic hard-sphere colloidal crystals by shear alignment, *Phys. Rev. E* **61**, 2929 (2000).
22. K. Visscher and S. M. Block, Versatile Optical Traps with Feedback Control, in: *Methods in Enzymology*, R B Vallee, ed Academic Press, San Diego, Vol. 298, (1997).
23. D. L. J. Vossen, T. van Dillen, M. J. A. de Dood, T. Zijlstra, E. van der Drift, A. Polman, A. van Blaaderen, Novel method for solution growth of thin silica films from tetraethoxysilane, *Adv. Materials* **12**, 1434 (2000).
24. P. Jiang, J. F. Bertone, K. S. Hwang *et al.*, Single-crystal colloidal multilayers of controlled thickness, *Chem. Mat.* **11**, 2132 (1999).
25. E. Snoeks, A. van Blaaderen, T. van Dillen *et al.*, Colloidal ellipsoids with continuously variable shape, *Adv. Materials*, **12**, 1511 (2000).
26. S. Neser, C. Bechinger, P. Leiderer *et al.*, Finite-size effects on the closest packing of hard spheres, *Phys. Rev. Lett.* **79**, 2348 (1997).
27. S. Pronk and D. Frenkel, Can stacking faults in hard-sphere crystals anneal out spontaneously?, *J. Chem. Phys.* **110**, 4589 (1999).
28. J. Aizenberg, P. V. Braun, and P. Wiltzius,Patterned colloidal deposition controlled by electrostatic and capillary forces, *Phys. Rev. Lett.* **84**, 2997 (2000).
29. R. Tao and J. M. Sun,3-Dimensional Structure of Induced Electrorheological Solid, *Phys. Rev. Lett.* **67**, 398 (1991).
30. R. Tao and Q. Jiang, Simulation of Structure Formation in an Electrorheological Fluid, *Phys. Rev. Lett.* **73**, 205 (1994).
31. A. Ashkin, Acceleration and trapping of particles by radiation pressure, *Phys. Rev. Lett.* **24**, 156 (1970).
32. A Ashkin and J M Dziedic, Optical levitation by radiation pressure, *Phys. Rev. Lett.* **19**, 283 (1971).
33. D G Grier, Optical tweezers in colloid and interface science, *Curr. Opin. Colloid Interface Sci.* **2**, 264 (1997).
34. E. R. Dufresne and D. G. Grier, Optical tweezer arrays and optical substrates created with diffractive optics, *Rev. Scient. Instr.* **69**, 1974 (1998).
35. F. Burmeister, W. Badowsky, T. Braun *et al.*, Colloid monolayer lithography-A flexible approach for nanostructuring of surfaces, *Appl. Surf. Sci.* **145**, 461 (1999).
36. P. Bartlett, R. H. Ottewill, and P. N. Pusey, Freezing of Binary-Mixtures of Colloidal Hard-Spheres *J. Chem. Phys.* **93**, 1299 (1990).
37. A. Moroz and C. Sommers, Photonic band gaps of three-dimensional face-centred cubic lattices, *J. Phys.-Condes. Matter* **11**, 997 (1999).
38. A. Blanco, E. Chomski, S. Grabtchak *et al.*, Large-scale synthesis of a silicon photonic crystal with a complete three-dimensional bandgap near 1.5 micrometres *Nature* **405**, 437 (2000).

THIN OPALINE PHOTONIC CRYSTALS

SERGEI G. ROMANOV, TORSTEN MAKA,
CLIVIA M. SOTOMAYOR TORRES
Institute of Materials Science and Department of Electrical & Information Engineering
University of Wuppertal, Gaußstr. 20, D-42097 Wuppertal, Germany

MANFRED MÜLLER, RUDOLF ZENTEL
Institute of Materials Science and Department of Chemistry
University of Wuppertal, Gaußstr. 20, D-42097 Wuppertal, Germany

1. Introduction

Among attractive features of the three-dimensional (3D) photonic crystal (PC) is its capability to cope with the emission of an arbitrary mode structure if the frequency of radiation matches the photonic band gap (PBG). To realise this effect one has to create a PC with omnidirectional PBG and to incorporate a light source of appropriate frequency without compromising the refractive index (RI) contrast. Numerous effects are anticipated in the case of strong coherent localisation of photons in the gain medium [1]. As far as visible light is concerned neither complete 3D PBGs nor a suitable technology for integrating the proper emitters have been reported so far.

One of the effective design solutions towards 3D PCs for the visible spectrum is templating a suitable high RI material in the opal [2]. Opal itself is a face centred cubic (fcc) package of identical silica spheres. The PBG of opals does not approach omnidirectionality because of the low RI contrast, symmetry considerations and overfilling of its space with dielectric [3]. Nevertheless opals have already demonstrated the ability to modify the fluorescence spectrum of light sources embedded in their volume [4,5,6]

Opals can be prepared from silica spheres [7] and polymer beads [8]. The forces controlling the assembly of these structures in a colloidal crystal are of the same strength as disorganising forces, which results in a large number of defects. In order to minimise disorder, the aspect ratio (area / thickness) of the opal package has to be as large as possible. The sedimentation of beads on a substrate allows the preparation of thin opals composed of few layers [9,10,11].

Infilling opals with high RI inorganic materials and subsequent inverting them pursues a twofold target: to increase the RI contrast and to optimise the volume fraction of scatterers. However, the choice of materials combining a wide electronic gap and an RI over critical value is extremely narrow. That is why inverted opals reported so far either cannot operate in the visible, e.g. Si replicas [12], or possess an insufficient RI contrast to exhibit a complete PBG, e.g. TiO_2 or CdS replicas [13,14]. Attempts to infill opal with GaP have yielded a volume fraction of semiconductor insufficient to realise inverted structures [15].

C.M. Soukoulis (ed.), Photonic Crystals and Light Localization in the 21st Century, 253–262.

The general feature of inorganic inverted opals is the nominally high RI contrast. However, the actual physical behaviour of inverted opaline structures can be questioned since it is based on the assumption that the infill has the RI of bulk semiconductor. In fact, the material synthesised in opal voids fills loosely the available space. For example, the filling factor of TiO_2 that reported in ref. [13] is about 10-15% out of up to 26% available template space. The low density of material constituting the body of replica results in the dramatically reduced RI contrast. Annealing of such composite [14] obviously brings closer together the nominal and effective values of RIs, but this procedure may not increase the gap because the PBG, which occurs between 8th and 9th bands, collapses rapidly with a deviation of the filling factor from the optimum value [16].

So far the radiation from PCs has been reported for RI contrast of about 1.5 : 1. In this case the propagation of the emission is suppressed within a small fraction of the solid angle (see, e.g. [17,18]). Obviously, this RI contrast is insufficient to localise even partially the emitted photon in the vicinity of the emitter and this emission is filtered by the stop-band due to the distributed Bragg reflection [18]. Nevertheless, the flow of energy appears spatially redistributed over the space [19] due to the anisotropy of dispersion surfaces in an incomplete PC [20]. In the inverted opaline structure the photon emitted with the frequency of the stop-band samples the severely restricted phase space. Therefore, its localisation appears stronger and the alteration of the emission properties of the embedded light source goes far beyond a simple band-pass filtering effect.

The aim of this paper is the comparative analysis of optical properties of PMMA opaline films and their semiconductor replicas. Organic dyes, emission bands of which overlap with the lowest stop-band of the corresponding PC, were used as light sources homogeneously distributed in the volume of PCs. Several tests have been performed to show the difference of the light source behaviour in PBG environments of different strengths.

2. Material preparation

The PMMA beads were prepared by a modified emulsion polymerisation [11]. The bead diameters of opaline structures studied were ~250 and ~286 nm.

Thin opaline films were prepared by spreading a few drops of the emulsion over hydrophilic substrates. Sedimentation proceeds during three days in an atmosphere of controlled humidity. Typical area covered by homogeneously diffracting opaline film is of 2×2 cm^2. The beads are self-assembled in the fcc package with the (111) plane along the substrate. SEM inspection revealed films consisting of 10 to 50 layers. Monocrystalline domains extend approximately over a hundred micrometers. A controlled amount of Coumarin 6 dye was added during the synthesis.

The replicas of PMMA opaline film were prepared from SnS_2 [21]. Due to its high RI contrast and wide electronic bandgap (~2.1 eV for the indirect transition and ~2.4 eV for the direct transition) [22] the inverse SnS_2 opaline structure has the potential for a complete PBG material operating up to the green part of the spectrum. Chemical vapour deposition of SnS_2 was performed with $SnCl_4$ vapour and H_2S gas at ambient pressure. To remove the PMMA beads, the films were subjected to tetrahydrofurane (THF). Details are given elsewhere [21]. On a microscopic scale the semiconductor replica is a perfect duplicate of the opal structure. The density of the semiconductor in the voids and thereby the effective RI depends, however, on the synthesis conditions. The Raman spectrum of SnS_2 inverted opal shows a peak centred at 311 cm^{-1} in accord with the frequency of lattice vibration in crystalline SnS_2. The relatively broad appearance of this peak suggests that the semiconductor consists of small crystallites.

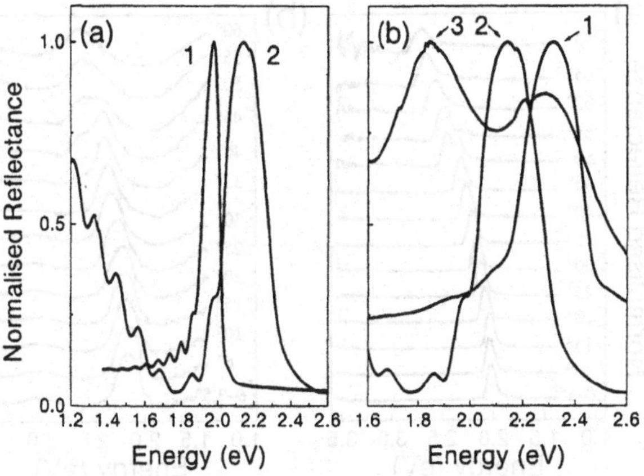

Figure 1. (a) Optical diffraction spectra from PMMA opaline film (D=287 nm) (curve 1) and its SnS_2 replica (curve 2). (b) Evolution of the Bragg peak with the increase of the density of SnS_2 in replica from 1 to 3. Bragg peaks are indicated by arrows.

These replicas were immersed in a 1:1000 mole solution of perylene dye and then dried. As a result dye molecules were deposited on the inner surface of replica voids.

3. Optical diffraction

The reflectance and transmission spectra of opaline films have been measured by illuminating a 0.2 cm^2 area with white light from a tungsten halogen lamp and collecting a reflected/transmitted light within a 2° solid angle.

Opaline films, both PMMA templates and SnS_2 replicas, demonstrate a uniform coloration due to diffraction over a whole area. Fig.1a shows the reflectance spectra of PMMA opaline template and its SnS_2 replica. The Bragg resonance shifts with the change of the effective RI of the structure as a whole. From peak positions at 629 and 596 nm for PMMA and SnS_2 films, respectively, the effective RIs 1.34, and 1.26 are deduced from the Bragg law $\lambda_{(111)} = 2n_{eff}a$, where $a = 0.816D$ is the interplane distance for (111) planes of the fcc lattice and D represents the bead diameter. Using the effective medium estimate of the average RI in the form $n_{PMMA-opal} = fn_{PMMA} + (1-f)n_{air} = 1.34$, where $n_{PMMA} = 1.4893$, $n_{air} = 1$, $f = 0.74$ is the bead filling fraction for an ideal fcc package, the Bragg estimate of the bead diameter is $D = 283$ nm, which deviates slightly from the average $D = 289$ nm obtained by SEM inspection. Dissolution of beads from the composite leads to an approximately 5% shrinkage of the lattice parameter. Assuming the same lattice parameter for the replica, the RI of the SnS_2 is 1.91 was obtained by fitting the expression $n_{SnS_2-replica} = (1-f_{SnS_2}) + f_{SnS_2}n_{SnS_2}$ with the Bragg estimate of the RI. It is reasonable to ascribe the difference between obtained n_{SnS_2} and its nominal value to the loose structure of the replica framework. If the effective RI depends linearly upon the density of the semiconductor, then SnS_2 fills only 60% of the template void volume, i.e. about 14 vol % of the whole composite. Reversibly, the effective medium expression with $n_{SnS_2} = 3.2$ and

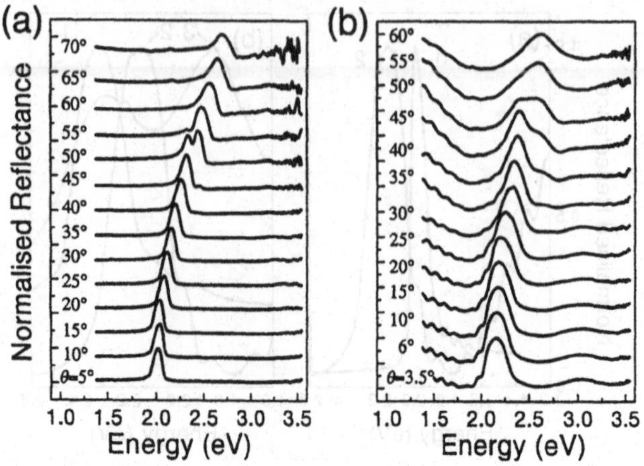

Figure 2. Angular dependence of the diffraction maximum for PMMA PC (a) and its SnS_2 replica (b). Curves are shifted vertically for clarity.

$f_{SnS_2} = 0.14$ produces an $n_{SnS_2-replica} \cup 1.3$ in accords with the Bragg estimate, especially if lattice shrinkage is taken into account.

The evolution of the Bragg peak with the change of the amount of semiconductor in the replica is demonstrated in Fig.1b. For different samples possessing $n_{SnS_2-replica}$ as 1.14, 1.26 and 1.43, the microscopic porosity of SnS_2 decreases and its relative density increases towards that of the bulk material from 0.49 to 0.60 to 0.83 over 24% of the replica space (curves 1, 2 and 3 of Fig. 1b, respectively). Thus, the actual contrast on which the properties of these PCs are based changes from 1.55 via 1.9 to 2.7. Curve 3 corresponds to a very thin film PC having fewer than 10 layers, where the deposition proceeds more effectively.

Fig. 1a shows the reflectance oscillations beside of the Bragg resonance, which appear due to the Fabry-Pérot resonance across the film. These fringes prove a millimeter scale uniformity of the film thickness, but the structuring of the film affects the intensity distribution of these oscillations over the spectrum appearance as compared with homogeneous film [23].

Angular resolved reflectance measurements were performed to study the PBG structure. To trace the angular dependence, the diffraction spectra were collected between 3° and 70° in the specular configuration, where the angle of incidence θ is equal to the angle of collection. Fig. 2 shows well resolved Bragg resonance over this range showing a high level of ordering of the scatterers in both template and replica. Splitting of the Bragg resonance into two peaks occurs around 50° (Fig. 2). This is so-called branching of the stop-band dispersion. The analysis of the band structure [23] shows that branching takes place at the boundary of the Brillouin zone of the PC, where two reflexes originating from (111) and (200) sets of fcc lattice planes fall in the solid angle of the detector simultaneously. Due to the higher RI contrast the Bragg resonance in replica is wider and its angular dispersion is flatter, correspondingly, the branching can be detected over a larger range of angles. This effect is common for most films studied, which is another evidence of the structural superiority of thin opaline films as compared with bulky opals.

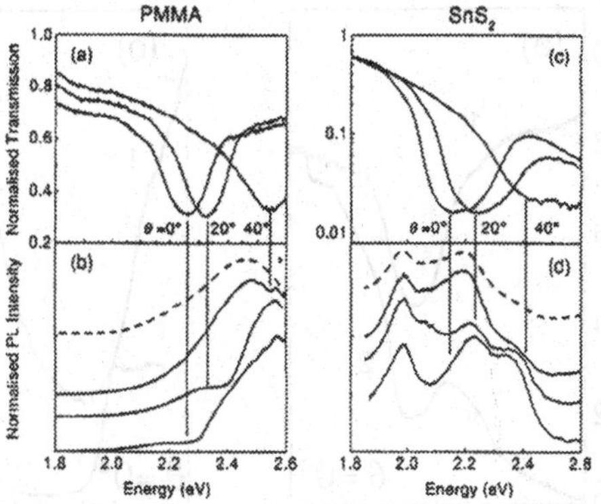

Figure. 3. (a,b) PL spectra of PMMA PC collected at angles 0°, 20° and 40° in comparison with transmission spectra at the same angles. (c,d) Similar spectra of inverted structure from SnS_2. Curves in panels b and d are shifted vertically for clarity. PL spectra of the reference samples are shown by dash lines. Arrows show the central frequency of the stop-band at the angle of the emission collection indicated at each arrow.

4. Emission of the light

Photoluminescence (PL) spectra were excited by an Ar^+-laser operating in cw mode. The excitation power was kept low to avoid the degradation of the dye. PL spectra were collected in the back window configuration. To catch the changes in the spectrum of the source embedded in the incomplete PC the emission has to be collected within the small fraction of the solid angle (about 5° in our case) along the direction of the stop-band appearance.

A direct comparison of dye PL spectra in PMMA and SnS_2 opaline films cannot be performed because different dyes were used to match the emission spectrum with PBG. However, both systems demonstrate a similar suppression of the emission intensity with angular variation of the stop-band (Fig. 3). A perylene dye was chosen for the SnS_2 replica because of its stability against degradation, but its spectrum, which consists of three lines at ~1.98, ~2.2 and ~ 2.4 eV, appears more complicated for analysis.

Firstly, the PL spectrum of the PC was divided by that of a reference sample, which does not show PBG in order to reveal the gap in the emission spectrum. Secondly, the PL spectrum of the reference sample was multiplied by the transmission spectrum of the opaline film to model the PBG-induced spectral redistribution of the emission intensity. Thirdly, the angular distribution of the PL intensity was drawn to demonstrate the directionality of emission propagation. Finally, the evolution of the PL spectrum shape with the increase of excitation power was analysed to pick up the amplified spontaneous emission.

Fig. 4a compares the stop-band obtained from emission and transmission of a PMMA PC. In both spectra the minimum appears at the same frequency and shows a similar depth. The latter feature is specific for thin films, whereas in bulky colloidal crystals the stop-band in emission seems much shallower than in transmission. A similar procedure applied to the replica spectrum shows a factor of 10 deeper stop-band in transmission than in emission as well as a strong distortion of the relative PL spectrum at 2.4 eV at the stop-band edge (Fig. 4b). The different relationship of relative PL and transmission spectra in the template

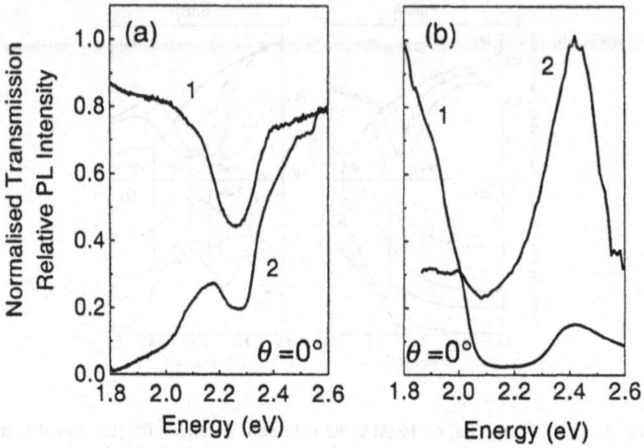

Figure 4. **Comparison of stop-band appearance in transmission (curves 1) and relative emission (curves 2) in PMMA PC (a) and SnS_2 PC (b). Curves are shifted vertically.**

and the replica can be accounted for stronger modification of the radiative recombination in the latter.

There are two scenarios can be followed by emission in PC. The first one is apparently realised in PMMA PC film, where the product of transmission spectrum and the PL spectrum of the reference reproduces the experimentally observed PL spectrum satisfactorily (Fig. 5a). Accordingly, PC does not affect the radiative recombination, but simply rejects the emission propagation from some directions in accord with the transmission function. Thus, the net effect of a low RI PC upon the emission is a spatial redistribution of the intensity. Another scenario is applicable to SnS_2 PC - peaks at 2.2 and 2.4 eV of the experimental spectrum do not survive in the similar product (curve 3, Fig. 5d) of curves 1 and 2 of Fig. 5c. Probably, an enhancement of spontaneous emission at peak 2.2 and especially 2.4 eV occurs when they appear at the stop-band edge. From the other hand, the closer fit to the experimental spectrum can be obtained with an artificially reduced depth of the transmission minimum (compare curves 4 and 6, Fig.5 d), which effectively means that emission detected outside the PC is that generated near its surface. However, this reduction may help with peak at 2.2 eV, but still does not explain the enhancement of emission at 2.4eV. This observation correlates with enhancement of a relative PL spectrum at the upper edge of the stop-band (curve 2 of Fig.4b).

In an incomplete PC the spatial distribution of the energy flow transported by EM waves in the PBG frequency range is governed by the symmetry of dispersion surfaces. Being the cross-section taken at constant frequency throughout the photon energy band diagram of PC, the dispersion surface in the PBG frequency range contains sections overlapping with the gap for some wavevectors and non-overlapping for others, the former eliminates these directions from a radiation propagation. In the case of incomplete PC the dispersion surface configuration depends dramatically on the frequency because a part of the solid angle covered by PBG changes considerably with the small increment of the frequency. Correspondingly, the angular distribution of the emission flow away from a PC changes with the frequency. Fig. 6 shows the angular diagrams of emission of a PMMA PC at two different frequencies and compares them with a standard distribution of the emission intensity given by $\cos^2\theta$.

For PCs of a higher RI contrast the configuration of the dispersion surface changes less with the same frequency increment as it happened for low contrast PC. Because of a larger increment required to reveal the directionality effect the angular diagrams for 2.08 and 2.4 eV bands of SnS_2 PC are compared in Fig. 7. The 2.4 eV band shows focusing along the normal to the film plane, whereas 2.08 eV band shows a minimum in this direction. This observation correlates with the angular position of the stop-band in reflectance spectra. Apparently, the dispersion surface configuration favours the focusing effect along the (111) direction if the upper edge of the stop-band (on its angular move) crosses the emission maximum. Evidently, it happens with both the Coumarin emission band in PMMA PC and 2.4 eV Perylene emission band in SnS_2 PC.

If a PC provides a dressing of the emitter with its own radiation [1], the shape of the PL spectrum should depend upon the emission intensity. The achieved level of the RI contrast in SnS_2 PCs is not enough to localise the radiation sufficiently, but it leaves a hope to reveal the precondition of this feedback in a same manner as it is made for resonators. The distortion of the PL spectrum was traced by changing the excitation power, provided that the pumping power is low enough to exclude saturation and two-photon processes among others. The intensity ratios taken between PL spectra collected at different excitation power are shown in Fig. 8 for different angles of the light collection. The ratio spectral band, which is ended with peak centred at 2.45 eV, correlates with the emission band of the perylene dye, i.e. it is a feature of electronic transitions, namely a matrix element of the transition and a photon density of states. The latter is to be affected somehow by a PBG of a PC. If the stop-band is

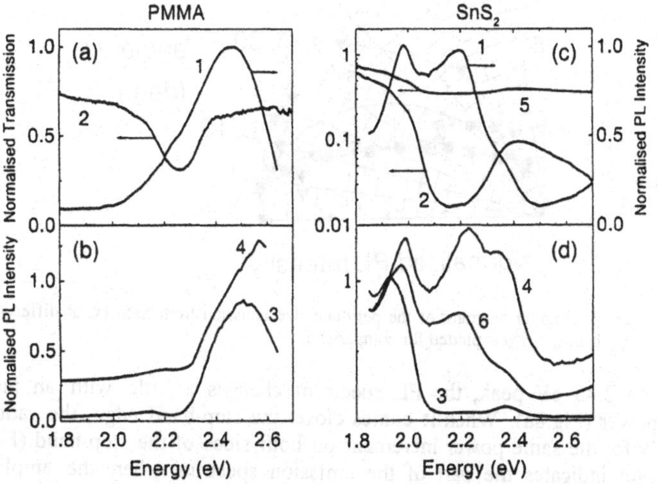

Figure 5. Reconstruction of PL spectra of PMMA (left) and SnS_2 (right) PCs. Panels (a, c): PL spectrum of the reference sample (curves 1) and the corresponding transmission spectrum (curves 2) for these PCs, respectively. Panels (b,d) curves 3 – product of spectra 1 and 2. Curves 4 - experimental spectra. Closer fit to the experimental PL of perylene/SnS_2 (curve 6, d-panel) can be obtained with artificially smeared transmission spectrum (curve 5 of c-panel).

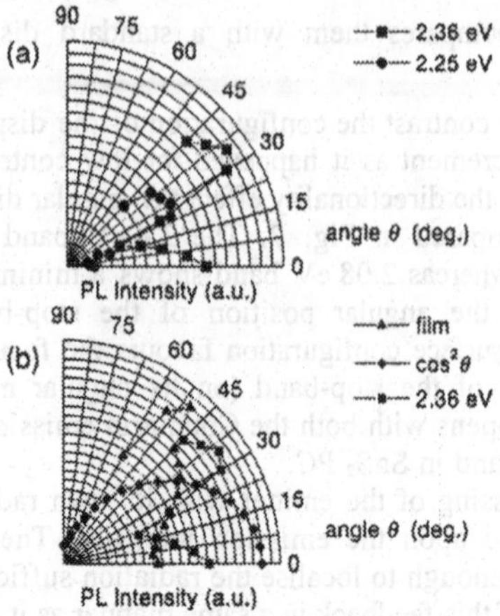

Figure 6. Angular diagrams of the coumarin dye emission from PMMA PC at different energies. (b) Comparison of angular diagrams of emission from PMMA PC, unstructured film of the same composition and $\cos^2\theta$.

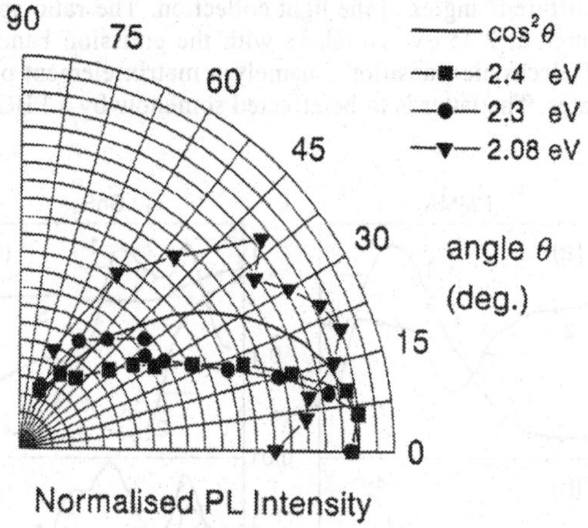

Figure 7. Angular diagrams of the perylene dye emission from SnS_2 PC at different energy bands; $\cos^2\theta$ is plotted for comparison.

far below the 2.45 eV peak, the PL spectrum changes a little with an increase of the excitation power (Fig.8a). When it comes closer the stop-band edge, the ratio peak grows more rapidly for the same power increment on both sides of the stop-band (Figs.8b,c). The ratio spectrum indicates the part of the emission spectrum where the amplification of a spontaneous emission takes place. This happens, if the stop-band edge appears in the vicinity of the electronic transition. For the photon density of states being the scalar value the directionality of the spontaneous emission rate cannot be accounted. However, the squeezing of the space available for the emission propagation appears effectively as the amplification of the emission occurring at the stop-band edge, where the permanent pumping as a necessary condition for this effect to be observed. This observation alone does not prove

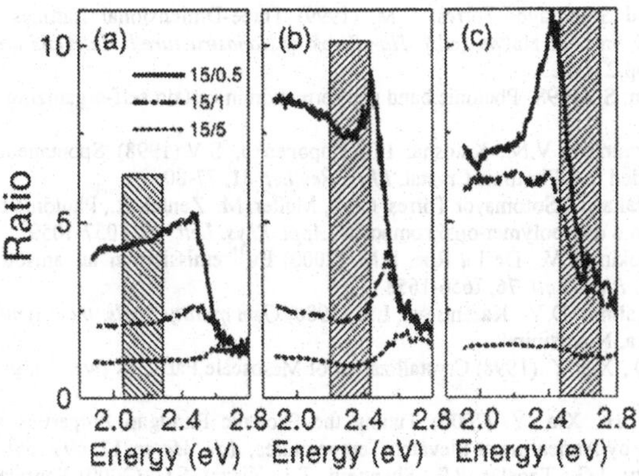

Figure 8. Intensity ratio spectra taken at excitation power increments 3, 15 and 30 for angles 0° (a), 30° (b) and 60° (c). Patterned bars represent the FWHM of stop-band for the same angles.

unambiguously the PBG-related enhancement of the spontaneous emission but can be considered as a pre-condition for the manipulation of the emission rate.

Taken altogether, all tests indicate a strong alteration experienced by the emission at 2.4 eV band in a perylene/SnS_2 PC. The changes in the emission radiated at the stop-band edge can be considered as the benchmark to prove theories dealing with emission efficiency in PBG structures.

In summary, we have exploited a non-expensive chemical routine to prepare large area opaline films by sedimentation of PMMA beads and converting these templates into SnS_2 inverted opaline structure through a gas phase reaction at ambient conditions. Potentially, SnS_2 PCs possess a RI, which is high enough to open an omnidirectional PBG in the visible range of light. The structural quality of prepared films has been confirmed by transmission/reflectance spectroscopy. Diffraction of the EM waves from these structures has shown the formation of incomplete PBG structure with the symmetry related to the fcc PC. Enhancement of the PBG with the increase of the RI contrast has been demonstrated. This high RI contrast structure allow the manipulation of the emission characteristics of light sources embedded in PCs. In particular, the suppression of the emission in the stop-band frequency range, the enhancement of the spontaneous emission and the directionality of the emission have been demonstrated.

5. Acknowledgement

This work was partly supported by the EU-IST project PHOBOS, no. 19009.

References

1 John, S. (1995) Localization of Light - theory of photonic band gap materials, in C.M Soukoulis (ed.), *Photonic Band Gap Materials*, Kluwer Academic Publishers, Dordrecht, pp.563-665

2 Romanov, S.G and Sotomayor Torres, C.M. (1999) Three-Dimensional Lattices of Nanostructures - the template approach, in H.S. Nalwa (ed.), *Handbook of Nanostructured Materials and Technology, v.4, ch.4*, Academic Press, pp.231-323,

3 Busch, K. and John, S. (1998) Photonic band gap formation in certain self-organizing systems, *Phys.Rev.E* **58**, 3896 -3908

4 Petrov, E.P., Bogomolov, V.N., Kalosha, I.I., Gaponenko, S.V.(1998) Spontaneous Emission of Organic Molecules Embedded in a Photonic Crystal, *Phys. Rev.Lett* **81**, 77-80

5 Romanov, S.G., Maka, T., Sotomayor Torres, C.M., Müller, M., Zentel, R., Photonic band-gap effects upon the light emission from a dye-polymer-opal composite, *Appl. Phys. Lett.* **75**, 1057-1059

6 Romanov, S.G., Fokin, A.V., De La Rue, R.M. (2000) Eu^{3+} emission in an anisotropic photonic band gap environment, *Appl. Phys. Lett.* **76**, 1656-1658

7 Deniskina, N.D, Kalinin, D.V., Kazantseva, L.K.(1980) *Gem quality opals, their synthesis and natural genesis* (in Russian), Nauka, Novosibirsk

8 Park, S. H., Qin, D., Xia, Y. (1998) Crystallization of Mesoscale Particles over Large Areas, *Adv. Mater.* **10**, 1028-1032

9 Gates, B., Park, S. H., Xia, Y. (2000) Tuning the Photonic Bandgap Properties of Crystalline Arrays of Polystyrene Beads by Annealing at Elevated Temperatures, *Adv. Mater.* **12**, 693 -656

10 Amos, R.M., Rarity, J.G., Tapster, P.R., Shepherd, T.J., Kitson, S.C. (2000) Fabrication of large-area face-centered-cubic hard-sphere colloidal crystals by shear alignment, *Phys. Rev. E* **61**, 2929-2935

11 Müller, M., Zentel, R., Maka, T., Romanov, S.G., Sotomayor Torres, C.M., (2000) Dye containing Polymer Beads as Photonic Crystals, *Chem Mater.*, 12, 2508-2512

12 Blanco, A., Chomski, E., Grabtchak, S., Ibisate, S., John, S., Leonard, S.W., Lôpez, C., Meseguer, F.O., Miguez, H., Mondia, J.P., Ozin, G.A., Toader, O., van Driel, H.M. (2000) Large-scale synthesis of a silicon photonic crystal with a complete three-dimensional bandgap near 1.5 micrometres, *Nature* **405**, 437-440

13 Wijnhoven, J.E.G.J., Vos, W.L. (1998) Preparation of Photonic Crystals Made of Air Spheres in Titania, *Science* **281**, 802-804

14 Vlasov, Y.A., Yao,N., Norris, D.J. (1999) Synthesis of Photonic Crystals for Optical Wavelengths from Semiconductor Quantum Dots, *Advanced Materials*. **11**, 165-169

15 Romanov, S.G., Yates, H.M., Pemble, M.E., De La Rue, R. M. (2000) Impact of GaP layer deposition upon photonic bandgap behaviour of opal, *J. Phys.: Condens. Matter* **12**, 339-348

16 Doosje, M., Hoenders, B. J., Knoester, J.(2000) Photonic bandgap optimization in inverted fcc photonic crystals, *J. Opt. Soc. Am. B* **17**, 600-606

17 Romanov, S.G., Fokin, A.V., Alperovich, V.I., Johnson, N.P., De La Rue, R.M (1997). The Effect of the Photonic Stop-Band upon the Photoluminescence of CdS in Opal, *phys. stat. sol. (a)* **164**, 169-173

18 Vlasov, Y.A., Deutsch, M., Norris, D.J. (2000) Single-domain spectroscopy of self-assembled photonic crystals, *Appl. Phys. Lett.* **76**, 1627-1629

19 Romanov, S.G., Maka, T., Sotomayor Torres, C.M., Müller, M., Zentel, R. (1999) Emission Properites of Dye-Polymer-Opal Photonic Crystals, *Journal of Lightwave Technology* **17**, 2121-2127

20 Kosaka, H., Kawashimaa, T., Tomita, A., Notomi, M., Tamamura, T., Sato, T., Kawakami, S.(1998) Superprism phenomena in photonic crystals, *Phys. Rev. B* **58**, R10096- R10099

21 Müller, M., Zentel, R., Maka, T., Romanov, S.G., Sotomayor Torres, C.M., Photonic Crystal Films with high Refractive Index Contrast, *Adv. Materials*, to be published

22 Domingo, G., Itoga, R.S., Cannewurf, C.R. (1966) Fundamental Optical Absorption in SnS_2 and $SnSe_2$, *Phys. Rev.* **143**, 536-541

23 Romanov, S.G., Maka, T., Sotomayor Torres, C.M., Müller, M., Zentel, R., Manzanares, J., Cassagne, D., Jouanin, C., submitted for publication

TUNABLE SHEAR-ORDERED FACE-CENTERED CUBIC PHOTONIC CRYSTALS

R M. AMOS, D.M. TAYLOR, T.J. SHEPHERD, J.G. RARITY AND P. TAPSTER
DERA
St. Andrews Road
Malvern
Worcestershire
WR14 3PS
UK
RAMOS@dera.gov.uk

1. Abstract

Large-area photonic crystals are produced by the shear-alignment of stabilized 720 nm diameter PMMA spheres dispersed in a range of liquids suspended between two parallel glass slides. An oscillatory linear shear aligns the initially small crystallites into a single domain many square centimeters in area. Reducing the shear to one lattice constant per layer produces a face-centered cubic crystal structure. This relaxes to a faulted twinned face-centered cubic structure on removal of the shear. Pure face-centered cubic crystals can be fabricated by dispersing the PMMA spheres directly in an epoxy resin. A 2-dimensional shearing scheme creates a stable face-centered cubic structure which is made permanent by exposing to UV light, thus solidifying the epoxy resin. The diffractive properties of the crystal can be monitored as the shear is applied and used to determine the crystal structure. Further, if the PMMA spheres are dispersed directly into a liquid crystal, the refractive index contrast and hence the diffraction properties can be controlled by temperature and by applying an electric field across the crystal.

2. Introduction

In this paper we will summarize the recent results and conclusions of three experiments in which photonic crystals are fabricated by applying a controlled shear to a colloidal suspension confined between two glass slides. We use 720 nm diameter polymethyl methacrylate (PMMA) spheres dispersed in octanol, an epoxy resin, or a liquid crystal at volume concentrations of between 49 and 54%.

There is currently much interest in photonic crystals. These are materials that possess a periodic modulation in refractive index on an optical wavelength scale. Such materials can Bragg reflect incident light at certain well-defined frequencies which are

C.M. Soukoulis (ed.), Photonic Crystals and Light Localization in the 21st Century, 263–278.

dictated by the periodicity, direction of propagation and polarization. Extending the periodicity to three- dimensions (3D) and by suitably increasing the dielectric contrast opens the prospect of creating a material wherein all electromagnetic propagation is disallowed for a range of optical frequencies [1,2]. This is known as a photonic band gap (PBG) material. Within the band gap the optical density of states is zero. Purcell [3] was the first to propose that spontaneous emission can be modified by controlling the density-of-states; PBG materials have enormous potential in tailoring the properties of many optical devices.

The formation of a photonic band gap depends on the detailed periodic structure of the material. Structures based on the face-centered cubic (FCC) unit cell have a near-spherical Brillouin zone and are good candidates for producing a wide band gap [4]. However, materials which possess a full photonic band gap at optical wavelengths have yet to be demonstrated experimentally and remain a significant fabrication challenge. There have been a number of fabrication techniques used to produce 3D photonic crystals that show a partial band gap. One such technique is self-assembly.

The formation of optical-scale hard-sphere crystals from monodisperse colloidal dispersions has been studied for some time. Such systems have proved extremely useful models for studies of the liquid-solid-glass phase transition [5-7]. It was shown that for hard-spheres spontaneous crystallization can occur for particular values of volume concentration. For volume concentrations $f > 0.49$ a polycrystalline phase separates from the initially liquid-like structure. The crystalline phase fills the entire sample when f reaches 0.54 and glassy states form for $f > 0.58$. In initial light scattering experiments the scattered intensity from many crystallites were studied as a function of angle [8]. This is equivalent to the well-known X-ray powder diffraction method, and study of the detailed structure of the Bragg ring allows the structure within the crystallites to be deduced. It was concluded that the crystalline phase was primarily made up of small (100μm) crystallites with structure primarily random close packed (RCP) consisting of a random stacking of hexagonally close packed (HCP) layers.

Synthetic opals can be fabricated by the sedimentation of silica spheres suspended in a liquid. The liquid can be evaporated and the resulting dry crystal infiltrated with other materials to increase the refractive index contrast [9,10]. Alternatively, the dry silica crystal can be heated (sintered) to fuse the spheres together. After infiltration with another material (such as TiO_2) the silica spheres can be removed by dissolving in acid, thus forming the inverse crystal structure [11,12]. A recent paper [13] has demonstrated that such inverse structures can also be created directly.

The methods discussed above are slow (sedimentation takes many days or weeks to form colloidal crystals) and tend to create small crystallites. There is no control over the dimensions of the crystal, its orientation or structure, and perhaps most importantly, there is no control over the defect density. Recent experiments [14,15] have shown that shearing along one direction during crystallization increases the size of the crystallites and can induce the formation of millimetre-sized FCC crystals. Shear-induced order has been reported for triblock copolymers in solution in a cylindrical geometry [16]. Six nm diameter miscelles are formed which align into HCP planes under steady shear and twinned FCC structures under oscillatory shear. Shear has also been applied by suspending a colloidal crystal between two parallel plates [17-21]. It was shown that under high strain conditions HCP layers of spheres formed aligned parallel with the flow direction. Application of low strain produced a polycrystalline structure consisting of HCP planes aligned perpendicular to the shear direction. Local disorder was observed using optical microscopy revealing dislocations, vacancies and stacking faults. In this paper we study the optical properties of shear-ordered colloidal crystals.

3. Shear-ordered crystals

720 nm diameter polymethyl methacrylate (PMMA) spheres were dispersed in octanol at volume concentrations of between 49 and 54%. A small amount was placed between two glass slides separated by 10-micron diameter spacer beads (Figure 1).

The sample was illuminated by a laser beam normal to the glass slides and the diffracted Bragg spot intensity monitored on a screen. The pattern consisted of a diffuse ring containing many bright spots, indicating the presence of many domains typically a few hundred microns in size and randomly orientated (Figure 2a)

The bottom glass slide was fixed to a computer-controlled translation stage with 1-micron precision and the top slide held fixed in space. To increase the size of the domains a large-scale oscillatory shear equivalent to many tens of lattice constants per layer was applied. This melted the domains and ensured hexagonal packing parallel to the glass slides. After a period of a few minutes, a single domain filled the entire cell (several cm^2). When the shear was removed the Bragg spot pattern consisted of six well-defined spots of roughly equal intensity, (Figure 2b). These spots were observable over the entire area of the sample and did not move or rotate as the probe laser was moved.

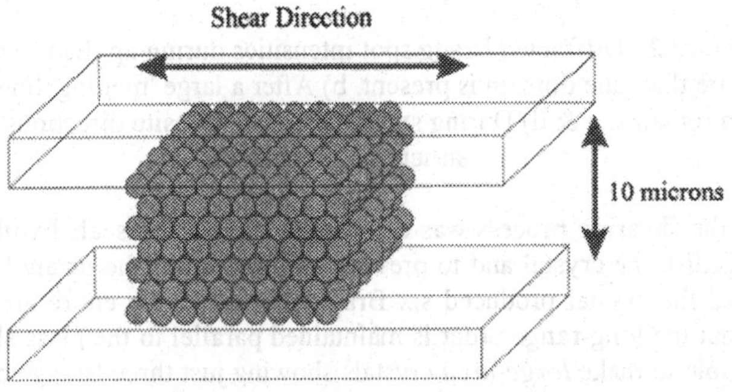

Figure 1. Sample geometry used for shear-ordering colloidal crystals

To influence the stacking sequence perpendicular to the glass slides (in the (111) direction), we applied a small-scale shear, equivalent to one lattice constant per layer and observed the intensity of the six Bragg spots. As shear was applied in one direction, three of the six spots separated by 120 degrees greatly increased in intensity. When shear was applied in the opposite direction, the alternative set of three spots increased in intensity, (Figures 2c and d). This was due to the formation of pure FCC in both cases (i.e., ABCABCABC- and ACBACBACB-type packing). A FCC crystal has 3-fold rotational symmetry in the (111) direction and so three diffracted Bragg spots are expected. On cessation of the shear the crystal slowly relaxed to a structure showing six Bragg spots.

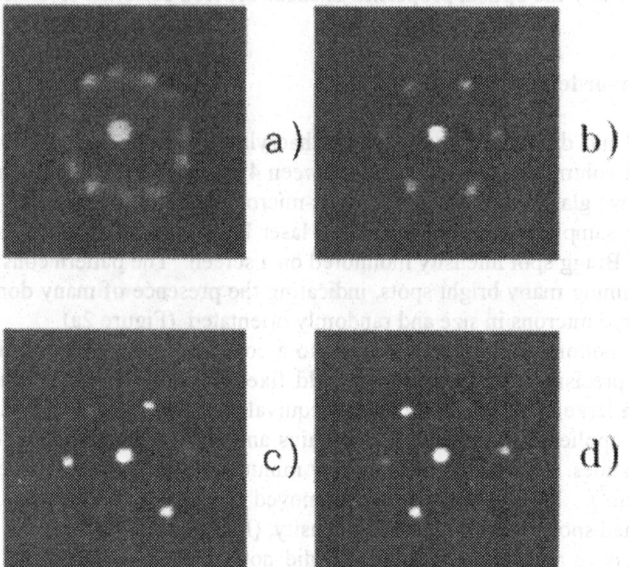

Figure 2. Diffracted Bragg spot intensities during applied shear. a) Before shearing more than one domain is present. b) After a large 'melting' linear shear a single domain remains. c & d) During small shears in opposite directions single FCC structures are selected

After the shearing process was complete, the cell was sealed with an epoxy resin glue to ruggedise the crystal and to prevent evaporation of the octanol. After the resin had hardened the crystal produced six Bragg spots over the entire area of the cell, an indication that the long-range order is maintained parallel to the glass slides. In general we were unable to make *large-area* crystals showing just three Bragg spots with a linear shear; the crystals tend to relax into a six Bragg spots configuration over a period of minutes as the glue dried. We attribute this change to relaxation processes after the shearing (residual movement in the apparatus and thermal movement of the spheres). The resultant crystal structure is actually *twinned* FCC, with both configurations coexisting in the same region of the sample. Similar results have been observed when oscillatory shear is applied to triblock copolymers [16]. We have confirmed the twinned FCC structure by optical characterisation [22].

The intensity of the six Bragg spots were first measured as a function of the incident angle θ between the laser beam and the normal to the glass slides. The crystal sample was placed on a rotation stage with an angular resolution of 0.2 degrees in the centre of a cylindrical bowl containing de-ionised water. A laser beam of wavelength

476 nm was aligned so that it was incident at the centre of rotation. The Bragg spot intensity and diffraction angle was measured with a simple photodiode detector.

We note that the angle at which the Bragg spots are observed can be analysed by considering each layer within the colloidal crystal as a 2D diffraction grating. The pitch of the grating is equal to $d\sqrt{3}/2$ where d is the effective sphere diameter. Following simple diffraction theory we can write

$$\sin\theta + \sin(\theta - \varphi) = \frac{2\lambda_0}{nd\sqrt{3}} \tag{1}$$

where θ is the angle of incidence, ϕ is the angle of the diffracted Bragg spot beam measured from the zero-order transmitted beam, n is the refractive index of the water and λ_0 the incident wavelength. Thus, if we plot sin θ against sin (θ-ϕ), we obtain a linear dependence with a gradient of -1 and an intercept of

$$\frac{2\lambda_0}{nd\sqrt{3}} \tag{2}$$

(see Figure 3). From this we can deduce the sphere size to be 790 nm if we assume that the spheres are touching. Since the volume concentration was 54% (compared to 74% for a close packed structure), we calculate the sphere diameter to be 711 nm. Measurements from SEM images indicate a sphere diameter of 720 nm± 20 nm in good agreement.

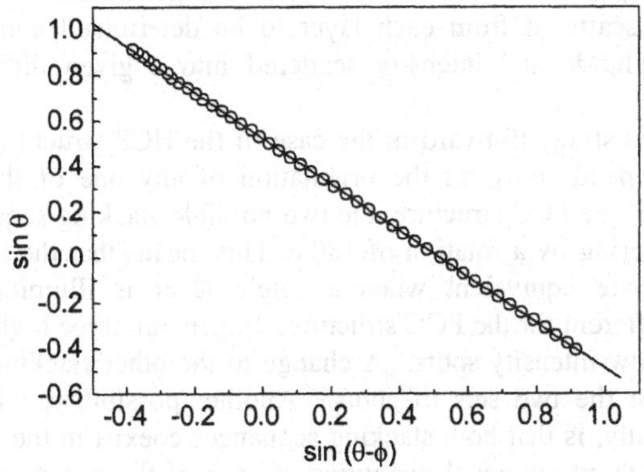

Figure 3. **Angular dependence of the Bragg spot intensities as a function of the incident angle as described in the text. The solid line is a linear fit to the experimental data and was used to calculate the sphere diameter.**

In order to determine the crystal structure a simple theory has been developed to model the light scattering properties of shear-ordered colloidal crystals. This was done by stacking hexagonally close packed layers of spheres in various ways, leading to several possible three-dimensional structures: FCC, HCP, and RCP were the alternatives selected for detailed study.

There is only a small refractive index contrast ($\Delta n=0.06$) between PMMA spheres and octanol, and hence the strength of scattering from individual spheres is expected to be weak. The samples are also thin so that a single-scattering approximation should be valid. The intensity scattered from a plane parallel incident wave into a given direction was calculated by simply summing the scattered amplitudes from each of the spheres in the sample. The scattered amplitude from each sphere was calculated from exact Mie scattering theory. The effect of this is simply to multiply the intensity scattered from a point source by a form factor dependent on the angle between incident and scattered waves.

The summation of scattering amplitudes was performed in two stages. Each layer in the sample is assumed to consist of a perfect two-dimensional hexagonal structure of infinite extent, with the spheres in contact with six nearest neighbours. The scattering from this layer is calculated analytically - the results are the same as for a two-dimensional diffraction grating. The intensity is zero except for a discrete set of scattering angles dependent on the wavelength and the incident direction. The intensity in each of these directions is simply given by the Mie form factor mentioned above. The phase is a function of the incident and scattered angles, together with a term representing the phase of the grating - this is determined by the coordinates of any one sphere within the layer. The second stage is the summation over the number of layers in the sample, which was done numerically. For each of the structures of interest, a set of coordinates for one sphere in each of the layers was generated. This allowed the complex amplitudes scattered from each layer to be determined and then summed, giving the total amplitude and intensity scattered into a given direction from the structure of interest.

This approach is straightforward in the case of the HCP structure, for which the diffraction pattern depends only on the orientation of any one of the layers in the sample. In the case of the FCC structure, the two possible stacking sequences give rise to two structures differing by a rotation of 180°. This means that the six lowest-order Bragg spots, which are equivalent when a single layer is illuminated at normal incidence, become different for the FCC structure. In general, three high-intensity spots alternate with three low-intensity spots. A change to the other stacking sequence will exchange the roles of the two sets of spots. Another possibility, which is actually observed experimentally, is that both stacking sequences coexist in the same sample as twinned FCC, and if there are equal quantities of each of the two possible structures, then six equal-intensity Bragg spots are observed. To model this structure we simply sum the intensities produced by each of the two possible FCC orientations

In the case of RCP we do not have a unique structure, but instead a statistical ensemble of alternative structures with equal probabilities. To model this, a Monte Carlo technique is used. A large number of alternative structures are generated, the diffraction from each is calculated, and the average intensity produced by all of them determined. We present the results from such calculations in Figure 4.

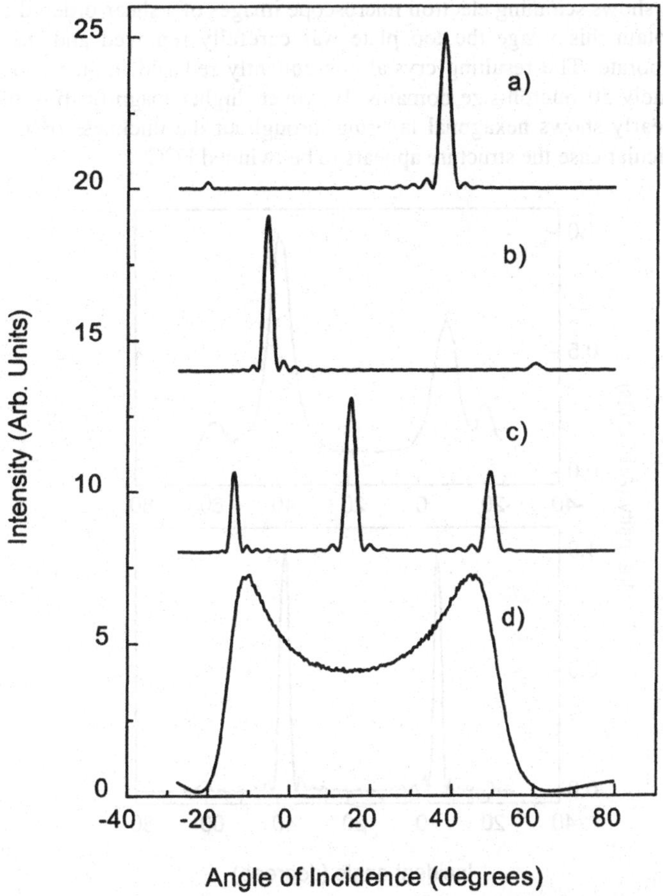

Figure 4. Theoretical Bragg spot intensity as a function of incident angle for a) Single FCC (ABCABCABC) b) Single FCC (ACBACBACB) c) HCP d) RCP.

The experimental intensity dependence of the Bragg spots (shown in Figure 5) compares well to that generated from weak scattering theory. The positions of the four main peaks show good agreement. However, the relative heights of the peaks clearly do not. The theoretical dependence assumes equal amounts of both types of FCC. The heights of the 2 main peaks in the experimental data are not equal indicating that there is more of one type of FCC than the other present in the sample (we estimate 60% of one type and 40% of the other based on the relative heights of the peaks). Also the widths of the peaks are greater than that predicted from theory. This is probably due to scattering from defects within the crystal. Work is currently in progress to examine more closely the defect type and density in shear-aligned colloidal crystals.

Figures 6 shows scanning electron microscope images of a shear-ordered colloidal crystal. To obtain this image the top plate was carefully removed and the octanol allowed to evaporate. The resulting crystal consequently reduced in size and cracked into approximately 50 micron-size domains. However, higher magnification of one of the domains clearly shows hexagonal layering throughout the thickness of the crystal and in this particular case the structure appears to be twinned FCC.

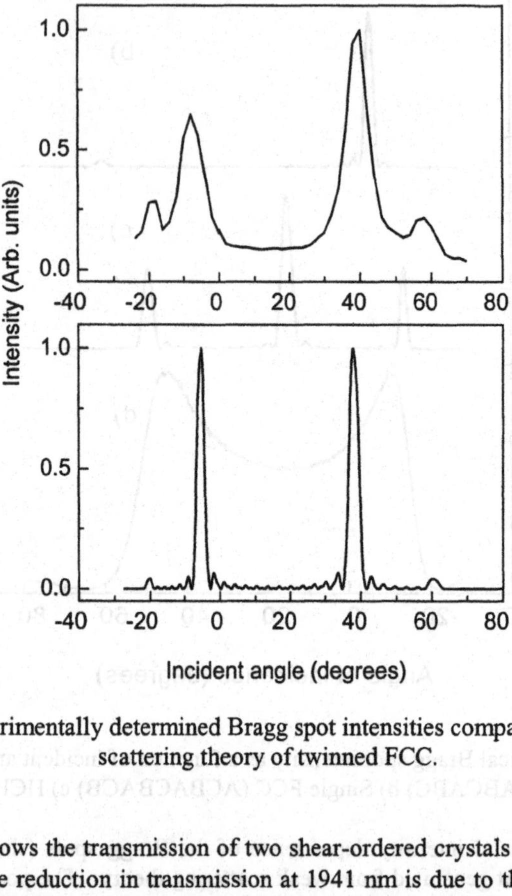

Figure 5. Experimentally determined Bragg spot intensities compared with the weak scattering theory of twinned FCC.

Figure 7 shows the transmission of two shear-ordered crystals of thickness 10 μm and 115 μm. The reduction in transmission at 1941 nm is due to the partial band gap. As expected, the reduction in transmission is larger for the thickest colloidal crystal due to the increased number of lattice planes giving rise to the reflection. At wavelengths outside the partial band gap, there is little difference in transmission indicating similar scattering and absorption properties. It should also be noted that the transmission is high, around 80%; a useful property for many potential applications such as optical limiting and optical switching. The transmission could be increased further if anti-reflection coated slides are used.

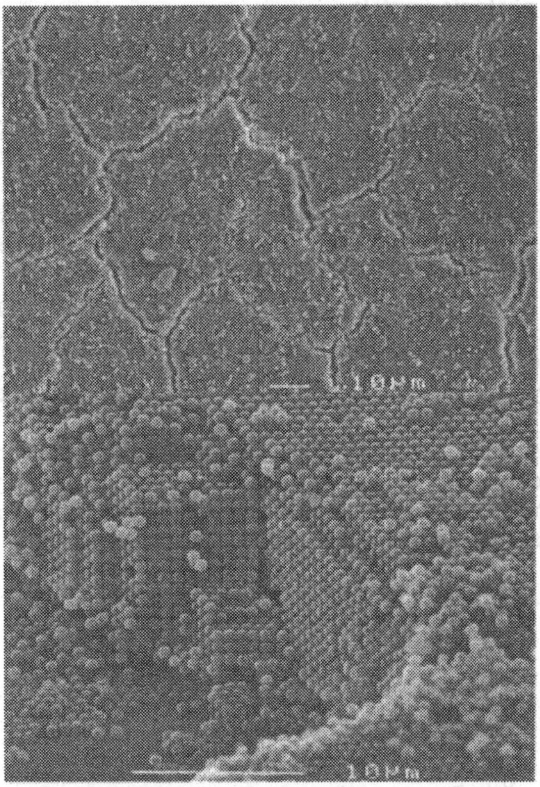

Figure 6. SEM images of a dried shear ordered crystal a) 125μm and b) 32μm across.

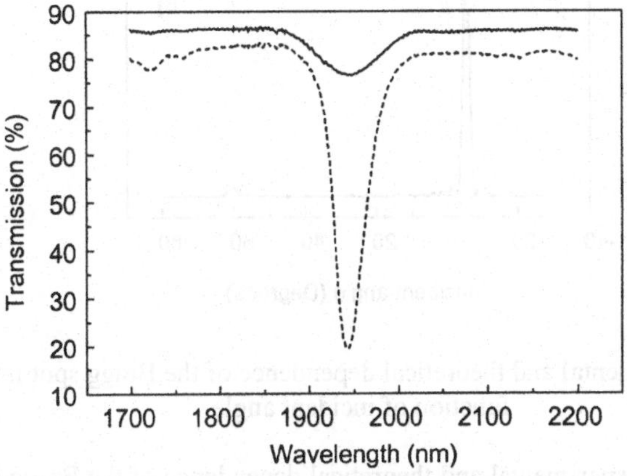

Figure 7. Transmission spectra of two shear-ordered colloidal crystals. The solid line is for a crystal thickness of 10 microns and the dash line is for a thickness of 115 microns.

4. Permanent photonic crystals

The PMMA spheres can be dispersed in a number of liquids, including a UV curable epoxy resin. Crystallization occurred for the same volume concentrations compared to the octanol system. As before a linear shear produced pure FCC stacking on the forward and reverse strokes of the shear and relaxation to a twinned FCC structure occurred when the shear was removed.

In order to select one of the pure FCC stacking sequences, we employed a 2-dimensional shearing scheme. This consisted of shearing successively in three directions 120 degrees apart to form a closed triangular loop. The magnitude of the shear was equal to one lattice constant per layer in the crystal. No relaxation to the twinned FCC structure was observed whilst the triangular shear was applied. The stacking sequence could be selected by choosing the direction of shear around the triangle; one way produced ABCABCABC-type stacking and the other ACBACBACB-type stacking.

Since the structure was stable whilst applying the 2-dimensional shear we were able to make the pure FCC structure permanent by exposing the crystal to UV light, thus rendering the epoxy resin solid. On cessation of shear the crystal remained in the pure FCC form showing just three Bragg spots.

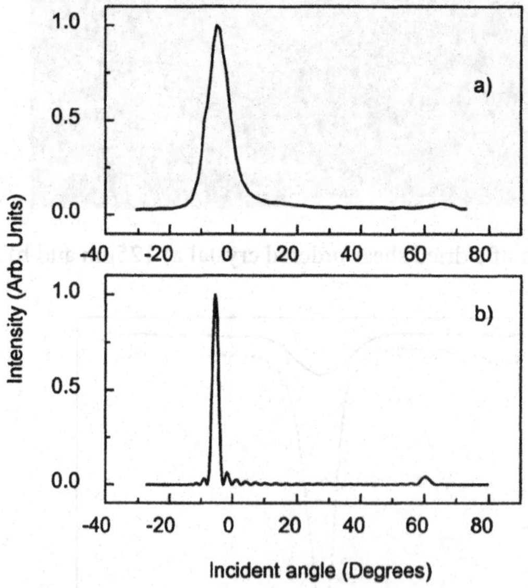

Figure 8. Experimental and theoretical dependence of the Bragg spot intensity as a function of incident angle.

Figure 8 shows the experimental and theoretical dependence of the Bragg spot intensity as a function of incident angle. The intensity greatly increases at an angle of 5.4 degrees, corresponding to the Bragg condition. The theoretical dependence is for a pure

FCC crystal structure consisting of 20 layers of close-packed PMMA spheres (of index 1.49) in an epoxy resin background (of index 1.43). The theoretical sphere diameter was chosen to be 790 nm, to account for the fact that in the experimental sample the volume concentration was 54% and so the spheres were not close-packed. The position of the two peaks in intensity show good agreement with experiment as before. The experimental widths of the peaks, however, are larger than that predicted by the theory. This is probably due to random scattering from defects within the crystal and the finite size distribution of the spheres (~5%).

The photonic crystal was also studied with a scanning electron microscope. We carefully removed the top glass slide which did produce some damage noticeably on the top surface of the crystal. However, regions many millimetres across still produced three Bragg spots indicating the presence of long-range order. Two scanning electron microscope images are shown in Figure 9. The crystal was scored with a scalpel blade to produce a clean edge for study. The total area of the crystal was approximately 2 cm^2. Figure 9a shows the crystal at low magnification and shows the scored region. Figure 9b shows a higher magnification image of the same part of the crystal. FCC packing can clearly be seen throughout the thickness of the film as well as the damage to the top few layers.

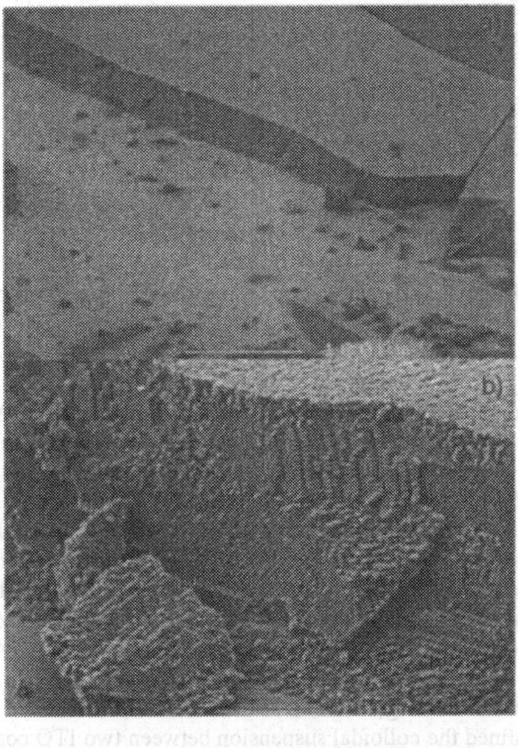

Figure 9. **SEM scans of an epoxy-set colloidal crystal (dismantled and cut in half) at different magnifications (450μm and 60μm wide scans)**

5. Tunable photonic crystals

Dynamical control over the refractive index contrast and hence the diffractive properties may be of great importance for filters, optical limiters and switches. In a recent theoretical study, Busch and John considered the properties of a 3-dimension optical lattice partially filled with a liquid crystal [23]. The refractive index contrast could be controlled by changing the orientation of the liquid crystal molecules. Their conclusion was that the band gap could be controlled by using standard materials (semiconductor and nematic liquid crystal refractive index values).

In a separate experimental study, Yoshino *et al* infiltrated liquid crystal into a synthetic opal host formed from silica spheres [24]. The transmission of the crystal at optical wavelengths at the partial band gap was studied as a function of temperature. They observed phase changes as a step-like change in the refractive index of the liquid crystal (and hence the transmission) as a function of temperature.

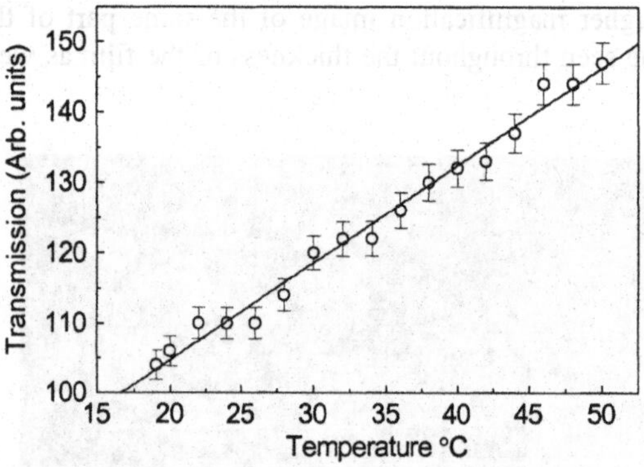

Figure 10. Graph showing the temperature dependence of the zero-order transmission of a colloidal crystal dispersed in 5CB, a nematic liquid crystal at room temperature. The solid line is a linear fit to aid the eye.

We have conducted similar studies with shear-ordered PMMA spheres in 5-carbonyl benzoate (5CB). We immersed the sample in a water bath and measured the intensity of the zero-order transmitted beam as a function of temperature at a wavelength of 632.8 nm (outside the partial band gap). Typical data is shown in Figure 10. 5CB has a nematic to isotropic phase transition at 34^{0}C that should be evident in this experiment as a step-like change in transmission at this temperature. Within the temperature range studied no such phase change was observed. This we attribute to strong surface anchoring of the liquid crystal at the surface of the PMMA spheres. We suggest that the difference between this sample and those in [24] are due to the differences in the surface aligning energies for PMMA and silica spheres. This is currently under further investigation.

We also confined the colloidal suspension between two ITO coated glass slides so that an electric field could be applied across the crystal. Applying a modest voltage (0-20V) influenced the liquid crystal molecular orientation. The intensity of the transmitted beam or the diffracted Bragg spot was then monitored with a photodiode connected to an oscilloscope. We applied a variety of AC and DC fields across the crystal and noted the results.

The Bragg spot intensity reduced as an electric field was applied. When the field was removed the intensity returned to its original value. AC fields were applied with a DC offset such that the magnitude alone, and not the direction of the field, changed. It was noted that changing the direction of the field doubled the modulation frequency of the Bragg spots intensity. We believe this is due to the symmetry of the LC alignment around the spheres.

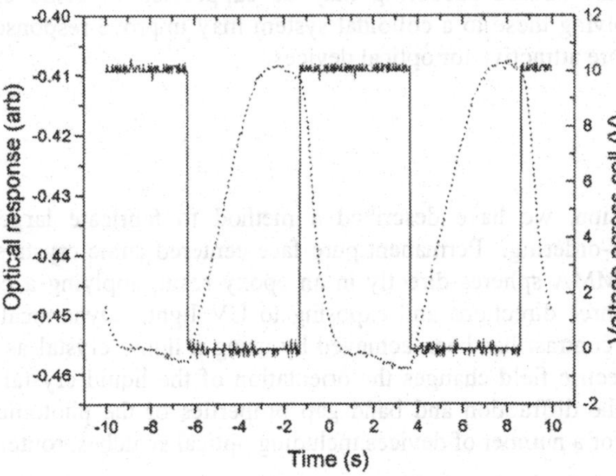

Figure 11. Typical optical response (dashed line) of a single Bragg spot to an oscillating electric field (solid line) shown here at 100mHz.

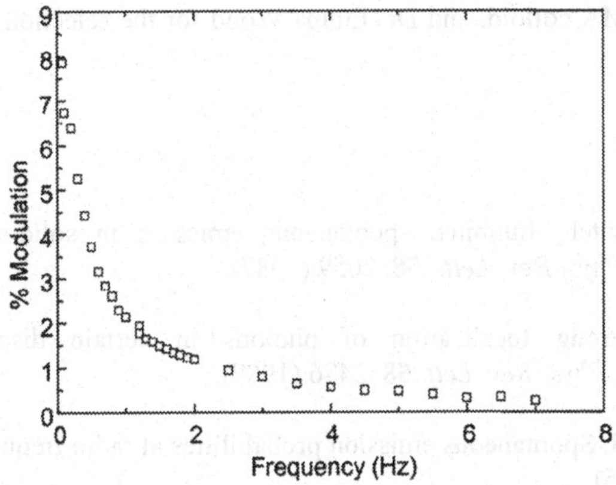

Figure 12. A graph showing how the amplitude of the oscillating Bragg spot intensity varies as a function of applied frequency.

Typical data can be seen in Figure 11. It appears from this that the response time of the liquid crystal is very slow. The rise and fall times were approximately 2 and 3 seconds, respectively. The optical response reduces sharply with increasing frequency. Figure 12 shows the frequency response of the device. No response was observed at frequencies greater than 20Hz.

We believe that this slow response is a result of strong surface anchoring forces. In our system the interstitial volumes are small; individual volumes between spheres are of the order of $0.1\mu m^3$. There are little or no details that can be found in the literature that describe the behaviour of liquid crystals in such small volumes. Some recent work [25] suggests that surface anchoring may be suppressed to some extent by using oligomers. Applying these to a colloidal system may improve response times making these crystals more attractive for optical devices.

6. Conclusion

In conclusion, we have described a method to fabricate large-area photonic crystals by shear-ordering. Permanent pure face-centered cubic crystals are fabricated by dispersing PMMA spheres directly in an epoxy resin, applying a controlled shear sequentially in three directions and exposing to UV light. Dynamical control of the refractive index contrast has been achieved by using a liquid crystal as the suspension medium. An electric field changes the orientation of the liquid crystal molecules and hence changes the diffraction and band gap properties of the photonic crystal. This could be useful for a number of devices including optical switches, routers and limiters.

7. Acknowledgements

We thank Professor Peter Pusey and Dr. Andrew Schofield for supplying us with the stabilized PMMA colloid, and Dr. Emma Wood for the selection and supply of the liquid crystal.

8. References

[1] E. Yablonovitch, Inhibited spontaneous emission in solid-state physics and electronics, *Phys. Rev. Lett.* **58**, 2059 (1987).

[2] S. John, Strong localization of photons in certain disordered dielectric superlattices, *Phys. Rev. Lett.* **58**, 2486 (1987).

[3] E. M. Purcell, Spontaneous emission probabilities at radio frequencies, *Phys. Rev.* **69**, 681 (1946).

[4] N. W. Ashcroft and N. D. Mermin, *Solid State Physics,* Saunders, Philadelphia (1979).

[5] N. A. Clark, A. J. Hurd, and B. J. Ackerson, Single colloidal crystals, *Nature* **281**, 57 (1979).

[6] P. N. Pusey and W. Van Megen, Phase behaviour of concentrated suspensions of nearly hard colloidal spheres, *Nature* **320**, 340 (1986).

[7] P. N. Pusey and W. Van Megen, Observation of a glass transition in suspensions of spherical colloidal particles, *Phys. Rev. Lett.* **59**, 2083 (1987)

[8] P. N. Pusey, W. Van Megan, P. Bartlett, B. J. Ackerson, J. G. Rarity, and S. M. Underwood, Structure of crystals of hard colloidal spheres, *Phys. Rev. Lett.* **63**, 2753 (1989).

[9] A. Blanco, C. Lopez, R. Mayoral, H. Miguez, F. Meseguer, A. Mifsud, and J. Herrero, CdS photoluminescence inhibition by a photonic structure, *Appl. Phys. Letts.* **73**, 1781 (1998).

[10] A. A. Zakhidov, R. H. Baughman, Z. Iqbal, C. Cui, I. Khayrullin, S. O. Dantes, J. Marti, and V. G. Ralchenko, Carbon structures with three-dimensional periodicity at optical wavelengths, *Science* **282**, 897 (1998).

[11] A. M. Kapitonov, N. V. Gaponenko, V. N. Bogomolov, A. V. Prokofiev, S. M. Samoilovich, and S. V. Gapanenko, Photonic stop band in three-dimensional SiO_2/TiO_2 lattice, *Phys. Stat. Sol.*, **165**, 119 (1998).

[12] J. E. G. J. Wijnhoven and W. L. Vos, Preparation of photonic crystals made of air and Titania, *Science* **281**, 802 (1998).

[13] G. Subramania, K. Constant, R. Biswas, M. M. Sigalas, and K. M. Ho, Optical photonic crystals fabricated from colloidal systems, *Appl. Phys. Letts.* **74**, 3933 (1999).

[14] C. Dux and H. Versmold, Light diffraction from shear ordered colloidal dispersions, *Phys. Rev. Letts.* **78**, 1811 (1997).

[15] B. J. Ackerson and N. A. Clark, Shear-induced partial translational ordering of a colloidal solid, *Phys. Rev. A* **30**, 906 (1984).

[16] T. M. Slawecki, C. J. Glinda, and B. Hammouda, Shear-induced micellar crystal structures in an aqueous triblock copolymer solution, *Phys. Rev. E* **58**, R4084 (1998).

[17] M. D. Haw, W. C. K. Poon, and P. N. Pusey, Direct observation of oscillatory-shear-induced order in colloidal suspensions, *Phys Rev. E*, **57**, 6859 (1998).

[18] M. D. Haw, W. C. K. Poon, and P. N. Pusey, Colloidal glasses under shear strain, *Phys Rev. E* **58**, 4673 (1998).

[19] S. H. Park and Y. Xia, Macroporous membranes with highly ordered and three-dimensional interconnected spherical pores, *Advanced Materials* **10**, 1045 (1998).

[20] S. H. Park and Y. Xia, Assembly of mesoscale particles over large areas and its application in fabricating tunable optical filters, *Langmuir* **15**, 266 (1999).

[21] S. H. Park, D. Qin, and Y. Xia, Crystallization of mesoscale particles over large areas, *Advanced Materials* **10**, 1028 (1998).

[22] R. M. Amos, T. J. Shepherd, J. G. Rarity, P. Tapster, and S. C. Kitson, Fabrication of large-area face-centered cubic hard-sphere colloidal crystals by shear alignment, *Phys. Rev. E* **61**, 2929 (2000).

[23] K. Busch and S. John, Liquid-crystal photonic-band-gap materials: The tunable electromagnetic vacuum, *Phys. Rev. Lett.* **83**, 976 (1999).

[24] K. Yoshino, Y. Shimoda, Y. Kawagishi, K. Nakayama, and M. Ozaki, Temperature tuning of the stop band in transmission spectra of liquid-crystal infiltrated synthetic opal as tunable photonic crystal, *Appl. Phys. Lett.* **75**, 932 (1999).

[25] G. P. Bryan-Brown, E. L. Wood, and I. C. Sage, Weak surface anchoring of liquid crystals, *Nature* **399**, 338 (1999).

PHYSICS AND APPLICATIONS OF PHOTONIC CRYSTALS

E. OZBAY*, B. TEMELKURAN, AND MEHMET BAYINDIR
Department of Physics, Bilkent University
Bilkent, 06533 Ankara, Turkey

Abstract. We have demonstrated the resonant cavity enhanced (RCE) effect by placing microwave detectors in defect structures built around dielectric based photonic crystals. A power enhancement factor of 3450 was measured for planar cavity structures. Similar defects were used to achieve highly directional radiation patterns from monopole antennas. We also used these defect structures to demonstrate waveguiding around layer-by-layer photonic crystals. An air gap introduced between two photonic crystal walls was used as waveguide. We observed full transmission of the electromagnetic (EM) waves through these planar waveguide structures within the frequency range of the photonic band gap. The dispersion relations obtained from the experiments were in good agreement with the predictions of our waveguide model. We presented experimental and theoretical investigation of eigenmode splitting due to coupling of the localized cavity modes in the three-dimensional photonic crystals. A new type of waveguiding mechanism, photons propagate through strongly localized coupled-cavity modes, in photonic band gap structures was demonstrated. It was also observed that the group velocity of photons tends towards zero at the waveguiding band edges of the periodic coupled cavities.

1. Introduction

The content of optics is the generation, propagation, and detection of light. In the recent years, the term photonics has come into use in analogy to electronics. Electronics deals with the behaviour of electric-charge, while photonics covers the behaviour of photons. The periodicity of atoms results in an energy band-gap for the electrons, where the electric-charge flow is forbidden. A decade ago, it was suggested that an artificially created periodic structure might result in a similar band gap for electromagnetic (EM)

C.M. Soukoulis (ed.), Photonic Crystals and Light Localization in the 21st Century, 279–303.

waves, where the propagation of the waves were inhibited in a certain range of frequencies in all directions [1, 2]. In analogy with electronic bandgaps in semiconductors, these structures are called photonic band gap (PBG) materials or photonic crystals [3, 4].

The initial interest in this area came from the proposal to use photonic crystals to control spontaneous emission in photonic devices [1]. However, the technological challenges restricted most of the experimental demonstrations and relevant applications of these crystals to millimeter wave and microwave frequencies [5-8]. Recently, a three-dimensional (3D) photonic crystal with a band gap at optical frequencies was reported [9-11]. With this breakthrough, initially proposed applications like thresholdless semiconductor lasers [12] and single-mode light-emitting diodes [13, 14] became feasible.

One other important issue of the photonic crystals is that, just like the donor or acceptor states in an electronic crystal, breaking the periodicity of the crystal results in localization of the EM field within the defect volume [15]. With these properties, photonic crystals are novel structures that can be used to control the behaviour of light. Very recently, the two-dimensional bandgap laser was reported [16, 17]. The cavity consisted of one filled hole (a defect) in an otherwise periodic array of holes penetrating a light emitting, semiconducting film [16].

In the first part of this paper, we will present three important applications of photonic band gap materials: detectors, antennas, and waveguides. The first one is the detection of the EM wave, in which we will introduce a detector whose sensitivity and selectivity are significantly improved using photonic crystals [6]. In the second application, we will show that the radiated field from a monopole antenna inserted within the defect volume of the photonic crystal is highly directional and enhanced [8]. In the last section, we will demonstrate the propagating EM wave through a waveguide built around photonic crystals [7].

In the second part, we have reported the eigenmode splitting, formation of bonding and antibonding modes (analogous to the electronic states in the diatomic molecules), due to the coupling of the evanescent defect modes in three-dimensional (3D) photonic crystals [18]. Moreover, a transition from the discrete atomic-like states to the continuous spectrum (formation of a photonic band) was observed, while increasing the number of defect cavities [18]. Recently, Bayer *et al.* observed formation of a photonic band due to coupling between the optical molecules [19].

A new type of waveguiding mechanism, guiding and bending of electromagnetic (EM) waves through localized coupled-cavity modes, was demonstrated [20, 21]. It was also observed that the photon lifetime increases drastically along with extremely small group velocity at the coupled-cavity waveguide (CCW) band edges [22].

2. Three-Dimensional Layer-by-Layer Photonic Crystals

In our experiments, we used a layer-by-layer structure [23, 24] which was constructed by using square-shaped alumina rods (0.32 cm × 0.32 cm × 15.25 cm) of refractive index 3.1 at 12 GHz. The stacking sequence repeats every four layers, which has the equivalent geometry of a face centered tetragonal (fct) lattice, corresponding to a single unit cell in the stacking direction. The crystal has a center to center separation of 1.12 cm, with a dielectric filling ratio of ∼ 0.29 [Fig. 1(a)]. The layer-by-layer photonic crystal is the first structure that was fabricated at optical frequencies [9-11].

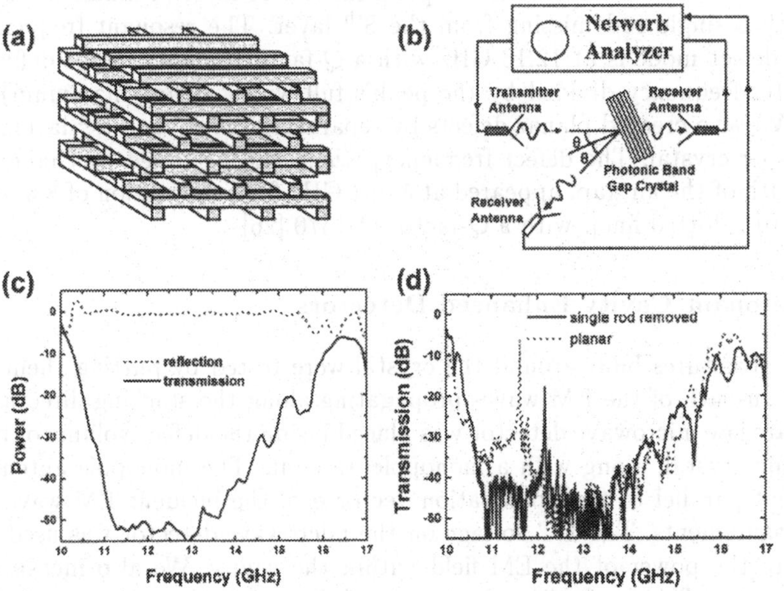

Figure 1. (a) Schematics of a three-dimensional layer-by-layer photonic crystal. (b) The experimental setup for measuring the transmission and reflection characteristics of the photonic crystal. (c) Transmission (solid line) and reflection (dotted line) profiles of 4-unit cell periodic structure along the stacking direction. (d) Transmission characteristics of a single rod removed (solid line) and planar (dotted line) defect structures.

We measured the transmission and reflection properties of the structure by using a Hewlett-Packard 8510C network analyzer. Standard gain horn antennas were used to transmit and receive the EM radiation [Fig. 1(b)]. Surroundings of the setup were covered with absorbers resulting in a sensitivity around 70 dB. Figure 1(c) shows the transmission (solid line) and reflection (dotted line) through a 4-unit cell crystal along the stacking direction. Almost all incident EM waves were reflected within the stop-band of the photonic crystal. The transmission is around -55 dB within the band gap, corresponding to 3.5 dB attenuation per layer. The transmission measurements performed at different angles and polarizations show that the three-dimensional stop band, referred to as the photonic band gap, extends from 10.6 to 12.7 GHz, which agrees well with the expectations of the theory [25].

Breaking the periodicity of the crystal resulted in evanescent modes within the PBG. We tested two types of such defect structures. Figure 1(d) (solid line) shows the transmission spectrum of a 16-layer (4-unit cell) crystal with a single rod missing from the 8th layer. The resonant frequency of the defect mode is at 12.16 GHz with a Q-factor (quality factor defined as center frequency divided by the peak's full width at half-maximum) is 1380. We also created planar defects by separating the 8th and 9th layers of a 16-layer crystal. The defect frequency, which can be tuned by changing the width of the air gap, appeared at 11.61 GHz for a separation of 8.6 mm [Fig. 1(d), dotted line], with a Q-factor of 1570 [26].

3. Resonant Cavity Enhanced Detectors

Defect structures built around the crystal were tested by putting them in the beam-path of the EM waves propagating along the stacking direction. A square law microwave detector was placed inside the defect volume of the photonic crystal, along with a monopole antenna. The monopole antenna was kept parallel to the polarization vector $\mathbf{e}$ of the incident EM wave in all measurements. The DC voltage on the microwave detector was used to measure the power of the EM field within the cavity. We also measured the enhanced field by feeding the output of the monopole antenna into the input port of the network analyzer. The monopole antenna was constructed by removing the shield around one end of a microwave coaxial cable. The exposed center conductor, which also acted as the receiver, was 2 mm long. The calibrated enhancement measurements were performed in the following manner. We first measured the enhanced EM field by the probe inside the cavity. While keeping the position of the probe fixed, we removed the crystal and repeated the same measurement. This single pass absorption data of the probe was then used for calibration of the first measurement.

We first investigated the planar defect structure described in the previous section. Figure 2(a) shows the enhancement characteristics of this defect structure with a separation width of 8.5 mm. The measurement was done by the network analyzer and the frequency was chosen to cover the

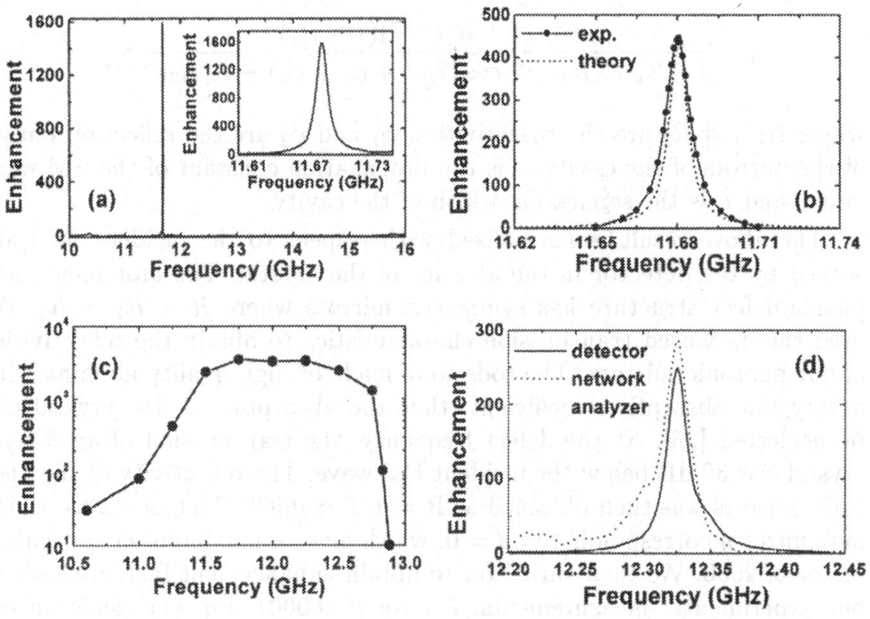

Figure 2. (a) Experimental enhancement factors obtained for a planar defect structure using the network analyzer. (b) Comparison of the experimental (solid line) and theoretical (dotted line) enhancement factors obtained for the RCE detector in the planar defect structure. (c) The power enhancement can be obtained at different resonant frequencies by changing the cavity width. This corresponds to a tuning band-width ranging from 10.5 to 12.8 GHz. (d) Enhancement characteristics of the box-like cavity measured by the network analyzer (dotted line) and the microwave detector (solid line).

photonic band gap of our crystal. We observed a power enhancement factor of 1600 at a defect frequency of 11.68 GHz with a Q-factor 900. We then measured the enhancement characteristics of the same defect structure, with a microwave detector inserted inside the same cavity. An enhancement factor of 450 along with a Q-factor of 1100 was observed at the same defect frequency [Fig 2(b) solid line].

The discrepancy between two measured enhancement factors can be explained by modeling our structure as a Fabry-Perot cavity. The crystals on each side of the cavity are considered as photonic mirrors of the Fabry-Perot cavity. The probe we used in our experiments was simulated by an absorption region of thickness d, with a relative absorption coefficient (α). We can write the power enhancement factor η, which is defined as the ratio of the stored power inside the absorption layer, to the incident EM wave, for the absorption region within the Fabry-Perot cavity,

$$\eta = \frac{(1 + R_2 e^{-\alpha d})(1 - R_1)}{1 - 2\sqrt{R_1 R_2} e^{-\alpha d} \cos(2\beta L + \phi_1 + \phi_2) + R_1 R_2 e^{-2\alpha d}}, \tag{1}$$

where R_1 and R_2 are the reflectivities, ϕ_1 and ϕ_2 are the reflection phases of the mirrors of the cavity, β is the propagation constant of the EM wave in air, and L is the separation width of the cavity.

The above result is normalized with respect to the incident field absorbed by the detector in the absence of the crystal. The aforementioned planar defect structure has symmetric mirrors where $R = R_1 = R_2$. We used the measured transmission characteristics to obtain the reflectivities of our photonic mirrors. The rods were made of high quality alumina with a very low absorption coefficient, thus the absorption in the crystal can be neglected [26]. At the defect frequency, the transmission of an 8-layer crystal was 30 dB below the incident EM wave. The reflectivity of the photonic mirrors was then obtained as R = 1-T = 0.999. The ideal case which maximizes η corresponds to $\alpha d = 0$, which gives a maximum enhancement factor of 2000. We then varied αd to obtain enhancement factors closer to our experimental measurements. For $\alpha d = 0.0001$, Eq. (1) yields an enhancement factor of 1600 (which corresponds to the value obtained from the network analyzer), while $\alpha d = 0.0011$ results in an enhancement factor of 450 (microwave detector). The increased absorption factor for the detector measurement can be explained by the relatively large volume size of the microwave detector compared to monopole antenna alone. Figure 2 (b) compares the measured (solid line) and simulated (dotted line) enhancements obtained for the RCE microwave detector within the planar defect structure. The theoretical Q-factor (1500) is comparable with the experimental Q-factor (1100).

The Fabry-Perot model suggests that η is maximized for the matching case $R_1 = R_2 e^{-2\alpha d}$ [27]. To increase the enhancement, we increased R_2 by adding one more unit cell (4 layers) to the mirror at the back. This resulted in an asymmetric planar cavity with a 2-unit cell thick front mirror, and a 3-unit cell thick back mirror. By varying the width of the planar cavity, we measured the enhancement factors at different resonant frequencies. As shown in Fig 2 (c), the tuning bandwidth of the RCE detector extends from 10.5 to 12.8 GHz. This tuning bandwidth of the RCE detector is in good agreement with the full photonic band gap (10.6-12.7 GHz) of the crystal [24]. As expected, the measured enhancement factors are relatively higher when compared with the symmetrical defect case. The maximum enhancement was measured as 3450 at a defect frequency of 11.75 GHz. The theory predicted enhancement factors around 5500, which is higher than the measured values. The discrepancy can be explained by the finite size of the photonic crystal, which limits the power enhancement of the field within the cavity.

In order to obtain a defect that is localized in three dimensions, we modified a 16-layer crystal structure in the following manner. Part of the rods on the 8th and 9th layers were removed to obtain a rectangular prism-like cavity. The dimensions of the cavity were $4a \times 4a \times 2d$, where $a = 1.12$ cm was the center-to-center distance between parallel rods, and $d = 0.32$ cm was the thickness of the alumina rods. We measured the power enhancement characteristics of this structure using the method described earlier. Figure 2 (d) (dotted line) shows the measurement made by the network analyzer. An enhancement factor of 290, and a Q-factor of 540 were measured at a defect frequency of 12.32 GHz. We then used a microwave detector within the cavity to probe the EM field inside the localized defect. As shown in Figure 2(d) (solid line), the maximum enhancement (245) occurred at the same frequency, along with a Q-factor of 680. Both measurements clearly indicate the resonant cavity enhancement for the localized defect.

4. Highly Directional Resonant Antennas

Among the most important applications of photonic crystals, there is a great deal of growing interest for photonic crystal-based antennas [28, 29]. In microwave and millimeter-wave integrated circuits, the control of the radiation from a dipole antenna is of great importance. In such circuits, the antenna is mounted on a semiconductor substrate, which enhances the performance and functionality of the circuit. But most of the power from the antenna on a dielectric substrate is radiated into the substrate. Standard antennas on GaAs or Si radiate only 2-3% of their power into the air. If a thin substrate is used to overcome the loss due to this trapping, another problem arises. A 180° phase shift comes from the reflection at the bottom conductor, causing the radiation to cancel out at driving point. These problems can be solved, if the antenna is mounted on a 3-D photonic crystal, from which the radiation will fully be reflected in all directions.

The reported experimental and theoretical studies on the antenna applications mostly made use of the total reflection property of photonic crystals. The antennas mounted on photonic crystal substrate surfaces exhibited high efficiency and directivity compared to conventional antennas on dielectric substrates [30, 31]. Although high directivities which could be achieved using array antennas on photonic crystals were suggested [32], the maximum directivity that was demonstrated by Brown and McMahon using a photonic crystal-based single dipole antenna was 10, along with a radiative gain of 8 [30]. Very recently, a higher gain around 80 was reported using a 2-D photonic crystal cavity and a metallic mirror [33].

In this section, we report a photonic crystal-based resonant antenna with a very high directivity and gain. The antenna was formed by a hybrid combination of a monopole radiation source and a cavity built around layer-by-layer photonic crystal [8].

We used the output port of a microwave network analyzer and a monopole antenna to obtain EM waves. The monopole antenna as in the previous section was constructed by removing the shield around one end of a microwave coaxial cable. The cleaved center conductor, which also acted as the radiation source this time, was 6 mm long. An input port of the network analyzer and a standard gain horn antenna were used to receive the radiated EM field from the monopole antenna. The receiver was kept free to rotate around the antenna as shown in Fig. 3.

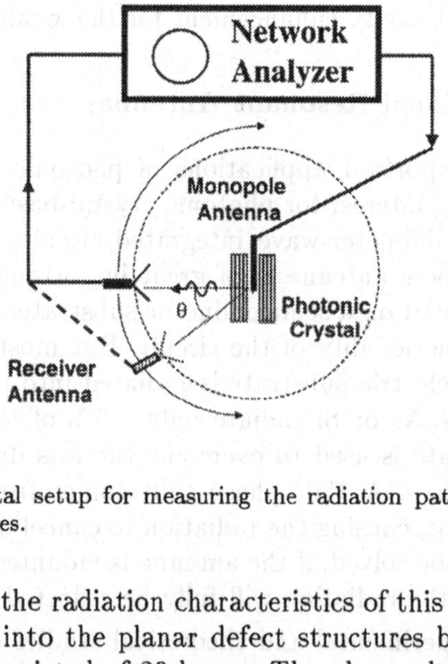

Figure 3. Experimental setup for measuring the radiation patterns of the monopole antenna at various angles.

We investigated the radiation characteristics of this monopole antenna, which was inserted into the planar defect structures built around a photonic crystal that consisted of 20 layers. The planar defect was formed by separating the 8th and 9th layers of the structure, as described in the previous section. In order to suppress the radiation in the backward direction, we intentionally chose one of the crystals of the cavity to have a higher reflectivity than the front crystal. This resulted in an asymmetric planar cavity with a two unit-cell (8 layers) front crystal, and a three-unit cell (12 layers) back crystal. The intensity through the back crystal is $\sim$ 18-20 dB lower than the front crystal in the 0° direction. If a symmetric cavity was used, two directional beams would emerge in both directions.

In the H-plane measurements, the antenna and the polarization axis of the receiver horn antenna were kept vertical and were parallel to each other at all incidence angles. We then rotated the antenna, photonic crystal and the horn antenna 90 degrees (so that the monopole antenna and the polarization axis of the horn were horizontal) to measure the radiation pattern in the perpendicular plane (E-plane). In all these measurements, the monopole antenna was kept close to the back crystal of the cavity. The antenna was parallel to the surface rods of the back crystal to maximize the directivity and the detected power.

Antenna radiation patterns were simulated with the widely used finite-difference-time-domain (FDTD) technique [29]. To reduce the FDTD computational space, a short dipole antenna was used in the simulations which should approximate well the monopole antenna. The time-dependent Maxwell's equations were numerically integrated with the fixed frequency dipole source inside the defect volume of the photonic crystal, to obtain the far-field radiation pattern. The calculations were repeated at different frequencies of the dipole source.

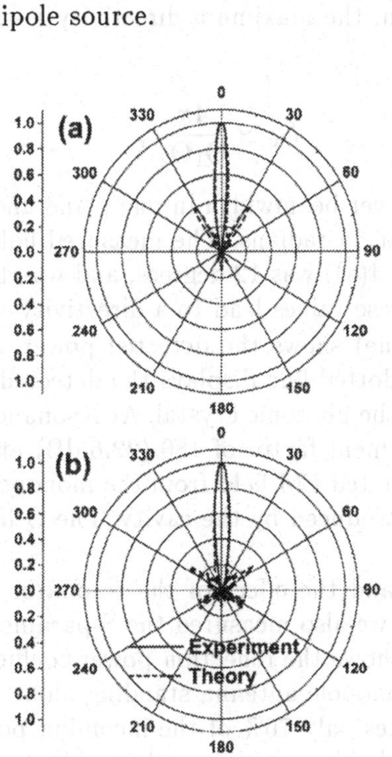

Figure 4. The measured (solid lines) and calculated (dotted lines) radiation patterns of the monopole antenna inside the cavity of the photonic crystal for (a) H-field and (b) E-field. The measurements and simulations were made at the resonance frequency of 11.7 GHz.

We first measured the detected power at the resonance frequency of the cavity as a function of angle. Figure 4(a) (solid line) shows the normalized radiation pattern in H-plane, which was measured at the resonance frequency of the cavity. We observed a strong radiation around $\theta = 0°$, where the radiation along other directions is highly suppressed. The measurements performed in the other plane (E-plane, Fig. 4(b), solid line) also resulted in a similar radiation pattern. The measured (solid lines) and calculated (dotted lines) radiation patterns for both planes agree well. The simulations also predict a directed radiation pattern that displays the same trends but has side lobes other than the major lobe. We also observed such radiations along similar angles in the experiment, but we were able to suppress them by slightly varying the position of the monopole antenna within the cavity. We repeated these measurements with antennas having different lengths, and we observed no significant change in the radiation patterns for both planes.

For antennas with one narrow major lobe and negligible minor lobes in the radiation pattern, the maximum directivity is approximately equal to [34]

$$D_0 \simeq \frac{4\pi}{\Theta_1 \Theta_2}, \tag{2}$$

where Θ_1 is the half-power beamwidth in one plane and Θ_2 in the perpendicular plane to the first, in radians. The measured half-power beamwidth along the H-plane (Fig. 4(a)) was 12 degrees, and was 11 degrees along the E-plane (Fig. 4(b)). These values lead to a directivity value around 310.

Figure 5(a) (solid line) shows the detected power as a function of frequency at $\theta = 0°$. The dotted line displays the detected power at the same angle in the absence of the photonic crystal. At resonance frequency, we observed a power enhancement factor of 180 (22.6 dB) at a defect frequency of 11.725 GHz. The radiated EM field from the monopole antenna has also frequency selectivity introduced by the cavity. The Q factor was measured to be 895.

In order to understand the effect of the resonator to the efficiency of the monopole antenna, we also measured the S-parameters of our antenna structure. Figure 5(b) shows the reflection power coefficient (S11) which is 30% (-5 dB) for the monopole antenna standing alone in air. This implies that the antenna radiates only 70% of the incoming power. When the antenna was inserted inside the cavity, we observed a very sharp drop (-35 dB) at resonance frequency in the reflection spectra [Fig. 5(b), solid line]. This drop indicates that most of the power (99.97%) is radiated out in the presence of the cavity. The maximum radiation gain for our antenna is related to the maximum directivity by $G_0 = (1 - R)(1 - A)D_0$, where R is the reflected power and A is the absorptivity of the antenna. In our case, the reflectivity at the resonance frequency is very small (0.0003). Assuming that the absorption in the antenna has a negligible value, the maximum gain has a value around 300.

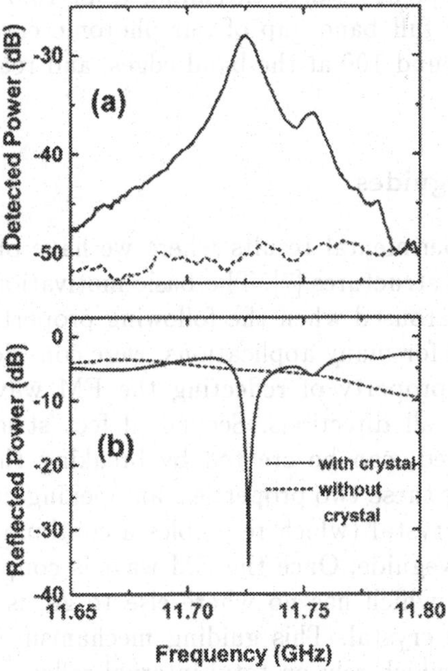

Figure 5. (a) Detected power of the monopole antenna with (solid line) and without (dashed line) photonic crystal around resonance frequency at $\theta = 0°$. (b) The reflection power coefficient (S11) measured with (solid line) and without (dashed line) photonic crystal.

Such a planar cavity built around a 3-D photonic crystal should not be confused with the Fabry-Perot type of resonators that are constructed by using distributed Bragg reflectors (which are known as 1-D photonic crystals). In the former structure, the EM field is always coupled to the evanescent defect mode within the band gap irrespective of the incidence angle. However, the resonant frequency shifts as the angle of incidence of the EM wave changes in the latter case [34, 35]. It is obvious that for planar waves, 3-D and 1-D resonant structures will result in similar enhancements and directivities. In our case, the monopole antenna radiates in all directions, and all the power radiated is coupled to the evanescent mode of the defect, regardless of the direction. This is the reason we have an antenna with a very high efficiency [see Fig. 5(b)]. However, for a 1-D structure, the radiated EM field, except a certain direction, will not be coupled to the corresponding resonant mode of the cavity.

Although our structure is suitable for narrow bandwidth applications, one can tune the defect frequency to any desired value by adjusting the width of the cavity. We observed that the resonance frequency could be tuned within a frequency range extending from 10.6 to 12.8 GHz, which corresponds to the full band gap of our photonic crystal. The directivity drops to values around 100 at the band edges, and reaches a peak value of 310 at 11.7 GHz.

5. Planar Waveguides

We report our experimental results where we have observed waveguiding in photonic crystal structures [7]. The basic motivation in photonic crystal based waveguides aroused when the following properties of these crystals, which are essential for many applications, were considered. First, photonic crystals have the property of reflecting the EM waves within the band gap frequencies in all directions. Second, defect structures in which the EM wave is trapped, can be created by breaking the periodicity of the crystal. Combining these two properties, an opening carved all through an otherwise-perfect crystal (which resembles a continuous defect structure), may serve as a waveguide. Once the EM wave is coupled inside the guide, the trapped wave, which has no where else to go, is guided through the opening inside the crystal. This guiding mechanism is superior to traditional waveguides which rely on total internal reflection of the EM waves. The serious leakage problem for the EM waves traveling around tight corners in a traditional waveguide can be solved by using a photonic crystal based waveguide, and smaller scale optoelectronic integrated circuits can be successfully built [36, 37].

Figure 6(a) shows the schematics of the measurement set up that was used in our experiments. We measured the transmission-phase and transmission-amplitude properties of the two different waveguide structures, namely a parallel-plate and an L-shape. We constructed the parallel-plate type waveguide by using two separate 3-unit cells thick layer-by-layer photonic crystals. The crystals were brought together along the stacking direction with a separation width (d) between them, while keeping a mirror type of symmetry between the rods of the two crystals [see Fig. 6(a)]. For the planar defect structure we have investigated in the first two sections, the propagation direction of the EM wave was perpendicular to the plane of the cavity. If the propagation direction is chosen to be parallel to the plane of the cavity, the structure will have the geometry of a parallel-plate waveguide. We expect the wave to be guided through the introduced air

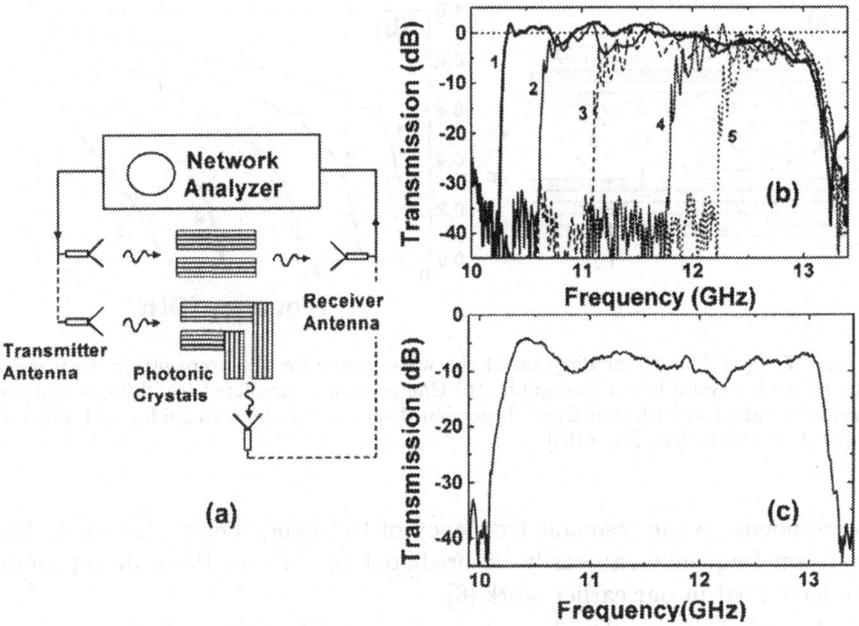

Figure 6. (a) Experimental set-up used to investigate the parallel-plate (upper case) and L-shaped (lower case) waveguide structures. (b) Transmission amplitude measured from parallel-plate waveguides as the separation width of the waveguide is changed. The numbers given in the plot are assigned to width of the guides as (1) 18, (2) 16, (3) 14, (4) 12, and (5) 10.5 mm. (c) Transmission characteristics of the L-shaped waveguide.

gap, starting from a cut-off frequency which depends on the width of the gap. The guiding is limited with the full band gap frequency range of the photonic crystal, for which the crystal has the property of reflecting the EM waves in all directions.

We tested this waveguiding argument by measuring the transmission properties of these structures along the plane of the cavity. Figure 6(b) shows the transmission properties of the waveguide structure for different separation widths. We observed full transmission (100%) of the EM waves along a certain frequency range. The waveguiding was first observed at a minimum separation width around 10 mm, and the cut-off shifted to lower frequency values as the width of the air gap was increased. Independent of the width of the cavity, the guiding was observed to vanish at a fixed upper cut-off frequency (13.2 GHz), which corresponds to the upper band-edge of the photonic band gap. This was along our expectations as the crystals do not act as mirrors (in all directions) beyond the full band gap frequencies. The lower cut-off frequency was determined by the width of the cavity and

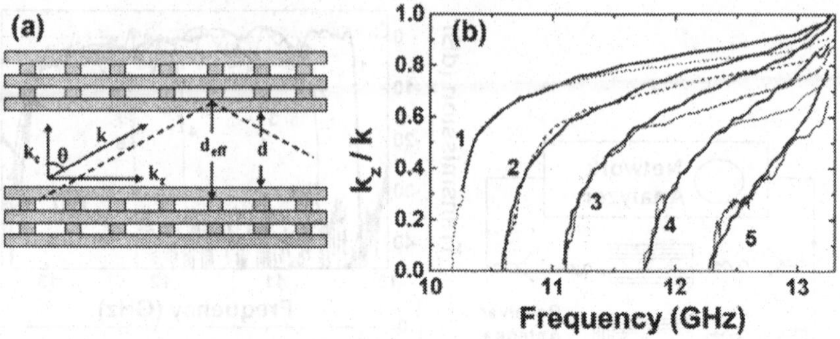

Figure 7. (a) The vector diagram of the wave vector for the propagating wave inside the photonic crystal based waveguide. (b) Comparison of predicted (solid lines) and theoretically calculated (dotted lines) dispersion diagrams for the waveguides with different separation widths [see Fig. 6(b)].

corresponds to the resonant frequency of the Fabry-Perot resonator. This resonant frequency can easily be predicted by a Fabry-Perot defect model we have used in our earlier work [6].

As we have pointed earlier, photonic crystal-based waveguides were predicted to have the property of guiding the wave through sharp bends [36]. To demonstrate this effect, we constructed an L-shaped waveguide in the following manner. We coupled the output of the previously described planar waveguide structure, to the input of another but identical waveguide making 90° with the first one, as shown in the second configuration of the set-up [see Fig. 6(a)]. Each wall of the waveguide is a 2-unit cell photonic crystal. The width of the cavity is kept at a value of 2 cm, for which the frequency range of the waveguide will overlap with the full band gap of the crystals. Figure 6(c) shows the transmission of the EM waves through the L-shaped waveguide. The maximum magnitude of the transmitted signal was 35% of the incident signal. The frequency range of the L-shaped waveguide again covers the full band gap frequencies of the photonic crystal. The exchange of the receiver and transmitter antennas did not affect the transmission characteristics. The relatively poor performance of the transmission magnitude can be further increased by a proper design of the bend [38]. These results show that photonic crystals can be used for various waveguide configurations.

We investigated the dispersion characteristics of the planar waveguide by measuring the phase difference of the transmitted wave introduced by the guide. This phase difference, ϕ_{trans}, can be written as $\phi_{\text{trans}} = kL - k_z L$, where $k = 2\pi f/c$ is the free space wavevector, k_z is the component of the wavevector along the waveguide [see Fig. 7(a)], and L is the length of the waveguide. This can be used to find the normalized propagation constant, k_z/k, as a function of frequency,

$$\frac{k_z}{k} = 1 - \frac{\phi_{\mathrm{trans}}}{kL} = 1 - \frac{\phi_{\mathrm{trans}} c}{2\pi f L} . \tag{3}$$

The dispersion relation calculated by this phase-measurement method is shown in Fig. 7(b) (solid lines) for different separation widths of the waveguide. The separation widths are chosen to be the same as those widths used in the transmission measurements given in Fig. 6(c).

The dispersion relations can also be calculated by a parallel-plate waveguide model. Since the dielectric photonic crystal walls of the waveguide have a certain penetration depth that can be calculated using the reflection-phase information from the walls of the cavity, we can define an effective width for the waveguide. This approach was previously used to investigate the defect characteristics built around dielectric and metallic photonic crystals [6]. In the calculation of this effective penetration depth, one must consider the angle dependence of the reflection phase, since the wave is considered to be bouncing between the walls of the waveguide at different angles for different frequencies. We measured the reflection phase of the EM waves from the walls of the cavity for the frequency range of the band gap, as a function of angle θ, where θ is taken to be the angle between the wavevector k and its component along the stacking direction of the crystal k_c as shown in Fig. 7(a). We calculated the effective width of the waveguide using the total phase contributions of both walls of the cavity, $\phi_{\mathrm{ref}}(\theta, f)$,

$$d_{\mathrm{eff}} = d + \frac{\phi_{\mathrm{ref}}(\theta, f)}{2k} , \tag{4}$$

where d is the actual separation width of the waveguide. The corresponding propagation angle for each frequency is obtained from Eq. (3) as,

$$\theta = \arcsin\left(\frac{k_z}{k}\right) = \arcsin\left(1 - \frac{\phi_{\mathrm{trans}} c}{2\pi f L}\right) . \tag{5}$$

This angle information can be used in Eq. (4) to find an effective width of the guide at each frequency. The k_c component of the wavevector can be calculated as $k_c = 2\pi/\lambda_c$, where $\lambda_c = 2d_{\mathrm{eff}}$ is the cut-off wavelength of the waveguide. The dispersion relation can now be expressed as

$$\frac{k_z}{k} = \frac{\sqrt{k^2 - k_c^2}}{k} . \tag{6}$$

Note that since k_c is considered to be constant, after some frequency the square-root becomes real, so that the waves after that cut-off frequency (defined by k_c) can propagate in the guide. For frequencies less than the cut-off frequency, k_z is imaginary, and such modes (evanescent modes) cannot propagate in the waveguide [39]. Figure 7(b) compares the parallel-plate waveguide model dispersion relations [obtained from Eq. (6], dotted lines) with the dispersion relations obtained from the transmission phase measurements [using Eq. (3], solid lines). As can be seen from the plots, the results are in good agreement for different separation widths of the guide, except for the higher frequency regions of the waveguide. This discrepancy is mainly related to the inaccurate reflection phase information (due to experimental limitations) at higher incidence angles, $\theta > 70°$.

6. Tight-binding description of the localized coupled-cavity modes in photonic crystals

As we have demonstrated in previous sections, by introducing a defect into the photonic crystals, it is possible to create highly localized defect modes within the photonic band gap, which is analogous to the localized impurity states in a semiconductor [15]. Although the modes of each cavity were tightly confined at the defect sites, overlap between the nearest-neighbor modes is enough to provide the propagation of photons via hopping [Fig. 8(a)]. This picture can be considered as the classical wave analog of the tight-binding (TB) method in solid state physics [18,40-43]. Recently, the TB scheme was also successfully used for various photonic structures. Waveguiding along the impurity chains in photonic insulators [40], waveguiding through coupled resonators [43], and one-dimensional superstructure gratings [41] were theoretically investigated by using TB formalism. Lidorikis *et al.* tested the TB model by comparing the *ab initio* results of two-dimensional PBG structures with and without defects [42]. They obtained the TB parameters by an excellent fitting to *ab initio* results. Splitting of the coherent coupling of whispering gallery mode in quartz polystyrene spheres was reported and explained within the TB photon picture [44]. The optical modes in the micrometer-sized semiconductor coupled cavities were investigated by Bayer *et al.* [45].

We used the 3D layer-by-layer dielectric photonic crystals. The defective unit cells were created by removing a single rod from a single layer of the cell, where each cell consists of 4 layers having the symmetry of a face-centered tetragonal structure. The experimental set-up consists of a HP 8510C network analyzer and microwave horn antennas to measure the transmission-amplitude and transmission-phase properties of various defect structures built around photonic crystals [Fig. 8(b)]. The electric field polarization vector of the incident EM wave **e** was parallel to the rods of the defect layer for all measurements.

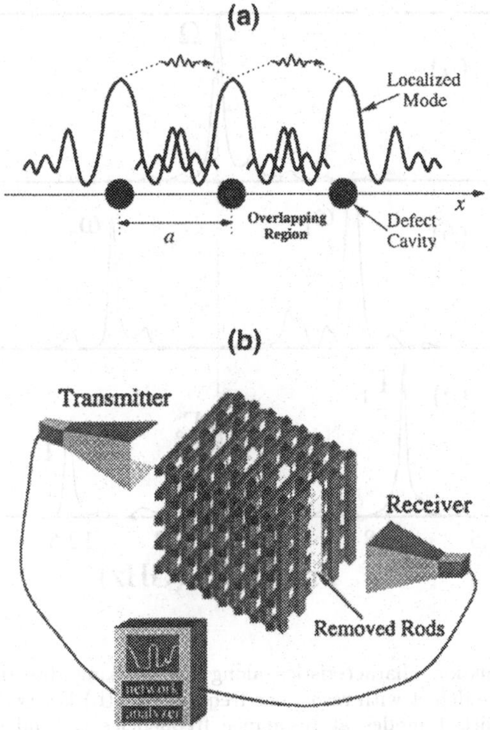

Figure 8. (a) Schematics of propagation of photons by hopping between the coupled evanescent defect modes. The overlap of the defect modes is large enough to provide propagation of the EM waves along tightly confined cavity modes. (b) The experimental setup for measuring the transmission characteristics of the coupled defect structures in three-dimensional photonic crystals. The electric field polarization is directed along the removed rods.

By using the aforementioned experimental setup, we first measured the transmission amplitude through a crystal with a single defective unit cell. This resulted in a localized defect mode within the PBG which is analogous to acceptor impurity state in semiconductor physics [15]. The defect mode occurred at a resonance frequency of $\Omega = 12.150$ GHz with a Q-factor (quality factor, defined as center frequency divided by the peak's full width at half-maximum) of ~ 1000 [Fig. 9(a)]. Next, we measured the transmission through the crystal that contains two consecutive single rods removed unit cells. We observed that the mode in the previous case split into two resonance modes at frequencies $\omega_1 = 11.831$ GHz and $\omega_1 = 12.402$ GHz [Fig. 9(b)]. The intercavity distance for this structure was $a = 1.28$

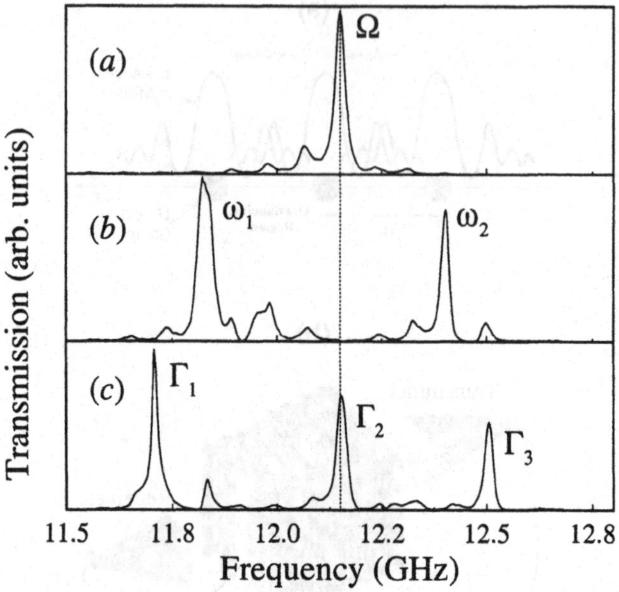

Figure 9. Transmission characteristics along the stacking direction of the photonic crystal: (a) For single defect with resonance frequency Ω. (b) For two consecutive defects resulting in two splitted modes at resonance frequencies ω_1 and ω_2 with intercavity distance a = 1.28 cm. (c) For three consecutive defects with resonance frequencies Γ_1, Γ_2, and Γ_3.

cm, which corresponds to single unit cell thickness in the stacking direction. Figure 9(c) shows the transmission characteristics of a crystal having three consecutive defective cells, where the resonant modes were observed at frequencies $\Gamma_1 = 11.708$ GHz, $\Gamma_2 = 12.153$ GHz and $\Gamma_3 = 12.506$ GHz.

In order to understand the observed splitting due to coupling of the individual cavity modes, we introduced the classical wave analog of the TB model. In our case, the eigenmodes of each cavity were tightly confined at the defect sites. However, the overlap of the modes is enough to provide the propagation of photons through neighboring defect sites via hopping. Various forms of this picture were successfully applied to the photonic systems in scientific literature [40-43]. In this paper, we adopted the notation used by Yariv *et al.* [43].

We first considered an individual localized mode $\mathbf{E}_\Omega(\mathbf{r})$ of a single defect that satisfies the Maxwell equations which can be further simplified as

$$\nabla \times [\nabla \times \mathbf{E}_\Omega(\mathbf{r})] = \epsilon_0(\mathbf{r})(\Omega/c)^2 \mathbf{E}_\Omega(\mathbf{r}) , \quad (7)$$

where $\epsilon_0(\mathbf{r})$ is the dielectric constant of the single defect and Ω is the corresponding eigenfrequency. Here, we assumed that $\mathbf{E}_\Omega(\mathbf{r})$ is real, nondegenerate and orthonormal, i.e. $\int d\mathbf{r}\epsilon_0(\mathbf{r})\mathbf{E}_\Omega(\mathbf{r})\cdot\mathbf{E}_\Omega(\mathbf{r}) = 1$. This merely describes the experimental structure used for Fig. 9(a).

In the case of two coupled defects, the eigenmode can be written as a superposition of the individual evanescent defect modes as $\mathbf{E}_\omega(\mathbf{r}) = A\mathbf{E}_\Omega(\mathbf{r}) + B\mathbf{E}_\Omega(\mathbf{r} - a\hat{x})$. The eigenmode $\mathbf{E}_\omega(\mathbf{r})$ also satisfies the Eq. (7), where $\epsilon_0(\mathbf{r})$ replaced with the dielectric constant of the system $\epsilon(\mathbf{r}) = \epsilon(\mathbf{r} - a\hat{x})$ and Ω replaced with eigenfrequency ω of the coupled defect mode.

Inserting $\mathbf{E}_\omega(\mathbf{r})$ into Eq. (7), and multiplying both sides from the left first by $\mathbf{E}_\Omega(\mathbf{r})$ and then by $\mathbf{E}_\Omega(\mathbf{r} - a\hat{x})$ and spatially integrating resulting equations, the single defect mode Ω is splitted into two eigenfrequencies

$$\omega_{1,2}^2 = \Omega^2(1 \pm \beta)/(1 \pm \alpha + \Delta\alpha) , \tag{8}$$

where the TB parameters are given by $\alpha = \int d\mathbf{r}\epsilon(\mathbf{r})\mathbf{E}_\Omega(\mathbf{r})\cdot\mathbf{E}_\Omega(\mathbf{r}-a\hat{x})$, $\beta = \int d\mathbf{r}\epsilon_0(\mathbf{r}-a\hat{x})\mathbf{E}_\Omega(\mathbf{r})\cdot\mathbf{E}_\Omega(\mathbf{r}-a\hat{x})$, and $\Delta\alpha = \int d\mathbf{r}[\epsilon(\mathbf{r}) - \epsilon_0(\mathbf{r})]\mathbf{E}_\Omega(\mathbf{r})\cdot\mathbf{E}_\Omega(\mathbf{r})$. By inserting the experimentally obtained eigenfrequencies ω_1 and ω_2 [see Fig. 2(b)] into Eq. (8), the TB parameters are determined as $\alpha = -0.102$ and $\beta = -0.149$. Here we assumed that $\Delta\alpha$ is negligible compared to α and β.

This splitting is analogous to the splitting in the diatomic molecules, for example H_2^+, in which the interaction between the two atoms produce a splitting of the degenerate atomic levels into *bonding* and *antibonding* orbitals. Our results are the first direct experimental observation of the bonding/antibonding mechanism in a photonic crystal which was theoretically proposed by Antonoyiannakis and Pendry [46].

Similarly, for a system with three coupled defects, the eigenfrequency Ω is splitted into three resonant frequencies:

$$\begin{aligned} \Gamma_2^2 &\simeq \Omega^2 , \\ \Gamma_{1,3}^2 &\simeq \Omega^2 \ (1 \pm \sqrt{2}\beta)/(1 \pm \sqrt{2}\alpha) , \end{aligned} \tag{9}$$

where we ignored the second nearest neighbor coupling between the cavity modes. This turns out to be a reasonable assumption for our case, since our experimental observations showed that the second nearest neighbor coupling parameters are one order of magnitude smaller than the first nearest neighbor coupling parameters. Table 1 compares the resonance frequencies, which were calculated by inserting TB parameters α and β into the Eq. (9), with the values obtained from the experiment [Fig. 9(c)]. The experimentally measured three-split modes coincides well with the theoretically expected values. This excellent agreement shows that the classical wave analog of TB formalism is valid for our structure.

TABLE 1. The measured and calculated values of resonant frequencies for the crystal with three defective unit cells.

	Measured [GHz]	Calculated [GHz]
Γ_1	11.708	11.673
Γ_2	12.153	12.150
Γ_3	12.506	12.492

In the presence of the coupled periodic defect array, the eigenmode can be written as linear combination of the individual defect modes [41, 43]

$$\mathbf{E}(\mathbf{r}) = E_0 \sum_n \exp(-inka)\ \mathbf{E}_\Omega(\mathbf{r} - na\hat{x}) \ . \tag{10}$$

The dispersion relation for this structure can be obtained from Eqs. (7) and (10) keeping only the nearest neighbor coupling terms [40, 43]

$$\omega^2(k) = \Omega^2 \frac{1 + 2\beta\cos(ka)}{1 + \Delta\alpha + 2\alpha\cos(ka)} \ . \tag{11}$$

If the TB parameters, α and β, are small compared to unity, Eq. (11) is simplified to $\omega(k)/\Omega \simeq 1 + \kappa\cos(ka)$, where $\kappa = \beta - \alpha = -0.047$.

When the number of defective unit cells is increased, a waveguiding band is expected to be formed due to the coupling of individual resonant modes. We measured the transmission through a 10-unit cell crystal, where a single rod is removed in each unit cell. As shown in Fig. 10, the waveguiding band stands within the PBG extending from 11.47 to 12.62 GHz, with a bandwidth of $\Delta\omega = 1.15$ GHz. Nearly 100 percent transmission was observed throughout the waveguiding band. The amplitude of the parameter κ can also be determined from the waveguiding bandwidth which gives us $|\kappa| = \Delta\omega/2\Omega \simeq 0.047$, exactly the same previously obtained value from the coupling of two cavities.

The dispersion relation for the waveguiding band can be obtained from the transmission-phase measurement as follows [25]. The net phase difference $\Delta\phi$ between the phase of the EM wave propagating through the photonic crystal and the phase of the EM wave propagating in free space for a total crystal thickness of L is given by $\Delta\phi = kL - 2\pi fL/c$. This expression can be used to determine the wave vector k of the crystal at each frequency f within the waveguiding band.

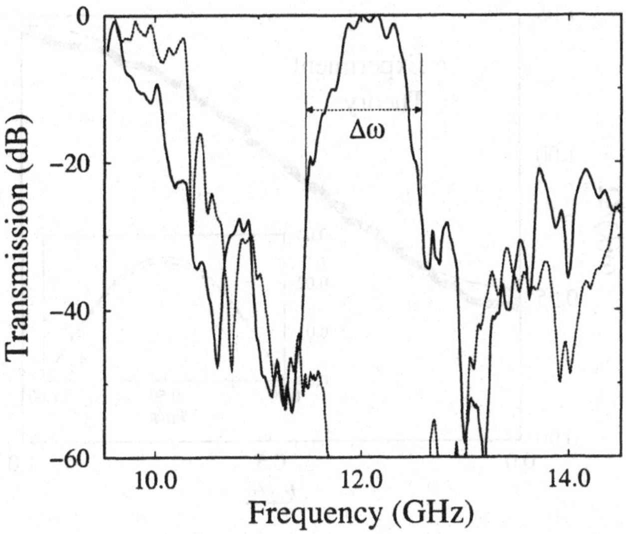

Figure 10. Transmission amplitude as function of frequency for a waveguide structure which consists of 10 consecutive defective crystal (solid line). Transmission through a perfect crystal is plotted for the comparison (dotted line).

Figure 11 shows the comparison of the measured (⋄ symbols) and calculated (solid line) dispersion relations. As shown in Fig. 11, the TB calculations gives good agreement with the measured results, and the deviations between the experiment and the theory is more pronounced around the edges of the waveguiding band. We expect this discrepancy to vanish as the number of unit cells used in the experiment is increased.

The inset in Fig. 11 shows the comparison of the theoretical (solid line) and experimental (dotted line) variation of the group velocity, $v_g(k) = \mathrm{d}\omega(k)/\mathrm{d}k \simeq -\Omega\kappa a \sin(ka)$, of the waveguiding band as a function of wave vector k. The theoretical curve is obtained from Eq. (11), while the experimental curve is obtained by taking the derivative of the best fitted cosines function to the experimental data. Notice that the group velocity vanishes at the waveguiding band edges [47]. It is important to note that, in the stimulated emission process, the effective gain is inversely proportional to the group velocity [48]. The group velocity can be made smaller if one can reduce the amplitude of the parameter κ.

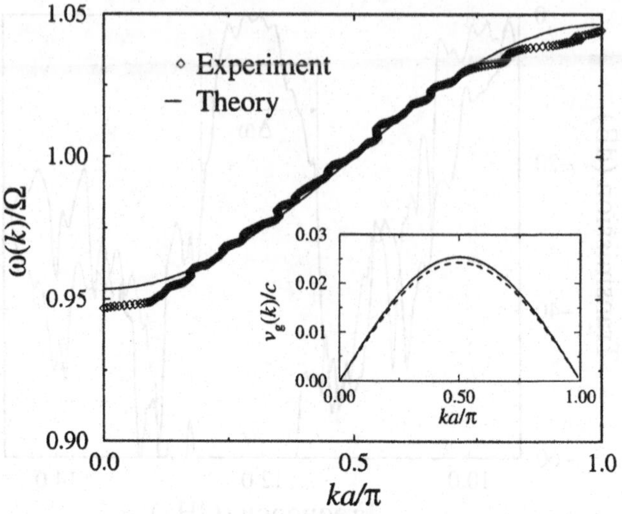

Figure 11. Dispersion diagram of the waveguiding band predicted from the transmission-phase measurements (◇ symbols) and calculated by using tight-binding formalism (solid line) with $\kappa = -0.047$. Inset: The normalized group velocity diagrams calculated by the theory (solid line) and obtained from the experimental data (dotted line) agree well and both vanish at the guiding band edges, where c is the speed of light.

7. Summary

In this paper, we have investigated the transmission and defect characteristics of layer-by-layer photonic crystals and suggested two applications based on this structure. First, we suggest the possibility of using an embedded detector inside the crystal, as an RCE detector. By using smaller size photonic crystals and higher frequency detectors, the RCE effect can also be obtained at millimeter and far-infrared frequencies. These frequency selective RCE detectors have increased sensitivity and efficiency when compared to conventional detectors, and can be used for various applications. In the second application, we used the hybrid combination of a monopole radiation source and a cavity built around photonic crystals. This combination exhibited a highly directional and enhancement radiation source. The third application is the guidance of the EM waves with 100% transmission, using photonic crystals. We have developed a parallel-plate waveguide model for our structures. The dispersion diagrams calculated using the transmitted phase measurements and by the waveguide model were in good agreement. We also observed 35% transmission for the EM waves traveling through a sharp bend in an L-shaped waveguide.

We have observed the splitting of the coupled localized cavity modes in the 3D microwave layer-by-layer photonic crystals and in the 1D optical photonic structures. We have also demonstrated formation of the waveguiding band within the stop band and compared the measured dispersion relation of the guiding band with the TB predictions. A new mechanism to manipulate propagation of EM waves in the photonic band gap structures was demonstrated. Photons hop from one evanescent defect mode to the next one, regardless of the direction of propagation. A complete transmission of the EM wave along a straight path was observed experimentally. The excellent agreement between experiment and theory is an indication of the potential applications of the tight-binding scheme in the photonic structures.

8. Acknowledgments

This work is supported by Turkish Department of Defense Grant No. KOBRA-001, NATO Grant No. SfP971970, and National Science Foundation Grant No. INT-9820646.

*To whom correspondence should be addressed:
Electronic mail: ozbay@fen.bilkent.edu.tr

References

1. E. Yablonovitch, "Inhibited spontaneous emission in solid-state physics and electronics," *Phys. Rev. Lett.* **58**, 2059 (1987).
2. S. John, "Strong localization of photons in certain disordered dielectric superlattices," *Phys. Rev. Lett.* **58**, 2486 (1987).
3. J. D. Joannopoulos, R. D. Meade, and J. N. Winn, *Photonic Crystals: Molding the Flow of Light* (Princeton University Press, Princeton, NJ, 1995).
4. For a recent review, see articles in *Photonic Band Gap Materials*, edited by C. M. Soukoulis (Kluwer, Dortrecht, 1996).
5. M. C. Wanke, O. Lehmann, K. Muller, Q. Wen, and M. Stuke, "Laser rapid prototyping of photonic band-gap microstructures," *Science* **275**, 1284 (1997).
6. B. Temelkuran, E. Ozbay, J. P. Kavanaugh, G. Tuttle, and K. M. Ho, "Resonant cavity enhanced detectors embedded in photonic crystals," *Appl. Phys. Lett.* **72**, 2376 (1998).
7. B. Temelkuran and E. Ozbay, "Experimental demonstration of photonic crystal based waveguides," *Appl. Phys. Lett.* **74**, 486 (1999).
8. B. Temelkuran, Mehmet Bayindir, E. Ozbay, R. Biswas, M. M. Sigalas, G. Tuttle, and K. M. Ho, "Photonic crystal based resonant antenna with a very high directivity," *J. Appl. Phys.* **87**, 603 (2000).
9. S. Y. Lin, J. G. Fleming, D. L. Hetherington, B. K. Smith, R. Biswas, K. M. Ho, M. M. Sigalas, W. Zubrzycki, S. R. Kurtz, and J. Bur, "A three-dimensional photonic crystal operating at infrared wavelength," *Nature (London)* **394**, 251 (1998).
10. J. G. Fleming and Shawn-Yu Lin, "Three-dimensional photonic crystal with a stop band from 1.35 to 1.95 μm," *Opt. Lett.* **24**, 49 (1999).

11. S. Noda "Three-dimensional photonic crystals operating at optical wavelength region," *Physica B* **279**, 142 (2000).
12. P. R. Villenevue, S. Fan, J. D. Joannopoulos,Kuo-Yi Lim, G. S. Petrich, L. A. Kolodziejski, and R. Reif, "Air-bridge microcavities," *Appl. Phys. Lett.* **67**, 167 (1995).
13. P. L. Gourley, J. R. Wendt, G. A. Vawter, T. M. Brennan, and B. E. Hammons, "Optical properties of two dimensional photonic lattices fabricated as honeycomb nanostructures in compound semiconductors," *Appl. Phys. Lett.* **64**, 687 (1994).
14. J. P. Dowling, M. Scalora, M. J. Bloemer, and C. M. Bowden, "The photonic band edge laser: A new approach to gain enhancement", *J. Appl. Phys.* **75**, 1896 (1994).
15. E. Yablonovitch, T. J. Gmitter, R. D. Meade, A. M. Rappe, K. D. Brommer, and J. D. Joannopoulos, "Donor and acceptor modes in photonic band structure," *Phys. Rev. Lett.* **67**, 3380 (1991).
16. O. Painter, R. K. Lee, A. Scherer, A. Yariv, J. D. O'Brien, P. D. Dapkus, and I. Kim, "Two-dimensional photonic band-gap defect mode laser," *Science* **284**, 5421 (1999).
17. A. Mekis, M. Meier, A. Dodabalapur, R.E. Slusher, and J.D. Joannopoulos, "Lasing mechanism in two-dimensional photonic crystal lasers," *Appl. Phys. A* **69**, 111 (1999).
18. Mehmet Bayindir, B. Temelkuran, and E. Ozbay, "Tight-binding description of the coupled defect modes in three-dimensional photonic crystals," *Phys. Rev. Lett.* **84**, 2140, (2000).
19. M. Bayer, T. Gutbrod, A. Forchel, T. L. Reinecke, P. A. Knipp, R. Werner, and J. P. Reithmaier, "Optical Demonstration of a Crystal Band Structure Formation," *Phys. Rev. Lett.* **83**, 5374 (1999).
20. Mehmet Bayindir, B. Temelkuran, and E. Ozbay, "Propagation of photons by hopping: A waveguiding mechanism through localized coupled-cavities in three-dimensional photonic crystals," *Phys. Rev. B* **61**, R11855 (2000).
21. Mehmet Bayindir, S. Tanriseven, and E. Ozbay, "Propagation of light through localized coupled-cavity modes in one-dimensional photonic band gap structures," *Appl. Phys. A*, to be published.
22. Mehmet Bayindir and E. Ozbay, "Heavy photons at coupled-cavity waveguide band edges in a three-dimensional photonic crystal," *Phys. Rev. B* **62**, R2247 (2000).
23. K. M. Ho, C. T. Chan, C. M. Soukoulis, R. Biswas, and M. Sigalas, "Photonic Band Gaps in Three Dimensions: New layer-by-layer periodic structures," *Solid State Commun.* **89**, 413 1994.
24. E. Ozbay, "Layer-by-layer photonic band gap crystals: From microwave to the far-infrared," *J. Opt. Soc. Am. B* **13**, 1945 (1996).
25. E. Ozbay, A. Abeyta, G. Tuttle, M. Tringides, R. Biswas, C. T. Chan, C. Soukoulis, and K. M. Ho, "Measurement of a three-dimensional photonic band gap in a crystal structure made of dielectric rods," *Phys. Rev. B* **50**, 1945 (1994).
26. E. Ozbay and B. Temelkuran, "Reflection properties and defect formation in photonic crystals," *Appl. Phys. Lett.* **69**, 743 (1996).
27. M. Selim Unlu and S. Strite, "Resonant cavity enhanced photonic devices," *J. Appl. Phys.* **78**, (1995).
28. E. R. Brown, C. D. Parker, and E. Yablonovitch, "Radiation properties of a planar antenna on a photonic-crystal substrate," *J. Opt. Soc. Am. B* **10**, 404 (1993).
29. M. M. Sigalas, R. Biswas, Q. Li, D. Crouch, W. Leung, R. Jacobs-Woodbury, B. Lough, S. Nielsen, S. McCalmont, G. Tuttle, and K. M Ho, "Dipole antennas on photonic band-gap crystals: Experiment and simulation," *Micro. Opt. Tech. Lett.* **15**, 153 (1997).
30. E. R. Brown, and O. B. McMahon, "High zenithal directivity from a dipole antenna on a photonic crystal," *Appl. Phys. Lett.* **68**, 1300 (1996).
31. R. Gonzalo, Peter de Maagt, and M. Sorolla, "Enhanced patch-antenna performance by suppressing surface waves using photonic-bandgap substrates," *IEEE Trans. Mi-*

crowave theory Tech. **47**, 2131 (1999).

32. G. Poilasne, P. Pouliguen, K. Mahdjoubi, J. Lenormand, C. Terret, and Ph. Gelin, "Theoretical study of grating lobes reduction using metallic photonic bandgap materials (MPBG)," *Micro. Opt. Tech. Lett.* **18**, 32 (1998).
33. M. Thevenot, C. Cheype, A. Reineix, and B. Jecko, "Directive photonic-bandgap antennas," *IEEE Trans. Microwave theory Tech.* **47**, 2115 (1999).
34. A. Yariv and P. Yeh, *Optical Waves in Crystals*, (Wiley, New York, 1984).
35. E. F. Schubert, N. E. J. Hunt, A. M. Vredenberg, T. D. Harris, J. M. Poate, D. C. Jacobson, Y. H. Wong, and G. J. Zydzik, "Increased fiber communications bandwidth from a resonant cavity light emitting diode emitting at $\lambda = 940$ nm," *Appl. Phys. Lett.* **63**, 2603 (1993).
36. A. Mekis, J. C. Chen, I. Kurland, S. Fan, P. R. Villeneuve, and J. D. Joannapoulos, "High transmission through sharp bends in photonic crystal waveguides," *Phys. Rev. Lett.* **77**, 3787 (1996).
37. Shawn-Yu Lin, E. Chow, V. Hietala, P. R. Villeneuve, and J. D. Joannopoulos, "Experimental demonstration of guiding and bending of electromagnetic waves in a photonic crystal," *Science* **282**, 274 (1998).
38. M. M. Sigalas, R. Biswas, K. M. Ho, C. M. Soukoulis, and D. D. Crouch, "Waveguides in three-dimensional metallic photonic band-gap materials," *Phys. Rev. B* **60**, 4426 (1999).
39. J. D. Jackson, *Classical Electrodynamics*, second ed. (Wiley, New York, 1975).
40. N. Stefanou and A. Modinos, "Impurity bands in photonic insulators," *Phys. Rev. B* **57**, 12127 (1998).
41. C. Martijn de Sterke, "Superstructure gratings in the tight-binding approximation," *Phys. Rev. E* **57**, 3502 (1998).
42. E. Lidorikis, M. M. Sigalas, E. N. Economou, and C. M. Soukoulis, "Tight-binding parametrization for photonic band gap materials," *Phys. Rev. Lett.* **81**, 1405 (1998).
43. A. Yariv, Y. Xu, R. K. Lee, and A. Scherer, "Coupled-resonator optical waveguide: a proposal and analysis," *Opt. Lett.* **24**, 711 (1999); Y. Xu, R. K. Lee, and A. Yariv, "Propagation and second-harmonic generation of electromagnetic waves in a coupled-resonator optical waveguide," *J. Opt. Soc. Am. B* **17**, 387 (2000).
44. T. Mukaiyama, K. Takeda, H. Miyazaki, Y. Jimba, and M. Kuwata-Gonokami, "Tight-binding photonic molecule modes of resonant bispheres," *Phys. Rev. Lett.* **82**, 4623 (1999).
45. M. Bayer, T. Gutbrod, J. P. Reithmaier, A. Forchel, T. L. Reinecke, P. A. Knipp, A. A. Dremin, and V. D. Kulakovskii, "Optical modes in photonic molecules," *Phys. Rev. Lett.* **81**, 2582 (1998).
46. M. I. Antonoyiannakis and J. B. Pendry, "Electromagnetic forces in photonic crystals," *Phys. Rev B* **60**, 2363 (1999).
47. K. Sakoda and K. Ohtaka, "Optical response of three-dimensional photonic lattices: Solutions of inhomogeneous Maxwell's equations and their applications," *Phys. Rev. B* **54**, 5732 (1996).
48. K. Sakoda, "Enhanced light ampli cation due to group-velocity anomaly peculiar to two- and three-dimensional photonic crystals," *Opt. Express* **4**, 167 (1999).

PHOTONIC CRYSTAL FIBERS: EFFECTIVE-INDEX AND BAND-GAP GUIDANCE

Douglas C. Allan, James A. West, James C. Fajardo,
Michael T. Gallagher, Karl W. Koch, and Nicholas F. Borrelli
Sullivan Park, Corning Incorporated
Corning, NY 14830 USA

1. INTRODUCTION

Conventional telecommunication optical waveguide glass fiber is the backbone of the internet revolution. This highly optimized and highly transparent waveguide consists of a higher refractive index core glass inside a lower index clad glass. Light is localized in the core by total internal reflection (TIR) at the core/clad boundary. The transmission distance between amplifiers of today's fibers, about 80-120 km, is limited in part by the small but nonzero absorption and scattering of the fiber. Longer transmission lengths could be possible by increasing the power at each amplifier, but this is limited by optical nonlinearity of the glass in the fiber.

It has recently been demonstrated, both theoretically [1] and experimentally,[2] that photonic band-gap confinement can be used to form a new kind of optical waveguide fiber. This photonic band-gap fiber (PBGF) guides light in a *low* index core, in contrast to conventional fiber waveguides. This low index core can be vacuum (or air), allowing for dramatic reduction in nonlinearity and scattering.

The concept of using Bragg reflection or diffraction to confine light in an optical fiber is not new.[3-6] It is only recently, however, that such fibers have been demonstrated.[2,7] These new photonic band-gap fibers use a microstructured silica fiber containing a periodic lattice of air columns surrounding a large central air column that constitutes the core. The central air column acts as a defect, breaking the periodicity of the lattice of air columns, and hence can create localized states at frequencies and wavevectors that fall within a band gap. Light localization near or within this core does not depend on total internal reflection, so the core index need not be higher than the index of the surrounding medium. This creates the possibility of light guidance in an air core. When the core is air, or, in general, when the core index is lower than the effective cladding index, only Bragg-guided modes will be localized in the core. If the core index is higher than the effective index of the cladding, then it is possible for both refractively guided (TIR) and Bragg-guided modes to be localized in the core.

When the core index is higher than that of the surrounding medium, the modes guided by total internal reflection have a close analogy to bound modes of a step index fiber.[9] The relatively high index contrast of air/silica (compared to that of conventional all-glass fibers) and the varying penetration of modes into the air regions as a function of wavelength, create

C.M. Soukoulis (ed.), Photonic Crystals and Light Localization in the 21st Century, 305–320.

a strong variation of effective cladding index with wavelength that confers some unusual properties to these effective index photonic crystal fibers.[9-15] In particular, the properties of being endlessly single mode,[10] having large or easily manipulated group velocity dispersion,[13] including anomalous dispersion, and having an easily manipulated mode area[15] are of interest.

This paper presents some unifying features of conventional glass fiber waveguides, effective index photonic crystal fibers (PCFs), and photonic band-gap fibers that guide by Bragg scattering. In the first section we unify the different regimes by presenting all the different guided modes on a single band structure diagram, depicting the possible frequencies of mode propagation versus wavevector (or propagation constant) down the fiber. In the second section we discuss fiber fabrication. In the third section we concentrate on the effective index fibers, discussing some of their useful properties. In the final section we concentrate on the Bragg-guiding fibers, which are possibly the most interesting because of the prospect of guiding in air.

2. GUIDED MODES AND BAND GAPS

In published literature much attention has been devoted to two-dimensional photonic crystals, where the direction of light propagation is in the plane of periodicity. Photonic crystal *fibers* may also be considered as two-dimensional in the sense that the periodic structure exists only in the plane transverse to the fiber axis. The direction of light propagation, however, is down the fiber axis, or out of the plane of periodicity. Naively, one might think that no band gap is possible for propagation in the direction that has continuous translational symmetry (down the fiber axis). An idea like this is suggested on page 66 of Ref. 16. Band gaps do arise, however, at higher values of the axial k-vector k_z (usually called the propagation constant β in optics literature). These gaps arise because the bandwidth at each β_z shrinks as β_z increases, shown in Fig. 1. (This is also pointed out on page 67 of Ref. 16.) In Fig. 1 we show the projected band diagram for a high dielectric material (dielectric constant, ε=13) with a triangular lattice of air holes of radius r and r/Λ=0.48. Here, Λ is the pitch or spacing between air holes. In this case there is an "omnidirectional" gap at β_z=0, i.e., a gap exists for all values of in-plane wavevector.[16] It is true that no band gap can exist for all values of β_z; one can see that the in-plane gap from $\omega\Lambda/(2\pi c)$=0.43 to 0.52 (see at β_z=0 in Fig. 1) vanishes by the time $\beta_z\Lambda/(2\pi)$ reaches 0.9. The absence of a gap extending over all axial wavevectors, however, is irrelevant for use in waveguide applications. Even the conventional mode of a single-mode telecommunication fiber exists in a band gap that does not extend to all wavevectors (it does not extend to zero). This does not matter because the mode will only be used over a limited range of frequencies and wavevectors.

Figures 1, 2a, and 2b are all calculated using a full vector solution to the Maxwell equations in a plane-wave basis in the frequency domain.[17] In these band calculations, no material dispersion is included. Figure 1 shows the situation with high dielectric contrast (ε=13 and 1) and no defect, while Figs. 2a and 2b show lower contrast (ε=2.1025 and 1) and two different kinds of defects. The main difference between Fig. 1 and Fig. 2b is the higher dielectric contrast of Fig. 1. As shown in Figs. 2a and b, a single diagram can capture all the different kinds of guided modes of a fiber waveguide. Figure 2b is a blow-up of the lower left corner of Fig. 2a, with labels for various features. These figures show the projected band structure for several fiber designs. Conventional waveguiding by TIR is not usually considered a band-gap effect, but may be considered so by reference to Fig. 2. Even a conventional fiber has a band gap, shown as the lowest open region on Fig. 2, below the line

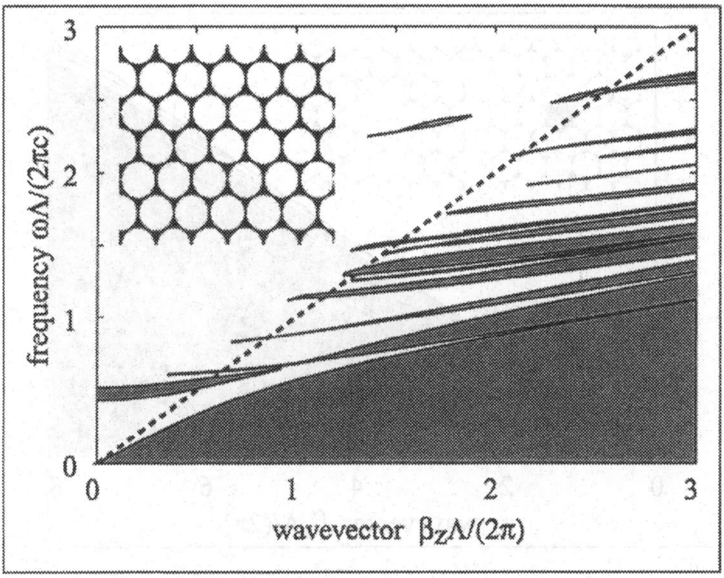

Figure 1. Projected band structure for triangular lattice of air holes in a high dielectric (ε=13), for out-of-plane wavevector β_z, with air hole r/Λ=0.48. Gaps are shaded gray. The inset shows the structure, where the white circles are air regions and dark is dielectric. (Similar to Fig. 11, page 66 of Ref. 16.)

labeled FSM. Here FSM denotes the fundamental space-filling mode, or the lowest mode that can propagate in the background index. At nonzero β_z, there is a lowest frequency that can propagate in a uniform medium of refractive index *n,* given by $\omega/c=\beta_z/n$. In a conventional fiber, these would be called cladding modes (or radiation modes) and the effective cladding index is equal to *n*. When a core of higher index is introduced (represented by the glass index line in Fig. 2), this creates a defect in the previous translationally continuous radial structure. With a raised index, new modes at lower frequencies can propagate in the band gap between the effective cladding and core index lines. (The core index line, denoted glass index line in Fig. 2b, has slope $1/n_{core}$.) These modes, denoted refractive modes in Fig. 2b, are localized to the core region and are the very modes used in optical fiber telecommunication. At short wavelength (large β_z), the refractive mode is almost entirely in the glass core and its dispersion curve approaches the glass index line. At long wavelength, the refractive mode spreads out into the background material and its dispersion curve approaches the FSM line. These features, depicted in Fig. 2, are schematically correct for a conventional telecommunication fiber. Similarly, TIR-guided modes exist in photonic crystal fibers that have a solid core surrounded by a pattern of lower index (e.g., air hole) regions. In this case the effective or average index of the surrounding region is lower than the index of the solid glass core, and the guidance is similar to that of the conventional fiber described above with the propagating modes appearing in the band gap between the core and effective cladding lines. The inset shown in the upper left of Fig. 2a shows the actual core/clad structure that produces this waveguide: one missing air hole (solid glass core) surrounded by a triangular lattice of air holes in glass. The air holes have radius/pitch, r/Λ=0.495.

Moving up to higher frequencies in Fig. 2a, a series of gaps is seen. In the present air/silica dielectric contrast, such gaps can only exist at nonzero β_z, and they arise by the narrowing of band widths described above. These gaps would not exist, were it not for the

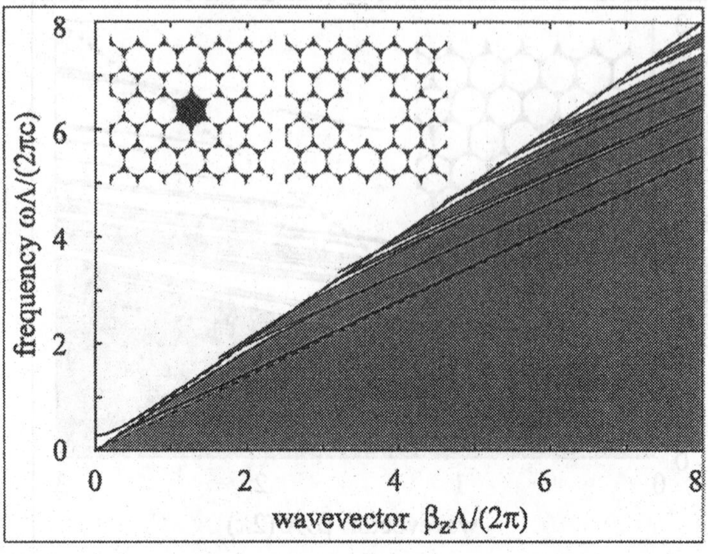

Figure 2a. **Band structure "finger diagram" for photonic crystal fiber. This diagram is calculated for air holes of r/Λ=0.495 in a triangular pattern running through a silica glass fiber. See Fig. 1b for labeling of lines and regions. Insets show the two defects (or waveguides) being considered, where white regions are air holes and dark regions are silica glass. Λ is the pitch or hole separation.**

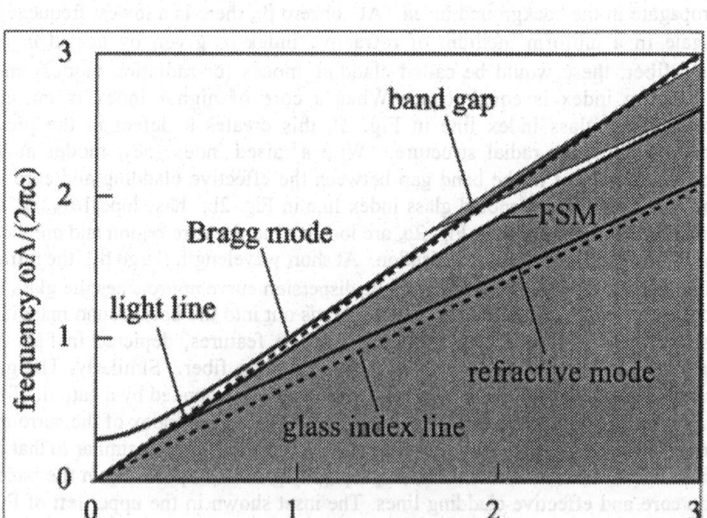

Figure 2b. **Same as Fig. 2a with expanded scale. Grey regions are band gaps, solid lines show where certain modes can exist, and dashed lines show boundaries explained in text. The light line has slope 1, shown as a dashed line. The Bragg mode is only localized inside the band gap.**

pattern of air columns running down the fiber. When a defect is introduced into this structure, in the form of any change in periodicity, modes can occur in the gaps and these modes must be localized near the defect. Note that a higher-index defect has the possibility of localizing modes by TIR (lowest gap) and also localizing modes by Bragg scattering (higher gaps). A lower-index defect (e.g., an oversized air hole) cannot localize a mode by TIR, so must localize the mode by Bragg scattering. When gaps extend above the vacuum light line (line of $\omega=c\beta_z$, lowest frequency of propagation in vacuum), it is then possible for the mode to be localized in the air region of an air defect. We show the dispersion curve for a typical defect state, labeled Bragg mode in Fig. 2b. The defect producing this localized mode is shown as the right inset in Fig. 2a (larger air hole in center). At places where the defect dispersion crosses a band gap above the light line, the mode can be localized in the air core. An example is shown in Fig. 2b, where the defect dispersion lies slightly above the light line and crosses the first band gap above the FSM. The propagation of light in air, trapped inside a flexible fiber, creates the possibility for negligible nonlinearity, low loss, and low dispersion, giving these fibers great potential for telecommunication applications, as we discuss later.

3. FABRICATION

3.1 Stack and Draw

The common method to fabricate glass/air microstructured fibers (including PCFs and PBGFs) is the stack and draw process, where glass capillaries are arranged in a lattice array and the assembly is drawn to fiber dimensions. This process has been successfully used to demonstrate a number of microstructured fiber waveguides, including endlessly single mode PCFs,[10] photonic band-gap fibers,[8] and fibers with enhanced nonlinear effects.[22] Using this technique, it is straightforward to make long lengths (> 1km) of robust coated fiber without resorting to the more complex methods discussed in the literature.[23]

A hollow core photonic band-gap fiber made by this technique is shown in Fig. 3. The pitch Λ between the large holes is about 7.5μm; the large core defect was produced by removing seven central lattice points. The image is generated using 2 meters of fiber, with one end illuminated by a broadband source, giving the refractively guided white light in the glass webbing and a bright green mode propagating down the air core (seen as light gray in Fig. 3).

By increasing the air-filling fraction in triangular structures, it becomes easier to fabricate structures that have lower-frequency and broader band gaps that transmit light in the near infrared. The fiber in Fig. 4 has an air filling fraction >87%, where the glass strands separating the holes are about 100nm in thickness. Unlike the fiber in Fig. 3, cladding light is easily stripped because of the very thin glass walls. Experimental and theoretical analyses of fibers with this cross-section is presented in our fourth section, where we concentrate on band-gap guidance.

The stack and draw technique can also be modified to fabricate all-glass PCFs. These are effective index microstructured fibers where the holes are replaced by lower index glass posts. This approach allows us to predetermine the hole size and shape making the fabrication process more straightforward and controlled. The obvious drawback, however, is the lower index contrast, making it difficult to demonstrate all-glass PBGFs or low bend-loss effective-index PCFs. For these fibers, the building block of the structure is a solid rod rather than a capillary. The rods are from a CVD preform which has an inverted index profile (i.e., where the core has a lower index than the clad). After assembly, the bundle of rods can be drawn under a vacuum such that the low index core of the original preform become the posts in the final fiber. A picture of such an all-glass PCF is shown in Fig. 5. The pattern of small dots is low-index columns that run the length of the fiber.

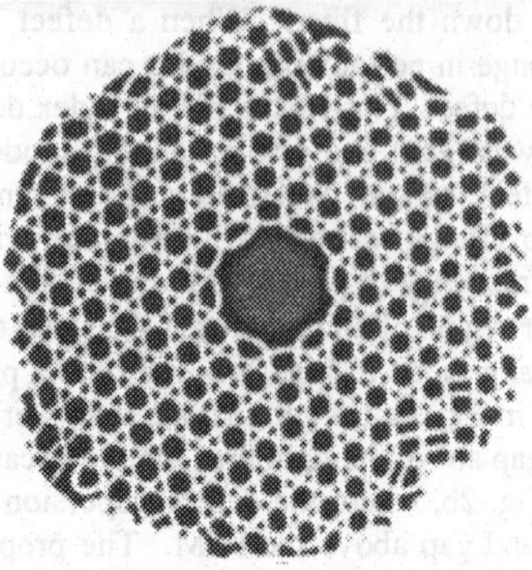

Figure 3. **Photonic band-gap fiber with mode in air core. Gray area in center air hole is actually green transmitted light. Dark areas are air holes, while light areas are glass. The larger air holes are 4.4µm in diameter and their pitch is 7.4µm.**

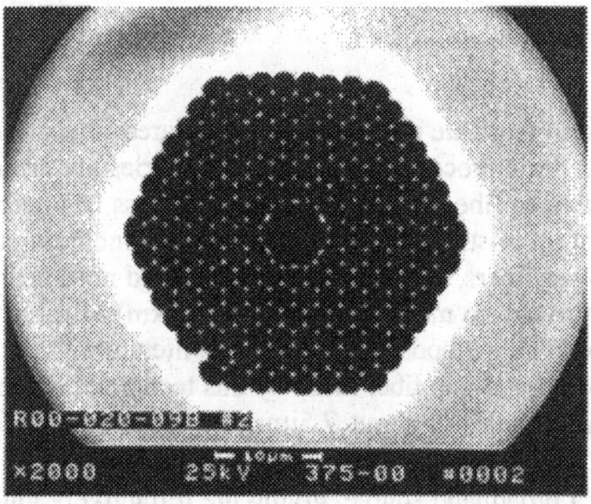

Figure 4. **Electron micrograph of photonic band-gap fiber with >87% air-filling fraction and pitch 2.2µm.**

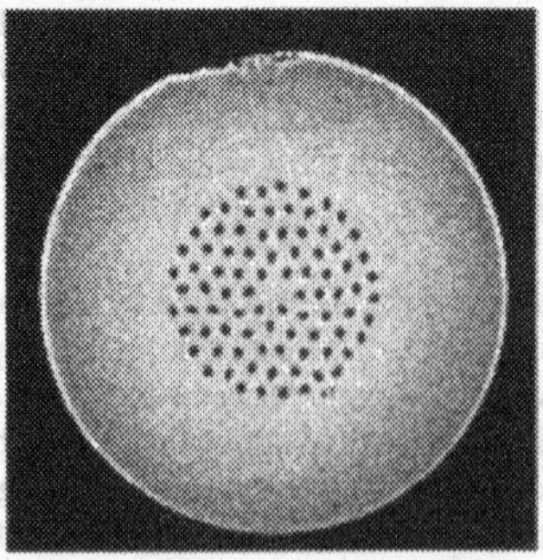

Figure 5. **All-glass photonic crystal fiber. The darker regions are glass columns running the length of the fiber, with lower index by fluorine-doping. The outer diameter of the fiber is 100µm, the pitch is 4.5µm, and the radius/pitch ratio is 0.2.**

3.2 Preform Extrusion

Although a useful tool to prototype band-gap fiber structures, the stack and draw method described above is a relatively slow process to make an optical preform. It is also difficult to make complex cross-sections that lack natural symmetry. We have investigated an alternative method for the production of PBG preforms using an extrusion process. Analogous to the extrusion process for the manufacture of Celcor® ceramic substrates for catalytic converters, it is a fast process that can generate many preforms at one time. It is also possible to fabricate a wide variety of more complicated microstructures than previously demonstrated by stack and draw.

The two preforms in Figs. 6a and 6b were made by extrusion. In Fig. 6a the holes in the preform round off during fiberization, forming the same triangular lattice commonly made by stack and draw. When drawn to a fiber, the preform in Fig. 6b reduces to form the honeycomb structure, which has been shown theoretically to exhibit photonic band gaps different from the triangular lattice.[20] Note, however, the fibers in Fig. 6 are effective index PCFs, where a solid core was made by inserting a silica rod into a channel in the preform.

As one would expect, contamination is a major concern in the extrusion technique for PBG preforms. A chemical purification process minimizes the effects of die wear and residual processing additives. Such content in the body not only leads to extrinsic absorption and scattering, but also disrupts the structure by inducing crystallization during the draw process.

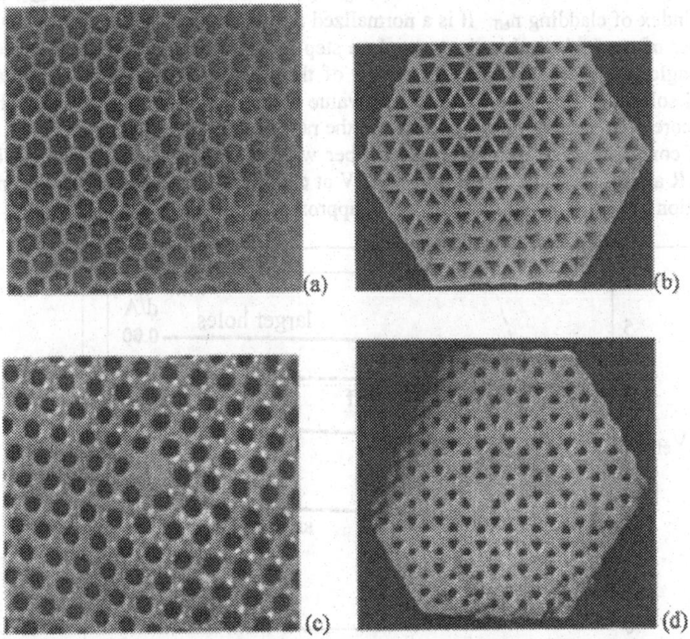

Figure 6a) **Extruded PCF preform for triangular lattice fiber.** ***b)*** **Preform (no defect) for honeycomb lattice.** ***c)*** **Fiber from extruded preform in 6a.** ***d)*** **Fiber from extruded preform in 6b, respectively. Holes in (c) are about 2μm in diameter with 3μm pitch; longest outer dimension of (d) is 75μm.**

4. EFFECTIVE INDEX WAVEGUIDES

Effective index guiding PCFs have a higher index core than the cladding. The cladding is typically any pattern of index variation, and while strict periodicity is obviously not required in the effective index regime, it is important for practical fabrication and performance reasons. We have made endlessly single mode air/silica PCFs with measured losses as low as 15dB/km, measured at 1550nm, in lengths exceeding 1km. We have made single mode all-glass PCFs with a measured loss as low as 12dB/km, measured below 1000nm. At longer wavelengths bend loss rapidly increases because the very low index contrast of the all-glass PCF only weakly binds the core mode. At these wavelengths, these losses are three orders of magnitude lower than the lowest values reported so far in the literature.

Effective index PCFs have interesting dispersion properties, due to the very strong wavelength dependence of the effective cladding index. At short wavelength, the lowest mode is confined primarily in high-index regions, and the effective index of the cladding is very close to that of the core (solid glass). At long wavelengths, the lowest mode spreads out over the low- and high-index regions and effectively averages them, so that the final cladding index depends on the air fraction of the structure. This can be seen in Fig. 7, where we show the fiber "V-number" vs. inverse wavelength for several sizes of air holes in glass. The V-number is defined as

$$V=(2\pi R/\lambda)\,(n_{core}^{2}-n_{eff}^{2})^{1/2}, \quad (1)$$

with the effective radius of core R, wavelength λ, refractive index of core n_{core}, and the effective index of cladding n_{eff}. It is a normalized frequency that can be used to determine the number of modes bound in the core. In a step index core profile fiber, the core binds only a single mode for $V<2.405$ (first zero of the Bessel function $J_0(V)$). In a PCF, numerical solutions show that the threshold value for multiple modes is $V\sim4.1$, when the effective core radius is assumed to be equal to the radius of the central air hole.[9] The correct choice of core radius is not obvious for a fiber with a microstructured cladding, but the choice of R affects the only the magnitude of V at cutoff and not its functional dependence. The variation of V with inverse wavelength is approximately linear for a conventional fiber,

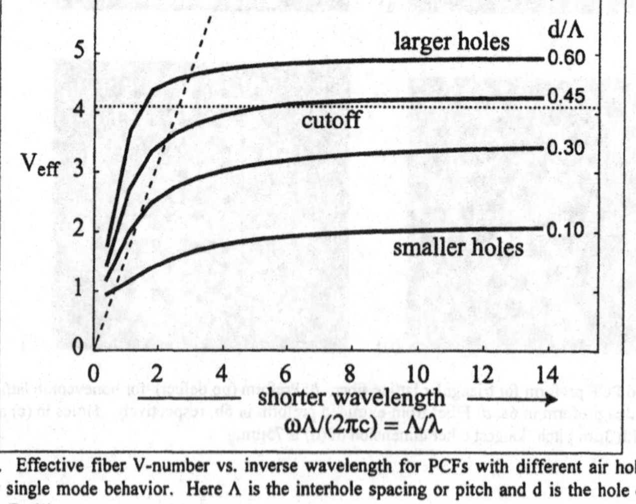

Figure 7. **Effective fiber V-number vs. inverse wavelength for PCFs with different air hole sizes, showing endlessly single mode behavior. Here Λ is the interhole spacing or pitch and d is the hole diameter. V_{eff} is defined in Eq.(1).**

as shown by the dotted line of Fig. 7. For a standard fiber the region of single-mode propagation only exists over a limited range of wavelengths; at shorter wavelengths, more modes can 'fit' into the core. The case for a PCF is very different: the V-curve bends over and flattens out as a function of inverse wavelength. (The case we consider assumes that the core material is the same as the cladding matrix material, i.e., silica in this case.) For small enough air holes ($r/\Lambda<0.2$), the entire curve of V remains below the single-mode cutoff, and hence, the fiber remains endlessly single mode. For larger air holes, the fiber can be made endlessly 2-moded, etc. Considering the usual telecommunication transmission band of 1530-1580nm, the enlarged range of single-mode propagation has no compelling advantage at the current time, especially when PCF bend loss at short wavelengths is considered.

High dispersion and zero dispersion shifted to shorter wavelengths are potentially more interesting consequences of the strong dependence of n_{eff} on wavelength. In Fig. 8 we show the experimentally measured[18] and theoretically calculated dispersions for an effective-index PCF. The fiber has a solid glass (silica) core, and a triangular lattice of air holes surrounding the core. The lattice has a pitch of about 2.2μm and a radius/pitch ratio of 0.37. The theoretical calculation includes explicit dependence of material index on wavelength (material dispersion). This shows an example of shifting the zero of dispersion to 860nm, so that the shorter wavelength range of 1300nm to 860nm is now a region of anomalous (positive) dispersion. Although high dispersions can also be achieved using a silica rod in air, photonic crystal fibers allow tailoring both dispersion and dispersion slope with greater flexibility. A simple silica rod has only one parameter (its size), while a PCF has other adjustable knobs: pitch and hole size, and other details of the microstructure.

5. BAND-GAP GUIDANCE

Unlike the effective index photonic crystal fiber, the air-core PCF has no analog in conventional waveguides. Bragg effects play an important role in modern optics (e.g., fiber Bragg gratings), but until the appearance of the band-gap PCF, Bragg reflections were not used for waveguiding. Not only is this fiber truly unique among waveguides, but as a photonic band-gap structure it is also quite unique. Typical PBG devices involve interaction

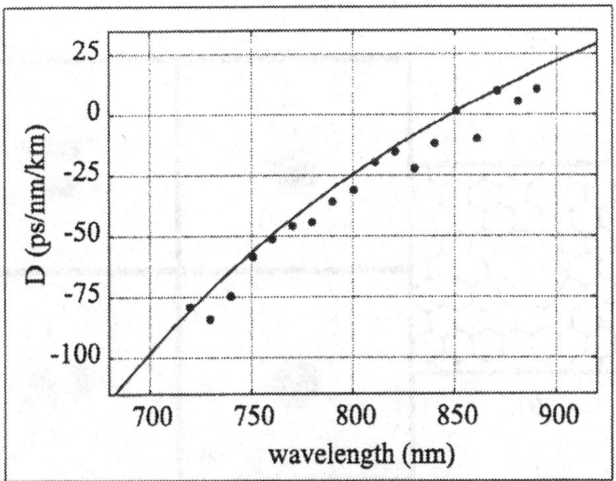

Figure 8. Dispersion parameter D of an effective index PCF comparing experimental data[18] (points) and theoretical curve (line). The experimental fiber has an average pitch of 2.2μm and an average radius/pitch ratio of 0.37, and the calculation assumed a perfectly periodic lattice using these average parameters. Discrepancy between theory and experiment can be attributed to variations in lattice parameters surrounding the core region.

lengths on the order of 10 to 1000 times the wavelength but we have demonstrated interaction lengths of greater than 10^7 times the wavelength with the PBGF!

There are many parameters that have considerable influence on the performance of the band-gap fiber: choice of lattice, lattice spacing, index fill fraction, choice of materials, size and shape of defect, and structural uniformity (both in-plane and along the axis of propagation). Because the first demonstration of these fibers was so recent,[2,8] there has been very little exploration of the various parameters, and the optimal design of a PBGF is yet undetermined. However, the standard triangular lattice suggested in the first discussion[7] of these fibers has proven to be the most fruitful design. It is simple to fabricate, has large band-gaps above the light line,[1] and to date, no other structure has demonstrated significant advantages based on modeling or measurement.[19] For these reasons we focus our discussion on the triangular lattice.

The design of the defect in the triangular lattice has been dictated largely by the nature of the fabrication process in which the defect is formed simply by the absence of the capillaries used in the stack-and-draw process. The defect must be large enough to support at least one guided mode[2] but, as in conventional waveguides, increasing the core size will eventually lead to the appearance of higher order modes.

The air-filling fraction f and the lattice spacing Λ are to some degree determined by the limits imposed by the fabrication process. For the triangular lattice with air holes of diameter d, the air-filling fraction is given by

$$f = \frac{\pi}{2\sqrt{3}}\left(\frac{d}{\Lambda}\right)^2. \tag{2}$$

For the standard triangular lattice, f is limited to a maximal value of 0.907 at which point the air holes touch and the structure collapses. To date, we have demonstrated fibers with f ~0.89 in which the structural integrity of the thin walls (~50nm thick) provide a practical limitation on the structure.

Structural uniformity along the length of the fiber remains the greatest challenge to practical development of these fibers. The position and width of the band gaps, as well as the location of the defect modes, all depend very sensitively on the structural parameters. Variations of only a few percent in the lattice spacing or hole size can greatly affect the transmission properties. Although demonstration of transmission over several centimeters is

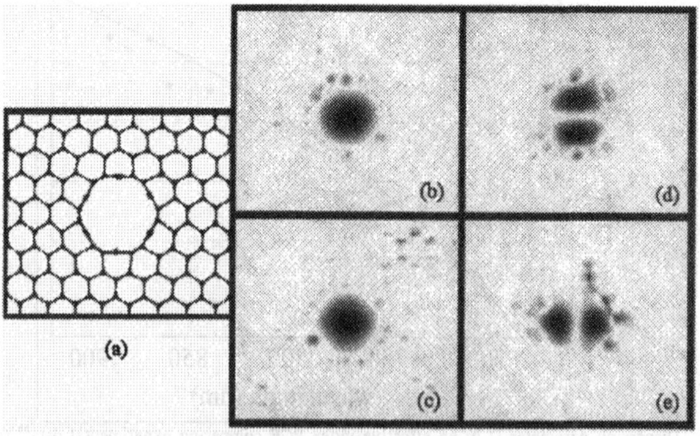

Figure 9. ***a)*** **Structure of experimental air/silica PBGF used in computer simulation.** ***(b)-(e)*** **Predicted bound modes for $\beta_z\Lambda/(2\pi)$=1.90 with normalized frequencies of $\omega\Lambda/(2\pi c)$ = 1.926, 1.926, 1.951, and 1.964, respectively.**

relatively easily achieved, transmission over tens or hundreds of meters is much more challenging. We report here transmission of light over more than 15 meters of fiber.

The fiber shown in Fig. 9a is an air-core PBGF with a pitch of Λ=3.1μm and an air-filling fraction of 0.89. These parameters were chosen not only to provide broad-band transmission at wavelengths commonly used for telecommunications, but also to use the lowest frequency band gap for this transmission. Previous demonstrations[2] of fibers with small air-fill fractions (f<50%) and large pitches utilized very high frequency band gaps producing narrow transmission bands in the visible. The larger air-fill fraction and smaller pitches reported here produce much larger transmission windows in which we believe the losses will be reduced. Another practical consequence of the choice of parameters is the ability to directly compare theory with experimental results. The calculation time for investigation of high frequency band gaps is prohibitive, but using a fiber with larger filling-fraction and smaller pitch reduces the computation time, allowing us to compare experimental results with theoretical predictions for the first time.

Figures 9(b)-(e) show the guided modes computed with the vector plane-wave model.[17] We must stress that this model used the measured structure as shown in Fig. 9a, including all the fabrication non-uniformities. Despite the fact that the structure is not perfectly periodic, we still see very well-confined fundamental and higher order modes. However, in addition to the modes localized in the air core, many additional modes appear in the band gap due to the presence of unintentional cladding defects. These 'cladding' modes are localized around the core region and are observed experimentally (see Fig. 10a). Even in relatively poor quality structures where unintentional defects are more numerous, we have observed guided modes in the core region indicating that strict periodicity is not essential for wave-guiding over short distances.

In order to observe the guided modes and spectrum experimentally, it is important to minimize the number and size of unintentional defects near the core region. The fiber shown in Figure 9a guided relatively little light in the cladding (<20%) making it possible to excite and detect only in the core region. Figure 10 shows the experimentally observed modes excited using a butt-coupled launch from standard single-mode fiber (8μm core diameter) into approximately 1 meter of PBGF. The output spectrum shown in Fig. 11 was collected using a butt-coupled multi-mode fiber (62.5μm core diameter) and an optical spectrum analyzer.

Although difficult to identify conclusively, the light in the air core of this fiber appears to be predominantly in the nearly-degenerate TE_{01}, TM_{01}, and HE_{21} modes that make up the LP_{11} mode in the weakly-guided limit. We also believe there is a contribution from the fundamental HE_{11} mode. Excitation with a 4μm core diameter step-index fiber did not eliminate the ring structure that surrounds the central mode. This light is guided in the 'cladding modes' discussed above and the computed intensity profile of such a mode is shown in Fig. 12.

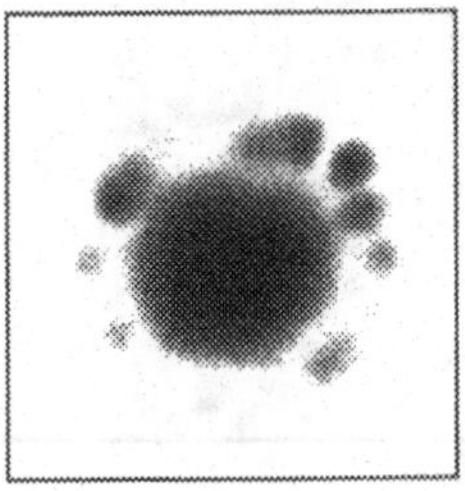
(a)

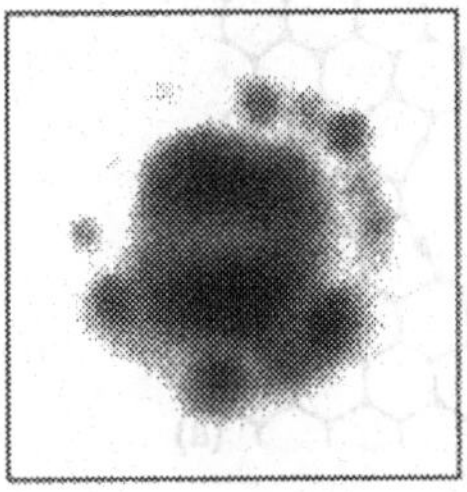
(b)

Figure 10. **Experimentally observed modes of the structure in Fig.9a at 1310nm. The images were recorded on an IR vidicon.**

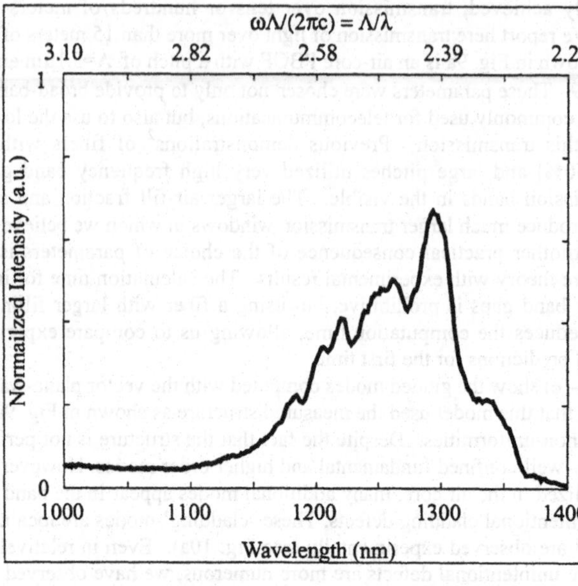

Figure 11. Transmission spectrum of defect modes in the band-gap fiber with Λ=3.1μm.

In Fig. 13 the band structure diagram of a perfect triangular lattice reveals a lowest band gap near $\omega\Lambda/(2\pi c)=2.0$. Numerical modeling of the experimental structure (see Fig. 14) indicates that the location of the defect modes can be approximated using the modes of a perfect reflector.[21] The radius R_d of this reflector is approximately equal to the physical radius of the defect. From Figs. 13 and 14 it appears the defect modes occur in the band gap from $\omega\Lambda/(2\pi c)$ =1.8 to 2.5. For Λ=3.1μm, this suggests that the observed spectrum should cover 1240 to 1720nm, however, the experimental data show a spectrum from 1150 to 1350nm. There are several possible explanations for this disagreement between theory and experiment. It is possible there are loss mechanisms that limit the transmission bandwidth of the guide modes, especially when the mode frequency approaches the edge of the gap. Also, the shift of the transmission band can be attributed to a difference in the air-filling fraction between the theoretical structure shown in Fig. 9a and the real structure. Figure 9a was obtained by thresholding a scanned image of a scanning electron micrograph.

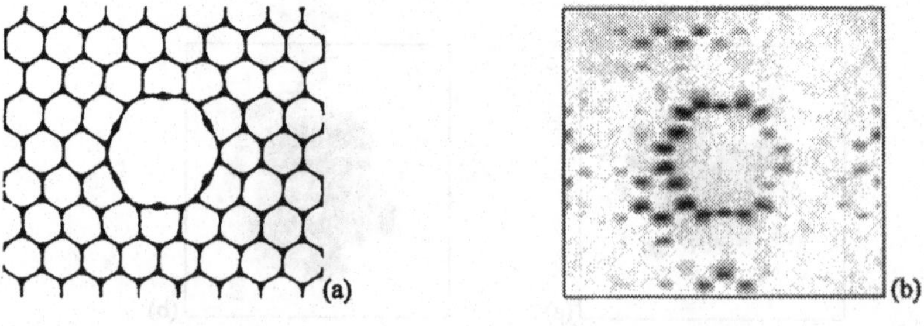

Figure 12 a) Structure of experimental air/silica PBGF used in computer simulation. *b)* Computed 'cladding' mode in the band gap for $\beta_z\Lambda/(2\pi)$=1.90 and normalized frequency of $\omega\Lambda/(2\pi c)$ = 1.936.

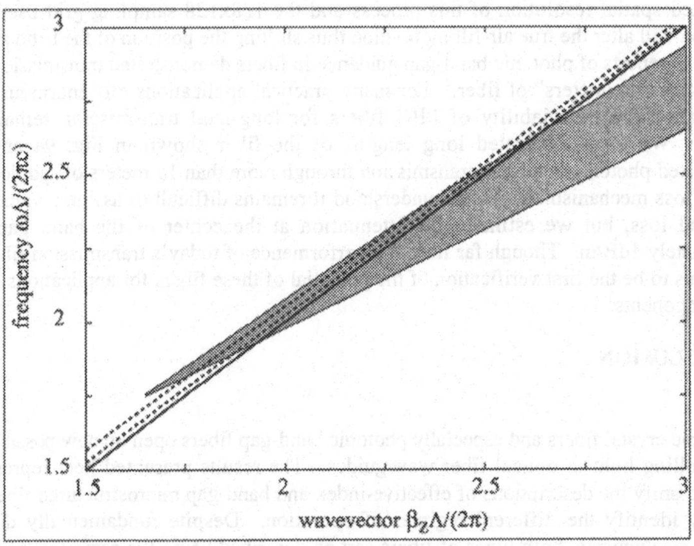

Figure 13. **Band structure diagram for perfect triangular lattice of air holes in silica. The ratio of the diameter of air holes to pitch was d/Λ=0.99 resulting in an air-filling fraction of *f*=0.889. The light line is the solid line $\omega\Lambda/(2\pi c)=\beta_z\Lambda/(2\pi)$, the band-gap is shaded and the dashed lines are the two lowest defect states assuming a perfect reflector of radius to pitch R_d/Λ=1.33.**

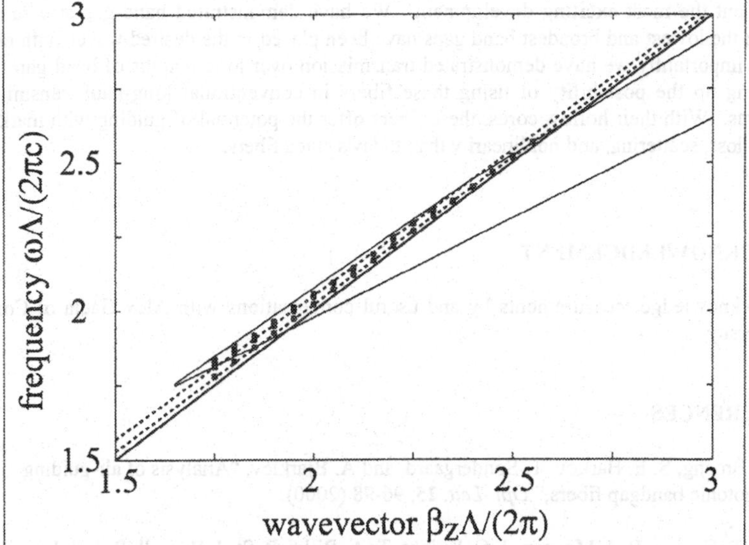

Figure 14. **The locations (points) of the localized defect modes (see Fig. 9b-e) calculated for the real structure shown in Fig. 9a are compared to the predictions (dashed lines) of the perfect reflector of radius R_d=1.33Λ. The band gap of the perfect structure is re-plotted from Fig. 13.**

The limited spatial resolution of this process and the 128x128 sampling grid used in the calculation will alter the true air-filling fraction thus shifting the position of the band gap.

Previous reports of photonic band-gap guidance in fibers demonstrated transmission in only "tens of centimeters" of fiber.[2] For many practical applications this enormous loss is unacceptable and the viability of PBG fibers for long-haul transmission remained in question. We have fabricated long lengths of the fiber shown in Fig. 9a and have demonstrated photonic band-gap transmission through more than 15 meters of spooled fiber. Until the loss mechanisms are better understood it remains difficult to assign a value to the distributed loss, but we estimate the attenuation at the center of the band gap to be approximately 1dB/m. Though far from the performance of today's transmission fibers, we believe this to be the first verification of the potential of these fibers for applications beyond small components.

6. CONCLUSION

Photonic crystal fibers and especially photonic band-gap fibers open up new possibilities for controlling light in optical fiber waveguides. The results presented here represent an attempt to unify the descriptions of effective-index and band-gap microstructured fibers, and to clearly identify the different regimes of operation. Despite fundamentally different guidance mechanisms, both types of fibers can be described using the same the theoretical model and language. It is important to build this unifying framework to prevent confusion between two fiber structures that appear to be so similar.

We discussed various experimental microstructured fibers including: air/silica effective index PCFs, all-glass PCFs, PCFs that shift the zero-dispersion wavelength, PCFs that are extruded, PBGFs that guide in the visible, and PBGFs that guide in the near IR. Although the effective index fibers have some remarkable attributes, it is the band-gap fibers that represent the most exciting development. We have demonstrated band-gap structures in which the lowest and broadest band gaps have been placed in the desired wavelength range. More importantly we have demonstrated transmission over long lengths of band-gap fiber, opening up the possibility of using these fibers in conventional long-haul transmission systems. With their hollow cores, these fibers offer the potential of guiding with markedly lower loss, scattering, and nonlinearity than today's silica fibers.

7. ACKNOWLEDGEMENT

We acknowledge measurements by and useful conversations with Alex Gaeta of Cornell University.

REFERENCES

1. J. Broeng, S. E. Barkou, T. Sondergaard, and A. Bjarklev, "Analysis of air-guiding photonic bandgap fibers," *Opt. Lett.* **25**, 96-98 (2000).

2. R. F. Cregan, B. J. Mangan, J. C. Knight, T. A. Birks, P. St. J. Russell, P. J. Roberts, and D. C. Allan, "Single-mode photonic band gap guidance of light in air," *Science* **285**, 1537-1539 (1999).

3. P. Yeh, A. Yariv, and E. Marom, "Theory of Bragg fiber," *J. Opt. Soc. Am.* **68**, 1196-1201 (1978).

4. N. J. Doran and K. J. Blow, "Cylindrical Bragg fibers: A design and feasibility study for optical communications," *J. Lightwave Techn.* **LT-1**, 588-590 (1983).

5. C. M. de Sterke, I. M. Bassett, and A. G. Street, "Differential losses in Bragg fibers," *J. Appl. Phys.* **76**, 680 (1994).

6. T. A. Birks, D. M. Atkin, G. Wylangowski, P. St. J. Russell, and P. J. Roberts, in *Microcavities and Photonic Bandgaps: Physics and Applications*, J. G. Rarity and C. Weisbuch, Eds., Kluwer, Dordrecht, Netherlands (1996), pp. 203-218.

7. T. A. Birks, P. J. Roberts, P. St. J. Russell, D. M. Atkin, and T. J. Shepherd, "Full 2-D photonic bandgaps in silica/air structures," *El. Lett.* **31**, 1941-1943 (1995).

8. J. C. Knight, J. Broeng, T. A. Birks, and P. St. J. Russell, "Photonic band gap guidance in optical fibers," *Science* **282**, 1476-1478 (1998).

9. T. A. Birks, D. Mogilevtsev, J. C. Knight, P. St. J. Russell, J. Broeng, P. J. Roberts, J. A. West, D. C. Allan, and J. C. Fajardo, "The analogy between photonic crystal fibres and step index fibres," in *Optical Fiber Communication Conference*, OSA Technical Digest, Optical Society of America, Wash. D.C. (1999), pp. 114-116.

10. J. C. Knight, T. A. Birks, P. St. J. Russell, and D. M. Atkin, "All-silica single-mode optical fiber with photonic crystal cladding," *Opt. Lett.* **21**, 1547-1549 (1996); **22**, 484-485 (1997).

11. T. A. Birks, J. C. Knight, and P. St. J. Russell, "Endlessly single-mode photonic crystal fiber," *Opt. Lett.* **22**, 961-963 (1997).

12. J. C. Knight, T. A. Birks, P. St. J. Russell, and J. P. de Sandro, "Properties of photonic crystal fiber and the effective index model," *J. Opt. Soc. Am. A* **15**, 748-752 (1998).

13. D. Mogilevtsev, T. A. Birks, and P. St. J. Russell, "Group-velocity dispersion in photonic crystal fibers," *Opt. Lett.* **23**, 1662-1664 (1998).

14. M. J. Gander, R. McBride, J. D. C. Jones, D. Mogilevtsev, T. A. Birks, J.C. Knight, and P. St. J. Russell, "Experimental measurement of group velocity dispersion in photonic crystal fiber," *El. Lett.* **35**, 63-64 (1999).

15. J. C. Knight, T. A. Birks, R. F. Cregan, P. St. J. Russell, and J.-P. de Sandro, "Large mode area photonic crystal fibre," *El. Lett.* **34**, 965-966 (1998).

16. J. D. Joannopoulos, R. D. Meade, and J. N. Winn, *Photonic Crystals: Molding the Flow of Light*, Princeton University Press, Princeton, NJ (1995).

17. Steven G. Johnson and J. D. Joannopoulos, The MIT photonic-bands package, http://ab-initio.mit.edu/mpb.

18. Alex Gaeta, School of Applied and Engineering Physics, Cornell University, private communication.

19. The inclusion of interstitial air holes into the triangular lattice has been suggested to increase gap bandwidths (see J. Broeng, S. E. Barkou, A. Bjarklev, J. C. Knight, T. A. Birks, and P. St. J Russell, "Highly increased photonic band gaps in silica/air structures," *Opt. Comm.* **156**, 240 (1998)). However, for the optimized parameter range discussed here, this modification does not result in improved performance.

20. S. E. Barkou, J. Broeng, and A. Bjarklev, "Silica-air photonic crystal fiber design that permits waveguiding by a true photonic bandgap effect," *Opt. Lett.* **24**, 1, 46-48 (1999).

21. N. S. Kapany and J. J. Burke, *Optical Waveguides*, Academic Press, Inc., NY (1972).

22. J. K. Ranka, R. S. Windeler, A. J Stentz, "Visible continuum generation in air-silica microstructure optical fibers with anomalous dispersion at 800 nm," *Opt. Lett.* **25**, 25-27 (2000).

23. P. J. Bennett, T. M. Monroe and D. J. Richardson, "Toward Practical holey fiber technology: Fabrication, splicing, modeling and characterization," *Opt. Lett.* **24**, 1203-1205 (1999).

APPLICATIONS OF PHOTONIC CRYSTALS TO DIRECTIONAL ANTENNAS

R. Biswas[1], E. Ozbay[2], B. Temelkuran[2], M. Bayindir[2], M. M. Sigalas[1], and K.-M. Ho[1]

[1]Department of Physics and Astronomy, Ames Laboratory and Microelectronics Research Center, Iowa State University, Ames, Iowa 50011
[2]Department of Physics, Bilkent University, Bilkent, Ankara 06533, Turkey

1. Introduction

One of the prime motivations for the rapid development of photonic band gap structures was the promise of manipulating and engineering the photonic densities of states (DOS) [1,2] for new applications. By altering the photonic DOS, spontaneous emission can be modified opening up novel applications to optical physics.

We describe in this paper a particularly simple but powerful way of modifying the photonic DOS by creating resonant cavities with photonic crystals and tailoring the emission of sources. This method has an analogy with efforts in optical physics in the 1980's to modify the photonic DOS. Atoms located near walls probe a modified photonic DOS and may change emission patterns. A very powerful construct was to fabricate a Fabry-Perot type of cavity of linear dimension L (Fig. 1). Such a cavity with perfectly reflecting walls only allows modes with wavelengths $\lambda_m = 2L/m$ or frequencies $\nu_m = mc_0/2L$. Indeed optical measurements in microcavities [3,4] found strongly modified and directional emission patterns of atoms placed inside microcavites when the cavity frequencies were tuned to the frequency of atomic emission.

Photonic band gap crystals offer a new twist to such cavity emission. The Fabry-Perot cavity modes are effectively the defect modes of a planar defect. The mode frequency (e.g. first mode, m=1) can be tuned to be within the photonic band gap. Then radiation can emerge from the cavity only at frequency ν_1, with all other frequencies in the band gap suppressed. The emission pattern of a source within the cavity can be a narrow directional pattern.

C.M. Soukoulis (ed.), Photonic Crystals and Light Localization in the 21st Century, 321–328.

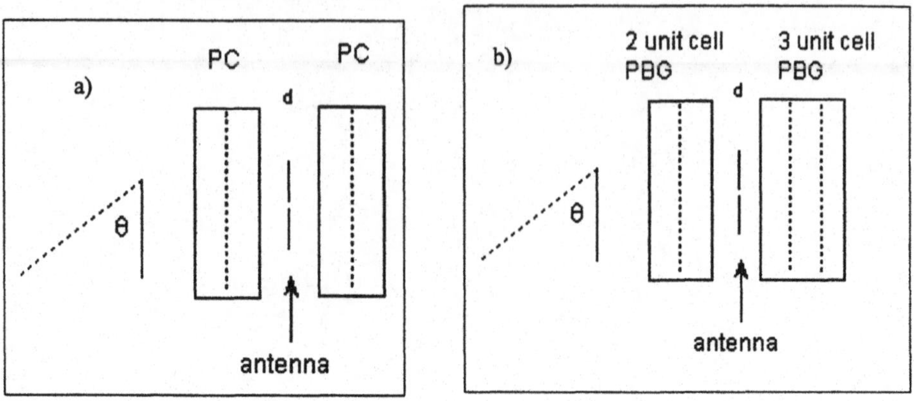

Fig. 1 a) Symmetric Fabry-Perot like cavity formed by photonic crystals or dielectric layers. b) Asymmetric cavity formed by a 3unit-cell PBG crystal separated from a 2 unit cell PBG crystal.

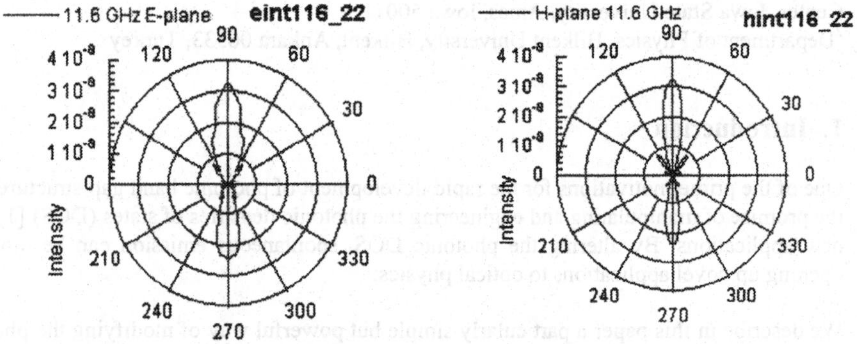

Fig. 2 Calculated radiation pattern from a dipole antenna at the center of a symmetric cavity, formed with two unit cells of PBG crystal as the wall.

2. Simulations and computational method

We simulate such photonic crystal cavities using the layer-by-layer structure composed of silicon rods that has a full robust three-dimensional photonic band gap. To compare with microwave measurements we have chosen dimensions in the cm range, but the dimensions can be scaled to generate any higher frequency. We utilize square rods of alumina (n=3.1) of square cross-section with a thickness of 0.3 cm and a rod-to-rod spacing of 1.1 cm. The structure has a complete photonic band gap between 11.3 and 14 GHz with an attenuation of ~12 dB/unit cell for the microwave structure.[5]

The cavity was simulated with the finite-difference time domain (FDTD) technique. The time-dependent Maxwell curl equations are numerically integrated to determine the radiation fields of a dipole source placed inside a cavity. The well known near-to-far field transformation is utilized to determine the far-field radiation patterns. Due to symmetry we only need to simulate one-fourth of the unit cell. Each layer of our PBG structure is composed of 15 rods. Past results [6] have demonstrated an excellent comparison between the results of FDTD simulation and experimental measurements for dipole antennas placed on the surface of these 3-D PBG crystals.

3. Directional sources and detectors

The first structure that we simulated was a cavity formed by two unit cells (8 layers) of PBG on each side of the cavity (Fig. 1). The cavity width, or the separation of the two sides of the cavity, was 0.8 mm modeled by 20 grid spaces. We checked that this cavity separation generates a defect mode near 12 GHz near the center of the band gap.

A dipole source was placed at the center of this symmetric cavity. Using FDTD we simulated the far-field radiation pattern of this dipole antenna at various frequencies. At 11.6 GHz we found the radiation pattern to consist of two narrow cones in the forward and backward directions through the cavity walls (Fig. 2). The radiation pattern has narrow half-widths of approximately 16° in the E-plane and 11° in the H-plane. Such directional patterns are virtually impossible to achieve with a broad dipole antenna source. Because of time-reversal symmetry of the electromagnetic fields, this pattern is also the pattern of a receiver.

The underlying reason for the directionality is that only at the frequency of the defect mode (~11.6 GHz) can radiation emerge from the cavity. Further the radiation is suppressed at angles away from the normal. Broad radiation patterns are observed at frequencies within the band edges.

The next step in modifying the resonant effect is to make the cavity asymmetric. We did this by having 3-unit cells at the back of the cavity and retaining the 2-unit cells on the front side. This attenuates the beam on the backside by ~12 dB and effectively generates a single radiation lobe in the forward direction. To optimize the pattern further we chose a dipole of length l = 1.25 λ. This longer dipole provides a much narrow radiation pattern for the free dipole that the short half-wave free dipole[7].

We obtain a single lobe radiation pattern through the front-side of the cavity (Fig. 3) with a exceedingly narrow full-width at half maxima of 14° in the E-plane and 12° in the H-plane. This uniquely directional pattern has only very weak sidelobes at ~30 ° to the normal and a radiation in the backside that is weaker by a factor of 10. Because of the time-reversal symmetry this also represents the response of a detector placed inside the cavity. Directional receivers can detect signals from a very narrow field of view, which is a desirable feature for detectors in astronomy applications.

By increasing the frequency of the source the pattern generates side-lobes above 11.8 GHz although the central feature remains similar. At lower frequencies the radiation patterns broadens. The simulations predict a window of about 0.2-0.4 GHz for this unique directionality.

Extensive experimental measurements at Bilkent University[8] have been performed on this cavity, created from 2- and 3-unit cells of PBG material and a monopole antenna source. For this geometry a resonant frequency of 11.725 GHz was obtained and the measured antenna radiation (Fig. 4) displays a half-power full-width of 12 ° in the E-plane and 11° in the H-plane[8]. The theoretical calculations are in very good agreement with these measurements.

In addition the power detected by a receiver placed in this resonant cavity was measured as a function of frequency. At the resonance frequency, a power enhancement of 180 (22.6 dB) was measured. The Q-factor, defined as the center frequency divided by the full width at half maximum, was measured to be 895. The measured (and computed) directivity reaches a peak value of ~310. This is a large improvement over the configuration where the dipole antenna was placed on the photonic crystal surface, which had a directivity of ~10 and a radiative gain of 8. Clearly this photonic-crystal based resonant antenna is a uniquely directional source/receiver that offers very high gain in a narrow bandwidth of frequencies.

The calculated bandwidth (Fig. 5) of this antenna is ~0.3-0.4 GHz, considerably broader than the experimentally determined value. The small frequency resolution (~0.2 GHz) resulting from the finite time of the simulations may account for this difference.

4. Discussion: comparison of 3-d with 1-d

Recently Thevenot et al [9] have modeled and fabricated a one-dimensional multilayer dielectric structure that has a single sharp defect mode. The system was driven by a patch antenna on a metal plate. The metal ground plane generated the image of the upper dielectric layers, so that only one-half of the structure was necessary for fabrication. At the resonant

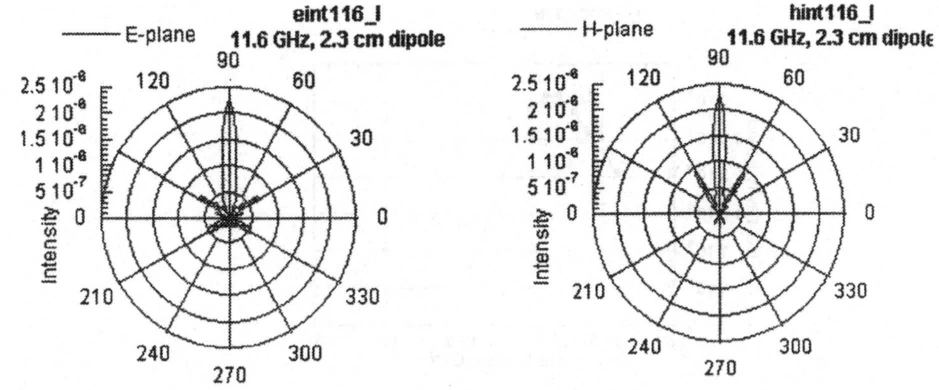

Fig. 3. Radiation pattern in the E-plane and H-plane for a dipole source placed inside a asymmetric cavity formed from creating a cavity between a 2-unit cell PBG and 3-unit cell PBG crystal. All the radsiation emerges in a narrow cone through the thinner (2-unit cell crystal).

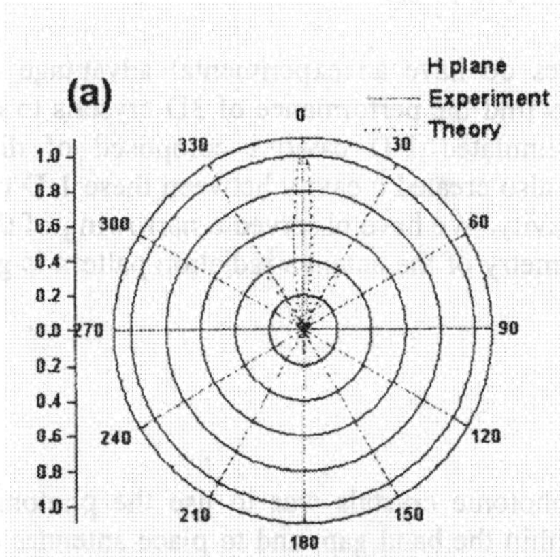

Fig. 4. Measured antenna radiation pattern from monople antenna placed inside asymmtric cavity of Fig. 1, along with the comparison with calculation.

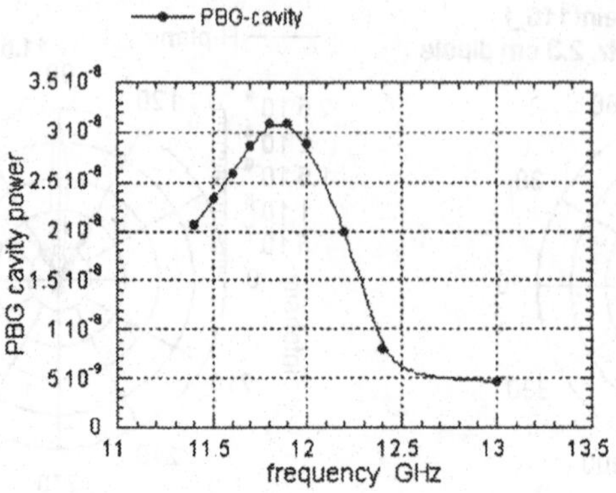

Fig. 5 Calculated output power of the dipole inside the asymmetric cavity as a function of the frequency. The dipole power is normalized with the radiation of a free dipole at each frequency.

frequency of their 1-D cavity they found a directive radiation pattern with the directivity of the structure increasing from 8 to 19 dB.

The simpler 1-D structures do have an experimental advantage of simplicity over 3-D structures. However we do find the performance of 3D crystals to be superior to their 1-D counterparts. We have simulated 1-D cavities composed of dielectric layers (n=3.1) separated by air. We have also created a cavity between these 1-D layers and have placed a dipole source within the cavity. We have observed a narrowing of the radiation pattern, but the directionality and symmetry of the antenna radiation pattern is generally inferior to that of the 3D crystal.

5. Discussion

The first application of photonic crystals was to use the photonic crystals as a perfect reflector at frequencies within the band gap, and to place antennas on the photonic crystal. When such antennas were driven at frequencies within the band gap all the power was radiated in the air side with no power emerging from the PBG side[6,10-12]. This cut down on the large power loss of antennas on semiconductor substrates, where most of the power (>90%) can be lost as substrate modes.

However the antennas on PBG substrates had patterns that were very sensitive to the height and lateral position of the antenna. This is because the antenna power depends on the local electric field at the substrate, that is very sensitive to both the lateral position and height of the antenna on the substrate.[6,11,12] In the present resonant antenna, the radiation patterns and gains are far superior to those achieved with antennas on the PBG crystals. The resonant antennas are also less sensitive to position within the cavity. However the band width of resonant antennas is less than the antennas on PBG substrates. Another promising approach is to integrate patch antennas on periodically textured metallic surfaces that have a band gap for surface modes. Such electromagnetic surfaces increase the gain and performance of patch antennas. [13-16]

The resonant cavities offer a practical way to test predictions expected in optical physics, with the antenna being the analog of an emitting atom. Uniquely directional high gain sources and detectors can be generated with this method.

6. Acknowledgements

We acknowledge Gary Tuttle and Costas Soukoulis for many helpful suggestions and discussions. Ames Laboratory is operated by the U.S. Department of Energy by Iowa State University under Contract No. W-7405-Eng-82. We also acknowledge support by the Department of Commerce through the Center of Advanced Technology Development (CATD) at Iowa State University.

References

1. For a review see C.M. Soukoulis, ed., *Photonic Band Gap Materials*, Proceedings NATO Advanced Study Institute (Kluwer, Dordrecht, 1996).
2. J. D. Joannopoulos, R.D. Meade, J.N. Winn, *Photonic Crystals: Molding the Flow of Light*, Princeton University Press (1995).
3. *Spontaneous Emission and Laser Oscillation in Microcavities*, edited by H. Yokohama and K. Ujihara, CRC Press, Boca Raton, 1995).
4. H. Yokohama, page 275 in Ref. 3; G. Bjork, and Y. Yokohama p. 189 in Ref. 3.
5. E. Ozbay *et al*, , Laser Micromachined millimeter wave photonic band gap structures *Appl. Phys. Lett.* **67**, 1969 (1995).
6. M. M. Sigalas, R. Biswas, Q. Li, D. Crouch, W. Leung, R. Jacobs-Woodbury, B. Lough, S. Nielsen, S. McCalmont, G. Tuttle, and K.-M. Ho, Dipole antennas on Photonic band gap crystals- experiment and simulation, *Microwave and Opt. Tech. Lett.* **15,** 153 (1997).
7. C. A. Balanis, *Antenna Theory, Analysis and Design* (Harper and Row, New York, 1982).
8. B. Temelkuran, M. Bayindir, E. Ozbay, R. Biswas, M. Sigalas, G. Tuttle, and K.-M. Ho, Photonic crystal based resonant antenna with a very high directivity, *J. Appl. Physics* **87**, 603 (2000).
9. M. Thevenot, C. Cheype, A. Reneix, B. Jecko, Directive photonic band gap antennas, *IEEE Transactions on Antennas and Propagation* **47**, 2115 (1999).

10. E. R. Brown and O. B. McMahon, High zenithal directivity from a dipole antenna on a photonic crystal, *Appl. Phys. Lett.* 68, 1300 (1994).
11. E. R. Brown, C. D. Parker, and E.J. Yablonovitch, Radiation properties of a planar antenna on a photonic crystal substrate, *J. Opt. Soc. Am. B* 10, 404 (1993).
12. M. P. Kesler, J. G. Maloney, B. L. Shirley, and G. S. Smith, Antenna design with the use of photonic band gap materials as all dielectric planar reflectors, *Microwave and Opt. Tech. Lett.* 11, 169 (1996).
13. D. Sievenpiper et al., High impedance electromagnetic surfaces with a forbidden frequency band, *IEEE Trans. On Microwave Theory and Techniques* 47, 2059 (1999).
14. J. D. Shumpert et al, Parallel platre mode reduction in conductor backed slots using electromagnetic bandgap structures, *IEEE Trans. on Microwave Theory and Techniques* 47, 2099 (1999).
15. R. Cocioli et al, Aperture-coupled patch antenna on UC-substrate, ibid 47, 2123 (1999).
16. R. Gonzalo et al, Enhanced patch-antenna performance by suppressing surface waves using photonic bandgap substrates, ibid 47, 2131 (1999).

INTENSE FOCUSING OF LIGHT USING METALS

JB PENDRY
The Blackett Laboratory, Imperial College
London SW7 2BZ, United Kingdom

1. Electron Plasmas and Negative ε

At optical frequencies the dielectric response of metals is dominated by the plasma like behaviour of the electron gas:

$$\varepsilon(\omega) = 1 - \frac{\omega_p^2}{\omega(\omega + i\gamma)}. \tag{1}$$

There is a characteristic plasma frequency which is the natural frequency of oscillation of the electron gas

$$\omega_p^2 = \frac{ne^2}{\varepsilon_0 m_e}. \tag{2}$$

Dissipation is introduced through the damping factor, γ, which in turn can be related to the conductivity of the metal if we assume that the same form persists to low frequencies,

$$\gamma = \sigma^{-1}\varepsilon_0. \tag{3}$$

It is customary to ignore the dependence of ε on wave vector, q, and this is a good approximation for many purposes. However in some circumstances, for example where we consider the response of nanostructures to light, we may have to worry about the short wavelength, large q behaviour of ε. One obvious cut-off length is the separation between electrons in the metal. Another might be the inelastic scattering length for electrons which is typically a few nanometres. The very short wavelength response of metals at optical frequencies has been studied in the electron microscope where losses at large momentum transfers can be measured.

Many of the most striking experiments are made on high conductivity metals such as silver where the following approximate formula describes the response,

$$\varepsilon \approx 5.7 - 9.0^2\omega^{-2} + 0.4i. \tag{4}$$

If we substitute into Maxwell's equations we obtain the following dispersion relationship for light in an ideal loss free metal,

$$q = \sqrt{\varepsilon}\,\omega c_0^{-1} = c_0^{-1}\sqrt{\omega^2 - \omega_p^2} \tag{5}$$

a result which is plotted in Figure 1.

C.M. Soukoulis (ed.), Photonic Crystals and Light Localization in the 21st Century, 329–349.

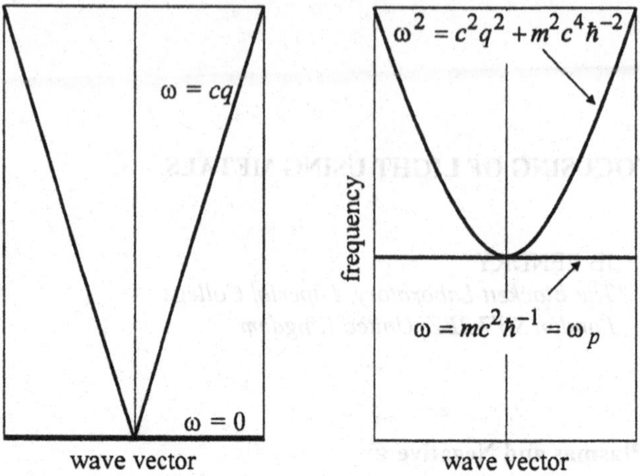

Figure 1. Dispersion of light in metals: Left: $\omega(q)$ for free space; right: for a perfect metal with no resistance.

Note that in a metal transverse light acquires a mass, and the longitudinal mode now has a finite frequency: the plasma frequency, ω_p. In the range $0 < \omega < \omega_p$, the dielectric function is negative and no modes are allowed in the bulk of the metal. This accounts for the fact that metals are extremely opaque at optical frequencies. It also accounts for the Meissner effect in a superconductor whereby a magnetic field, in fact any low frequency electromagnetic field, is expelled from the superconductor.

However, most striking for our purpose is the fact that ε in a metal is essentially negative below the plasma frequency. This fact is entirely responsible for the striking and unique optical properties of structured metals. First, we observe that if we take a flat metal surface there are solutions of Maxwell's equations, bound to the surface, known as surface plasmons [1]. At very short wavelength these are essentially electrostatic in nature. They decay exponentially into the bulk of the metal and into vacuum with exponent $|\mathbf{q_P}|$, where $\mathbf{q_P}$ is the wave vector parallel to the surface. The condition for their existence at a vacuum/ metal interface is,

$$\varepsilon(\omega) + 1 = 0, \tag{6}$$

which from (1) implies, if we neglect losses,

$$\omega_{sp} = \omega_p / \sqrt{2}, \tag{7}$$

where ω_{sp} is the surface plasma frequency. Every surface of a metal is decorated with surface plasmons and the more complex the surface geometry, the more complex the structure of the resulting surface plasma modes. Furthermore, although surface plasmons on a flat surface do not couple to externally incident radiation, more complicated surface geometries do result in coupling to external radiation and it is through this coupling that the rich response of metallic structures to light is generated.

A further point to note is that the surface modes extend down to wavelengths very much shorter than the wavelength of light in free space. The cut off to the surface plasma spectrum is essentially given by the average electron electron separation in the metal which is typically 0.1nm compared with a free space wavelength of a few hundred nm. The implication is that the density of surface modes is very large, perhaps a million times greater than the density of freely propagating modes.

Some insight into how negative ε can create surface modes, and the essentially resonant nature of these modes, can be had by considering the following simple analogy. Consider the capacitor/inductor circuit in Figure 2.

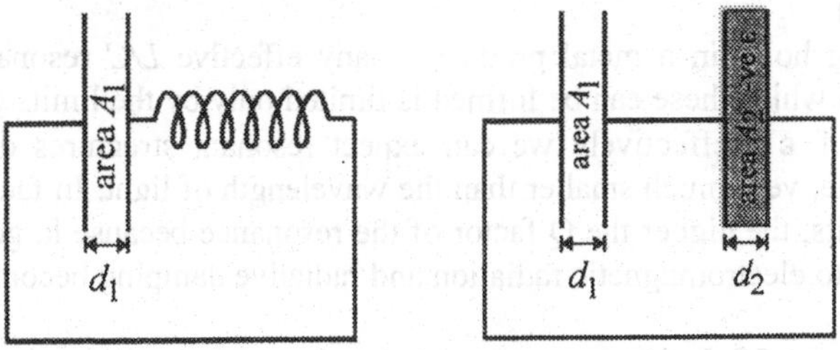

Figure 2. A capacitor and inductor form a resonant circuit, but a capacitor and a second capacitor may also form a resonant circuit if one is filled with negative ε material!

The capacitor and inductor resonate when,

$$Z_C + Z_L = \frac{1}{i\omega C_1} + i\omega L = 0 \tag{8}$$

and the capacitance is given in terms of the cross sectional area, A_1, and plate separation, d_1, by:

$$C_1 = \frac{\varepsilon_0 A_1}{d_1}. \tag{9}$$

Now consider a different circuit, shown on the right-hand side of Figure 2, in which the inductor is replace by a second capacitor. Normally we would regard such a circuit as non resonant and rather uninteresting, but suppose that the dielectric introduced into the second capacitor is in fact a plasma with ε given by (1):

$$C_2 = \frac{\varepsilon\varepsilon_0 A_2}{d_2} = \left(1 - \frac{\omega_p^2}{\omega^2}\right)\frac{\varepsilon_0 A_2}{d_2} \approx -\frac{\omega_p^2 \varepsilon_0 A_2}{\omega^2 d_2}, \quad \omega << \omega_p. \tag{10}$$

Hence, the effective impedance of the capacitor at low frequencies is,

$$Z_2 = \frac{1}{i\omega C_2} \approx \frac{-\omega d_2}{i\omega_p^2 \varepsilon_0 A_2} = i\omega L_2, \tag{11}$$

where,

$$L_2 = \frac{d_2}{\omega_p^2 \varepsilon_0 A_2}. \tag{12}$$

Thus a capacitor with a negative-dielectric filling appears to be an inductor and the circuit is in fact resonant at a frequency given by,

$$\frac{1}{i\omega C_1}+\frac{1}{i\omega C_2}=0=\frac{d_1}{i\omega\varepsilon_0 A_1}+\frac{d_2}{i\omega\varepsilon\varepsilon_0 A_2}.$$

If the two capacitors have the same area, then this is equivalent to the surface plasma condition given in (6).

Think of the internal surfaces of a metallic structure as capacitor plates and suppose that surfaces separated by metal now behave like inductors. This gives an idea of the complex resonances that arise within these structures. And negative ε is the central concept.

So cutting holes in a metal produces many effective *L/C* resonant circuits. The length scale on which these can be formed is limited only by the limits to validity of the plasma form of ε - effectively we can expect resonant structures down to the sub nanometre scale, very much smaller than the wavelength of light. In fact the smaller the effective circuits, the higher the Q factor of the resonance because large circuits couple more strongly to electromagnetic radiation and radiative damping becomes big.

Non-Uniqueness of Solutions

In the electrostatic limit, in the absence of external charges,

$$\nabla\cdot\mathbf{D}(\mathbf{r})=\nabla\cdot[\varepsilon(\mathbf{r})\nabla\phi(\mathbf{r})]=0. \tag{13}$$

It follows that

$$\int_V \varepsilon_0\varepsilon\mathbf{E}\cdot\mathbf{E}dV=0. \tag{14}$$

If ε is everywhere positive, then the implication is that,

$$\mathbf{E}=0,\quad \text{everywhere}. \tag{15}$$

However, if the volume contains a photonic metallic structure within which ε is alternately negative and positive in different parts of the structure, then the theorem no longer holds. *Metallic systems (negative ε) may support localised resonances.* This is yet another way to understand how the complexity of structured metallic systems arises. A good example of the activity of structured metals is governed by colloidal silver such as is found in exposed and developed photographic film. Solid silver is a highly reflective material, but the colloidal form is highly absorbing and appears black. The surface plasma resonances are responsible for this property.

The Focusing Effect is Due to Concentration in These Resonances

In the Raman effect, light is scattered from a molecule and simultaneously creates a vibrational excitation, see Figure 3. The Raman signal is proportional to the 4th power of the electric field at the molecule,

$$|\mathbf{E}_s|^4/|\mathbf{E}_0|^4, \tag{16}$$

where $\mathbf{E}_S$ is the field measure at the molecule and $\mathbf{E}_0$ is the field in free space. Therefore the Raman signal is a probe of local enhancement of the field. Various computational tools have been developed which are reviewed in [2]. Some early work by Francisco Garcia Vidal and myself [3] modelled a rough metal surface assuming a simple array of metal cylinders, diameter $2r$, lattice spacing d=20nm. The dielectric function of silver is modelled by (4).

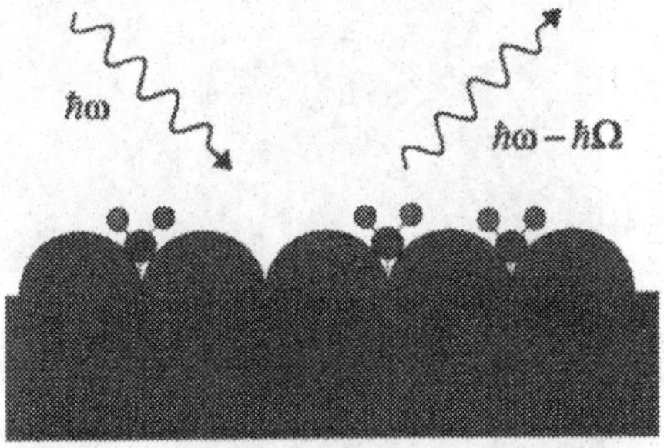

Figure 3. Our model of a rough surface: a chain of silver semi cylinders placed upon a silver slab with thickness l = 2R, where R is the radii of the semi cylinders. For the calculations shown in Figs. 4 and 5, $2R = l = 30$ nm and $d = 2R$.

As it happens the surface is particularly active when the cylinders just touch. It seems that crevices or spikes attract a high density of surface modes. In Figure 4 we see the electric field amplitude round the cylinder for normally incident radiation polarised so that the electric vector lies normal to the axes of the cylinders. Clearly, very strong enhancement is taking place. Local enhancement also occurs for isolated cylinders or spheres, but for an array of close packed cylinders the effect is much greater and occurs over a broad band of frequencies: something highly unusual for a resonant phenomenon.

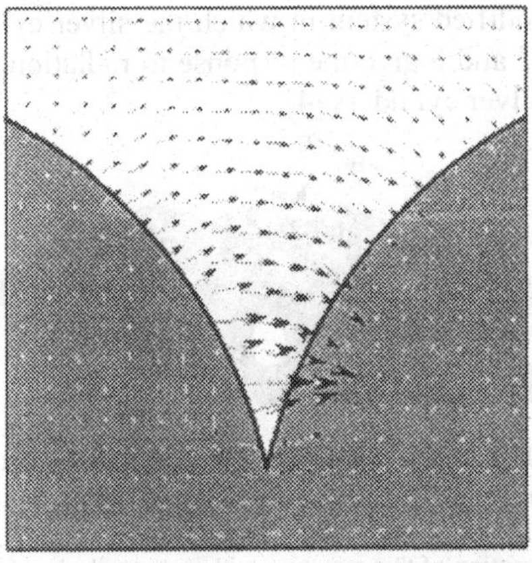

Figure 4. A picture of the **E** field generated by a normally incident plane wave at the frequency of maximum enhancement, 2.7 eV and for $2R = d = l = 30\text{nm}$: see the full curve in Fig. 5.

Figure 5 shows enhancement of the Raman signal as a function of wavelength. The broad band nature is apparent, a phenomenon explained by the fact that the enhancement comprises a whole series of overlapping mini resonances each on of which is individually very narrow but which taken together give the broad band effect. The magnitude of the enhancement is very great, rising to 10^8, which implies an energy density enhanced by 10^4 , just where the cylinders touch.

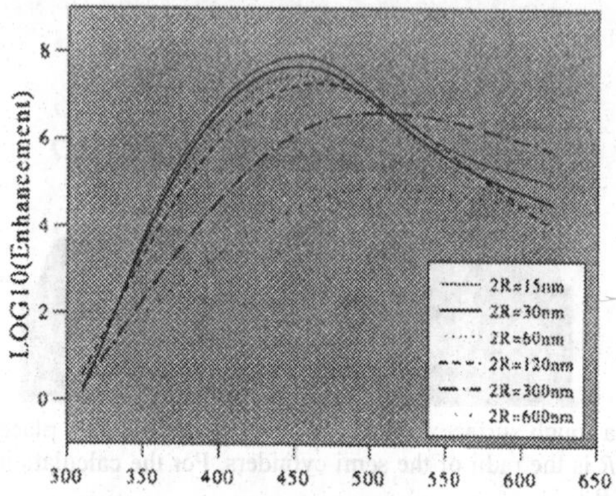

Figure 5. The local enhancement evaluated at the crevices between the semi cylinders shown in Fig. 3, for different values of the ratio $d/2R$, with $2R = d = 1 = 30\text{nm}$. The spacing between cylinders, *d*, varies from *2R* to 1.2*R*. In this regime the cylinders intersect and roughness of the surface decreases.

Note also the reduced enhancement in Figure 5 when the diameters of the cylinders become comparable to the wavelength of light in free space. Radiative coupling improves as the structures become larger and hence radiative damping of the resonances increases. To observe highly resonant metallic systems, dimensions must be kept well below the free space wavelength.

Figure 6 shows a modified system in which the silver cylinders have been coated with carbon and Figures 7 and 8 give the response to radiation corresponding to Figure 4 and 5 for the touching silver cylinders [4].

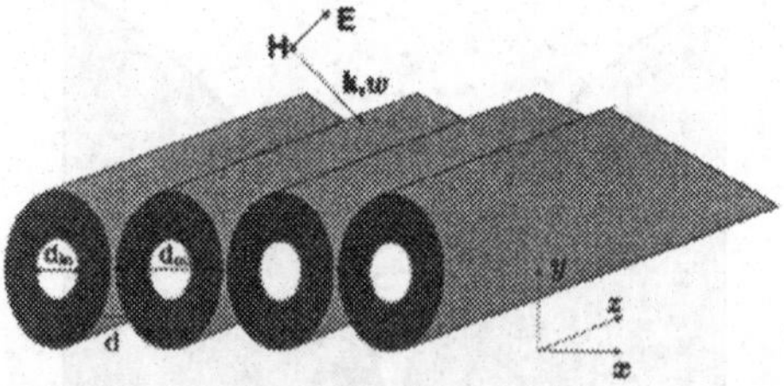

Figure 6. An array of Ag-filled carbon nanotubes: the cylinders of outer diameter $d_{out} = 10\text{nm}$ are infinitely long in the *z* direction and are distributed periodically in the *x* direction with a separation of $d = 10.3\text{nm}$. The inner core filled with silver will be varied between 3 and 9.5nm in our calculations. We study the electromagnetic interaction of this structure with a normally incident plane wave polarised with the electric field perpendicular to the axes of the cylinders.

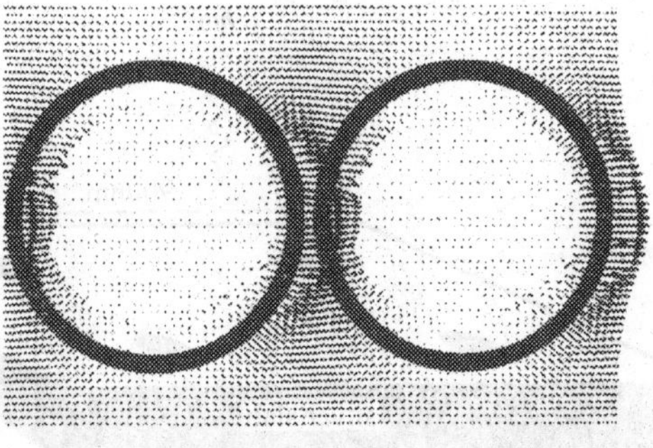

Figure 7. A detailed picture of the total **E** field generated by a normally incident plane wave impinging on the array of Ag-filled carbon nanotubes of Figure 6 with $d_{in} = 8\text{nm}$. The **E** field is evaluated at $\omega = 2.5\text{eV}$, the frequency at which the optical reflectance is minimum for this case. The total **E** field is shown for two unit cells of the array.

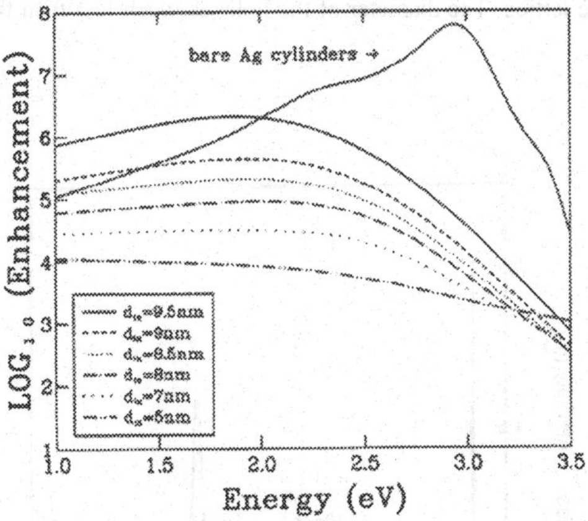

Figure 8. The local enhancement of the Raman signal evaluated at the region between the nanotubes, for different values of d_{in} and as a function of the energy of the incoming photon. The same quantity, as evaluated for bare Ag cylinders of diameter 9.5 nm and separated by 10.3 nm, is also shown.

The message of this calculation is that separating the cylinders considerably reduces the enhancement but still leaves a very large enhancement of the order of 10^6.

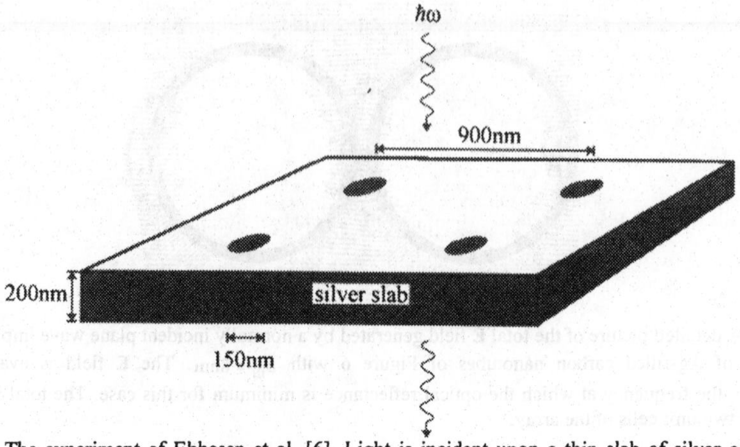

Figure 9. The experiment of Ebbesen et al. [6]. Light is incident upon a thin slab of silver containing holes arranged in a square lattice. The diameter of the holes is much less than the typical wavelength of light: 1000nm.

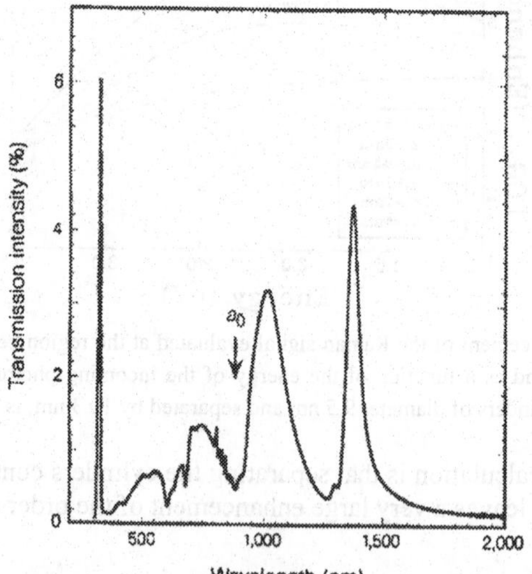

Figure 10. Zero order transmission spectrum measured by Ebbesen et al. [6] for the structure shown in Figure 9. a_0 is the spacing between the holes.

Another enhancement effect will be treated in greater detail by Francisco Garcia Vidal in his talk [5] so I mention it only briefly here. Figure 9 shows details of an experiment by Ebbesen et al. [6]. The important point is that the diameter of the holes is much smaller than the wavelength of light. Conventional theory for transmission through holes in an absorbing material predicts essentially zero transmission: the light cannot squeeze through such a tiny aperture. However once again metals prove that they do not obey the normal rules and in Figure 10 we show the results of Ebbesen's experiment. The transmitted intensity at around 5% rises to many times the expected value and theoretical calculations show that in principle, for an ideal system, the peak transmitted intensity may rise to 100%. This is yet another instance of metals focusing light into a confined space. In fact the intensity of light inside the holes is many orders of magnitude greater than in free space.

2. Artificial Plasmas

At all frequencies below ω_p the effective dielectric function is negative and the wave vector imaginary. Hence ω_p is a cut-off frequency. Many other unusual properties follow when epsilon is negative.

We have seen the remarkable effects created by structuring metals and observed that these depend on the negative ε property of the metal. Formula (1) for ε shows that for frequencies $\omega < \gamma$, resistive effects become dominant. Since typically,

$$\gamma \approx 0.1\text{eV}, \tag{17}$$

we do not expect to see materials with negative ε at microwave frequencies. This is a pity because it prevents us from exploiting all the enhancement and other tricks that we can use at optical frequencies. However, it turns out that we can design artificial materials for use at microwave frequencies, structured on a scale much less than the wavelength of radiation, which have an *effective* ε which is negative. One such structure is shown in Figure 11 [7].

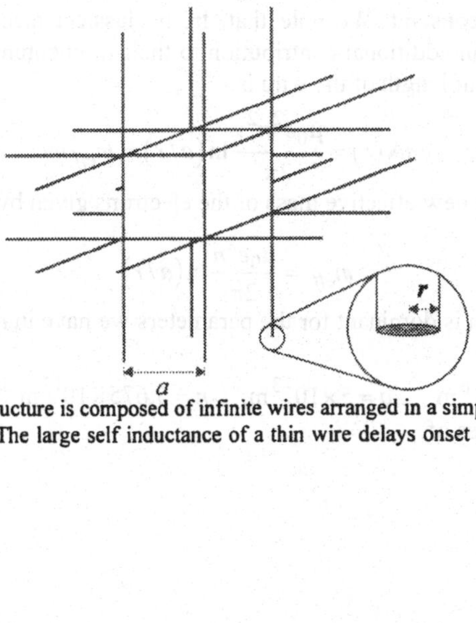

Figure 11. The periodic structure is composed of infinite wires arranged in a simple cubic lattice, joined at the corners of the lattice. The large self inductance of a thin wire delays onset of current mimicking the effect of electron mass.

It is possible to make a full solution of Maxwell's equations for this system but much more light is shed by a very simple calculation that gives the correct result to within 5%. Consider a displacement of electrons along one of the cubic axes: the active wires will be those directed along that axis. If the density of electrons in these wires is n, the density of these active electrons in the structure as a whole is given by the fraction of space occupied by the wire,

$$n_{eff} = n\frac{\pi r^2}{a^2}. \tag{18}$$

Before we rush to substitute this number into formula (1) for the plasma frequency, we must pause to consider another effect which is at least as important: any restoring force acting on the electrons will not only have to work against the rest mass of the electrons, but also against self-inductance of the wire structure. This effect is not present in the original calculation of the plasma frequency but in our structure it is the dominant effect. It can be represented as a contribution to the electron mass. The important point is that the inductance of a thin wire diverges logarithmically with the radius. Suppose a current I flows in the wire creating a magnetic field circling the wire,

$$H(R) = \frac{I}{2\pi R} = \frac{\pi r^2 ve}{2R}, \tag{19}$$

where R is distance from the wire's centre. We have also re-expressed the current in terms of electron velocity, v, and charge density, NE. We write the magnetic field in terms of a vector potential,

$$\mathbf{H}(R) = \mu_0^{-1}\nabla\times\mathbf{A}(R), \tag{20}$$

where,

$$A(R) = \frac{\mu_0 r^2 nve}{2}\ln(a/R), \tag{21}$$

and a is the lattice constant. We note that, from classical mechanics, electrons in a magnetic field have an additional contribution to their momentum of $e\mathbf{A}$, and therefore the momentum per unit length of the wire is,

$$en\mathbf{A}(r) = \frac{\mu_0 e^2 n^2 v}{2\pi}\ln(a/r) = m_{eff}nv, \tag{22}$$

where and m_{eff} is the new effective mass of the electrons given by,

$$m_{eff} = \frac{\mu_0 e^2 n}{2\pi}\ln(a/r). \tag{23}$$

This new contribution is dominant for the parameters we have in mind. For instance, for aluminium wires,

$$r = 1.0\times10^{-6}\,\text{m},\quad a = 5\times10^{-3}\,\text{m},\quad n = 5.675\times10^{17}\,\text{m}^{-3}\,\text{(aluminium)}, \tag{24}$$

gives an effective mass of,

$$m_{eff} = 2.4808\times10^{-26}kg$$
$$= 2.7233\times10^{4} m_e = 14.83 m_p \tag{25}$$

In other words, by confining electrons to thin wires we have enhanced their mass by four orders of magnitude so they are now as heavy as nitrogen atoms!

Having both the effective density, n_{eff}, and the effective mass, m_{eff}, we can substitute into (1),

$$\omega_p^2 = \frac{n_{eff} e^2}{\varepsilon_0 m_{eff}} = \frac{2\pi c_0^2}{a^2 \ln(a/r)} \approx [8.2GHz]^2 . \tag{26}$$

Here is the reduction in the plasma frequency promised.

Note in passing that although the new reduced plasma frequency can be expressed in terms of electron effective mass and charge, these microscopy quantities cancel, leaving a formula containing only macroscopic parameters of the system: wire radius and lattice spacing. It is possible to formulate this problem entirely in terms of inductance and capacitance of circuit elements. However, in doing so we miss the analogy with the microscopic plasmon.

One remaining worry: does electrical resistance in the wires swamp the effect? A more careful calculation including resistance gives the following expression for an effective dielectric function of the structure,

$$\varepsilon_{eff} = 1 - \frac{\omega_p^2}{\omega\left(\omega + \dfrac{i\varepsilon_0 a^2}{\pi r^2 \sigma}\right)}, \tag{27}$$

where σ is the conductivity of the metal. Typically for aluminium,

$$\sigma = 3.65\times10^{7}\,\Omega^{-1}\mathrm{m}^{-1} \text{ (aluminium)} \tag{28}$$

and,

$$\varepsilon_{eff} \approx 1 - \frac{\omega_p^2}{\omega(\omega + i\times 0.1\omega_p)} \text{ (aluminium)} \tag{29}$$

Thus our new plasmon is about as well-defined relative to its resonant frequency as the original plasmon.

This simple theory is confirmed by more detailed calculations, and also by experimental measurements on a system of wires. The measurements are shown in Figure 12 and the threshold for observing transmission compared to the onset of the real wave vector as predicted by theory. The agreement is excellent confirming our simple picture of the physical processes at work.

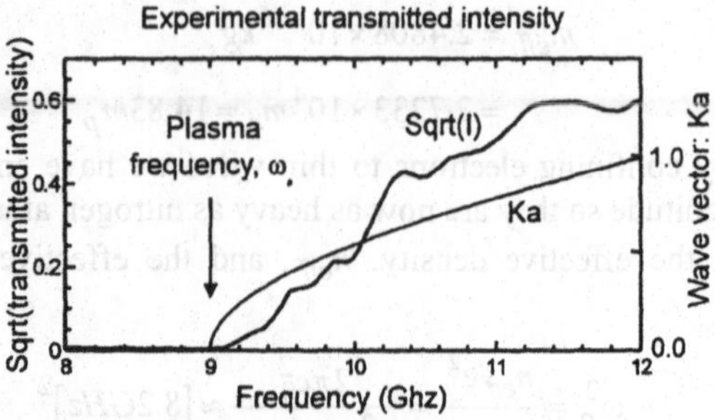

Figure 12. Experimental measurements of the transmitted amplitude (i.e., square root of the intensity) through 120mm of a dense photonic wire structure with a 5mm×5mm×6mm unit cell containing two sets of wires at right angles. Also shown is the theoretical plasma dispersion. Notice that the wave vector becomes real just as the experimental transmission coefficient begins to rise confirming theoretical predictions of the plasma frequency.

The theme of these lectures is enhancement of electromagnetic fields. A transverse wave, $\omega > \omega_p$, propagating through our structure gives a magnetic field close to the wires enhanced in intensity by $\approx 10^7$ over the free space value:

$$\frac{1}{2}\mu_0 H^2(r) \approx \left(\frac{a}{2r}\right)^2 \frac{1}{2}\mu_0 H^2\left(\frac{a}{2}\right) = 2.5\times10^7 \times \frac{1}{2}\mu_0 H^2\left(\frac{a}{2}\right) \tag{30}$$

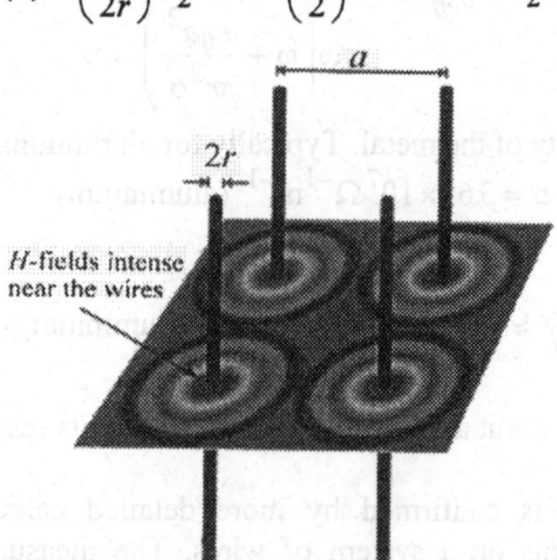

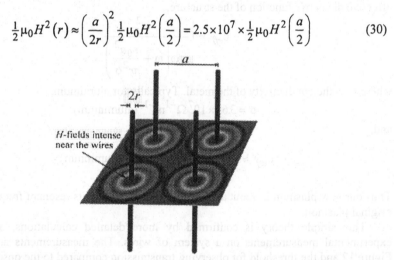

Figure 13. Distribution of magnetic fields around the thin wire conductors in our negative ε structure. Note the massive enhancement near the wires.

The enhanced magnetic fields in the vicinity of the wires is shown in Figure 13.

These enhanced magnetic fields can be exploited to modify the properties of the structure. For example, coating the wires even with a very thin layer of magnetic material will increase the mass enhancement of the electrons and lower the plasma frequency. If the magnetic material is non linear, it is possible to exploit this property in switching applications: a DC current in the wires would shift the plasma frequency and could be exploited to 'open' and 'shut' a window of frequencies on the microwave region. Alternatively, two beams of radiation may interact and scatter from one another.

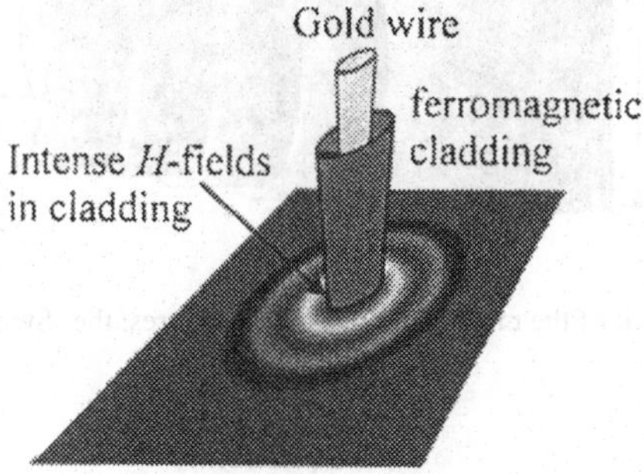

Figure 14. The enhanced magnetic field couples strongly to magnetic material placed close to the wire.

These wire structures show all the consequences of negative epsilon and some novel ones besides:

- Highly reflecting for $\omega < \omega_p$ - no modes below ω_p, therefore radiation is not allowed inside.
- The Meißner effect - at finite ω, $\gamma < \omega < \omega_p$, magnetic fields are expelled from the structure because there are no modes below ω_p - and even at $\omega = 0$ provided that the wires are superconducting, $\gamma = 0$.
- Surfaces of the composite support surface plasmon modes at $\omega_s = \omega_p / \sqrt{2}$.
- Strong effects are generated by a very small amount of metal: parts per million - c.f. doping of semiconductors.
- Heavy electrons implies very strong electron/**phonon** coupling - the lattice shakes violently as an em wave passes through it.
- A low frequency plasma mode implies very strong electron/**photon** coupling with applications to microwave devices, travelling wave tubes etcetera - electron beams passing through the voids essentially Cerenkov radiate into the plasmon modes.

3. Magnetism Without Magnets

Given the symmetry in Maxwell's equations between electric and magnetic field, it is natural to ask if we can engineer novel magnetic structures by analogy with the way we developed the wires structures. The challenge is: can we micro-engineer a structure entirely from non-magnetic metal that behaves as though it had macroscopic magnetic properties? The answer is yes we can [8]! Figures 15 through 17 show a magnetically active structure.

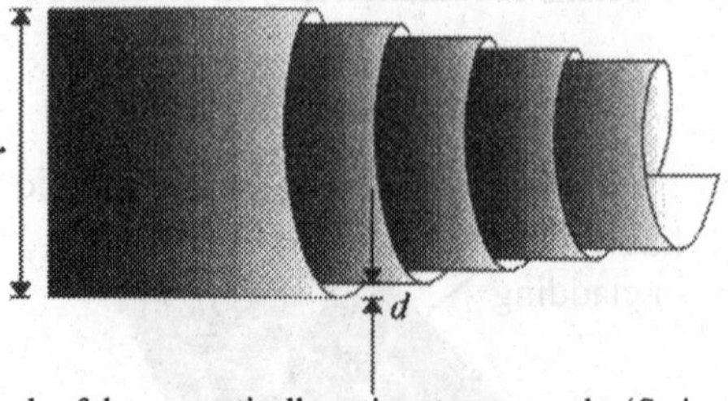

Figure 15. Basic building block of the magnetically active structures: the 'Swiss roll' comprising a coil of metal sheeting.

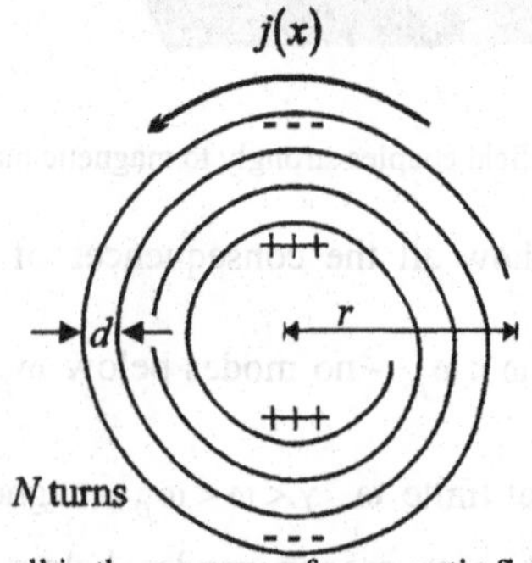

Figure 16. End view of the Swiss roll in the presence of a magnetic field: current flows only by virtue of the capacitance between layers.

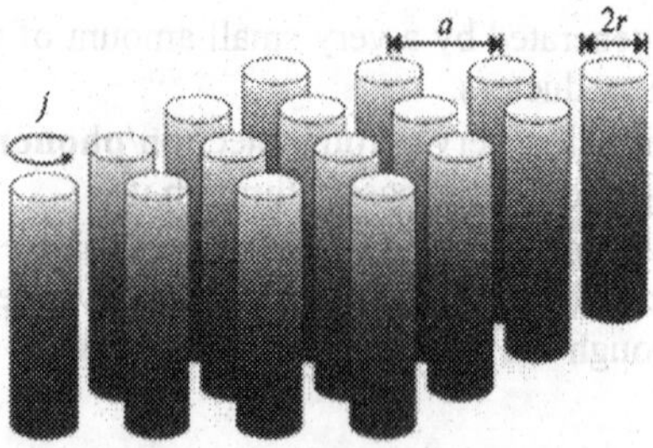

Figure 17. Making a 3D structure by stacking 'Swiss rolls'.

A magnetic penetrating to the interior of the roll induces currents around the coil which charge the capacitance acting between the two ends of the coil. This capacitance, together with the inductance of the coil, forms a resonant circuit. Just as a metal wire conducts electrons from one end to the other, so this structure appears to transmit magnetic monopoles: north poles appear at one end, south poles at the other. This is an illusion, of course, because there are no magnetic monopoles. The capacitance and inductance per unit length for an individual roll can easily be calculated, and hence the magnetic response. This, in turn, enables us to calculate the effective permeability of an array of rolls,

$$\mu_{eff} = 1 - \frac{\dfrac{\pi r^2}{a^2}}{1 + \dfrac{2Ri}{\omega r \mu_0 (N-1)} - \dfrac{d c_0^2}{2\pi^2 r^3 (N-1)\omega^2}}. \tag{31}$$

We choose the following parameters:

$$r = 2.0\times10^{-4}\,\text{m},\ a = 5.0\times10^{-4}\,\text{m},\ d = 1.0\times10^{-5}\,\text{m},\ N=3, \tag{32}$$

and a resistivity of the conducting sheets, $R = 2\Omega$.

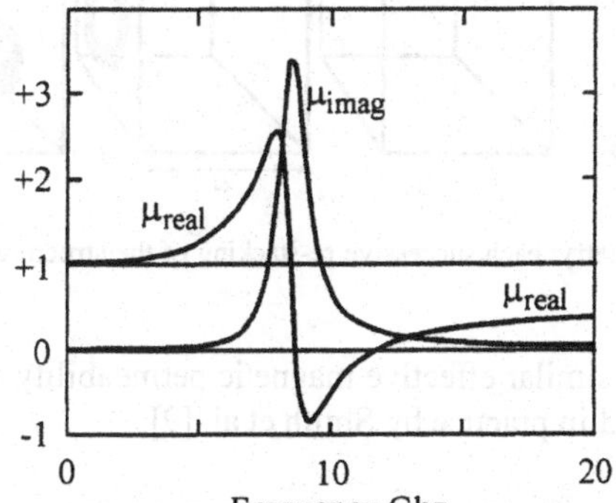

Figure 18. The effective magnetic permeability of an array of Swiss rolls calculated for the parameter values given in (31).

Figure 18 shows the resulting permeability. Characteristically it takes the form of a structure centred on the capacitance/inductance resonance of the individual rolls (essentially the peak in μ_{imag}). To the low frequency side of the resonance, a large positive enhancement is seen in μ_{imag}, and at high frequencies μ_{eff} is suppressed below unity to a value given by the fraction of the cross sectional area of the unit cell not filled by the Swiss roll. This filling fraction determines the 'activity' of the structure and the breadth and strength of the resonant region. For the structure we chose to present here, μ_{real} dips below zero. This signals the existence of a magnetic plasma oscillation in the bulk of the structure at this crossing frequency.

Another structure with similar philosophy and similar properties is the split ring structure shown in Figures 19 and 20.

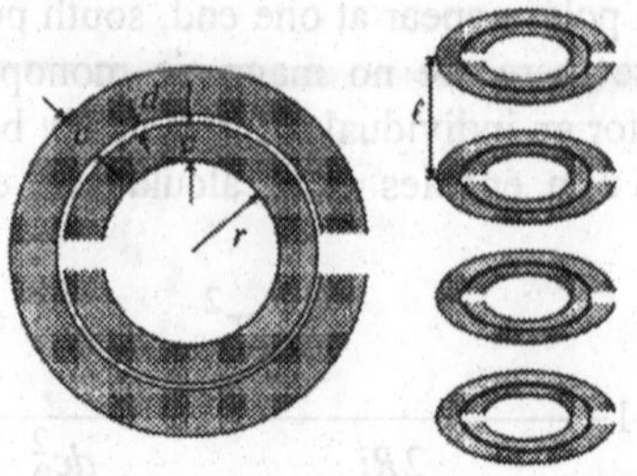

Figure 19. Left: a plan view of a split ring showing definitions of distances. Right a sequence of split rings shown in their stacking sequence. Each split ring comprises two thin sheets of metal.

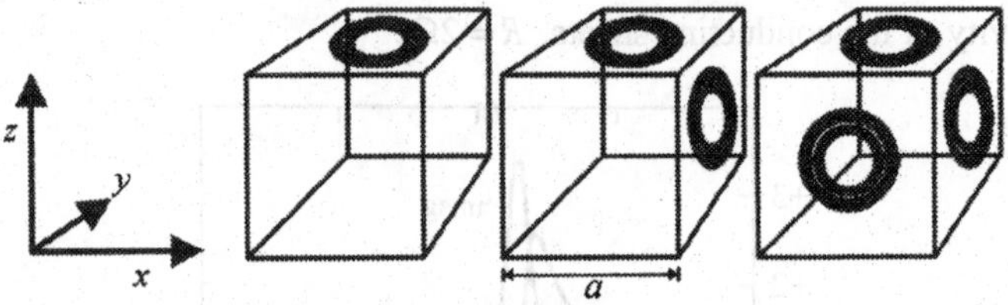

Figure 20. Building 3D symmetry: each successive re-stacking of the structure adds a ring to another side of the unit cell.

These structures display similar effective magnetic permeability to that shown in Figure 18 and have been realised in practice by Smith et al. [9].

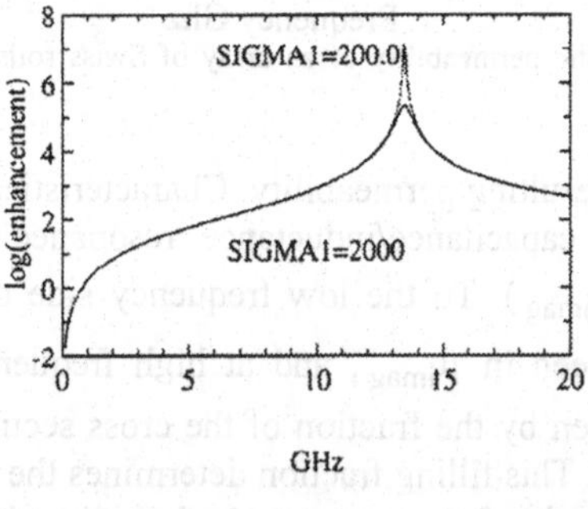

Figure 21. Enhancement of the energy density of the electric field within the gap between the split rings for two different values of the resistivity of the metal sheet: Upper curve for copper rings, $\sigma_1 = 200.0\Omega$; lower curve for more resistive rings, $\sigma_1 = 2000.0\Omega$.

Returning again to our theme of the concentration of fields, both the split ring and the Swiss roll structures show strongly enhanced electrical fields. In the case of the split ring, the magnetic field induces currents which charge the capacitance between inner and outer ring. Hence a large fraction of the electromagnetic energy is at some stage stored in the electric fields acting across this small gap. If we take some typical values,

$$r = 2.0mm, c = 1.0mm, d = 0.1mm, l = 10mm, \tag{33}$$

then we can calculate the enhancement of energy density in the electrical field at the mid point of the gap for some typical values of resistance on the rings. This particular structure shows a resonance around 13GHz. For example: a beam of microwaves at 13.41GHz with power flux of 10^4 watts-m^{-2} has an electric field strength of the order of $2\times10^3\,\mathrm{Vm}^{-1}$ in vacuo. If this beam were incident on, and entirely transmitted into, our magnetic structure, it would generate a field strength of the order of $10^7\,\mathrm{Vm}^{-1}$ in the space between the split rings, or of the order of $10^3\,\mathrm{V}$ between the edges of the two rings: more than enough to cause electrical breakdown in air! It is evident that these structures have considerable potential for enhancing non-linear phenomena. Furthermore, the non-linear medium need only be present in the small volume within which the energy is concentrated, opening the possibility of using small quantities of expensive material, and reducing any requirements of mechanical integrity that a larger structure would impose.

4. The Perfect Lens

We have shown how first the dielectric function and next the magnetic permeability can be negative. Smith and Schultz first combined these two attributes in the single structure. If both ε and μ are negative, the result is a medium with a refractive index, $n = \sqrt{\varepsilon\mu}$, that is negative. This work will be described elsewhere at this meeting. The reader is referred to David Smith's paper [9] and to an earlier paper by Veselago [10]. Smith and Schultz went on to point out that such a negative refractive index medium would focus light because light is bent to a negative angle with the surface normal by refraction: (see Figure 22).

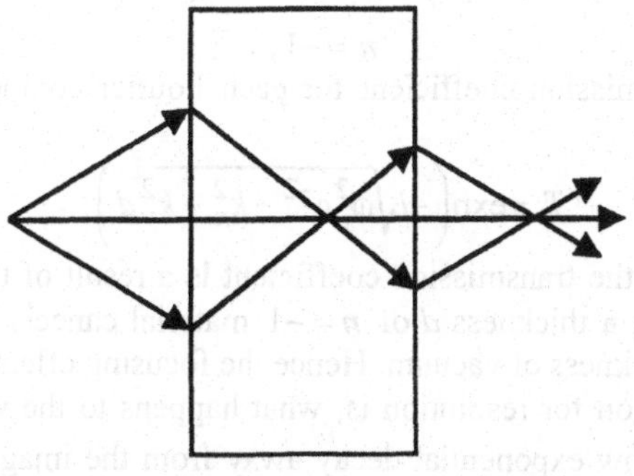

Figure 22. A negative refractive index medium bends light to a negative angle with the surface normal. Light formerly diverging from a point source is set in reverse and converges back to a point. Released from the medium, the light reaches a focus for a second time.

Recently my group has realised that this system can in fact bring light to a perfect focus unlimited by the constraints of free space wavelength [11]. First, let us look more closely at the reasons for limitation in performance of a conventional lens. Consider an infinitesimal dipole of frequency ω in front of a lens. The electric component of the field will be given by some 2D Fourier expansion,

$$\mathbf{E}(\mathbf{r},t) = \sum_{\sigma,k_x,k_y} \mathbf{E}_\sigma\left(k_x,k_y\right)\exp\left(ik_z z + ik_x x + ik_y y - i\omega t\right), \tag{34}$$

where we choose the axis of the lens to be the z-axis. Maxwell's equations tell us that,

$$k_z = +\sqrt{\omega^2 c^{-2} - k_x^2 - k_y^2}, \quad \omega^2 c^{-2} > k_x^2 + k_y^2, \tag{35}$$

The function of the lens is to apply a phase correction to each of the Fourier components so that at some distance beyond the lens the fields reassemble to a focus and an image of the dipole source appears. Except that something is missing: for larger values of the transverse wave vector,

$$k_z = +i\sqrt{k_x^2 + k_y^2 - \omega^2 c^{-2}}, \quad \omega^2 c^{-2} < k_x^2 + k_y^2, \tag{36}$$

these evanescent waves decay exponentially with z and no phase correction will restore them to their proper amplitude. They are effectively removed from the image which generally comprises only the propagating waves. Since the propagating waves are limited to,

$$k_x^2 + k_y^2 < \omega^2 c^{-2}, \tag{37}$$

the maximum resolution in the image can never be greater than,

$$\Delta \approx \frac{2\pi}{k_{\max}} = \frac{2\pi c}{\omega} = \lambda, \tag{38}$$

and this is true no matter how perfect the lens and how large the aperture.

Now let us ask what it is about the slab of negative refractive index material that enables it to focus light. Assuming for simplicity that,

$$\varepsilon = -1 \text{ and } \mu = -1, \tag{39}$$

so that,

$$n = -1, \tag{40}$$

we calculate the transmission coefficient for each Fourier component as described in (34),

$$T = \exp\left(-i\sqrt{\omega^2 c^{-2} - k_x^2 - k_y^2}\, d\right). \tag{41}$$

The negative phase of the transmission coefficient is a result of the negative refractive index. Thus, traversing a thickness d of $n = -1$ material cancels the phase acquired in traversing an equal thickness of vacuum. Hence the focusing effect of the new medium.

The crucial question for resolution is, what happens to the waves with very large k_P? They normally show exponential decay away from the image as described above. Let us calculate the transmission coefficient of the slab for these waves. It works out to be,

$$\lim_{\substack{\varepsilon\to-1\\ \mu\to-1}} T_P = \lim_{\substack{\varepsilon\to-1\\ \mu\to-1}} \frac{2\varepsilon k_z}{\varepsilon k_z + k_z'} \frac{2k_z'}{k_z' + \varepsilon k_z} \frac{\exp\left(ik_z'd\right)}{1-\left(\dfrac{k_z'-\varepsilon k_z}{k_z'+\varepsilon k_z}\right)^2 \exp\left(2ik_z'd\right)} \tag{42}$$

$$= \exp\left(-ik_z d\right).$$

Remember that in this calculation, k_z is imaginary. For exponentially decaying waves, a medium with $n=-1$ cancels the exponential decay experienced in the vacuum and restores the amplitude to its original value. This double function of the medium: restoration of both the *phase* and the *amplitude*, means that all the original components of the object's wavefunction are brought together so that a precise and perfect reconstruction of the object is made in the image plane. This is the ideal. In practice resistive losses in the medium will make reconstruction less than perfect but still possibly better than a wavelength limited lens.

There is a further intriguing possibility of realising this superlens. We have given above a general prescription for a superlens. However, if we are willing to accept a few limitations then life becomes much easier. Imagine that we want to use visible radiation to make an image of a very small object which is much smaller than the wavelength of light, but that the distance between object and image is also very small. Under these circumstances all the Fourier components of the image satisfy,

$$k_P >> \omega c_0^{-1} \tag{43}$$

so that,

$$k_z = i\sqrt{k_x^2 + k_y^2 - \omega^2 c^{-2}} \approx i\sqrt{k_x^2 + k_y^2} \tag{44}$$

and,

$$k_z' = i\sqrt{k_x^2 + k_y^2 - \varepsilon\mu\omega^2 c^{-2}} \approx i\sqrt{k_x^2 + k_y^2} \tag{45}$$

so that,

$$\lim_{k_P >> \omega c_0^{-1}} T_P = \lim_{k_P >> \omega c_0^{-1}} \frac{2\varepsilon k_z}{\varepsilon k_z + k_z'} \frac{2k_z'}{k_z' + \varepsilon k_z} \frac{\exp\left(ik_z'd\right)}{1-\left(\dfrac{k_z'-\varepsilon k_z}{k_z'+\varepsilon k_z}\right)^2 \exp\left(2ik_z'd\right)} \tag{46}$$

$$= \frac{4\varepsilon \exp\left(-k_P d\right)}{(1+\varepsilon)^2 - (1-\varepsilon)^2 \exp\left(-2k_P d\right)}.$$

Hence the transmission coefficient for P polarised waves of very short wavelength depends only on ε and not at all on μ. Therefore I propose that we use a slab of dielectric with radiation tuned to the condition,

$$\varepsilon = -1. \tag{47}$$

Then we have,

$$\lim_{\substack{\varepsilon\to -1 \\ k_P \gg \omega c_0^{-1}}} T_P = \lim_{\varepsilon\to -1} \frac{4\varepsilon\exp(-k_P d)}{(1+\varepsilon)^2-(1-\varepsilon)^2\exp(-2k_P d)} = \exp(+k_P d) \tag{48}$$

and the slab of dielectric cancels the exponential decay of the vacuum. We note that (47) is also exactly the condition for the existence of a surface plasmon and therefore in this limit image formation can be said to be surface plasmon assisted.

If we use a slab of silver, the best approximation we can get to (47) is,

$$\varepsilon = -1 + 0.4i. \tag{49}$$

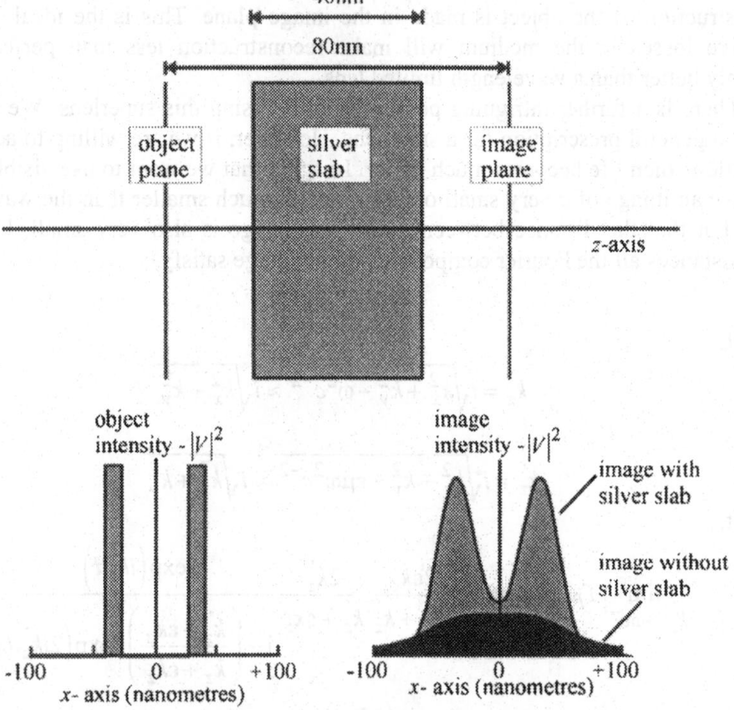

Figure 23. Top: plan view of the new lens in operation. A quasi-electrostatic potential in the object plane is imaged by the action of a silver lens. Bottom: The electrostatic field in the object plane is shown on the left. On the right is the electrostatic field in the image plane with and without the silver slab in place. The reconstruction would be perfect were it not for finite absorption in the silver.

Figure 23 shows a simulation of this result using the approximate dielectric function of silver. The image is less than perfect due to the finite electrical resistance present even in silver. Nevertheless considerable focusing is apparent.

We conclude that the minus sign, whether it appears in ε, μ, or n, has remarkable consequences for the electromagnetic properties of the materials concerned. Perhaps the most notable of these is the occurrence of strong focusing effects which vary in nature from resonant interactions with incoming radiation, to squeezing of light through small apertures, to our final example of the superlens. I am sure that I have not exhausted the possibilities in these lectures!

5. References

1. R.H. Ritchie, *Phys. Rev.*, **106,** 874 (1957).
2. J.B. Pendry, *J. Phys.* [Condensed Matter] **8** 1085-1108 (1996); A.J. Ward and J.B. Pendry *Phys. Rev.* **B58,** 7252-9 (1998); A.J. Ward and J.B. Pendry, *Comp. Physics Comm.* **112,** 23 (1998); J.B. Pendry and P.M. Bell: 'Transfer Matrix Techniques for Electromagnetic Waves' in *Photonic Band Gap Materials* NATO ASI series ed. C.M. Soukoulis (Kluwer, Dordrecht, 1996)
3. F.J. Garcia Vidal and J.B. Pendry, *Phys. Rev. Lett.* **77,** 1163 (1996).
4. F.J. Garcia Vidal, J.M. Pitarke, and J.B. Pendry, *Phys. Rev.* **B58,** 6783 (1998).
5. J.A. Porto, F.J. Garcia Vidal, and J.B. Pendry, *Phys. Rev. Lett.* **83,** 2845 (1999).
6. T. W. Ebbesen *et al., Nature* (London) **391,** 667 (1998).
7. D.F. Sievenpiper M.E. Sickmiller, and E. Yablonovitch, *Phys. Rev. Lett.*, **76,** 2480 (1996); J.B. Pendry, A.J. Holden, W.J. Stewart, and I. Youngs, *Phys. Rev. Lett.* **76,** 4773 (1996); J.B. Pendry, A.J. Holden, D.J. Robbins, and W.J. Stewart, *J. Phys.* [Condensed Matter] **10,** 4785 (1998).
8. J.B. Pendry, A.J. Holden, D.J. Robbins, and W.J. Stewart, *IEEE Transactions on Microwave Theory and Techniques* **47**, 2075 (1999).
9. D. R. Smith, Willie J. Padilla, D. C. Vier, S. C. Nemat-Nasser, and S. Schultz, *Phys. Rev. Lett.* **84,** 4184 (2000).
10. V.G. Veselago, *Soviet Physics USPEKHI* **10**, 509 (1968).
11. J.B. Pendry, submitted to *Phys. Rev. Lett.* (2000).

LEFT-HANDED METAMATERIALS

D. R. SMITH, W. J. PADILLA, D. C. VIER, R. SHELBY,
S. C. NEMAT-NASSER, N. KROLL, S. SCHULTZ
Department of Physics, University of California, San Diego
9500 Gilman Drive, La Jolla, California, 92093-0319, USA

The response of a material to electromagnetic radiation can be entirely characterized by the *material parameters*: the electrical permittivity, or ε, and the magnetic permeability, or μ. The range of possible values for the material parameters, as dictated by fundamental considerations such as causality or thermodynamics, extends beyond that found in naturally occurring materials. We thus seek to extend the material parameter space by creating electromagnetic *metamaterials*—ordered composite materials that display electromagnetic properties beyond those found in naturally occurring materials. Recently, we have demonstrated a metamaterial made of a repeated lattice of conducting, nonmagnetic elements that exhibits an effective μ and an effective ε, both of which are simultaneously negative over a band of frequencies [1]. Such a medium has been termed *Left-Handed* [2], as the electric field (**E**), magnetic intensity (**H**) and propagation vector (**k**) are related by a left-hand rule. We introduce the reader to the expected properties predicted by Maxwell's equations for Left-Handed media, and describe our recent numerical and experimental work in developing and analyzing this new metamaterial.

1. Electrodynamic Metamaterials

The term *Photonic Band Gap* (PBG) structure has come to refer to a periodic arrangement of dielectric or metallic scatterers, generally characterized by a gap or partial gap in the spectrum of propagating electromagnetic modes [3,4]. While this describes a very general structure, PBG has come to be more specifically understood as the optical (or electromagnetic) analogy to electrons in solids, with most of the band structure concepts and analytical techniques associated with solid state physics being carried over to PBG analysis. PBG structures are thus most often thought of as periodic structures possessing gaps in propagating modes due to *Bragg reflection*, when the wavelength of radiation is on the order of the spacing between the periodic scatterers.

When the wavelength of the incident radiation is much larger than the size and spacing of a collection of scatterers, the response of the scatterers to the incident fields can be treated by *effective medium theory* [5]. While the techniques of PBG analysis can be applied in the effective medium limit—and indeed we apply those techniques in the work reported here—it is expected that in the long wavelength limit, simpler, perhaps even analytic, descriptions will suffice to describe wave propagation.

C.M. Soukoulis (ed.), Photonic Crystals and Light Localization in the 21st Century, 351–371.

Both the PBG analysis and effective medium theory have as a common goal the solution of Maxwell's equations for electromagnetic fields, possibly in the presence of currents and charges. At a fundamental level, all known electromagnetic wave phenomena associated with a medium can be understood by determining self-consistently the electric field **E**, the magnetic induction **B**, and the responding current and charge densities (**j** and ρ, respectively). Such a description, however, is inconvenient and entirely unnecessary when the constituent current and charge densities vary on a scale much smaller than the scale of variation of the applied fields. It is therefore common practice under these conditions to replace the *microscopic* form of Maxwell's equations with a *macroscopic* form that includes, in an averaging sense, the electromagnetic properties of the medium [6].

The result of the averaging process is to introduce two auxiliary fields: **D**, the electric displacement, and **H**, the magnetic intensity. Maxwell's equations in the presence of responding media then take the form (in MKS, or SI, units)

$$\nabla\times\mathbf{E} = -\frac{\partial\mathbf{B}}{\partial t} \qquad \nabla\cdot\mathbf{D} = 0$$
$$\nabla\times\mathbf{H} = \frac{\partial\mathbf{D}}{\partial t} \qquad \nabla\cdot\mathbf{B} = 0 \qquad (1)$$

In order to solve these equations, it is necessary to assume two further relations between the field quantities. As we will be concerned with linear media here, we assume the four fields are related by the following:

$$\mathbf{B} = \mu(\omega)\mathbf{H} \qquad \mathbf{D} = \varepsilon(\omega)\mathbf{E}, \qquad (2)$$

where μ is the *magnetic permeability* and ε is the *electric permittivity*. The detailed properties of a medium's electromagnetic response are thus contained in μ and ε, which we refer to here as the *material parameters*. While the underlying composition of a material may be very complicated, being composed of arrangements of atoms, molecules or structured elements providing responding currents and fields, we need only determine μ and ε to have a complete description accurate for electrodynamic wave propagation.

Since the possible values (and spatial/frequency dependence) associated with the material parameters determine the range of behavior of electromagnetic wave propagation in media, it is reasonable to consider what possible values are available in naturally occurring materials. If we take a practical approach and survey the properties of materials as tabulated in various handbooks or other published reports, we find that values for the material parameters appear to have restrictions, dependent on the frequency range. Large positive values for the permittivity, for example, are found in many insulating materials at low frequencies (GHz and below). At higher frequencies, such as infrared and optical, the electrical response from insulators starts to tail off; however, conductors display a wide range of electric response at high frequencies, including negative values of the permittivity near and below the plasma frequency.

The possible values for the permeability in naturally occurring materials are much more restricted than those associated with the permittivity. The basis for this difference is the lack of a magnetic charge (or magnetic monopole) analogous to the electric charge—the entity responsible for the large electric response in dielectric materials. At DC and very low frequencies, inherently magnetic materials (i.e., materials possessing spin) can exhibit a wide range of permeability values. These effects diminish rapidly, however, at higher frequencies, where for most known materials $\mu(\omega)$ is positive, and always very close to unity. Negative values of $\mu(\omega)$ in particular are not found, although the magnetic susceptibility is frequently found to be less than zero (diamagnetism).

Although we find empirically that the set of values for the material parameters appears to be restricted, we may ask the question: are there fundamental limits on ε and μ, and if so, what are they?

If we restrict our attention to passive, linear media, the only constraints on the material parameters appear to be those set by causality. An analysis of the general analytic properties of ε and μ leads to the following conclusions [7]:

1. $\varepsilon_r(\omega)$ and $\mu_r(\omega)$ tend to unity for large ω.
2. $d(\omega\varepsilon_r(\omega))/d\omega>1$ and $d(\omega\mu_r(\omega))/d\omega>1$.

Note that we have introduced the relative material parameters $\varepsilon_r(\omega)=\varepsilon(\omega)/\varepsilon_0$, and $\mu_r(\omega)=\mu(\omega)/\mu_0$; in the rest of this paper, we will always be referring to the relative material parameters, without writing the 'r' subscript.

The first point above is a statement that, beyond some frequency all materials stop responding; however, the statement is a mathematical one, with 'large ω' having the same meaning as 'ω approaches infinity.' The second point is that a pair of relations, derived from a Kramers-Kronig analysis, places the only restriction on the frequency dispersion characteristics of the material parameters. In particular, the relations show that negative values for either of the material parameters are possible when there is sufficient frequency dispersion. Thus, while we do not find naturally occurring materials with negative permeability, causality does not preclude the occurrence. In fact, since the constraints set by causality on either ε or μ are identical, we might conclude that the same range of values observed for the permittivity in dielectric materials is possible also for the permeability.

We can therefore hope to gain access to a broader range of material parameters by creating heterogeneous structured composites that have electromagnetic properties differing from the inherent properties of the constituent materials or elements. Such composites have been termed *metamaterials* [8]. Electromagnetic metamaterials, which may offer additional advantages in other physical properties such as strength, elasticity or heat conduction, possess unique electromagnetic attributes that can be entirely encapsulated in the *effective* material parameters ε_{eff} and μ_{eff}. Note that in this context, the structured composites are not required to be periodic, as the wavelengths of interest are much larger than any length scale associated with the medium. This is in contrast to PBG systems, which rely on periodicity to produce band edges and stop bands, and which can be very sensitive to even minor amounts of disorder [9].

There are a variety of materials from which to construct electromagnetic metamaterials, but conductors are particularly good candidates because of their innate strong response to electromagnetic fields. By arranging conducting scatterers in various configurations, a broad range of electromagnetic responses can be achieved that can be characterized by effective material parameters. Alternatively, it is also possible to apply circuit models to analyze conducting scatterers—which, after all, behave as resistors, capacitors, or inductors—and derive an equivalence between the material and lumped circuit parameters. This approach has led, for example, to the use of periodic wire structures as circuit analogs for microwave propagation through the ionosphere [10-11], or arrays of resonant split rings to display an enhanced permeability response [12]. More recently, arrays of conducting elements have been used in applications from high-energy accelerator cavities [13] to high-impedance antenna substrates [14,15]. It is thus not surprising that the metamaterial we discuss here owes its unique properties to the presence of metal scattering elements, and that this metamaterial exhibits a combination of effective material parameters unlike any found in naturally occurring materials!

2. Left-Handed Media

In 1999, Pendry *et al.* suggested that certain configurations of nonmagnetic conducting elements would have a very strong *magnetic* response to applied electromagnetic fields [16]. In particular, Pendry *et al.* predicted that these configurations could have a *negative* effective permeability over a finite frequency range. As mentioned in Section 1, the magnetic response of naturally occurring materials known to us tails off rapidly with increasing frequency, and in particular is never found to be negative (at least without accompanying large losses). In contrast, if the conducting elements described by Pendry *et al.* were embedded into some structurally robust host material (e.g., polymer or ceramic), the resulting material could be classified as a metamaterial, having a magnetic response not available by other means. Indeed, Pendry *et al.* suggested a variety of uses for such a metamaterial, including magnetic shielding.

Professor Pendry presented the magnetic structures in 1999 at the Workshop on Electromagnetic Crystal Structures, held in Laguna Beach, California. We became very interested in the experimental demonstration of the magnetic structures, as we felt having the ability to tune the magnetic properties of a surface would be of great significance. To illustrate why a tunable permeability might be of importance, we recall that the reflection coefficient of a wave from a surface has the form

$$r=\frac{\sqrt{\dfrac{\varepsilon_1}{\mu_1}}\cos\theta_R-\sqrt{\dfrac{\varepsilon_2}{\mu_2}}\sqrt{1-\left(\dfrac{n_1}{n_2}\right)^2\sin^2\theta_R}}{\sqrt{\dfrac{\varepsilon_1}{\mu_1}}\cos\theta_R+\sqrt{\dfrac{\varepsilon_2}{\mu_2}}\sqrt{1-\left(\dfrac{n_1}{n_2}\right)^2\sin^2\theta_R}} \qquad (3)$$

for the electric field perpendicular to the plane of incidence (exchange ε and μ for electric field parallel to the plane of incidence) [17]. The possibility to "match" waves normally incident ($\theta_R=0$) from medium 1 to the surface of medium 2 is increased by having control over the permeability of the second layer, as there is no reflection for normal

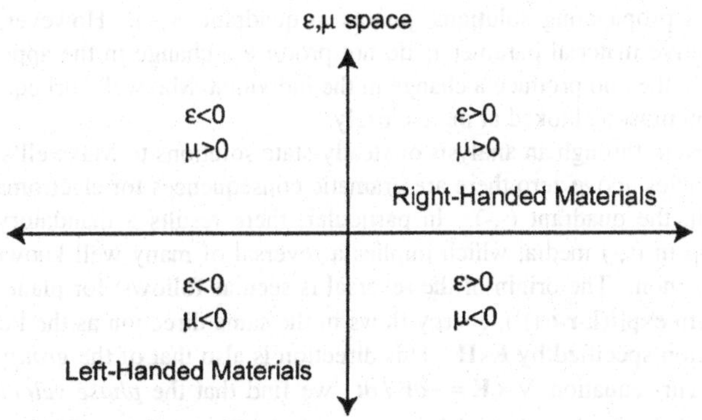

Figure 1. Material parameter space can be conveniently visualized on a set of (ε,μ) axes. Materials which posses a positive permeability are represented by points in the upper half plane.

incidence when $\sqrt{\varepsilon/\mu}$ is the same for both media. For waves incident from other angles, the reflectance can at least be minimized by matching impedance, provided the indices of refraction are also similar in magnitude between the two media.

While fabricating the proposed magnetic structures for testing was not a difficult task, unambiguously characterizing the observed scattering behavior as being due distinctly to an inherent permeability represented a challenge. As we initiated a program to construct and characterize test models of the magnetic metamaterial, we realized that the simplest means of demonstrating the negative magnetic permeability was to combine a negative permittivity medium with the magnetic medium and observe the effect of the composite medium on wave propagation. These experimental and computational details are described in Section 4; however, we first describe generally the propagation properties of a medium that has simultaneously negative material constants. This analysis was first carried out in an early paper by V. G. Veselago, who termed such materials *Left-Handed* [2], and this section paraphrases the contents of that paper.

Consider the chart in Figure 1, which depicts the various regimes of electromagnetic wave propagation in nearly transparent (low loss) materials for all possible values of $\mu(\omega)$ and $\varepsilon(\omega)$. In what follows we will refer to pairs of algebraic signs to indicate the real parts of $\mu(\omega)$ and $\varepsilon(\omega)$ for any possible material. Thus (+,+) indicates the first quadrant, (+,-) the second quadrant, and so on. Naturally occurring materials generally appear in the upper half plane, where $\mu>0$. In quadrant (+,+), the product of $\mu(\omega)\varepsilon(\omega)$ is positive, and the wavevector $k = n\omega/c$ is real [$n(\omega) = \sqrt{\varepsilon(\omega)\mu(\omega)}$]. Plane wave electromagnetic solutions, which have an e^{inkx} dependence, are thus propagating. In quadrant (+,-) the product $\mu(\omega)\varepsilon(\omega)$ is negative, and the index of refraction, being the square root of a negative number, leads to a pure imaginary k-value. An imaginary k implies an evanescent wave, or a wave in which field amplitudes decay exponentially.

If we had access to materials with $\mu<0$, the lower half-plane in Figure 1 would be accessible. At first glance, this might seem an uninteresting detail, as the wave equation is symmetric in ε and μ. Thus, in quadrant (-,+) we find a negative product of $\mu(\omega)\varepsilon(\omega)$, and k values are pure imaginary as in quadrant (+,-). And, in quadrant (-,-), the positive product $\mu\varepsilon$ indicates propagating solutions, just as in quadrant (+,+). However, while simultaneously negative material parameters do not produce a change in the appearance of the wave equation, they do produce a change in the individual Maxwell curl equations, and thus the situation must be looked at more closely.

Veselago showed, through an analysis of steady-state solutions to Maxwell's Equations, that at frequencies above zero there are dramatic consequences for electromagnetic wave propagation in the quadrant (-,-). In particular, there results a mandatory "left-handed" relationship in (-,-) media, which implies a reversal of many well known electromagnetic phenomenon. The origin of the reversal is seen as follows: for plane waves (solutions of the form $\exp[i(\mathbf{k}\cdot\mathbf{r}-\omega t)]$), energy flows in the same direction as the Poynting vector, or the direction specified by **ExH**. This direction is also that of the *group velocity*, $\mathbf{V_g}$. From the curl equation $\nabla\times\mathbf{E} = -\partial\mathbf{B}/\partial t$, we find that the *phase velocity* $\mathbf{V_p}$, determined by **ExB**, is in the direction of the wavevector **k**. Thus, when $\mu(\omega)$ is positive, the set of vectors **E**, **H** and **k,** and the set of vectors **E**, **B** and **k**, both obey "right-hand" rules, and $\mathbf{V_g}$ and $\mathbf{V_p}$ are in the same direction.

When $\mu(\omega)$ is negative, however, **B** and **H** are *antiparallel*. Since the curl equation relating **E**, **B**, and **k** does not change in media where μ and ε are negative, we must conclude that the sign of **ExH** (energy flow) changes. If we require on physical grounds that

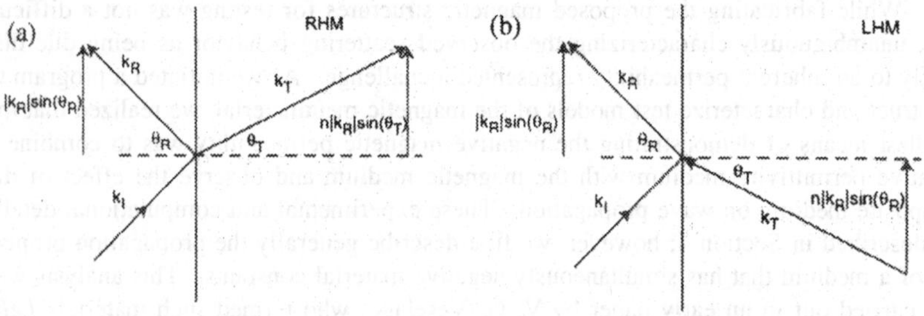

Figure 2. (a) Snell's law illustrated for light passing between two Right-Handed materials with different indices of refraction. (b) Snell's law illustrated for light passing from a Right-Handed to a Left-Handed material.

the direction of energy flow must be outward from a radiating source, we find that the wavevector (and thus V_p) of the underlying plane waves must be directed towards the source. Veselago characterized quadrant (-,-) as "Left-Handed," noting that the vectors **E**, **H**, and **k** satisfy a left-hand rule. We follow Veselago's terminology here, referring to media with simultaneously negative material parameters as Left-Handed, and to media with simultaneously positive material parameters as Right-Handed.

One of the dramatic effects on wave propagation occurring in Left-Handed media, first pointed out by Veselago, can be seen in the application of Snell's law to interfaces between Right- and Left-Handed media. Figure 2a shows a diagram of the incident, reflected, and transmitted waves for a wave passing from a Right Handed medium (RHM), in this case vacuum (n=1), to a second RHM with refractive index n. The vectors drawn in the diagram represent the magnitudes and directions of the propagation vectors of the three waves; note that if the magnitude of the incident and reflected propagation vector is $|\mathbf{k}|$, then the magnitude of the transmitted propagation vector is $|n\mathbf{k}|$, where n is the refractive index. In order to maintain the correct phase relationship at the interface between the waves, for all times and for all positions along the interface, the projection of the propagation vectors parallel to the interface must have the exact same magnitude and orientation for each of the three waves. This results in Snell's Law, or $\sin(\theta_R) = n\sin(\theta_T)$, where θ_T is the angle of the transmitted propagation vector measured from the normal to the interface. Snell's law describes the manner in which waves "bend" as they traverse a boundary between two media with differing refractive indices.

If the second material is Left-Handed, the situation is as presented in Figure 2b, where the propagation vectors for the incident and reflected waves are unchanged from Figure 2a. However, the propagation vector corresponding to the wave inside the Left-Handed medium must point opposite to the group velocity. Therefore, the phase relationship along the interface can only be satisfied if the propagation vector of the refracted wave has the same magnitude as that in a corresponding Right-Handed medium, *but bends to an angle on the other side of the normal.* That is, the angle of refraction is "reversed" (angles measured upward from the normal in the usual RHM are called posi-

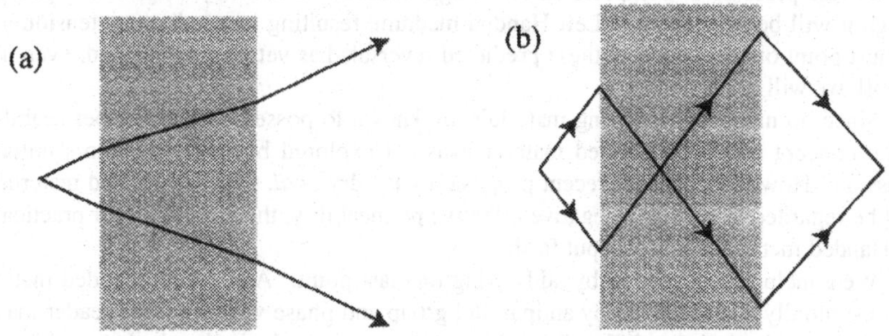

Figure 3. (a) Rays from a point source passing through a Right-Handed medium will diverge. (b) Rays emanating from a point in a Right-Handed medium and incident on a Left-Handed medium with ε=-1 and μ=-1, will be refracted in such a manner as to refocus inside the material. On exiting the Left-Handed medium, rays will focus yet again to produce a real image outside the slab.

tive, and those that have to be measured downward from the normal are considered negative).

A self-consistent interpretation for Left-Handed media is that Snell's law holds as usual, but we must regard the index of refraction (n) as corresponding to the negative square root of the product of $\mu(\omega)\varepsilon(\omega)$, even though the product itself is positive. Thus, Left-Handed materials possess refractive indices that are negative. While it is not obvious that the refractive index should always be negative when both material constants are negative, a detailed analysis taking into account the analytic nature of the permittivity and permeability shows this in fact to be generally true [18].

The reversal of Snell's Law and the existence of negative refractive index imply an entirely new form of geometrical optics, as Veselago pointed out. A striking example is shown in Figure 3, which contrasts the focusing of the rays from a point source near a slab of RHM (Figure 3a) with that from a point source near a slab of LHM (Figure 3b). In the typical case, rays entering a RHM (positive refractive index) are refracted at the interfaces such that the emerging rays appear to emanate from a point source somewhat closer to the observer than the actual point source. In addition, there will always be a reflected ray (not shown in the figure) whenever the impedance of the slab differs from that of the surrounding medium. If the slab has negative refractive index, however, the modification of Snell's law causes the refracted rays to be redirected toward a focus provided the slab has sufficient thickness. If the permittivity and permeability (and therefore the index) of the slab are equal to –1, and the point source is close enough to the slab surface, the rays will be brought to a focus inside the slab and once again to a point external to the slab. Moreover, there will be no ray reflected from the surfaces, as they are perfectly matched; all energy is transmitted through the medium. Professor Pendry has recently suggested that such a slab can constitute a "perfect lens," recovering not only the propagating but also the evanescent components of the point source [19].

In addition to the reversal of Snell's Law, Veselago concluded that several other properties would undergo reversal in Left-Handed materials, including the Doppler shift (a source moving towards a detector in a Left-Handed medium results in a *lower* frequency at the detector), the Cerenkov effect (the radiation emitted when a charged particle passes through a medium faster than the speed of light in that medium), and radiation pressure (the pressure of compression on a Right-Handed medium by a light wave going through it will be reversed in a Left-Handed medium, resulting in a radiation "tension"). We must point out that none of these predicted reversals has yet been confirmed, even in the work we will describe below.

Since no naturally occurring materials are known to possess a negative permeability, the concept of a Left-Handed material was not explored beyond Veselago's initial discussion. However, with the recent proposal by Pendry *et al.* that a structured material could be regarded as having a negative effective permeability, the possibility for practical Left-Handed metamaterials was put forth.

We conclude this section by addressing one last point. As the Left-Handed material is essentially characterized by antiparallel group and phase velocities, the reader may question how this situation differs from the negative group velocity bands that are inherent in PBG dispersion diagrams. First, because PBG effects occur only when the wavelength is on the order of or smaller than the periodicity, an effective medium theory that would identify unambiguously a negative permeability is not possible. As we have shown above, a negative permeability defines a Left-Handed medium. Second, the bands in PBG structures correspond to Bloch waves rather than plane waves, and this complicates the description of problems involving an interface between different types of media, most notably in the appearance of bound surface waves. The focusing effect of a parallel slab of Left-Handed material, for example, depends on the plane wave analysis used in Left-Handed media. While recent evidence [20] suggests that scattering phenomena (e.g., negative refraction) similar to that described here can be observed at certain band edges in PBG structures, the key descriptions of "Left-Handed" and negative refractive index should be properly reserved for materials with identifiable material parameters that are simultaneously negative.

3. The Split Ring Resonator

As we have discussed in Section 1, naturally occurring materials almost universally have a positive permeability, and thus a Left-Handed material, while not ruled out by fundamental considerations, seemed unlikely to be practical. However, in 1999, Pendry *et al.* [16] introduced several configurations of conducting scattering elements that, when grouped into an interacting array, would display a magnetic response to applied electromagnetic fields. One of the suggested configurations was an array of Split Ring Resonators (SRRs), a single example of which is shown in the inset to Figure 4a.

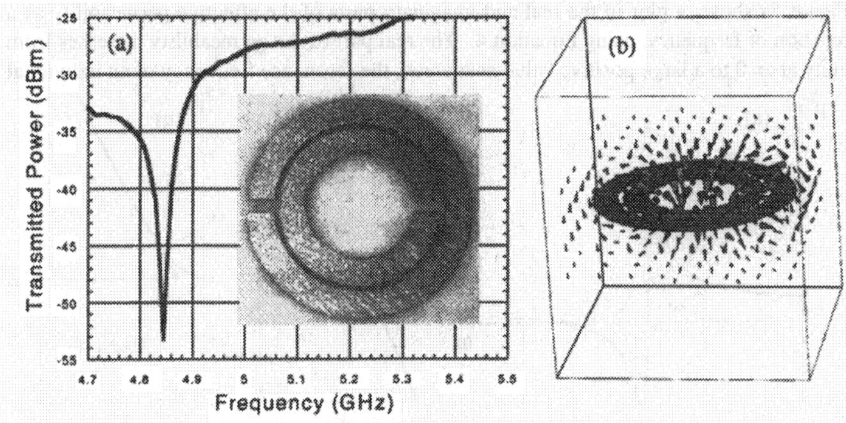

Figure 4. (a) Resonance curve for a single SRR. The resonant frequency occurred at 4.845 GHz, with a Q-factor of roughly 600. Inset: A photograph of a single copper SRR, produced by the lithographic process described in the text. (b) Magnetic field vector plot of an SRR near resonance, taken from simulation data.

An individual SRR acts like a magnetic dipole, with a current circulating in the rings and a dipolar magnetic field pattern (Figure 4b). By placing splits in and between the rings, highly capacitive regions are produced and a resonance formed, with the resonance wavelength being significantly larger than the dimensions of the SRR. Since the excitation wavelength is so much larger than the dimensions of the ring, the SRR can be conveniently approximated as a "point" magnetic dipole. Figure 4a shows a measured absorption curve of a SRR similar to that shown in the inset, taken by placing an input and an output loop antenna near the SRR. The Q-factor, as measured from the absorption curve, was found to be greater than 600 at the resonance frequency of ~4.85 GHz. We note that the free space resonance wavelength is 9.37 times the 6.6 mm outer diameter of the SRR.

Because the individual SRRs are magnetically active at a wavelength roughly eight times larger than the lattice spacing, an array of interacting SRRs can be treated as an effective medium. Pendry *et al.* carried through this analysis, finding a generic function for the effective permeability, or

$$\mu_{eff}(\omega) = 1 - \frac{F\omega^2}{\omega^2 - \omega_0^2 + i\Gamma\omega}, \tag{4}$$

where F and ω_0 are constants relating to the details of the structure. Equation (4) indicates that propagating modes occur up until the frequency ω_0, followed by a gap where no propagating modes exist, followed by propagating modes starting from the frequency $\omega_0/\sqrt{1-F}$. The reason for the gap in propagation is of particular significance: this is where Equation (4) predicts that the effective permeability should be negative. Figure 5a shows a plot of the real and imaginary parts of the effective permeability as a function of frequency, using Equation 4. The real part of the permeability increases from unity at ω=0 to a large positive value near $\omega=\omega_0$, the resonance frequency of an individual

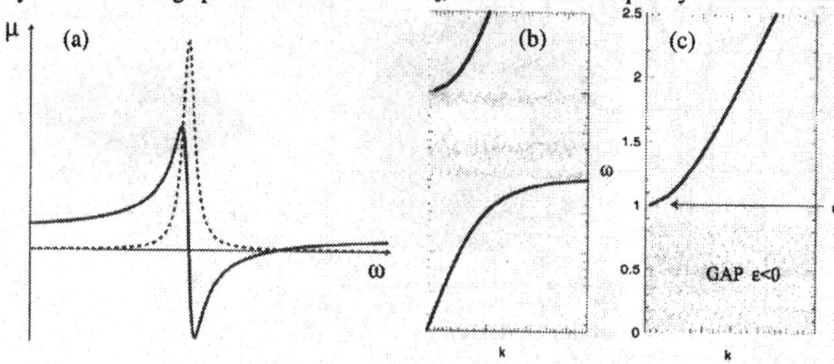

Figure 5. (a) A generic permeability curve, showing both real (solid curve) and imaginary (dashed curve) parts, as calculated from Equation (2). (b) The resulting generic dispersion curve, using the permeability from Equation (2) and setting ε=1. (c) A generic dispersion curve, using the permittivity from Equation (3) and setting μ=1.

SRR, where it then abruptly passes to a large negative value, crossing μ=0 at $\omega=\omega_{mp}$. Pendry *et al.* have termed this latter frequency the *magnetic plasmon frequency* [16]. The peak value of the permeability, infinite in the case of no loss, is constrained by the magnitude of the material losses in the SRR. The width of the negative permeability region is determined mainly by the filling factor F. At high frequencies Equation 4 implies that the permeability tends toward 1-F; however, it is understood that the material will stop responding at very high frequency, and the permeability will actually reach unity.

Assuming that there is no electrical response, the permeability can be used to determine the dispersion relation $\omega = ck/\sqrt{\mu}$, as shown in Figure 5b. The region of negative permeability is manifested as a gap in the photonic band structure, although we must keep in mind that this gap occurs well below the band edge frequency set by π/d, which differentiates it from the type of gap that would occur in a PBG structure.

The work described in [16] relied on analytical estimates and did not present either experimental data or numerical simulations based on actual structures. It was our goal to verify experimentally the magnetic properties and other predictions for these magnetic structures. Because of fabrication issues, we chose to focus our efforts on the SRR medium, which could be produced by straightforward lithographic techniques.

The most direct method of investigating the electromagnetic modes of an arbitrary structure is to solve Maxwell's equations numerically. There are a variety of computational methods available for this purpose, but we chose to use a finite-difference technique using the commercial software MAFIA [21]. In the finite difference computational method, a unit cell is discretized and boundary conditions applied to simulate an infinitely repeated structure. An example of a unit cell for the SRR is shown in Figure 4b, where the discretization effects can be seen in the grid lines across the SRR surface, and the graininess of the circular boundary. Because the field variation in metal structures can occur on a scale much smaller than the applied wavelength, many simulations were run with increasing mesh density to ensure numerical convergence.

Figure 6 shows the dispersion relation as calculated using the discretized cell in Figure 4b. Along the z-direction, (front and back of box in 4b), periodic boundary conditions were applied with increasing phase advance. Because of a limitation in MAFIA, periodic boundary conditions could only be applied along one of the directions, with electric (tangential electric field set to zero) and magnetic (tangential magnetic field set to zero) boundary conditions used to simulate periodic boundary conditions on the other surfaces. A comparison of Figures 6 and 5b shows that the SRR dispersion diagram computed via direct simulation and that predicted by Pendry *et al.* agree qualitatively very well.

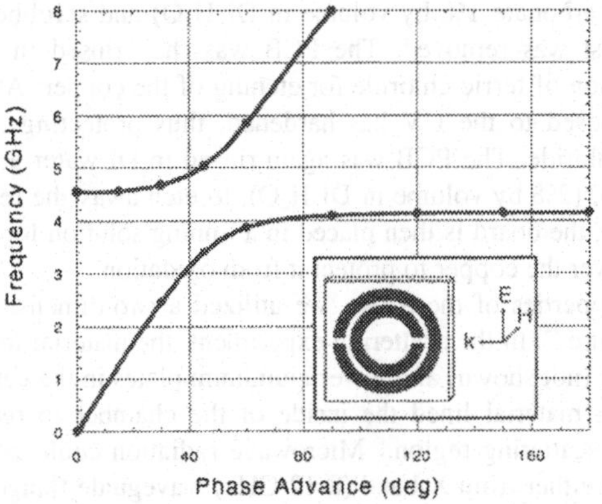

Figure 6. Calculated dispersion curve for the SRR array for the polarization of the field indicated in the inset. Inset: The field incident on the SRRs had H parallel to the axes of the rings.

4. Fabrication and Experiment

Having established that the dispersion relation of a realistic geometry conformed to that predicted by Equation 4, we constructed a SRR medium for experimental confirmation. The SRRs, being planar elements, were well suited to fabrication by an inexpensive circuit-board lithographic process. The split ring resonator shown in the inset to Figure

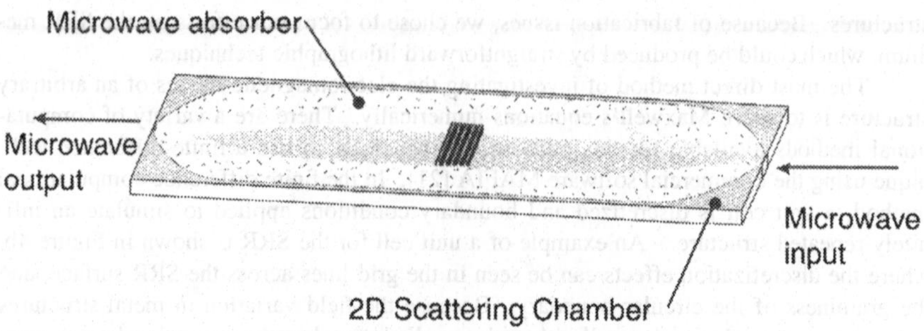

Figure 7. Depiction of the microwave scattering chamber. Microwaves can be coupled via X-band ports on either side of the chamber, resulting in plane-wave like excitation of the test structure. Microwave absorber around the inside of the chamber serves both to adiabatically expand the input radiation, and to minimize reflections back into the scattering region. An aluminum plate covers the chamber during experiments. Holes drilled into the cover plate (not shown) allow coupling to and from the chamber via coaxial antennas.

4a was fabricated using a commercially available printed circuit board (PCB) technique. The PCB consisted of a 216 micron layer of G10 fiberglass, a 16 micron layer of copper, a layer of photoresist, and a thin layer of mylar. A negative was made of the desired design with a high-density printer onto a high quality transparency and placed print side against the PCB. The PCB and negative were exposed to UV light in the spectral range of 350-425nm for 4.5 minutes. The mylar layer was then removed and the PCB placed in film developer (sodium carbonate 1% by volume in DI H_2O) and scrubbed gently until the unexposed photoresist was removed. The PCB was then rinsed in DI water and placed into a warm solution of ferric chloride for etching of the copper. At this point the photoresist that was exposed to the UV has hardened, thus protecting the underlying copper from the ferric chloride. The PCB was again rinsed in DI water and then placed into potassium hydroxide, (2% by volume in DI H_2O), to etch away the remaining hardened photoresist. Finally, the board is then placed in a tinning solution for 20 seconds to place a thin layer of tin over the copper to protect it from oxidation.

To measure the properties of the SRRs, we utilized a two-dimensional scattering chamber, depicted in Figure 7. In the scattering experiment, the material to be tested was placed between the upper (not shown) and lower aluminum plates in the central region of the chamber. Absorbing material lined the inside of the chamber to reduce spurious reflections back into the scattering region. Microwave radiation could be injected into the chamber and detected either from X-band (8-12 GHz) waveguide flanges on the outer plates, or via antennas inserted into holes drilled into the upper plate. As the frequencies of interest in the structures measured were well below X-band, we used the latter method in the work presented here.

The two-dimensional geometry was convenient, as only one unit cell needed to be placed in the vertical direction; however, caution is necessary when replacing periodic with electric boundary conditions, as unit cells that deviate from symmetry will exhibit different behaviors under the two types of terminations. We later compared the effect of electric versus periodic boundary conditions on the structures described here using GdfdL—another commercial finite-difference electromagnetic mode solver [22]—and found agreement between the two methods of termination.

Sheets of the SRRs, as shown in Figure 8a, were cut into strips, assembled into a unit that was fourteen centimeters in length and approximately 6 centimeters deep (in the propagation direction), and placed into the scattering chamber. The SRR medium was excited by microwaves from an antenna inserted through the upper plate near one end of the scattering structure, and probed via a second antenna placed at the opposite end of the chamber. The antennas were moved as far apart as possible to avoid any possible inter-

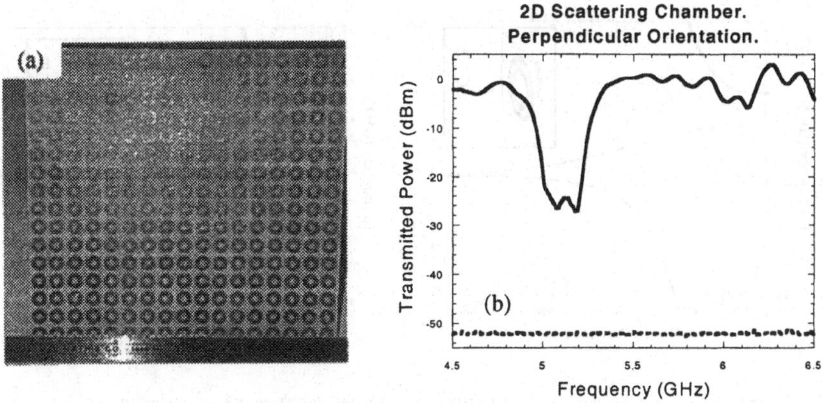

Figure 8. (a) A single sheet of the fabricated SRR medium. (b) Transmitted power (solid curve) through a lattice of SRRs. The dashed curve shows the transmission through the wire medium, which is coincident with the noise floor of the network analyzer.

ference effects from the antenna near fields, which are on the order of the wavelength (~6 cm). The transmission spectrum associated with the SRR medium is shown in Figure 8b, where, as expected, we see that there is a dip in transmission corresponding to the gap in the simulated modes (Figure 6).

5. The SRR-Wire Medium

While both the numerical dispersion curve and the experimental transmission measurement confirm the predicted behavior of the SRR medium, neither demonstrates whether the gap region is actually due to a magnetic or electric response. The reason for this is that both methods probe only the dispersion relation $\omega=ck/n$, where the square of the refractive index $n^2=\varepsilon(\omega)\mu(\omega)$. Clearly, if there is a frequency band where either the permittivity or the permeability is less than zero, the refractive index is imaginary, and a gap in transmission (or dispersion) will occur. To experimentally determine independent values for μ and ε from the transmission measurements would require phase sensitive measurements of both the transmitted and reflected waves (or S-parameters)—a more complicated and time consuming experiment, and one which would require a great deal of care to interpret unambiguously.

As an immediate alternative to an S-parameter experiment, we decided to pursue a different approach, altering the dielectric properties of the SRR material. While there were a number of possible methods of accomplishing this, we noted that if we made a second medium with presumed negative permittivity overlapping the negative permeability region associated with the SRR medium, then the combined medium would exhibit a region of propagation where previously there had been attenuation in either medium alone. This was, perhaps, the most direct and dramatic means of confirming the negative permeability region of the SRR medium.

Structures possessing a negative effective permittivity at microwave frequencies

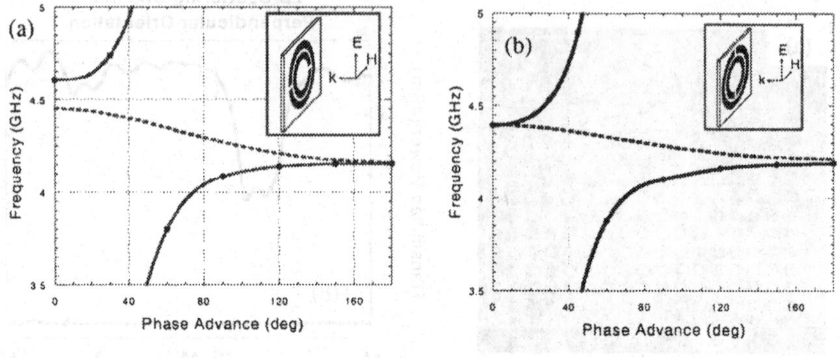

Figure 9. Dispersion curves for the combined SRR and post medium. The solid curves in either figure correspond to the SRR medium alone, and are shown as a guide. (a) SRRs are oriented with the gaps perpendicular to the incident electric field. (b) SRRs are oriented with the gaps parallel to the electric field.

can be easily constructed using metal scatterers. One of the simplest, the thin wire medium, was analyzed by Pendry *et al.* in 1996 [23] and shown to have an effective permittivity identical to that of a dilute, collisionless plasma, or

$$\varepsilon(\omega) = 1 - \frac{\omega_p^2}{\omega^2}, \tag{3}$$

where the plasma frequency ω_p is determined by the radius and spacing of the wires. This permittivity function corresponds to a frequency gap in propagating modes between zero frequency and the plasma frequency. The analysis presented in [23] required wires thin in relation to the skin depth; however, this is not a necessary condition unless one is concerned with differentiating the plasma frequency from the band edge frequency. By interlacing the SRR array with a wire array having a plasma frequency significantly above the SRR magnetic plasmon frequency ω_{mp}, the negative permeability gap band should turn into a propagation band.

To create the negative permittivity host for the SRR array, we utilized a periodic array of conducting posts of diameter 1/16" and spacing 8.0 mm, identical with the spacing of the SRRs. The onset of propagation for the wires alone, as determined by simulations, occurred at a frequency of ~20 GHz. This frequency corresponds to the band edge, with the plasma frequency occurring somewhat higher [24]. Combining a SRR and a conducting post in a unit cell led to the dashed dispersion curve shown in

Figure 9a. As a guide, the solid lines correspond to the SRR medium alone, and indicate where the negative permeability frequency gap occurs. When the posts are added to the cell, what was previously a gap in propagation becomes a propagation band, and what previously corresponded to propagation bands now become stop bands. Note that the slope of the propagation band in the SRR-post medium is negative, indicating that phase and group velocities are antiparallel, consistent with the interpretation of a simultaneously negative permittivity and permeability.

The simulations also indicated that the orientation of the gap region in the SRRs relative to the direction of the applied electric field would have a significant influence on the character of the band gap. Two orientations that were considered are shown in the insets to Figures 9a and 9b, with their respective dispersion curves. The slight difference of the dispersion curves is due to the greater dielectric response of the SRR when in orientation (a) as opposed to orientation (b). The effect is manifested as the upward shift of the upper band edge in Figure 9a. The SRR gap contains both a region of negative permeability, which becomes a propagation band when combined with the wire medium, and a region of negative permittivity, which continues to be a gap when the wires are added. This is in contrast to the case of Figure 9b, where the entire SRR frequency gap becomes a propagation band when the wire medium is added. The presence of the permittivity gap in orientation (a) has also been observed experimentally [25].

(a) (b)

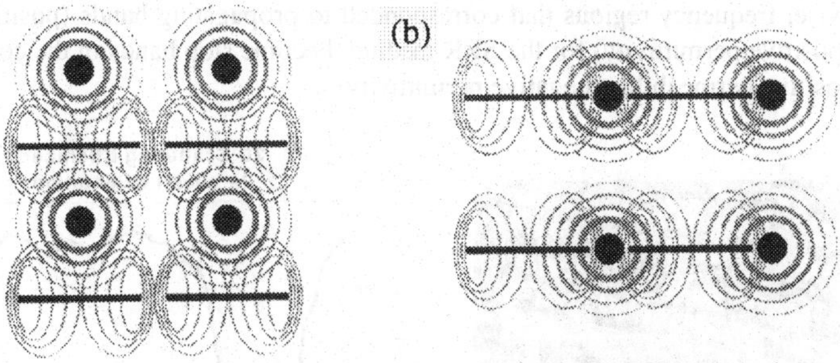

Figure 10. (a) Depiction of a configuration of posts and SRRs that gives rise to a Left-Handed frequency band. (b) Depiction of a configuration of posts and SRRs that does not give rise to a Left-Handed frequency band. All views are from above where the circle represents the post and the line represents the SRR.

Further numerical simulations revealed the spatial location of the SRR element with respect to the wire element to be of critical importance in forming the Left-Handed propagation band. The best results were obtained when the posts were centered between SRRs, with the axes of the posts intersecting the SRR axes, as depicted in Figure 10a. Presumably, this configuration minimizes the interaction between the SRR medium and the post medium, allowing a division of the magnetic and electric responses. As can be seen from Figure 10a, the strong magnetic fields circulating around the posts responding to the incident electric field fall off rapidly toward the SRRs, and also have a polarization that does not couple strongly to the SRRs. Likewise, the predominantly magnetic fields induced by the incident magnetic field in the SRRs tend to fall off considerably at the positions of the posts. In contrast, Figure 10b depicts an example of a geometry that failed to produce a Left-Handed band, presumably due to the strong magnetic coupling between the SRRs and the posts. This explanation of the observed results is, of course, qualitative, and should be checked by actual calculation of the coupling between elements.

To confirm the numerical results, we fabricated a composite medium for testing by combining a post medium with an SRR medium, as shown in Figure 11a. To make the post medium, an aluminum plate was drilled with an 18x7 array of holes using a numerically controlled milling machine. Commercially available brass dowel pins with diameters of 1/16" and height 1/2" were inserted into the plate. The bottom plate of the scattering chamber was milled out such that the top of the base plate of the post medium was flush with the inside bottom surface of the scattering chamber. Slight grooves in the base plate (Figure 11a) allowed positioning of the SRR strips, which were further held in place by Styrofoam spacers.

As in the case of the SRR medium alone (Section 3), we performed microwave transmission measurements on the composite medium using coaxial antennas for the input and detection of the microwave signals. The result of this measurement is shown by the lower dashed curve in Figure 11b. The transmission for the SRR lattice alone is also plotted in Figure 11b for comparison, and the transmitted power for the case of the posts alone (coincident with the noise floor of the sweeper) is plotted in Figure 9. The essential feature here is that the frequency region corresponding to the magnetic band gap (negative permeability, positive permittivity) for the SRR medium alone becomes a region of propagation for the combined medium (negative permeability, negative permittivity). Likewise, frequency regions that corresponded to propagating bands (positive permeability, positive permittivity) for the SRR medium become stop bands in the combined medium (positive permeability, negative permittivity).

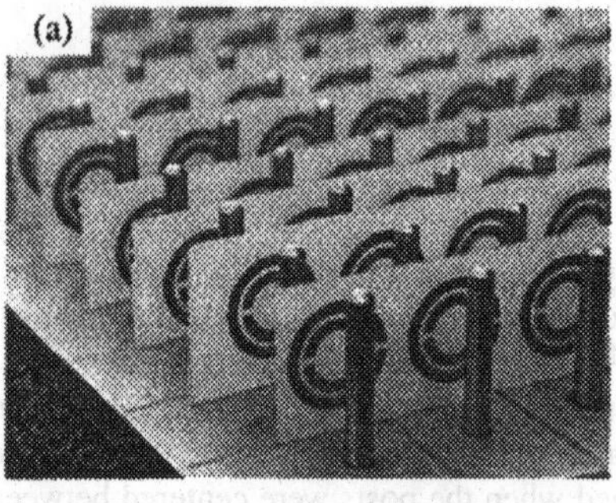

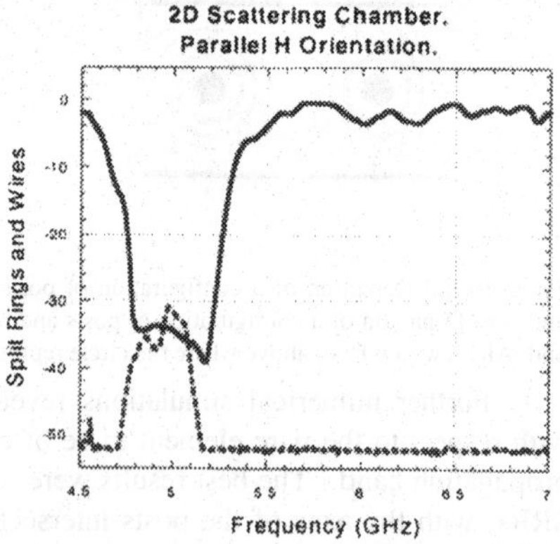

Figure 11. (a) Photograph of the fabricated SRR/post array used in the scattering experiments. (b) Microwave transmission measurements on the SRR medium alone (solid curve) and the combined medium (dashed curve).

6. A 2-D Isotropic Left-Handed Metamaterial at X-Band Frequencies

The center frequency for the Left-Handed region in the first test structure was 5 GHz. This longer wavelength was convenient to work with from a practical point-of-view, as the rings and posts were easy to fabricate, and the lateral unit cell dimension (including one SRR and one post) was appropriate to the chamber height. Thus, the test structure and boundary conditions were consistent with the numerically simulated structure and imposed boundary conditions. However, the scattering chamber used in the experiments was initially designed for X-band (8-12 GHz) transmission measurements; to obtain the best data from our system, we required a structure with a Left-Handed transmission region at X-band frequencies. In addition, the Left-Handed properties of the lattice used in the initial experiments were restricted to one dimension. Since any experiment validating the anticipated reversals of electromagnetic properties would require at least 2-D isotropy, we also wanted the next structure to exhibit a Left-Handed band for any angle of incidence.

Raising the Left-Handed region to higher frequencies required raising the resonant frequency of the SRRs, and the effective plasma frequency of the wires. The SRR resonant frequency is generally raised both by reducing the overall dimension, as well as reducing the internal capacitance, while the plasma frequency is trivially raised by decreasing the distance between the posts (or wires). After contemplating a number of different designs, we found via numerical simulations that the SRR structure shown in Figure 12a produced a negative permeability region with a bandwidth of nearly 1 GHz, starting at ~10.5 GHz. We were constrained by the height of our experimental apparatus to having an integer number of unit cells in one centimeter, and this is the reason that the structure has three SRRs in the vertical direction.

Because of the smaller size of the unit cell, the increased number of posts would have required a considerable effort in fabrication. We thus investigated structures in which wires were placed by the same lithographic process on the reverse side of the circuit board material, as can be seen in Figure 12a. An initial concern was that electrical continuity should maintained in the wire medium to ensure that the effective permittivity matched Equation 3. However, the effect of small gaps between the otherwise continuous wires is to introduce a resonance into the effective permittivity, such that the equation

$$\varepsilon(\omega) = 1 - \frac{\omega_p^2}{\omega^2 - \omega_0^2} \tag{5}$$

holds; that is, the wire medium with broken electrical connectivity scatters light as a medium of bound charges rather than free charges [14]. The result is that the region of negative permittivity, rather than extending from zero to the effective plasma frequency, now starts at a resonant frequency ω_0. As long as this negative permittivity frequency region is at least as large or larger than the negative permeability region, a Left-Handed medium can be formed, as demonstrated by the simulation results in Figure 12b (dashed curve).

In order to test the feasibility of making a 2-D isotropic structure, the X-band structure was simulated and constructed to have SRRs and wires in two directions (Figure 12a). The unit was assembled from two-sided circuit board, on which the SRR structure was patterned, with a wire structure patterned on the reverse side (shown schematically in Figure 13a). Identical strips were then cut from the circuit board, with smaller cuts placed between each unit cell, such that two sets of strips could be interlocked to make the isotropic (2-D) final assembly. The final structure was rigid enough that no other material was used in the positioning. Microwave transmission measurements were carried out on the structure in the scattering chamber, this time utilizing the X-band waveguide ports on the ends of the chamber to couple microwaves into and out of the scattering region. Previous work has shown that microwaves introduced in this manner

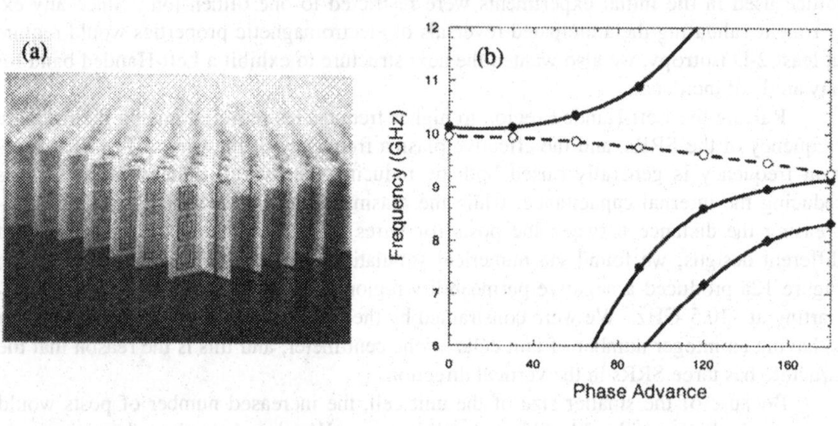

Figure 12. (a) Photograph of an SRR/wire structure possessing an isotropic Left-Handed frequency band near 10 GHz. (b) Calculated dispersion diagram for the X-band medium. Solid circles: Dispersion diagram for just the SRRs. Solid diamonds: Lowest propagation band of the dispersion diagram for both SRRs and wires. This lowest band occurs because the continuity of the wires has been broken. Open circles: The Left-Handed propagation band for the SRR-wire medium.

to the chamber scatter as plane waves, thus allowing a more favorable comparison between experimental results and numerical calculations.

The result of the transmission measurements on the X-band structure is shown in Figure 13b. Three curves are shown, corresponding to three orientations [(1,0), (0,1) and (1,1)] of the structure relative to the incident radiation. As can be seen, the onset frequency and bandwidth of the measured transmission curves are roughly consistent with that predicted by the simulations, although the three curves are shifted relative to each other. It was found on closer inspection of the fabricated structure that a slight systematic shift in relative positions of the rings had occurred during assembly, such that the medium as viewed from one of the two symmetry directions had slightly different properties than the other. This bias probably accounts for the shifts observed in the experimental transmission curves.

The general shape of the transmission curve was found to be quite similar to that found from a simple 1-D transmission calculation assuming a uniform medium with the effective material properties that we believe characterize the actual structure. This indicates that the construction of SRRs and wires indeed behaves as an effective medium. Furthermore, the experimental results on the X-band system suggest that a 2-D isotropic system is possible to construct, providing us a platform on which to further investigate the various reversals of electromagnetic properties described in Section 2.

8. Conclusion

We have demonstrated that a composite medium of conducting, non-magnetic elements can form a Left-Handed frequency band, where the effective permittivity and the effective permeability are simultaneously negative. This material fits the definition of an electromagnetic metamaterial, as the electromagnetic properties of the composite structure are not observed in naturally occurring materials.

Left-Handed metamaterials, which can also be equivalently regarded as negative refractive index materials, were first proposed and analyzed by V. G. Veselago, who predicted dramatic effects on the propagation of electromagnetic waves passing through such materials. Having developed the first known examples of Left-Handed structures, we are now in a position to study the predicted reversals in a systematic manner, and search for applications. The prospect of surfaces with reduced electromagnetic reflection is clearly of immediate relevance, but interesting applications are also very likely to result from the reversals of the Doppler shift, Cerenkov radiation and radiation pressure. The scattering from combinations of Left-Handed and Right-Handed materials should also lead to novel effects.

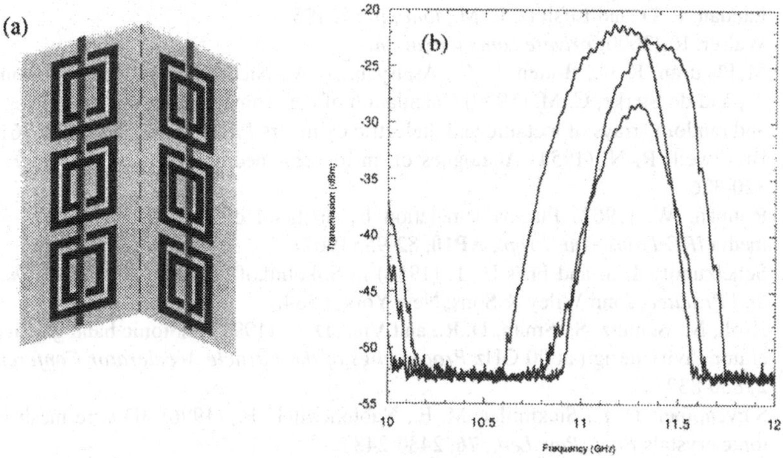

Figure 13. (a) Depiction of a single unit cell of the isotropic Left-Handed medium. (b) Transmission measurements, made in the scattering chamber, of the isotropic structure.

9. Acknowledgements

We thank Professor J. B. Pendry for numerous discussions and communications regarding negative permeability materials. This work was supported by the DARPA, through a grant from the ONR (Contract No. N00014-00-1-0632), the NSF (Contract No. NSF-DMR-97-24535), and the DOE (Contract Nos. DE-FG-03-93ER40793 and DE-FG-03-93ER40759).

9. References

1. Smith, D. R., Padilla, W., Vier, D. C., Nemat-Nasser, S. C., and Schultz, S. (2000) A composite medium with simultaneous negative permittivity and permeability *Phys. Rev. Lett.* **84**, 4184-4187.
2. Veselago, V. G. (1968) The electrodynamics of substances with simultaneously negative values of ε and μ *Soviet Physics USPEKHI* **10**, 509-514.
3. Yablonovitch, E. (1987) Inhibited spontaneous emission in solid-state physics and electronics *Phys. Rev. Lett.* **58**, 2059-2062.
4. John, S. (1987) Strong localization of photons in certain disordered dielectric superlattices *Phys. Rev. Lett.* **58**, 2486-2489.
5. Shalaev, V. M. (1996) Electromagnetic properties of small-particle composites *Physics Reports*, **272**, 61-137.
6. Landau, L. D. and Lifshitz, E. M. (1987) *Electrodynamics of Continuous Media, 2nd Edition* Pergamon Press, Oxford, p257.
7. Landau, L. D. and Lifshitz, E. M., *ibid.*, p287, 1987.
8. Walser, R. (2000) *private communication*.
9. McPhedran, R. C., Botten, L. C., Asatryan, A. A., Nicorovici, N. A., Robinson, P. A., and de Sterke, C. M. (1999) Calculation of electromagnetic properties of regular and random arrays of metallic and dielectric cylinders *Phys. Rev. E*, **60**, 7614-7617.
10. Bracewell, R. N. (1954) Analogues of an ionized medium *Wireless Engineer*, **31**, 320-326.
11. Rotman, W. (1962) Plasma simulation by artificial dielectrics and parallel-plate media *IRE Trans. Ant. Prop.*, **AP10**, 82-95 (1962).
12. Schelkunoff, I. S. and Friis H. T. (1952) in Sokolnikoff, S. (ed.) *Antennas: Theory and Practice*, John Wiley & Sons, New York, p584.
13. Kroll, N., Schultz, S., Smith, D. R., and Vier, D. C. (1999) Photonic band gap accelerator cavity design at 90 GHz *Proceedings of the Particle Accelerator Conference*, **2**, 830-832.
14. Sievenpiper, D. F., Sickmiller, M. E., Yablonovitch, E., (1996) 3D wire mesh photonic crystals *Phys. Rev. Lett.*, **76**, 2480-2483.
15. Sievenpiper, D. F., Zhang, L., Jimenez Broas, R. F., Alexopolous, N. G., Yablonovitch, E., (1999) High-impedance electromagnetic surfaces with a forbidden frequency band *IEEE MTT*, **47**, 2059-2074.
16. Pendry, J. B., Holden, A. J., Robbins, D. J., and Stewart, W. J. (1999) Magnetism from conductors and enhanced nonlinear phenomena *IEEE Trans. MTT*, **47**, 2075-2084.
17. Jackson, J. D. (1975) *Classical Electrodynamics, 2nd Edition,* John Wiley & Sons,

New York, p281.
18. Smith, D. R. and Kroll, N. (2000) Negative refractive index in left-handed materials *Phys. Rev. Lett.*, **85**, 2933-2936.
19. Pendry, J. B. (2000) Negative refraction makes a perfect lens *Phys. Rev. Lett.*, in press.
20. Notomi, M. (2000) Theory of light propagation in strongly photonic crystals: Refraction-like behavior in the vicinity of the photonic bandgap *Phys. Rev. B*, submitted.
21. Weiland, T. (1994) Recent advances and applications of the MAFIA codes *AIP Conference Proceedings* **297**, 291-302.
22. Bruns, W. (1995) GdfidL: a finite difference program for arbitrarily small perturbations in rectangular geometries *IEEE Trans. Mag.*, **32**, 1453-1456.
23. Pendry, J. B., Holden, A. J., Stewart, W. J., and Youngs, I. (1996) Extremely low frequency plasmons in metallic mesostructures *Phys. Rev. Lett.* **76**, 4773-4776.
24. Shelby, R. and Smith, D. R. (2000) unpublished.
25. Wiltshire, M. (2000) private communication.

TOWARDS COMPLETE PHOTONIC BAND GAP STRUCTURES BELOW INFRARED WAVELENGTHS

Alexander Moroz[1]

Debye Institute, Utrecht University,
P.O. Box 80000, 3508 TA Utrecht, The Netherlands

1. INTRODUCTION

Photonic crystals are structures with a periodically modulated dielectric constant. In analogy to the case of an electron moving in a periodic potential, certain photon frequencies can become forbidden, independent of photon polarization and the direction of propagation - a complete photonic bandgap (CPBG) [1, 2]. As early as 1975, photonic crystals with such a gap have been shown to offer the possibility of controlling the spontaneous emission of embedded atoms and molecules in volumes much greater than the emission wavelength [3] and, later on, to be an important ingredient in a variety of technological applications [4]. However, as yet no two- (2D) and three-dimensional (3D) photonic crystals are available with complete bandgaps below infrared (IR) wavelengths and fabrication of photonic crystals with such a gap poses a significant technological challenge already in the near-IR [5, 6]. One faces the extreme difficulty in satisfying combined requirements on the dielectric contrast and the modulation (the total number and the length of periodicity steps). In order to achieve a CPBG below the IR wavelengths, the modulation is supposed to be on the scale of optical wavelengths or even shorter and, as for any CPBG structure, must be achieved with roughly ten periodicity steps in each direction. This task is currently beyond the reach of reactive ion and chemical etching techniques even for 2D structures, because the hole filling fraction must be rather high and the etching must be deep enough [7]. (See, however, [8] for a recent progress using holographic techniques.) Fortunately, in 3D, such a modulation occurs naturally in colloidal crystals formed by monodisperse colloidal suspensions of microspheres. The latter are known to self-assemble into 3D crystals with excellent long-range periodicity on the optical scale [9], removing the need for complex and costly microfabrication. Colloidal systems of microspheres crystalize either in a face-centered-cubic (fcc) or (for small sphere filling fraction) in a body-centered-cubic (bcc) lattice [9]. Since larger sphere filling fractions favour opening of larger gaps, simple fcc structures of spheres have been one of the main subjects of our investigation.

[1] www.amolf.nl/research/photonic_materials_theory

C.M. Soukoulis (ed.), Photonic Crystals and Light Localization in the 21st Century, 373–382.

The outline of the contributions is as follows. First, we shall concentrate on the 3D photonic structures. In Sec. 2 we discuss photonic properties of purely dielectric fcc structures of homogeneous and coated spheres. In Sec. 3 we review our recent work [10, 11, 12] which shows a way to avoid the restrictions on the critical dielectric contrast required for the formation of a CPBG and discuss recent experimental progress towards fabrication of a CPBG structure below IR wavelengths. In Sec. 4 we discuss the application of ideas, presented in Sec. 3, to lower dimensional photonic structures. Sec. 5 deals with nonlinear properties of metallo-dielectric structures. In Sec. 6 we review a few approaches to fabricate the proposed structures, and, in Sec. 7 we give our conclusions and outlook for future investigations.

2. SELF-ORGANIZING COLLOIDAL STRUCTURES

Self-organization of small colloidal particles into regular crystals on an optical scale has been known for a long time and occurs, for example, in natural opals. Indeed, the origin of the nice colours of opals is Bragg scattering. However, the crystalline order by itself is not enough to open a CPBG. Let ε_h and ε_s be the host and sphere dielectric constant, respectively. If ε_s is less than ε_h, the so-called "air spheres" case, calculations show that a CPBG can open in a simple fcc structure [13], provided the dielectric contrast $\delta = \max(\varepsilon_h/\varepsilon_s, \varepsilon_s/\varepsilon_h) \gtrsim 8$ [14, 15]. This puts a large constraint on the materials choice which is yet to be overcome. Motivated by the experimental progress, we have investigated if it is possible to avoid the constraint on the dielectric contrast by making the scatterers more complex, for instance, by using coating spheres [15]. For the so-called stop gap (a photonic band gap in a given direction of propagation) in the (111) crystal direction, which corresponds to the L point of the Brillouin zone, the results are rather interesting. Imagine, we can fabricate fcc photonic crystals of spheres with different respective refractive indices, say n_1 and $n_2 < n_1$, with the sphere filling fraction and the host refractive index being the same in both cases. Let us assume that the homogeneous spheres can be substituted by coated spheres with the core and shell refractive indices n_1 and n_2, respectively. Then the L-gap width can increase by as much as 50% relative to the larger of the L-gap widths of the two fcc photonic crystals of homogeneous spheres. Apart from larger L-gap, a suitable coating can be used to manipulate optical properties of particles in a controlled way. Using this way we can tune properties of the photonic structures which the core-shell spheres form. Unfortunately, a coating does not affect much the critical dielectric contrast necessary for the formation of a CPBG [15, 16]. One way to avoid the restriction on the dielectric contrast is to make a radical departure from purely dielectric structures.

3. COLLOIDAL STRUCTURES OF METALLIC SPHERES

Development in photonic crystals has been partly stimulated by the lack of good metallic mirrors below the IR wavelengths where a typical metal absorption increases (see Figure 1). By some strange turn, a promising new route to achieve a CPBG below the IR wavelengths is to use scatterers with a negative dielectric constant [10, 11, 12], which is usually associated with metals. For example, let us take the Drude-like dielectric

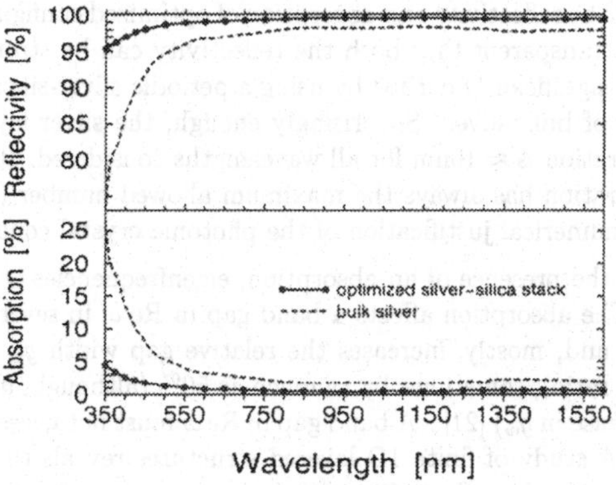

Figure 1: Reflectivity at normal incidence of bulk silver compared to that of optimized finite silver-silica stack. Each data point is an optimum over ≈ 2.9 million different configurations examined.

function,

$$\varepsilon_s(\omega) = 1 - \frac{\omega_p^2}{\omega(\omega + i/\tau)}, \tag{1}$$

where ω is the angular frequency, τ is the relaxation time, and ω_p is the plasma frequency, $\omega_p^2 = 4\pi n_e e^2/m$, where n_e, e, and m are the carrier density, charge, and mass, respectively. The absorption in the Drude model is controlled by the damping term $\gamma = 1/\tau$. For a typical metal $\gamma/\omega_p \approx 10^{-2}$. Hence, the absorption can be rather small for frequencies $0.1\omega_p \le \omega_p$ (cca $0.5\omega_p \le \omega_p \le 1.2\omega_p$ for real materials), in which case metals behave as a conventional, although highly dispersive, dielectric. A good example of such a metal is silver for wavelengths 310 − 520 nm [17]. Strong dispersion makes band-structure calculation quite involved and apparently outside the reach of the well-established plane-wave method [1]. To avoid the problems with dispersion, we have used a Korringa-Kohn-Rostocker (KKR) method for electromagnetic waves [18]. Dispersion does not cause any complication for the KKR method and computational time is the same as without dispersion.

Despite recent claims, simple fcc structure was shown to yield a CPBG down to ultraviolet wavelengths [11, 12]. Up to four CPBG's can open in the nonabsorptive frequency window $0.5\omega_p \le \omega \le 1.1\omega_p$. The relative gap width g_w can be as large as 10%, even if the host refractive index $\varepsilon_h = 1$ [11]. In addition, there is also a sizeable CPBG with $g_w \approx 40\%$ present outside of this nonabsorptive window [19]. Surprisingly enough, the critical metallic filling fraction to open a CPBG is around 52%, the same as the critical air filling fraction to open a CPBG for inverted opals. It seems as if CPBG's open as the result of enhanced capacitance, when metallic surfaces are closer than a critical distance. Periodicity seems to do all the magic in curbing absorption and raising reflectivity of a periodic metallo-dielectric structure, which can have rather different properties from the underlying bulk metal. In order to illustrate our results obtained for 2D and 3D metallo-dielectric photonic structures [10, 11, 12], one can perform a simple numerical experiment for a finite periodic silver-silica layered stack, i.e., a 1D photonic crystal. Let us allow for up to 25 unit cells, vary the silver and silica layers thickness with 1nm in the intervals [5, 200]nm and [10, 600]nm, respectively, and, for a given wavelength, select the configuration with the highest reflectivity at normal incidence. In total for every wavelength ≈ 2.9 million different configurations are scanned over. The reflectivity and absorption of optimized configurations are plotted in Figure 1. It is transparent that both the reflectivity can be strongly increased and absorption can be significantly curbed by using a periodic silver-silica layered structure compared to that of bulk silver. Surprisingly enough, the silver layer thickness in an optimized configuration is $\approx$ 10nm for all wavelengths considered. It turns out that an optimized configuration has always the maximum allowed number (=25) of unit cells, which provides a numerical justification of the photonic crystal concept.

Generally, in the presence of an absorption, eigenfrequencies ω turn into complex resonances [20]. The absorption affects a band gap in Re ω in several ways. It pushes band edges down and, mostly, increases the relative gap width g_w (gap width to the midgap frequency ratio), sometimes by as much as 50% (although, in some cases it can also lead to a decrease in g_w) [21]. A band gap in Re ω must not necessarily imply a very high reflectivity. A study of finite 1D layered structures reveals that, in the presence of a strong absorption, the reflectivity at the gap center can, for instance, saturate at 60% or less, depending on a single bilayer, or, a single unit cell absorption [21]. The latter yields a lower bound on the absorption of a composite structure. The reflectivity at the gap center is usually more than twice that for frequencies within a band, almost exclusively as a result of decreased absorption within the gap which approaches that of a single bilayer. In both cases transmissions are small. If T denotes the transmission for frequencies within a band, then the transmission within a gap is typically T^2 [20]. The effect of absorption on the band gap is negligible (both in shifting the gap edges and in changing gap width) if and only if (Im ε_s)/(Re ε_s) ≤ 0.1.

3.1 Photonic Structures of Coated Spheres

The exceptional band-gap properties of Drude spheres, i.e., spheres with a Drude-like dielectric function, are rather robust against coating these spheres with a semiconductor or an insulator [12]. By using a coating which can be subsequently index-matched, one can continuously tune the metallic filling fraction. However, the coating can play a much more important role. Coating can actually facilitate the preparation of photonic colloidal crystals of Drude spheres because it can (i) stabilize metallic microparticles by preventing, or, at least, by significantly reducing their oxidation; (ii) prevent aggregation of metallic particles by reducing Van der Waals forces between them. In the latter case, a coating of roughly 30 nm is required. Except from enlarging of some of the stop gaps (gaps in a fixed direction of propagation) by as much as 50% [15], the coating with an optically nonlinear material can reduce the required intensity for the onset of optical bistability [22, 23] due to the enhancement of local fields near the surface-plasmon resonance. Using a procedure in which fluorescent organic groups are placed inside the silica shell with nm control over the radial position [24] makes it, in principle, possible to perform a precise position-dependent testing of the spontaneous emission within such a photonic crystal. Last but not least, using a semiconductor coating may allow a matching of the photonic and electronic bandgaps, which is important for many applications involving photonic crystals [4]. Our results show that for coated Drude microspheres with a coating width $l_c/\lambda_p \leq 10\%$ (up to $l_c = 30$ nm for $\lambda_p = 328$ nm which corresponds to silver) and the coating and host refractive indices n_c and n_h, respectively, between 1 and 1.47, one can always find a sphere radius r_s such that the relative gap width g_w is larger than 5% and, in some cases, g_w can even exceed 9% [12]. This provides a sufficiently large margin for gap-edge distortions due to omnipresent imperfections and impurities to allow both technological and experimental applications involving the proposed structures. Using different coatings and by changing the refractive index n_h of the supporting liquid (this can be easily achieved), one can tune the width and midgap frequency of a CPBG considerably. In principle, the midgap frequency ω_c can be tuned to whatever frequency within a nonabsorptive window ($0.6\omega_p \leq \omega \leq 1.1\omega_p$ for silver [17]).

It is important to realize that, because the metallic core size parameter $x = 2\pi r_c/\lambda$ satisfies $x \geq 3.4$ for all wavelengths within a CPBG for all CPBG's considered here in the frequency region $0.55\omega_p \leq \omega \leq 1.1\omega_p$, the absorption is still dominated by bulk properties, i.e., can be negligible [17], since the plasmon-induced absorption becomes relevant only for particle sizes much smaller than the wavelength [25].

4. TWO-DIMENSIONAL PHOTONIC STRUCTURES

For many technological applications it is enough to achieve a photonic bandgap (PBG) for in-plane propagation and, for applications involving highly polarized light sources, it can be sufficient to obtain a PBG for a single polarization only (Note that for in-plane propagation, the two photon polarizations do not mix and Maxwell's equations reduce to two scalar equations, one for each polarization.). Numerous applications have been suggested involving 2D photonic structures, i.e., new designs for light-emitting diodes [26], polarizers [27], high transmission through sharp bends [28], efficient bandpass filters, channel drop filters, and, in one-dimension (1D), waveguide crossing without cross-talk [29]. For such structures, only an in-plane CPBG can ensure light propagation control whatever the in-plane light propagation. Fortunately, many of the ideas discussed for 3D photonic structures also apply to 2D metallo-dielectric structures. For square and triangular lattices of Drude cylinders, i.e., cylinders with a Drude-like behaviour of their dielectric function, we have showed that such systems can possess complete in-plane CPBG's below IR wavelengths [10]. Of the two geometries, the optimal one for ideal Drude-like behaviour is a square lattice, whereas for Drude-like behaviour in silver, using experimental data [17], the optimal geometry is a triangular lattice [10]. If the lattice spacing is tuned to a characteristic plasma wavelength, several CPBG's open in the spectrum and their relative gap width can be as large as 36.9% (9.9% in a nonabsorptive window) even if the host dielectric constant $\varepsilon_h = 1$ [10].

The observed magnitude and robustness of the in-plane CPBG of the metallo-dielectric structures allows one to speculate that an inclusion of metallic (silver) wires could boost the performance of the photonic crystal fibre designed by Knight et al. [30]. The photonic crystal fibre [30] is a 2D photonic periodic arrangement of thin cylindrical glass fibres where the light is sent along the cylinder axis. In lateral directions, the localization of light is achieved in complete analogy to the case of electrons: by introducing a defect at the center of the photonic crystal fibre, for instance, by omitting one cylinder such that it induces a transversally localized mode with frequency within a 2D CPBG. The light can then propagate with that frequency along the cylinder axis even if the core of the photonic crystal fibre is air and if cladding has a higher refractive index.

5. NONLINEAR PROPERTIES OF METALLO-DIELECTRIC STRUCTURES

There are many potentially interesting applications involving photonic crystals with nonlinear components, for instance, as optical limiters, optical switches, optical diodes, and optical transistors, for multiple-beam second-harmonic generation (SHG), ring cavity SHG, multiple wavelength frequency conversion, and realization of the optical bistability [22, 23]. The main obstacle in fabricating such devices is to find out materials with sufficiently high optical nonlinearities. For example, optically nonlinear Bragg diffracting nanosecond optical switches have been fabricated by doping of polymer particles with an absorptive dye. However, its switching efficiency has been only $\approx 2\%$ [31].

Metals have been known to possess one of the largest nonlinear susceptibilities. Unfortunately, due to a strong metallic reflection, the light was reflected back before it could have ever experienced the metallic nonlinearity. This changes dramatically if metallic components are arranged periodically in space. It has been demonstrated in 1D that the periodicity makes metals transparent [32], thereby allowing the light to access the metallic nonlinearity [33]. This situation should not change qualitatively for 2D and 3D periodic structures. Therefore, we expect metallo-dielectric structures to be promising candidates for many nonlinear applications which can be experimentally studied in the presence of a CPBG.

6. EXPERIMENTAL REALIZATION

Metallo-dielectric structures can have a significant commercial impact due to their exceptional properties. We list only a few of them:

- They can yield sizeable CPBG. Depending on the scale and chosen material, a CPBG can be opened anywhere in the range from radiowaves [34] down to ultraviolet wavelengths, making the crystals an excellent template for multiplexing, waveguiding, and optical chips.
- Since metals are known to possess large nonlinear susceptibilities, the photonic crystals are inherently nonlinear, i.e., the crystals are promising candidates for various nonlinear applications.
- By applying an electric field one can switch reverseably in ms from an fcc colloidal crystal to a body-centered-tetragonal crystal: a so-called martensitic transition [35, 36, 37]. Hence, the crystals are also promising candidates for the CPBG structures with switchable bandgaps.
- Their properties can be tuned, in an irreversible way, by an ion irradiation which induces a plastic deformation of colloidal particles [38].
- A combination of a suitable coating, doping, and the presence of a metallic component allows for large freedom in optimizing specific properties of the photonic crystals.
- A nonzero electric conductivity can be used in pumping and/or in a fabrication of a new class of displays.

The main experimental problem in fabricating the proposed photonic structures in 3D is to synthesize large enough spheres (e.g., with radius $r_s \approx 150$ nm for silver) to reach the threshold value $r_s/\lambda_p \gtrsim 0.9n_h$, where $\lambda_p = 2\pi\omega_p/c$, c the speed of light in a vacuum, is the plasma wavelength and n_h is the host refractive index. (Surprisingly enough, the same threshold value r_c/λ_p, where r_c is the Drude cylinder radius, is also required to open a complete bandgap in a 2D close-packed square lattice.) Thus, the main

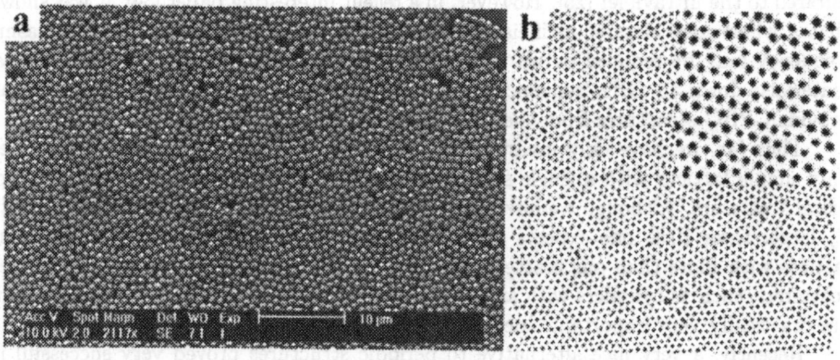

Figure 2: Large silver spheres fabricated by K.P. Velikov and G.E. Zegers. a) Scanning electron micrograph (SEM) of dried silver particles with radius $r_s = 349$ nm and polydispersity $\delta_d = 16\%$. Only small ordered regions are observed. b) Confocal image of the bottom layer of a charge stabilized crystal of silver particles ($r_s = 320$ nm, $\delta_d < 17\%$) in water. Large single crystals with a pitch of 1 μm are observed, as shown in the inset.

task is opposite to that using etching techniques which aim at ever shorter length scales. For gold, a method to produce monodisperse colloids of several hundred nm radius and larger has been developed [39]. Recent results on the fabrication of such spheres from silver are promising. Figure 2 shows images of the samples fabricated by K.P. Velikov and G.E. Zegers from our group. Figure 2a shows scanning electron micrograph (SEM) of dried silver particles with radius $r_s = 349$ nm and polydispersity $\delta_d = 16\%$. In this case only small ordered regions are observed. Figure 2b shows a confocal image of the bottom layer of a charge stabilized crystal of silver particles ($r_s = 320$ nm, $\delta_d < 17\%$) in water. Large single crystals are observed, as shown in the inset. The only remaining problem is to control the size polydispersity of spheres and reduce it below 5% to trigger 3D crystallization [9] with smaller interparticle spaces. Recent progress in so-called do-it-yourself crystallization (see contribution by A. van Blaaderen), which allows to reduce defects in colloidal structures beyond thermodynamic limits, may help to overcome even the last hurdle.

In 2D, the proposed structures could be realized by introducing, for instance, by electrochemical deposition, a Drude-like material into the holes of a periodic structure of air holes in a dielectric, a structure that has no CPBG without the Drude-like material inserted. Regarding photonic crystal fibre [30], before thermal treatment and stretching out, some of the dielectric fibres can be, in a regular way, replaced by silver wires and then processed in the standard way, by the stack-and-draw method or by fibre-pulling.

7. CONCLUSION

In recent years, photonic crystals have turned out to be a very exciting subject, truly interdisciplinary, involving physics, chemistry, and engineering. For many applications it would be desirable to achieve a CPBG for optical or even shorter wavelengths. We have shown that metallo-dielectric structures can serve this purpose. They can yield sizeable CPBG's in two- and three-dimensions [10, 11, 12]. Moreover, these structures are inherently nonlinear and their CPBG can be tuned or switched on/off in a controlled way. The region of plasma frequencies of conventional materials ranges from the near-infrared to the ultraviolet [25]. However, in a recent interesting paper [34], it was shown that a whole new class of artificial materials can be fabricated in which the plasma frequency may be reduced by up to 6 orders of magnitude compared to conventional materials, down to GHz frequencies. Correspondingly, the proposed structures can provide CPBG structures from the GHz up to ultraviolet frequencies.

Thus far, we have only investigated the simplest geometries and scatterers, i.e., only simple lattices with a single scatterer per unit cell, and only spherical and cylindrical scatterers. Although we have shown that one can achieve the relative gap width g_w larger than 10%, one expects that the width can yet be enlarged by considering lattices with more than one scatterer per unit cell [1, 40], or, using more complicated scatterers, such as cylinders with an ellipsoidal cross section [41]. These generalizations are practically very important since such structures can be now fabricated.

Recently, a very nice alternative to periodic structures proved very successful in opening a CPBG [42]. The latter involves quasicrystals which can be devised to make the Brillouin zone more spherical (circular in 2D). A quasicrystal with metallic components may be very interesting object to investigate. Likely, many open problems and many surprises are still ahead of us.

ACKNOWLEDGEMENTS

I should like to thank my colleagues A. van Blaaderen, M.J.A. de Dood, H. van der Lem, A. Polman, A. Tip, K.P. Velikov, and G.E. Zegers for careful reading of the manuscript and useful comments. This work is part of the research program by the Stichting voor Fundamenteel Onderzoek der Materie (Foundation for Fundamental Research on Matter) which was made possible by financial support from the Nederlandse Organisatie voor Wetenschappelijk Onderzoek (Netherlands Organization for Scientific Research).

References

[1] K.M. Ho, C.T. Chan, and C.M. Soukoulis, Existence of photonic gap in periodic dielectric structures, *Phys. Rev. Lett.* **65**, 3152 (1990).

[2] E. Yablonovitch, T.J. Gmitter, and K.M. Leung, Photonic band structure: The face-centered-cubic case employing nonspherical atoms, *Phys. Rev. Lett.* **67**, 2295 (1991).

[3] V.P. Bykov, Spontaneous emission from a medium with a band spectrum, *Sov. J. Quant. Electron.* **4**, 861 (1975).

[4] E. Yablonovitch, Inhibited spontaneous emission in solid-state physics and electronics, *Phys. Rev. Lett.* **58**, 2059 (1987).

[5] T.F. Krauss, R.M. De La Rue, and S. Brandt, Two-dimensional photonic-bandgap structures operating at near-infrared wavelengths, *Nature* **383**, 699 (1996).

[6] S.Y. Lin et al., A three-dimensional photonic crystal operating at infrared wavelengths, *Nature* **394**, 251 (1998).

[7] T.F. Krauss and R.M. De La Rue, Photonic crystals in the optical regime - past, present and future, *Prog. Quant. Electronics* **23**, 51 (1999).

[8] M. Campbell, D.N. Sharp, M.T. Harrison, R.G. Denning, and A.J. Turberfield, Fabrication of photonic crystals for the visible spectrum by holographic lithography, *Nature* **404**, 53 (2000).

[9] W.B. Russel, D.A. Saville, and W.R. Schowalter, *Colloidal Dispersions*, Cambridge University Press, Cambridge (1995).

[10] H. van der Lem and A. Moroz, Towards two-dimensional complete photonic band gap structures below infrared wavelengths, *J. Opt. A: Pure Appl. Opt.* **2**, 395 (2000).

[11] A. Moroz, Three-dimensional complete photonic-bandgap structures in the visible, *Phys. Rev. Lett.* **83**, 5274 (1999).

[12] A. Moroz, Photonic crystals of coated metallic spheres, *Europhys. Lett.* **50**, 466 (2000).

[13] H.S. Sözüer, J.W. Haus, and R. Inguva, Photonic bands: convergence problem with the plane-wave method, *Phys. Rev. B* **45**, 13962 (1992).

[14] R. Biswas, M.M. Sigalas, G. Subramania, and K.-M. Ho, Photonic band gaps in colloidal systems, *Phys. Rev. B* **57**, 3701 (1998).

[15] A. Moroz and C. Sommers, Photonic band gaps of three-dimensional face-centered cubic lattices, *J. Phys.: Condens. Matter* **11**, 997 (1999).

[16] K. Busch and S. John, Photonic band gap formation in certain self-organizing systems, *Phys. Rev. E* **58**, 3896 (1998).

[17] E.D. Palik et al., *Handbook of Optical Constants of Solids I*, Academic Press, San Diego (1991).

[18] A. Moroz, Density-of-states calculation and multiple scattering theory for photons, *Phys. Rev.* B **51**, 2068 (1995).

[19] W.Y. Zhang, X.Y. Lei, Z.L. Wang, D.G. Zheng, W.Y. Tam, C.T. Chan, and P. Sheng, Robust photonic band gap from tunable scatterers, *Phys. Rev. Lett.* **84**, 2853 (2000).

[20] A. Tip, J.-M. Combes, and A. Moroz, Band structure of absorptive photonic crystals, *J. Phys. A: Math. Gen.* **33**, 6223 (2000).

[21] A. Moroz, A. Tip, and J.-M. Combes, Absorption in periodic layered structures, *Synthetic Metals* **115**, (2000) (to appear).

[22] K.M. Leung, Optical bistability in the scattering and absorption of light from nonlinear microparticles, *Phys. Rev. A* **33**, 2461 (1986).

[23] D.S. Chemla and D.A. Miller, Mechanism for enhanced optical nonlinearities and bistability by combined dielectric-electronic confinement in semiconductor nanocrystallites, *Opt. Lett.* **11**, 522 (1986).

[24] A. van Blaaderen and A. Vrij, Synthesis and characterization of colloidal dispersions of fluorescent, monodisperse silica spheres, *Langmuir* **8**, 2921 (1992).

[25] C.F. Bohren and D.R. Huffman, *Absorption and scattering of light by small particles*, Wiley, New York, (1984), Chap. 9, 12.

[26] S. Fan, P.R. Villeneuve, J.D. Joannopoulos, and E.F. Schubert, High extraction efficiency of spontaneous emission from slabs of photonic crystals, *Phys. Rev. Lett.* **78**, 3294 (1997).

[27] A.R. McGurn and A.A. Maradudin, Photonic band structures of two- and three-dimensional periodic metal or semiconductor arrays, *Phys. Rev. B* **48**, 17576 (1993).

[28] A. Mekis, J.C. Chen, I. Kurland, S. Fan, P.R. Villeneuve, and J.D. Joannopoulos, High transmission through sharp bends in photonic crystal waveguides, *Phys. Rev. Lett.* **77**, 3787 (1996).

[29] G. Johnson, C. Manolatou, S. Fan, P.R. Villeneuve, J.D. Joannopoulos, and H.A. Haus, Elimination of cross talk in waveguide intersections, *Opt. Lett.* **23**, 1855 (1998).

[30] J.C. Knight, J. Broeng, T.A. Birks, and P.St.J. Russell, A photonic crystal fibre, *Science* **282**, 1476 (1998).

[31] G. Pan, R. Kesavamoorthy, and S.A. Asher, Optically nonlinear Bragg diffracting nanosecond optical switches, *Phys. Rev. Lett.* **78**, 3860 (1997).

[32] M. Scalora, M.J. Bloemer, A.S. Pethel, J.P. Dowling, C.M. Bowden, and A.S. Manaka, Transparent, metallo-dielectric, one-dimensional, photonic band-gap structures, *J. Appl. Phys.* **83**, 2377 (1998).

[33] R.S. Bennink, Y.-K. Yoon, R.W. Boyd, and J.E. Sipe, Accessing the optical nonlinearity of metals with metal-dielectric photonic bandgap structures, *Opt. Lett.* **24**, 1416 (1999).

[34] J.B. Pendry, A.J. Holden, W.J. Stewart, and I. Youngs, Extremely low frequency plasmons in metallic mesostructures, *Phys. Rev. Lett.* **76**, 4773 (1996).

[35] A. van Blaaderen, From the de Broglie to visible wavelengths: Manipulating electrons and photons with colloids, *MRS Bulletin* (October) **23**, 39 (1998).

[36] W. Wen, N. Wang, H. Ma, Z. Lin, W.Y. Tam, C.T. Chan, and P. Sheng, Field induced structural transition in mesocrystallites, *Phys. Rev. Lett.* **82**, 4248 (1997).

[37] U. Dassanayake, S. Fraden, and A. van Blaaderen, Structure of electrorheological fluids, *J. Chem. Phys.* **112**, 3851 (2000).

[38] E. Snoeks, A. van Blaaderen, T. van Dillen, C.M. van Kats, M.L. Brongersma, and A. Polman, Colloidal ellipsoids with continuously variable shape, *Adv. Materials* **12**, (2000) (to appear).

[39] D.V. Goia and E. Matijecic, Tailoring the particle size of monodispersed colloidal gold, *New Journal of Chemistry* **146**, 139 (1999).

[40] D. Cassagne, C. Jouanin, and D. Bertho, Hexagonal photonic-band-gap structures, *Phys. Rev. B* **53**, 7134 (1996).

[41] M. Qiu and S. He, Large complete band gap in two-dimensional photonic crystals with elliptic air holes, *Phys. Rev. B* **60**, 10610 (1999).

[42] M. E. Zoorob, M. D. B. Charlton, G. J. Parker, J. J. Baumberg, and M. C. Netti, Complete photonic bandgaps in 12-fold symmetric quasicrystals, *Nature* **404**, 740 (2000).

EFFECT OF MODERATE DISORDER ON THE ABSORBANCE OF PLASMA SPHERES DISTRIBUTED IN A HOST DIELECTRIC MEDIUM

V. YANNOPAPAS * and A. MODINOS
Department of Physics, National Technical University of Athens, Zografou Campus, GR-157 73,Athens, Greece

N. STEFANOU
Section of Solid State Physics, University of Athens, Panepistimioupolis, GR-157 84, Athens, Greece

Abstract. Using a coherent-potential approximation, in conjunction with the on-shell method we developed for the study of photonic crystals, we study the effect of moderate disorder on light absorption by composite materials consisting of plasma spheres embedded in a host dielectric medium. We analyze our results by reference to the properties of a single sphere and to those of an infinite crystal. We find, in particular, that the absorption of light by a thin slab (a two-dimensional array of plasma spheres) is affected more strongly by disorder, in comparison to the absorbance of thick slabs consisting of many layers of spheres.

The promising properties of photonic band gap materials, i.e. composite structures with a dielectric function which is a periodic function of the position, have attracted a growing interest in recent years [1]-[3]. Among the methods which have been developed for the theoretical study of photonic crystals, the so-called on-shell methods [4],[5] allow a direct comparison with experiment since they provide, besides the frequency band structure of the infinite crystal, the transmission, reflection and absorption coefficients of light incident on a finite slab of the crystal. Our method [4] treats multilayers of non-overlapping spherical scatterers in a host medium of different dielectric function. As in all on-shell methods, the dielectric function of the scatterers can be a function (possibly complex) of the frequency ω, which would be the case in the study of light scattering by arrays of metallic particles [6]-[8]. Depending on the size and distribution of the metallic spheres, such arrays can be very good absorbers of light [9]-[11], or photonic crystals with a robust photonic band gap in the GHz regime [12]. In previous work, we dealt with periodic two-dimensional (2D) [13] and three-dimensional (3D) [14] arrays of metallic spheres. However, in reality such structures are rarely periodic because

* vyannop@cc.uoa.gr

C.M. Soukoulis (ed.), Photonic Crystals and Light Localization in the 21st Century, 383–387.

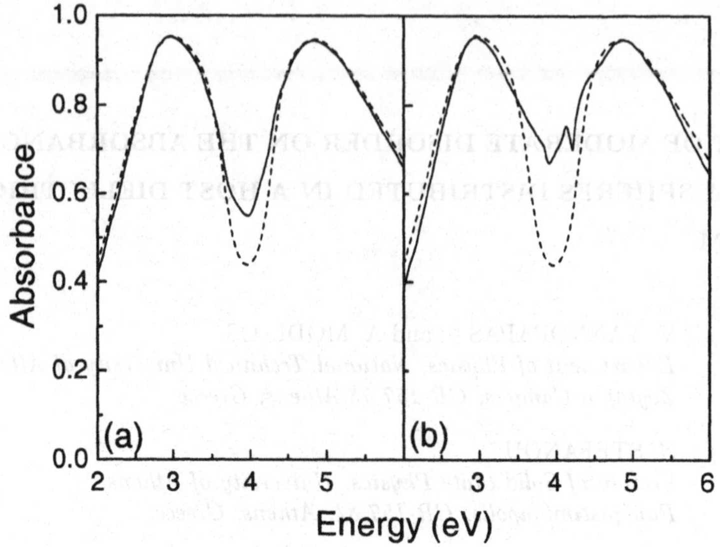

Figure 1. Absorption of light incident normally on a slab of an fcc crystal consisting of plasma spheres ($S = 50$ Å , $\hbar\omega_p = 9.2$ eV, $\hbar\tau^{-1} = 0.2$ eV) in gelatine ($\epsilon = 2.37$) and occupying randomly (a) 75% and (b) 50% of the lattice sites (solid lines). The slabs consist of 129 planes parallel to the (001) surface and the volume fraction occupied by the spheres $f = 0.1$. The broken lines are obtained for an ordered system with the same f.

the size, shape and distribution of the particles is usually not uniform [9],[10]. In order to deal with the intrinsic disorder of these systems we developed a coherent-potential-approximation (CPA) method to treat light scattering by 2D and 3D disordered systems consisting of non-overlapping spheres [15],[16]. In this paper we present some results of our CPA calculations with the emphasis on the role of dimensionality.

We consider a slab of 129 (001) fcc planes. The lattice sites on each plane are occupied randomly by metallic spheres. The latter are described by a Drude dielectric function

$$\epsilon_p(\omega) = 1 - \frac{\omega_p^2}{\omega(\omega + i\tau^{-1})} \tag{1}$$

where ω_p stands for the bulk plasma frequency of the metal and τ is the relaxation time of the conduction-band electrons. We have chosen $\hbar\omega = 9.2$ eV and $\hbar\tau^{-1} =$ 0.2 eV which correspond to silver. In all our calculations, the radius of the spheres is $S = 50$ Å. The spheres are embedded in gelatine ($\epsilon = 2.37$) and we assume that the same medium extends to infinity on the left and right of the slab.

In Figs. 1a and 1b we show the absorbance curves obtained [16] for two slabs with random occupancy of the lattice sites of 75% and 50%, respectively. The volume fraction occupied by the spheres $f = 0.1$ in both cases. We have also calculated the absorbance of a fully occupied (periodic) lattice of metallic spheres having the same volume fraction $f = 0.1$. Fig. 1a shows that the CPA results for

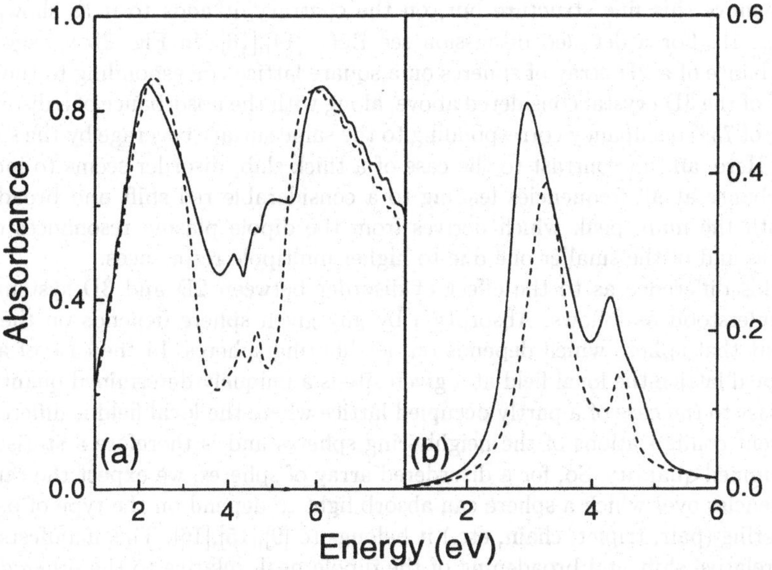

Figure 2. Absorption of light incident normally on a (001) slab of an fcc crystal of plasma spheres ($S = 50$ Å , $\hbar\omega_p = 9.2$ eV, $\hbar\tau^{-1} = 0.2$ eV) in gelatine ($\epsilon = 2.37$). (a): slab of 129 layers; (b): slab of one layer. Solid lines: random occupancy of 75% of the lattice sites. Broken lines: ordered system with volume coverage by the spheres 30% in (a) and surface coverage by the spheres 43% in (b); these coverages being the same with those of the corresponding disordered systems.

the 75% occupancy are almost the same with those of the corresponding periodic system. The dip between the two peaks in the absorbance curve is due to a gap in the band structure of the corresponding infinite crystal when the metallic spheres are assumed to be non-absorbing ($\tau = \infty$ in Eq. (1)). This gap is generated by hybridization of a narrow band resulting from the coupling of dipole resonant states centered on the spheres with a wide band of freely propagating waves in an effective homogeneous background [14]. Dipole absorption occurs mainly at and about the edges of the above mentioned gap leading to the two main peaks in the absorbance curves. Evidently disorder increases the absorption in the region of this dip. Increasing the fraction of the non-occupied sites to 50% (Fig. 1b), and with it the amount of disorder in the system, leads to an additional peak, not obtained for the periodic system, in the region of the dip. This peak has been attributed to a cluster-induced dipole resonance which lies well above the dipole resonance of an isolated sphere [16].

In Fig. 2a we compare the absorbance curve of a disordered system [a thick (001) fcc slab with 75% occupancy of the lattice sites and $f = 0.3$] with that of a corresponding ordered system. Again, we see no big difference except in the dip between the two dipole peaks. The structure in this region, in the case of the periodic system, derives from multipole bands of the corresponding infinite crystal associated with 2^l-pole resonances (with $l > 1$) of the single sphere. Disorder does not remove this fine structure but, on the contrary, it adds to it as shown also in Fig. 1b. For a detailed discussion see Refs. [14],[16]. In Fig. 2b we show the absorbance of a 2D array of spheres on a square lattice corresponding to the (001) plane of the 3D crystal considered above, along with the absorbance of a disordered plane of 75% occupancy corresponding to the same surface coverage by the spheres 43%. Here, and in contrast to the case of a thick slab, disorder seems to increase absorbance at all frequencies leading to a considerable red shift and broadening of both the main peak which derives from the dipole plasma resonances of the spheres and of the smaller one due to higher multipole resonances.

This difference as to the effect of disorder between 2D and 3D systems can be understood as follows. Absorption by any given sphere depends on the local field at that sphere which depends on neighboring spheres. In the case of a fully occupied lattice the local field at a given site is a uniquely determined quantity, in contrast to the case of a partly occupied lattice where the local field is different for different configurations of the neighboring spheres and is therefore a statistically determined quantity. So, for a disordered array of spheres, we expect the range of frequencies over which a sphere can absorb light to depend on the type of particle clustering (pair, triplet, chain, etc.) it belongs to [9],[15],[16]. This manifests itself as a relative shift and broadening of the dipole peak relative to the ordered case. However, the probability of having varying particle clusters in a disordered structure similar to a binary alloy, such as the one we consider here, decreases with increasing coordination number and therefore particle clustering effects become more prominent as the dimensionality of the structure is reduced [17].

Acknowledgements

V. Yannopapas was supported by the State Scholarship Foundation (I.K.Y.), Greece.

References

1. Joannopoulos, J. B., Meade, R. D., and Winn, J. W. (1995) *Photonic Crystals*, Princeton University Press, Princeton, N.J.
2. Soukoulis, C. M. (editor) (1996) *Photonic Band Gap Materials*, Kluwer Academic, Dordrecht.
3. Krauss, T. F. and De La Rue, R. M. (1999) Photonic crystals in the optical regime - past, present and future, *Prog. Quant. Elec.* **23**, 51-96.
4. Stefanou, N., Karathanos, V., and Modinos, A. (1992) Scattering of electromagnetic waves by periodic structures, *J. Phys.: Condensed Matter* **4**, 7389-7400; Stefanou, N., Yannopapas, V., and Modinos, A. (1998) Heterostructures of photonic crystals: frequency bands and transmission coefficients, *Comput. Phys. Commun.* **113**, 49-77; Stefanou, N., Yannopapas, V., and Modinos, A. (2000) MULTEM 2: A new version of the program for transmission and band-structure calculations of photonic crystals, *Comput. Phys. Commun.* **132**, 189-196.
5. Ohtaka, K. and Tanabe, Y. (1996) Photonic bands using vector spherical waves. Reflectivity, coherence and local field, *J. Phys. Soc. Jpn.* **65**, 2276-2284; Pendry, J. B., and MacKinnon, A. (1992) Calculation of photon dispersion relations, *Phys. Rev. Lett.* **69**, 2772-2775; Pendry, J. B. (1994) Photonic band structures, *J. Mod. Opt.* **41**, 209-229; Qiu, Y.,

Leung, K. M., Cavin, L., and Kralj, D. (1995) Dispersion curves and transmission spectra of a two-dimensional photonic band gap crystal-Theory and experiment, *J. Appl. Phys.* **77**, 3631-3636; McPhedran, R. C., Botten, L. C., Asatryan, A. A., Nicorovici, N. A., Robinson, P. A., and de Sterke, C. M. (1999) Ordered and disordered photonic band gap materials, *Aust. J. Phys.* **52**, 791-809.

6. Lamb, W., Wood, D. M., and Ashcroft, N. W. (1980) Long-wavelength electromagnetic propagation in heterogeneous media, *Phys. Rev. B* **21**, 2248-2266.
7. Persson, B. N. J., and Liebsch, A. (1983) Optical properties of two-dimensional systems of randomly distributed particles, *Phys. Rev. B* **28**, 4247-4254.
8. Liebsch, A. and Persson, B. N. J. (1983) Optical properties of small metallic particles in a continuous dielectric medium, *J. Phys. C: Solid State Phys.* **16**, 5375-5391.
9. Kreibig, U., Althoff, A., and Pressmann, H. (1981) Veiling of optical single-particle properties in many-particle systems by effective medium and clustering effects, *Surf. Sci.* **106**, 308-317.
10. Abelès, F., Borensztein, Y., and López-Rios, T. (1984) Optical properties of discontinuous thin films and rough surfaces of silver, *Festkörperprobleme (Advances in Solid State Physics, Braunschweig: Vieweg)* **24**, 93-117.
11. Granqvist, C. G. and Wittwer, V. (1998) Materials for solar energy conversion: An overview, *Sol. Energy Mater. and Sol. Cells* **54**, 39-48; Joerger, R., Gampp, R., Heinzel, A. Graf, W., Köhl, M., Gantenbein, P., and Oelhafen, P. (1998) Optical properties of inhomogeneous media, *Sol. Energy Mater. and Sol. Cells* **54**, 351-361; Taleb, A., Russier, V., Courty, A., and Pileni, M. P. (1999) Collective optical properties of silver nanoparticles organized in two-dimensional superlattices, *Phys. Rev. B* **59**, 13350-13358.
12. Zhang, W. Y., Lei, X. Y., Wang, Z. L., Zheng, D. G., Tam, W. Y., Chan, C. T., and Sheng, P. (2000) Robust photonic band gap from tunable scatterers, *Phys. Rev. Lett.* **84**, 2853-2856.
13. Stefanou, N. and Modinos, A. (1991) Scattering of light from a two-dimensional array of spherical particles on a substrate, *J. Phys.: Condens. Matter* **3**, 8135-8148; Stefanou, N. and Modinos, A. (1991) Optical properties of thin discontinuous metal films, *J. Phys.: Condens. Matter* **3**, 8149-8157.
14. Yannopapas, V., Modinos, A., and Stefanou, N. (1999) Optical properties of metallodielectric photonic crystals, *Phys. Rev. B* **60**, 5359-5365.
15. Stefanou, N. and Modinos, A. (1993) Scattering of electromagnetic waves by a disordered two-dimensional array of spheres, *J. Phys.: Condens. Matter* **5**, 8859-8868.
16. Modinos, A., Yannopapas, V., and Stefanou, N. (2000) Scattering of electromagnetic waves by nearly periodic structures, *Phys. Rev. B* **61**, 8099-8107.
17. Economou, E. N. (1979) *Green's Functions in Quantum Physics*, Springer-Verlag, New York.

RANDOM LASERS WITH COHERENT FEEDBACK

H. CAO, J. Y. XU, Y. LING
Department of Physics and Astronomy, Materials Research Center, Northwestern University, Evanston, IL 60208-3112
S.-H. CHANG, S. T. HO
Department of Electrical and Computer Engineering, Materials Research Center, Northwestern University, Evanston, IL 60208-3118
AND
E. W. SEELIG, X. LIU, R. P. H. CHANG
Department of Materials Science and Engineering, Materials Research Center, Northwestern University, Evanston, IL 60208-3116

In a random medium, optical scattering may induce a phase transition in the photon transport behavior [1]. When the scattering is weak, the propagation of light can be described by a normal diffusion process. With an increase in the amount of scattering, recurrent light scattering events arise. Interference between the counter-propagating waves in a disordered structure gives rise to the enhanced backscattering, also called weak localization [2, 3]. When the amount of scattering is increased beyond a critical value, the system makes a transition into a localized state. Light propagation is inhibited due to the interference in multiple scattering [4, 5, 6, 7, 8]. This phenomenon is called Anderson localization of light. It is an optical analog to Anderson localization of electrons in solid.

Apart from the remarkable similarities, there are striking differences between electron transport and photon transport in a disordered medium. For example, the number of electrons is always conserved, while the number of photons may not be. In an amplifying random medium, a photon may induce the stimulated emission of a second photon. A fascinating phenomenon, which would never occur in an electronic system, is the lasing action in a disordered gain medium. Such lasers are called random lasers. There are two kinds of random lasers: one is with nonresonant (incoherent) feedback, the other is with resonant (coherent) feedback. Lasing with non-

C.M. Soukoulis (ed.), Photonic Crystals and Light Localization in the 21st Century, 389–404.

resonant feedback occurs in the regime of weak scattering and low gain. Above the threshold, a sudden increase of peak emission intensity and a drastic narrowing of emission spectrum occur. However, there are no discrete lasing modes due to the lack of resonant feedback. Lasing with nonresonant feedback has been observed in laser dye solutions containing microparticles or laser crystal powders [9, 10, 11]. The experimental result can be explained by the theory of light diffusion with gain, where the phase of optical field and interference effect are neglected [12, 13, 14, 15, 16].

Lasing with resonant feedback occurs in the regime of strong scattering and high gain [17, 18, 19, 20, 21]. In the presence of strong optical scattering, light may return to a scatterer from which it was scattered before, and thereby forming closed loop paths. If the amplification along such a loop path exceeds the loss, laser oscillation could occur in the loop which serves as a laser resonator. The requirement of the phase shift along the loop being equal to a multiple of 2π determines the lasing frequencies. The picture of a closed loop is intuitive but naive. The light may come back to its original position through many different paths and interfere. Thus, this laser can be called randomly distributed feedback laser.

We will first demonstrate the difference between lasing with non-resonant feedback and lasing with resonant feedback, and then focus on the random lasers with coherent feedback.

1. Transition from lasing with no-resonant feedback to lasing with resonant feedback

To study the transition, we use is the laser dye solution containing semiconductor nanoparticles. The advantage of the suspension is that the gain medium and the scattering elements are separated. Thus, we can independently vary the amount of scattering by particle density and the optical gain by dye concentration.

Experimentally, rhodamine 640 perchlorate dye and zinc oxide (ZnO) particles are mixed in methanol. The ZnO particles have a mean diameter of 100 nm. To keep the particles from clustering, the solution, contained in a flask, is shaken in an ultrasonic cleaner for 20 minutes just before the photoluminescence experiment. The frequency-doubled output ($\lambda = 532$ nm) of a mode-locked Nd:YAG laser (10 Hz repetition rate, 25 picosecond pulse width) is used as a pump light. The pump beam is focused by a lens (10 cm focal length) to the solution contained in a 1 cm $\times$ 1 cm $\times$ 3 cm cuvette at nearly normal incidence. Emission into the direction $\sim 45°$ from the normal of the cell front window is collected by a fiber bundle and directed to a 0.5-meter spectrometer with a cooled CCD detector array.

By changing the ZnO particle density in the solution, we continuously

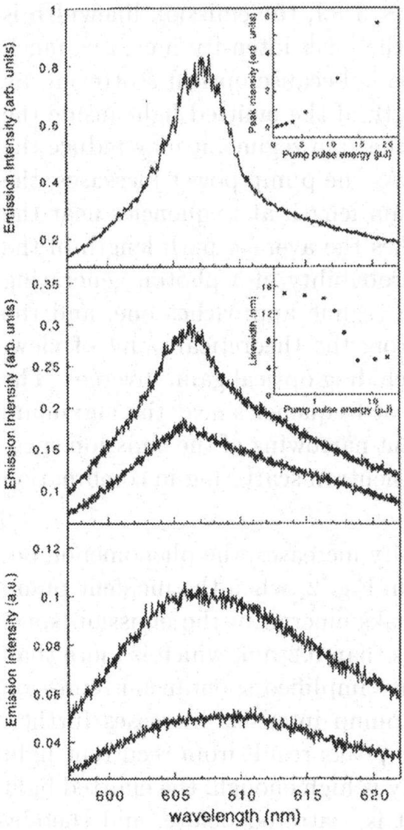

Fig. 1

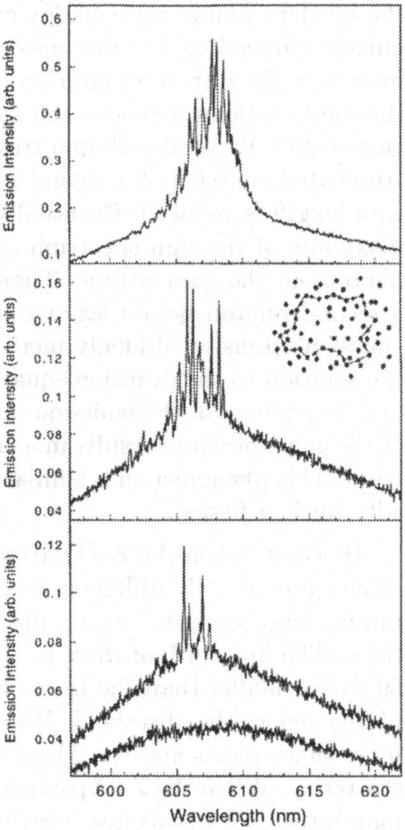

Fig. 2

Figure 1. **Emission spectra when the incident pump pulse energy is (from bottom to top) 0.68, 1.5, 2.3, 3.3, 5.6 μJ. The ZnO particle density is $\sim 3 \times 10^{11}$ cm^{-3}. The upper inset is the emission intensity at the peak wavelength versus the pump pulse energy. The middle inset is the emission linewidth versus the pump pulse energy.**

Figure 2. **Emission spectra when the incident pump pulse energy is (from bottom to top) 0.68, 1.1, 1.3, 2.9 μJ. The ZnO particle density is $\sim 1 \times 10^{12}$ cm^{-3}. The inset shows the emission intensity versus the pump pulse energy.**

vary the amount of scattering. Figures 1 and 2 show the evolution of the emission spectra with the pump intensity when the ZnO particle density is $\sim 2.5 \times 10^{11}$ cm^{-3} and $\sim 1.0 \times 10^{12}$ cm^{-3}, respectively. The dye concentration is fixed at 5×10^{-3} M. As shown in the inset of Fig. 1, when the incident pump pulse energy exceeds ~ 3 μJ, the emission linewidth is quickly reduced to ~ 5 nm; meanwhile, the peak intensity increases much more rapidly with the pump power. This is because optical scattering by the ZnO particles increases the path length of the emitted light inside the gain region. When the photon travels in the gain regime, it may induce the stimulated emission of a second photon. As the pump power increases, the gain length is reduced. Eventually the gain length at frequencies near the maximum of the gain spectrum approaches the average path length of the photons in the gain regime. Then the probability of a photon generating a second photon before leaving the gain regime approaches one, and the emission intensity suddenly increases. From the theoretical point of view, the solution to the diffusion equation, including optical gain, diverges. The drastic increase of the emission intensity at frequencies near the maximum of the gain spectrum results in a significant narrowing of the emission spectrum. This phenomenon is similar to the neutron scattering in combination with nuclear fission.

However, when the ZnO particle density increases, the phenomenon becomes dramatically different. As shown in Fig. 2, when the incident pump pulse energy exceeds 1.0 μJ, discrete peaks emerge in the emission spectrum. The linewidth of these peaks is less than 0.2 nm, which is more than 50 times smaller than the linewidth of the amplified spontaneous emission (ASE) below the threshold. When the pump intensity increases further, more sharp peaks appear. These discrete peaks result from recurrent light scattering. When the ZnO particle density is high enough, the emitted light may return to a scatterer from which it is scattered before, and thereby forming a closed loop path. When the amplification along such a loop path exceeds the loss, laser oscillation can occur in the loop which serves as a laser resonator. The requirement of the phase shift along the loop being equal to a multiple of 2π determines the oscillation frequencies. Laser emission from these cavities results in discrete narrow peaks in the emission spectrum. Because the ZnO particles are mobile in the solution, the frequencies of the lasing modes changes from pulse to pulse. The emission spectra in Figs. 1 and 2 are taken for a single pump pulse. When the pump power increases further, the gain exceeds the loss in more cavities formed by multiple scattering. Laser oscillation in those cavities gives additional peaks in the emission spectrum.

Furthermore, we have studied the transition from lasing with non-resonant feedback to lasing with resonant feedback. Figure 3 shows the evolution of the emission spectra with the pump intensity when the ZnO particle density is ~ 5×10^{11} cm^{-3}. As the pump power increases, a drastic spectral narrowing occurs first. Then at higher pump intensity, discrete narrow peaks emerge in the emission spectrum. In the solution, there is some but not a large probability of a photon scattered back to the same scatterer from which it is scattered before. In other words, the cavities formed by multiple scattering is quite lossy. The pump intensity required to reach lasing threshold in these cavities is high. Thus, the pump intensity first reaches the threshold where the gain length near the maximum of the gain spectrum becomes equal to the average path length of photons in the excitation volume. A significant spectral narrowing and a sudden increase of peak emission intensity occur, similar to what happens in Fig. 1. Then the pump intensity reaches a second threshold where the amplification along some closed loop paths formed by scattering exceeds the loss. Lasing oscillation occurs in these cavities, adding discrete peaks to the emission spectrum. However, the number of lasing modes in Fig. 3 is less than that in Fig. 2 under similar pump power. When the gain length and excitation volume are the same, a smaller number of scatterers leads to weaker optical scattering. Hence, the number of loops where the lasing threshold can be reached is less.

Therefore, we have demonstrated the transition from lasing with non-resonant feedback to lasing with resonant feedback by increasing the amount of optical scattering [20].

2. Random lasers with coherent feedback

In this section, we focus on our experimental studies of lasing with coherent feedback in highly disordered zinc oxide (ZnO) powder and polycrystalline films [17, 18, 21].

ZnO nanoparticles are synthesized with the precipitation reaction. The process involves the hydrolysis of zinc salt in a polyol medium. Through the process of electrophoresis, ZnO powder films are made. The film thickness varies from a few μm to 50 μm. Figure 4 (a) is the scanning electron microscope (SEM) image of the ZnO particles. The average particle size is about 50 nm.

We characterize the scattering mean free path l in the coherent backscattering (CBS) experiment [2, 3]. ZnO has a direct band gap of 3.3 eV. To avoid absorption, the frequency-doubled output (λ = 410 nm) of a mode-locked Ti:Sapphire laser (76 MHz repetition rate, 200 femtosecond pulse width) is used as the probe light. Figure 4 (b) shows the measured backscattering cone of the ZnO powder film. From the angle of cusp, we estimate that $l \approx 0.5\ \lambda$, after taking into account the internal reflection [22].

In the photoluminescence experiment, the ZnO powder film is optically pumped by the fourth harmonics (λ = 266 nm) of a mode-locked Nd:YAG laser. The pump beam is focused to a $\sim 20\ \mu$m spot on the film surface with normal incidence. Electrons in the valence band absorbed pump photons and jumped to the conduction band. They subsequently relaxed to the

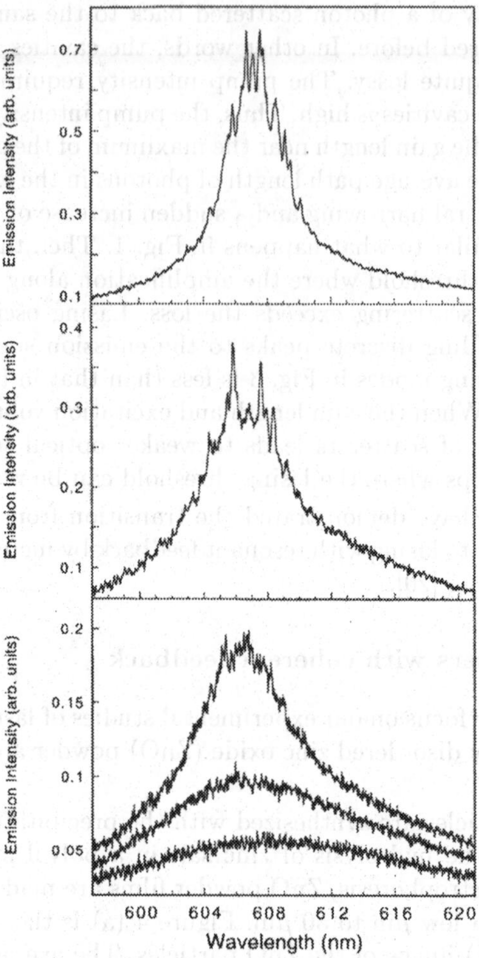

Figure 3. Emission spectra when the incident pump pulse energy is (from bottom to top) 0.74, 1.35, 1.7, 2.25, and 3.4 μJ. The ZnO particle density is $\sim 6 \times 10^{11}$ cm^{-3}.

bottom of the conduction band before radiative decay. The spectrum of emission from the powder film is measured by a spectrometer with 0.13 nm spectral resolution. At the same time, the spatial distribution of the emitted light intensity in the film is imaged by an ultraviolet (UV) microscope onto a UV sensitive charge-coupled device (CCD) camera. The amplification of the microscope is about 100 times. The spatial resolution is around 0.24 μm. A bandpass filter is placed in front of the microscope objective to block the pump light.

Figure 5 shows the measured spectra and spatial distribution of emission in a ZnO powder film at different pump power. At low pump intensity,

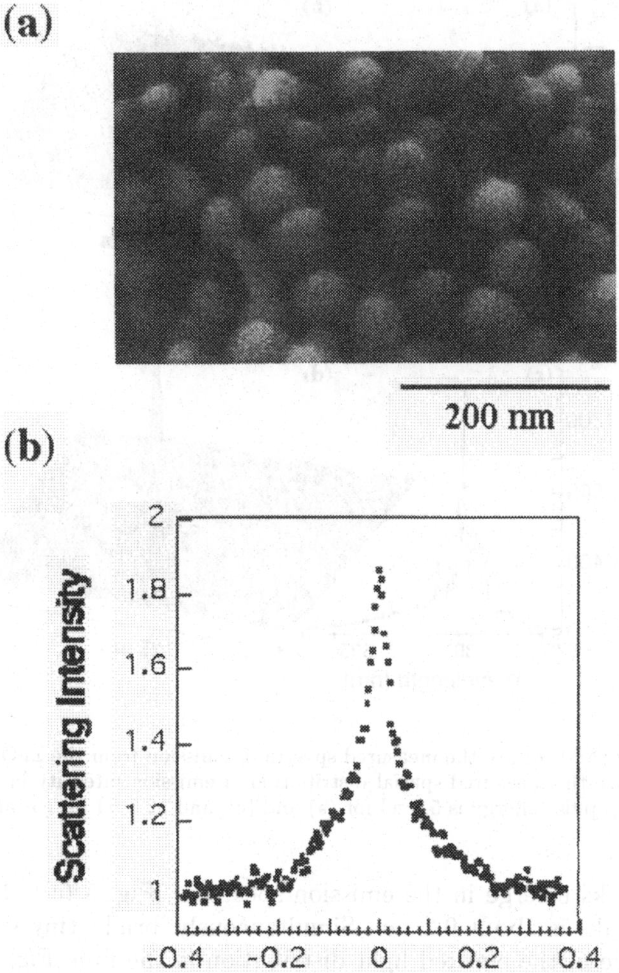

Figure 4. (a) SEM image of the ZnO nanoparticles. (b) Measured backscattering cone from the ZnO powder film.

the spectrum consists of a single broad spontaneous emission peak. Its full width at half maximum (FWHM) is about 12 nm [Fig. 5 (a)]. In Fig. 5 (b), the spatial distribution of the spontaneous emission intensity is smooth across the excitation area. Due to the pump intensity variation over the excitation spot, the spontaneous emission in the center of the excitation spot is stronger. When the pump intensity exceeds a threshold, very narrow

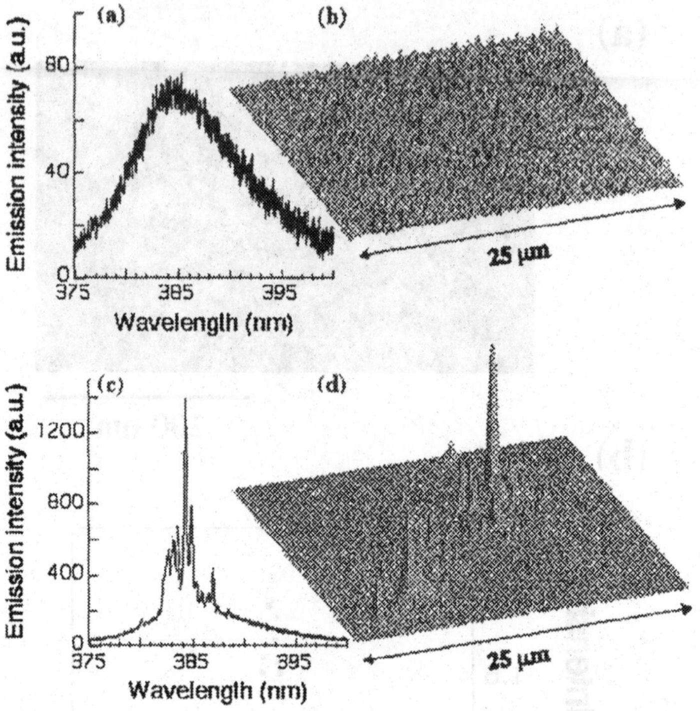

Figure 5. (a) and (c) are the measured spectra of emission from the ZnO powder film. (b) and (d) are the measured spatial distribution of emission intensity in the film. The incident pump pulse energy is 5.2 nJ for (a) and (c), and 12.5 nJ for (b) and (d).

discrete peaks emerge in the emission spectrum [Fig. 5 (c)]. The FWHM of these peaks is about 0.2 nm. Simultaneously, bright tiny spots appear in the image of the emitted light distribution in the film [Fig. 5 (d)]. The size of the bright spots is between 0.3 and 0.7 μm. When the pump intensity is increased further, additional sharp peaks emerge in the emission spectrum. Correspondingly, more bright spots appear in the image of the emitted light distribution. The frequencies of the sharp peaks depends on the sample position. Namely, when we move the excitation spot across the film, the frequencies of the sharp peaks change. Figure 6 plots the spectrally integrated emission intensity as a function of the pump power. A threshold behavior is clearly seen: above the pump power at which multiple sharp peaks emerged in the emission spectrum, the integrated emission intensity increased much more rapidly with the pump power.

We also measured the temporal profile of the emission from the ZnO powder film with a Hamamatsu streak camera. As the pump power exceeds

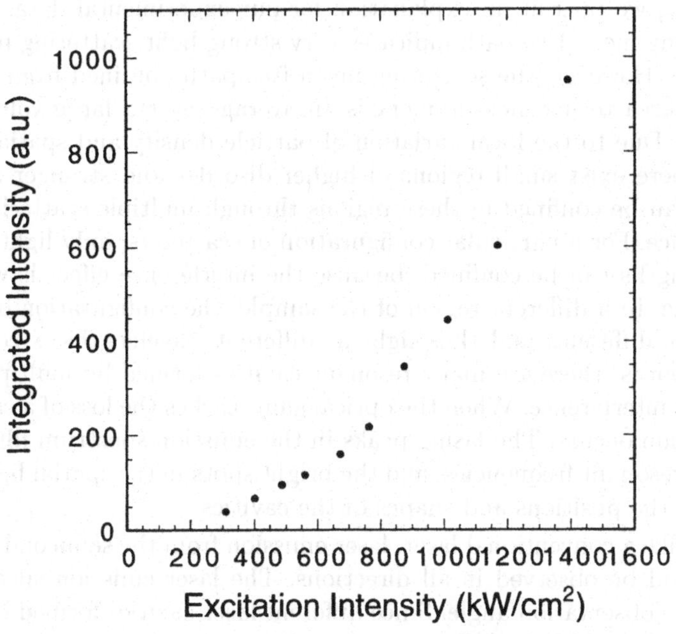

Figure 6. Spectrally integrated intensity of emission from the ZnO powder versus the excitation intensity.

the threshold, the emission pulse is dramatically shortened from 200 to 30 ps. From the threshold behavior of the emission intensity, the very narrow spectral peaks, and the dramatic shortening of the emission pulses, we conclude that lasing occurs in the ZnO powder film.

The experimental fact that the bright spots in the emission pattern and the lasing modes in the emission spectrum always appear simultaneously suggests that the bright spots are related to the laser light. There seems to be two possible explanations for the bright spots. One is the laser light intensity at the locations of the bright spots is high. The other is the laser light is not particularly strong at the locations of the bright spots. However, there are some efficient scattering centers at the locations of the bright spots, and thus the laser light is strongly scattered. In the latter case, these scattering centers should also strongly scatter the spontaneously emitted light below the lasing threshold, because scattering is a linear process. Hence, these bright spots should exist below the lasing threshold. However, there are no bright spots below the lasing threshold. Therefore, these bright spots are caused not by efficient scatterers, but by the strong laser light in the medium.

Next, we present an explanation for our experimental data. The short scattering mean free path indicates very strong light scattering in the powder film. However, the scattering mean free path obtained from the coherent backscattering measurement is an average over a large volume of the sample. Due to the local variation of particle density and spatial distribution, there exist small regions of higher disorder and stronger scattering. Light can be confined in these regions through multiple scattering and interference. For a particular configuration of scatterers, only light at certain wavelengths can be confined, because the interference effect is wavelength sensitive. In a different region of the sample, the configuration of the scatterers is different, and thus light at different wavelengths is confined. In other words, there are many resonant cavities formed by multiple scattering and interference. When the optical gain reaches the loss of a cavity, laser oscillation occurs. The lasing peaks in the emission spectrum illustrate the cavity resonant frequencies, and the bright spots in the spatial light pattern exhibit the positions and shapes of the cavities.

Unlike a conventional laser, laser emission from the semiconductor powder could be observed in all directions. The laser emission spectra varied with the observation angle. Since different laser cavities formed by multiple scattering could have different output directions, lasing modes observed at different angles are different.

3. Microlasers made of disordered media

Disorder-induced optical scattering not only provides coherent feedback for lasing, but also leads to spatial confinement of light in micrometer-sized volume. Based on this new physical mechanism of optical confinement, we have fabricated microlasers with disordered medium [23].

The micrometer-sized random material is made of ZnO powder. The ZnO nanoparticles are synthesized with precipitation reaction. The process involves hydrolysis of zinc salt in a polyol medium. Specifically, 0.05 mol of zinc acetate dihydrate is added to 300 ml diethylene glycol. The solution is heated to 160° C. As the solution is heated, more zinc acetate is dissociated. When the Zn^{2+} concentration in the solution exceeds the nucleation threshold, ZnO nanocrystallites precipitate and agglomerate to form clusters. The size of the clusters can be controlled by varying the rate at which the solution is heated. The inset of Fig. 7 is the scanning electron microscope (SEM) image of a typical ZnO cluster. The ZnO nanocrystallites have an average size of $\sim$ 50 nm. The size of the clusters varies from submicron to a few micron.

The ZnO cluster is optically pumped by the fourth harmonics ($\lambda = 266$ nm) of a mode-locked Nd:YAG laser (10 Hz repetition rate, 15 picosecond

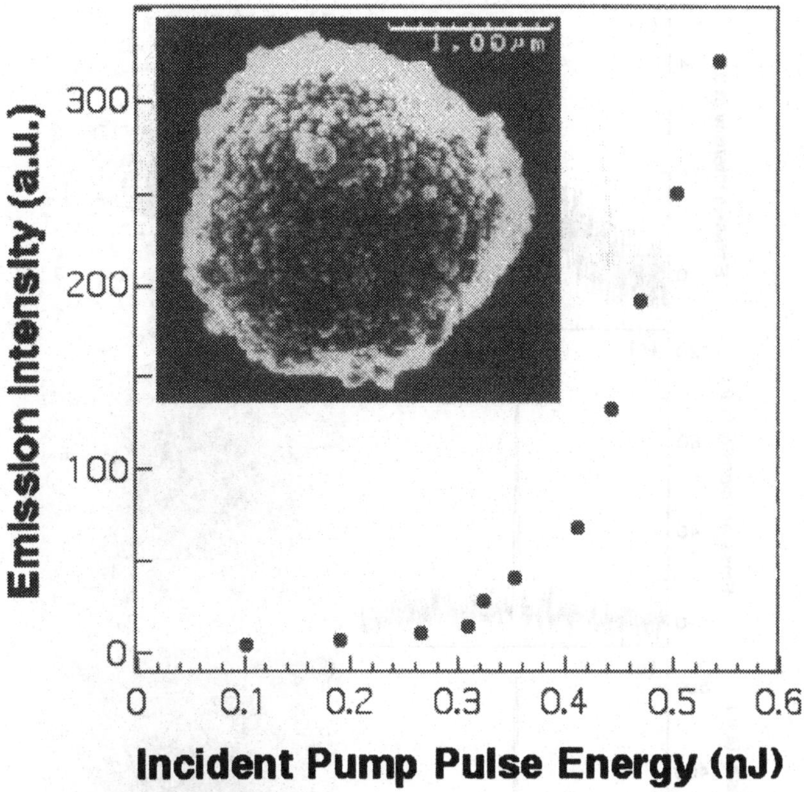

Figure 7. Spectrally integrated intensity of emission from the ZnO cluster versus the incident pump pulse energy. The inset is the SEM image of the ZnO cluster.

pulse width). The pump light is focused by a microscope objective onto a single cluster. The spectrum of emission from the cluster is measured by a spectrometer with 0.13 nm spectral resolution. In the meanwhile, the spatial distribution of the emitted light intensity in the cluster is imaged by an ultraviolet (UV) microscope onto a UV sensitive CCD camera. The amplification of the microscope is $\sim$ 100 times. The spatial resolution is $\sim$ 0.25 μm. A bandpass filter is placed in front of the microscope objective to block the pump light.

We have performed optical measurement of the cluster shown in the inset of Fig. 7. The pump light is focused by a microscope objective onto this cluster. The size of the cluster is $\sim$ 1.7 μm. It contains $\sim$ 20000 ZnO nanocrystallites. As shown in Fig. 8 (a), at low pump power, the emission spectrum consists of a single broad spontaneous emission peak. Its full with at half maximum (FWHM) is 12 nm. The spatial distribution of the spontaneous emission intensity is uniform across the cluster [see Fig. 8 (b)]. When

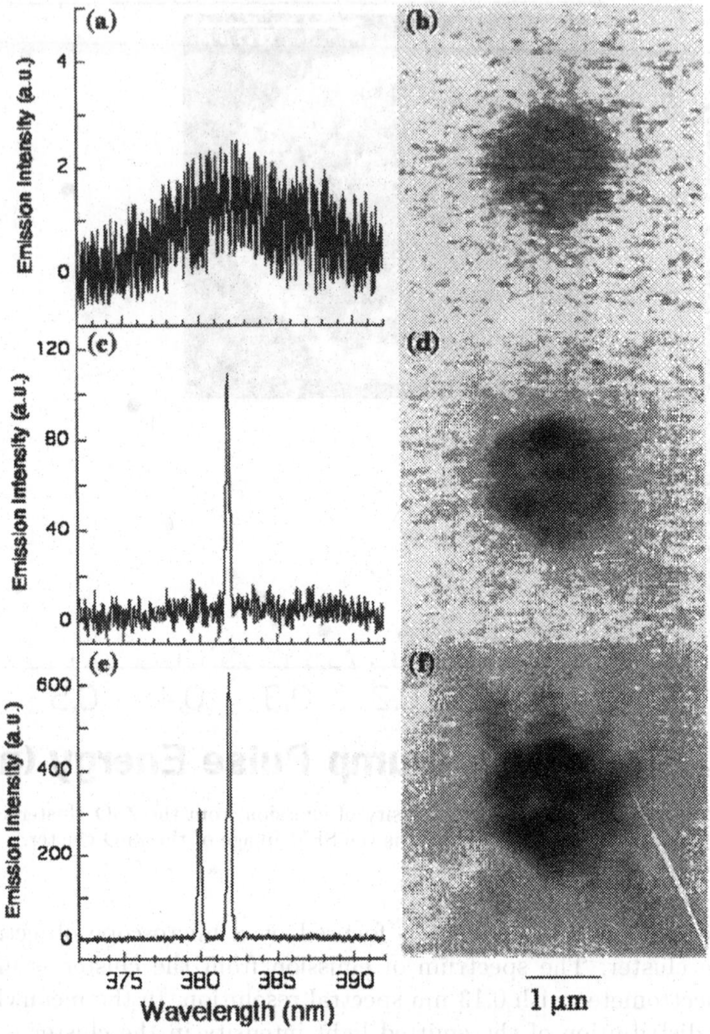

Figure 8. (a), (c), and (e) are the spectra of emission from the ZnO cluster shown in fig. 1. (b), (d), and (f) are the corresponding spatial distribution of emission intensity in the cluster. The incident pump pulse energy is 0.26 nJ for (a) and (b), 0.35 nJ for (c) and (d), and 0.50 nJ for (e) and (f).

the pump power exceeds a threshold, a sharp peak emerges in the emission spectrum shown in Fig. 8 (c). Its FWHM is 0.22 nm. Simultaneously, a couple of bright spots appear in the image of the emitted light distribution in the cluster in Fig. 8 (d). The size of the bright spot is ~ 0.3 μm. When the pump power is increased further, a second sharp peak emerges in the emission spectrum [see Fig. 8 (e)]. Correspondingly, additional bright spots appear in the image of the emitted light distribution in Fig. 8 (f).

As shown in Fig. 7, above the pump power at which sharp spectral peaks and bright spots appear, the emission intensity increases much more rapidly with the pump power. These data suggest that lasing action has occurred in the micrometer-sized cluster. The incident pump pulse energy at the lasing threshold is ~ 0.3 nJ. Note that only ~ 1 % of the incident pump light is absorbed. The rest is scattered.

The highly disordered structure of the cluster leads to strong light scattering. Hence, light can be trapped inside the cluster through the process of multiple scattering and wave interference. For the particular configuration of scatterers in a cluster, only light at certain frequencies can be localized, because the interference effect is wavelength sensitive. Because of the finite size of the random medium, some photons escape through the surface of the cluster. This gives rise to the loss of a localization cavity. When the optical gain exceeds the loss of a localization cavity, laser oscillation occurs in the cavity mode. The spatial distribution of the laser light intensity exhibits the spatial profile of the cavity mode. There may be several localization cavities in a cluster. Since different localization cavities have different losses, their lasing thresholds are different. Thus, with an increase of optical gain, lasing occurs in a second localization cavity, leading to an additional peak in the emission spectrum. The simultaneous addition of bright spots in the spatial light pattern not only confirms that lasing occurs in a different cavity, but also reveals the spatial profile of the cavity mode.

Since the cluster is very small, optical reflection from the boundary of the cluster might have some contribution to light confinement in the cluster. However, the laser cavity is not formed by total internal reflection at the boundary. Otherwise, the spatial pattern of laser light would be a bright ring near the edge of the cluster.

4. Theoretical modeling

Several models have been set up in the theoretical study of the stimulated emission in an active random medium, e.g., the diffusion equation with gain [13, 14], the Monte Carlo simulation [16], and the ring laser with non-resonant feedback [15]. However, these models cannot predict lasing with coherent feedback because the phase of the optical field is neglected. We take a different approach: namely, we directly calculate the electromagnetic field distribution in a random medium by solving the Maxwell equations using the finite-difference time-domain (FDTD) method [24]. The advantage of this approach is that we can model the real structure of a disordered medium, and calculate both the emission pattern and the emission spectrum.

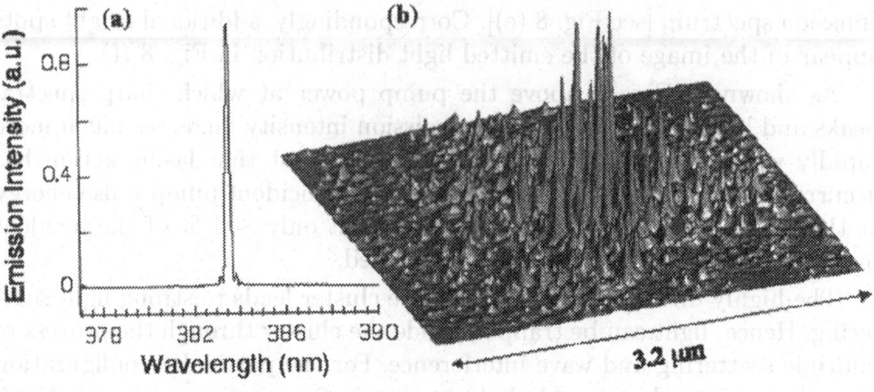

Figure 9. (a) The calculated emission spectrum. (b) The calculated spatial distribution of emission intensity in the random medium.

In our model, ZnO particles are randomly distributed in space. The particle size is 50 nm. The random medium has a finite size, and it is surrounded by air. To model the situation that the random medium is located in infinitely large space, we use the uniaxial perfect matched layer (UPML) absorbing boundary condition to absorb all the outgoing light wave in the air [25]. We solve the Maxwell curl equations

$$\begin{aligned} \frac{\partial \vec{H}}{\partial t} &= - \frac{1}{\mu_0} \nabla \times \vec{E} \\ \frac{\partial \vec{E}}{\partial t} &= \frac{1}{\epsilon} \nabla \times \vec{H} - \frac{\sigma}{\epsilon} \vec{E} \end{aligned} \tag{1}$$

in the time domain after introducing optical gain by negative conductance σ [26]. The randomness is introduced to the Maxwell equations through the dielectric constant ε, which varies spatially due to the random distribution of the ZnO particles. The refractive index of ZnO is about 2.3.

In our simulation, a seed pulse, whose spectrum covers the ZnO emission spectrum, is launched in the center of the random medium at $t = 0$. When the optical gain is above the lasing threshold, the electromagnetic field oscillation builds up in the time domain. Using the discrete Fourier transform of the time domain data, we obtain the emission spectrum. Figure 9 shows the calculated emission spectrum and emission pattern for a specific configuration of scatterers. The size of the random medium is 3.2 μm. The filling factor of ZnO particles is 0.5. When the optical gain is just above the lasing threshold, the emission spectrum, shown in Fig. 9 (a), consists of a single peak. Figure 9 (b) represents the light intensity distribution in the random medium. There are a few bright spots near the center. At the edge of the random medium, the light intensity is almost zero. To check the effect of the boundary, we change the spatial distribution of the scatterers near the edges of the random medium. We find both the emission frequency and the emission pattern remain the same. Their independence of the boundary condition indicates that the lasing mode is formed by multiple scattering and interference inside the disordered medium. When the optical gain is increased further, additional lasing modes appear.

In summary, we have observed lasing with resonant feedback in active random media. Disorder-induced optical scattering provides coherent feedback for lasing. When the pump power exceeds the threshold, discrete lasing modes appear in the spectrum, the emission intensity increases significantly, and the emission pulses are shortened dramatically. The laser emission from the random media can be observed in all directions.

In addition, we have achieved spatial confinement of laser light in micrometer-sized random media. Since the scattering mean free path is less than the optical wavelength, the optical confinement is attributed to the disorder-induced scattering and interference. Using the finite-difference time-domain method, we simulate lasing with coherent feedback in active random media. We find that the lasing modes are insensitive to the boundary conditions.

This work is supported partially by the United States National Science Foundation under Grant No. ECS-9877113. H. C. acknowledges support from the David and Lucile Packard Foundation.

References

1. S. John, *Phys. Today*, 32 (May, 1991).
2. M. P. van Albada, and A. Lagendijk, *Phys. Rev. Lett.* **55**, 2692 (1985).
3. P. E. Wolf, and G. Maret, *Phys. Rev. Lett.* **55**, 2696 (1985).
4. A. Z. Genack, and N. Garcia, *Phys. Rev. Lett.* **66**, 2064 (1991).
5. R. Dalichaouch, J. P. Armstrong, S. Schultz, P. M. Platzman, and S. L. McCall, *Nature* **354**, 53 (1991).
6. D. S. Wiersma, P. Bartolini, A. Lagendijk, and R. Righini, *Nature* **390**, 671 (1997).
7. F. J. P. Schuurmans, D. Vanmaekelbergh, J. van de Lagemaat, and A. Lagendijk, *Science* **284**, 141 (1999).
8. F. J. P. Schuurmans, M. Megens, D. Vanmaekelbergh, and A. Lagendijk, *Phys. Rev. Lett* **83**, 2183 (1999).
9. N. M. Lawandy, R. M. Balachandran, A. S. L. Gomes, and E. Sauvain, *Nature* **368**, 436 (1994)
10. W. Sha, C.-H. Liu, and R. Alfano, *Opt. Lett.* **19**, 1922 (1994).
11. C. Gouedard, D. Husson, C. Sauteret, F. Auzel, and A. Migus, *J. Opt. Soc. Am. B* **10**, 2358 (1993).
12. V. S. Letokhov, *Sov. Phys. JETP* **26**, 835 (1968).
13. D. S. Wiersma, and A. Lagendijk, *Phys. Rev. E* **54**, 4256 (1996).
14. S. John, and G. Pang, *Phys. Rev. A* **54**, 3642 (1996).
15. R. M. Balachandran, and N. M. Lawandy, *Opt. Lett.* **22**, 319 (1997).

16. G. A. Berger, M. Kempe, and A. Z. Genack, *Phys. Rev. E* **56**, 6118 (1997).
17. H. Cao, Y. G. Zhao, H. C. Ong, S. T. Ho, J. Y. Dai, J. Y. Wu, and R. P. H. Chang, *Appl. Phys. Lett.* **73**, 3656 (1998).
18. H. Cao, Y. G. Zhao, S. T. Ho, E. W. Seelig, Q. H. Wang, and R. P. H. Chang, *Phys. Rev. Lett.* **82**, 2278 (1999).
19. S. V. Frolov, Z. V. Vardeny, K. Yoshino, A. Zakhidov, and R. H. Baughman, *Phys. Rev. B* **59**, 5284 (1999).
20. H. Cao, J. Y.Xu, S.-H. Chang, and S. T. Ho, *Phys. Rev. Lett.* **61**, 1985 (2000).
21. H. Cao, J. Y. Xu, D. Z. Zhang, S.-H. Chang, S. T. Ho, E. W. Seelig, X. Liu, and R. P. H. Chang, *Phys. Rev. Lett.* **84**, 5584 (2000).
22. J. X. Zhu, D. J. Pine, and D. A. Weitz, *Phys. Rev. A* **44**, 3948 (1991).
23. H. Cao, J. Y. Xu, E. W. Seelig, and R. P. H. Chang, *Appl. Phys. Lett.* **76**, 2997 (2000).
24. A. Taflove, *Computational Electrodynamics The Finite-Difference Time Domain Method* (Artech House, 1995).
25. Z. S. Sacks, D. M. Kingsland, R. Lee, and J. F. Lee, *IEEE Trans. Antennas and Propagation* **43**, 1460 (1995).
26. S. C. Hagness, R. M. Joseph, and A. Taflove, *Radio Science* **31**, 931 (1996).

ANALYSIS OF RANDOM LASERS IN THIN FILMS OF π-CONJUGATED POLYMERS

R.C. Polson, J.D. Huang, and Z.V. Vardeny
Department of Physics, University of Utah, Salt Lake City, UT 84112

Abstract

Mirrorless laser action has been observed in thin films of a π-conjugated polymer. The many mode emission spectrum from a stripe excitation geometry suggests true lasing. Analytical tools developed for microring polymer lasers are applied to the laser emission spectra of films to determine the dominant resonator lengths. Using the coherent backscattering technique the light mean free path, l^* is determined to be $15\mu m$. With the obtained resonator loops of 155 μm, the dominant laser cavity consists of $\sim$10 scatterers.

1. Introduction

The familiar configuration of a laser consists of an active gain medium placed inside a cavity resonator that consists of two mirrors. The light beam reflects inside the resonator, stimulates emission in the gain medium to obtain optical amplification, and eventually escapes through one of the mirrors. Laser action has also been shown in systems with no clear cavities, such as saturated scatterers in dye solutions [1], films of π-conjugated polymers [2], and semiconductor polycrystalline films [3]. These disordered systems rely on scattering in the medium to provide optical feedback necessary for laser emission. Coherent backscattering measurements[4-6] can give a value for the light mean free path inside the medium.

In this work we show that Fourier transform of the emission spectra can provide an effective cavity length inside the disordered polymer films. The cavity length may be related to the mean free path inside the film determined by the method of coherent backscattering.

C.M. Soukoulis (ed.), Photonic Crystals and Light Localization in the 21st Century, 405–415.

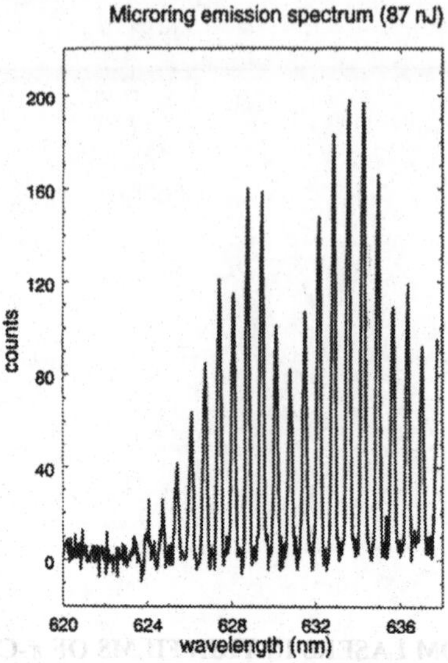

Figure 1: Typical DOO-PPV polymer microring emission spectrum for a 125 μm diameter core at an excitation energy per pulse of 87 nJ.

2. Microring polymer laser

We begin with a laser system that has a known resonator in order to develop the machinery used to later analyze the laser emission of polymer films. The polymer microring laser is an optically pumped device which consists of a thin layer of active medium supported by a cylindrical glass core[7]. The polymer microring laser devices studied here were made from poly(dioctyloxy) phenylene vinylene, DOOPPV, which was synthesized by modifying a published procedure[8]. A thin polymer film was self-assembled to coat glass fibers with diameter of 125 μm[9]. These devices were excited with the second harmonic of a Nd:YAG laser at 532 nm with pulses lasting 100 ps at 100 Hz repetition rate. The measurements were done in a dynamic rough vacuum of 2 torr. The excitation beam was focused through a cylindrical lens that excited a narrow stripe on the coated fiber. The emission light was collected using a second fiber (1 mm in diameter) approximately 3 cm from the microring laser and sent to a Spex 1200 triple spectrometer, where a charged coupled device (CCD) camera recorded the light intensity. The overall spectral resolution was 0.05 nm. Figure 1 is a typical emission spectrum of a DOO-PPV microring polymer laser above threshold at an excitation energy, E_p of 87 nJ per pulse.

One simple model system to use when analyzing the emission spectra of microrings is a Fabry-Perot cavity. The microring geometry is not exactly the same, nevertheless this model has been used successfully[10]. An important property of a Fabry-Perot cavity is the mode spacing with a constant index of refraction, n, and mirror spacing, L. The expected mode spacing is then given by

$$\Delta\lambda = \frac{\lambda^2}{2nL} = \frac{\lambda^2}{\pi n D}, \tag{1}$$

where λ is wavelength. In the case of a microring, the round trip cavity length 2L in Eq. (1) is replaced by the circumference, πD, where D is the diameter of the ring. For the spectrum in Fig. 1 the separation ranges from 0.65-0.70 nm that corresponds to nD between 178-183 μm. Assuming a diameter of 125μm, this gives n as 1.424-1.624 which is an intermediate value not between the refractive index of the glass core of 1.5 and that of the polymer of 1.7, but between the polymer and the surrounding vacuum.

The next often discussed property of Fabry-Perot cavities is either the resolving power of an interferometer, or the Q factor of the resonator [11]. This is given by

$$Q = \frac{2\pi nL}{\lambda}\frac{\sqrt{r}}{1-r} \quad . \tag{2}$$

In Eq. (2) r is defined as $R\exp((\gamma-\alpha)L)$, where R is the mirror reflectivity γ is the gain per unit length and α is the loss per unit length. When r >1, then Eq. (2) is no longer valid since a negative Q value has no meaning. In the realm where Eq. (2) is not valid the important criterion for lasing is met; namely gain exceeds loss. Q has other definitions too; one such definition comes from the laser mode line width, $\delta\lambda$, that can be measured directly from the emission spectrum near the threshold excitation intensity. This defines Q as:

$$Q = \frac{\lambda}{\delta\lambda}, \tag{3}$$

where $\delta\lambda$ is the full width at half maximum of a longitudinal laser emission mode. The Q value can also tell the photon coherence time inside the laser resonator [11] that is

$$Q = \omega\tau, \tag{4}$$

where ω is the laser angular frequency and τ is the characteristic time.

The Fourier transform of the emission spectrum gives a more accurate value of nL than that extracted from $\delta\lambda$. The expected intensity of the Fourier transform of a Fabry-Perot cavity was derived in Ref. [12] . It consists of a series of equally spaced diminishing lines given by

$$I(d) = |1 - Rexp(2i\Phi)|^2 \sum_{m=0}^{\infty}\sum_{l=0}^{\infty} \frac{R^{l+m} exp(-2i\Phi(l-m))}{kL(l+m+1) + i(\pi d + nL(l-m))} \quad . \tag{5}$$

In Eq. (5) k is the wavevector, k=$2\pi/\lambda$, d is the conjugate variable to wavevector, l, m are integers, Φ is the phase change upon reflection at the mirrors, and R is the mirror reflectivity. The important part of this expression is that peaks are produced whenever the imaginary part of the denominator goes to zero. This occurs when d is a multiple of nL/π or nD/2 with the circular geometry of a microring.

In simple cases of small absorption and narrow wavelength window [13], then the ratio of one Fourier transform harmonic peak to the next is r, which is given by

$$r = R\exp((\gamma-\alpha)L), \tag{6}$$

where α is loss and γ is gain per unit length. The numeric value of the ratio can be also substituted into Eq. (2) to obtain a variant Q to Eq. (3).

Figure 2 is the Fourier transform of the microring emission spectrum of Fig. 1 plotted on a linear scale; the inset is the same Fourier transform plotted on a logarithmic scale. If the emission spectrum is measured in wavevector space, k=$2\pi/\lambda$, with unconventional units of μm^{-1}, then the units of the Fourier transform come out in μm. Multiple, evenly spaced harmonics are readily seen in Fig. 2. The large component at d=0 is uninteresting as it

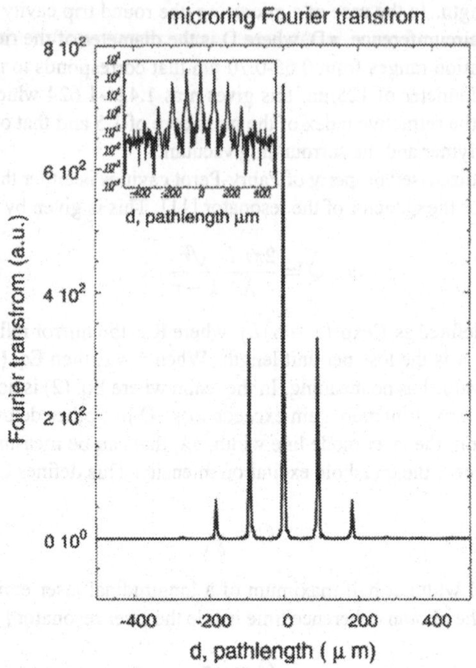

Figure 2: Fourier transform of the polymer microring laser shown in Fig. 1. The inset is the same figure plotted on a semi-log scale.

corresponds to a "dc offset" which only indicates that the emission spectrum is not symmetric about zero. The first peak is theoretically at d=nD/2 and has a numeric value from the Fourier transform of 91.1μm. The second peak is theoretically d=nD and has a value from the Fourier transform of 182.3μm. Additionally, with this accurate value for nD, one can assign each emission peak to an integral Bessel function [14]. From Fig. 1 the FWHM of the maximum peak at 633.6 nm is 0.25 nm. This gives a Q value of 2500 using Eq. (3). From Eq. (4) the laser coherence time is $\sim$ 1 ps.

Equation (2) has a singularity when r =1, at lasing threshold. Additionally, at excitation energies, E_p, above the threshold, E_0, Q would have a negative value. The functional dependence of Q on I changes sharply at lasing threshold. A similar change in r versus E_p is expected near threshold. In Fig. 3 we plot the emission intensity versus excitation energy, E_p, for the microring laser shown in Fig. 1. There is a clear change of slope near E_p =60 nj/pulse. The lower inset of Fig. 3 is r vs E, again there is a clear change at E_p =55 nj/pulse, where r goes from increasing to decreasing. We therefore conjecture that the device threshold excitation energy E_0 is between 55 and 63 nJ. The top inset of Fig. 3 is the emission at E_p = 49 nj/pulse. There are clear modes present below E_0. Since the Q factor of the microring cavity is high, these are not lasing modes because loss is greater than gain, but cavity modes.

For the two points with $E_p < E_0$ that still show cavity modes and using Eq. (6), we calculate the loss and gain per unit length. The amplitude ratio of the peaks in the Fourier transform gives us r. Assuming a linear relation between gain and excitation energy, E_p, i.e., $\gamma = gE_p$, with g a constant, then α is 29.2 cm^{-1} and g=469.6 $(cm\ \mu j)^{-1}$.

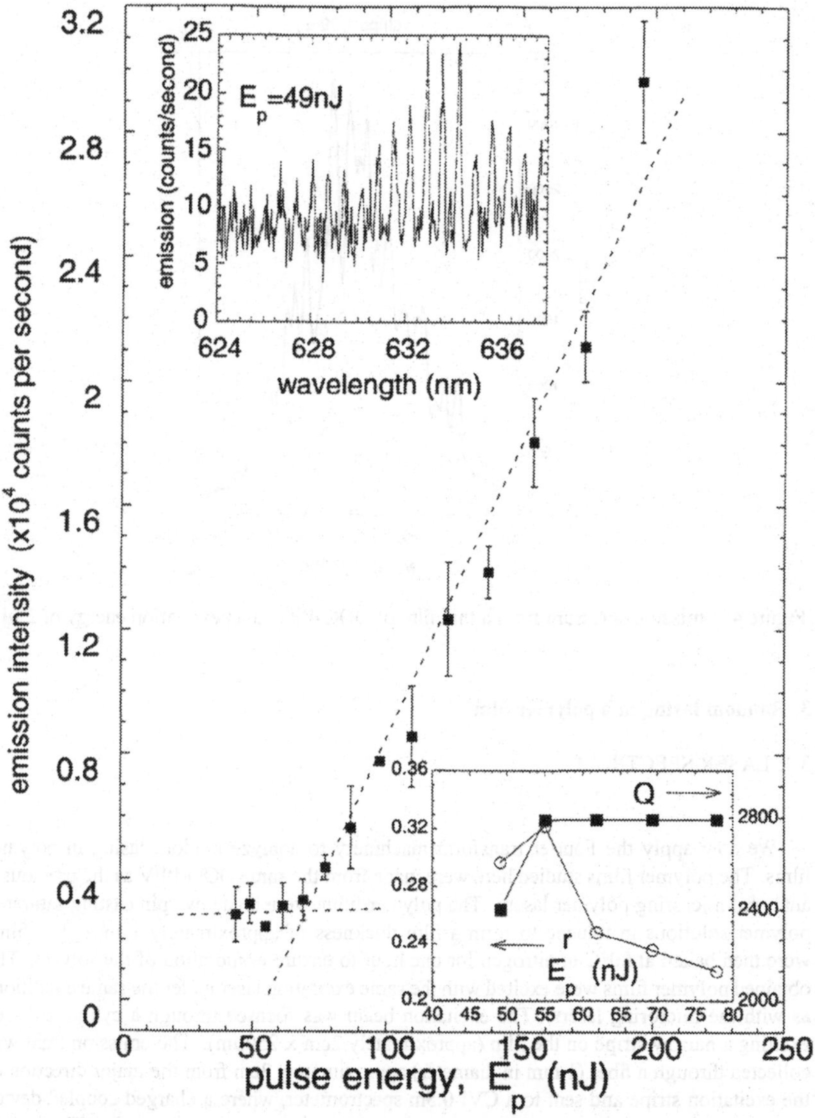

Figure 3: Emission intensity versus excitation pulse energy, E_p, for the polymer microring laser. The top inset is the first emission spectrum below threshold. The bottom inset is r and Q vs. E_p.

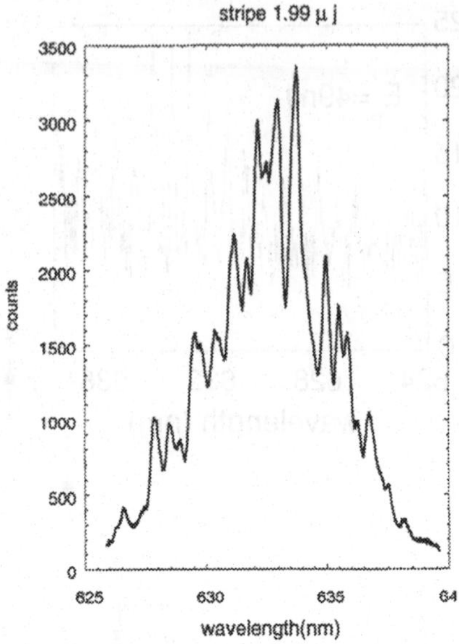

Figure 4: Emission spectrum from a thin film of DOO-PPV at an excitation energy of 2 μj.

3. Random lasing in a polymer film

3.1. LASER SPECTRUM

We now apply the Fourier transform machinery to analyze random lasing in polymer films. The polymer films studied here were made from the same DOO-PPV as the previously analyzed microring polymer lasers. The polymer films were made by spin casting saturated polymer solutions in toluene to form a film thickness of approximately 1 μm. The films were then baked at 80°C in nitrogen for one hour to ensure evaporation of the solvent. The obtained polymer films were excited with the same excitation laser under the same conditions as with the microring lasers. The excitation beam was focused through a cylindrical lens exciting a narrow stripe on the film (approximately 2cm x 250μm). The emission light was collected through a fiber (1 mm in diameter) approximately 3cm from the major direction of the excitation stripe and sent to a CVI 0.5m spectrometer, where a charged coupled device camera (Santa Barbara Instrument Group) recorded the emission light intensity. The overall spectral resolution for this spectrometer and CCD was 0.02 nm.

Figure 4 is a typical spectrum of random lasing from a DOO-PPV polymer film. One important note is that the entire spectrum is reproducible at the same excitation intensity and film spot. No intentional scatterers were added to the film. Local density variations or dust particles may be the scatterers; these will be collectively referred to as inhomogeneities. The emission spectrum changes at different excitation intensities or different spots on the polymer film, since different paths or random cavities inside the film may fit the requirement of gain.

Figure 5 is the absolute value of the Fourier transform for the thin film emission of Fig. 4. Once again, the peak at d=0 is uninteresting, since it is caused by the values of the recorded emission spectrum being positive. Although every component is important in creating the

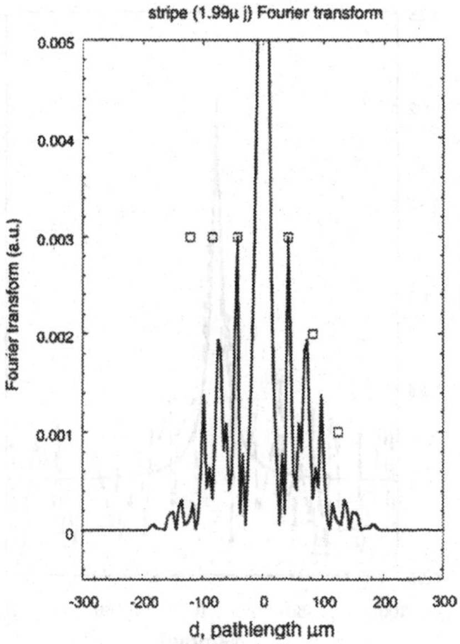

Figure 5: Fourier transform of the film emission spectrum in Fig. 4. The square symbols indicate the main peak, twice the main peak, and three times the main peak. The third peak is not the third harmonic of the first.

final spectrum, three dominant transform peaks occur at d$\simeq$ 41, 74, 97μm. The discrete spacing of points in the Fourier transform is 4.5μm, the second peak can be considered as a multiple of the first harmonic. The third peak is not the third multiple of the first peak, this is illustrated with the square symbols in Fig. 4. The peak at 97μm may correspond to the first harmonic of a second cavity. Alternatively, it may be the third harmonic of the first peak of a very anharmonic cavity. The round trip optical pathlengths in real space are $2\pi d$, which are 260 and 610μm, respectively. We note that both of these cavity lengths are much greater than the film thickness of 1μm, indicating that internal reflection between the film and substrate or vacuum is not a fundamental length scale for the laser emission.

3.2. COHERENT BACKSCATTERING

The traditional technique to study light scattering processes in a disordered medium is coherent backscattering[4-6]. The slope and shape of the backscattered cone near zero degree angle give an indication of the light mean free path, l^*, within the medium[15]. Coherent backscattering was measured in a thick aggregation (approx. 3mm) of DOO-PPV as shown in Fig. 6. Ensemble averaging of approximately 50 slightly different initial inclination angles and sample translations were necessary to obtain a build-up of the coherent backscattering cone seen in Fig. 6. From the shape of the cone in Fig. 6, a light mean free path (l^*) of approximately 15 μm is determined.

From direct measurement of line widths of the spectrum in Fig. 4, Q for random cavity in the film is about 450. Taking the value for Q, we calculate from Eq. (4) the average photon

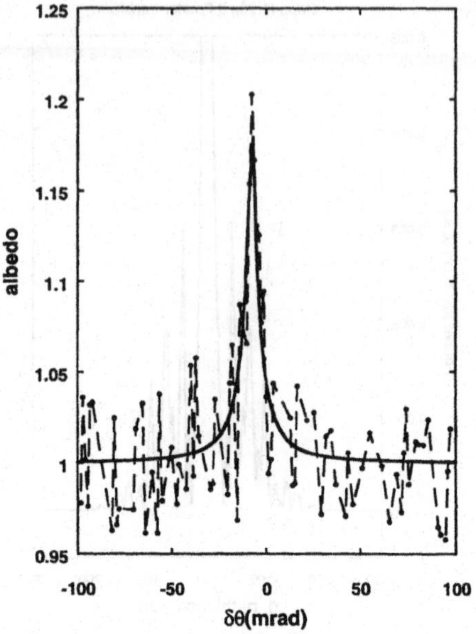

Figure 6: Coherent backscattering cone in the albedo from a DOO-PPV film with no optical gain. The cone was measured by ensemble averaging 50 different spot illuminations.

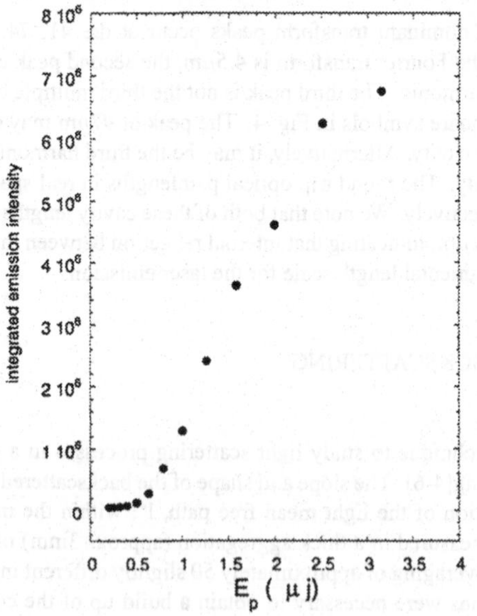

Figure 7: Emission intensity versus excitation energy per pulse for the random laser in the film.

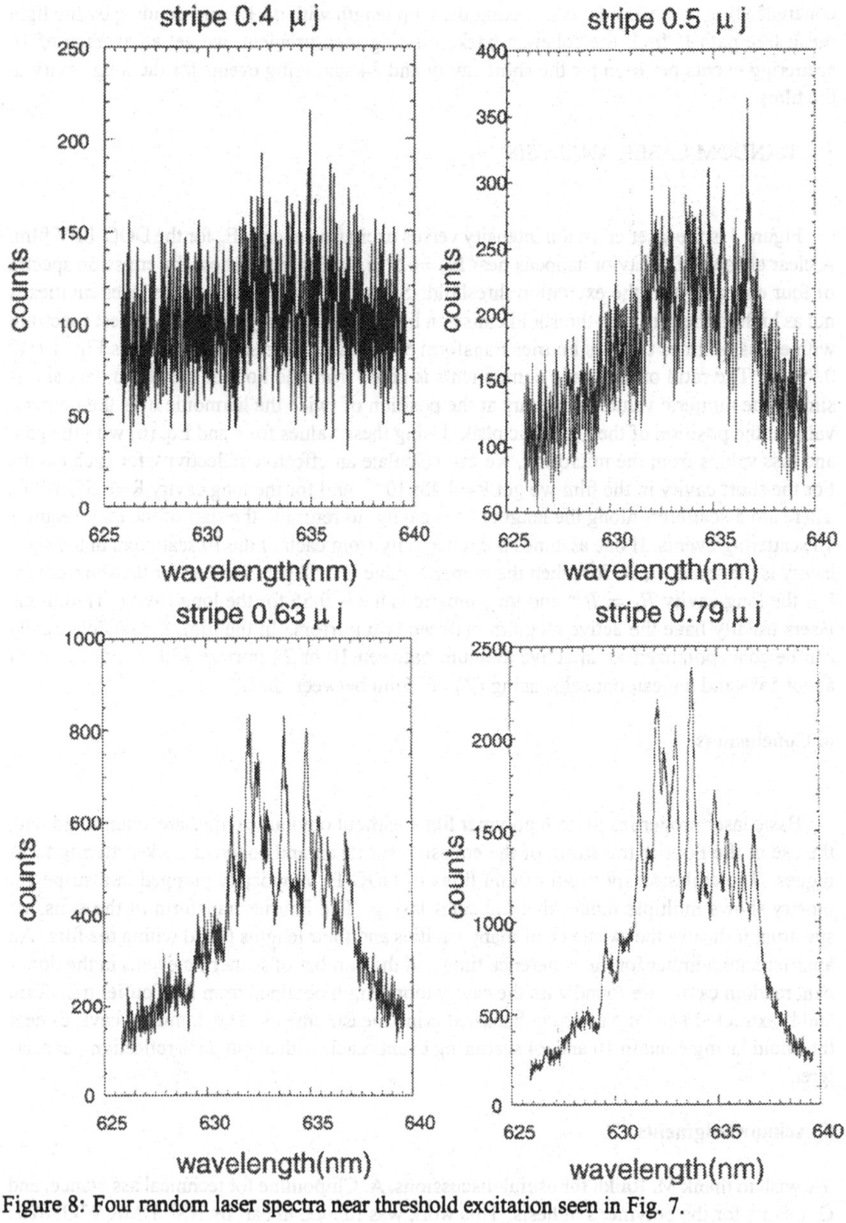

Figure 8: Four random laser spectra near threshold excitation seen in Fig. 7.

coherence time to be 250 fs. Also taking the loop length with n=1.7 and dividing by the light mean free path l* from the coherent backscattering measurement, we get an average of 10 scattering events per loop for the short cavity and 24 scattering events for the long cavity in the films.

3.3. RANDOM LASER ANALYSIS

Figure 7 is the laser emission intensity versus excitation energy E_p for the DOO-PPV film. A clear change of behavior happens near E_p =0.5 μj. In Fig. 8 we show the emission spectra of four energies near the excitation threshold. Since the Q of these random laser cavities is not as high as the ring, sub-threshold emission lines are not clearly seen. The lowest spectrum with emission lines that has Fourier transform harmonics at the same position as Fig. 4 is at 0.79 μj. The ratio of harmonic components is taken from the Fourier transform data and is simply the numeric value that occurs at the position of twice the harmonic over the numeric value at the position of the harmonic peak. Using these values for r and Eq. (6) with the gain and loss values from the microring, we can calculate an effective reflectivity for each cavity. For the short cavity in the film we get R=4.45x10^{-3}, and for the long cavity R=6.55x10^{-7}. There are 5 scatterers along the length of the cavity; to return to the start of the loop requires 10 scattering events. If one assumes the reflectivity from each of the 10 scatterers in the short cavity is the same, $R_t = R^{10}$, then the numeric value is 0.58 per scatterer for the short cavity. For the long cavity $R_t = R^{24}$ and the numeric value is 0.55 for the long cavity. Traditional lasers usually have the active medium between two mirrors. In the film, the random cavity can be conceptualized as an active medium between 10 or 24 mirrors with a reflectivity of about 55% and a mean optical spacing (l*) of 15μm between them.

4. Conclusions

Basic laser properties for thin polymer films without obvious cavities are determined with the use of the Fourier transform of the emission spectrum and coherent backscattering techniques. The emission spectrum of thin films of DOO-PPV optically pumped in a stripe geometry shows multiple modes that indicates lasing. The Fourier transform of the emission spectrum indicates the existence of many cavities and their lengths found within the film. An approximate number for the coherence time and the number of scattering events in the dominant random cavity are found with the cavity loop length obtained from the Fourier transform and l* extracted from the coherent backscattering measurements. The dominant cavities near threshold lasing contain 10 and 24 scattering events each with about 55% reflection per scatterer.

5. Acknowledgments

We wish to thank M. Raikh for useful discussions, A. Chipouline for technical assistance, and G. Levina for the polymer synthesis. This work was funded in part by NSF DMR 97-32820.

References

[1] N.M. Lawandy, R.M. Balachandran, A.S.L. Gomes, and E. Sauvain, *Nature* **368**, 436 (1994).

[2] S. Frolov, K. Yoshino, and Z. Vardeny, *Phys. Rev B.* **57**, 9141 (1998).

[3] H. Cao, Y.G. Zhao, H.C. Ong, S.T. Ho, J.Y. Dai, J.Y. Wu, and R.P.H. Chang, *Appl. Phys. Lett.* **73**, 3656 (1998).

[4] Meint P. Van Albada, and Ad Lagendijk, *Phys. Rev. Lett.* **55**, 2692 (1985).

[5] P. Wolf, and G. Maret, *Phys. Rev. Lett.* **55**, 2696 (1985).

[6] S. Etemad, R. Thompson, and M.J. Andrejco, *Phys. Rev. Lett.* **57**, 575 (1986).

[7] M. Kuwata-Gonokami, R.H. Jordan, A. Dodabalapur, H.E. Katz, M.L. Schilling, and R.E. Slusher, *Optics Lett.* **20**, 2093 (1995).

[8] N.N. Barashkov, D.J. Guerrero, H.J. Olivos, and J.P. Ferraris, *Synth. Metals* **75**, 153 (1995).

[9] S. Frolov, M. Shkunov, Z.V. Vardeny, and K. Yoshino, *Phys. Rev. B* **56**, R4363 (1997).

[10] H.P. Weber, and R. Ulrich, *Appl. Phys. Lett.* **19**, 38 (1971).

[11] Karlov, N.V., *Lectures on Quantum Electronics* (CRC Press, Boca Raton, 1993).

[12] D. Hofsttetter, and R.L. Thornton, *Appl. Phys. Lett.* **72,** 404 (1998).

[13] D. Hofsttetter, and R.L. Thornton, *Optics Lett.* **32,** 1831 (1997).

[14] R.C. Polson, G. Levina and Z.V. Vardeny, *Appl. Phys. Lett.*, **76**, 3858 (2000).

[15] E. Akkermans, P.E. Wolf, and G. Maret, J. Phys. (France) **49**, 77 (1988).

THEORY AND SIMULATIONS OF RANDOM LASERS

XUNYA JIANG AND C. M. SOUKOULIS
Ames Laboratory and Department of Physics and Astronomy,
Iowa State University, Ames, IA 50011

Abstract. We present a model to simulate the phenomenon of random lasers. It couples Maxwell's equations with the rate equations of electronic population in a disordered system and includes the interaction of EM waves with electrons and the gain is saturable. Finite difference time domain methods are used to obtain the field pattern and the spectra of localized lasing modes inside the system. A critical pumping rate P_r^c exists for the appearance of the lasing peak(s) for periodic and random systems. The number of lasing modes increases with the pumping rate and the length of the random system. There is a lasing mode repulsion related to localization effects. This property leads to a saturation of the number of modes for a given size system and a relation between the localization length ξ and average mode length L_m. The dynamic processes of the random laser systems are studied. We find some properties for evolving processes of the localized lasing modes .

1. Introduction

Laser physics and localization theory were almost developed at the same time. The interplay of localization and amplification is an old and interesting topic in physics research [1]. With promising properties, mirror-less random laser systems are widely studied [2-9] both experimentally and theoretically. Recently, new observations [2] of laser like emission were reported and showed new interesting properties of amplifying media with strong randomness. First, sharp lasing peaks appear when the gain or the length of the system is over a well defined threshold value. Although a drastic spectral narrowing has been previously observed [3], discrete lasing modes were missing. Second, more peaks appear when the gain or the system size fur-

C.M. Soukoulis (ed.), Photonic Crystals and Light Localization in the 21st Century, 417–433.

ther increases over the threshold. Third, the spectra of the lasing system is direction-dependent, not isotropic. To fully explain such an unusual behavior of stimulated emission in random systems with gain, we need new theoretical ideas.

Theoretically, many methods have been used to discuss the properties of such random lasing systems. Based on the time-dependent diffusion equation, earlier work by Letokhov [1] predicted the possibility of lasing in a random system and Zyuzin [5] discussed the fluctuation properties near the lasing threshold. Recently, John and Pang [6] studied the random lasing system by combining the electron number equations of energy levels with the diffusion equation. Such a consideration predicted a reduction in the threshold gain for laser action, due to the increased optical path from diffusion. It also verified the narrowing of the output spectrum when approaching the gain threshold. By using the diffusion approach it is not possible to explain the lasing peaks observed in the recent experiments [2] in both semiconductor powders and in organic dyes-doped gel films. The diffusive description of photon transport in gain media neglects the phase coherence of the wave, so it give limited information for the wave propagation in the gain media and can not get the modes for a certain configuration. Genack's group [9] used Monte Carlo method to simulate random walk of photons with frequency-dependent gain, and they acquired the similar narrowing of the output peak as in [6] and some dynamic processes. Theoretically, this method [9] is also based on diffusion theory, and it could not get the lasing modes, too. Another approach [7, 10-13] which is based on the time-independent wave equations for the random gain media can go beyond the diffusive description, but as was shown recently [14], the time-independent method is only useful in determining the lasing threshold pumping or length. When the gain or the length of system is larger than the threshold value, the time-independent description will give a totally unphysical picture for such a system. To fully understand the random lasing system, we must deal with three basic elements of such systems: *randomness* which will cause the localization or fluctuation effects, *saturable gain* which is due to the EM field-electrons interaction and will make the system stable at certain amplitudes of the field, and *time – dependent wave propagation*. Thus we need time-dependent wave equations in random systems by coupling Maxwell's equations with the rate equations of electron population within a semi-classical [15, 16] theory.

We have introduced [17] a model by combining these semi-classical laser theories with Maxwell's equations. By incorporating a well-established FDTD (Finite Difference Time Domain) [18] method, we calculate the wave propagation in random media with gain. Because this model couples electronic number equations at different levels with field equations, the amplification is nonlinear and saturated, so stable state solutions can be obtained after a long relaxation time. The advantages of this FDTD model are obvious, since one can follow the evolution of the electric field and electron numbers inside the system. From the field distribution inside the system, one can clearly distinguish the localized modes from the extended ones. One can also examine the time dependence of the electric field inside and just outside the system. Then, after Fourier transformation, the emission spectra and the modes inside the system can be obtained. Further more, we can study dynamic processes, such as relaxation in such systems.

Our system is essentially a one-dimensional simplification of the real experiments [2, 3]. It consists of many dielectric layers (see Fig. 1) of real dielectric constant of fixed thickness, sandwiched between two surfaces, with the spacing between the dielectric layers filled with gain media (such as the solution of dye molecules). The distance between the neighboring dielectric layers is assumed to be a random variable. The overall length of the system is L.

The paper is organized as follows. In Sec. 2 we introduce the theoretical model we are studying. The explanation of the experimental results by our theoretical model is presented in Sec. 3. We also introduce the concept of localized modes in Sec. 3. In Sec. 4 we present our predictions about the mode repulsion property, the saturated number of modes in high gain, and the relation of the average mode length with the localization length. These predictions have been checked experimentally [19]. In Sec. 5 we present some dynamic processes of our random laser system and the role of localized modes is emphasized. We also show the essential role of the local electron populations in the lasing process. Finally, Sec. 6 is devoted to a discussion of our results and gives some conclusions.

2. Theoretical Model

The binary layers of the system (shown in Fig. 1) are made of dielectric materials with dielectric constant of $\varepsilon_1 = \varepsilon_0$ and $\varepsilon_2 = 4 \times \varepsilon_0$, respectively. The thickness of the first layer (white color in Fig. 1), which simulates the gain medium, is a random variable $a_n = a_0(1 + W\gamma)$, where $a_0 = 300$nm, W is the strength of randomness and γ is a random value in the range [-0.5, 0.5]. The thickness of second layer (black color in Fig. 1), which simulates the scatterers, is a constant $b = 180$nm. In the layers representing the gain medium, there is a four-level electronic material mixed inside. An external mechanism pumps electrons from ground level (N_0) to third level (N_3) at a certain pumping rate, P_r, proportional to the pumping intensity in experiments. After a short lifetime, τ_{32}, electrons can non-radiative transfer to the second level (N_2). The second level (N_2) and the first level (N_1) are called the upper and the lower lasing levels. Electrons can be transfered from the upper to the lower level by both spontaneous and stimulated emission. At last, electrons can non-radiative transfer from the first level (N_1) back to the ground level (N_0). The lifetimes and energies of upper and lower lasing levels are τ_{21}, E_2 and τ_{10}, E_1, respectively. The center frequency of radiation is $\omega_a = (E_2 - E_1)/\hbar$ chosen to be equal to $2\pi \times 6 \cdot 10^{14}\ Hz$, which corresponds to a wavelength $\lambda = 499.7\ nm$. Based on real laser dyes [20], the parameters τ_{32}, τ_{21} and τ_{10} are chosen to be 1×10^{-13}s, 1×10^{-9}s, and 1×10^{-11}s. The total electron density $N_0^0 = N_0 + N_1 + N_2 + N_3$ and the pump rate P_r are the controlled variables according to the experiments [2].

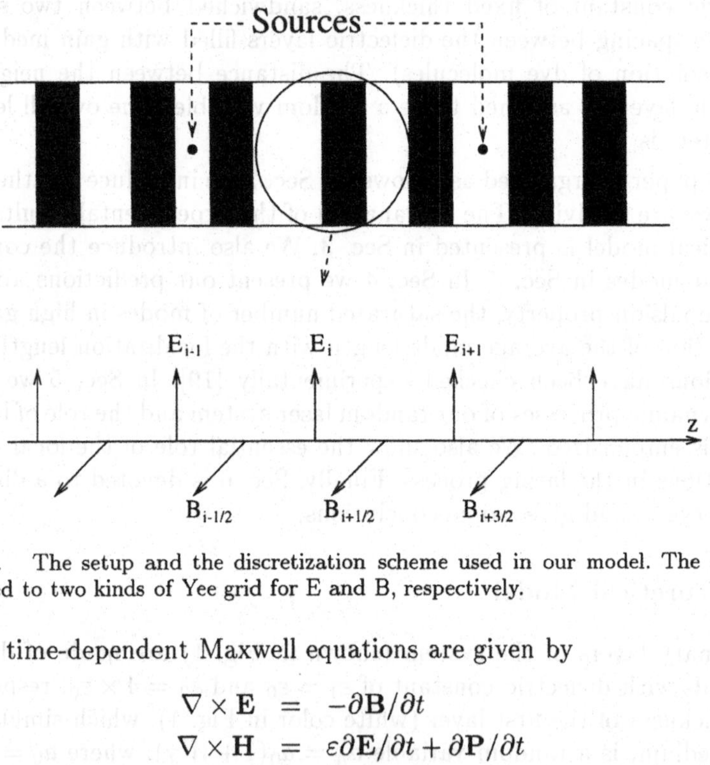

Figure 1. The setup and the discretization scheme used in our model. The space is discretized to two kinds of Yee grid for E and B, respectively.

The time-dependent Maxwell equations are given by

$$\begin{aligned} \nabla \times \mathbf{E} &= -\partial \mathbf{B}/\partial t \\ \nabla \times \mathbf{H} &= \varepsilon \partial \mathbf{E}/\partial t + \partial \mathbf{P}/\partial t \end{aligned} \tag{1}$$

where $\mathbf{B} = \mu \mathbf{H}$ and $\mathbf{P}$ is the electric polarization density from which the amplification or gain can be obtained. Following the single electron case, one can show [16] that the polarization density $P(x,t)$ in the presence of an electric field obeys the following equation of motion

$$\frac{d^2P(t)}{dt^2} + \Delta\omega_a \frac{dP(t)}{dt} + \omega_a^2 P(t) = \frac{\gamma_r}{\gamma_c}\frac{e^2}{m}\Delta N(t)E(t) \tag{2}$$

where $\Delta\omega_a = 1/\tau_{21} + 2/T_2$ is the full width at half maximum linewidth of the atomic transition. T_2 is the mean time between dephasing events which is taken to be 2.18×10^{-14}s, $\Delta N(x,t) = N_1(x,t) - N_2(x,t)$, and $\gamma_r = 1/\tau_{21}$ is the real decay rate of the second level and $\gamma_c = \frac{e^2}{m}\frac{{\omega_a}^2}{6\pi\varepsilon_0 c^3}$ is the classical rate. It is easy to derive [16] from Eq. (1) that the amplification line shape is Lorentzian and homogeneously broadened. Equation (1) can be thought of as a quantum mechanically correct equation for the induced polarization density $P(x,t)$ in a real atomic system.

The equations giving the number of electrons on every level can be expressed as follows:

$$
\begin{aligned}
\frac{dN_3(x,t)}{dt} &= P_r N_0(x,t) - \frac{N_3(x,t)}{\tau_{32}} \\
\frac{dN_2(x,t)}{dt} &= \frac{N_3(x,t)}{\tau_{32}} + \frac{E(x,t)}{\hbar\omega_a}\frac{dP(x,t)}{dt} - \frac{N_2(x,t)}{\tau_{21}} \\
\frac{dN_1(x,t)}{dt} &= \frac{N_2(x,t)}{\tau_{21}} - \frac{E(x,t)}{\hbar\omega_a}\frac{dP(x,t)}{dt} - \frac{N_1(x,t)}{\tau_{10}} \\
\frac{dN_0(x,t)}{dt} &= \frac{N_1(x,t)}{\tau_{10}} - P_r N_0(x,t)
\end{aligned}
\tag{3}
$$

where $\frac{E(x,t)}{\hbar\omega}\frac{dP(x,t)}{dt}$ is the induced radiation rate from level 2 to level 1 when it is negative or the excitation rate from level 1 to level 2 when it is positive. This term couples the Maxwell equations with the electron population equations.

To excite the system, we must introduce sources into the system[21]. To simulate the real laser system, we introduce sources homogeneously distributed in the system to simulate the spontaneous emission. We make sure that the distance between the two sources L_s is smaller than the localization length ξ. Each source generates waves of a Lorentzian frequency distribution centered around ω_a, with its amplitude depending on N_2. Details of the role of sources in the FDTD scheme can be found in [18]. In real lasers, the spontaneous emission is the most fundamental noise [15, 16], but generally submerged in other technical noises which are much larger. In our system, the simulated spontaneous emission is the *only* noise present, and is treated self-consistently. This is the reason for the small background in the emission spectra shown below.

There are two leads, both with a width of 300 nm, at the right and the left sides of the system. At the end of the leads, we use the Liao method [18] to impose absorbing-boundary conditions (ABC). In the FDTD calculation, we discretize both the space and time, the discrete time step and space steps are chosen to be $\Delta t = 10^{-17}$s and $\Delta x = 10^{-9}$m, respectively, as shown in Fig. 1. In the FDTD scheme the boundary conditions for the field at the interfaces between the two media are automatically satisfied, since we are numerically solving Maxwell's equations. So, for a given random configuration and based on the previous time steps, we can calculate the next time step ($n+1$ step) values. First, we obtain the $n+1$ time step of the electric polarization density P by using Eq. (2), then the $n+1$ step of the electric and magnetic fields are obtained by Maxwell's equations and at last the $n+1$ step of the electron numbers at each level are calculated by Eq. (3). The FDTD calculation details are shown in the following equations:

$$
\begin{aligned}
P_i^{n+1} &= \frac{2-{\omega_a}^2\Delta t^2}{1+\Delta\omega\Delta t/2}P_i^n + \frac{\Delta\omega\Delta t/2-1}{1+\Delta\omega\Delta t/2}P_i^{n-1} + \frac{\Delta t^2}{1+\Delta\omega\Delta t/2}\frac{\gamma_r}{\gamma_c}\frac{e^2}{m}\Delta N_i^n E_i^n \\
E_i^{n+1} &= E_i^n + \frac{\Delta t}{\varepsilon_i \Delta x}(H_{i+1/2}^{n+1/2} - H_{i+1/2}^{n-1/2}) - \frac{1}{\varepsilon_i}(P_i^{n+1} - P_i^n) \\
B_i^{n+1/2} &= B_i^{n-1/2} + \frac{\Delta t}{\Delta x}(E_{i+1}^n - E_i^n) \\
N_{3,i}^{n+1} &= \frac{2\Delta t \tau_{23}}{2\tau_{23}+\Delta t}P_{r,i}N_{0,i}^n + \frac{2\tau_{23}-\Delta t}{2\tau_{23}+\Delta t}N_{3,i}^n \qquad (4) \\
N_{2,i}^{n+1} &= \frac{2\tau_{21}-\Delta t}{2\tau_{21}+\Delta t}N_{2,i}^n + \frac{\tau_{21}\Delta t(N_{3,i}^{n+1}+N_{3,i}^n)}{\tau_{32}(2\tau_{21}+\Delta t)} + \frac{\tau_{21}(E_i^{n+1}+E_i^n)(P_i^{n+1}+P_i^n)}{(2\tau_{21}+\Delta t)\hbar\omega} \\
N_{1,i}^{n+1} &= \frac{2\tau_{10}-\Delta t}{2\tau_{10}+\Delta t}N_{1,i}^n + \frac{\tau_{10}\Delta t(N_{2,i}^{n+1}+N_{2,i}^n)}{\tau_{21}(2\tau_{10}+\Delta t)} - \frac{\tau_{10}(E_i^{n+1}+E_i^n)(P_i^{n+1}+P_i^n)}{(2\tau_{10}+\Delta t)\hbar\omega} \\
N_{0,i}^{n+1} &= (1-\Delta P_{r,i})N_{0,i}^n + \frac{\Delta t}{2\tau_{10}}((N_{1,i}^{n+1}+N_{1,i}^n)
\end{aligned}
$$

The initial condition is that all electrons are in the ground state, so there is no field, no polarization, and no spontaneous emission. Then the electrons are pumped from N_0 to N_3 (then to N_2) with a constant pumping rate P_r. The system begins to evolve according to the above equations. It takes about 30 hours to calculate an 80-cell system for 10^7 steps on a DEC 433 MHz alpha workstation. Generally, we do not need such a long time to reach equilibrium, except for near the threshold for lasing.

3. Localized Modes of Random Laser Systems

We have performed numerical simulations for periodic and random systems. First, for all the systems, a well-defined lasing threshold exists. As expected, when the randomness becomes stronger, the threshold intensity decreases because localization effects make the paths of waves propagating inside the gain medium much longer.

For a periodic or *short* ($L < \xi$) random system, generally only one mode dominates the entire system, even if the gain increases far above the threshold. This is due to the fact that the first mode can extend in the whole system, and its strong electric field can force almost all the electrons of the upper level N_2 to jump down to the N_1 level quickly by stimulated emission. This leaves very few upper electrons for stimulated emission of the other modes. In other words, all the other modes are suppressed by the first lasing mode even though their threshold values are only a little bit smaller than the first one. This phenomenon also exists in common homogeneously broadening lasers [15].

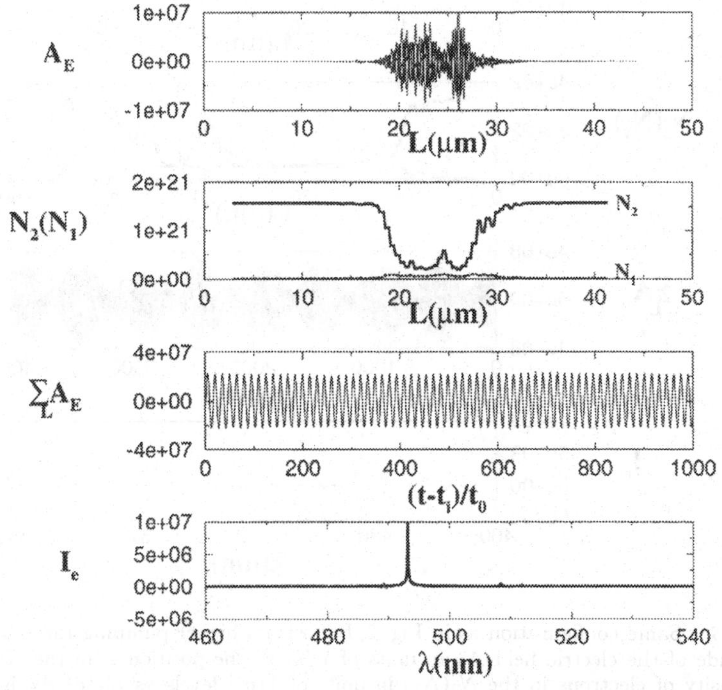

Figure 2. (a) The amplitude of the electric field A_E in units of V/m vs the position L in the system, (b) the density of electrons in the $N_2(N_1)$ in units of $1/m^3$ levels vs L, (c) A_E in units of V/m average over length vs $(t - t_i)/t_0$, where $t_0 = 2.78 \times 10^{-17}$s and $t_i = 7 \times 10^{-10}$s, and (d) the spectra I_e in units of V/m vs the wavelength for an 80-cell system with $W = 1.4$, $N_0{}^0 = 5.5 \times 6.02 \times 10^{23}/m^3$ and $P_r = 1 \times 10^6\ s^{-1}$.

For *long* ($L >> \xi$) random systems, a richer behavior is observed. First, we find that all the lasing modes are localized and stable around their localization centers after a long relaxing time. Each mode has its own specific frequency and corresponds to a peak in the spectrum inside the system.

When the gain is a little above the threshold value, we can observe one localized lasing mode as showed in Fig. 2a. Notice that N_2 is small (Fig. 2b) in the position where the mode is, due to a stimulated emission. In Fig. 2c, we show the time dependence of the averaged A_E over all the spatial points. It is a very good sine function. The spectrum intensity I_e inside the system (see Fig. 2d) gives a sharp lasing peak. I_e is obtained by taking the Fourier transform of the spatial averaged $A_E(t)$.

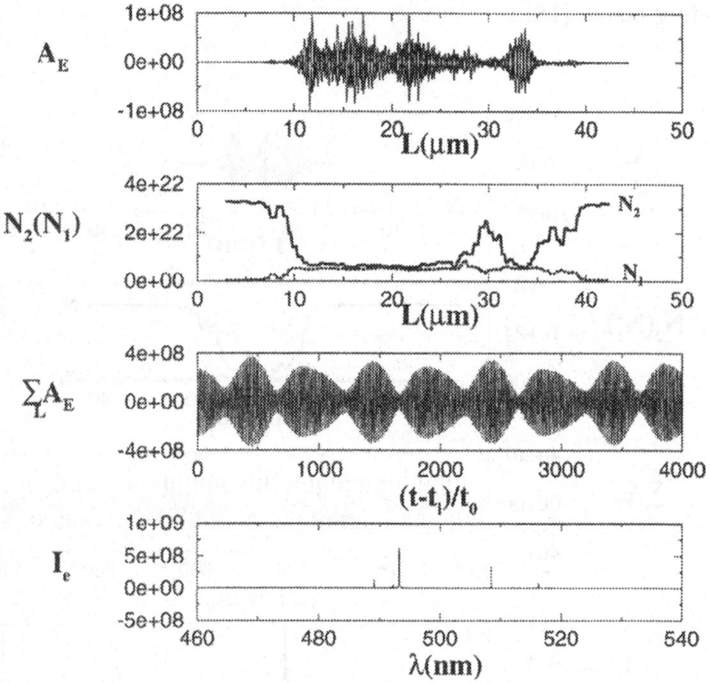

Figure 3. Same configuration as in Fig. 2, but with a higher pumping rate P_r. (a) The amplitude of the electric field A_E in units of V/m vs the position L in the system, (b) the density of electrons in the $N_2(N_1)$ in units of $1/m^3$ levels vs L, (c) A_E in units of V/m average over length vs $(t-t_i)/t_0$, where $t_0 = 2.78 \times 10^{-17}$s and $t_i = 7 \times 10^{-10}$s and (d) the spectra I_e in units of V/m vs the wavelength for an 80-cell system with $W = 1.4$, $N_0{}^0 = 5.5 \times 6.02 \times 10^{23}/m^3$, and $P_r = 1 \times 10^7 s^{-1}$.

When the gain increases beyond the threshold, the electric field pattern (see Fig. 3a) shows that more localized lasing modes appear in the system. The spectrum intensity I_e inside the system (see Fig. 3d) gives more sharp peaks, observed in the experiments [2]. Notice that N_2 is small (Fig. 3b) at the same location where the amplitude of the electric field A_E (Fig. 3a) is large. In Fig. 3c, the time-dependence of the averaged A_E over all the spatial points is shown. In Fig. 3d, I_e is also shown, with more than one peak.

We can explain the experimental multi-lasing peaks phenomena from the results shown in Figs. 2 and 3. Because the first lasing mode has a strong localized field, this field only reduces N_2 locally. If the center of the second localized mode is far from the center of the first lasing mode and the pumping rate is large enough, N_2 can increase in this region and make the second mode lase afterward. If the pumping rate is even larger and the system size is large enough, multi-modes can lase simultaneously.

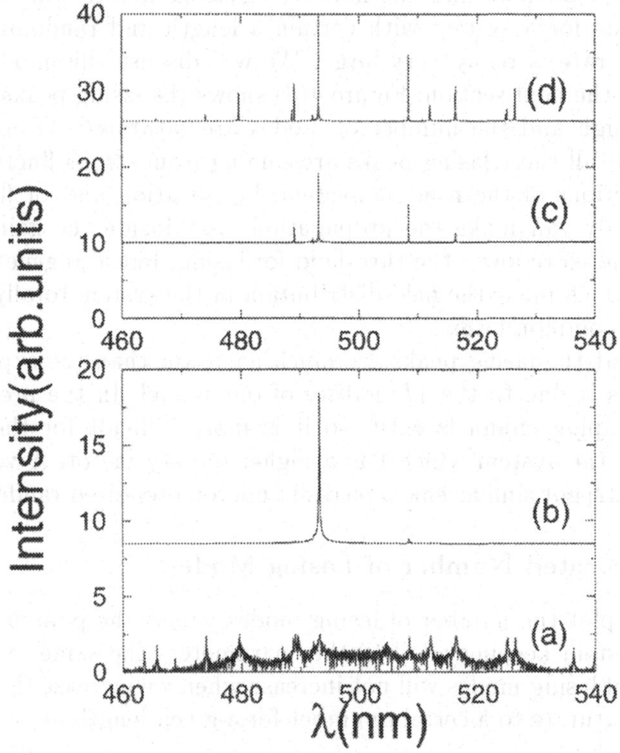

Figure 4. **The spectral intensity in arbitrary units vs the wavelength for the 80-cell system with W=1.4 for different pumping rates P_r. P_r in units of s^{-1} is (a) 10^4, (b) 10^6 and (c) 10^{10}. To be able to plot all the curves in one figure, we have multiplied (a), (b) and (c) by 10^{-3}, 10^{-6} and 10^{-8}, respectively, and shifted them apart.**

So far, we call these lasing modes *localized modes* just because we see the field distribution of these lasing modes is localized and the effect on the electron population is localized. But, do these modes really arise from localized states of the random system? The spectrum of these lasing modes supports this conclusion. In Fig. 4, we plot the spectral intensity vs the wavelength for different pumping rates (proportional to the input intensity in the experiments). When the pumping rate is very small, we see the spectrum of spontaneous emission and find many peaks with large background noise (Fig. 4(a)). We have checked the transmission coefficient of the random system, and, indeed, a lot of structure is obtained. The exact frequency of these peaks is determined by the random configuration of the system. When the gain is increased, one mode goes over its threshold and begins to lase, therefore giving a sharp peak in the spectra as seen in Fig. 4(b). When gain is increased further, more and more lasing peaks appear as in Fig. 4(c). But, we find the number of lasing modes will saturate to a certain value for a system with certain a length and randomness when the pumping rate is really very large. We will discuss this mode number saturation in the next section. Figure 4(d) shows the lasing peaks when the intensity is high and the number of modes are saturated. We obtain numerically that all these lasing peaks are coming from strong fluctuations in the wavefunctions of the random system. Localization and/or fluctuation effects not only can make the propagation path inside the gain medium longer and therefore lower the threshold for lasing, but also generate localized modes which make the field distribution in the system totally different from that of common lasers.

Notice that the lasing peaks are much narrower than the experimental ones [2]. This is due to the $1D$ nature of our model. In the present case, only two escaping channels exist, so it is more difficult for the wave to get out from the system which has a higher quality factor. A very recent experiment [22] got similar sharp peaks in micrometer-sized random media.

4. The Saturated Number of Lasing Modes

In Fig. 5 we plot the number of lasing modes versus the pumping rate for an 80-cell system keeping all the other parameters the same. Notice that the number of lasing modes will not increase when we increase the pumping rate, it will saturate to a certain number for a given length and strength of randomness.

From Fig. 5, we see that the critical pumping rate $P_r^c \simeq 10^6 s^{-1}$. In the experiments of Cao *et al* [2] and Frolov *et al* [2], the critical pumping intensity I_p^c is given instead. To relate P_r^c and I_p^c for a given sample of dimensions $a \times b \times d$, where d is the thickness of the sample, we equate the power used in the experiments with the one used in the numerical simulations. We have:

$$I_p ab\eta = P_r N_0 abd\hbar\omega_a \quad (5)$$

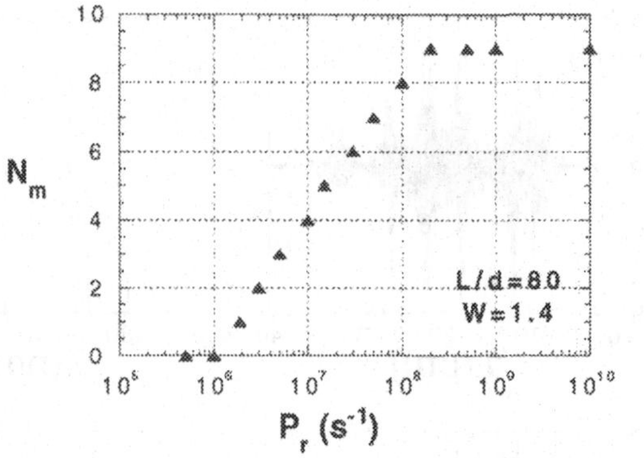

Figure 5. The lasing mode number N_m vs the pumping rate P_r in the system of 80 cells. $W = 1.4$, and $N_0{}^0 = 5.5 \times 6.02 \times 10^{23}/m^3$.

where η is the absorption ratio, the order of 1%, $\hbar\omega_a$ is the energy difference between the lasing energy levels N_2 and N_1, and N_0 is the number of ground states. Using Eq.(5) we obtain

$$P_r = \frac{I_p \eta}{N_0 \hbar\omega_a} \tag{6}$$

In Cao *et al.*'s experiments [2] the critical pumping intensity $I_p^c = 7.63 \times 10^9\ W/m^2$, $d = 6\ \mu m$, $\hbar\omega_a = 3.3\ eV$ and $N_0 = 22 \times 6.02 \times 10^{23}\ (1/m^3)$. By using Eq.(6), we obtain that the critical pumping rate, $P_r^c \simeq 2 \times 10^6\ s^{-1}$, is in qualitatively agreement with our prediction shown in Fig. 5. In Frolov *et al.*'s experiments [2], $I_p^c = 2.5 \times 10^6\ W/m^2$, $d = 30\ \mu m$, $\hbar\omega_a = 2.64\ eV$, and $N_0 = 5 \times 6.02 \times 10^{23}$, $(1/m^3)$ and by using Eq.(6), we obtain that $P_r^c \simeq 9 \times 10^6\ s^{-1}$ again in qualitatively agreement with our prediction.

To understand this mode number saturation phenomenon, we compared systems with different lengths and very high pumping rates, P_r, to insure that the number of lasing modes is saturated. In Fig. 6, we show the amplitude of the electric field A_E vs L (in Figs. 6a and 6c) and the spectrum I_e (in Figs. 6b and 6d) for an 80-cell system and a 160-cell system with the same strength of randomness and the same pumping rate. First, from Figs. 6a and 6c we can see that the localized modes are almost evenly distributed over the entire space of the systems. Second, more localized modes exist in the longer system (Fig. 6c) than the shorter system (Fig. 6a). This is also shown in the spectrum I_e of both systems where more lasing peaks exist for the long system in Fig. 6d than for the short system in Fig. 6b. Third, the intriguing result is that the average sizes of lasing modes are almost the same for both systems. Many systems with different lengths and different

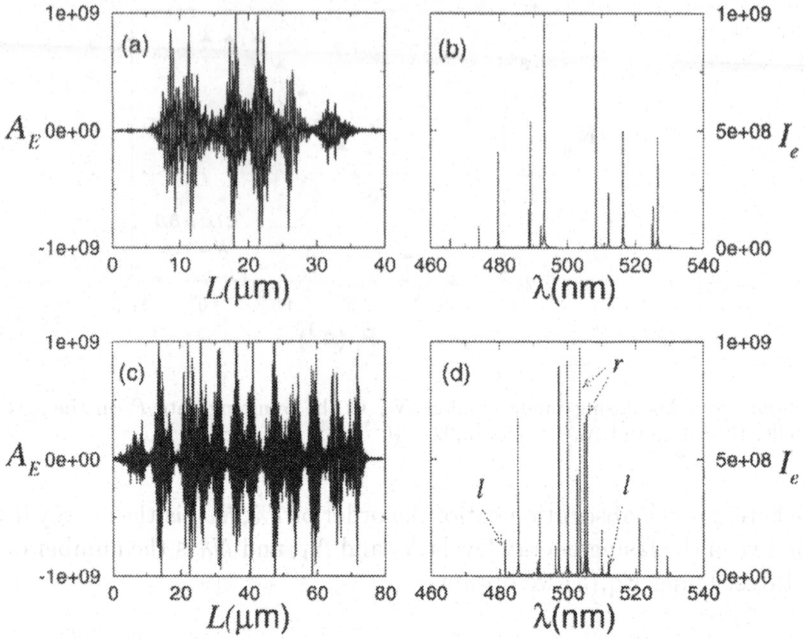

Figure 6. (a) The amplitude of the electric field A_E in units of V/m vs the position L in the system of 80 cells. (b)The spectra in units of V/m of (a) system. (c) The amplitude of the electric field A_E in units of V/m vs the position L in the system of 160 cells. (d) the spectra in units of V/m of (c) system. In both system, $W = 1.4$, $N_0{}^0 = 5.5 \times 6.02 \times 10^{23}/m^3$ and $P_r = 3 \times 10^9 s^{-1}$.

pumping rates (very large to insure the number of lasing modes saturated) are examined. We find the average size of the lasing modes is almost independent of the length of system and pumping rate, only dependent on the strength of the randomness. So, it is reasonable to assume this saturation of the lasing modes is related to localization too.

The saturated-mode-number phenomena are due to the interplay between localization and amplification. Localization makes the lasing mode strong around its localization center and exponentially small away from its center so that it only suppresses the modes in this area by reducing N_2. When a mode lases, only those modes which are *far enough* from this mode can lase afterwards. So, more than one mode can appear for a long system and each mode seems to *repel* each other. Because every lasing mode dominates a certain area and is separated from other modes, only a limited number of lasing modes can exist for a finite long system even

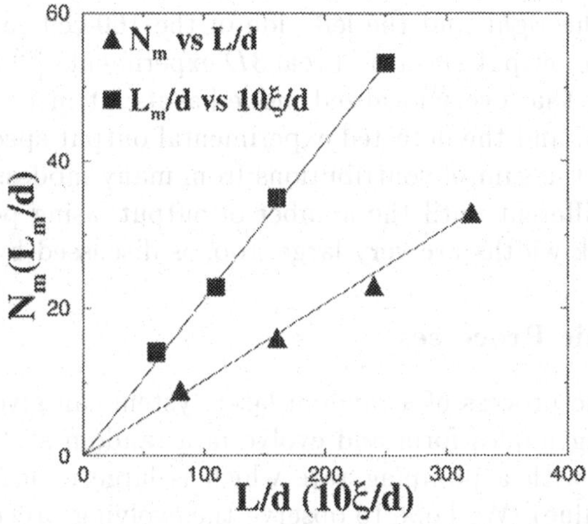

Figure 7. The number of modes N_m vs the length of the system L/d, where d=$< a_n >$+b=480 nm is the size of the cell. Also the average mode length L_m/d vs the localization length $10 \times \xi/d$ for different disorder strength W for a 320 cell system. $P_r = 1 \times 10^8$ and the rest of the parameters are the same as the ones of Fig. 2.

in the case of large amplification. We therefore expect that the number of surviving lasing modes N_m should be proportional to the length of the system L when the amplification is very large. Since the *mode – repulsion* property is coming from the localization of the modes, we expect that the average mode length $L_m = L/N_m$ should be related to the localization length ξ, which determines the decay rate of localized field. Our numerical results show that L_m is proportional to the localized length ξ at a large range except very strong randomness. In Fig. 7, we plot N_m vs the length of the systems L when we increase the length from 80 cells to 320 cells and keep all other parameters the same. In Fig. 7, we also plot the average mode length L_m vs the localization length ξ, when we change the random strength W for a 320-cell system. The localization lengths are calculated using the transfer-matrix method by averaging 10,000 random configurations. These results confirm that, indeed, $N_m \propto L$ and $L_m \propto \xi$. It will be very interesting to checke these predictions experimentally [19].

For our 1D system, the output spectra are quite anisotropic. The emission spectra at the right and left side of the systems generally are quite different for random laser systems. This can be explained from the field pattern shown in Fig. 6a and 6c. Notice the localized modes are quite different at both sides of the system. The right (left) output spectrum generally is dominated by the right (left) edge modes because of the localization effect which makes the photons of the center modes much more difficult to escape from the system. In Fig. 6d, we use "r" and "l" to denote the output spectra of the right and the left side of the 160-cell random system. The non-isotropic output spectra of real $3D$ experiments [2] might be explained by assuming that every localized mode has its intrinsic direction, strength, and position, and the detected experimental output spectra at different directions are the sum of contributions from many modes. So, generally they should be different until the number of output lasing peaks are very large and the peak widths are very large, too, as discussed by Letokhov [1].

5. Dynamic Processes

The dynamic process of a random laser system can give us a clear picture of how lasing modes form and evolve in a random system. We use a 120-cell system with a pumping rate which is large enough (larger than the threshold value). We hope to observe the evolving process of lasing modes from the very beginning.

As we discussed above, at first all electrons are at the ground state and there is no field at all. Then, an outside mechanism begins to pump the electrons up. There is a spontaneous emission field generated by sources and the magnitude of the spontaneous emission field is proportional to the local $\Delta N = N_2 - N_1$. Because N_1 is very small relatively to N_2 before a lasing mode appears, $\Delta N \simeq N_2$. When N_2 increases but still not large enough to lase, the spontaneous emission field inside the system is like a random field and the spectrum of this field is similar to that shown in Fig. 4(a). N_2 and N_1 are almost the same over the whole system.

When N_2 gets above a certain value, 1.6×10^{22} for our system (at a time 13.1 *ps* after the pumping process began), a mode suddenly grows up rapidly and dominates the whole system as shown in Fig. 8(a). Exactly at the same spatial position and same moment, *local* N_2 decreases while N_1 increases rapidly as shown in Fig. 8(b). The only reason for this sudden change of N_2 and N_1 is the term $\frac{E(x,t)}{\hbar\omega}\frac{dP(x,t)}{dt}$ in Eq. (3) which is negative and very large at the mode position. This shows that the induced radiation is a dominant mechanism around this mode area. A sharp peak appears at the spectra of the system too. All these signs signify a localized lasing mode.

At a later time (17.5 ps after the pumping process began), another mode at the left edge of the system suddenly grows rapidly as shown in Fig. 9(a). N_2 decreases locally while N_1 increases rapidly as shown in Fig. 9(b). We find another peak in the spectrum. So the second mode lases after the first one. Because our pumping rate is large, there will be more modes that will lase afterward. After a long relaxing time, every lasing mode reduces the local $\Delta N = N_2 - N_1$ dramatically, so the gain which the mode receives will decrease. When the loss of the mode field is equal to the gain from the local

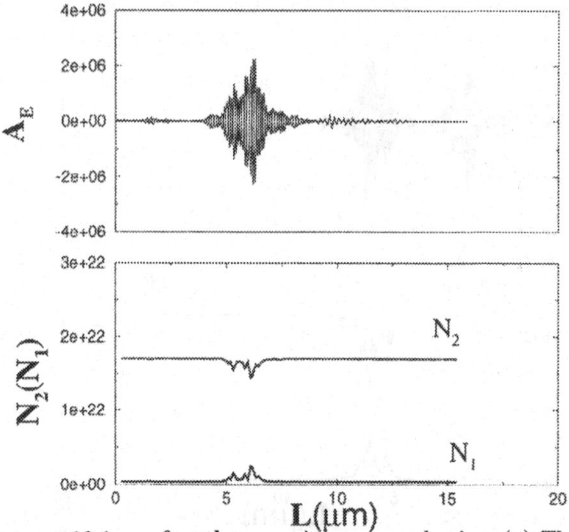

Figure 8. Data at 13.1 ps after the pumping process begins. (a) The amplitude of the electric field A_E in units of V/m vs the position L in the system of 120 cells. (b) The number of electrons on upper N_2 and lower N_1 lasing levels. Both (a) and (b) data are from the system with a new setup $a_n = a_0(1+W_1\gamma)$, $b_n = b_0(1+W_2\gamma)$, where $a_0 = 48$nm, $b_0 = 80$nm, $W_1 = 0.4$, $W_2 = 1.4$, and γ is a random value in the range [-0.5, 0.5]. $\varepsilon_1 = \varepsilon_0$, $\varepsilon_2 = 5.29 \times \varepsilon_0$, $N_0 = 50 \times 6.02 \times 10^{23}$, $P_r = 5 \times 10^6$.

ΔN, the amplitude of the mode becomes stable.

We have changed the pumping rate to larger and smaller values (but always larger than the threshold) and observe the mode evolving process. We find that one mode lases always at almost the same local value of N_2. This strongly suggests this local value of N_2 represents the individual threshold of the mode [19] if we suppose the build-up time of the modes are very short.

6. Conclusions

Our results can be summarized as follows: (*i*) As expected for a periodic and *short* ($L < \xi$, ξ is the localization length) random system, an extended mode dominates the field and the spectra. (*ii*) For either strong disorder or the long ($L \gg \xi$) system, we obtain a low threshold value for lasing. By increasing the length or the gain (a higher gain can be achieved by increasing the pumping intensity), more peaks appear in the spectra. By examining the field distribution inside the system, one can clearly see that these lasing peaks are coming from localized modes. (*iii*) The emission spectra are not the same for different output directions, which show that the emission is not isotropic. This anisotropic spectra can be explained

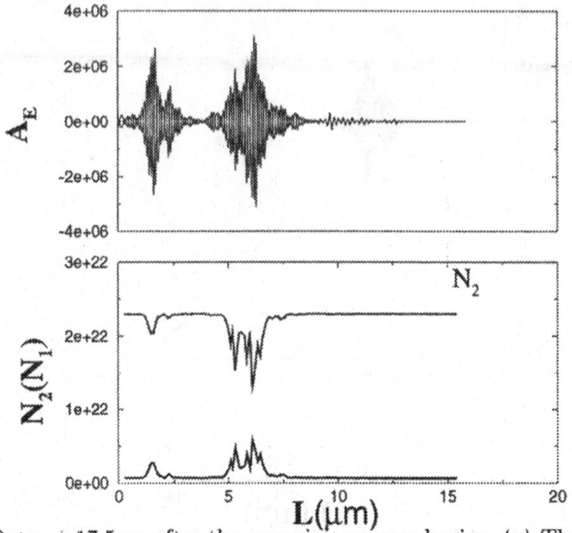

Figure 9. Data at 17.5 ps after the pumping process begins. (a) The amplitude of the electric field A_E in units of V/m vs the position L in the system of 120 cells. (b)The number of electrons on upper N_2 and lower N_1 lasing levels. All parameters are the same as Fig. 8.

by the property of localized lasing mode, too. (*iv*) When the gain or the pumping intensity increases even further, the number of lasing modes do not increase further, but saturate to a constant value, proportional to the length of the system for a given randomness. (*v*) The dynamic processes of random lasing systems can be also understood. These findings are in agreement with recent experiments [2] and also make new predictions. We want to point out that our model is $1D$, unlike the experiments done in $3D$ samples. However, the experimental results are strongly dependent on the shape of the excitation area [2]. Sharp lasing peaks are observed if the excitation area is stripe-like, close to our $1D$ model. In the $1D$ case, we expect the number of lasing modes to be less than the $3D$ case but much sharper. This is due to the fact that the modes are more localized and there are less propagating paths in $1D$.

In summary, by using a FDTD method, we constructed a random lasing model to study the interplay of localization and amplification. Unlike the time-independent models, the present formulation calculates the field evolution beyond the threshold amplification. This model allows us to obtain the field pattern and spectra of localized lasing modes inside the system. For random systems, we can explain the multi-peaks and the non-isotropic properties in the emission spectra seen experimentally. Our numerical results predict the mode-repulsion property, the lasing-mode saturated number, and the average modelength. We also observed the energy exchange between the localized modes, which is much different from common lasers and this is essential for further research of mode competition and evolution in random laser.

We wish to thank E. Lidorikis, M. Sigalas, and Qiming Li for helpful discussions. Ames Laboratory is operated for the U.S. Department of Energy by Iowa State University under Contract No. W-7405-Eng-82. This work was supported by the director for Energy Research, Office of Basic Energy Sciences.

References

1. V. S. Letokhov, *Sov. Phys. JEPT* **26**, 835 (1968).
2. H. Cao, Y. G. Zhao, S. T. Ho, E .W. Seelig, Q. H. Wang, and R. P .H .Chang, *Phys. Rev. Lett.* **82**, 2278 (1999); S. V. Frolov, Z. V. Vardeny, K. Yoshino, A. Zakhidov and R. H. Baughman, *Phys. Rev. B* **59**, 5284 (1999).
3. N. M. Lawandy, R. M. Balachandran, S. S. Gomers and E. Sauvain, *Nature* **368**, 436 (1994).
4. D. S. Wiersma, M. P. van Albada and Ad Lagendijk, *Phys. Rev. Lett.* **75**, 1739 (1995); D. S. Wiersma et. al., *Phys. Rev. E* **54**, 4256(1996).
5. A. Yu. Zyuzin, *Phys. Rev. E* **51**, 5274 (1995).
6. S. John and G. Pang, *Phys. Rev. A* **54**, 3642 (1996), and references therein.
7. Qiming Li, K. M. Ho and C. M. Soukoulis, to be published in *Physica B.*
8. K. Totsuka, G. van Soest, T. Ito, A. Lagendijk and M. Tomita, *J. of Appl. Phys.* **87**, 7623 (2000).
9. G. A. Berger, M. Kempe, and A. Z. Genack, *Phys. Rev. E* **56**, 6118 (1997).
10. P. Pradhan and N. Kumar, *Phys. Rev. B* **50**, 9644 (1994).
11. Z. Q. Zhang, *Phys. Rev. B* **52**, 7960 (1995).
12. J. C. J. Paasschens, T. Sh. Misirpashaev and C. W. J. Beenakker, *Phys. Rev. B* **54**, 11887 (1996).
13. Xunya Jiang and C. M. Soukoulis, *Phys. Rev. B* **59**, 6159 (1999).
14. Xunya Jiang, Qiming Li, and C. M. Soukoulis, *Phys. Rev. B* **59** R9007 (1999).
15. A. Maitland and M. H. Dunn, *Laser Physics* (North-Holland Publishing Com., Amsterdam, 1969). See chapters 3, 8 and 9.
16. Anthony E. Siegman, *Lasers* (Mill Valley, California, 1986). See chapters 2, 3, 6 and 13.
17. Xunya Jiang and C. M. Soukoulis, *Phys. Rev. Lett.* **85**, 70 (2000).
18. A. Taflove, *Computational Electrodynamics: The Finite-Difference Time-Domain Method* (Artech House, London, 1995). See chapters 3, 6, and 7.
19. Xunya Jiang, C. M. Soukoulis and H. Cao et al. to be published.
20. Such as the coumarine 102 or uranin with meth as solvent. Our results are of general validity and are not sensitive to the lasing dyes used.
21. The structure of our $1D$ random medium is an alternate of layers of random thickness representing the gain medium and dielectric layers of constant thickness representing the scatterers. Theoretically, every discrete grid point of the layers representing the gain medium is a source that can generate spontaneous emission. Because this is very time consuming, we selected a finite number (20 to 50) of sources. To simulate real spontaneous emission, every source needs a proper vibration amplitude and a Lorentzian frequency distribution. We have checked that the spatial distribution of the sources does not influence the calculation results.
22. H. Cao et. al. *Phys. Rev. Lett.* **84**, 5584 (2000).

CAVITY APPROACH TOWARDS A COHERENT RANDOM LASER

J.P. WOERDMAN, J. DINGJAN AND M.P. VAN EXTER
Huygens Laboratory, Leiden University
P.O. Box 9504, 2300 RA Leiden, The Netherlands
e-mail: qo@molphys.leidenuniv.nl
fax: ++ 31 71 5275819
tel: ++ 31 71 5275823

Abstract. We explore the possibility of a coherent random laser based upon a suitably modified conventional laser cavity. Particularly promising is a nonparaxial variety of an open resonator based upon ideal spherical mirrors. Phase locking allows spatial redistribution of the intracavity field into localized closed-loop ray paths.

C.M. Soukoulis (ed.), Photonic Crystals and Light Localization in the 21st Century, 435–446.

1. Introduction

A random laser is defined as a laser in which the feedback is due to some random scattering mechanism, as opposed to reflective feedback by the mirrors of a conventional laser. Typical examples are laser-crystal powders or laser-dye solutions containing microparticles. The concept of a random laser dates back to the early days of laser physics [1]. From that time, until recently, interest has been focused on the *incoherent* variety of the random laser. In this variety the phase relations are considered to be irrelevant so that the feedback is basically *intensity* feedback [2]. The physics is then not dramatically different from the case of amplified spontaneous emission without feedback, or the case of a conventional multi-mode laser in the limit of infinitely many, randomly phased modes. In all these cases, a space-time photon diffusion picture is sufficient, leading to thermal photon statistics and a relatively broad laser linewidth (*i.e.*, in practical cases not very much smaller than the gain linewidth).

However, it is in principle incorrect to neglect the phase relations in the random scattering process, in particular when the scattering is very strong [3]. Random amplitude-feedback is not the same as random intensity-feedback! A spectacular illustration of this point is the phenomenon of strong localization of light. This has recently been observed in light scattering experiments on a passive semiconductor powder, where a series of subsequent light scattering events can form a closed loop [4]. In the active case, *i.e.*, when adding gain, such a loop can be seen as a microscopic ring laser, emitting a very narrow spectral line since the condition for localization depends on interference (when using the analogue of a ring laser, an integer number of wavelengths must fit along the cavity length) [3]. Such a so-called *coherent* random laser has recently been demonstrated experimentally in an optically pumped semiconductor powder [5]. Depending on the pumping conditions, one or more localized loops may oscillate [6]. If several loops oscillate they do so at different wavelengths, corresponding to the generally different configurations of the scattering particles.

We address here the question whether a coherent random laser can also be realized with a suitably modified conventional laser cavity (*e.g.*, a 2-mirror resonator), *without* using randomly placed microscopic scatterers. The ray propagation in this cavity must have a chaotic nature due to the geometry of the mirrors; such chaotic ray manifolds are well-known for the case of stadium resonators [7,8]. In the present paper we propose a route towards this goal: the 2-mirror resonator, based upon two ideal spherical mirrors, must be sufficiently nonparaxial and must support many transverse modes.

The motivation to develop a random laser based upon a macroscopic cavity instead of microscopic volume scattering is twofold. *(i)* The system can be much better controlled since the gain medium and the random feedback are spatially separated; in principle, any desired gain medium can be used. *(ii)* The thresh-

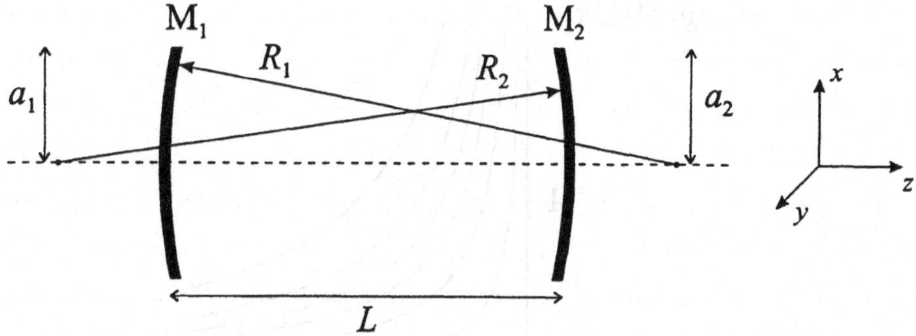

Figure 1. Fabry Perot resonator consisting of two spherical mirrors M_1 and M_2. These mirrors have radii of curvature R_1 and R_2, and diameters $2a_1$ and $2a_2$.

old is anticipated to be much lower, thus allowing continuous instead of pulsed operation. These advantages should facilitate experimental study of the excess quantum noise properties that have been predicted for a coherent random laser [9–11].

The structure of our paper is as follows. In Section 2 we give an overview of some properties of a paraxial optical resonator, emphasizing the connection between ray optics and wave optics; even when remaining within the paraxial regime this leads to results that may be surprising for some readers. In Section 3 the discussion is extended to the nonparaxial case, emphasizing the concepts of ray localization and phase locking. Section 4 introduces a coherent random laser constructed along these lines, and Section 5 gives a concluding discussion.

2. Paraxial analysis of an optical resonator

We consider a Fabry-Perot resonator consisting of two spherical mirrors M_1 and M_2 (Fig. 1). We assume the paraxial approximation, *i.e.*, $\sin\alpha \approx \alpha$ where α is the angle between a wavefront normal ("ray") and the axis. The paraxial regime is in fact not sharply defined; its extent depends greatly on the specific phenomenon that one studies and the desired accuracy of the paraxial prediction for this phenomenon.

The stability of a paraxial resonator can be judged from the well-known stability diagram displayed in Fig. 2 [12]. The resonator is stable if it satisfies $0 \leq g_1 g_2 \leq 1$, where $g_i = 1 - (L/R_i)$, with R_i as the radius of curvature of mirror i and L as the separation of the mirrors. Stable means, in a wave-optical sense, that the (Hermite)-Gaussian beam "fitting" between the two mirrors has a positive value for w_0^2, where w_0 is the minimum waist radius of the beam. In a geometrical-optical sense, stability implies that a ray bouncing back and forth between the mirrors remains confined in the transverse direction. In the present

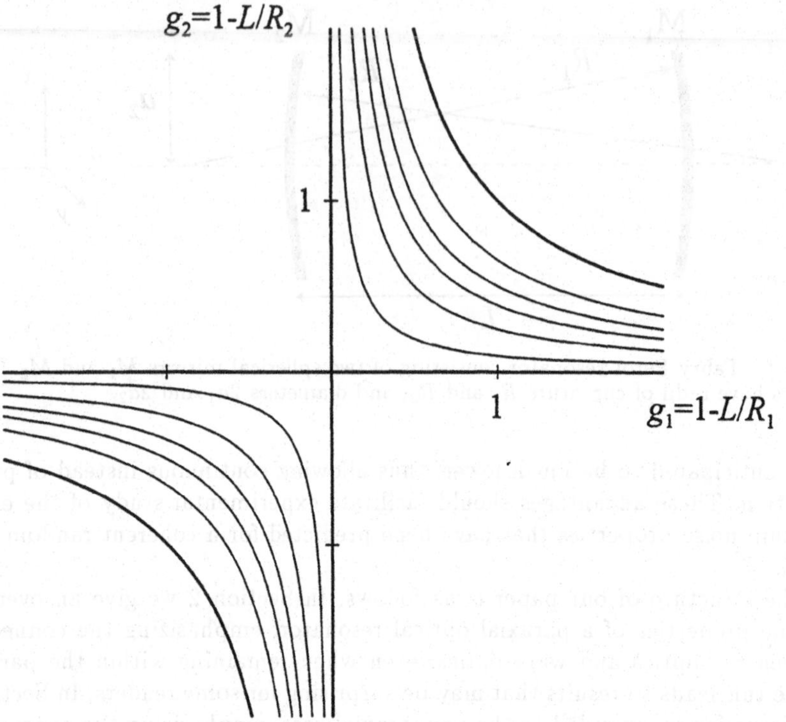

Figure 2. Stability diagram of a 2-mirror resonator. The shaded area corresponds with stable resonators; the hyperbolas inside this area correspond with resonators which have a relatively low-order rational Gouy phase. These resonators have a large degeneracy of their longitudinal and transverse modes.

paper we will restrict ourselves to this stable regime (*i.e.*, the shaded area in Fig. 2).

It is not well known that there is considerable structure within the stable regime; this was a popular issue in the 1960s (see [14] and references therein). In a wave-optical context the structure becomes evident by studying the well-known equation for the resonance frequency [12]

$$\nu_0 = \frac{c}{2L}\left\{q + (1+m+n)\frac{\theta}{2\pi}\right\} , \quad (1)$$

where q is the longitudinal mode index, m and n are the transverse mode indices of the Hermite-Gaussian eigenmode and the Gouy phase angle θ has been introduced via

$$\cos^2(\frac{1}{2}\theta) = g_1 g_2 \quad . \quad (2)$$

Note that the Gouy phase θ is a function of the cavity length and the radii of curvature of the mirrors; it gives the "extra" propagation phase of a curved wavefront as compared to a plane wave. We assume the special case that θ is a rational fraction of 2π, *i.e.*, $\theta = (K/N)2\pi$ with K and N integers (without a common factor); in that case we obtain

$$\nu_0 = \frac{c}{2NL}\{Nq + K(1+m+n)\} \ . \tag{3}$$

This shows that an arbitrary intra-cavity travelling wave field reproduces itself after N roundtrips. There are in fact N sets of degenerate transverse modes within one axial free spectral range of the cavity, since increasing the sum $(m+n)$ by N and decreasing q by K leaves the resonant frequency unchanged. The smaller N is, the higher the degeneracy of these sets. In fact the number of low-loss transverse modes of the cavity, which is of the order of $(N_F)^2$, is divided among the N degenerate sets. Here N_F is the Fresnel number, given by $N_F = a_1 a_2/\lambda L$ [12]. According to Eq. (2), each N corresponds to a certain hyperbola inside the stable region of Fig. 2.

In a geometrical-optical description the condition that a travelling wave repeats itself after N roundtrips (*i.e.*, 2 N transits) translates into the requirement that the associated $2N$ rays form a *closed* path. This case has been well studied in the context of folded optical delay lines [15]. Figure 3 shows some examples of the ray paths (for $N = 3$ and 4) and the corresponding vertices on the mirrors. For $K = 1$ the transverse motion of the ray during the N roundtrips is one trip back-and-forth. In the general case, the transverse motion consists of K trips back-and-forth. Generally, the rays are in the surface of a hyperboloid, with the vertices forming ellipses on the mirrors [15]. Under special conditions the ellipses may become a circle or a line. In the case of a circle the Gouy phase θ has a direct geometrical interpretation; it translates into the difference in polar angle of two neighboring vertices on the mirror.

We emphasize that, if Eq. (3) is satisfied, a ray leaving at *any* (paraxial) angle α and from *any* (paraxial) position r on the mirror reproduces itself after N roundtrips; this spatial indifference is a consequence of the paraxial approximation. Folded optical delay lines usually operate in this regime.

3. Beyond the paraxial approximation: ray localization and phase locking

Very interesting phenomena occur when we consider a resonator as in Fig. 1, but now *outside* the paraxial regime. In that case the longitudinal and transverse degrees of freedom are no longer separable. The factorization of the cavity mode function U into a transverse mode and a longitudinal mode,

$$U(x,y,z) = f(x,y)g(z) \ , \tag{4}$$

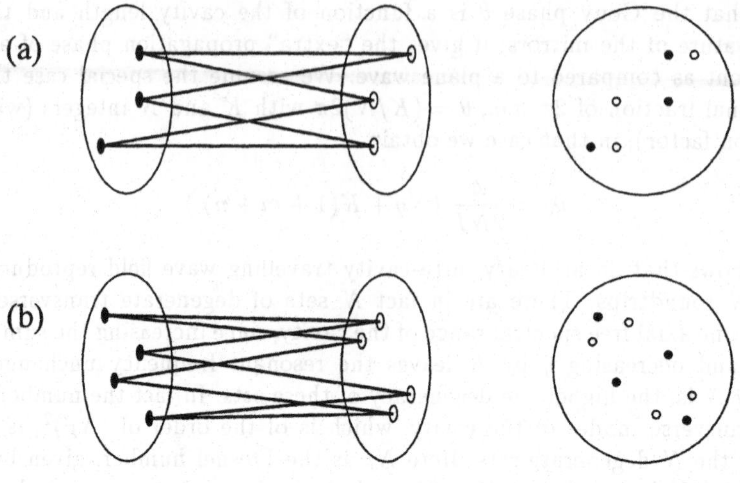

Figure 3. Closed ray paths in a resonator with a low-order rational Gouy phase $2\pi(K/N)$. In (a) we have $K = 1, N = 3$ and in (b) $K = 1, N = 4$.

is invalidated, as are Eqs. (1) and (3). Although this makes the nonparaxial situation extremely complex, it is still possible to recognize some generic aspects [14].

Specifically, one finds by elementary ray tracing that the spatial indifference of the closed (K, N) paraxial path disappears. That is to say, when considering a resonator with length L in the nonparaxial case, a path specified by (K, N) and starting from one of the mirrors at a radial position r, the starting axial angle being α, survives only as a closed path for a *specific* choice of r ($r = r_{K,N}$) and a *specific* choice of α ($\alpha = \alpha_{K,N}$). Thus, nonparaxiality implies *localization* of closed ray paths. When slightly changing L, one may again construct a closed path with the same values (K, N) but different values of $R_{K,N}$ and $\alpha_{K,N}$. When L is changed too much, a ray path (K, N) can no longer be constructed since the vertices would be off the mirrors, *i.e.*, $r_{K,N} > a$, where a is the mirror radius.

In the frequency domain, this "tolerance" in L corresponds effectively to a "tolerance" in the resonance condition Eq. (3). A closed ray path (K, N) can exist for a *range* of values of the cavity length L, at the *same* frequency ν as given by Eq. (3). This range δL is given by [14]

$$\delta L \sim \frac{a^2}{L} \; . \tag{5}$$

The relative tolerance $\delta L/L$ is of the order of $(NA)^2$, where $NA \sim a/L$ is the numerical aperture of the resonator. Equivalently, the relative tolerance $\delta\nu/\nu$

which is allowed when realizing a closed path (K, N), at fixed L, is also given by $(NA)^2$.

In the language of coupled-mode theory, this frequency tolerance can be seen as frequency locking (or phase locking) due to dissipative coupling of a set of modes. Generally, dissipative coupling originates from spatial (x, y) nonuniformities in loss or gain [16]. For a formal description of this phenomenon, we denote the optical field as a state vector

$$| e\rangle = \sum_i a_i \mid u_i\rangle , \tag{6}$$

where $| u_i\rangle$ is a convenient, orthogonal basis, like the eigenmodes of the loss-free system. We denote the effective loss (*i.e.*, the difference between loss and gain) by the operator $g(x, y)$. In this notation the roundtrip loss experienced by a propagating optical field is proportional to

$$\frac{\langle e \mid g \mid e\rangle}{\langle e \mid e\rangle} = \frac{\sum\limits_{i,j} a_i^* a_j \langle u_i \mid g \mid u_j\rangle}{\sum\limits_i \mid a_i \mid^2} . \tag{7}$$

The diagonal elements of the matrix $g_{ij} \equiv \langle u_i \mid g \mid u_j\rangle$ correspond to the modal losses of the various eigenmodes $| u_i\rangle$. The off-diagonal elements represent the dissipative couplings between these modes. The situation of minimum loss (or maximum gain), which is preferred according to the Maximum Emission Principle [17], will not correspond to either of the modes $| u_i\rangle$, but will be a phase-locked linear combination of these modes.

A classic example of dissipative frequency locking is formed by the synchronization of the two pendulum clocks of Huygens [18]. A more recent example is frequency locking of the *cw* and *ccw* modes in a ring laser gyro [12,16,19,20]. In both examples we deal with two, detuned modes; the frequency difference of these modes changes into a loss difference by a linear transformation of the basis of eigenmodes.

In the case of our nonparaxial resonator the unperturbed transverse-mode frequencies satisfy Eq. (3); they are locked by the spatial nonuniformity of the loss represented by the *finite* size of the mirrors [14]. Analogous to the 2-mode case [16,19,20], the frequency differences of the unperturbed modes are transformed into loss differences of the locked modes. A simple, anthropomorphic interpretation of this transverse mode locking is as follows. Assume that the cavity length L is slightly changed from the (K, N) resonance condition implied by Eq. (3). It is then energetically advantageous for the transverse Gaussian modes to keep their frequencies the same; this is topologically allowed in the nonparaxial case. In this way the superposition state maintains a compact, closed ray path (K, N) that "fits" on the mirrors. When δL becomes too large, the lock is broken and the superposition state spreads out beyond the mirror area.

The same anthropomorphic interpretation applies to frequency (or phase) locking of the two modes, *cw* and *ccw*, in a ring laser gyro [12]. In practice, these modes are coupled, *e.g.*, by backscattering from a dust particle on one of the mirrors. The *cw* and *ccw* modes, nominally detuned by the Sagnac effect when the ring laser rotates, prefer to keep the same frequency, since this leads to a standing wave pattern that optimally avoids the dust particle, namely by positioning a node at the dust particle. This treatment can be generalized to include a complex-valued coupling coefficient, thus allowing a transition from "dissipative" to "conservative" coupling when the coupling coefficient goes from real to imaginary [16,19,20].

We stress that this frequency locking phenomenon is a consequence of a (properly phased) *linear* coupling. If we add a gain medium to the cavity and operate the system as a multimode laser, the modes may also be coupled *nonlinearly*, by cross-saturation. However, as long as the nonlinear coupling is much smaller than the linear coupling, the simple picture outlined above remains valid. It has been demonstrated experimentally that this is often a reasonable approximation if the laser involved is not too far above threshold [20].

4. Nonparaxial resonator as coherent random laser

All ingredients of a cavity random laser are now in place. One should start from a paraxial multi-mode resonator operating in the stable regime (*i.e.*, the shaded area in Fig. 2). The resonator should have a low-N rational Gouy phase, $\theta = 2\pi(K/N)$. By adding a suitable nonparaxial perturbation, the degenerate mode manifold belonging to (K, N) is split, leading to a dense spectrum of sharp resonances, assuming a high finesse of the resonator. This eigenvalue spectrum is, in principle, chaotic due to the nonseparable nature of wave equation annex boundary conditions (= mirrors). The dissipative coupling implied by the finite diameter of the mirrors leads to frequency locking within this chaotic spectrum and thus to localized, closed ray paths. If a gain medium is inserted in the resonator, each closed path acts as a ring laser.

This scenario possibly represents a *bona fide* implementation of the coherent random laser, analogous to the implementation based upon scattering in a microparticle system. In both cases the conventional modes of the system (Gaussian beams, plane waves, ...) are nondegenerate due to nonseparable boundary conditions; these modes are phase locked to create a closed loop. In the microscopic case the line sections of a closed loop [4,5] have only a diagrammatical meaning, in the sense of Feynman, since the spatial dimension is typically of order λ. In the macroscopic case the line sections correspond to propagating plane waves, *i.e.*, the rays of geometrical optics. Localization refers now to a transverse spatial dimension $\leq \sqrt{a_1 a_2}/N_F$, *i.e.*, again limited by the wave nature of light. In both cases a spatial increase of the pumped gain volume leads to the appearance of more, higher-order (*i.e.*, larger-N) loops; the reason is that a high-order loop is "larger" than a low-order loop and thus requires a larger pumped volume.

A key question is how large the nonparaxiality must be in order to produce a chaotic ray manifold/eigenvalue spectrum. The effect of a nonparaxial aberration δ_{nonpar} is nonperturbative if it causes a shift in the mode frequencies that is large compared to the mode spacings [8]. Since we deal with a *degenerate* (K, N) mode manifold, this condition translates into the requirement that the nonparaxial aberration must be larger than the cold-cavity linewidth $\Delta\nu_c$ of the modes. On the other hand, the nonparaxial aberration must remain smaller than the dissipative locking bandwidth $(NA)^2\nu$. Thus, we anticipate that we have to satisfy as *necessary* condition

$$\Delta\nu_c < \delta_{nonpar} < (NA)^2\nu \ . \tag{8}$$

It is unclear whether this is also a *sufficient* condition; nonseparability of the wave equation may lead to ray motion that is only partially instead of fully chaotic.

An attractive way to introduce a large violation of the paraxial condition is to make the resonator strongly *astigmatic*, by inserting a thick Brewster plate (Fig. 4(a)) or using a three-mirror cavity with a curved folding mirror (Fig. 4(b)). Although these resonators seem approximately paraxial relative to their "chief ray," they are in fact highly nonparaxial; this is quantified by the angle α in Fig. 4. This angle can be of the order of 1 radian. We expect that such a strongly astigmatic resonator has still relatively small losses, since it stems from a paraxially stable configuration; in other words, we deal with a system that is still dominantly conservative. As a historical aside, the configurations in Fig. 4 were popular in the very first generation of continuous dye lasers [21], where the dye flowed through a thick Brewster cell as in Fig. 4(a). The (undesired) astigmatism introduced by this cell was compensated by using a folding mirror as in Fig. 4(b); the two astigmatisms have opposite signs.

An essential feature of a random laser is its statistical nature. One should measure the property under investigation (optical spectrum, intensity noise spectrum, ...) for many individual implementations of the random system; the measured values of this property may differ greatly. The statistical distribution function is a signature of localization (if it occurs) [22]. In the case of a random laser based upon microparticle scattering, an individual implementation corresponds to a specific spatial arrangement of the scattering particles. In the case of a cavity random laser an individual implementation corresponds to a set of specific values of cavity length, mirror diameters, strength of astigmatism, etc. Also, these can be changed, e.g., by mounting one of the mirrors on a piezo element to vary the cavity length L.

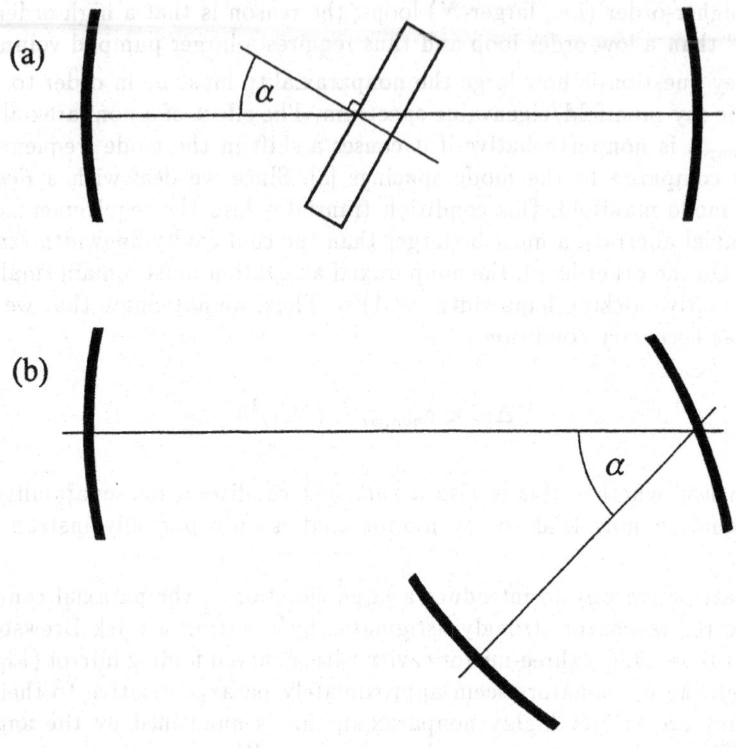

Figure 4. Astigmatic resonator configurations, based upon a thick Brewster plate (a) or a folded resonator (b).

5. Concluding discussion

Obviously, the ideas outlined above need further theoretical and experimental elaboration. This is highly nontrivial, since the ray and wave dynamics of a nonparaxial open cavity is largely a *terra incognita.* Three potentially useful observations are as follows.

(i) There are many similarities with lasers based on the chaotic ray dynamics in an optical stadium resonator [8]. It would be very interesting to work out the precise connections. An important practical advantage of our open 2-mirror cavity is that any gain medium can be used, contrary to the case of a (closed) stadium resonator.

(ii) Also, other lens aberrations than astigmatism may be useful. Optical aberrations in a near-paraxial system have been intensively studied for more than a century; they can be classified as mathematical catastrophes [23]. In

third-order aberration theory (*i.e.*, $\sin\alpha \approx \alpha - \frac{1}{6}\alpha^3$) one finds the 5 primary (Seidel) aberrations, one is the astigmatism encountered above. In order to account for the propagation effect of the primary aberrations, one should proceed to fifth-order theory. This theoretical foundation is possibly useful for better understanding of the nonparaxial 2-mirror laser resonator.

(iii) When we unfold the rays in a near-paraxial cavity, we obtain a lens guide. Lens guides were a popular topic of (mainly theoretical) study in pre-fiber-optics times when they were thought to hold promise of optical broadband communication [24]. As it was realized that the lenses in such a guide had necessarily some aberrations, there have been rudimentary numerical simulations, on computers of the 1960s, of a guide composed of imperfect lenses. It was found that lens imperfections lead to beam break up after a sufficient number of transits; the conclusion was that no simple relation between wave dynamics and ray dynamics in an aberrated-lens-guide [24] exists. This early finding seems highly relevant in the present context.

As already mentioned before, it is uncertain how strongly nonparaxial the resonator must be made for a realization of chaotic scattering. It would be interesting to inject a *passive* nonparaxial resonator with a monochromatic beam and measure its reflection/transmission; this could reveal signatures of chaos such as level repulsion [7,25], coherent backscattering, and exponential transmission [3,4].

Having an open-cavity implementation of a coherent random laser will greatly simplify experimental efforts to verify the predictions of excess quantum noise ("Petermann factor K_P") which have been based upon a universal random matrix model of the random laser [9–11]. Interestingly, the key aspect of this model is that excess noise occurs only if the eigenmodes that contribute to the laser output overlap each other and if their losses are *distributed* over some range. Such a spread of losses occurs naturally in the cavity random laser since the dissipative frequency locking mechanism transforms frequency nondegeneracy of wave modes that contribute to a closed ray path into loss nondegeneracy.

We note this aspect of having overlapping modes with a distribution of losses is also the key requirement for the appearance of excess quantum noise ($K_P > 1$) in *nonrandom* cavity lasers [13]. Thus, it could well be that a nonparaxial multi-transverse-mode-laser, as proposed here, will always lead to $K_P > 1$, but this may only be associated with chaotic scattering when the nonparaxiality is strong enough. The signature of the latter is, of course, the occurrence of a statistical distribution of K_P. It would be very interesting to study this gradual transition from a "deterministic" to a "random" Petermann factor.

Very recently, we observed phase locking of transverse modes into a closed ray path as discussed in Section 3. In this experiment we use a Nd^{3+}:YVO_4 laser, with a folded cavity configuration to introduce astigmatism [26]. Presently, we are studying the noise properties of this device.

References

1. R.V. Ambartsumyan, N.G. Basov, P.G. Kryukov, and V.S. Letokhov, "Non-resonant feedback in lasers", in: *Progress in Quantum Electronics*, edited by J.H. Sanders and K.W.H. Stevens, Pergmanon Press, Oxford, 1970, Vol. 1, p. 107.
2. M. Kempe, G.A. Berger, and A.Z. Genack, "Stimulated emission from amplifying random media", in: *Handbook of Optical Properties*, Vol. 2, R.E. Hummel and P. Wissman, editors, 1997, CRC Press, Boca Raton (LA), p. 301.
3. D.S. Wiersma and A. Lagendijk, Light diffusion with gain and random lasers, Phys. Rev. E 54, 4256 (1996).
4. D.S. Wiersma, P. Bartolini, A. Lagendijk, and R. Righini, Localization of light in a disordered medium, Nature 390, 671 (1997).
5. H. Cao, Y.G. Zhao, S.T. Ho, E.W. Seelig, Q.H. Wang, and R.P.H. Chang, Random laser action in semiconductor powder, Phys. Rev. Lett. 82, 2278 (1999).
6. H. Cao, J.Y. Xu, E.W. Seelig, and R.P.H. Chang, Microlaser made of disordered media, Appl. Phys. Lett. 76, 2997 (2000).
7. H.J. Stöckmann, *Quantum Chaos*, Cambridge University Press, Cambridge, 1999.
8. C. Gmachl, F. Capasso, E.E. Narimanov, J.U. Nöckel, A.D. Stone, J. Faist, D.L. Sivco, and A.Y. Cho, High-power directional emission from microlasers with chaotic resonators, Science 280, 1556 (1998).
9. M. Patra, H. Schomerus, and C.W.J. Beenakker, Quantum-limited linewidth of a chaotic laser cavity, Phys. Rev. A 61, 023810 (2000).
10. K. Frahm, H. Schomerus, M. Patra, and C.W.J. Beenakker, Large Petermann factor in chaotic cavities with many scattering channels, Europhys. Lett. 49, 48 (2000).
11. C.W.J. Beenakker, "Photon statistics of a random laser", in: *Diffuse Waves in Complex Media*, edited by J.P. Fouque, NATO ASI Series, Kluwer, Dordrecht, 1999.
12. A.E. Siegman, *Lasers*, University Science Books, Mill Valley (CA), 1986.
13. M.A. van Eijkelenborg, Å.M. Lindberg, M.S. Thijssen, and J.P. Woerdman, Resonance of quantum noise in an unstable cavity laser, Phys. Rev. Lett. 77, 4314 (1996).
14. I.A. Ramsay and J.J. Degnan, A ray analysis of optical resonators formed by two spherical mirrors, Appl. Opt. 9, 385 (1970).
15. D. Herriott, H. Kogelnik, and R. Kompfner, Off-axis paths in spherical mirror interferometers, Appl. Opt. 3, 523 (1964).
16. J.P. Woerdman and R.J.C. Spreeuw, "Optical level crossings", in: *Analogies in Optics and Micro Electronics*, edited by W. van Haeringen and D. Lenstra, Kluwer, Dordrecht, 1990, p. 135.
17. L.A. Westling, M.G. Raymer, and J.J. Snyder, Single-shot spectral measurements and mode correlations in a multimode pulsed dye laser, J. Opt. Soc. Am. B 1, 150 (1984).
18. C. Huygens, *Oeuvres Complètes de Christiaan Huygens*, Vol. 5, Société Hollandaise des Sciences, La Haye, Martinus Nijhoff, 1893, p. 243.
19. H.A. Haus, H. Statz, and I.W. Smith, Frequency locking of modes in a ring laser, IEEE J. Quantum Electronics 21, 78 (1985).
20. R.J.C. Spreeuw, R. Centeno Neelen, N.J. van Druten, E.R. Eliel, and J.P. Woerdman, Mode-coupling in a He-Ne ring laser with backscattering, Phys. Rev. A 42, 4315 (1990).
21. H.W. Kogelnik, E.P. Ippen, A. Dienes, and C.V. Shank, Astigmatically compensated cavities for cw dye lasers, IEEE J. Quantum Electronics 8, 373 (1972).
22. A.A. Chabanov, M. Stoytchev, and A.Z. Genack, Statistical signatures of photon localization, Nature 404, 850 (2000).
23. M.V. Berry and C. Upstill, "Catastrophe optics: Morphologies of caustics and their diffraction patterns", in: *Progress in Optics*, Vol. 18, edited by E. Wolf, North Holland, Amsterdam, 1980, p. 257.
24. D. Marcuse, *Light Transmission Optics*, Krieger Publishing Company, Malabar (FA), 1989.
25. F. Haake, *Quantum Signatures of Chaos*, Springer, Berlin (1991).
26. J. Dingjan, M.P. van Exter, and J.P. Woerdman, Geometric modes in a single-frequency Nd:YVO_4 laser, to be published.

PROPAGATION OF LIGHT IN DISORDERED SEMICONDUCTOR MATERIALS

AD LAGENDIJK , JAIME GOMEZ RIVAS , ARNOUT IMHOF , FRANK J.P. SCHUURMANS AND RUDOLF SPRIK
van der Waals-Zeeman Institute, University of Amsterdam, Valckenierstraat 65, 1018 XE Amsterdam, The Netherlands

1. Introduction

The analogy between the propagation of electron waves and classical waves has led to a revival in the research of the transport of light in disordered scattering systems [1]. The first indications of the role of interference in multiple scattering has been indicated in experiments on enhanced backscattering in the late 1980's [2]. Over the past decade many studies have been performed to characterize and understand this intricate interplay of scattering and interference [3]. The improved understanding of the optical systems stimulated the studies of the propagation of waves in disordered systems in general and applications in e.g. the field of medical imaging [4].

The 'holy grail' has been to observe the optical analogue of Anderson localization in electronic systems [5]. Anderson localization refers to an inhibition of the wave propagation in disordered scattering systems due to interference. Localization is essentially a wave phenomenon and it should hold for all kinds of waves i.e. electrons, electromagnetic and acoustic waves [6]. For isotropic scatterers Anderson localization is established if $kl_s \sim 1$, where k is the wave vector in the medium and l_s is the scattering mean free path, or the average length that the wave propagates in between two elastic collisions. The transition between extended and localized states occurs when $kl_s < 1$. This is known as the Ioffe-Regel criterion for localization [7]. To approach the Ioffe-Regel criterion, l_s can be reduced by using scatterers with a high refractive index, n, and an optimal size where the scattering cross-section is a maximum.

Experimental difficulties in realizing a random medium where the optical absorption is low enough and the light scattering is efficient enough to induce localization has been the reason why, for a long time, only mi-

C.M. Soukoulis (ed.), Photonic Crystals and Light Localization in the 21st Century, 447–473.

crowave localization was realized [8]. In this experiment the absorption is large and, therefore, complicates the interpretation of the results. Recently, near-infrared localization in GaAs powders was observed [9]. However, the validity of these measurements has been questioned by the possibility of absorption [10].

To achieve localization the parameter kl_s needs to be reduced. The light wavevector, k, is defined as $k = \frac{2\pi n_e}{\lambda}$ where λ is the wavelength and n_e is the effective refractive index of the disordered medium. The scattering mean free path, l_s, is given in first approximation by $l_s \sim \frac{1}{\rho\sigma_s}$, where ρ is the density of scatterers and σ_s their scattering cross section. The scattering cross section depends on the size of the scatterers relative to λ and on the refractive index contrast between the scatterers (n) and the surrounding medium (n_0), $m = \frac{n}{n_0}$, being larger for higher values of m.

Contrary to electronic systems, for light it is not possible to reach the localization transition ($kl_s \approx 1$) just by reducing k. In the Rayleigh scattering limit or when $\lambda \gg r$, where r is the radius of the scatterers, σ_s is proportional to λ^{-4} and therefore $kl_s \propto \lambda^3$. In this limit a reduction of k by increasing the light wavelength will give rise to an increase of the localization parameter. In the opposite limit or the geometric optics limit, $\lambda \ll r$, the scattering cross section equals $2\pi r^2$ and $kl_s \propto \frac{1}{\lambda r^2}$. Thus reducing λ will not help either to approach the localization transition. Therefore, localization of light will only be possible at an intermediate wavelength window where the scattering cross section is maximal, that is, when the size of the scatterers is of the order of the wavelength, $\lambda \sim r$. Even then the refractive index contrast needs to be high enough to reach the localization transition.

Here we present an overview of our recent measurements on Si [11] and Ge powders and on a unique form of porous GaP[12, 13]. We will discuss the method to observe deviations from diffusive transport and the occurrence of localization. Important are good characterization of the materials by a systematic study of static and dynamical properties. We will discusss the role of residual absorption, effective refractive index on internal reflection and topology of the sample.

2. Disordered semiconductor systems

Much experimental work has been done on powders of TiO_2 [14, 15, 16]. TiO_2 is the dielectric with the highest refractive index in the visible, $n = 2.7$, and, although the TiO_2 samples were strongly scattering, the lowest value of the localization parameter was still far from the transition ($kl_s \approx 6$). Some semiconductors like Ge, GaAs, Si and GaP have larger refractive indices than TiO_2 and very low absorption for $\lambda > \lambda_{\text{gap}}$, where λ_{gap} is the wavelength of the semiconductor energy band gap. In table 1 we list, for

TABLE 1. refractive index, n, and wavelength of the energy band gap, λ_{gap}, of several semiconductors. The lowest reported value of the localization parameter, kl_s, and the structure of the samples are also listed.

Material	n	λ_{gap} (nm)	Reported kl_s (at λ)	Structure	Reference
GaAs	3.5	890	< 1 (1.067 μm)	powder	[9]
GaP	3.2	550	$\sim$2 (0.633 μm)	porous	[12]
Ge	4.1	1850	$\sim$3 (2 μm)	powder	[24]
Si	3.5	1100	$\sim$3.5 (6.5 μm)	powder	[11]
TiO_2	2.7	> 300	$\sim$7 (0.633 μm)	powder	[15]

these semiconductors, the refractive index n and λ_{gap}. Therefore, they are good candidates to prepare a material where light is localized. We have also included in table 1 the lowest measured value of kl_s. Strong localization of light ($kl_s < 1$) was first and solely reported in GaAs powders [9]. However, an alternative explanation for these measurements was proposed in terms of classical light diffusion and optical absorption [10]. It was clear that a thorough characterization of these novel materials was necessary.

We have prepared samples with different structure, powders and porous materials, as it is indicated in table 1. In the following we describe the preparation method for the different samples. The starting material of the Si samples was commercially available powder of high purity Si particles (Cerac S-1049) with sizes ranging from a few hundred nanometers to about 40 μm. To reduce the polydispersity in the particle size we suspended the particles in spectroscopic grade chloroform and we let them sediment for 5 minutes. Only the particles that did not sediment were used in the experiments. Fig. 1(a) is an scanning electron microscopy (SEM) image of these particles. We can see that the Si particles are rounded and that they tend to aggregate into clusters. Considering the clusters as single particles, the average particle radius is $\bar{r} = 690 \pm 410$ nm. Layers of Si powder with different thickness were made by putting a few drops of the suspension on CaF_2 substrates and letting the chloroform evaporate [11].

The Ge samples were prepared starting from bulk pieces of Ge that were gently milled. Sedimentation of the biggest particles was necessary in order to keep the milling time and intensity as low as possible. A SEM image of the resulting Ge particles is shown in Fig. 1(b). As may be noticed, the Ge particles do not form clusters and their shape is different from that of the Si particles. The average Ge particle size is $\bar{r} = 980 \pm 680$ nm. The still high polydispersity of the Si and Ge particles has serious disadvantages, since

Figure 1. Scanning electron microscope images of disordered semiconductor samples. (a) Si powder, (b) Ge powder and (c) porous GaP (PA-GaP).

the average scattering cross section becomes lower as the polydispersity increases. Layers of Ge particles were made in a similar way as for Si, for which we suspended the particles in spectroscopic grade methanol.

The GaP samples are porous or sponge-like layers of GaP. The porous structure was formed by anodic etching of n-type single crystalline GaP wafers [12]. Samples of two types were made: anodically etched GaP (A-GaP) with a porosity of 35% and photoanodically etched GaP (PA-GaP) with a porosity of 50%. The PA-GaP samples were prepared by further etching A-GaP using homogeneous photo-assisted etching [12]. The resulting samples are layers of different thickness of porous GaP on bulk GaP wafers or substrates. Figure 1(c) is a SEM image of PA-GaP sample. The average pore size in the A-GaP samples is estimated to be $\bar{r} = 92 \pm 30$ nm while for the PA-GaP samples $\bar{r} = 132 \pm 30$ nm.

Finally, it is necessary to mention that the structure of the samples will play an important role in its scattering properties. For instance, it has been demostrated that the values of kl_s for the inverse structure of air spheres in high dielectric materials (porous material) is lower that those for the direct structure of spheres of high dielectric material in air (powder) [17]. Also the shape of the particles or pores will influence the scattering.

3. Static characterization

In this section we describe the static measurements. From these measurements important sample parameters as l_s, l, L_a and n_e are obtained. The optical absorption in the medium is characterized by the absorption lenght, L_a. The transport mean free path, l, is defined as the distance over which the direction of propagation of the wave is randomized and vanishes in the localization regime. The scattering mean free path, l_s, constitutes a measure of the disorder quantified by the localization parameter. Let us briefly describe the propagation of light in disordered scattering media. In the weak scattering limit, $kl_s \gg 1$, the propagation of light is well described by the diffusion equation [18]. The diffusion approximation neglects the interference of waves propagating along different paths since, on average, this interference cancels out. The light diffuses in the medium with a diffusion constant given by

$$D_B = \frac{v_e l_B}{3}, \tag{1}$$

where v_e is the energy velocity and l_B the Boltzmann mean free path, defined as the transport mean free path in the absence of interference. If a sample is illuminated, the source of diffuse radiation is given by the light scattered out of the incident or coherent beam. The incident beam decays as $\exp(-z/l_s)$ where z is the depth in the sample. The diffuse total transmission, defined as the transmitted light flux normalized by the incident flux, can be calculated by solving the diffusion equation with the proper boundary conditions. The boundary conditions are determined by considering that the diffuse fluxes entering the sample are due to a finite boundary reflectivity [19, 20]. This reflectivity arises from the refractive index mismatch between the sample and the outside world. The total transmission will, therefore, depend on the boundary reflectivities by means of the so-called extrapolation factors τ_1 and τ_2 where the index 1 refers to the interface where the incident beam enters the sample and the index 2 to the opposite interface. The extrapolation factors τ_1 and τ_2 are given by [20]

$$\tau_1 = \frac{2}{3}\left(\frac{1+\overline{R}_1}{1-\overline{R}_1}\right), \tag{2}$$

and a similar expression for τ_2. Where $\overline{R}_1$ is the polarization and angular averaged reflectivity of the boundary. The extrapolation lengths z_1 and z_2 are defined as the extrapolation factors times the transport mean free path. Thus, in the weak scattering limit we have $z_1 = \tau_1 l_B$ and $z_2 = \tau_2 l_B$.

In the case of non-absorbing samples, represented by the condition $L_a > L$, where L_a is the optical absorption length and L is the sample thickness, the total transmission is

$$T = \frac{l_B + z_1}{L + z_1 + z_2}. \tag{3}$$

The total transmission decays as the inverse of the sample thickness, similarly to Ohm's law for the electronic conductance. If significant absorption is present in the samples, $L_a < L$, the total transmission decays exponentially with sample thickness,

$$T = \frac{2L_a(l_B + z_1)}{L_a^2 + (z_1 + z_2)L_a + z_1 z_2} \exp\left(-\frac{L}{L_a}\right). \tag{4}$$

As the localization transition is approached the diffusion constant is renormalized by wave interference, which, according to the scaling theory of localization [21], is given by

$$\frac{D}{D_B} = \frac{l}{l_B} = l_B\left(\frac{1}{\xi_0} + \frac{1}{L_a} + \frac{1}{L}\right), \tag{5}$$

where the coherence length ξ_0 represents the length over which the interference is important. At the localization transition ξ_0 diverges, thus in an infinite and non-absorbing medium D and l vanish. At the transition the transport of light is inhibited.

In a non-absorbing medium in the strong localization regime ($kl_s < 1$) the total transmission is

$$T \propto \exp\left(-\frac{L}{L_{loc}}\right), \tag{6}$$

and the wave is spatially localized on length scales given by the localization length, L_{loc}. Notice that the equal dependence of the transmission on the sample thickness in the case of classical light diffusion in an absorbing medium (Eq. 4) and in the case of strong localization in a non-absorbing medium (Eq. 6) greatly complicates the analysis of these measurements. However, optical absorption is not necessarily a disadvantage. The role of absorption in the localization process has been never experimentally investigated and this can not be done in electronic systems since the number of electrons is conserved.

In the following we describe the static measurements that we have performed on disordered semiconductors materials. The simplest experiment consists in measuring the decay of intensity of the coherent beam sent through the samples. The transmitted fraction of the coherent beam, T_{coh}, is given by the expression

$$T_{\text{coh}} = \exp(-L/l_s). \tag{7}$$

TABLE 2. Scattering mean free path, l_s, effective refractive index, n_e, and localization parameter, kl_s, of A-GaP and PA-GaP samples.

Sample	l_s (μm) at $\lambda = 740$ nm	n_e	kl_s
A-GaP	0.4 ± 0.1	~ 2.0	6.8
PA-GaP	0.25 ± 0.05	1.5 ± 0.2	3.2

To measure T_{coh} one can place a detector at a long distance behind the sample and in the direction of the incident beam. By doing this the detected diffuse transmission is negligible compared to the coherent transmitted fraction. Unfortunately due to the exponential decay of T_{coh} these measurements can only be done for thin samples and an intense light source is needed. To avoid semiconductor band gap absorption the wavelength must be greater than λ_{gap}. For the GaP samples we used as radiation source a mode-locked Ti:Sapphire laser (Spectra Physics Tsunami) at a central wavelength of 740 nm. The values of l_s in the GaP samples at $\lambda = 740$ nm obtained from the measurement of T_{coh} are summarized in table 2. The scattering mean free path is shorter in PA-GaP due to its higher porosity.

The band gap of Ge is at $\lambda = 1.85$ μm, therefore we used as radiation source a Free Electron Laser (FELIX, Rijnhuizen, The Netherlands), which could be easily tuned in the near and mid-infrared (from 4.5 to 200 μm) [1]. We measured T_{coh} at $\lambda = 5$, 6.5, 7 and 8 μm. In the inset of Fig. 2 we plot the measurements at $\lambda = 8$ μm as function of the sample thickness and a fit to Eq. 7, from which we obtain $l_s = 3.8 \pm 0.2$ μm. Figure 2 shows the wavelength dependance of l_s. As expected l_s increases as λ becomes larger. This is due to the reduction of the scattering cross section when the wavelength becomes significantly larger than the scatterers size.

To obtain the localization parameter, $k = \frac{2\pi n_e}{\lambda} l_s$, we still need to know the effective refractive index of the samples, n_e. By measuring the angular dependence of the diffuse transmission it is possible to obtain this important parameter. This is because the angular distribution of the transmitted light is affected by the refractive index mismatch between the sample and the exterior, but not by l or l_s. Defining θ_i as the angle at which the diffuse light is incident on the interior side of the sample boundary with respect to the sample surface normal, and θ_e as the angle at which the light exits the sample (θ_i and θ_e are related by Snell's law), the transmission probability

[1]The experiments at FELIX where done in collaboration with C.W. Rella and L.D. Noordam from the FOM-Institute for Atomic and Molecular Physics (AMOLF, The Netherlands).

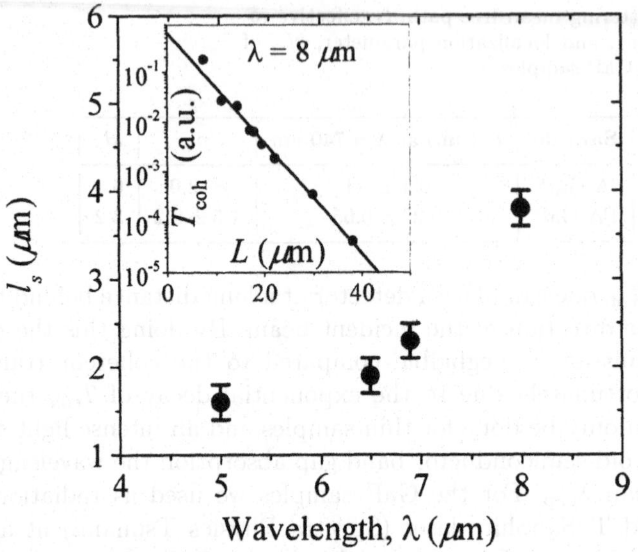

Figure 2. Wavelength dependence of the scattering mean free path, l_s, in Ge powder samples. Inset: measurements of the transmitted fraction of the coherent beam in the Ge samples as function of the sample thickness, L, for $\lambda = 8$ μm. The solid line is an fit to $T_{coh} = \exp(-L/l_s)$, with and scattering mean free path $l_s = 3.8 \pm 0.2$ μm.

at an angle θ_e, $P(\theta_e)$, is given by [22]

$$\frac{P(\theta_e)}{\cos\theta_e} \propto (\tau_2 + \cos\theta_i)(1 - R_2(\theta_i)) \tag{8}$$

where $R_2(\theta_i)$ is the Fresnel reflection coefficient at an incidence angle θ_i on interface 2. As $R_2(\theta_i)$ and τ_2 are functions of the refractive index contrast between the sample and the outside medium, it is possible to obtain n_e from the measurements $P(\theta_e)$. The measurements of $P(\theta_e)$ are done by rotating a detector around the sample. In Fig. 3 we plot as squares $P(\theta_e)/\cos(\theta_e)$ as a function of $\cos(\theta_e)$ for a 10 μm thick PA-GaP sample. By placing a polarizer between the sample and the detector we also measured the s and p-polarization components (triangles and circles in Fig. 3). The three measurements are fitted to Eq. 8 with the appropriate Fresnel reflection coefficients and with n_e as single free fitting parameter obtaining $n_e = 1.5 \pm 0.2$. For the A-GaP samples it is not possible to obtain n_e from the measurements of $P(\theta_e)$ because these samples have a thin low-porosity overlayer of 0.1-0.2 μm. As $P(\theta_e)$ is determined by the sample interface characteristics, for A-GaP samples these measurements are affected by the

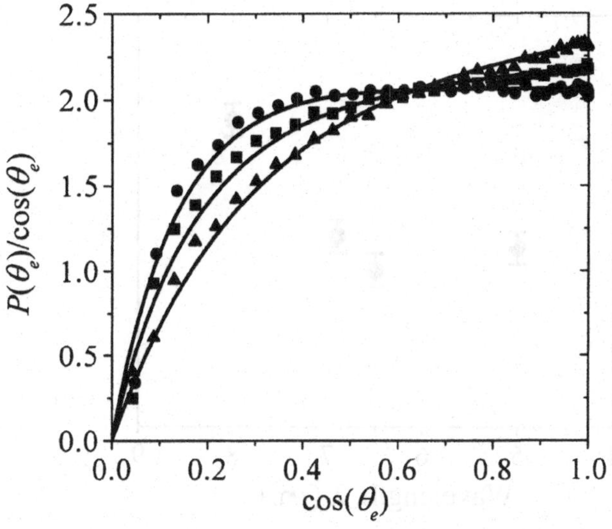

Figure 3. Transmission probability of a PA-GaP as a function of $\cos(\theta_e)$, where θ_e is the transmission angle with respect to the sample surface normal. The triangles and circles are the measurements for s and p-polarization detection while the squares correspond to unpolarized detection. The solid lines represent fits to classical diffusion theory from which the effective refractive index of the samples, $n_e = 1.5 \pm 0.2$, is obtained.

thin overlayer, making it impossible to infer from them a bulk property as n_e. Photo-assisted etching of the A-GaP to form PA-GaP removes the overlayer. However, we can estimate n_e knowing their porosity (35%). A good estimate of n_e is given by the Maxwell-Garnett effective refractive index [23], which in the case of A-GaP gives $n_e \sim 2.0$. In table 2 the measured value of n_e for PA-GaP and the estimated one for A-GaP are listed, together with the localization parameter. PA-GaP is very close to the localization transition, $kl_s = 3.2$, being the strongest scattering material of visible light to date.

By weighing the Ge powder samples we have estimated a material volume fraction of ~ 40. The corresponding value of the Maxwell-Garnett effective refractive index is $n_e \sim 1.6$. The localization parameter as a function of λ for the Ge samples is plotted in Fig. 4. The relatively high value of the localization parameter, regarding the high refractive index of Ge, and the nearly constant value of the localization parameter with λ can be understood in terms of the high polydispersity in the Ge particle size. As it is discussed in Ref.[11], due to the polydispersity the resonances in σ_s are

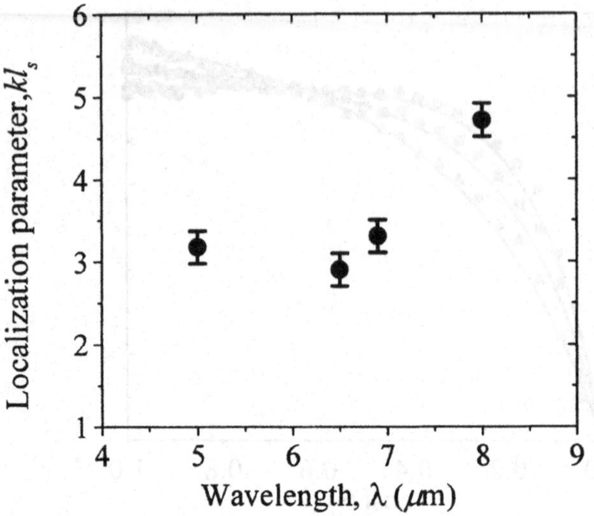

Figure 4. **Wavelength dependence of the localization parameter in the Ge powder samples.**

smoothed out and the average scattering cross section becomes in general larger than in a monodisperse system. Therefore to achieve localization in the Ge powder samples the polydispersity needs to be further reduced by, for instance, selective sedimentation.

The transport mean free path can be obtained from the total transmission measurements. The samples were mounted at the input of a $BaSO_4$ coated integrating sphere. The integrating sphere collected the diffuse transmitted light that was detected with a detector placed at the output port. To obtain an absolute value of the total transmission the measurements were normalized by the incident intensity. In all the samples (GaP, Ge and Si) the incoming beam was incident on the air-sample interface and the transmitted light exited the sample through the sample-substrate interface. For simplicity, in the determination of τ_2 we have not considered the reflections at the interface substrate-air. These reflections give rise to a larger value of τ_2. However, the total transmission through thick samples ($L \gg l$) is almost insensitive to the value of τ_2, as is clear from Eq. 3, and an underestimate of τ_2 will not affect the values of l. The inverse of the total transmission of the GaP samples, at $\lambda = 740$ nm, versus the sample thickness is plotted in Fig. 5. The circles are the measurement of A-GaP, while the squares corre-

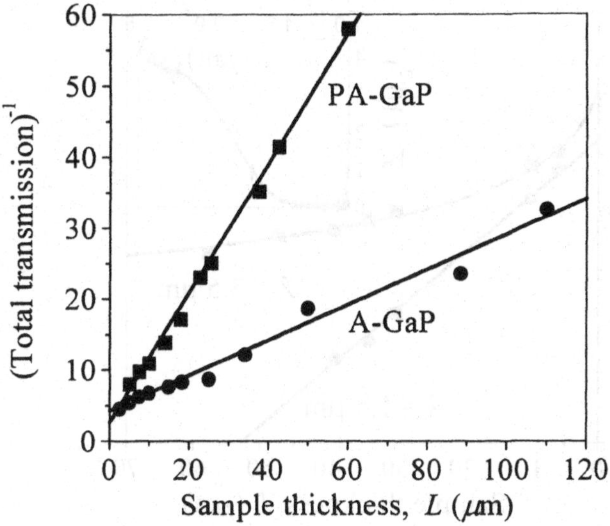

Figure 5. Inverse of the total transmission versus the sample thickeness, L, for PA-GaP (squares) and A-GaP (circles) samples. The solid lines are fits using the diffusion theory.

spond to PA-GaP. The linear dependence of T^{-1} on L is a clear signature that absorption is negligible, that is $L_a > 110$ μm in the A-GaP samples and $L_a > 60$ μm in the PA-GaP samples. With the values of n_e (table 2) and Eq. 2 the extrapolation factor τ_1 can be calculated, being $\tau_1 = 5.14$ for A-GaP and $\tau_1 = 2.42$ for PA-GaP. The solid lines in Fig. 5 are fits using Eq. 3. From the slope of these lines and with τ_1 we obtain $l = 0.65 \pm 0.03$ μm for A-GaP and $l = 0.32 \pm 0.04$ μm for PA-GaP. These values of l are slightly larger than l_s, which means that the scatterers are not fully isotropic.

We have also measured the total transmission of the Ge samples in the mid-infrared using the free electron laser [24], but lets here discuss the measurements on the Si samples. For the Si powder samples a tungsten halogen lamp was used as a light source and the total transmission spectra were measured with a Fourier transform infrared spectrometer (BioRad FTS-60A). The spectrum of a 57.8 μm thick sample is shown in the inset of Fig. 6. In Fig. 6 we plot the total transmission of the Si samples as a function of their thickness, L, for $\lambda = 1.4$ μm (circles) and 2.5 μm (squares). From the Si volume fraction (~ 40 %), n_e is estimated to be ~ 1.5 and the extrapolation factors of the interfaces sample-air, τ_1, and sample-substrate, τ_2, are ~ 2.4 and ~ 0.78 respectively. The solid lines in Fig. 6 represent

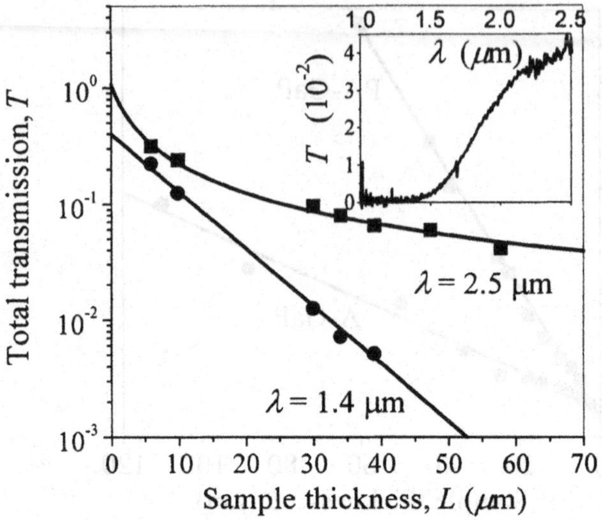

Figure 6. Total transmission through Si powders as a function of the sample thickness, L, for $\lambda = 1.4$ μm and $\lambda = 2.5$ μm. The solid lines are fits using classical diffusion theory. The inset shows the total transmission spectrum of a $L = 57.8$ μm sample.

fits to the measurements using classical diffusion theory (Eqs. 3 and 4). At $\lambda = 2.5$ μm we find $l = 0.83 \pm 0.09$ μm and $L_a > 60$ μm, while at $\lambda = 1.4$ μm, $l = 0.56 \pm 0.05$ μm and $L_a = 8.8 \pm 0.1$ μm.

The wavelength dependence of L_a is plotted in Fig. 7. The strong absorption at $\lambda < 2.0$ μm is due to strain in the Si lattice structure, which creates band gap tails that increase considerably the absorption at sub-band gap energies with respect to the strain-free material. We have confirmed the presence of strain by means of X-ray diffraction.

The dots in Fig. 8 represent the transport mean free path in the Si powder samples as a function of the wavelength. In collaboration with C.M. Soukoulis and K. Busch we have calculated the transport mean free path in the Si samples using the Energy Density Coherent Potential Approximation (EDCPA) [23, 25]. For the calculation we considered spherical and isotropic ($l = l_s$) scatterers. The dotted line in Fig. 8 is the calculated l of a monodisperse system of Si spheres with a volume fraction of 40% and a sphere radius equal to $\bar{r}$. The solid line in the same figure represents the averaged l over the particle size polydispersity. The resonances in l are smoothed out due to the polydispersity and in general l becomes larger. A

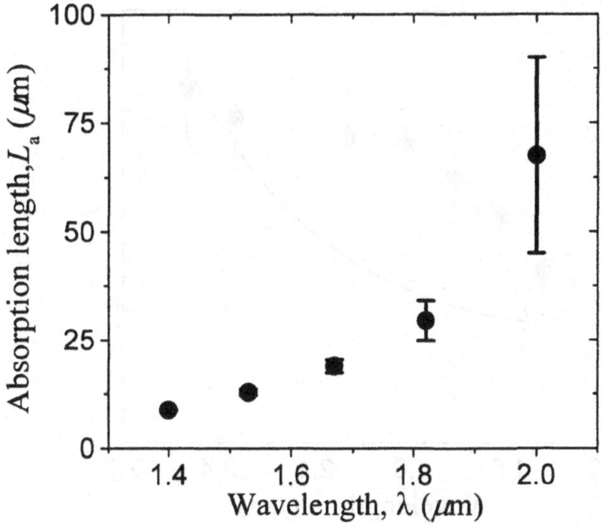

Figure 7. Absorption length, L_a, in Si powders as a function of the wavelength, λ.

good qualitative agreement is found between experiments and theory. The small quantitative difference can be attributed to the non-spherical shape of the Si particles and the ambiguous definition of the $\bar{r}$ due to the particle clustering. Assuming that the scatterers are isotropic and that $n_e = 1.5$ (Maxwell Garnett refractive index of the samples), we find a nearly constant value of $kl_s \sim 3.5$ in the studied wavelength range. As discussed for Ge, a reduction in the polydispersity of the Si particles will give rise to a lower value of the localization parameter.

We have also done enhanced backscattering (EBS) measurements on the GaP samples [13]. With these measurements we can check the consistency of the total transmission measurements and look for localization effects. We have measured the EBS of A-GaP and PA-GaP using the off-centered rotation technique [26]. The EBS measurements at $\lambda = 685$ nm are shown in Fig. 9. From the width of the cones the values of the transport mean free path can be inferred. For A-GaP (narrow cone) we find $l = 0.58 \pm 0.05$ μm, while for PA-GaP (wide cone) $l = 0.23 \pm 0.03$ μm, thus in good agreement with the total transmission measurements. The scattering efficiency can be reduced by decreasing the refractive index contrast in the samples. This can be achieved by filling the air voids in the samples with a non-absorbing liquid. In Fig. 10 the EBS of a PA-GaP sample filled with 1-dodecanol

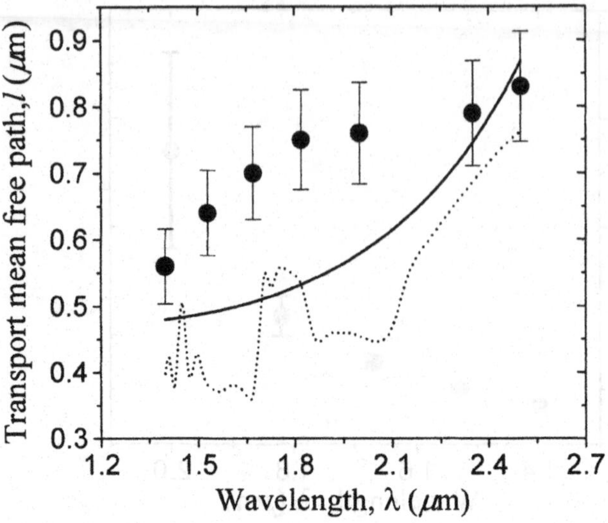

Figure 8. Transport mean free path of light, l, in the Si powder samples versus the wavelength, λ. The dotted line is l, calculated using the energy density coherent potential approximation, of a system of 40% by volume of Si spheres with a size equal to the average Si particle size. The solid line is the calculated l considering the polydispersity of the particles.

($n \sim 1.44$ and no absorption at $\lambda = 685$ nm) together with the EBS of the same non-filled sample are shown. The cone of the non-filled sample is a factor 2.1 ± 0.1 broader than the filled one, corresponding to an increase of the transport mean free path. Of special interest is the rounding of the cone top, $\Delta\Theta_R$, as is shown in the inset of Fig. 10. Within the classical diffusion approximation this rounding can be due to two factors: absorption and the finite size of the samples. The expression relating the rounding with the absorption length and the sample thickness can be derived to be [13]

$$\Delta\Theta_R = \frac{1}{kL_a} \coth\left(\frac{L_e}{L_a}\right), \tag{9}$$

where $L_e = L + z_1 + z_2$ is the effective sample thickness. In the absence of absorption, $L \ll L_a$, Eq. 9 reduces to

$$\Delta\Theta_R = \frac{1}{kL_e}. \tag{10}$$

To investigate the mechanisms of the cone rounding, we measured the EBS for various sample thicknesses. The cone rounding of A-GaP, PA-GaP and

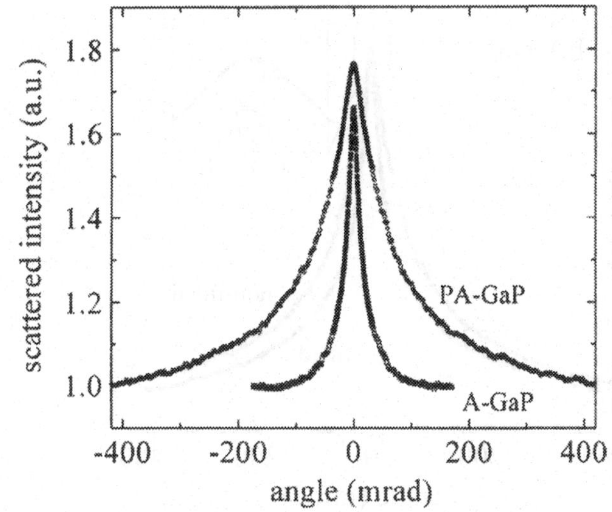

Figure 9. Enhanced backscattering of A-GaP and PA-GaP.

PA-GaP filled with 1-dodecanol are shown in Fig. 11 as open squares, open circles and filled triangles respectively as a function of $(kL_e)^{-1}$. Clearly, the cone rounding of A-GaP and filled PA-GaP follow Eq. 10. Absorption plays no role for these two types of samples and the rounding can be fully described in terms of the finite sample size. In contrast, the cone rounding of PA-GaP does not tend to zero for thick samples. If the measurements are fitted with Eq. 9 we find $L_a = 33 \pm 2$ μm. This contradicts the total transmission measurements from which we concluded that $L_a > 60$ μm. Moreover, if absorption is responsible for the rounding of the cone of PA-GaP, an extra rounding in the cone of the filled samples should also be apparent, which clearly is not the case. The extra rounding is only observed in the strongest scattering material which is the closest to the localization transition. It is expected that interference effects due to the proximity of the localization transition change the EBS cone shape. This change should be more significant in the cone cusp, since only at Θ close to 0 long paths contribute to the EBS. In particular it has been demonstrated that due to localization the cone cusp becomes rounded [27], similarly to our observation in PA-GaP.

Finally, we should mention that by filling the samples with non-absorbing liquids it is possible to verify if an exponentially decreasing total transmis-

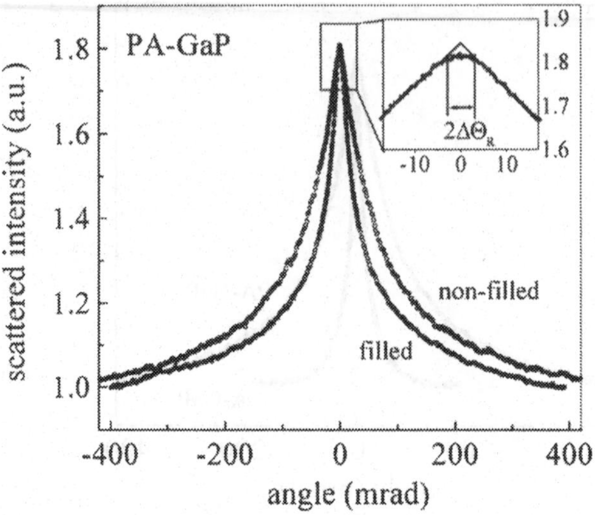

Figure 10. Enhanced backscattering of a PA-GaP sample with the air voids filled with 1-dodecanol and the same sample with non-filled pores. The inset is the a magnification of the cone top of the filled sample where the rounding of the cusp, $\triangle\Theta_R$, is visible.

sion with L is due to strong localization (Eq. 6) or if absorption needs to be considered. We have realized this experiment in Ge samples close to the band gap as is shown in Ref. [28].

4. Dynamic characterization

In this section we describe an interferometric technique for measuring time-resolved light transmission by random scattering media [29]. In this technique an incident ultrashort laser pulse is interfered with light transmitted by the medium. Since diffusely scattered light is incoherent an interferogram is obtained only if the scattered light is limited to a single (or just a few) coherence area, or speckle spot, at a time. Properties of light transport are then determined by repeating the measurement for many different configurations of scatterers and taking the appropriate average. This way one can measure the diffusion coefficient D, and with it the energy velocity v_e [16]. Due to the high dynamic range of the technique the decay rate $1/t_d \propto D/L^2$ of the tail of the diffusely transmitted pulse can be accurately determined. We use this to search for deviations that are expected to occur when the localization threshold is reached and D becomes thickness-dependent. For

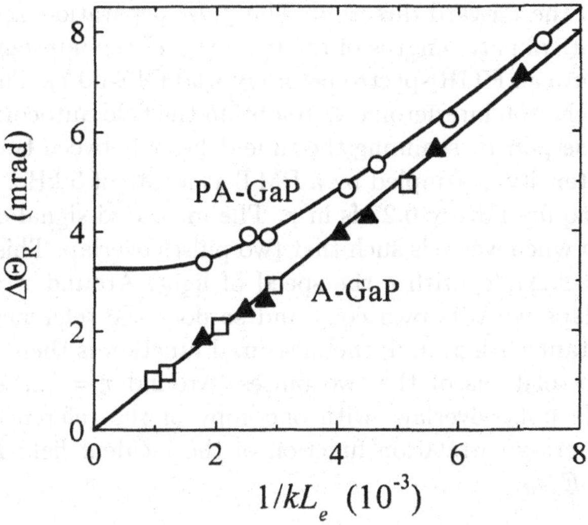

Figure 11. Cone roundings, $\Delta\Theta_R$, of A-GaP (open squares), PA-GaP (open circles), and PA-GaP filled with 1-dodecanol (filled triangles) as a function of the inverse of the effective sample thickness. The solid straight line is the theoretical prediction assuming a negligible absorption, Eq. 10 , using no adjustable parameters. PA-GaP shows an extra rounding for thick samples. The measurements are fitted to Eq. 9 with $L_a = 33 \pm 2$ μm. This absorption length is not consistent with the total transmission measurements.

example, near the mobility edge one expects to find $1/t_d \propto 1/L^3$ [30]. Furthermore, we will show that with our technique statistical information can be obtained on the fluctuations in the phases and amplitudes of multiply scattered light. This kind of dynamical information was hitherto unavailable for light, and makes possible a more detailed dynamical study of light propagation in strongly scattering media. Results are presented for samples of A-GaP.

In these experiments we used bandwidth-limited ultrashort pulses (~100 fs) from a Ti:Sapphire laser (Spectra Physics Tsunami) at 740 nm, with a repetition rate of 82 MHz. The spectral bandwidth of the pulses is about 1% of the central frequency, so that the mean free paths can be considered constants over this range. A double-pulsed signal is obtained with a fixed Mach-Zehnder interferometer in which the reference arm is empty and the sample arm contains the scattering sample. The sample beam and reference beam which emerge from the interferometer are carefully overlapped. This produces a pair of pulses: an undisturbed pulse followed by a pulse scattered by the sample into the forward direction. The pulse separation ΔL is the difference in the optical path lengths of the two arms of the interferometer. This beam is sent into an FTIR spectrometer (Biorad FTS-60A). The FTIR uses a scanning Michelson interferometer to obtain the field autocorrelation function of the pulse pair by scanning the time delay τ between two copies of the pair. The intensity is sampled by a PMT at a rate of 5 kHz. By this way samples are acquired every 0.27 fs in τ. The measured signal contains interference fringes whenever τ is such that two pulses overlap. This occurs if $\tau = 0$ or if $\tau = \pm\Delta L/c$, with c the speed of light. Around $\tau = 0$ the sample pulse overlaps with its own copy and so does the reference pulse. Apart from a constant background, the measured function is then the sum of the field autocorrelations of the two pulses. Around $\tau = \pm\Delta L/c$ one copy of the sample pulse overlaps with one copy of the reference pulse. This produces the cross correlation function of the incident field E_{in} and the scattered field E_{scat}:

$$C(\tau) = \frac{1}{\Delta T}\int_{-\Delta T/2}^{\Delta T/2} E_{in}^*(t)E_{scat}(t-\tau)dt, \qquad (11)$$

which contains both *amplitude* and *phase* information on the pulse transport through the sample. ΔT is the repetition time of the laser, which is much longer than the pulse width.

The sample was placed between two identical lenses of 60 mm focal length, which are in confocal position. The first lens is used to focus the beam onto the sample in a small spot. The second lens collects the scattered light into a parallel beam which is then sent through an aperture. By moving the sample close to the common focal point the illuminated area can be reduced to about 10 μm. This increases the angular size of the speckles such that a single speckle spot can be selected in the scattered beam with the aperture. Different configurations of scatterers are produced by moving the sample in the plane perpendicular to the beam by a distance larger than the illuminated spot. Typically, 60 configurations were measured. For each configuration 50 scans were averaged to reduce noise. The power incident upon the sample was ~0.1 W. Identical results were obtained when the incident power was halved, so nonlinear effects were absent.

In Fig. 12 the measured interferograms of a number of different speckles are shown. Each of these signals represents the temporal profile of the field transmitted in a different speckle spot, convoluted with the incident field. The signals are filled with fringes resulting from the rapid oscillations of the electromagnetic field. It is clear that the signal of each speckle is completely different because it consists of a unique sum of fields that have propagated along different paths, each of which has its own random amplitude and phase.

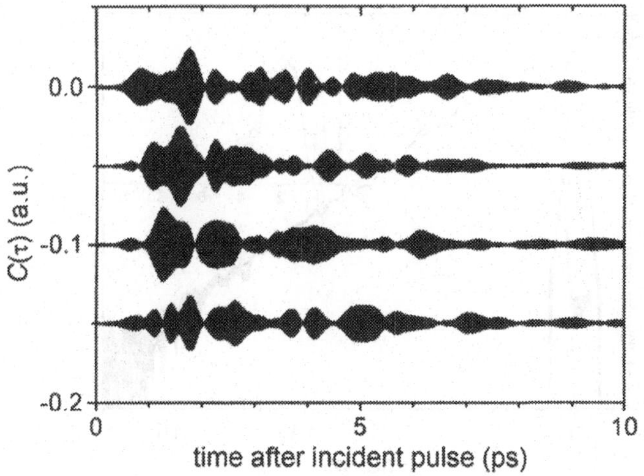

Figure 12. **Interferograms from a number of different speckles measured on a sample of A-GaP of L =15 μm thickness.**

The most important dynamical parameter describing propagation of light in random media is the diffusion coefficient D. The most direct way to measure it is a time resolved measurement in which a short laser pulse is incident upon the sample and one measures the time dependence of the transmitted intensity using a fast detector. This can then be compared to the prediction of diffusion theory to obtain D. Solving the diffusion equation with the proper boundary conditions for a slab of scattering material of thickness L one gets for the total transmission T [31]

$$T(t) = \frac{-2\pi D e^{-Dt/L_a^2}}{(L+z_1+z_2)^2} \sum_{n=1}^{\infty} n \quad \sin(\pi n \tfrac{l+z_1}{L+z_1+z_2}) \cos(\pi n \tfrac{L-l+z_1}{L+z_1+z_2}) \times \exp(-\tfrac{\pi^2 n^2 Dt}{(L+z_1+z_2)^2}). \qquad (12)$$

Here, z_1 and z_2 are the extrapolation lengths on the incident and transmitting side of the slab, respectively. In interferometric measurements a fast detector is not needed because time is measured by the optical retardation of the interferometer. The time dependence of the transmitted intensity is obtained by squaring the measured cross correlations, and averaging over all speckles. The fringes average out because their phases are random. To

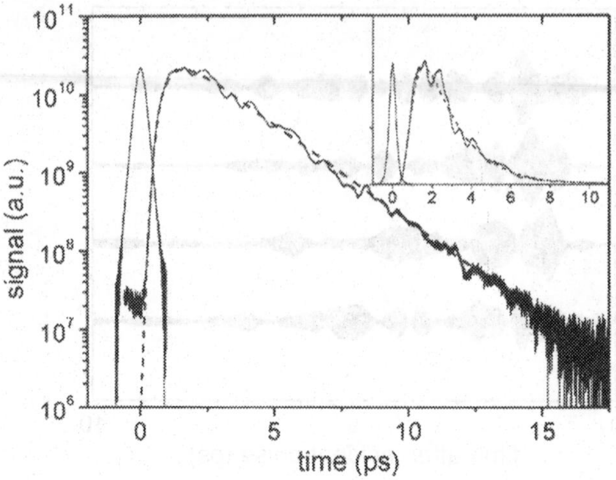

Figure 13. The diffusely transmitted pulse obtained by summing the squares of the interferograms of 60 different speckles of a sample of A-GaP of 15 μm thickness. The narrow pulse centered around the time origin is the incident pulse. The dashed line is Eq. 12 with $D = 21$ m^2/s and $L_a = \infty$. Inset: same data on a linear scale.

remove the remaining fringes the function is Fourier filtered. The result is shown in Fig. 13. The wiggles in the transmitted pulse form are due to the limited number of speckles (sixty). The time origin is found by moving the sample out of the beam and measuring the arrival time of the (now undistorted) pulse, which is also shown in Fig. 13. The semilog-plot demonstrates the high dynamic range of the measurement: An exponential decay over more than 3 orders of magnitude of the intensity is observed. This can be compared to Eq. 12 , which at long times predicts a single exponential decay with a rate $1/t_d$ given by

$$\frac{1}{t_d} = \frac{D}{L_a^2} + \frac{\pi^2 D}{(L + z_1 + z_2)^2}. \tag{13}$$

By plotting the decay rate against $1/L^2$ the validity of the diffusion equation is verified, and the values of L_a and D can be found. This is done in Fig. 14, where the expected linear relation is indeed found. From the slope we find $D = 21$ m^2/s. The intercept is zero within the experimental error, setting a lower limit on the diffuse absorption length: $L_a > 30$ μm. This means that the samples do not suffer from absorption (which was also

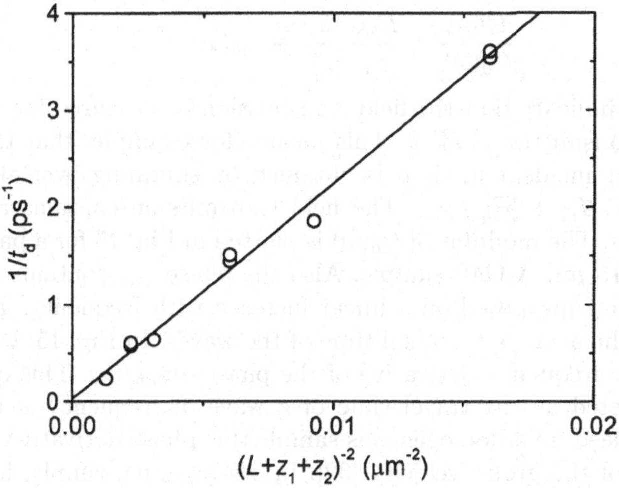

Figure 14. Decay rate of the tail of the transmitted pulse versus the inverse of the thickness squared. The solid line is a linear fit to Eq. 13.

clear from the total transmission measurements). Using only the value of D in Eq. 12 the form of the transmitted pulse is described very well, see Fig. 13. Using Eq. 1 and the value of l from the total transmission measurements an energy velocity of $0.32c$ is found, where c is the speed of light in vacuum.

An alternative way to obtain D is from dynamical speckle measurements. Using a tunable single frequency laser one can measure the intensity autocorrelation function within a single speckle spot, $C_I(\Delta\omega) = \langle \delta I(\omega)\delta I(\omega + \Delta\omega)\rangle$, where $\delta I(\omega) \equiv I(\omega) - \langle I(\omega)\rangle$. This function is related to the Fourier transform of the time dependence of the transmitted pulse [31]. The autocorrelation function of the scattered field $C_E(\Delta\omega) = \langle E(\omega)E^*(\omega+\Delta\omega)\rangle$ is similarly, and even more directly, related to the transmitted pulse shape. These functions can also be obtained from the interferometric data, as we shall see below.

Now we examine the phases and amplitudes contained in the data. The complex Fourier transform of the interferogram of a speckle, Eq. 11, gives $C(\omega) \sim E^*_{in}(\omega)E_{scat}(\omega)$. If this is divided by the Fourier transform of a reference interferogram measured without the sample, $C_0(\omega)$, the field transmission coefficient $t_{ab}(\omega)$ is obtained:

$$\frac{C(\omega)}{C_0(\omega)} = \frac{E_{scat}(\omega)}{E_{in}(\omega)} \equiv t_{ab}(\omega) \tag{14}$$

The subscripts indicate that the field transmission is measured for incident mode a and transmitted mode b. This means, for example, that the total transmission for incident mode a is obtained by summing over all transmitted speckles, $T_a = \sum_b |t_{ab}|^2$. The field transmission contains real and imaginary parts. The modulus of $t_{ab}(\omega)$ is plotted in Fig. 15 for a particular speckle of the 15 μm A-GaP sample. Also the phase ϕ_{ab} contains fluctuations. These are superposed on a linear increase with frequency, given by ωt, where t is the average traversal time of the waves. In Fig. 15, we therefore plotted the frequency derivative of the phase, $d\phi_{ab}/d\omega$. This quantity can be interpreted as the travel time of a wave of frequency ω through the sample. Indeed, in a homogeneous sample this phase derivative is equal to the inverse of the group velocity [32]. In a scattering sample, however, there are large fluctuations around a well-defined average, which is proportional to the inverse of the energy velocity. The average value of the phase derivative in this sample is equal to 2.32 ps and corresponds to the average traversal time $t_{av} = (L + z_1 + z_2)^2/6D$. For this sample we find $D = 23$ m^2/s, which agrees well with the value found from the decay of the tail of the transmitted intensity. It is also a clear from Fig. 15 that the amplitude and phase are strongly correlated: large positive and negative values of the phase derivative coincide with the zeroes or near-zeroes of the amplitude. This indicates that, as one crosses over from one speckle to a neighboring speckle in the frequency domain, a phase jump is encountered.

The complex field transmission coefficient $t_{ab}(\omega)$ in Fig. 15 can be autocorrelated and averaged together with data from the other speckles. The result is proportional to the field autocorrelation function $C_E(\Delta\omega)$. Similarly, the intensity autocorrelation function $C_I(\Delta\omega)$ can be found by autocorrelating $|t_{ab}(\omega)|^2$. The results are shown in Fig. 16. The data should be compared with the theoretical results [33]

$$C_E(\Delta\omega) = Re\left(\frac{q(L + z_1 + z_2)}{\sinh(q(L + z_1 + z_2))}\right), \tag{15}$$

$$C_I(\Delta\omega) = \left|\frac{q(L + z_1 + z_2)}{\sinh(q(L + z_1 + z_2))}\right|^2, \tag{16}$$

where $q = \sqrt{2\Delta\omega/D}$. The agreement is excellent at low frequency shifts, but deviations appear at larger shifts due to the limited number of speckles. From the fits, the value $D = 21$ m^2/s is found, as before. It should be noted that Eq. 16 is only the highest order term in the intensity correlations. Other terms contain the long range fluctuations and the universal conductance

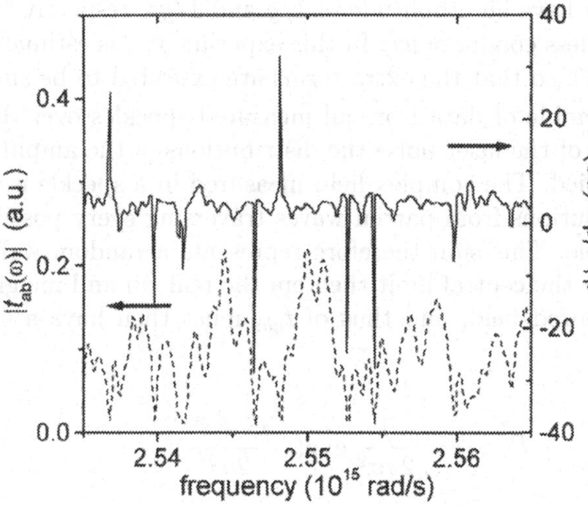

Figure 15. **Modulus (dashed line, left scale) and phase derivative (full line, right scale) of t_{ab} measured on a sample of A-GaP of $L = 15$ μm.**

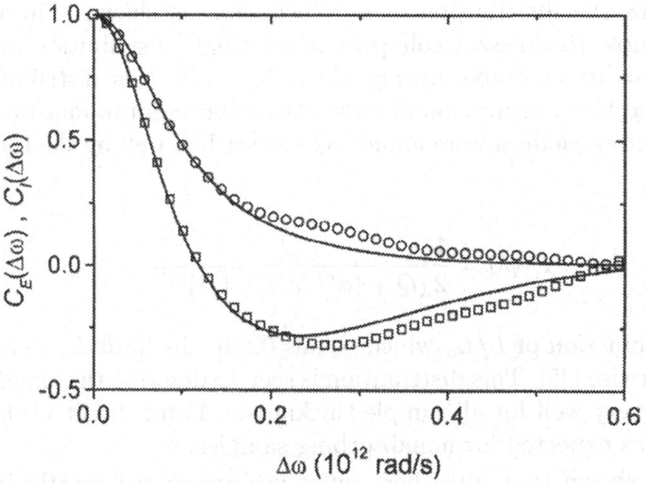

Figure 16. **Field (squares) and intensity (circles) correlation functions measured on the sample of Fig. 15. The lines are Eqs. 15 and 16 with $D = 21$ m^2/s.**

fluctuations which have an amplitude of $1/g$ and $1/g^2$, respectively, where g is the dimensionless conductance. In this experiment g is estimated to be on the order of 100, so that the extra terms are expected to be small.

Using the ensemble of data from all measured speckles over the whole frequency content of the laser pulse the distributions of the amplitude and phase can be studied. The complex field measured in a speckle is the sum of random contributions from partial waves traversing every possible path through the sample. This sum therefore represents a random walk in the complex plane. By the central limit theorem the real (r) and imaginary (i) parts of the measured field, and thus of t_{ab}, must then have a Gaussian distribution:

$$P(r,i) = \frac{1}{2\pi\sigma^2}\exp(-\frac{r^2+i^2}{2\sigma^2}) \tag{17}$$

The measured distributions are shown in Fig. 17. To remove the instrumental response the real and imaginary parts of t_{ab} have been normalized by the ensemble average of the modulus $|t_{ab}| = (r^2+i^2)^{1/2}$. The Gaussian distribution provides a very good fit. There was no correlation between r and i: $\langle ri\rangle = 0$. The parameter σ was found to be 0.793, close to the expected value of $\sqrt{2/\pi}$. The phase ϕ_{ab} is seen to be evenly distributed over 2π, as expected.

In Fig. 18 the distribution of $\phi' = d\phi_{ab}/d\omega$ is shown. The data for different sample thicknesses collapse onto a single distribution after normalizing ϕ' to its ensemble average $\langle\phi'\rangle$. Recently, this distribution was also measured for transmission of microwaves through random waveguides [34]. The microwave data were found to be described well by the theoretical distribution

$$P(\phi') = \frac{1}{2}\frac{Q}{(Q+(\phi'/\langle\phi'\rangle-1)^2)^{3/2}}. \tag{18}$$

Here Q is a function of L/L_a which equals 0.4 in the limit $L_a \to \infty$ and is smaller otherwise [35]. This distribution is seen to describe the experimental distribution very well for all sample thicknesses. From the fit we find $Q = 0.43 \pm 0.05$, as expected for nonabsorbing samples.

We have shown that ultrashort pulse interferometry greatly increases the amount of dynamical information that one can obtain on the propagation of light in strongly scattering samples. Deviations from diffusion theory are expected to show up in the measured quantities as the localization threshold is approached. In the present samples of anodically etched GaP all the data can still be described completely with diffusion theory.

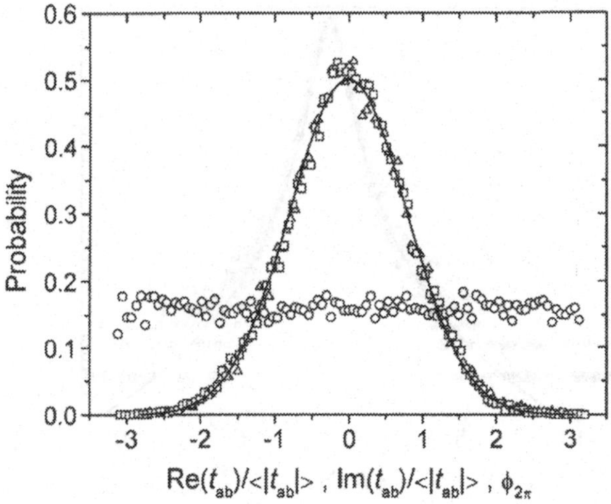

Figure 17. Probability distribution function of the real (triangles) and imaginary (squares) parts of the field transmission coefficient t_{ab} and of its phase modulo 2π (circles). The full line is a Gaussian fit.

5. Conclusion

In conclusion, disordered semiconductor samples based on powders of Si, Ge, GaAs, and macroporous GaP display many effects that are associated with strongly multiple scattering of light. A combination of careful static and dynamic measurements on a range of sample thicknesses is necessary to fully characterize the optical transport. All the semiconductor samples we studied have kl_s values that are in the range of strong localization effects, assuming that the precise location of the transition is determined by kl_s of order 1. The exact position of the localization transition and the behavior at the transition is still pendent and may depend on other sample characteristics such as powder size distribution and topology, residual absorption, boundary reflection associated with the effective refractive index of the sample and finite sample size effects. The scaling behavior of dynamical quantities associated with the diffusion constant and the energy velocity in systems near localization may differ considerably from the static properties such as the kl_s product. For example, recent theoretical work indicated that the mean free path near localization is position dependent and gradually changes from the smallest value in the bulk to larger values near the edges of the sample [27]. Further study on e.g. monodisperse powders and other

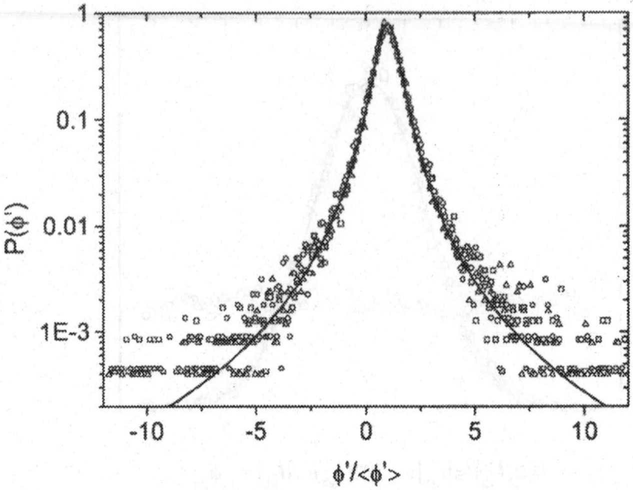

Figure 18. Probability distribution of the phase derivative for sample thickness $L = 5$ (triangles), 10 (circles), and 18 (squares) μm. The full line is Eq. 18 with $Q = 0.4$.

topologically well-defined samples is necessary to uncover the localization behavior in these strongly scattering systems.

6. Acknowledgments

We are inbdeted to D. Vanmaekelbergh and J. van de Lagemaat for preparing the GaP samples, to C.M. Soukoulis and K. Busch for the EDCPA calculations, and to L.D. Noordam and C.W. Rella for their collaboration with the work done on Ge samples. We gratefully acknowledge P. de Vries, R. H. J. Kop, D. S. Wiersma, W. L. Vos, H. P. Schriemer, M. Megens, Duong Dau, G. van Soest, and Gerard Wegdam for fruitful discussions and contributions. Financial support has been supplied for JGR by the European Commission through Grant No. ERBFM- BICT971921. This work is part of the research program of the Stichting voor Fundamenteel Onderzoek der Materie, which is financially supported by the Nederlands Organisatie voor Wetenschappelijk Onderzoek.

References

1. P. Sheng, *Introduction to Wave Scattering, Localization, and Mesoscopic Phenomena*, (Academic Press, New York) 1995.

2. M.P. van Albada, A. Lagendijk, Phys. Rev. Lett. 55: 2692 (1985); P.E. Wolf, G. Maret, Phys. Rev. Lett. 55: 2696 (1985).
3. 'Photonic Band Gaps and Localization', NATO ASI B 308, Edited by C.M. Soukoulis. Proc. of ARW, Heraklion, Crete (Greece), 1992, Kluwer (1993).
4. 'Advances in Optical Imaging and Photon Migration 1998', Edited by James G. Fujimoto and Michael S. Patterson, Trends in Optics and Photonics Series, Vol. 21, OSA (1998).
5. P.W. Anderson, Phys. Rev. 109: 1492 (1958).
6. S. John, Phys. Rev. Lett. 53: 2169 (1984); P.W. Anderson, Philos. Mag. B 52: 505 (1985).
7. A.F. Ioffe and A.R. Regel, Prog. Semicond. 4: 237 (1960).
8. N. Garcia and A.Z. Genack, Phys. Rev. Lett. 66: 1850 (1991).
9. D.S. Wiersma, P. Bartolini, A. Lagendijk, and R. Righini, Nature 390: 671 (1997).
10. F. Scheffold, R. Lenke, R. Tweer, and G. Maret, Nature 398: 206 (1999).
11. J. Gómez Rivas, R. Sprik, C.M. Soukoulis, K. Busch, and A. Lagendijk, Europhys. Lett. 48: 22 (1999).
12. F.J.P. Schuurmans, D. Vanmaekelbergh, J. van de Lagemaat, and A. Lagendijk, Science 284: 141 (1999).
13. F.J.P. Schuurmans, M. Megens, D. Vanmaekelbergh, and A. Lagendijk, Phys. Rev. Lett. 83: 2183 (1999).
14. A.Z. Genack, Phys. Rev. Lett. 58: 2043 (1987).
15. M.P. van Albada, B.A. van Tiggelen, A. Lagendijk, and A. Tip, Phys. Rev. Lett. 66: 3132 (1991).
16. R. H. J. Kop, P. de Vries, R. Sprik, and A. Lagendijk, Phys. Rev. Lett. 79: 4369 (1997).
17. A. Kirchner, K. Busch and C.M. Soukoulis, Phys. Rev. B 57: 277 (1998).
18. A. Ishimaru, *Wave Propagation and Scattering in Random Media* (Academic Press, New York, 1995).
19. A. Lagendijk, R. Vreeker, and P. de Vries, Phys. Lett. A 136: 81 (1989).
20. J.X. Zhu, D.J. Pine, and D.A. Weitz, Phys. Rev. A 44: 3948 (1991).
21. E. Abrahams, P.W. Anderson, D.C. Licciardello, and T.V. Ramakrishnan, Phys. Rev. Lett. 42: 673 (1979).
22. M.U. Vera and D.J. Durian, Phys. Rev. B 53: 3215 (1996).
23. S. Datta, C.T. Chan, K.M. Ho, and C.M. Soukoulis, Phys. Rev. B 48: 14936 (1993).
24. J. Gómez Rivas, R. Sprik, A. Lagendijk, L.D. Noordam, and C.W. Rella, accepted for publication in Phys. Rev. E RC.
25. K. Busch and C.M. Soukoulis, Phys. Rev. Lett. 75: 3442 (1995); A. Kirchner, K. Busch, and C.M. Soukoulis, Phys. Rev. B 49: 3800 (1994).
26. D.S. Wiersma, M.P. van Albada, and A. Lagendijk, Rev. Sci. Instruments. 66: 5473 (1995).
27. B.A. Tiggelen, A. Lagendijk, and D.S. Wiersma, Phys. Rev. Lett. 84: 4333 (2000).
28. J. Gómez Rivas, R. Sprik, and A. Lagendijk, Ann. Phys. (Leipzig) 8: 77 (1999) Spec. Issue.
29. R. H. J. Kop and R. Sprik, Rev. Sci. Instrum. 66: 5459 (1995).
30. S. John, Phys. Rev. Lett. 58: 2486 (1987).
31. A. Z. Genack and J. M. Drake, Europhys. Lett. 11: 331 (1990).
32. A. Imhof, W. L. Vos, R. Sprik, and A. Lagendijk, Phys. Rev. Lett. 83: 2942 (1999).
33. S. Feng, C. Kane, P. A. Lee, and A. D. Stone, Phys. Rev. Lett. 61: 834 (1988).
34. A. Z. Genack, P. Sebbah, M. Stoytchev, and B. A. van Tiggelen, Phys. Rev. Lett. 82: 715 (1999).
35. B. A. van Tiggelen, P. Sebbah, M. Stoytchev, and A. Z. Genack, Phys. Rev. E **59**, 7166 (1999).

RADIATIVE TRANSFER OF LOCALIZED WAVES

A local diffusion theory

B.A. VAN TIGGELEN
CNRS/Laboratoire de Physique et Modélisation des Milieux Condensés, Université Joseph Fourier, Maison des Magistères, B.P. 166, 38042 Grenoble Cedex 9, France
A. LAGENDIJK
Van der Waals-Zeeman Laboratory, University of Amsterdam, Valckenierstraat 65-67, 1018 XE Amsterdam, The Netherlands

AND

D.S. WIERSMA
European Laboratory for non-Linear Spectroscopy and Istituto Nazionale per la Fisica della Materia, Largo E. Fermi 2, 50125 Florence, Italy

1. Introduction

Almost twenty years ago, after one century of radiative transfer, and twenty years after the first paper by Anderson on localization [1], the first publications of the self-consistent theory of localization appeared. Following ideas of Götze [2], Vollhardt and Wölfle demonstrated in a series of pioneering papers [3-5] the importance of the so-called "most-crossed" diagrams for the renormalization of the diffusion coefficient in wave diffusion. These diagrams are now known to be at the very base of all kinds of weak localization phenomena, such as the Sharvin-Sharvin effect [6] and enhanced backscattering [7]. Twenty years ago it became very urgent to understand the role of wave localization in a context that concerns *transport* of waves in *open* media, and to include interference effects into transport theory. This goal was, and still is very ambitious. Earlier studies had shown localization to be a non-perturbational phenomenon [8]. Very few people believed that localization could once be understood by generalizing an ordinary, classical Boltzmann equation. At the same time, however, researchers were eager to give "great" principles, such as the Thouless criterion [9], and finite-size

C.M. Soukoulis (ed.), Photonic Crystals and Light Localization in the 21st Century, 475–487.

scaling [10] a more microscopic base. This requires an understanding of localization in open media.

Anno 2000, random-matrix theory [11] and the self-consistent theory of localization have provided us a wealth of information how transport of waves in a disordered medium is affected by the nearness of localization. Such studies were particularly stimulated by experiments with classical waves, such as microwaves [12-14], visible and infrared light [15, 16, 17] and acoustic waves [18], whose natural language had always been radiative transfer. To generalize classical transport for interferences, one has the choice of either solving simplified models exactly, or to find approximate solutions of "exact" models.

Random-matrix theory (RMT) is of the first kind. Based on the elegant chaos theory by Dyson and others, RMT is now able to predict many features of wave diffusion, including fluctuations, even in the localized regime [19], and even in a non-perturbational way. Two aspects are still unsolved. First, RMT was constructed for quasi-one dimensional systems, for which no mobility edge is believed to exist, and a generalization to higher dimensional systems does not seem feasible. This eliminates RMT as a candidate to understand features like enhanced backscattering or anomalous transmission. Second, standard RMT is basically a stationary theory. Only very recently, Beenakker *et al.* published a dynamic variant of RMT in reflection [20].

The strong point of the self-consistent theory is that it is based on a *rigorous* argument - reciprocity - applied to an "exact" equation - the Bethe-Salpter equation - that applies in any random system. A weak point is that the theory can only be worked out approximately, for instance, by employing the diffusion approximation and a low-disorder expansion. Unfortunately, this weak point is often misused as an argument against the whole principle. The approximate theory gives critical exponents around the transition, which are typical of mean field approximations and do not agree with *ab-initio* studies of the Anderson Tight Binding model [21]. In addition, the theory only applies to field-field correlation functions, and does not do any predictions about fluctuations of e.g., conductance. Recent experimental work by Genack etal. [17] has demonstrated the importance of fluctuations to get a complete view on Anderson localization. Finally, the self-consistent theory seems to fail in the absence of time-reversal symmetry, e.g., when a magnetic field is present in the medium [5], probably because this violates one of the two basic assumptions of the theory. Despite the above weak points, the self-consistent theory has given us deeper insight into the role of Anderson localization in wave transport. It has confirmed the Thouless criterion as a universal criterion for wave localization in open media and has put forward the Ioffe-Regel criterion, anticipated already in the early sixties [22], as a criterion for localization in infinite 3D media. As was shown and emphasized by Wölfle and Vollhardt [5], the self-consistent theory agrees in great detail with scaling arguments for the dynamic diffusivity $D(\Omega)$ [23] and with the scaling theory for the DC conductance [10].

One pertinent controversy initiated by the self-consistent theory concerns the scale-dependence of the diffusion kernel itself. Scaling theory has led to a homogeneous but "scale-dependent" diffusivity kernel $D(\Omega, \mathbf{r}-\mathbf{r}')$, with Fourier transform $D(\Omega, \mathbf{q})$. Near the mobility edge one has suggested $D(\Omega, q) \sim q$ [24-26]. The absence of such q-dependence in the self-consistent theory is sometimes considered as a serious failure, in spite of its other successes mentioned above. Recently, we presented a local formulation of the self-consistent theory [27] that will be explained below. We find that weak localization effects lower the diffusion coefficient, but we also infer that the suppression is different near the boundaries. As a result, we encounter a new feature: a spatially inhomogeneous, but *local* diffusion coefficient $D(\mathbf{r})$. At the mobility edge, our local formulation predicts a scale-dependence $D(z) \sim 1/z$ of the diffusion coefficient of a slab geometry, leading to a transmission $T \sim 1/L^2$ of a slab with thickness L, and a rounding of line shape in enhanced backscattering. Both properties have been observed [15, 16], but were previously interpreted in terms of a scale-dependent diffusivity $D(q) \sim q$ [26]. As a bonus, our local variant of the self-consistent theory is able to deal explicitly with boundary conditions in an almost conventional way. This facilitates "engineering" with the self-consistent theory.

2. Basic Elements of the Selfconsistent Theory

The Green's function $G(\mathbf{r}_1, t_1 \to \mathbf{r}_2, t_2)$ describes the propagation of a wave at position $\mathbf{r}_1$ at time t_1 to position $\mathbf{r}_2$ at time t_2 and can be constructed from the underlying wave equation. We denote its ensemble average by $\langle G \rangle$. In its most general form, transport theory is a theory for the ensemble-averaged "two-particle" Green's function

$$\langle G(\mathbf{r}_1, t_1 \to \mathbf{r}_3, t_3) G^*(\mathbf{r}_2, t_2 \to \mathbf{r}_4, t_4) \rangle \equiv \Gamma(\mathbf{r}_1, t_1, \mathbf{r}_2, t_2, \mathbf{r}_3, t_3, \mathbf{r}_4, t_4) . \tag{1}$$

This object is related to the total intensity of the radiation field. It relates intensity properties at the "source" (indices 1 and 2) to the ones at the "detector" (indices 3 and 4). In a linear random medium, an object $U(\mathbf{r}_1, t_1 \cdots \mathbf{r}_4, t_4)$ should exist that generates the two-particle Green's function in the following symbolical way,

$$\Gamma = U + U \cdot \langle G \rangle \times \langle G^* \rangle \cdot \Gamma \equiv U + R . \tag{2}$$

The new object U is called the *irreducible vertex*. The dots denote convolutions in space-time. This so-called Bethe-Salpeter equation can be formally iterated to yield a multiple scattering series for the two-particle Green's function with U as an elementary building block. This iteration provides a new "reducible vertex" R that contains all multiple scattering events except the elementary block U.

Although U may look like a complicated object, it has one simple, but important property that we will now discuss. Let us for simplicity adopt monochromatic waves with frequency ω so that the time dependence $\exp(-i\omega t_i)$ becomes trivial. We first observe that spatial reciprocity (i.e., interchanging detector and source) imposes the following reciprocity relations for the two-particle Green's function [5, 28],

$$\Gamma(\mathbf{r}_1, \mathbf{r}_2, \mathbf{r}_3, \mathbf{r}_4) = \Gamma(\mathbf{r}_3, \mathbf{r}_4, \mathbf{r}_1, \mathbf{r}_2) = \Gamma(\mathbf{r}_3, \mathbf{r}_2, \mathbf{r}_1, \mathbf{r}_4) . \tag{3}$$

The first identity is the well-known, classical reciprocity relation in radiative transfer [29], and is also obeyed by R and U separately. However, neither U nor R is expected to obey the second reciprocity identity. A somewhat technical inspection learns that interchanging source and detector *only* for the field going $1 \to 3$ without doing the same procedure for the field that travel from $2 \to 4$ turns *any* contribution to R into an irreducible contribution to U [30]. The reverse, however, is not true. This is expressed by the following, unique decomposition

$$U(\mathbf{r}_1, \mathbf{r}_2, \mathbf{r}_3, \mathbf{r}_4) = C(\mathbf{r}_1, \mathbf{r}_2, \mathbf{r}_3, \mathbf{r}_4) + S(\mathbf{r}_1, \mathbf{r}_2, \mathbf{r}_3, \mathbf{r}_4) , \tag{4}$$

where the vertex C is obtained from R using the reciprocity operation,

$$C(\mathbf{r}_1, \mathbf{r}_2, \mathbf{r}_3, \mathbf{r}_4) = R(\mathbf{r}_3, \mathbf{r}_2, \mathbf{r}_1, \mathbf{r}_4) , \tag{5}$$

and S is a set of scattering diagrams that is transformed into itself,

$$S(\mathbf{r}_1, \mathbf{r}_2, \mathbf{r}_3, \mathbf{r}_4) = S(\mathbf{r}_3, \mathbf{r}_2, \mathbf{r}_1, \mathbf{r}_4) . \tag{6}$$

Single scattering can easily be seen to be part of S. The classical picture of radiative transfer emerges when for U and S single scattering is adopted as an approximate building block for multiple scattering [31]. However, this procedure disregards the existence of C, so that *classical radiative transfer does not obey the reciprocity principle* (3). The vertices C and S give rise to physical phenomena that are not described by classical radiative transfer. The object C is the most general formulation possible to describe enhanced backscattering, an interference effect that has been observed with light [7] and acoustic waves [32], and recently even in a cold rubidium gaz [33]. In addition to single scattering, the set S contains recurrent scattering events. They are known to affect the celebrated enhancement factor of two in backscattering [28] as also observed [34].

For practical calculations, one can observe that the vertices R and C typically start and end at a scattering particle that is assumed small compared to the mean free path. Therefore, one expects the relations [35]

$$\begin{aligned} R(\mathbf{r}_1, \mathbf{r}_2, \mathbf{r}_3, \mathbf{r}_4) &\approx \delta(\mathbf{r}_1 - \mathbf{r}_2)\delta(\mathbf{r}_3 - \mathbf{r}_4)F(\mathbf{r}_1, \mathbf{r}_3)\,, \\ C(\mathbf{r}_1, \mathbf{r}_2, \mathbf{r}_3, \mathbf{r}_4) &\approx \delta(\mathbf{r}_3 - \mathbf{r}_2)\delta(\mathbf{r}_1 - \mathbf{r}_4)F(\mathbf{r}_1, \mathbf{r}_3)\,, \end{aligned} \tag{7}$$

leaving only two independent positions by means of the function $F(\mathbf{r}_1, \mathbf{r}_3)$. The reciprocity principle (5) imposes the appearance of the same, symmetric function F in both R and C. Physically, the function F describes how (stationary) multiple scattering transfers radiation from one place to the other. It has a hydrodynamic long range behavior: in an infinite 3D medium it decays as $1/|\mathbf{r}_1 - \mathbf{r}_3|$ for large separations. This in sharp contrast to the vertex S, which represents a kind of "super" single scattering, including loops in the medium. One may assert short range behavior, i.e.,

$$S(\mathbf{r}_1, \mathbf{r}_2, \mathbf{r}_3, \mathbf{r}_4) \approx \delta(\mathbf{r}_1 - \mathbf{r}_2)\delta(\mathbf{r}_3 - \mathbf{r}_4)\delta(\mathbf{r}_1 - \mathbf{r}_3)S(\mathbf{r}_1)\,, \tag{8}$$

as it should be if S is to be a good "building block."

The relations (2), (4) and (5) show that reciprocity relates the output Γ of the transport equation directly to its input U. As a result, the problem of writing down and solving a transport equation is a *self-consistent* problem. This is the basic message of the self-consistent theory of localization. We refer to the excellent review by Wölfle and Vollhardt [5] for some subtle complications and for more details.

2.1. DIFFUSION APPROXIMATION

The self-consistent problem has so far only been worked out in the diffusion approximation. On length scales larger than the mean free path, the transport equation for $F(\mathbf{r}_1, \mathbf{r}_2)$ reduces to a diffusion equation. This is a well-known consequence of flux conservation [31]. The diffusion coefficient is related to the irreducible vertex U [31]. The Boltmann diffusion coefficient D_B is obtained if for U ordinary single scattering is adopted. Inclusion of C gives the following equation,

$$\frac{1}{D(\mathbf{r})} = \frac{1}{D_B} + \frac{F(\mathbf{r}, \mathbf{r})}{\pi v_E(k)\rho(k)}\,. \tag{9}$$

The physics behind the "weak localization" term is the constructive interference of reciprocal paths at position $\mathbf{r}$, expressed by the "return probability" $F(\mathbf{r}, \mathbf{r})$. We will ignore the difference between extinction length, scattering and Boltzmann transport mean free path and represent all by ℓ. With v_E the transport speed of light and k its wave number we have (in 3D) the familiar relations $D_B = \frac{1}{3}v_E\ell$ [31], and $\rho(k) \approx k^2/\pi^2 v_E$ for the density of states per unit volume. Both k, ℓ and v_E have been calculated near the localization threshold [36].

The stationary diffusion equation for F is

$$-\nabla \cdot D(\mathbf{r})\nabla F(\mathbf{r},\mathbf{r}') = \frac{4\pi}{\ell}\delta(\mathbf{r}-\mathbf{r}')\,. \tag{10}$$

The factor $4\pi/\ell$ appears when single scattering is adopted as a source for multiple scattering.

Equations (9) and (10) must contain *one and the same* diffusion coefficient, and one seeks for a "self-consistent" solution. In infinite media, $F(\mathbf{r},\mathbf{r}')$ is translationally invariant, so that the return probability $F(\mathbf{r},\mathbf{r})$ and diffusion coefficient $D(\mathbf{r})$ do not depend on $\mathbf{r}$. In reciprocal space is $C(q) = 4\pi/\ell D q^2$, so that $C(\mathbf{r},\mathbf{r}) = \sum_{\mathbf{q}} C(q) \sim \mu/D\ell^2$, assuming an upper cut-off $q_{\mathrm{max}} = \mu/\ell$ to regularize the diverging wavenumber integral. Hence,

$$D = D_B\left(1 - \frac{\mu}{k^2\ell^2}\right). \tag{11}$$

This is the standard "Vollhardt and Wölfle" result in three dimensions. The mobility edge, if defined by $D = 0$ [8], obeys a Ioffe-Regel type criterion as derived microscopically by John *et al.* [37] and Economou *et al.* [38], and agrees with numerical studies of the Anderson Tight Binding model [39, 40]. The obligation to use a cut-off, which somewhat arbitrarily eliminates wave paths shorter than the mean free path from the return probability, highlights the partial failure of the diffusion approximation. Some controversy existed about the choice of this cut-off, an important issue as it influences the exact location of the mobility edge [38, 41, 42]. A careful analysis of the exact formulas demonstrated the choice $q_{\mathrm{max}} = \mu/\ell$ to be approximately correct [43]. For $\mu = 1$, the mobility edge is conveniently located at $k\ell = 1$, which is close to predictions made by the Potential Well Analogy ($k\ell = 0.84$) [38] and by point scatterer models ($k\ell = 0.97$) [43].

The essence of our work is that absence of translational symmetry in finite media imposes the diffusion coefficient $D(\mathbf{r})$ to depend on $\mathbf{r}$. This conclusion is unavoidable if one doesn't wish to give up the basic ingredients of the self-consistent theory of localization: reciprocity and flux conservation. Previous applications of the self-consistent theory accounted for the boundaries by means of a second, lower cut-off [3, 4].

3. Application to a Slab Geometry

We consider stationary propagation in a slab geometry of thickness L and infinite width, and Fourier transform ($\mathbf{q}_{||}$) the transverse coordinate. For $0 < z < L$, Eqs. (9) and (10) become

$$-\partial_z D(z)\,\partial_z F(z,z',q_{||}) + D(z)q_{||}^2 F(z,z',q_{||}) = \frac{4\pi}{\ell}\delta(z-z'), \quad (12)$$

$$\frac{1}{D(z)} = \frac{1}{D_B} + \frac{2}{k^2\ell}\int_0^{1/\ell} \mathrm{d}q_{||}\, q_{||} F(z,z,q_{||}), \quad (13)$$

$$F(0,z',q_{||}) - z_e(0)\partial_z F(0,z',q_{||}) = 0, \quad (14)$$

$$F(L,z',q_{||}) + z_e(L)\partial_z F(L,z',q_{||}) = 0. \quad (15)$$

The last two equations are the familiar radiative boundary conditions at both sides of the slab, featuring the "extrapolation lengths" $z_e(0/L) \equiv 3z_0 D(0/L)/v_E$ [44]. They contain the diffusion coefficient, $D(0/L)$, at the boundaries so that z_e is always non-zero, even in the localized regime, when D vanishes in the bulk. The value, $z_0 = \frac{2}{3}$, corresponds to no internal reflection, but is much larger in recent localization experiments [15, 16] due to internal reflection. Equation (12) is recognized as an ordinary, second order differential equation with a source term. Without the latter, two independent solutions $f_\pm(z)$ exist with a non-zero Wronskian $W(q_{||}) \equiv D(z) \times (f'_+ f_- - f'_- f_+)$, independent of z.

We first discuss the semi-infinite medium $L = \infty$. Let $f_+(z)$ be the growing solution. As $F(z,z',q_{||})$ must be bounded at large z, z', Eq. (12) is solved for

$$F(z,z',q_{||}) = \frac{f_+(z_<)f_-(z_>)}{W(q_{||})\ell/4\pi} - P(q_{||})f_-(z)f_-(z'), \quad (16)$$

where $z_< = \min(z,z')$, $z_> = \max(z,z')$ and $P(q_{||})$ follows easily from the boundary condition (14). At the mobility edge we assert the simple algebraic form,

$$D(z) = \frac{D(0)}{1 + z/\xi_c}, \quad (17)$$

with two free parameters $D(0)$ and ξ_c. The homogeneous solutions would then be,

$$f_+(z) = (z+\xi_c)I_1\left(q_{||}[z+\xi_c]\right),$$
$$f_-(z) = (z+\xi_c)K_1\left(q_{||}[z+\xi_c]\right), \quad (18)$$

in terms of the modified Bessel functions I_1 and K_1 with Wronskian $W = D(0)\xi_c$ [45]. Equation (16) learns that $C(z,z,q_{||})$ rises linearly in z for large z and that Eq. (13) is indeed asymptotically satisfied. Equation (13) evaluated at $z = 0$ gives a relation between $D(0)$ and ξ_c. The remaining freedom in ξ_c can be used to optimize self-consistency below 0.05 %. Both ξ_c and $D(0)$ depend heavily on the parameter z_0 in the boundary condition (see Table 3).

Table 1. Solution $D(z) = D(0)/(1 + z/\xi_c)$ of the self-consistent equations at the mobility edge $k\ell = 1$ for a semi-infinite slab as a function of the parameter z_0 that controls internal reflection at the boundary. The middle column reveals that $D(0) \sim 1/z_0$. For $z_0 = \infty$ one expects $D = 0$ for all z.

z_0	$D(0)/D_B$	ξ_c/ℓ
2/3	0.642	1.5
3	0.336	3
5	0.249	4
7	0.203	6
10	0.159	8
20	0.0968	25

The line shape $I_c(\theta)$ in enhanced backscattering can be obtained from $C(z, z', q_{||})$ using standard methods [46]. Insight is provided by the approximate formula $I_c(\theta) \approx C(z = \ell, z' = \ell, q_{||} = 2k \sin\theta/2)$, used by De Vries *et al.* [44]. The line shape exhibits a logarithmic rounding

$$I_c(\theta) \sim 1 + z_e(0)\xi_c q_{||}^2 \log(q_{||}\xi_c) , \tag{19}$$

when $q_{||}\xi \ll 1$, rather than the familiar cusp $I_c(\theta) \sim 1 - z_e|q_{||}|$ [46]. Berkovits and Kaveh [26] predicted a rounding of the line shape on the basis of the non-local diffusion kernel $D(q)$.

The localized regime corresponds to $k\ell < 1$. We may assert the solution $D(z) = D(0)\exp(-2z/\xi)$, with ξ the localization length. We find $f_\pm(z) = \exp(-\lambda_\pm z)$ with $\lambda_\pm = 1/\xi \pm \sqrt{q_{||}^2 + 1/\xi^2}$, and Wronskian $W = 2D(0)\sqrt{q_{||}^2 + 1/\xi^2}$. Equation (13) is indeed satisfied for $z \gg \xi$ if we adopt the localization length $\xi/\ell = 2(k\ell)^2/[1 - (k\ell)^4]$, with a critical exponent of unity. The same equation evaluated at $z = 0$ provides $D(0)$. The above exponential ansatz for D is found to be satisfactory for all z if $z_0 > 10$, but for smaller internal reflection we found less agreement. The line shape is approximately given by

$$I_c(\theta) \approx \frac{1}{1 - z_e(0)/\xi + z_e(0)\sqrt{q_{||}^2 + 1/\xi^2}} . \tag{20}$$

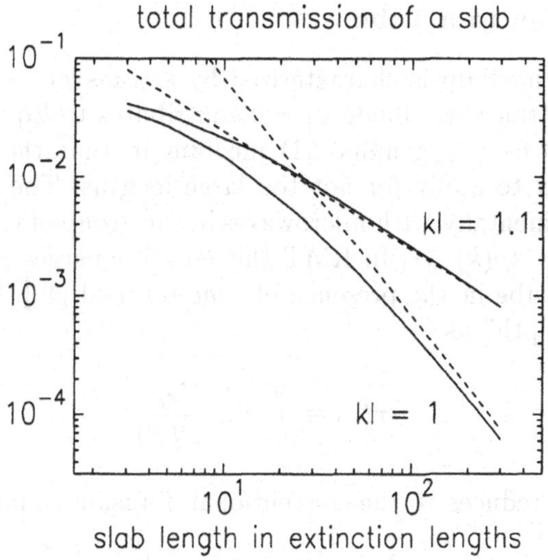

Figure 1. Numerical solution of the self-consistent equations for a finite slab. Total transmission coefficient as a function of the slab length, L, for the critical value $k\ell = 1$, and in the delocalized regime $k\ell = 1.1$. The dashed lines have slopes -2 and -1. We have adopted an internal-reflection parameter $z_0 = 10$.

This indicates an analytical rounding for $\theta < 1/k\xi$, reminiscent of an absorbing semi-infinite medium in the delocalized regime, a case that must be excluded experimentally [16].

One can use the solution $D_\infty(z)$ for the semi-infinite medium to estimate the length dependence of the total transmission $T(L)$ of a slab with length L. We expect that $D(z) \approx D_\infty(\frac{1}{2}L - |\frac{1}{2}L - z|)$ i.e., symmetric in the central plane $z = \frac{1}{2}L$. For a point source close to the boundary $z = 0$, the diffusion equation predicts,

$$T(L) = z_0\ell \left(2z_0\ell + \int_0^L \mathrm{d}z\, \frac{D_B}{D(z)}\right)^{-1} . \tag{21}$$

The integral is proportional to the "optical thickness" of the slab. Equation (21) gives,

$$T(L) \to \begin{cases} 4z_0\,(D_\infty(0)/D_B)\,(\xi_c/\ell) \times (\ell/L)^2 & k\ell = 1 \\ z_0\,(D_\infty(0)/D_B)\,(\ell/\xi) \times \exp(-L/\xi) & k\ell < 1 \end{cases} . \tag{22}$$

This scale dependence agrees with scaling theory [5, 47], but has large and precise prefactors: 2.6 for $k\ell = 1$ and $z_0 = \frac{2}{3}$, and increasing with z_0.

Figure 1 shows that $1/L^2$ law predicted at the mobility edge rapidly disappears in the delocalized regime $k\ell > 1$. It has been reported by Genack*et al.* [14] for microwaves and by Wiersma *et al.* [15] for GaAs samples.

4. Application to a Tube

A "quasi 1D" medium is characterized by a transverse surface $A < \ell^2$, so that only the transverse mode $q_{\|} = 0$ contributes to Eq. (13), with weight $1/A$. It differs from a genuine 1D medium in that the diffusion picture is still believed to apply for not too large lengths. The tube geometry is studied experimentally with microwaves in the group of Genack [48]. Define the length $\xi = A\rho(k)v_E\ell$. In RMT this length emerges as the localization length of the tube in the presence of time-reversal [49]. Upon introducing the "optical depth" as

$$\tau(z) \equiv \int_0^z \mathrm{d}z' \, \frac{D_B}{D(z')}\,, \tag{23}$$

Equation (12) reduces to the conventional diffusion equation,

$$-\partial_\tau^2 F(\tau,\tau') = \delta(\tau - \tau')\,, \tag{24}$$

whose solution is easily obtained using the radiative boundary conditions at $\tau(0) = 0$ and $\tau(L) = b$. The self-consistent Eq. (13) imposes that

$$\frac{\mathrm{d}\tau}{\mathrm{d}z} = 1 + \frac{1}{\xi} F(\tau,\tau) = 1 + \frac{1}{\xi} \frac{(\tau + z_0)(b + z_0 - \tau)}{b + 2z_0}\,. \tag{25}$$

For a semi-infinite quasi 1D medium ($b = \infty$) this equation has the exact solution

$$D(z) = \left[\frac{1}{D_B} + \frac{2z_0}{v_E\xi}\right]^{-1} \exp(-2z/\xi)\,. \tag{26}$$

For a finite length of the tube the total transmission, calculated from Eq. (21), is plotted in Figure 2. It compares very well to the solution of RMT published by Zirnbauer [49], in particular the cross-over from ℓ/L to $\exp(-L/\xi)$. The RMT result has an extra $1/L^{3/2}$ factor in the transmission. Not unexpectedly, Eq. (26) shows the diffusion coefficient at the boundary to be sensitive to the amount of internal reflection, as quantified by the extrapolation parameter z_0. This was also seen to be the case for the slab geometry.

5. Application to a Sphere: Thouless' Criterion

For a sphere with radius a one expects a diffusion coefficient $D(r)$ that depends only on the distance r to the origin. An expansion into spherical

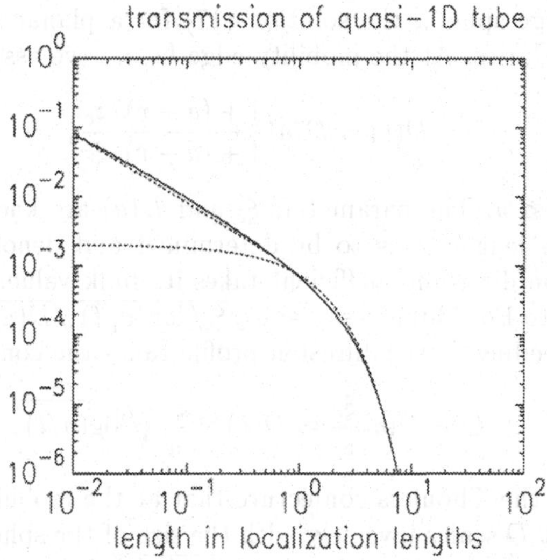

Figure 2. **Solution of the self-consistent equations for a quasi-1D medium. Plotted is the average transmission as a function of the thickness of the tube. Dashed lines denote the Ohmic $1/L$ behavior that applies for small lengths and the localized exponential law that applies for large lengths. The extrapolation length has been chosen much smaller than the localization length.**

harmonics yields the self-consistent problem,

$$-\partial_r r^2 D(r) \partial_r F_l(r, r') + D(r) l(l+1) F_l(r, r') = \delta(r - r') \quad (27)$$

$$\frac{1}{D(r)} = \frac{1}{D_B} + \frac{1}{k^2 \ell} \sum_l (2l+1)\, F_l(r, r) \quad (28)$$

$$F_l(a, r') + \frac{3 z_0 D(a)}{v_E} \partial_r F_l(a, r') = 0\,. \quad (29)$$

The sum over the angular quantum numbers l diverges. It is reasonable to adopt an upper cut-off $l_{\max} \approx r/\ell$ which is consistent with the choice $q_{\max} = 1/\ell$ made earlier. In particular, close to the center ($r < \ell$) only the s-wave spherical harmonic $l = 0$ contributes. The above equations will be solved for a very large sphere $a \gg \ell$ and for the critical value $k\ell = 1$. We will verify Thouless' assertion that the diffusion coefficient at the mobility edge scales inversely with the size of the sphere, i.e., $D \sim 1/a$ (see e.g., Ref. [31] for a good discussion).

Equation (27) can easily be solved analytically for $l = 0$. Inserting its solution into Eq. (28) yields,

$$\frac{1}{D(0)} = \frac{1}{D_B} + \frac{1}{k^2 \ell} \left[\int_\ell^a \frac{\mathrm{d}r}{r^2 D(r)} + \frac{z_0 \ell}{v_E a^2} \right]\,. \quad (30)$$

For a very large sphere, the solution (17) for a planar slab should apply near the boundaries. At the mobility edge $k\ell = 1$ we assert the profile,

$$D(r) = D(a)\frac{1+(a-r)/z_c}{1+(a-r)/\xi_c}, \tag{31}$$

with $\xi_c \ll z_c \ll a$. The parameters ξ_c and $D(a)$ are known from the slab geometry. The length z_c is to be determined and denotes the depth beyond which the diffusion coefficient takes its bulk value. Putting the conjecture (31) into Eq. (30) gives $z_c \approx a\sqrt{\xi_c/\log(a/\ell)}\sqrt{D(a)/D_B}$. As a result, at depths exceeding z_c the diffusion profile takes the constant value

$$D \approx D(a)\frac{\xi_c}{z_c} \approx D(a) \times \frac{\xi_c}{a}\sqrt{\log(a/\ell)}\,. \tag{32}$$

This confirms the Thouless conjecture that at the mobility edge the diffusion coefficient D scales inversely with the size of the sphere. Note that, for our approach to be valid, we demand $\sqrt{\log(a/\ell)}$ to be a large number. The sphere must thus really be very large.

The work at LPM2C is supported by the GdR 1847 PRIMA of the french CNRS. The work at UvA is part of the dutch FOM research program and is made possible by financial support of NWO. The work at LENS is supported by the EC grant HPRI-CT1999-00111.

References

1. P.W. Anderson, *Phys. Rev.* **109**, 1492 (1958).
2. W. Götze, *J. Phys. C* **12**, 1279 (1979).
3. D. Vollhardt and P. Wölfle, *Phys. Rev. Lett.* **45**, 842 (1980). D. Vollhardt and P. Wölfle, Phys. Rev. B **22**, 4666 (1980).
4. P. Wölfle and D. Vollhardt, in: *Anderson Localization*, edited by Y. Nagaoka and H. Fukuyama (Springer-Verlag, Berlin 1982).
5. P. Wölfle and D. Vollhardt, in: *Electronic Phase Transitions* (Elsevier Science, Amsterdam, 1992).
6. B.L. Altshuler, A.G. Aronov, and B.Z. Spivak, *JETP Lett.* **33**, 94 (1981); D. Yu. Sharvin and Yu.V. Sharvin, *JETP Lett.* **34**, 272 (1981).
7. Research Group POAN (ed.), *New Aspect of Electromagnetic and Acoustic Wave Diffusion*, (Springer-Verlag, Heidelberg, 1998).
8. For a recent review see: B.A. van Tiggelen, in: *Diffuse Waves in Complex Media*, edited by J.P. Fouque (Kluwer, Dordrecht, 1999).
9. D.J. Thouless, in: *Ill-Condensed Matter*, edited by R. Balian, R. Maynard, and G. Toulouse (North-Holland, Amsetrdam, 1979).
10. E. Abrahams, P.W. Anderson, D.C. Licciardello, and T.V. Ramakrishnan, *Phys. Rev. Lett.* **42**, 673 (1979).
11. See for a recent review: C.W.J. Beenakker, *Phys. Rep.* **69**, 731 (1997).
12. S. John, *Comments on Cond. Matt. Phys.* **14**, 193 (1988); *Physics Today*, May 1991.
13. P. Sheng (editor), *Scattering and Localization of Classical Waves*, (World Scientific, Singapore, 1990).

14. N. Garcia and A.Z. Genack, *Phys. Rev. Lett.* **66**, 1850 (1991). A.Z. Genack and N. Garcia, *Phys. Rev. Lett.* **66**, 2064 (1991).
15. D.S. Wiersma, P. Bartolini, A. Lagendijk, and R. Righini, *Nature* **390**, 671 (1997).
16. F.J.P. Schuurmans, M. Megens, D. Vanmaekelbergh, and A. Lagendijk, *Phys. Rev. Lett.* **83**, 2183 (1999).
17. A. Chabanov, M. Stoytchev, and A.Z. Genack, *Nature* **404** 850 (2000).
18. R.L. Weaver, *Wave Motion* **12**, 129 (1990).
19. S.A. van Langen, P.W. Brouwer, and C.W.J. Beenakker, *Phys. Rev. E* **53**, R1344 (1996).
20. H. Schomerus, K.J.H. van Bemmel and C.W.J. Beenakker, preprint Cond-mat/0004049 (2000); M. Titov and C.W.J. Beenakker, preprint Cond-mat/0005042 (2000)
21. A. MacKinnon, *J. Phys. Cond. Matt.* **6**, 2511 (1994).
22. A.F. Ioffe and A.R. Regel, *Progress in Semi-Conductors* **4**, 237 (1960).
23. F.J. Wegner, *Z. Phys. B* **25**, 327 (1976).
24. Y. Imry, Y. Gefen, and D. Bergmann, *Phys. Rev. B* **26**, 3436 (1982).
25. E. Abrahams and P.A. Lee, *Phys. Rev. B* **33**, 683 (1986).
26. R. Berkovits and M. Kaveh, *Phys. Rev. B* **36**, 9322 (1987).
27. B.A. van Tiggelen, A. Lagendijk, and D.S. Wiersma, *Phys. Rev. Lett.* **84**, 4341 (2000).
28. B.A. van Tiggelen A. Lagendijk, and D.S. Wiersma, *Europhys. Lett.* **30**, 1 (1995).
29. H.C. van de Hulst, *Multiple Light Scattering*, Vol. 1, Chapter 3 (Academic, New York, 1980).
30. B.A. van Tiggelen and R. Maynard, in: *Wave Propagation in Complex Media*, edited by G. Papanicolaou (Springer-Verlag, New York, 1998).
31. P. Sheng, *Introduction to Wave Scattering, Localization and Mesoscopic Phenomena* (Academic, San Diego 1995).
32. A. Tourin, Ph. Roux, A. Derode, B.A. van Tiggelen, and M. Fink, *Phys. Rev. Lett.* **79**, 3637 (1997).
33. G. Labeyrie, F. de Tomasi, J.-C. Bernard, C.A. Müller, C. Miniatura, and R. Kaiser, *Phys. Rev. Lett.* **83**, 5266 (1999).
34. D.S. Wiersma, M.P. van Albada, B.A. van Tiggelen, and A. Lagendijk, *Phys. Rev. Lett.* **74**, 4193 (1995).
35. M.B. van der Mark, M.P. van Albada, and A. Lagendijk, *Phys. Rev. B* **37**, 3575 (1988).
36. K. Busch and C.M. Soukoulis, *Phys. Rev. Lett.* **75**, 3442 (1995).
37. S. John, H. Sompolinsky, and M.J. Stephen, *Phys. Rev. B* **27**, 5592 (1983).
38. E.N. Economou, C.M. Soukoulis, and A.D. Zdetsis, *Phys. Rev. B* **30**, 1686 (1984).
39. A.D. Zdetsis, C.M. Soukoulis, E.N. Economou, and G.S. Grest, *Phys. Rev. B* **32**, 7811 (1985).
40. J. Kroha, T. Kopp, and P. Wölfle, *Phys. Rev. B* **41**, 888, 1990.
41. T.R. Kirkpatrick, *Phys. Rev. B* **31**, 5746 (1985).
42. P. Sheng and Z.Q. Zhang, *Phys. Rev. Lett.* **57**, 1879 (1986).
43. B.A. van Tiggelen, A. Lagendijk, A. Tip, and G.F. Reiter, *Europhys. Lett.* **15**, 535 (1991).
44. A. Lagendijk, B. Vreeker, and P. de Vries, *Phys. Lett. A* **136**, 81 (1989).
45. M. Abramovitz and I.A. Stegun, *Handbook of Mathematical Functions* (Dover, New York, 1972), section 9.6.1.
46. E. Akkermans, P.E. Wolf, and R. Maynard, *Phys. Rev. Lett.* **56**, 1471 (1986).
47. P.W. Anderson, *Phil. Mag. B* **52**, 505 (1985).
48. A.Z. Genack, in Ref. [13].
49. M.R. Zirnbauer, *Phys. Rev. Lett.* **69**, 1584 (1992).

Dynamics of localization in a waveguide

C.W.J. Beenakker
Instituut-Lorentz, Universiteit Leiden
P.O. Box 9506, 2300 RA Leiden, The Netherlands

Abstract. This is a review of the dynamics of wave propagation through a disordered N-mode waveguide in the localized regime. The basic quantities considered are the Wigner-Smith and single-mode delay times, plus the time-dependent power spectrum of a reflected pulse. The long-time dynamics is dominated by resonant transmission over length scales much larger than the localization length. The corresponding distribution of the Wigner-Smith delay times is the Laguerre ensemble of random-matrix theory. In the power spectrum the resonances show up as a t^{-2} tail after N^2 scattering times. In the distribution of single-mode delay times the resonances introduce a dynamic coherent backscattering effect, that provides a way to distinguish localization from absorption.

1. Introduction

Light localization, one of the two central themes of this meeting, has its roots in electron localization. Much of the theory was developed first for electrical conduction in metals at low temperatures, and then adapted to propagation of electromagnetic radiation through disordered dielectric media [1, 2]. Low-temperature conduction translates into propagation that is monochromatic in the frequency domain, hence static in the time domain.

This historical reason may explain in part why much of the literature on localization of light deals exclusively with static properties. Of course one can think of other reasons, such as that a laser is a highly monochromatic light source. It is not accidental that one of the earliest papers on wave localization in the time domain [3] appeared in the context of seismology, where the natural wave source (an earthquake or explosion) is more appropriately described by a delta function in time than a delta function in frequency.

Our own interest in the dynamics of localization came from its potential as a diagnostic tool. The signature of static localization, an exponential decay of the transmitted intensity with distance, is not unique, since absorption gives an exponential decay as well [4]. This is at the origin of the difficulties surrounding an unambiguous demonstration of three-dimensional localization of light [5]. The dynamics of localization and absorption are, however, entirely different. One such dynamical signature of localization [6] is reviewed in this lecture.

C.M. Soukoulis (ed.), Photonic Crystals and Light Localization in the 21st Century, 489–508.

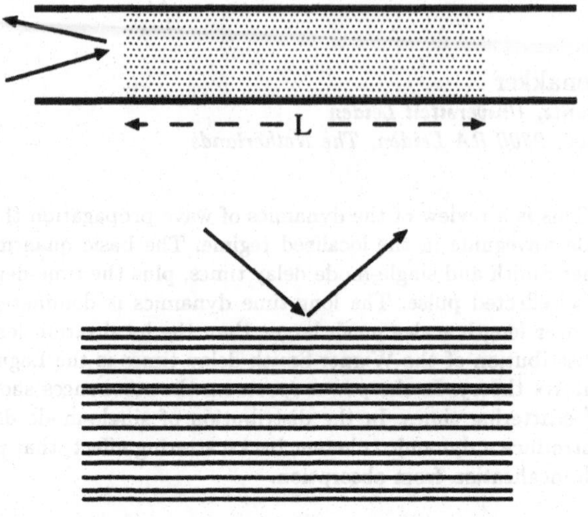

Figure 1. **The top diagram shows the quasi-one-dimensional geometry considered in this review. The waveguide contains a region of length L (dotted) with randomly located scatterers that reflects a wave incident from one end (arrows). The number of propagating modes N may be arbitrarily large. The one-dimensional case $N = 1$ is equivalent to the layered geometry shown in the bottom diagram. Each of the parallel layers is homogeneous but differs from the others by a random variation in composition and/or thickness.**

Localization is a non-perturbative phenomenon and this severely complicates the theoretical problem. In two- and three-dimensional geometries (thin films or bulk materials) not even the static case has been solved completely [7]. The situation is more favorable in a one-dimensional waveguide geometry, where a complete solution of static localization exists [7, 8]. The introduction of dynamical aspects into the problem is a further complication, and we will therefore restrict ourselves to the waveguide geometry (see Fig. 1). The number N of propagating modes in the waveguide may be arbitrarily large, so that the geometry is more appropriately called *quasi*-one-dimensional. (The strictly one-dimensional case $N = 1$ is equivalent to a layered material.)

The basic dynamical quantity that we will consider is the auto-correlator of the time-dependent wave amplitude $u(t)$,

$$a_\omega(t) = \int_{-\infty}^{\infty} dt'\, e^{-i\omega t'}\, u(t)u(t+t'). \tag{1}$$

If the incident wave is a pulse in time, then the transmitted or reflected wave consists of rapid fluctuations with a slowly varying envelope (see Fig. 2). The correlator $a_\omega(t)$ selects the frequency component ω of

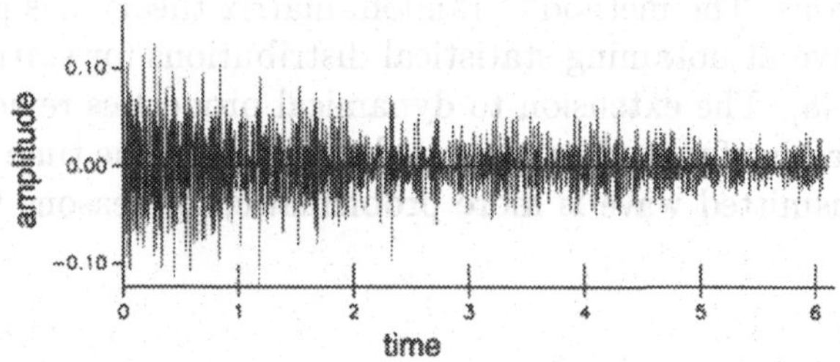

Figure 2. **Computer simulation of an acoustic plane wave pulse reflected by a randomly layered medium. The medium is a model for the subsurface of the Earth, with a sound velocity that depends only on the depth. The figure shows the reflected wave amplitude as a function of time (arbitrary units). The incident pulse strikes the surface at time zero. From Ref. [9].**

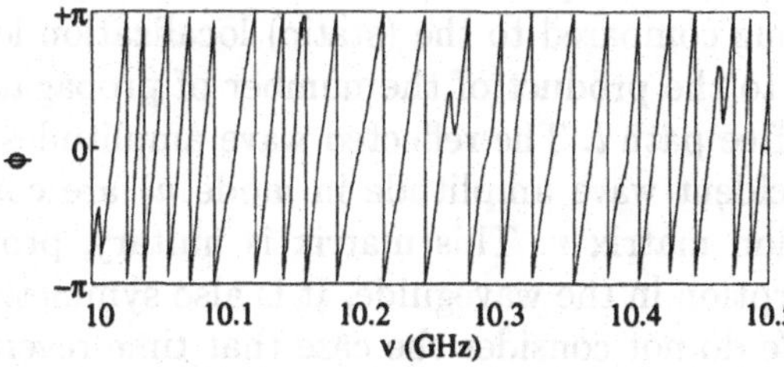

Figure 3. **Frequency dependence of the phase (modulo 2π) of microwave radiation transmitted through a disordered waveguide. The waveguide consists of a 1 m long, 7.6 cm diameter copper tube containing randomly positioned polystyrene spheres (1.27 cm diameter, 0.52% volume filling fraction). Wire antennas are used as the emitter and detector at the two ends of the tube. From Ref. [10].**

the rapid fluctuations. The remaining t-dependence is governed by the propagation time through the waveguide.

If the incident wave is not a pulse in time but a narrow band in frequency, then it is more convenient to study the frequency correlator

$$a_\omega(\delta\omega) = \int_{-\infty}^{\infty} dt\, e^{i\delta\omega t} a_\omega(t) = u^*(\omega)u(\omega+\delta\omega). \qquad (2)$$

The Fourier transformed wave amplitude $u(\omega) = \int dt\, e^{i\omega t}u(t) \equiv I^{1/2}e^{i\phi}$ is complex, containing the real intensity $I(\omega)$ and phase $\phi(\omega)$. Most of the dynamical information is contained in the phase factor, which winds around the unit circle at a speed $d\phi/d\omega$ determined by the propagation time (see Fig. 3).

The correlator a depends sensitively on the random locations of the scatterers in the waveguide, that give rise to the localization. This calls for a statistical treatment, in which we consider the probability distribution of a in an ensemble of waveguides with different scatterer configurations. The method of random-matrix theory has proven to be very effective at obtaining statistical distributions for static scattering properties [8]. The extension to dynamical properties reviewed here is equally effective for studies of the reflected wave. The time dependence of the transmitted wave is more problematic, for reasons that we will discuss.

2. Low-frequency dynamics

The low-frequency regime is most relevant for optical and microwave experiments [4, 10, 11], where one usually works with an incident beam that has a narrow frequency bandwidth relative to the inverse propagation time through the system. We assume that the length L of the waveguide is long compared to the (static) localization length $\xi = Nl$, which is equal to the product of the number of propagating modes N and the mean free path l. The reflected wave amplitudes r_{mn} in mode m (for unit incident wave amplitude in mode n) are contained in an $N \times N$ reflection matrix r. This matrix is unitary, provided we can disregard absorption in the waveguide. It is also symmetric, because of reciprocity. (We do not consider the case that time-reversal symmetry is broken by some magneto-optical effect.)

The correlator

$$C_\omega(\delta\omega) = r^\dagger(\omega) r(\omega + \delta\omega) \tag{3}$$

is the product of two unitary matrices, so it is also unitary. Its eigenvalues $\exp(i\phi_n)$, $n = 1, 2, \ldots N$, contain the phase shifts ϕ_n. Since $\phi_n \equiv 0$ for all n if $\delta\omega = 0$, the relevant dynamical quantity at low frequencies is the limit

$$\tau_n = \lim_{\delta\omega \to 0} \frac{\phi_n}{\delta\omega}, \tag{4}$$

which has the dimension of a time. It is known as the Wigner-Smith delay time, after the authors who first studied it in the context of nuclear scattering [12, 13]. The τ_n's may equivalently be defined as the eigenvalues of the Hermitian time-delay matrix Q,

$$Q(\omega) = -ir^\dagger \frac{dr}{d\omega} = U^\dagger \mathrm{diag}(\tau_1, \tau_2, \ldots \tau_N) U. \tag{5}$$

Experiments typically measure not the product of matrices, as in Eq. (3), but the product of amplitudes, as in Eq. (2). The amplitude measured within a single speckle (or coherence area) corresponds to a single matrix element. The typical observable is therefore not the Wigner-Smith delay time but a different dynamical quantity called the single-channel (or single-mode) delay time [10, 11]:

$$\tau_{mn} = \lim_{\delta\omega \to 0} \mathrm{Im} \frac{r^*_{mn}(\omega) r_{mn}(\omega + \delta\omega)}{\delta\omega |r_{mn}(\omega)|^2}. \tag{6}$$

If we decompose the complex reflection amplitude into intensity and phase, $r_{mn} = I^{1/2} e^{i\phi}$, then the single-channel delay time is the phase derivative, $\tau_{mn} = d\phi/d\omega \equiv \phi'$. Since the reflection matrix $r(\omega + \delta\omega)$ has for small $\delta\omega$ the expansion

$$r_{mn}(\omega + \delta\omega) = \sum_k U_{km} U_{kn} (1 + i\tau_k \delta\omega), \tag{7}$$

we can write the single-channel delay time as a linear combination of the Wigner-Smith times,

$$\tau_{mn} \equiv \phi' = \mathrm{Re} \frac{A_1}{A_0}, \quad A_k = \sum_i \tau_i^k U_{im} U_{in}. \tag{8}$$

We will consider separately the probability distribution of these two dynamical quantities, following Refs. [6, 14].

2.1. Wigner-Smith delay time

There is a close relationship between dynamic scattering problems without absorption and static problems with absorption [15]. Physically, this relationship is based on the notion that absorption acts as a "counter" for the delay time of a wave packet [16]. Mathematically, it is based on the analyticity of the scattering matrix in the upper half of the complex plane. Absorption with a spatially uniform rate $1/\tau_a$ is equivalent to a shift in frequency by an imaginary amount $\delta\omega = \mathrm{i}/2\tau_a$.[1] If we denote the reflection matrix with absorption by $r(\omega, \tau_a)$, then $r(\omega, \tau_a) = r(\omega + \mathrm{i}/2\tau_a)$. For weak absorption we can expand

$$r(\omega + \mathrm{i}/2\tau_a) \approx r(\omega) + \frac{\mathrm{i}}{2\tau_a} \frac{d}{d\omega} r(\omega) = r(\omega) \left[1 - \frac{1}{2\tau_a} Q(\omega) \right]. \tag{9}$$

As before, we have assumed that transmission can be neglected so that r is unitary and Q is Hermitian. Eq. (9) implies that the matrix product

[1] To see this, note that absorption is represented by a positive imaginary part of the dielectric constant $\varepsilon = 1 + i/\omega\tau_a$ (for $\omega\tau_a \gg 1$). Since ε is multiplied by ω^2 in the wave equation, a small imaginary increment $\omega \to \omega + i\delta\omega$ is equivalent to absorption with rate $2\delta\omega$. In the presence of a fluctuating real part of ε, an imaginary shift in frequency will lead to a spatially fluctuating absorption rate, but this is statistically equivalent to homogeneous absorption with an increased scattering rate.

$rr^\dagger$ for weak absorption is related to the time-delay matrix Q by a unitary transformation [14],

$$r(\omega,\tau_a)r^\dagger(\omega,\tau_a) = r(\omega)\left[1 - \frac{1}{\tau_a}Q(\omega)\right]r^\dagger(\omega). \qquad (10)$$

The eigenvalues $R_1, R_2, \ldots R_N$ of $rr^\dagger$ in an absorbing medium are real numbers between 0 and 1, called the reflection eigenvalues. Because a unitary transformation leaves the eigenvalues unchanged, one has $R_n = 1 - \tau_n/\tau_a$. This relationship between reflection eigenvalues and Wigner-Smith delay times is useful because the effects of absorption have received more attention in the literature than dynamic effects. In particular, the case of a single-mode disordered waveguide with absorption was solved as early as 1959, in the course of a radio-engineering problem [17]. The multi-mode case was solved more recently [18, 19]. The distribution is given by the Laguerre ensemble, after a transformation of variables from R_n to $\lambda_n = R_n(1-R_n)^{-1}$:

$$P(\{\lambda_n\}) \propto \prod_{i<j}|\lambda_i - \lambda_j|^\beta \prod_k \exp[-(\alpha\tau_s/\tau_a)(\beta N + 2 - \beta)\lambda_k]. \qquad (11)$$

Here τ_s is the scattering time of the disorder and α is a numerical coefficient of order unity.[2] The symmetry index $\beta = 1$ in the presence of time-reversal symmetry. (The case $\beta = 2$ of broken time-reversal symmetry is rarely realized in optics.) The eigenvalue density is given by a sum over Laguerre polynomials, hence the name "Laguerre ensemble" [20].

The relationship between the reflection eigenvalues for weak absorption and the Wigner-Smith delay times implies that the τ_n's are distributed according to Eq. (11) if one substitutes $\lambda_n/\tau_a \to 1/\tau_n$ (since $\lambda_n \to (1-R_n)^{-1}$ for weak absorption). In terms of the rates $\mu_n = 1/\tau_n$ one has [14]

$$P(\{\mu_n\}) \propto \prod_{i<j}|\mu_i - \mu_j|^\beta \prod_k \exp[-\gamma(\beta N + 2 - \beta)\mu_k]. \qquad (12)$$

[2] The coefficient α depends weakly on N and on the dimensionality of the scattering: $\alpha = 2$ for $N = 1$; for $N \to \infty$ it increases to $\pi^2/4$ or $8/3$ depending on whether the scattering is two or three-dimensional. The mean free path l, that we will encounter later on, is defined as $l = \alpha' c\tau_s$, with $\alpha' = 2$ for $N = 1$ and $\alpha' \to \pi/2$ or $4/3$, respectively, for $N \to \infty$ in two or three dimensions. (The wave velocity is denoted by c.) Finally, the diffusion coefficient $D = c^2\tau_s/d$ with $d = 1$ for $N = 1$ and $d \to 2$ or 3 for $N \to \infty$. The dimensionality that determines these coefficients is a property of the scattering. It is distinct from the dimensionality of the geometry. For example, a waveguide geometry (length much greater than width) is one-dimensional, but it may have $d = 3$ (as in the experiments of Ref. [11]) or $d = 2$ (as in the computer simulations of Ref. [6]).

We have abbreviated $\gamma = \alpha\tau_s$. For $N = 1$ it is a simple β-independent exponential distribution [21, 22, 23], or in terms of the original variable τ,

$$P(\tau) = 2\gamma\tau^{-2}\exp(-2\gamma/\tau). \quad (13)$$

The slow τ^{-2} decay gives a logarithmically diverging mean delay time. The finite localization length ξ is not sufficient to constrain the delay time, because of resonant transmission. Resonant states may penetrate arbitrarily far into the waveguide, and although these states are rare, they dominate the mean (and higher moments) of the delay time. The divergence is cut off for any finite length L of the waveguide. Still, as long as $L \gg \xi$, the resonant states cause large sample-to-sample fluctuations of the delay times. These large fluctuations drastically modify the distribution of the single-channel delay time, as we will discuss next.

2.2. SINGLE-CHANNEL DELAY TIME

In view of the relation (8), we can compute the distribution of the single-channel delay time ϕ' from that of the Wigner-Smith delay times, if we also know the distribution of the matrix of eigenvectors U. For a disordered medium it is a good approximation to assume that U is uniformly distributed in the unitary group, independent of the τ_n's. The distribution $P(\phi')$ may be calculated analytically in the regime $N \gg 1$, which is experimentally relevant ($N \simeq 100$ in the microwave experiments of Ref. [11]).

In the large-N limit the matrix elements U_{mn} become independent complex Gaussian random numbers, with zero mean and variance $\langle |U_{mn}|^2\rangle = 1/N$. Since Eq. (8) contains the elements U_{im} and U_{in}, we should distinguish between $n = m$ and $n \neq m$. Let us discuss first the case $n \neq m$ of different incident and detected modes. The average over the U_{in}'s amounts to doing a set of Gaussian integrations, with the result [6]

$$P(\phi') = \langle \tfrac{1}{2}(B_2 - B_1^2)(B_2 + \phi'^2 - 2B_1\phi')^{-3/2}\rangle. \quad (14)$$

The average $\langle\cdots\rangle$ is over the two spectral moments B_1 and B_2, defined by $B_k = \sum_i \tau_i^k |U_{im}|^2$. The joint distribution $P(B_1, B_2)$, needed to perform the average, has a rather complicated form, for which we refer to Ref. [6].

The result (14) applies to the localized regime $L \gg \xi$. In the diffusive regime $l \ll L \ll \xi$ one has instead [11, 24]

$$P(\phi') = (Q/2\bar{\phi}')[Q + (\phi'/\bar{\phi}' - 1)^2]^{-3/2}. \quad (15)$$

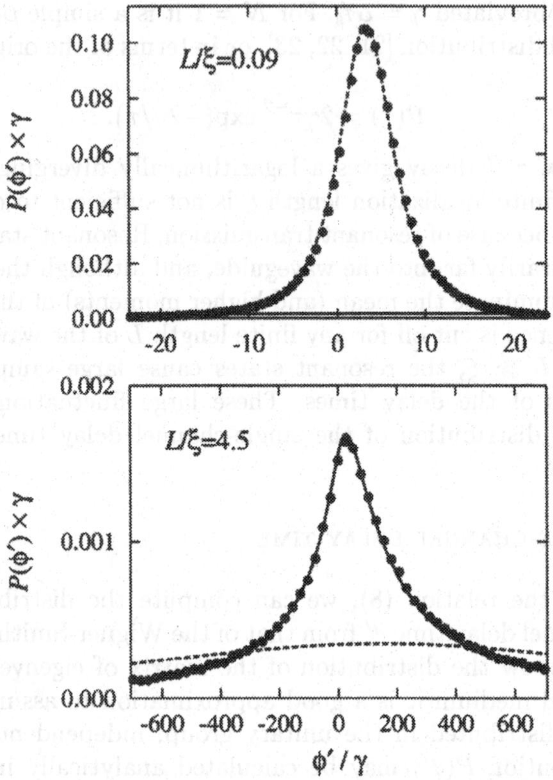

Figure 4. Distribution of the single-channel delay time ϕ' in the diffusive regime (top panel) and localized regime (bottom panel). The results of numerical simulations (data points) are compared to the predictions (14) (solid curve) and (15) (dashed). These are results for different incident and detected modes $n \neq m$. From Ref. [6].

The constants are given by $Q \simeq L/l$ and $\bar{\phi}' \simeq L/c$ up to numerical coefficients of order unity. Comparison of Eqs. (14) and (15) shows that the two distributions would be identical if statistical fluctuations in B_1 and B_2 could be ignored. However, as a consequence of the large fluctuations of the Wigner-Smith delay times in the localized regime, the distribution $P(B_1, B_2)$ is very broad and fluctuations have a substantial effect.

This is illustrated in Fig. 4, where we compare $P(\phi')$ in the two regimes. The data points are obtained from a numerical solution of the wave equation on a two-dimensional lattice, in a waveguide geometry with $N = 50$ propagating modes. They agree very well with the analytical curves. The distribution (15) in the diffusive regime decays $\propto |\phi'|^{-3}$, so that the mean delay time is finite (equal to $\bar{\phi}'$). The distribution in the localized regime decays more slowly, $\propto |\phi'|^{-2}$.

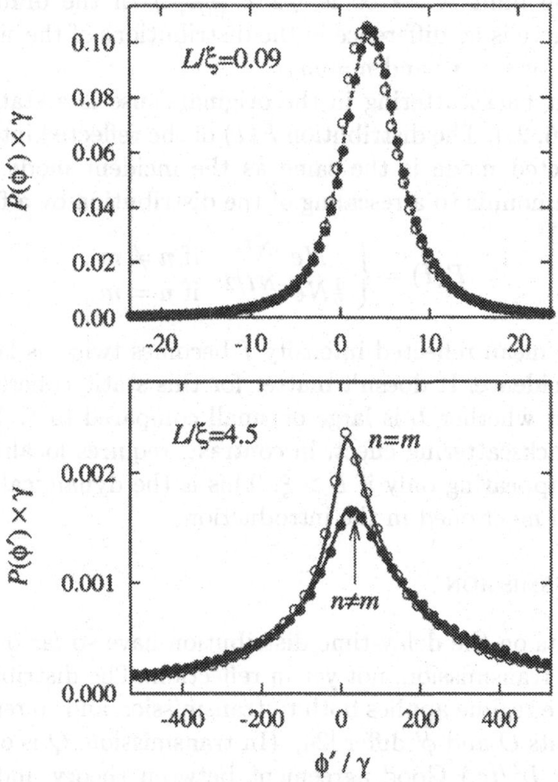

Figure 5. **Same as the previous figure, but now comparing the case $n \neq m$ of different incident and detected modes (solid circles) with the equal-mode case $n = m$ (open circles). A coherent backscattering effect appears, but only in the localized regime. From Ref. [6].**

The resulting logarithmic divergence of the mean delay time is cut off in the simulations by the finiteness of the waveguide length.

Notice that, although the most probable value of the single-channel delay time is positive, the tail of the distribution extends both to positive and negative values of ϕ'. This is in contrast to the Wigner-Smith delay time τ_n, which takes on only positive values. The adjective "delay" in the name single-channel delay time should therefore not be taken literally. The difficulties in identifying the phase derivative with the duration of a scattering process have been emphasized by Büttiker [25].

We now turn to the case $n = m$ of equal-mode excitation and detection. An interesting effect of coherent backscattering appears in the localized regime, as shown in Fig. 5. The maximal value of $P(\phi')$ for $n = m$ is larger than for $n \neq m$ by a factor close to $\sqrt{2}$. (The precise value in the limit $N \to \infty$ is $\sqrt{2} \times \frac{4096}{1371\pi}$.) In the diffusive regime, however, there is no difference in the distributions of the single-channel delay time for $n = m$ and $n \neq m$.

Coherent backscattering in the original sense is a static scattering property [26, 27]. The distribution $P(I)$ of the reflected intensity differs if the detected mode is the same as the incident mode or not. The difference amounts to a rescaling of the distribution by a factor of two,

$$P(I) = \begin{cases} Ne^{-NI} & \text{if } n \neq m\,, \\ \frac{1}{2}Ne^{-NI/2} & \text{if } n = m\,, \end{cases} \tag{16}$$

so that the mean reflected intensity $\bar{I}$ becomes twice as large near the angle of incidence. It doesn't matter for this static coherent backscattering effect whether L is large or small compared to ξ. The dynamic coherent backscattering effect, in contrast, requires localization for its existence, appearing only if $L > \xi$. This is the dynamical signature of localization mentioned in the introduction.

2.3. TRANSMISSION

Experiments on the delay-time distribution have so far only been carried out in transmission, not yet in reflection. The distribution (15) in the diffusive regime applies both to transmission and to reflection, only the constants Q and $\bar{\phi}'$ differ [24]. (In transmission, Q is of order unity while $\bar{\phi}' \simeq L^2/lc$.) Good agreement between theory and experiment has been obtained both with microwaves [11] and with light [4]. The microwave data is reproduced in Fig. 6. Absorption can not be neglected in this experiment (L exceeds the absorption length l_a by a factor 2.5), but this can be accounted for simply by a change in Q and $\bar{\phi}'$. The localization length is larger than L by a factor of 5, so that the system is well in the diffusive regime. It would be of interest to extend these experiments into the localized regime, both in transmission and in reflection. This would require a substantial reduction in absorption, to ensure that $L < \xi < l_a$.

Theoretically, much less is known about the delay-time distribution in transmission than in reflection. While we have a complete theory in reflection, as described in the previous subsection, in transmission not even the $N = 1$ case has been solved completely. Regardless of the value of N, one would expect $P(\phi')$ for $L \gg \xi$ to have the same $1/\phi'^2$ tail in transmission as it has in reflection, since in both cases the same resonances allow the wave to penetrate deeply into the localized region. For $N = 1$ this is borne out by numerical simulations by Bolton-Heaton et al. [28]. These authors also used a picture of one-dimensional resonant transport through localized states to study the decay of the

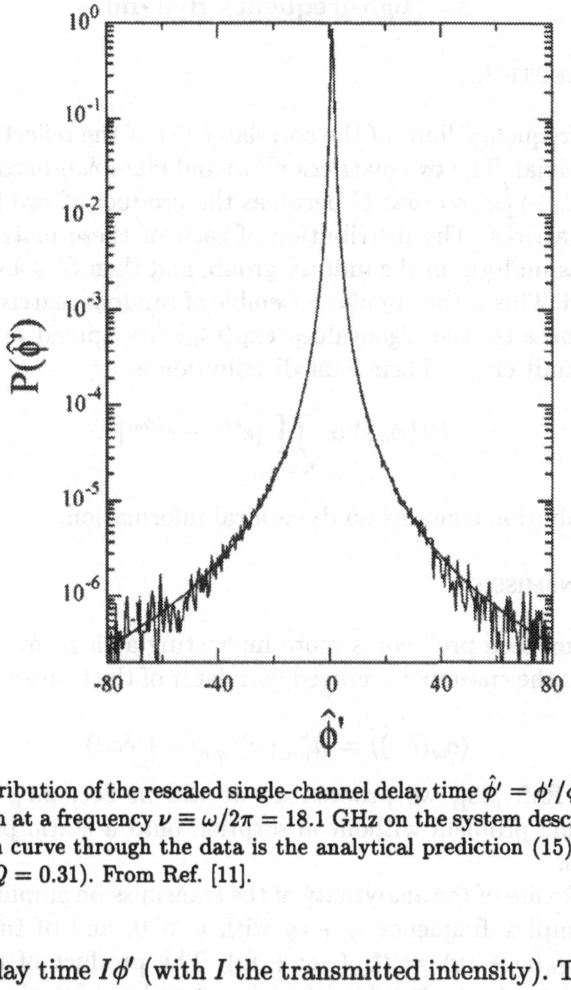

Figure 6. **Distribution of the rescaled single-channel delay time $\hat{\phi}' = \phi'/\bar{\phi}'$, measured in transmission at a frequency $\nu \equiv \omega/2\pi = 18.1$ GHz on the system described in Fig. 3. The smooth curve through the data is the analytical prediction (15) of diffusion theory (with $Q = 0.31$). From Ref. [11].**

weighted delay time $I\phi'$ (with I the transmitted intensity). They found an algebraic decay for $P(I\phi')$, just as for $P(\phi')$, but with a different exponent $-4/3$ instead of -2. It is not known how this carries over to $N > 1$.

Because of the finite length L of the waveguide, these algebraic tails are only an intermediate asymptotics. For $N = 1$ and exponentially large times $|\phi'| > \tau_s e^{L/l}$ the delay-time distribution has the more rapid decay [28, 29]

$$P(\phi') \propto \exp[-(l/L)\ln^2(\phi'/\tau_s)]. \tag{17}$$

Such a log-normal tail is likely to exist in the multi-mode case as well, but this has so far only been demonstrated in the diffusive regime $l \ll L \ll \xi$ [30, 31, 32]. The $1/\phi'^2$ intermediate asymptotics does not appear in that regime.

3. High-frequency dynamics

3.1. Reflection

The high-frequency limit of the correlator (3) of the reflection matrices is rather trivial. The two matrices $r^\dagger(\omega)$ and $r(\omega+\delta\omega)$ become uncorrelated for $\delta\omega \to \infty$, so that C becomes the product of two independent random matrices. The distribution of each of these matrices may be regarded as uniform in the unitary group, and then C is also uniformly distributed. This is the circular ensemble of random-matrix theory [20], so called because the eigenvalues $\exp(i\phi_n)$ are spread out uniformly along the unit circle. Their joint distribution is

$$P(\{\phi_n\}) \propto \prod_{n<m} |e^{i\phi_n} - e^{i\phi_m}|^\beta. \tag{18}$$

This distribution contains no dynamical information.

3.2. Transmission

The transmission problem is more interesting at high frequencies. Let us consider the ensemble-averaged correlator of the transmission matrix elements

$$\langle a_\omega(\delta\omega)\rangle = \langle t^*_{mn}(\omega)t_{mn}(\omega+\delta\omega)\rangle. \tag{19}$$

Following Ref. [33], we proceed as we did in Sec. 2.1, by mapping the dynamic problem without absorption onto a static problem with absorption.

We make use of the analyticity of the transmission amplitude $t_{mn}(\omega+iy)$, at complex frequency $\omega+iy$ with $y>0$, and of the symmetry relation $t_{mn}(\omega+iy) = t^*_{mn}(-\omega+iy)$. The product of transmission amplitudes $t_{mn}(\omega+z)t_{mn}(-\omega+z)$ is an analytic function of z in the upper half of the complex plane. If we take z real, equal to $\frac{1}{2}\delta\omega$, we obtain the product $t_{mn}(\omega+\frac{1}{2}\delta\omega)t^*_{mn}(\omega-\frac{1}{2}\delta\omega)$ in Eq. (19) (the difference with $t_{mn}(\omega+\delta\omega)t^*_{mn}(\omega)$ being statistically irrelevant for $\delta\omega \ll \omega$). If we take z imaginary, equal to $i/2\tau_a$, we obtain the transmission probability $T = |t_{mn}(\omega+i/2\tau_a)|^2$ at frequency ω and absorption rate $1/\tau_a$. We conclude that the ensemble average of a can be obtained from the ensemble average of T by analytic continuation to imaginary absorption rate:

$$\langle a_\omega(\delta\omega)\rangle = \langle T\rangle \ \text{ for } 1/\tau_a \to -i\delta\omega. \tag{20}$$

Higher moments of a are related to higher moments of T by $\langle a^p\rangle = \langle T^p\rangle$ for $1/\tau_a \to -i\delta\omega$. Unfortunately, this is not sufficient to determine the entire probability distribution $P(a)$, because moments of the form $\langle a^p a^{*q} \rangle$ can not be obtained by analytic continuation. This is a complication of the transmission problem. The reflection problem is simpler, because the (approximate) unitarity of the reflection matrix r provides additional information on the distribution of the correlator of the reflection amplitudes. This explains why in Sec. 2.1 we could use the mapping between the dynamic and absorbing problems to calculate the entire distribution function of the eigenvalues of $r^\dagger(\omega)r(\omega+\delta\omega)$ in the limit $\delta\omega \to 0$.

We will apply the mapping first to the single-mode case ($N = 1$) and then to the case $N \gg 1$ of a multi-mode waveguide.

3.2.1. *One mode*

The absorbing problem for $N = 1$ was solved by Freilikher, Pustilnik, and Yurkevich [34]. Applying the mapping (20) to their result we find[3]

$$\langle a_\omega(\delta\omega) \rangle = \exp(i\delta\omega L/c - L/l), \tag{21}$$

in the regime $c/l \ll \delta\omega \ll (\omega^2 c/l)^{1/3}$. (The high-frequency cutoff is due to the breakdown of the random-phase approximation [35].) The absolute value $|\langle a \rangle| = \exp(-L/l)$ is $\delta\omega$-independent in this regime. For $L \ll l$ one has ballistic motion, hence $\langle a \rangle = \exp(i\delta\omega L/c)$ is simply a phase factor, with the ballistic time of flight L/c. Comparing with Eq. (21) we see that localization does not change the frequency dependence of the correlator for large $\delta\omega$, which remains given by the ballistic time scale, but only introduces a frequency-independent weight factor.

The implication of this result in the time domain is that $\langle a_\omega(t) \rangle$ has a peak with weight $\exp(-L/l)$ at the ballistic time $t = L/c$. Such a ballistic peak is expected for the propagation of classical particles through a random medium, but it is surprising to find that it applies to wave dynamics as well.

3.2.2. *Many modes*

Something similar happens for $N \gg 1$. The transmission probability in an absorbing multi-mode waveguide was calculated by Brouwer [36],

$$\langle T \rangle = \frac{l}{N\xi_a \sinh(L/\xi_a)} \exp\left(-\frac{L}{2Nl}\right), \tag{22}$$

for absorption lengths $\xi_a = \sqrt{D\tau_a}$ in the range $l \ll \xi_a \ll \xi$. The length L of the waveguide should be $\gg l$, but the relative magnitude of L and

[3] The coefficient in front of the factor L/l in the exponent in Eq. (21) would be $-\frac{1}{3}$ according to the results of Ref. [34]. This would disagree with numerical simulations, which clearly indicate $|\langle a \rangle| = \exp(-L/l)$ (K. J. H. van Bemmel, unpublished). The error can be traced back to Eq. (39) in Ref. [34].

ξ is arbitrary. Substitution of $1/\tau_a$ by $-i\delta\omega$ gives the correlator

$$\langle a_\omega(\delta\omega)\rangle = \frac{l\sqrt{-i\tau_D\delta\omega}}{NL\sinh\sqrt{-i\tau_D\delta\omega}}\exp\left(-\frac{L}{2Nl}\right), \tag{23}$$

where $\tau_D = L^2/D$ is the diffusion time. The range of validity of Eq. (23) is $L/\xi \ll \sqrt{\tau_D\delta\omega} \ll L/l$, or equivalently $D/\xi^2 \ll \delta\omega \ll c/l$. In the diffusive regime, for $L \ll \xi$, the correlator (23) reduces to the known result [37] from perturbation theory.

For $\max(D/L^2, D/\xi^2) \ll \delta\omega \ll c/l$ the decay of the absolute value of the correlator is a stretched exponential,

$$|\langle a_\omega(\delta\omega)\rangle| = \frac{2l}{NL}\sqrt{\tau_D\delta\omega}\exp\left(-\sqrt{\tfrac{1}{2}\tau_D\delta\omega} - \frac{L}{2Nl}\right). \tag{24}$$

In the localized regime, when ξ becomes smaller than L, the onset of this tail is pushed to higher frequencies, but it retains its functional form. The weight of the tail is reduced by a factor $\exp(-L/2Nl)$ in the presence of time-reversal symmetry. (There is no reduction factor if time-reversal symmetry is broken [33].)

In Fig. 7 we compare the results of numerical simulations in a two-dimensional waveguide geometry with the analytical high-frequency prediction. We see that the correlators for different values of L/ξ converge for large $\delta\omega$ to a curve that lies somewhat above the theoretical prediction. The offset is probably due to the fact that N is not $\gg 1$ in the simulation. Regardless of this offset, the simulation confirms both analytical predictions: The stretched exponential decay $\propto \exp(-\sqrt{\tau_D\delta\omega/2})$ and the exponential suppression factor $\exp(-L/2\xi)$. We emphasize that the time constant $\tau_D = L^2/D$ of the high-frequency decay is the diffusion time for *the entire length* L of the waveguide — even though the localization length ξ is up to a factor of 12 smaller than L.

We can summarize these findings [33] for the single-mode and multimode waveguides by the statement that the correlator of the transmission amplitudes *factorises* in the high-frequency regime: $\langle a_\omega(\delta\omega)\rangle \to f_1(\delta\omega)f_2(\xi)$. The frequency dependence of f_1 depends on the diffusive time through the waveguide, even if it is longer than the localization length. Localization has no effect on f_1, but only on f_2.

4. Propagation of a pulse

If the incident wave is a short pulse, then the separation into low- and high-frequency dynamics is less natural. Ideally one would like to know

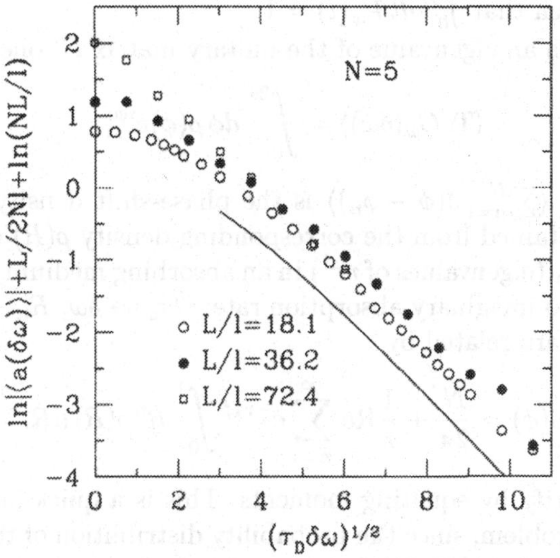

Figure 7. **Frequency dependence of the logarithm of the absolute value of the correlator $\langle a_\omega(\delta\omega)\rangle$. The data points follow from a numerical simulation for $N = 5$, the solid curve is the analytical high-frequency result (24) for $N \gg 1$. The decay of the correlator is given by the diffusive time constant $\tau_D = L^2/D$ even if the length L of the waveguide is greater than the localization length $\xi = 6\,l$. The offset of about 0.6 between the numerical and analytical results is probably a finite-N effect. From Ref. [33].**

the entire time dependence of the correlator $a_\omega(t)$ introduced in Eq. (1). A complete solution exists [38] for the ensemble-averaged correlator in the case of reflection,

$$\begin{aligned}\langle a_\omega(t)\rangle &= \int_{-\infty}^{\infty}\frac{d\delta\omega}{2\pi}e^{-i\delta\omega t}\langle r^*_{mn}(\omega)r_{mn}(\omega+\delta\omega)\rangle \\ &= \frac{1+\delta_{mn}}{N(N+1)}\int_{-\infty}^{\infty}\frac{d\delta\omega}{2\pi}e^{-i\delta\omega t}\langle \mathrm{Tr}\, C_\omega(\delta\omega)\rangle. \end{aligned} \tag{25}$$

The second equality follows from the representation

$$r(\omega\pm\delta\omega/2) = U^{\mathrm{T}}e^{\pm i\Phi/2}U, \tag{26}$$

with $\Phi = \mathrm{diag}(\phi_1, \phi_2, \ldots \phi_N)$ a diagonal matrix and U uniformly distributed in the unitary group. The factor $1+\delta_{mn}$ is due to coherent backscattering. It is convenient to work with the normalized power spectrum,

$$\mathcal{P}_\omega(t) = \frac{N+1}{1+\delta_{mn}}\langle a_\omega(t)\rangle = \frac{1}{N}\int_{-\infty}^{\infty}\frac{d\delta\omega}{2\pi}e^{-i\delta\omega t}\langle \mathrm{Tr}\, C_\omega(\delta\omega)\rangle, \tag{27}$$

normalized such that $\int_0^\infty dt\, \mathcal{P}_\omega(t) = 1$.

Since $e^{i\phi_n}$ is an eigenvalue of the unitary matrix C, one can write

$$\langle \mathrm{Tr}\, C_\omega(\delta\omega) \rangle = \int_0^{2\pi} d\phi\, \rho(\phi) e^{i\phi}, \tag{28}$$

where $\rho(\phi) = \langle \sum_{n=1}^N \delta(\phi - \phi_n) \rangle$ is the phase-shift density. This density can be obtained from the corresponding density $\rho(R)$ of reflection eigenvalues R_n (eigenvalues of $rr^\dagger$) in an absorbing medium, by analytic continuation to imaginary absorption rate: $i/\tau_a \to \delta\omega$, $R_n \to \exp(i\phi_n)$. The densities are related by

$$\rho(\phi) = \frac{N}{2\pi} + \frac{1}{\pi} \mathrm{Re} \sum_{n=1}^{\infty} e^{-in\phi} \int_0^1 R^n \rho(R)\, dR, \tag{29}$$

as one can verify by equating moments. This is a quick and easy way to solve the problem, since the probability distribution of the reflection eigenvalues is known [18, 19]: it is given by the Laguerre ensemble (11). The density $\rho(R)$ can be obtained from that as a series of Laguerre polynomials, using methods from random-matrix theory [20]. Eq. (29) then directly gives the density $\rho(\phi)$.

One might wonder whether one could generalize Eq. (29) to reconstruct the entire distribution function $P(\{\phi_n\})$ from the Laguerre ensemble of the R_n's. The answer is no, unless $\delta\omega$ is infinitesimally small (as in Sec. 2.1). The reason that the method of analytic continuation can not be used to obtain correlations between the ϕ_n's is that averages of negative powers of $\exp(i\phi_n)$ are not analytic in the reflection eigenvalues. For example, for the two-point correlation function one would need to know the average $\langle \exp(i\phi_n - i\phi_m) \rangle \to \langle R_n R_m^{-1} \rangle$ that diverges in the absorbing problem. It *is* possible to compute $P(\{\phi_n\})$ for any $\delta\omega$ — but that requires a different approach, for which we refer to Ref. [38].

The calculation of the power spectrum from Eqs. (27)—(29) is easiest in the absence of time-reversal symmetry, because $\rho(R)$ then has a particularly simple form. One obtains the power spectrum [38]

$$\mathcal{P}_\omega(t) = -\frac{1}{N} \frac{d}{dt} F(t/2N\gamma), \tag{30}$$

$$F(t) = \frac{1}{t+1} \sum_{n=0}^{N-1} \left(\frac{t-1}{t+1} \right)^n P_n \left(\frac{t^2+1}{t^2-1} \right), \tag{31}$$

where P_n is a Legendre polynomial. (Recall that $\gamma = \alpha\tau_s$, cf. Sec. 2.1.) In the single-mode case Eq. (30) simplifies to [3]

$$\mathcal{P}_\omega(t) = 2\gamma(t + 2\gamma)^{-2}. \tag{32}$$

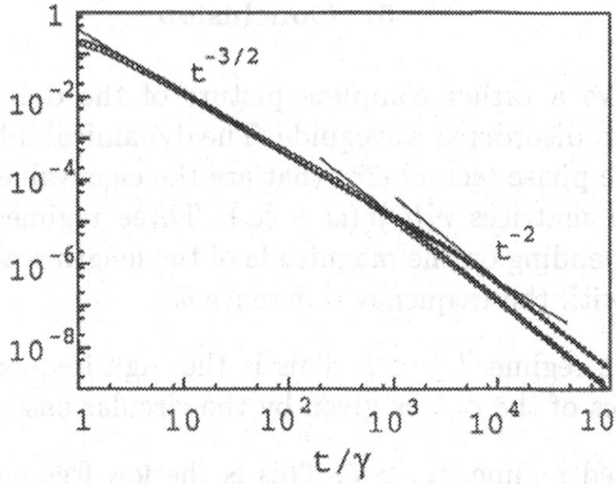

Figure 8. Time dependence of the power spectrum of a reflected pulse in the absence of time-reversal symmetry, calculated from Eq. (30) for $N = 7$ (open circles) and $N = 21$ (filled circles). The intermediate-time asymptote $\propto t^{-3/2}$ and the large-time asymptote $\propto t^{-2}$ are shown as straight lines in this double-logarithmic plot. The prefactor is N-independent for intermediate times but $\propto N$ for large times (notice the relative offset of the large-time asymptotes). Courtesy of M. Titov.

It decays as t^{-2}. For $N \to \infty$ Eq. (30) simplifies to

$$\mathcal{P}_\omega(t) = t^{-1}\exp(-t/\gamma)I_1(t/\gamma), \tag{33}$$

where I_1 is a modified Bessel function. The power spectrum now decays as $t^{-3/2}$. For any finite N we find a crossover from $\mathcal{P} = \sqrt{\gamma/2\pi}\,t^{-3/2}$ for $\tau_s \ll t \ll N^2\tau_s$ to $\mathcal{P} = 2N\gamma t^{-2}$ for $t \gg N^2\tau_s$. This is illustrated in Fig. 8.

In the presence of time-reversal symmetry the exact expression for $\mathcal{P}_\omega(t)$ is more cumbersome but the asymptotics carries over with minor modifications. In particular, the large-N limit (33) with its $t^{-3/2}$ decay remains the same, while the t^{-2} decay changes only in the prefactor: $\mathcal{P} = (N+1)\gamma t^{-2}$ for $t \gg N^2\tau_s$.

The quadratic tail of the time-dependent power spectrum of a pulse reflected from an infinitely long waveguide is the same as the quadratic tail of the delay-time distribution that we have encountered in Sec. 2. It is natural to assume that the power spectrum for transmission through a localized waveguide of finite length has the same quadratic decay, with a cross-over to a log-normal tail for exponentially large times, cf. Sec. 2.3.

5. Conclusion

We now have a rather complete picture of the dynamics of a wave reflected by a disordered waveguide. The dynamical information is contained in the phase factors $e^{i\phi_n}$ that are the eigenvalues of the product of reflection matrices $r^\dagger(\omega)r(\omega+\delta\omega)$. Three regimes can be distinguished, depending on the magnitude of the length scale $l_{\delta\omega} = \sqrt{D/\delta\omega}$ associated with the frequency difference $\delta\omega$:

- Ballistic regime, $l_{\delta\omega} < l$. This is the high-frequency regime. The statistics of the ϕ_n's is given by the circular ensemble, Eq. (18).

- Localized regime, $l_{\delta\omega} > \xi$. This is the low-frequency regime. The ϕ_n's are now distributed according to the Laguerre ensemble (12).

- Diffusive regime, $l < l_{\delta\omega} < \xi$. The distribution of the ϕ_n's does not belong to any of the known ensembles of random-matrix theory [38].

The emphasis in this review has been on the localized regime. The dynamics is then dominated by resonances that allow the wave to penetrate deep into the waveguide. Such resonances correspond to large delay times $\tau_n = \lim_{\delta\omega\to 0}\phi_n/\delta\omega$. The distribution of the largest delay time $\tau_{\rm max}$ follows from the distribution of the smallest eigenvalue in the Laguerre ensemble [39]. For $\beta = 1$ it is given by

$$P(\tau_{\rm max}) = \gamma N(N+1)\tau_{\rm max}^{-2}\exp(-\gamma N(N+1)/\tau_{\rm max}). \qquad (34)$$

It has a long-time tail $\propto 1/\tau_{\rm max}^2$, so that the mean delay time diverges (in the limit of an infinitely long waveguide). A subtle and unexpected consequence of the resonances is the appearance of a dynamic coherent backscattering effect in the distribution of the single-mode delay times. Unlike the conventional coherent backscattering effect in the static intensity, the dynamic effect requires localization for its existence. The recent progress in time-resolved measurements of light scattering from random media, reported at this meeting [4], should enable observation of this effect.

Extension of the theory to two- and three-dimensional localization remains a challenging problem for future research. We believe that the dynamic coherent backscattering effect will persist in higher dimensions, provided the localization length remains large compared to the mean free path. Several methods have been proposed to distinguish absorption from localization in the static intensity [40, 41]. The effect reviewed here could provide this information from a different, dynamic, perspective.

Acknowledgements

It is a pleasure to acknowledge the fruitful collaboration on this topic with K. J. H. van Bemmel, P. W. Brouwer, H. Schomerus, and M. Titov. This research was supported by the "Nederlandse organisatie voor Wetenschappelijk Onderzoek" (NWO) and by the "Stichting voor Fundamenteel Onderzoek der Materie" (FOM).

References

1. *Scattering and Localization of Classical Waves in Random Media*, edited by P. Sheng (World Scientific, Singapore, 1990).
2. B. A. van Tiggelen, in *Diffuse Waves in Complex Media*, edited by J.-P. Fouque, NATO Science Series C531 (Kluwer, Dordrecht, 1999).
3. B. White, P. Sheng, Z. Q. Zhang, and G. Papanicolaou, Phys. Rev. Lett. **59**, 1918 (1987).
4. A. Lagendijk, J. Gómez Rivas, A. Imhof, F. J. P. Schuurmans, and R. Sprik, in this volume.
5. F. Scheffold, R. Lenke, R. Tweer, and G. Maret, Nature **398**, 206 (1999); D. S. Wiersma, J. Gómez Rivas, P. Bartolini, A. Lagendijk, and R. Righini, Nature **398**, 207 (1999).
6. H. Schomerus, K. J. H. van Bemmel, and C. W. J. Beenakker, cond-mat/0004049; cond-mat/0009014.
7. K. Efetov, *Supersymmetry in Disorder and Chaos* (Cambridge University, Cambridge, 1997).
8. C. W. J. Beenakker, Rev. Mod. Phys. **69**, 731 (1997).
9. M. Asch, W. Kohler, G. Papanicolaou, M. Postel, and B. White, SIAM Review **33**, 519 (1991).
10. P. Sebbah, O. Legrand, and A. Z. Genack, Phys. Rev. E **59**, 2406 (1999).
11. A. Z. Genack, P. Sebbah, M. Stoytchev, and B. A. van Tiggelen, Phys. Rev. Lett. **82**, 715 (1999).
12. E. P. Wigner, Phys. Rev. **98**, 145 (1955).
13. F. T. Smith, Phys. Rev. **118**, 349 (1960).
14. C. W. J. Beenakker and P. W. Brouwer, cond-mat/9908325.
15. V. I. Klyatskin and A. I. Saichev, Usp. Fiz. Nauk **162**, 161 (1992) [Sov. Phys. Usp. **35**, 231 (1992)].
16. S. A. Ramakrishna and N. Kumar, Phys. Rev. B **61**, 3163 (2000).
17. M. E. Gertsenshtein and V. B. Vasil'ev, Teor. Veroyatn. Primen. **4**, 424 (1959); **5**, 3(E) (1960) [Theor. Probab. Appl. **4**, 391 (1959); **5**, 340(E) (1960)].
18. C. W. J. Beenakker, J. C. J. Paasschens, and P. W. Brouwer, Phys. Rev. Lett. **76**, 1368 (1996).
19. N. A. Bruce and J. T. Chalker, J. Phys. A **29**, 3761 (1996); **29**, 6681(E) (1996).
20. M. L. Mehta, *Random Matrices* (Academic, New York, 1991).
21. A. M. Jayannavar, G. V. Vijayagovindan, and N. Kumar, Z. Phys. B **75**, 77 (1989).
22. J. Heinrichs, J. Phys. Condens. Matter **2**, 1559 (1990).
23. A. Comtet and C. Texier, J. Phys. A **30**, 8017 (1997).

24. B. A. van Tiggelen, P. Sebbah, M. Stoytchev, and A. Z. Genack, Phys. Rev. E **59**, 7166 (1999).
25. M. Büttiker, in *Electronic Properties of Multilayers and Low-Dimensional Semiconductor Structures*, edited by J. M. Chamberlain, L. Eaves, and J. C. Portal, NATO ASI Series B231 (Plenum, New York, 1990).
26. M. P. van Albada and A. Lagendijk, Phys. Rev. Lett. **55**, 2692 (1985).
27. P.-E. Wolf and G. Maret, Phys. Rev. Lett. **55**, 2696 (1985).
28. C. J. Bolton-Heaton, C. J. Lambert, V. I. Fal'ko, V. Prigodin, and A. J. Epstein, Phys. Rev. B **60**, 10569 (1999).
29. B. L. Altshuler and V. N. Prigodin, Pis'ma Zh. Eksp. Fiz. **47**, 36 (1988) [JETP Lett. **47**, 43 (1988)].
30. B. L. Altshuler, V. E. Kravtsov, and I. V. Lerner, in *Mesoscopic Phenomena in Solids*, edited by B. L. Altshuler, P. A. Lee, and R. A. Webb (North-Holland, Amsterdam, 1991).
31. B. A. Muzykantskii and D. E. Khmelnitskii, Phys. Rev. B **51**, 5480 (1995).
32. A. D. Mirlin, Phys. Rep. **326**, 259 (2000).
33. C. W. J. Beenakker, K. J. H. van Bemmel, and P. W. Brouwer, Phys. Rev. E **60**, R6313 (1999).
34. V. Freilikher, M. Pustilnik, and I. Yurkevich, Phys. Rev. B **50**, 6017 (1994).
35. V. Freilikher and M. Pustilnik, Phys. Rev. B **55**, R653 (1997).
36. P. W. Brouwer, Phys. Rev. B **57**, 10526 (1998).
37. R. Berkovits and S. Feng, Phys. Rep. **238**, 135 (1994).
38. M. Titov and C. W. J. Beenakker, cond-mat/0005042.
39. A. Edelman, Lin. Alg. Appl. **159**, 55 (1991).
40. A. A. Chabanov, M. Stoytchev, and A. Z. Genack, Nature **404**, 850 (2000).
41. B. A. van Tiggelen, A. Lagendijk, and D. S. Wiersma, Phys. Rev. Lett. **84**, 4333 (2000).

FROM PROXIMITY RESONANCES TO ANDERSON LOCALIZATION

ARKADIUSZ ORŁOWSKI & MARIAN RUSEK
Instytut Fizyki, Polska Akademia Nauk, Warszawa, Poland

1. Introduction

This paper serves as a guide for a tour from proximity resonances to Anderson localization. It can be quite a long trip. To see a proximity resonance it is enough to have just two scatteres placed very close together. To observe Anderson localization we need, in general, an infinite number of scatterers. It is hard to count from two to infinity within ten pages. Therefore we will have to stop somewhere in between. We are able to manage 1000 scatterers and, fortunately, this number seems to be large enough to justify some reasonable conclusions.

The phenomenon of Anderson localization of electronic wave functions became a prominent part of contemporary condensed matter physics and it is still a vivid subject of theoretical and experimental research. As shown by Anderson [3], in a sufficiently disordered infinite material an entire band of electronic states can be spatially localized. In fact, the Anderson localization may be viewed as a transition from particle-like behavior described by the diffusion equation to wave-like behavior, which results in localization by interference. Indeed, the most plausible explanation of Anderson localization is based on the interference effects in multiple elastic scattering of electrons on the material impurities.

As interference is the common property of all wave phenomena, the quest for some analogs of electron localization for other types of waves has been undertaken and many generalizations of electron localization exist, especially in the realm of electromagnetic waves [11, 4, 13, 21]. So-called weak localization of electromagnetic waves manifesting itself as enhanced coherent backscattering is presently relatively well understood theoretically [2, 22, 18] and established experimentally [16, 23, 28]. The question is whether interference effects in 3D random dielectric media can reduce

C.M. Soukoulis (ed.), Photonic Crystals and Light Localization in the 21st Century, 509–518.

the diffusion constant to zero leading to strong localization. The crucial parameter is the mean free path l which should be rather short [12, 14].

Of course, apart from remarkable similarities between scattering of electrons and light waves, there are also striking differences. Very different is, e.g., the long-wavelength limit of elastic scattering. For electrons we have mainly s-wave scattering which is spatially isotropic and wavelength independent. For light we observe p-wave scattering. In this case there is forward-backward symmetry but scattering is non-isotropic. In inelastic scattering electrons change their energy but their total number is conserved. For light we have strong absorption and the intensity decreases. Moreover electrons are described by scalar wave functions (or two-component spinors if the spin is included). To describe correctly scattering and localization of electromagnetic waves we need to consider, in general, three-dimensional vector fields.

The Anderson localization of electromagnetic waves could be observed experimentally in the scaling properties of the transmission T. Imagine a slab of thickness L containing randomly distributed non-absorptive scatterers. Usually propagation of electromagnetic waves in weakly scattering random media can be described adequately by a diffusion process [9, 15]. Thus the equivalent of the Ohm's law holds and the transmission decreases linearly with the thickness of the sample, i.e., $T \propto L^{-1}$ (for sufficiently large L). However, when the fluctuations of the dielectric constant become large enough, the electromagnetic field ceases to diffuse and becomes localized due to interference. Anderson localization occurs when this happens. In such a case the material behaves as an optical equivalent of an insulator and the transmission decreases exponentially with the size of the system $T \propto e^{-L/\xi}$ [4, 1].

An experiment suggesting that Anderson localization is indeed possible in three-dimensional disordered dielectric structures has been given recently [27]. The strongly scattering medium has been provided by semiconductor powders with a very large refractive index. By decreasing the average particle size it was possible to observe a clear transition from linear scaling of transmission ($T \propto L^{-1}$) to an exponential decay ($T \propto e^{-L/\xi}$). Some localization effects have been also reported in previous experiments on microwave localization in copper tubes filled with metallic and dielectric spheres [6]. However, the latter experiments were plagued by large absorption, which makes the interpretation of the data quite complicated.

Thus from the experimental point of view there are indeed some reasonable indications that strong localization could be possible in three-dimensional random dielectric structures. On the other hand, it would be desirable to have a reasonably simple yet realistic theoretical model providing deeper insight into localization of light. It concerns especially those problems where the polarization effects have to be taken into account. Such considerations should assume the vector character of electromagnetic fields from the very beginning. To achieve this goal in a consistent way they should be based directly on the Maxwell equations. On the other hand, they should be simple enough to provide calculations without too many too-crude approximations. In this chapter we construct explicitly such a model for the three-dimensional localization of electromagnetic waves. The resulting model is thoroughly analyzed and its major consequences are elaborated.

2. Point-scatterers

Usually localization of light is studied experimentally in microstructures consisting of dielectric spheres with diameters and mutual distances being comparable to the wavelength [14]. On the other hand the theory of multiple scattering of electromagnetic waves by dielectric particles is tremendously simplified in the limit of point scatterers. In principle this approximation is justified only when the size of the scattering particles is much smaller than the wavelength. In practical calculations, however, many multiple-scattering effects can be obtained qualitatively for coupled electrical dipoles. Examples are: universal conductance fluctuations [17], enhanced backscattering [24], and dependent scattering [26]. What really counts for localization is mainly the scattering cross section and not the bare size of the scatterer. Therefore, trying to understand the problem, we replace the dielectric spheres located at the points $\vec{r}_a$ by *single* electric dipoles

$$\vec{\mathcal{P}}(\vec{r}) = \sum_{a=1}^{N} \vec{p}_a \, \delta(\vec{r} - \vec{r}_a), \tag{1}$$

with properly adjusted scattering properties.

To use safely the point dipole approximation it is essential to use a representation for the scatterers that fulfills the optical theorem rigorously and conserves energy in the scattering processes. This requirements give the following form of the coupling between the dipole moment and the electric field incident on the dipole [20]:

$$\frac{2}{3}\, i k^3 \, \vec{p}_a = \frac{e^{i\phi} - 1}{2} \, \vec{\mathcal{E}}'(\vec{r}_a), \tag{2}$$

where $k = \omega/c$ is the wavenumber in vacuum. The field acting on the ath dipole

$$\vec{\mathcal{E}}'(\vec{r}_a) = \vec{\mathcal{E}}^{(0)}(\vec{r}_a) + \sum_{\substack{b=1 \\ b \neq a}}^{N} \vec{\nabla} \times \vec{\nabla} \times \vec{p}_b \, \frac{e^{ik|\vec{r}_a - \vec{r}_b|}}{|\vec{r}_a - \vec{r}_b|}, \tag{3}$$

is the sum of some incident free field $\vec{\mathcal{E}}^{(0)}$, which obeys the Maxwell equations in vacuum, and waves scattered by all *other* dipoles.

The scatterers necessarily have an internal structure. Thus in general the phase shift ϕ from Eq. (2) should be regarded as a function of frequency ω. For example to model a simple scatterer with one internal Breit-Wigner type resonance one can write:

$$\cot\phi = -\frac{\omega-\omega_0}{\gamma_0}. \tag{4}$$

The total scattering cross-section σ takes then the familiar Lorentzian form:

$$k^2\,\sigma = 6\pi\,\sin^2\phi = \frac{6\pi\,\gamma_0^2}{(\omega-\omega_0)^2+\gamma_0^2}. \tag{5}$$

3. Localized waves

By definition, an electromagnetic wave is localized in a certain region of space if its magnitude is (at least) exponentially decaying in any direction from this region. We will show now that electromagnetic waves localized in the finite dielectric medium (1) correspond to nonzero solutions $\vec{\mathcal{E}}'(\vec{r}_a) \neq 0$ of Eqs. (2) and (3) for the incoming wave equal to zero, i.e., $\vec{\mathcal{E}}^{(0)}(\vec{r}_a) \equiv 0$.

If we solve Eqs. (2) and (3) and use again Eq. (2) to find $\vec{p}_a$, then we are able to find the electromagnetic field everywhere in space:

$$\vec{\mathcal{E}}(\vec{r}) = \vec{\mathcal{E}}^{(0)}(\vec{r}) + \vec{\mathcal{E}}^{(1)}(\vec{r}), \tag{6}$$

where the scattered field $\vec{\mathcal{E}}^{(1)}$ can be written in the following form [5]:

$$\vec{\mathcal{E}}^{(1)}(\vec{r}) = \sum_{a=1}^{N} \vec{\nabla}\times\vec{\nabla}\times\vec{p}_a\,\frac{e^{ik|\vec{r}-\vec{r}_a|}}{|\vec{r}-\vec{r}_a|} \tag{7}$$

Let us now suppose that the field is exponentially localized in the vicinity of the dielectric medium (1). First let us observe that, due to Eqs. (7), the scattered field $\vec{\mathcal{E}}^{(1)}(\vec{r})$ tends to zero if $|\vec{r}| \to \infty$. Thus if the total field (6) is exponentially localized, then the free field $\vec{\mathcal{E}}^{(0)}(\vec{r})$ must also tend to zero in this limit. But it is known from the vector form of the Kirchhoff integral formula [10] that if the free field vanishes on a closed surface, then it is zero everywhere inside this coupling surface.

The proof works also the other way round. Suppose that $\vec{\mathcal{E}}(\vec{r})$ is a solution of Eqs. (2) and (3), (7), and (6) for $\vec{\mathcal{E}}^{(0)}(\vec{r}) \equiv 0$. For $z \to \infty$ (the choice of the z axis is arbitrary) the scattered field $\vec{\mathcal{E}}^{(1)}(\vec{r})$ can be expanded into the plane waves propagating into the positive z direction and the evanescent plane waves.

As the considered medium is non-dissipative, the time average energy stream integrated over a closed surface surrounding it must vanish. This means that there are no propagating plane waves in the scattered field (which in the case $\vec{\mathcal{E}}^{(0)}(\vec{r}) \equiv 0$ is equal to the total field). Therefore the field consists only of evanescent plane waves and thus is exponentially localized.

4. Proximity Resonances

A way of dealing with *resonances* in this formalism is to look for resonance poles in the complex ω plane. Resonance poles are frequencies ω for which it is possible to solve Eqs. (2) and (3) as a homogeneous equations, i.e., for the incoming wave $\vec{\mathcal{E}}^{(0)}$ equal to zero. The real and imaginary parts of the resonance frequencies determine the positions and widths of the resonances. This method has been applied recently to the analysis of resonances in a system of $N = 2$ s-wave scatterers [7, 8]. A similar problem of scattering of light from two spherical particles has been discussed in [19].

It is seen from Eqs. (2) and (3) that for $\vec{\mathcal{E}}^{(0)} \equiv 0$ the latter system of equations is equivalent to the *eigenproblem* for the $\hat{G}$ matrix:

$$\sum_{b=1}^{N} \hat{G}_{ab} \cdot \vec{\mathcal{E}}'(\vec{r}_b) = \lambda \vec{\mathcal{E}}'(\vec{r}_a), \quad a = 1, \ldots, N \tag{8}$$

where

$$\lambda = -1 - i \cot \phi. \tag{9}$$

The elements of the $\hat{G}$ matrix from Eq. (8) are equal to the Green function (tensor) calculated for the differences between the positions of the scatterers:

$$\frac{2}{3} ik^3 \hat{G}_{ab} = \begin{cases} \vec{\nabla} \times \vec{\nabla} \times \frac{e^{ik|\vec{r}_a - \vec{r}_b|}}{|\vec{r}_a - \vec{r}_b|} & \text{for } a \neq b \\ 0 & \text{for } a = b \end{cases}. \tag{10}$$

The Green matrix defined by Eq. (10) depends only on the the scaled distances between all pairs of the scatterers $k|\vec{r}_a - \vec{r}_b|$. Therefore for fixed positions of the scatters $\vec{r}_a$, its eigenvalues still remain functions of frequency ω. Using an explicit model of the scattering phase shift $\phi(\omega)$ and solving Eq. (9) in a complex ω plane it is possible to determine the positions and widths of the resonances. In the particular case of the Breit-Wigner type scatterers Eq. (4) the real and imaginary parts of the eigenvalues of the $\hat{G}$ matrix have a nice physical interpretation: they are equal to the relative widths $(\gamma - \gamma_0)/\gamma_0$ and positions $(\omega - \omega_0)/\gamma_0$ of the resonances. Indeed, using the explicit form of the complex frequency $\omega \to \omega - i\gamma$ and substituting the Breit-Wigner model of the scattering into Eq. (9) we get:

$$\omega - i\gamma = \omega_0 - i\gamma_0[1 + \lambda(\omega - i\gamma)] \tag{11}$$

This system of two coupled nonlinear equations determines the values of the resonance poles $\omega - i\gamma$. In many physically interesting cases Eqs. (11) can be solved numerically by iteration. For instance in solving it up to the first order in γ_0/ω_0 one substitutes $\lambda(\omega_0)$ for $\lambda(\omega - i\gamma)$ getting:

$$\operatorname{Re}\lambda(\omega_0) \simeq \frac{\gamma - \gamma_0}{\gamma_0}, \quad \operatorname{Im}\lambda(\omega_0) \simeq \frac{\omega - \omega_0}{\gamma_0}. \tag{12}$$

Let us start with a simplest possible example of a system of $N = 2$ scatterers separated by a distance d. In this case the $\hat{G}$ matrix from Eq. (10) has four eigenvalues: $\lambda_{\pm}^{(T)} = \mp\frac{3}{2}\frac{e^{ikd}}{ikd}\left(\frac{1}{(kd)^2} - i\frac{1}{kd} - 1\right)$ corresponding to the transverse oscillations of the dipoles, and $\lambda_{\pm}^{(L)} = \pm\frac{3}{2}\frac{e^{ikd}}{ikd}\left(\frac{2}{(kd)^2} - i\frac{2}{kd}\right)$ corresponding to the longditual oscillations of the dipoles. The upper sign (+) describes oscillations in phase, whereas the lower sign (−) corresponds to the oscillations in anti-phase. For $k = k_0 = \omega_0/c$ the eigenvalues $\lambda_{\pm}^{(T)}$ and $\lambda_{\pm}^{(L)}$ may be considered as an approximate solution of Eq. (11) up to the first order in γ_0/ω_0.

The eigenvalues $\lambda_{\pm}^{(T)}$ and $\lambda_{\pm}^{(L)}$ are depicted in Fig. 1. They form a characteristic four-arms spiral. We see that for scatterers very close to each other ($d \to 0$) two arms of this spiral corresponding to the oscillations in anti-phase approach the axis $\operatorname{Re}\lambda = -1$ ($\gamma = 0$). They are related to the very narrow "antisymmetric" resonances. On the other hand in this limit the remaining two arms corresponding to the oscillations in phase tend asymptotically to the axis $\operatorname{Re}\lambda = 1$ ($\gamma = 2\gamma_0$). These arms are related to the "symmetric" resonances of the pair which are about twice as broad as the resonance of the single scatterer. For $d \to \infty$ both arms meet in the point $\lambda = 0$ ($\omega = \omega_0, \gamma = \gamma_0$) reproducing the results of the single scattering.

5. Self-averaging

To illustrate the appearance of the band of localized electromagnetic waves, emerging in the limit of infinite system, we have to study the properties of *finite* systems for increasing number of dipoles N (while keeping the density constant). For each distribution of the dipoles $\vec{r}_a$ placed randomly inside a sphere with the uniform scaled density $n = 1$ dipole per wavelength cubed we have diagonalized numerically the $\hat{G}$ matrix from Eq. (10) and obtained the complex eigenvalues λ. The resulting probability distribution $P(\lambda)$,

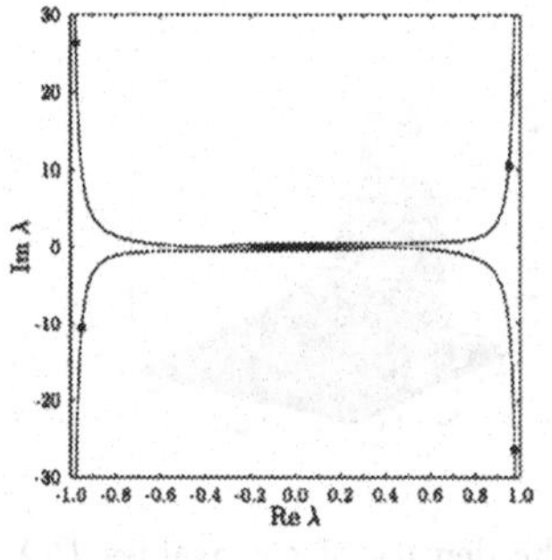

Figure 1. **Eigenvalues λ of a $\hat{G}$ matrix corresponding to a system of $N = 2$ point-like scatterers. All four types of resonances all clearly visible. The four black dots correspond to the eigenvalues calculated for a certain specific value of the distance between the scatterers $k\,d$.**

calculated from several different distributions of N dipoles is normalized in the standard way $\int d^2\lambda\, P(\lambda) = 1$. Let us now compare the surface plots of $P(\lambda)$ (treated as a function of two variables $\mathrm{Re}\,\lambda$ and $\mathrm{Im}\,\lambda$) calculated for systems consisting of different numbers of dipoles N. The plot for $N = 1000$ is presented in Fig. 2. It turns out that, for increasing size of the system, at some $\mathrm{Im}\,\lambda$ the probability distribution $P(\lambda)$ apparently moves towards the $\mathrm{Re}\,\lambda = -1$ axis and simultaneously its variance decreases. This tendency is easily seen, e.g., for values of $|\mathrm{Im}\,\lambda|$ that are close to 0. Our numerical investigations indicate, that in the limit of an infinite medium, the probability distribution $P(\lambda)$ tends to the delta function in $\mathrm{Re}\,\lambda$:

$$\lim_{N\to\infty} P(\lambda) = \delta(\mathrm{Re}\,\lambda + 1)\, f(\mathrm{Im}\lambda). \tag{13}$$

We have some numerical evidence that this fact is a general property of $\hat{G}$ matrices, not restricted to the considered case of one dipole per wavelength cubed $n = 1$. Of course we could justify Eq. (13) by more orthodox approach based on a version of the finite size scaling analysis which leads however to an analogous conclusion.

It follows from Eq. (13) that in the limit $N \to \infty$ the distribution function $P(\lambda)$ has only one value of $\mathrm{Re}\,\lambda$ for which it is non-zero. The quantity $\mathrm{Re}\,\lambda$ is then "self-averaging" and the average value applies to *every single* realization of the system except for a few special ones (with measure zero). This means that for "almost every" random distribution of the dipoles $\vec{r}_a$, the equation $\mathrm{Re}\,\lambda = -1$ holds. Therefore Eq. (9) can be fulfilled if the phase shift of the scatterers satisfies: $\mathrm{Im}\,\lambda = -\cot\phi$. In this case the corresponding eigenvector $\vec{\mathcal{E}}'(\vec{r}_a)$ of the $\hat{G}$ matrix is a nonzero

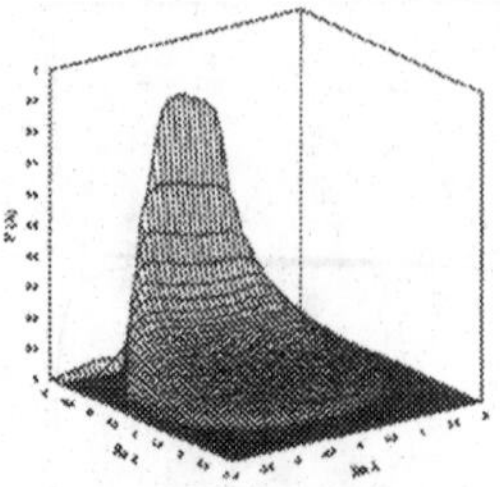

Figure 2. Surface plot of the density of eigenvalues $P(\lambda)$ calculated for 500 different distributions of $N = 1000$ point-like scatterers placed randomly inside a sphere, with uniform density $n = 1$ scatterer per wavelength cubed. For increasing values of N, the probability distribution $P(\lambda)$ apparently moves towards the $\mathrm{Re}\lambda = -1$ axis and, simultaneously, its variance along the $\mathrm{Im}\lambda = \mathrm{const}$ axes decreases.

solution of the system of linear equations (2) and (3) for the incoming wave $\vec{\mathcal{E}}^{(0)}(\vec{r}_a)$ equal to zero. Thus, as shown in Sec. 3, a localized wave exists.

6. Anderson localization

Let us now apply our model to a system of Breit-Wigner scatterers Eq. (4) located randomly with uniform physical density η. In this case the parameter ϕ from Eq. (2) remains a function of the frequency, i.e., $\phi = \phi(\omega)$. It follows from Eq. (13), for almost any random distribution of the scatterers $\vec{r}_a$ (except maybe for a few special ones with measure zero) an infinite number of eigenvalues λ of the $\hat{G}$ matrix satisfies the condition: $\mathrm{Re}\,\lambda_j(\omega) = -1$ (note that we added an index j which labels the localized waves). As pointed out before, this occurs not only for $n = 1$ but for a whole range of n and therefore, for fixed physical density ρ, for a range of frequencies ω. Therefore at real values of frequency ω_j determined by the equation:

$$\mathrm{Im}\,\lambda_j(\omega_j) = -\cot\phi(\omega_j) \tag{14}$$

these eigenvalues are solutions of Eq. (9). Thus the corresponding eigenvectors $\vec{\mathcal{E}}'_j(\vec{r}_a)$ of the $\hat{G}$ matrix describe localized states which exist at *discrete* frequencies ω_j. Note, that this result does not depend on the particular model of the scatterer used.

It seems reasonable to expect that the function f from Eq. (13) has compact support: $f(\mathrm{Im}\,\lambda) = 0$ for $|\mathrm{Im}\,\lambda| > \mathrm{Im}\,\lambda_{\mathrm{cr}}$ (the values of $\mathrm{Im}\,\lambda_{\mathrm{cr}}$ should be regarded as functions of ω). According to Eq. (14) this means that localized waves of frequency ω can exist only if

$$|\phi(\omega)| \geq \phi_{\mathrm{cr}}(\omega), \tag{15}$$

where $\cot \phi_{cr}(\omega) = \mathrm{Im}\, \lambda_{cr}(\omega)$. We see from Eqs. (5) and (15) that the total scattering cross section of individual particles σ must exceed some critical value $\sigma_{cr} = \sigma(\phi_{cr})$ before localization will take place in the limit $N \to \infty$. This fact is in perfect agreement with the scaling theory of localization [1]: in 3D random media a certain critical degree of disorder is needed for localization.

From Eqs. (15) and (4) we conclude that in three-dimensional media consisting of Breit-Wigner-type scatteres localization of light is possible only in a certain frequency window:

$$\omega_{\min} \leq \omega \leq \omega_{\max}. \tag{16}$$

In the limit $N \to \infty$ a countable set of discrete frequencies ω_j corresponding to localized waves becomes dense in this finite interval given by Eq. (16). Thus an entire *band* of spatially localized waves appears in the limit of an infinite medium.

7. Brief Summary

We have presented a quite realistic point-scatterer model describing scattering of electromagnetic waves by a disordered dielectric medium. Its relative simplicity allowed us to discover some new features of the Anderson localization of electromagnetic waves in 3D dielectric media without using any averaging procedures. Within our theoretical approach one can easily see how localization "sets in" for increasing size of the system. Very striking universal properties of the spectra of random matrices describing the scattering from a collection of randomly distributed point-like scatterers have been observed. Self-averaging of the real parts of the eigenvalues emerging in the limit of an infinite medium has been discovered numerically. For the first time (to our knowledge) the appearance of the band of localized electromagnetic waves in 3D was demonstrated. It can be understood as a counterpart of Anderson localization in solid state physics.

Acknowledgments

We are grateful to Costas Soukoulis for his hospitality extended to one of us (A.O.) in Crete. This work was supported in part by the Polish Committee for Scientific Research (KBN) under Grants 2 P03B 023 17 and 2 P03B 044 19.

References

1. E. Abrahams, P. W. Anderson, D. C. Licciardello, and T. V. Ramakrishnan, Scaling theory of localization: Absence of quantum diffusion in two dimensions, *Phys. Rev. Lett.* **42**, 673 (1979).

2. E. Akkermans, P. E. Wolf, and R. Maynard, Coherent backscattering of light by disordered media: Analysis of the peak line shape, *Phys. Rev. Lett.* **56**, 1471 (1986).
3. P. W. Anderson, Absence of diffusion in certain random lattices, *Phys. Rev.* **109**, 1492 (1958)
4. P. W. Anderson, The question of classical localization. A theory of white paint? *Phil. Mag. B* **52**, 505 (1985).
5. M. Born and E. Wolf, *Principles of Optics* (Pergamon Press, Oxford-London, 1965).
6. A. Z. Genack and N. Garcia, Observation of photon localization in a three-dimensional disordered system, *Phys. Rev. Lett.* **66**, 2064 (1991).
7. E. J. Heller, Quantum proximity resonances, *Phys. Rev. Lett.* **77**, 4122 (1996).
8. J. S. Hersch and E. J. Heller, Observation of proximity resonances in a parallel-plate waveguide, *Phys. Rev. Lett.* **81**, 3059 (1998).
9. A. Ishimaru, *Wave Propagaton and Scattering in Random Media* (Academic, New York, 1978).
10. J. D. Jackson, *Classical Electrodynamics* (Wiley, New York, 1962).
11. S. John, Electromagnetic absorption in a disordered medium near a photon mobility edge, *Phys. Rev. Lett.* **53**, 2169 (1984).
12. S. John, Localization and absorption of waves in a weakly dissipative disordered medium, *Phys. Rev. B* **31**, 304 (1985).
13. S. John, Strong localization of photons in certain disordered dielectric superlattices, *Phys. Rev. Lett.* **58**, 2486 (1987).
14. S. John, Localization of light, *Physics Today* **44**, 32 (May 1991).
15. A. Kerker, *The Scattering of Light and Other Electromagnetic Radiation*, (Academic, New York, 1969).
16. Y. Kuga and A. Ishimaru, Retroreflectance from a dense distribution of spherical particles, *J. Opt. Soc. Am. A* **1**, 831 (1984).
17. P. A. Lee and A. D. Stone, Universal conductance fluctuations in metals, *Phys. Rev. Lett.* **55**, 1622 (1985).
18. F. C. MacKintosh and S. John, Coherent backscattering of light in the presence of time-reversal-noninvariant and parity-nonconserving media, *Phys. Rev. B* **37**, 1884 (1988).
19. V. A. Markel, Scattering of light from two interacting spherical particles, *Journal of Modern Optics* **39**, 853 (1992).
20. M. Rusek, A. Orłowski, and J. Mostowski, Localization of light in three-dimensional random dielectric media, *Phys. Rev. E* **53**, 4122 (1996).
21. C. M. Soukoulis, editor, *Photonic Band Gaps and Localization*, NATO ASI Series, (Plenum, New York, 1993).
22. M. J. Stephen and G. Cwillich, Rayleigh scattering and weak localization: Effects of polarization, *Phys. Rev. B* **34**, 7564 (1986).
23. M. P. van Albada and A. Lagendijk. Observation of weak localization of light in a random medium, *Phys. Rev. Lett.* **55**, 2692 (1985).
24. M. B. van der Mark, M. P. van Albada, and A. Lagendijk, Light scattering in strongly scattering media: Multiple scattering and weak localization, *Phys. Rev. B* **37**, 3575 (1988).
25. W. van Haeringen and D. Lenstra, editors, *Analogies in Optics and Micro Electronics* (Kluwer, Dordrecht, 1990).
26. B. A. van Tiggelen, A. Lagendijk, and A. Tip, Multiple-scattering effects for the propagation of light in 3d slabs, *J. Phys. C* **2**, 7653 (1990).
27. D. S. Wiersma, P. Bartolini, A. Lagendijk, and R. Righini, Localization of light in a disordered media, *Nature* **390**, 671 (1997).
28. P.-E. Wolf and G. Maret, Weak localization and coherent backscattering of photons in disordered media, *Phys. Rev. Lett.* **55**, 2696 (1985).

BAND-STRUCTURE AND TRANSMITTANCE CALCULATIONS FOR PHONONIC CRYSTALS BY THE LKKR METHOD

I. E. PSAROBAS* and N. STEFANOU
Section of Solid State Physics, University of Athens, Panepistimioupolis, GR-157 84, Athens, Greece

A. MODINOS
Department of Physics, National Technical University of Athens, Zografou Campus, GR-157 73, Athens, Greece

Abstract. We developed a multiple scattering method for the calculation of the frequency band structure of a phononic crystal consisting of non-overlapping elastic spheres arranged periodically in a host medium of different elastic properties. Using a variation of the same method we can also calculate, with the same ease and accuracy, the coefficients of transmission, reflection and absorption of elastic waves incident on a slab of the material of finite thickness. The elastic coefficients for the spheres and/or the host medium can be complex and frequency dependent. We demonstrate the effectiveness of the method by applying it to specific examples.

Phononic crystals are composite materials consisting of homogeneous particles distributed periodically in a homogeneous host medium characterized by a different mass density ρ and different propagation velocities c_l and c_t (for longitudinal and transverse waves, respectively). With an appropriate choice of the values of these parameters, one may obtain phononic crystals with absolute frequency gaps (phononic gaps) in selected regions of frequency [1]. An elastic wave, whose frequency lies within an absolute gap of a phononic crystal, will be completely reflected by it; from which follows the possibility of constructing non-absorbing mirrors of elastic waves and vibration-free cavities which might be very useful in high-precision mechanical systems operating in a given frequency range. In an experiment one usually measures the reflection and/or transmission coefficients of an elastic wave incident on a finite slab of the phononic crystal and, consequently, theory should be able to provide reliable estimates of these, the experimentally measured quantities. The so-called on-shell methods developed in relation to photonic crystals can do exactly that, besides an accurate evaluation of the frequency band structure [2]-[4]. In these methods one views the crystal as a sequence of planes of scatterers parallel to a given surface: a crystallographic plane described by a two-dimensional (2D) lattice $\{\mathbf{R}_n\}$. The corresponding to $\{\mathbf{R}_n\}$ 2D reciprocal

* ipsarob@cc.uoa.gr

C.M. Soukoulis (ed.), *Photonic Crystals and Light Localization in the 21st Century*, 519–525.

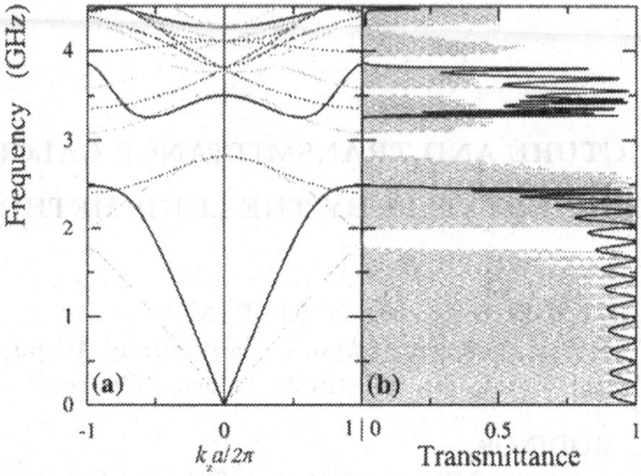

Figure 1. The frequency band structure normal to the (001) surface of an fcc crystal of silica spheres in ice (a); and the corresponding transmittance curve of a slab of 16 layers parallel to the same surface (b). The lattice constant is 1 μm and the radius of the spheres is 0.25 μm. In (a) the black lines represent longitudinal modes (in the sense defined in the text), the grey lines transverse modes, and the dotted lines are deaf bands. Correspondingly, in (b) the solid line shows the transmittance for normally incident longitudinal elastic waves; and the shaded curve that for normally incident transverse waves.

lattice we denote by $\{\mathbf{g}\}$. In the region between the nth and the $(n+1)$th planes a Bloch wave solution of the elastic-field equations, corresponding to a given frequency ω and a given reduced wave vector $\mathbf{k}_{\parallel}$ within the surface Brillouin zone (SBZ) of the given surface, has the form:

$$\mathbf{u}(\omega;\mathbf{k}_{\parallel}) = \sum_{\mathbf{g}} \mathbf{u}^{+}_{\mathbf{g}n} \exp\left[\mathrm{i}\mathbf{K}^{+}_{\mathbf{g}\nu}\cdot(\mathbf{r}-\mathbf{A}_n)\right] + \mathbf{u}^{-}_{\mathbf{g}n} \exp\left[\mathrm{i}\mathbf{K}^{-}_{\mathbf{g}\nu}\cdot(\mathbf{r}-\mathbf{A}_n)\right] , \quad (1)$$

where

$$\mathbf{K}^{\pm}_{\mathbf{g}\nu} = \left(\mathbf{k}_{\parallel}+\mathbf{g},\, \pm\left[(\omega/c_{\nu})^2-(\mathbf{k}_{\parallel}+\mathbf{g})^2\right]^{1/2}\right), \quad (2)$$

with $\nu = l$ (t) for the longitudinal (transverse) component of the field, and $\mathbf{A}_n$ is a point between the nth and $(n+1)$th planes. A generalized Bloch wave satisfies the equation

$$u^{\pm}_{\mathbf{g}n+1} = \exp\left(i\mathbf{k}\cdot\mathbf{a}_3\right) u^{\pm}_{\mathbf{g}n} , \quad (3)$$

where $\mathbf{a}_3 = \mathbf{A}_{n+1} - \mathbf{A}_n$ and $\mathbf{k} = (\mathbf{k}_{\parallel}, k_z(\omega;\mathbf{k}_{\parallel}))$.There are infinite many such solutions for given $\mathbf{k}_{\parallel}$ and ω, corresponding to different values of the z-component $k_z(\omega;\mathbf{k}_{\parallel})$ of the reduced wave vector $\mathbf{k}$, but in practice one needs to calculate only a finite number (a few tens at most) of these generalized Bloch waves. We have propagating waves [for these $k_z(\omega;\mathbf{k}_{\parallel})$ is real] which constitute the normal modes of the infinite crystal; and evanescent waves [for these $k_z(\omega;\mathbf{k}_{\parallel})$ is imaginary] which do not represent real waves, they are mathematical entities which enter directly or indirectly (depending on the method of calculation) into the evaluation of the reflection and transmission coefficients of a wave, with the same ω and $\mathbf{k}_{\parallel}$, incident on a slab of the crystal parallel to the given surface. On-shell methods have certain advantages over other band-structure methods, even if one is only interested in the frequency band structure and the corresponding normal modes of vibration of the infinite phononic crystal. In an on-shell method one can easily allow c_l and c_t of any of the constituent materials of the crystal to be complex and frequency dependent, as is necessary in some cases, without any difficulty, which is not the case with the ordinarily used plane-wave method [5]. And, as a rule, on-shell methods are also computationally more efficient [4, 6].

We have recently developed an on-shell method for phononic crystals [7] which constitutes an extension of the method some of us have developed for photonic crystals [3]. It applies to systems which consist of non-overlapping homogeneous spherical particles arranged periodically in a host medium characterized by different elastic coefficients. The basic ideas of the method are the same with those of the so-called layer Korringa-Kohn-Rostoker (LKKR) methods, initially developed to describe the multiple scattering of electrons in crystals [8]. The method provides the complex band structure [the functions $k_z(\omega; \mathbf{k}_\parallel)$] of the infinite phononic crystal associated with a given crystallographic plane (taken as the xy plane), which incorporates the ordinary frequency band structure of the crystal; and also the transmission, reflection, and absorption coefficients of an elastic wave incident at any angle on a slab of the crystal, parallel to the xy plane, of finite thickness. Moreover, one can calculate, by a slight variation of the method, the above quantities for a heterogeneous slab consisting of different planes of spheres, as long as these planes have the same 2D periodicity.

We demonstrate the applicability of our method by applying it, to begin with, to a specific example, which has also been considered by Sprik and Wegdam [5]: a system of silica spheres of radius $S = 0.25$ μm centered on the sites of an fcc lattice with a lattice constant $a = 1$ μm; the host material being ice. The relevant parameters are, for silica: $\rho = 2200$ Kgm^{-3}, $c_l = 5970$ ms^{-1}, $c_t = 3760$ ms^{-1}, and for ice (at -16 °C): $\rho = 940$ Kgm^{-3}, $c_l = 3830$ ms^{-1}, $c_t = 1840$ ms^{-1}. We view the crystal as a succcession of planes of spheres parallel to the (001) surface. Figure 1 shows the frequency band structure of the infinite crystal normal to the (001) plane ($\mathbf{k}_\parallel = \mathbf{0}$), and the corresponding transmission spectra for longitudinal and transverse waves incident normally on a slab of the crystal consisting of 16 layers (planes of spheres). Our results for the band structure, obtained with an angular momentum cutoff $\ell_{\max} = 4$ and 13 $\mathbf{g}$ vectors, are converged within an accuracy of 10^{-3}, and they agree with those of Sprik and Wegdam within the stated accuracy (of a few percent) of their results, which were obtained by the plane-wave method using 343 plane waves. Also, the transmission coefficient, easily obtainable by our method but not possible by the plane-wave method, confirms the validity of the band-structure calculation [see Figure 1b]. As expected, for frequencies within a gap the corresponding transmission coefficient vanishes. The eigenmodes of the phononic crystal are strictly speaking always hybrid, having a longitudinal and a transverse component, but along symmetry directions the following situation may arise. We consider for simplicity the normal modes corresponding to $\mathbf{k}_\parallel = \mathbf{0}$. In this case the component of the field described by Eq. (1) associated with the $\mathbf{g} = \mathbf{0}$ beam is either longitudinal or transverse; the field associated with

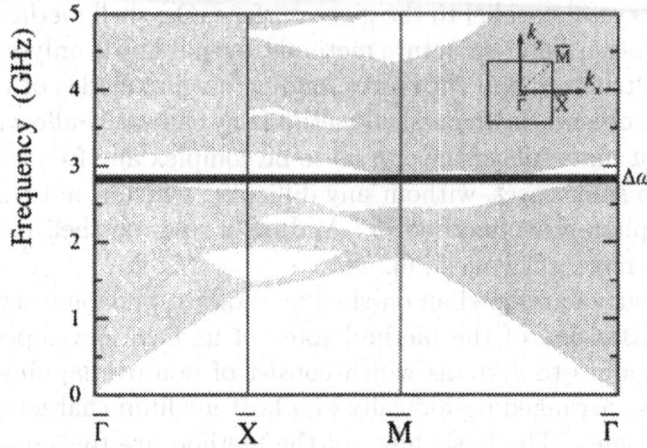

Figure 2. Projection of the frequency band structure on the SBZ of the (001) surface of the fcc phononic crystal described in the caption of Figure 1. The blank areas show the frequency gaps in the considered frequency region. The inset shows the SBZ of the (001) surface. The black strip corresponds to an absolute gap.

the $\mathbf{g} \neq \mathbf{0}$ components need not be of the same type. However, only the $\mathbf{g} = \mathbf{0}$ component couples to the external field (incident, reflected and transmitted waves), if $(\mathbf{k}_{\|} + \mathbf{g})^2 > (\omega/c_{l,t})^2$ for $\mathbf{g} \neq \mathbf{0}$. Therefore, an incident longitudinal or transverse wave will excite a mode (or modes) inside the crystal with a $\mathbf{g} = \mathbf{0}$ component of the same type. As long as the amplitude of the $\mathbf{g} = \mathbf{0}$ component of these modes is much greater than those of the $\mathbf{g} \neq \mathbf{0}$ components, which is the case in the example we have considered, the transmitted and reflected waves will be of the same type as the incident wave, but this need not be the case in general. The modes in Figure 1 are termed longitudinal or transverse in the above sense. For waves incident at an angle on the surface of the slab ($\mathbf{k}_{\|} \neq \mathbf{0}$) the above distinction between longitudinal and transverse waves no longer applies (the $\mathbf{g} = \mathbf{0}$ component of the elastic field inside the crystal is a hybrid one) and therefore an incident wave of a specific type (longitudinal or transverse) will give rise to reflected and transmitted waves of a mixed type. Finally, the oscillations in the transmittance curves are due to multiple reflections at the edges of the slab (Fabry-Pérot like oscillations).

In Figure 2 we show the projection of the frequency band structure on the surface Brillouin zone (SBZ) of the (001) plane along its symmetry lines. This is obtained, for a given $\mathbf{k}_{\|}$, as follows: the regions of ω for which there are no propagating states in the infinite crystal [the corresponding values of $k_z(\omega; \mathbf{k}_{\|})$ are all complex], are shown blank, against the light-shaded areas which correspond to regions over which propagating states do exist [for a given ω there is at least one Bloch wave with $k_z(\omega; \mathbf{k}_{\|})$ real]. We note the existence of a narrow absolute gap (black strip), of width $\Delta\omega_G$, extending from 2.82 to 2.89 GHz. An absolute gap at approximately the same frequency and of approximately the same width was found by Sprik and Wegdam [5].

Below this gap we have two bands of transverse waves, which are doubly de-

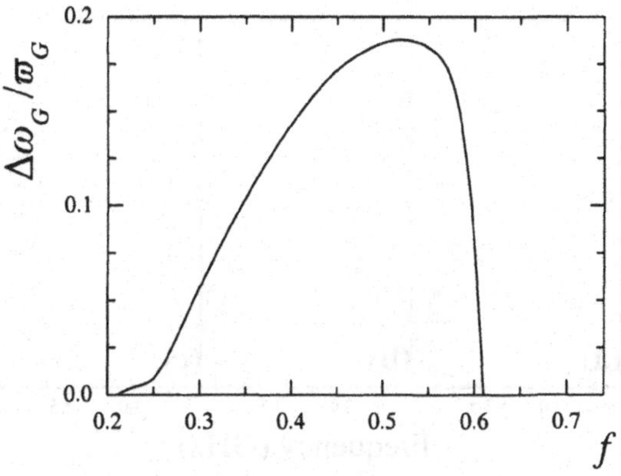

Figure 3. Gap width over midgap frequency versus volume filling fraction of an fcc phononic crystal of silica spheres in ice.

generate, extending from 0 to 1.77 GHz and from 2.01 to 2.82 GHz, with a gap in between. On the other hand, a non-degenerate band of longitudinal waves extends from 0 to 2.48 GHz. In addition to these bands, we find a non-degenerate deaf band, extending from 2.40 to 2.82 GHz. The $\mathbf{g} = \mathbf{0}$ component of the corresponding eigenmode of the elastic field vanishes, and, because the $\mathbf{g} = \mathbf{0}$ beam is the only one which matches (couples with) a propagating wave outside the crystal, this mode is not excited by an incident wave. Therefore, if this were the only band over the stated frequency region, the wave would be totally reflected. However, in our example, transmission through the slab in the frequency range of this deaf band occurs, because other bands with non-vanishing $\mathbf{g} = \mathbf{0}$ components exist in the same frequency region.

The long wavelength limit ($k_z \to 0$) is represented by the linear segments of the dispersion curves, the slopes of which determine the propagation velocities of longitudinal and transverse waves ($\bar{c}_l = 3893$ ms^{-1}, $\bar{c}_t = 2033$ ms^{-1}) in a corresponding effective medium.

We need not say anything more about the many bands which exist above the gap (see Figure 1).

In Figure 3, we show the ratio of the gap width to its respective midgap frequency ($\Delta\omega_G/\bar{\omega}_G$) against the volume fraction occupied by the silica spheres, f. Our results converge to an accuracy of 10^{-3} with an angular momentum cutoff $\ell_{\max} = 4$ and 13 $\mathbf{g}$ vectors at small f, but $\ell_{\max} = 7$ and 45 $\mathbf{g}$ vectors are needed to achieve the same accuracy at high volume filling fractions. It is seen that the maximum value of $\Delta\omega_G/\bar{\omega}_G$ is obtained for a value of f less than its possible maximum value (touching spheres), which shows that non-overlapping spheres (cermet topology) favor the formation of absolute frequency gaps in phononic crystals [9].

Next we consider a heterostructure: a slab consisting of five planes of spheres, one of which may be different from the other four; it has the same 2D periodicity

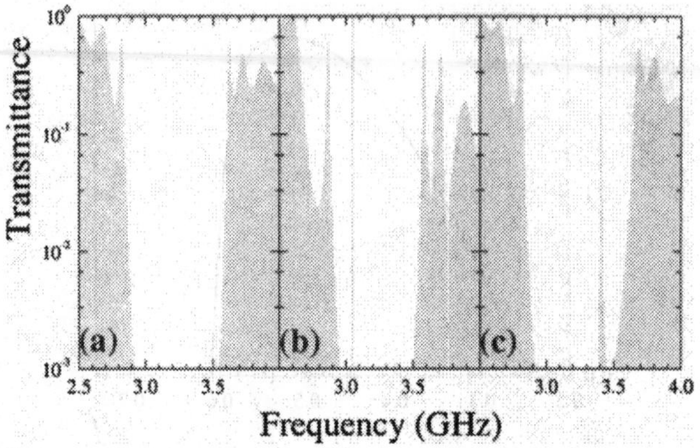

Figure 4. Transmittance of a transverse elastic wave incident normally on a slab of an fcc crystal of silica spheres in ice with lattice constant a. The slab consists of five planes of spheres parallel to the (001) surface. The spheres have a radius $S = 0.29a$, except those of the middle plane which have a different radius S_i [(a): $S_i = S$, (b): $S_i = 0.9S$, (c): $S_i = 0.7S$].

parallel to the surface of the slab as the other planes, but the spheres of this, so-called, impurity plane may be different: they have a smaller or larger radius than the spheres of the other planes. Our results are summarized in Figure 4, which shows the transmittance of a transverse elastic wave incident normally on the slab. For Figure 4a the spheres in all five planes are the same ($S = 0.29a$), and the transmittance vanishes, as expected, over the frequency region corresponding to the frequency gap of the infinite crystal for $\mathbf{k}_\parallel = \mathbf{0}$. For Figures 4b and 4c the middle plane is different from the other four; the spheres of this plane have a smaller radius: $S_i = 0.9S$ for Figure 4b and $S_i = 0.7S$ for Figure 4c, where $S = 0.29a$ is the radius of the spheres in the other planes. The transmission resonance that now appears at a frequency within the gap signifies the existence of a state of the elastic field centered on the impurity plane: a mode of vibration of the elastic field that extends to infinity parallel to the surface of the slab (in the manner of a Bloch wave), but decays rapidly normal to the impurity plane on either side of it. It appears that the normal mode of vibration (with $\mathbf{k}_\parallel = \mathbf{0}$) at the top of the valence band of the pure crystal (we use the term by analogy to semiconductor physics to denote the frequency band below the gap), splits off this band, becoming a localized (on the impurity plane) vibration, with a frequency higher in the gap the smaller the radius of the impurity spheres. The same happens, but to a lesser degree, for a longitudinal incident wave. We note that the transmission coefficient equals unity at the resonance frequency, when the impurity plane is the middle plane of the slab. When the impurity plane is removed from the center of the slab by one plane, the value of the transmission coefficient at resonance diminishes by at least two orders of magnitude, and the resonance disappears altogether when the impurity plane is removed to the surface of the slab [10].

Acknowledgements

I. E. Psarobas was partly supported by The University of Athens, and partly by the Institute of Communication and Computer Systems (ICCS) of the National Technical University of Athens.

References

1. Economou, E. N. and Sigalas, M. (1992) Elastic and acoustic wave band structure, *J. Sound Vib.* **158**, 377-382; Kushwaha, M. S., Halevi, P., Dobrzynski, L., and Djafari-Rouhani, B. (1993) Acoustic Band Structure of periodic elastic composites, *Phys. Rev. Lett.* **71**, 2022-2025.
2. Ohtaka, K. (1979) Energy band of photons and low-energy photon diffraction, *Phys. Rev. B* **19**, 5057-5067; Ohtaka, K. and Tanabe, Y. (1996) Photonic bands using vector spherical waves. Reflectivity, coherence and local field, *J. Phys. Soc. Jpn.* **65**, 2276-2284.
3. Stefanou, N., Karathanos, V., and Modinos, A. (1992) Scattering of electromagnetic waves by periodic structures, *J. Phys.: Condensed Matter* **4**, 7389-7400; Stefanou, N., Yannopapas, V., and Modinos, A. (1998) Heterostructures of photonic crystals: frequency bands and transmission coefficients, *Comput. Phys. Commun.* **113**, 49-77; Stefanou, N., Yannopapas, V., and Modinos, A. (2000) MULTEM 2: A new version of the program for transmission and band-structure calculations of photonic crystals, *Comput. Phys. Commun.* **132**, 189-196.
4. Pendry, J. B., and MacKinnon, A. (1992) Calculation of photon dispersion-relations, *Phys. Rev. Lett.* **69**, 2772-2775; Pendry, J. B. (1994) Photonic band structures, *J. Mod. Opt.* **41**, 209-229.
5. Sprik, R. and Wegdam, G. H. (1998) Acoustic band structure in composites of solids and viscous liquids, *Solid State Commun.* **106**, 77-81.
6. Qiu, Y., Leung, K. M., Carin, L., and Kralj, D. (1995) Dispersion-curves and transmission spectra of a 2-dinensional photonic band-gap crystal: Theory and experiment, *J. Appl. Phys.* **77**, 3631-3636.
7. Psarobas, I. E., Stefanou, N., and Modinos, A. (2000) Scattering of elastic waves by periodic arrays of spherical bodies, *Phys. Rev. B* **62**, 278-291.
8. Pendry, J. B. (1974) *Low Energy Electron Diffraction*, Academic Press, London; Modinos A. (1984) *Field, Thermionic and Secondary Electron Emission Spectroscopy*, Plenum Press, New York.
9. Economou, E. N. and Sigalas, M. M. (1993) Classical wave propagation in periodic structures: Cermet versus network topology, *Phys. Rev. B* **48**, 13434-13438.
10. Psarobas, I. E., Stefanou, N., and Modinos, A. (2000) Phononic crystals with planar defects, *Phys. Rev. B* **62**, 5536-5540.

MULTIPOLE METHODS FOR PHOTONIC CRYSTAL CALCULATIONS

N.A. NICOROVICI[1], A.A. ASATRYAN[1], L.C. BOTTEN[2], K. BUSCH[3], R. C. MCPHEDRAN[1], C. M. DE STERKE[1], P. A. ROBINSON[1], G.H. SMITH[2], D.R. MCKENZIE[1] and A.R. PARKER[4]
[1] *School of Physics, University of Sydney, NSW 2006, Australia*
[2] *School of Mathematical Sciences, University of Technology, Sydney, NSW 2007, Australia*
[3] *Department of Physics, University of Karlsruhe, P. O. Box 6980, 76128 Karlsruhe, Germany*
[4] *Department of Zoology, University of Oxford, South Parks Road, Oxford OX1 3PS, UK*

1. INTRODUCTION

There are a variety of general theories for computing band structures of photonic crystals, including finite difference methods[1], plane wave methods[2], and multipole methods[3]. While the finite difference and plane wave methods are more general in terms of the range of geometries to which they can be applied, the multipole (or Rayleigh) methods are computationally more efficient and superior in terms of their analytic tractability, coming into their own in derivations of theoretical modelling in areas such as long-wavelength localization and homogenization, and in predicting numerically-difficult outcomes (e.g. anomalously large absorption in crystals with fine metallic wires). In this paper, we outline the development of a multipole theory in a manner applicable to both finite and infinite, periodic structures. The former is applied in the computation of the local density of states (which gives emission probability as a function of position), while the latter is used in the computation of the band structure (including complex gap states) of photonic crystals and studies of disordered media, localization and homogenization.

2. THEORETICAL FORMULATION

Here, we develop a general framework that handles field problems for photonic crystals composed of finite or infinite collections of cylinders in either of the fundamental polarizations. The common thread is the use of the Rayleigh method[3] to develop a field identity expressing the regular part of the field (i.e., associated with the non-singular terms), in the vicinity of each cylinder, in terms of sources on all the other cylinders, plus contributions from other external sources. Outside the cylinders, the general form of the field $V(\mathbf{r})$,

C.M. Soukoulis (ed.), Photonic Crystals and Light Localization in the 21st Century, 527–534.

satisfying the Helmholtz equation ($\nabla^2 V + k^2\varepsilon(\mathbf{r})V = 0$), may be written as

$$V(\mathbf{r}) = \sum_{\ell \in C} \sum_{n=-\infty}^{\infty} B_n^\ell H_n^{(1)}(k\,|\mathbf{r} - \mathbf{r}_\ell|) \exp[in \arg(\mathbf{r} - \mathbf{r}_\ell)] + \text{other source terms}, \quad (1)$$

comprising outgoing waves sourced from the set of all cylinders C, plus other specified sources, possibly at infinity. In an annular region outside each cylinder ℓ, the field is expressed in a cylindrical harmonic series $V(\mathbf{r}) = \sum[A_n^\ell J_n(kr_\ell) + B_n^\ell H_n^{(1)}(kr_\ell)]e^{in\theta_\ell}$. Similarly, within each cylinder, $V(\mathbf{r}) = \sum[C_n^\ell J_n(k\nu_\ell r_\ell) + D_n^\ell H_n^{(1)}(k\nu_\ell r_\ell)]e^{in\theta_\ell}$, where ν_ℓ denotes the refractive index. The D_n terms providing for the possibility of a source within cylinder ℓ — are required for density of states calculations. Then, the Rayleigh field identity (derived using Green's Theorem), in the vicinity of cylinder ℓ, has the following form, where the E_n^ℓ denote contributions to the nth harmonic from external sources,

$$A_n^\ell = -i \sum_{j \in C} \sum_{m=-\infty}^{\infty} S_{n-m}^{\ell j} B_m^\ell + E_n^\ell. \quad (2)$$

The $S_n^{\ell j}$ arise from the expansion of outgoing waves from cylinders $j \neq \ell$ using Graf's addition theorem. Field continuity conditions at the interface of each cylinder yield relations of the form $B_n^\ell = R_n^\ell A_n^\ell + T_n^\ell D_n^\ell$, where the R_n^ℓ and T_n^ℓ are, respectively, cylindrical harmonic reflection and transmission coefficients for incoming regular (J_n) waves sourced on other cylinders and at infinity, and outgoing irregular waves ($H_n^{(1)}$) sourced within cylinder ℓ. Each harmonic term analytically satisfies the boundary conditions, a feature underpinning the method's efficiency and accuracy. The Rayleigh identity (2) and the above boundary conditions combine to form an inhomogeneous system of equations, whose solution yields the source coefficients from which the field may be reconstructed.

As is discussed later, the *local density of states* (LDOS) of a finite crystal is computed from the imaginary part of the Green's function G with coincident line source ($\mathbf{r}_s$) and field ($\mathbf{r}$) points. The Green's function $G(\mathbf{r}, \mathbf{r}_s; k) = (-i/4)H_0^{(1)}(k|\mathbf{r} - \mathbf{r}_s|)$ satisfies $[\nabla_{\mathbf{r}}^2 + k^2\varepsilon(\mathbf{r})]G(\mathbf{r}, \mathbf{r}_s; k) = \delta(\mathbf{r} - \mathbf{r}_s)$. In this case, the source contribution coefficients in (2) are given by $S_n^{\ell j} = H_n^{(1)}(kr_{\ell j})e^{-in\theta_{\ell j}}$ where $(r_{\ell j}, \theta_{\ell j}) = \mathbf{r}_\ell - \mathbf{r}_j$. For an inhomogeneous source term at $\mathbf{r} = \mathbf{r}_s$ exterior to all cylinders, we have $E_n^\ell = H_n^{(1)}(kr_{\ell s})e^{-in\theta_{\ell s}}$, while for an interior source, the form is more complex. The solution of the field identity then yields the $\{B_n^\ell\}$, from which the Green's function is reconstructed using (1).

The same theory may be used to model *photonic crystals* formed from finite or infinite stacks of laterally infinite gratings lying parallel to the xz plane and with generators aligned with the z-axis. For each grating, the period cell has length d_1 and contains N_c non-intersecting cylinders (of arbitrary radii, position and materials properties). For each grating, we derive [4] reflection and transmission scattering matrices by solving diffraction problems for all incidence channels p associated with a period d_1 structure with Bloch condition $\mathbf{E}(\mathbf{r} + d_1\widehat{\mathbf{x}}) = \mathbf{E}(\mathbf{r})\, e^{i\alpha_0 d_1}$. The incidence channels are characterized by direction sines and cosines $\alpha_p = \alpha_0 + 2\pi p/d_1$ and $\chi_p = (k^2 - \alpha_p^2)^{1/2}$ respectively.

Quasiperiodicity conditions reduce the field problem to the solution of the source coefficients B_n^ℓ in the central cell. The field identity is structurally identical to (2), with quasiperiodicity introducing contributions from periodic replicas of each cylinder of the central cell into the corresponding terms of $S_n^{\ell j}$. For periodic systems, the $S_n^{\ell j}$ are lattice sums[4] that are given by $S_n^{\ell\ell} = \delta_{n0} + \sum_{m\neq 0} H_n^{(1)}(|n|kd_1)e^{i\alpha_0 md_1}e^{in\arg(m)}$ and, for $\ell \neq j$ by, $S_n^{\ell j} = \sum_{m=-\infty}^{\infty} H_n^{(1)}(k|md_1\hat{\mathbf{x}} + \mathbf{c}_{\ell j}|)e^{i\alpha_0 md_1}e^{in\arg(mD\hat{\mathbf{x}}+\mathbf{c}_{\ell j})}$, where $\mathbf{c}_{\ell j}$ denotes the position of cylinder ℓ relative to j. External sources correspond to incident plane wave fields from either side of the grating, and their Fourier-Bessel expansions yields the coefficients E_n^ℓ in Eq. (2).

By solving (2), the source coefficients B_n^ℓ are used to reconstruct the plane wave fields directly above and below the grating, and by considering all possible incidence configurations, we may form plane-wave scattering matrices. For simplicity, we assume up-down symmetry (as arises for collinear placement of the cylinders) permitting a subdivision of the problem into symmetric ($\oplus$) and anti-symmetric ($\ominus$) parts. In matrix form, we have reflection and transmission matrices $\mathbf{R} = (\mathbf{S}^\oplus + \mathbf{S}^\ominus)/2$ and $\mathbf{T} = (\mathbf{S}^\oplus - \mathbf{S}^\ominus)/2$ with

$$\mathbf{S}^{\oplus/\ominus} = \pm\mathbf{I} \mp 2\mathbf{K}^{\oplus/\ominus}\left(\boldsymbol{\sigma}^{\oplus/\ominus} + i\mathbf{M}\right)^{-1}\mathbf{J}^{\oplus/\ominus}. \tag{3}$$

In what follows, we outline briefly the structure of the solution, referring readers to previous work[4] for details. In (3), the identity matrices represent scattering operators that are the solutions of the diffraction problem in the absence of the grating, and which correspond respectively to "magnetic" and "electric" mirrors on the line of symmetry ($y = 0$). The factor $\mathbf{J}$ denotes a change of basis from plane waves into cylindrical harmonics, while the factor $\mathbf{K}$ denotes a basis transformation in the opposite direction. The central factor $(\boldsymbol{\sigma} + i\mathbf{M})^{-1}$ is the scattering operator expressed in cylindrical harmonic basis and has two parts—the first term $\boldsymbol{\sigma}$ being a block matrix characterizing the structural geometry through the lattice sums, and the second term, $\mathbf{M}$, being a block diagonal matrix arising from the boundary conditions and encapsulating material properties of the cylinders.

The scattering matrices of the entire stack $(\mathcal{R}_s, \mathcal{T}_s)$ are formed from the scattering matrices of each layer $(\mathbf{R}_s, \mathbf{T}_s)$ through matrix recurrence relations. Thus, for a stack of gratings uniformly separated by h with propagation matrix $\mathbf{P} = \mathrm{diag}(\chi_p h)$,

$$\mathcal{R}_s = \mathbf{R}_s + \mathbf{T}_s\mathbf{P}\mathcal{R}_{s-1}\mathbf{P}(\mathbf{I} - \mathbf{R}_s\mathbf{P}\mathcal{R}_{s-1}\mathbf{P})^{-1}\mathbf{T}_s, \quad \mathcal{T}_s = \mathcal{T}_{s-1}\mathbf{P}(\mathbf{I} - \mathbf{R}_s\mathbf{P}\mathcal{R}_{s-1}\mathbf{P})^{-1}\mathbf{T}_s. \tag{4}$$

3. FROM SCATTERING MATRICES TO BAND DIAGRAMS

Plane wave scattering matrices may be used to determine the band structure of photonic crystals. Here, we extend a technique developed originally by McRae in low energy electron diffraction, and applied recently to photonic crystals by Gralak *et al.*[5]. We consider an infinite lattice, with basis vectors $\mathbf{e}_1 = (d_1, 0)$, $\mathbf{e}_2 = (d_2, d_3)$, composed of identical 1-D grating layers. Above ($j = 1$) and below ($j = 2$) the grating, fields are expanded in a plane wave basis with centred phase origins at ($x_j = \pm d_2/2, y_j = \pm d_3/2$):

$$V^{(j)}(x,y) = \frac{1}{\sqrt{d_1}}\sum_{p=-\infty}^{\infty} \chi_p^{-1/2}\left[f_p^{(j)-}e^{-i\chi_p(y-y_j)} + f_p^{(j)+}e^{i\chi_p(y-y_j)}\right]e^{i\alpha_p(x-x_j)}. \tag{5}$$

Relative to the coordinate origins (x_j, y_j), the field properties are expressed in terms of scattering matrices corresponding to incidence from both above $(\mathbf{R}, \mathbf{T})$, and from below

$(\mathbf{R}', \mathbf{T}')$, in the most general case. The general treatment of the scattering problem may be then expressed in terms of the $\mathcal{T}$-matrix as follows:

$$\mathcal{F}_2 = \mathcal{T}\mathcal{F}_1, \text{ where } \mathcal{F}_j = \begin{bmatrix} \mathbf{f}_j^- \\ \mathbf{f}_j^+ \end{bmatrix} \text{ and } \mathcal{T} = \begin{bmatrix} \mathbf{T} - \mathbf{R}'\mathbf{T}'^{-1}\mathbf{R} & \mathbf{R}'\mathbf{T}'^{-1} \\ -\mathbf{T}'^{-1}\mathbf{R} & \mathbf{T}'^{-1} \end{bmatrix}. \quad (6)$$

The band structure is then generated from the eigenvalue problem $\mathcal{T}\mathcal{F}_1 = \mu\mathcal{F}_1$ established from the Bloch-condition $V(\mathbf{r} + \mathbf{e}_2) = \mu V(\mathbf{r})$ satisfied by the fields, with $\mu = \exp(i\mathbf{k}_0 \cdot \mathbf{e}_2)$ and with $\mathbf{k}_0 = (\alpha_0, \beta_0)$. For up-down symmetric gratings arranged in rectangular or hexagonal lattices, however, it is possible to reformulate the eigenvalue problem, halving its dimension and simultaneously improving the numerical stability of the method. In the case of a rectangular array, the eigenproblem reduces to $\mathbf{F}_i^{-1}\mathbf{T}\mathbf{g}_i = (2c)^{-1}\mathbf{g}_i, i = 1, 2$, where $\mathbf{g}_i = \pm\mathbf{f}_1 + \mathbf{f}_2, \mathbf{F}_i = \mathbf{I} + (\mathbf{T} \mp \mathbf{R})(\mathbf{T} \pm \mathbf{R}))$, and $2c = \mu + \mu^{-1}$.

The eigenvalues of $\mathcal{T}$ may be partitioned according to their direction of propagation. Evanescent states (i.e. complex states in band gaps) are readily classified according to their magnitudes, with $|\mu| < 1$ and $|\mu| > 1$ respectively corresponding to forward and backward propagation. The classification of the propagating states, however, requires the y-component of the group velocity, proportional to $dk/d\beta_0 = \mathcal{E}_F/(k\mathcal{E}_D)$, the sign of which determines the propagation direction. Here, $\mathcal{E}_F$ and $\mathcal{E}_D$ respectively denote the energy flux and energy density per unit cell. From this, the eigenvalue equations are then similarly partitioned into forward and backward going sets, leading to the spectral decomposition $\mathcal{T} = \widetilde{\mathbf{F}}\widetilde{\mathbf{\Lambda}}\widetilde{\mathbf{F}}^{-1}$. The matrix $\widetilde{\mathbf{F}}$ is partitioned into left and right halves, respectively associated with forward ($\mathbf{F}$) and backward ($\mathbf{F}'$) propagation. In turn, both $\mathbf{F}$ and $\mathbf{F}'$ are partitioned into "eigenincidence" $\mathbf{F}_-$ and "eigenreflection" $\mathbf{F}_+$ matrices as in $\mathbf{F}^T = [\mathbf{F}_-^T \ \mathbf{F}_+^T]$, with corresponding definitions applying to $\mathbf{F}'$. The eigenvalues μ_i and μ_i' are similarly partitioned into diagonal matrices $\mathbf{\Lambda}$ and $\mathbf{\Lambda}'$.

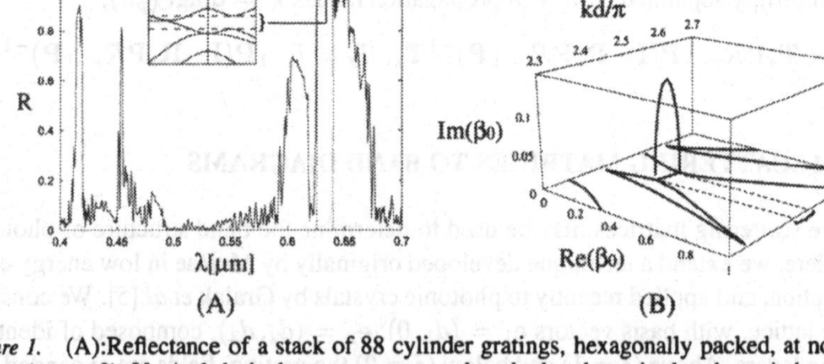

Figure 1. (A):Reflectance of a stack of 88 cylinder gratings, hexagonally packed, at normal incidence ($\alpha_0 = 0$). Vertical dashed curves correspond to the band gap in the photonic band diagram shown in the inset. (B): Complex band diagram for the partial gap of the sea mouse, showing the gap states. The brace in (A) and (B) indicates the location of the partial band gap.

In Fig. 1(A), we demonstrate the technique by calculating the complex band structure associated with a biological specimen, the sea mouse, which is a marine worm with a broad, segmented body found worldwide in shallow to moderately deep sea water. Its dorsal surface is covered by long, felt-like threads that, through some remarkable photonic engineering—the finest and most regular living structure identified in nature—yield a brilliant iridescence[6]. The stacking of 88 regular, hexagonally packed layers overcomes the low reflectance available from each layer and forms a partial band gap that is associated with high reflectance in the red at normal incidence. Fig. 1(B) displays the band gap in complex $\mathbf{k}_0$ space and the trajectory of the fundamental evanescent state crossing the gap.

Explicit forms of the reflection and transmission scattering matrices of finite crystals may be deduced from $\mathcal{T}_s = \mathcal{T}^s = \widetilde{\mathbf{F}}\widetilde{\mathbf{\Lambda}}^s\widetilde{\mathbf{F}}^{-1}$, their derivation revealing an important matrix $\mathbf{R}_\infty$, corresponding to reflection from a semi-infinite crystal. Its explicit form, $\mathbf{R}_\infty = \mathbf{F}_+\mathbf{F}_-^{-1}$, may be understood in terms of the "ratio" of the "eigenreflections" to the "eigenincidence". In a band gap, the net incident and reflected fluxes of each state are identical, a result embodied in the unitary form $\mathbf{R}_\infty^H\mathbf{R}_\infty = \mathbf{I}$ for the propagating order channels of the matrix and showing explicitly that the crystal behaves as a mirror.

Given $\mathbf{R}_\infty$, and its back propagation counterpart $\mathbf{R}'_\infty$, the scattering matrices for an s layer stack take the form $\mathbf{T}_s = (\mathbf{I}-\mathbf{R}'_\infty\mathbf{R}_\infty)[\mathbf{F}_-\mathbf{\Lambda}^{-s}\mathbf{F}_-^{-1}+\mathbf{F}'_-\mathbf{\Lambda}'^{-s}\mathbf{F}'^{-1}_-\mathbf{R}'_\infty\mathbf{R}_\infty]^{-1}$, the structure of which closely mirrors the corresponding scalar relationship for 1-D Fabry-Perot's interferometer. We note that the evaluation of $\mathbf{R}_\infty$ does not rely upon the full set of eigenvectors and, in fact, comparatively few eigenvectors are needed, with $\mathbf{F}_-^{-1}$ being computed as a generalized inverse through a singular value decomposition. At long wavelengths, $\mathbf{R}_\infty$ provides a mechanism by which the effective permittivity can be deduced. At these wavelengths, the specular order is the significant element, defining a reflection coefficient from which an effective refractive index and permittivity may be deduced.

4. DISORDERED PHOTONIC CRYSTALS

A significant issue in the design of photonic devices is their tolerance to imperfections, a problem closely related to the effects of disorder on their transmission properties. Despite its significance, only relatively few papers[7] have considered the matter. Here, we consider the effects of disorder on the transmittance of 2-D photonic crystals.

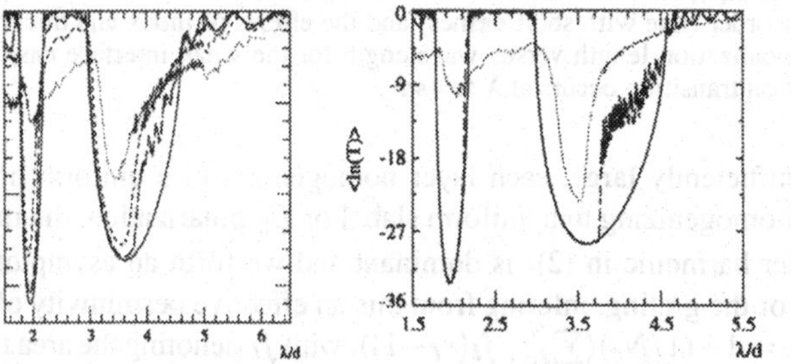

(A) (B)

Figure 2. $\langle \ln T \rangle$ versus λ for $E_{\|}$ polarization. (A): Effect of index disorder for $Q_\nu = 0$ (solid), 0.2 (dashed), 0.4 (short dashed), 0.8 (dotted). (B): Effect of radius disorder for $Q_a = 0$ (solid), $0.01d$ (dashed) and $0.08d$ (dotted).

Fig. 2(A) shows the ensemble averages over 100 realizations of the logarithm of the transmittance in $E_{\|}$ polarization for *refractive index disorder*. The refractive indices of the cylinders are given by $\nu_\ell = \bar{\nu} + \delta_\ell$, with δ_ℓ distributed uniformly in the interval

$[-Q_\nu, Q_\nu]$, and $\bar{\nu} = 3$. The structure consists of $s = 10$ grating layers characterized by $N_c = 5$ equally spaced ($d = 1$) cylinders per period ($d_1 = 5$). The effect of disorder is strongest in the first gap ($3 \leq \lambda/d \leq 5$), and most prominent on the long λ side.

Fig. 2(B) shows the effects of *radius disorder*. Here, the radii are given by $a_\ell = \bar{a} + \delta_l$, where δ_l is distributed uniformly with $\delta_l \in [-Q_a, Q_a]$. In Fig. 2(B), $\bar{a} = 0.3d$, for $N_c = 10$ equally spaced cylinders per period ($d_1 = 10$) and $s = 20$ layers. Again, the effects of randomness are most pronounced in the first gap, with disorder inducing "resonances" between $3.8 < \lambda/d < 4.5$ in the first gap. The behaviour is generally similar to that of index disorder, although with slightly more pronounced resonances, the number of which varies in proportion to the stack length, leading us to the conclusion that resonant behavior is essentially that of a randomized interferometer.

Figure 3(A) shows the effects of a combination of randomness (for a square lattice with $\bar{\nu} = 3$ and $\bar{a} = 0.3d$) with strong disorder in refractive index ($Q_\nu = 1.5$), radius ($Q_a = 0.1d$), vertical separation ($Q_h = 0.05d$) and lateral position of layers (i.e. sliding of layers) ($Q_x = 0.5d$). Index and radius disorder have by far the greatest effect and are able to eliminate any band structure[7]. Similar results apply to $H_{||}$ polarization.

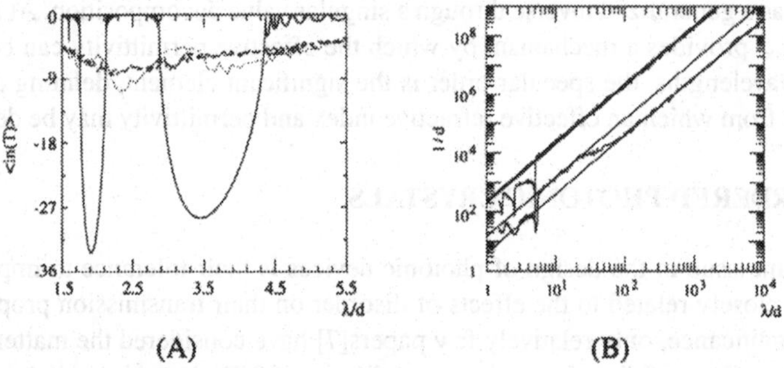

Figure 3. (A): Combination of strong disorder for $E_{||}$ polarization. Results are shown for the regular structure (solid line), the combination of all four types of disorder (dashed line), the effects of index and radius disorder (line with short dashes) and the effects of index and thickness disorder (dotted line). (B): Localization length versus wavelength for the weak interface case. The localization to homogenization transition occurs at $\lambda \approx 4sd$.

For λ sufficiently large, each layer homogenizes to a uniform film, with the stack eventually homogenizing to a uniform slab. For $E_{||}$ polarization, the monopole term (i.e. the 0th order harmonic in (2)) is dominant and we form an asymptotic estimate of the reflectance of the grating, infering from this an effective permittivity of the homogenized layer, $\langle\varepsilon_{\text{eff}}\rangle = 1 + (1/N_c)\langle\sum_{\ell=1}^{N_c} f_\ell(\varepsilon_\ell - 1)\rangle$, with f_ℓ denoting the area fraction of cylinder ℓ. For $E_{||}$ polarization, the specular order is the only significant channel of communication between layers and thus, for statistically equivalent layers, the structure eventually homogenizes to a uniform slab of the same permittivity. For $H_{||}$ polarization the situation is different, requiring both monopole and dipole terms. Taking ensemble averages and assuming that the cylinders each occupy the same area fraction, we derive the Maxwell-Garnett formula $\langle\varepsilon_{\text{eff}}\rangle = 1 + 2f/[(\bar{\varepsilon}+1)/(\bar{\varepsilon}-1) - fS_2/\pi]$ (for weak disorder only). For a single layer, the static dipole lattice sum is $S_2 = \pi^2/3$, while for an infinite array $S_2 = \pi$ due to both specular and evanescent order coupling between layers[7].

Localization occurs when waves undergo multiple scattering off a random potential and is characterized by the localization length l defined by $l/d = -\lim_{s\to\infty} 2s/\langle \ln T\rangle$ where T is the transmittance of the stack of s layers, each of thickness d. When each layer has homogenized, an asymptotic analysis[7] gives the localization length by

$$\frac{d}{l} \approx -\frac{\langle \ln T\rangle}{2s} = \frac{\alpha^2}{8}\left[\langle \eta^2\rangle + N(\alpha, s)\tilde{\varepsilon}^2\right], \tag{7}$$

where $\tilde{\varepsilon} = \langle \varepsilon_s\rangle - 1$, $\alpha = kd$ and η denotes the random component of the dielectric constant with zero mean. The first term, involving $\langle \eta^2\rangle$, does not depend on the stack length and determines the true localization length l. The second term is length dependent and describes the multiple reflections between the first and last interfaces of the isotropic stack, representing the eventual homogenization of the entire structure. For short wavelengths, the term $N(\alpha, s) = 2 + [\sin(s\alpha)\sin(s-2)\alpha]/(s\sin^2\alpha)$ has a magnitude of approximately unity and switches quite suddenly to the number of the layers in the stack at long wavelengths. The crossover between localization and homogenization occurs when $\lambda \approx 4sd$, the longest wavelength for which a quarter wave fits into the stack. Fig. 3(B) shows the variation of l/d with λ, and displays asymptotes generated from the pure localization terms and the combined localization and homogenization terms.

5. DENSITIES OF STATES

A key quantity determining the radiation dynamics of atoms in a photonic crystal is the spatially resolved, or local, density of states $\rho(\mathbf{r}; k)$. It gives the coupling strength of an atom to the modes of the crystal at wavenumber k and position $\mathbf{r}$, and encapsulates how the photonic crystal affects an atom's emission rate. It has been calculated before for an *infinite* photonic crystal[8]. In the band gaps of these structures the LDOS vanishes and there is no coupling between an atom and the radiation field. Here, we calculate the LDOS for *finite* structures, in which the density of states may be low but not zero, and with a line source, rather than a point source. These results thus pertain directly to emission measurements of finite samples. The LDOS is given by

$$\rho(\mathbf{r}; k) = -\frac{2k}{\pi c}\mathrm{Im}[G(\mathbf{r}, \mathbf{r}; k)], \tag{8}$$

where $G(\mathbf{r}, \mathbf{r}_S; k)$ is the electromagnetic Green's function for a line source at $\mathbf{r}_S$ and observation at $\mathbf{r}$. Below we show results for $\rho(\mathbf{r}; k)$ for a two-dimensional square array with lattice constant $d = 1$ of 81 circular cylinders of radius $a = 0.3d$ and refractive index $\nu = 3$ in vacuum, in which the electric field ia aligned with the cylinder axes.

The Green's function is formed with the techniques of Sec. 2 and the LDOS computed according to (8). The solid line in Fig. 4(A) is identical to the solid lines in Figs. 2, and shows two low-transmission regions. Fig. 4(B) gives $\pi c\rho(\mathbf{r}; k)/(2k)$ for $\lambda/d = 3.5$, near the centre of the first low-transmission region, while Fig. 4(C) is for $\lambda/d = 2.5$, where the transmission is high. From Fig. 4(B) we see that $\rho(\mathbf{r}; k)$ is small everywhere in the interior of the structure, and that there is a boundary layer with a thickness of roughly a single lattice constant. In the central region of the central unit cell, $\rho(\mathbf{r}; k)$ is about 3.3×10^{-5}, almost four orders of magnitude smaller than the vacuum level of 0.25. Thus, the emission by a line antenna located here is drastically reduced. From Fig. 4(C) we see that the $\rho(\mathbf{r};k)$ does not decrease inside the structure and varies around the vacuum value. However, there are notable features inside the central Wigner-Seitz cell, as shown in the inset. For this wavelength $\rho(\mathbf{r};k)$ is as high as 0.87—much larger than the vacuum value.

The dashed line in Fig. 4(A) is the total density of states $\rho(k) = \langle \varepsilon(\mathbf{r})\rho(\mathbf{r};k)\rangle$ computed by averaging the LDOS over the central Wigner-Seitz cell of the cluster. While a high transmission T always corresponds to a large density of states, the converse is not true, as exemplified by $3.8 < \lambda/d < 5.0$ for which the T is low, yet the DOS is high. The transmission spectrum in Fig. 4(A) is for normal incidence, while for non-normal incidence, the low-transmission region shifts to shorter wavelengths, indicating the presence of states (included in the LDOS) that are not accessible at normal incidence. This argument can be cast also in the language of infinite media, though the finite structures we are dealing with makes this somewhat hazardous. Normal incidence transmission depends only on states on the periodic edge of the Brillouin zone, while the LDOS and the DOS samples the entire Brillouin zone. Indeed, a calculation of the band structure along the anti-periodic edge of the Brillouin zone reveals states in $3.8 < \lambda/d < 5.0$.

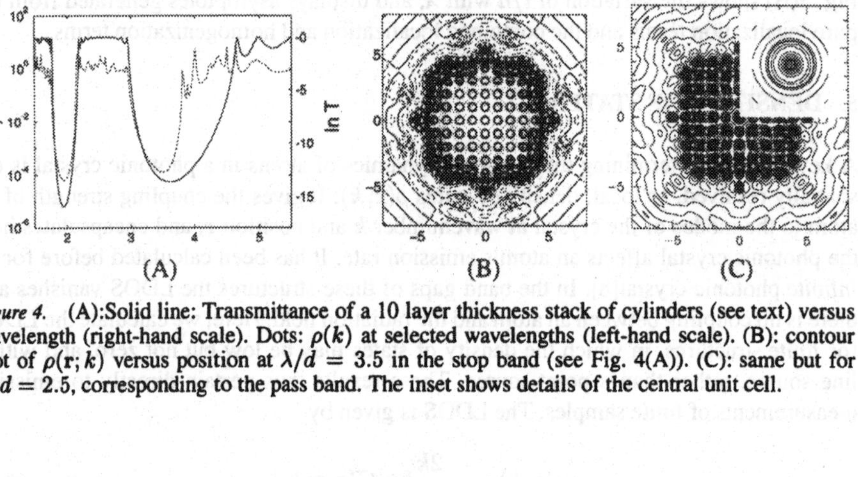

(A) (B) (C)

Figure 4. (A):Solid line: Transmittance of a 10 layer thickness stack of cylinders (see text) versus wavelength (right-hand scale). Dots: $\rho(k)$ at selected wavelengths (left-hand scale). (B): contour plot of $\rho(\mathbf{r};k)$ versus position at $\lambda/d = 3.5$ in the stop band (see Fig. 4(A)). (C): same but for $\lambda/d = 2.5$, corresponding to the pass band. The inset shows details of the central unit cell.

References

1. J. B. Pendry and A. MacKinnon, Phys. Rev. Lett. **69**, 2772 (1992); M. M. Sigalas *et al.*, Phys. Rev. B **52**, 11744 (1995).
2. K. M. Ho, C. T. Chan, and C. M. Soukoulis, Phys. Rev. Lett. **65**, 3152 (1990).
3. N. A. Nicorovici, R. C. McPhedran, and L. C. Botten, Phys. Rev. E **52**, 1135 (1995); K. Ohtaka, Phys. Rev. B **19**, 5057 (1979); Y. Qiu *et al.*, J. Appl. Phys. **77**, 3631 (1995); N. Stefanou, V. Yannopapas and A. Modinos, Comput. Phys. Comm. **113**, 49 (1998).
4. R. C. McPhedran *et al.*, Aust. J. Phys. **52**, 791 (1999); L. C. Botten *et al.*, J. Opt. Soc. Am. A **17** (2000), in press; D. Felbacq *et al.*, J. Opt. Soc. Am. A **11**, 2526 (1994).
5. E. G. McRae, Surface Science **11**, 479 (1968); Surface Science **11**, 492 (1968); B. Gralak, S. Enoch, and G. Tayeb, J. Opt. Soc. Am. A **17**, 1012 (2000).
6. A. R. Parker *et al.*, Nature (2000), in press.
7. M. M. Sigalas *et al.*, Phys. Rev. B, **53**, 8340 (1996); A. A. Asatryan *et al.*, Phys. Rev. E **60**, 6118 (1999); A. A. Asatryan *et al.*, Phys. Rev. E **62** (1999), in press.
8. S. John and K. Busch, J. Lightwave Technol. **17**, 1931 (1999).

UNDERSTANDING SOME PHOTONIC BAND GAP PROBLEMS BY USING PERTURBATION

Z. Q. ZHANG, X. ZHANG, Z-Y. LI, T-H. LI and C. T. CHAN
Department of Physics, Hong Kong University of Science and Technology, Clear Water Bay, Kowloon, Hong Kong

1. Introduction

During the past decade, a significant effort has been devoted to the study of photonic crystals (PC) [1-2]. The existence of a spectrum gap in PC provides an opportunity to confine and control the propagation of electromagnetic waves. It can give rise to some peculiar physical phenomena, as well as wide applications in several scientific and technical areas [2-3]. Since all the novel properties as well as the application of PC rely on the existence of photonic band gaps (PBG), it is essential to design a crystal structure that can produce a large spectrum gap. Despite the tremendous progress that has been made in this direction, it remains an important issue to find a generic method that allows us to engineer a gap. In this work, as the first example of using the perturbative approach to the study of PC, we show that a perturbation analysis can provide us a simple, systematic, and efficient way to engineer an existing PBG.

Nonuniformities inevitably occur in the fabrication of PCs, especially when the crystals are of micrometer and submicrometer sizes. How various kinds of randomness may affect the quality of a PBG have been studied in the past [4-6]. By extending the perturbation analysis to a disordered PC, we can explain why a gap is robust against the randomness in the positions of the scatterers and sensitive to the randomness in the size of the scatterers.

Inverse-opal techniques provide a promising route of fabricating 3D PC with a full band gap in the visible and infrared regimes. In the third example, we will use perturbativa analysis to explain why an incomplete infiltration has a larger PBG in an inverse opal PC. By careful mode analysis, we see that the enlargement of the PBG due to incomplete infiltration in inverse opal is the result of subtle changes in the photonic bands at two particular k-points in the Brillouin zone due to the depletion of high dielectric material.

2. The Engineering of Photonic Band Gaps

In a PC with a periodic dielectric constant $\varepsilon(\vec{r})$, a Bloch state for the magnetic field at the nth band and wave vector $\vec{k}$ satisfies the Maxwell equation

C.M. Soukoulis (ed.), Photonic Crystals and Light Localization in the 21st Century, 535–544.

$c^2\nabla\times[\varepsilon^{-1}(\vec{r})\nabla\times\vec{H}_{n\vec{k}}(\vec{r})]=\omega_{n\vec{k}}^2\vec{H}_{n\vec{k}}(\vec{r})$, where the eigenfrequencies $\omega_{n\vec{k}}$ give the band structures [2]. Here we would like to know how the eigenfrequencies at two band edge states would respond to the change of microstructures in the system. For a small change of the dielectric constant, $\delta\varepsilon(\vec{r})=\tilde{\varepsilon}(\vec{r})-\varepsilon(\vec{r})$, the new eigenfrequency $\tilde{\omega}_{n\vec{k}}$ can be estimated from the first-order perturbation theory, which gives [8]

$$\left(\frac{\tilde{\omega}_{n\vec{k}}}{\omega_{n\vec{k}}}\right)^2-1\approx\frac{\int[\tilde{\varepsilon}^{-1}(\vec{r})-\varepsilon^{-1}(\vec{r})]\,|\vec{D}_{n\vec{k}}(\vec{r})|^2\,d\vec{r}}{\int\varepsilon^{-1}(\vec{r})\,|\vec{D}_{n\vec{k}}(\vec{r})|^2\,d\vec{r}},\tag{1}$$

where the displacement field satisfies $\vec{D}_{n\vec{k}}(\vec{r})=(-ic/\omega_{n\vec{k}})\nabla\times\vec{H}_{n\vec{k}}(\vec{r})$ and the integration is performed in a unit cell. Equation (1) provides a simple way to estimate the shift in eigenfrequency due to the change of microstructure. For the two Bloch states at the band edges of a gap, we denote the shifts as $\Delta\omega_l=\tilde{\omega}_{nL}-\omega_{nL}$ and $\Delta\omega_u=\tilde{\omega}_{mU}-\omega_{mU}$, where L and U represent the symmetry points of the band structures at the lower and upper edges of the gap, respectively. It is their relative change, $\Delta\omega_g=\Delta\omega_u-\Delta\omega_l$, that determines the enlargement or reduction of the gap. The value of $\Delta\omega_g$ can be positive or negative, depending sensitively on the difference in the field-energy distribution of the two states at the band edges as well as the change of microstructure. For instance, let us consider the case of inserting a third component scatterer in each unit cell. In this case $\tilde{\varepsilon}^{-1}(\vec{r})-\varepsilon^{-1}(\vec{r})$ is nonzero, say δ, only at the insertion position. If the minimum of $|D_{nL}|^2$ occurs at the same position as the maximum of $|D_{mU}|^2$, an optimal enlargement of the gap can be achieved by inserting a third component with positive δ at this position. A negative δ can also enhance the gap, if $|D_{nL}|^2$ is at the maximum at the insertion position, whereas $|D_{mU}|^2$ is at the minimum. Thus, Eq. (1) provides a useful guide for the engineering of gaps in 3D PCs or 2D PCs with p-polarized waves.

For s waves in 2D PCs, we use the electric field that is perpendicular to the 2D plane to describe a Bloch state. The Maxwell equation in a scalar form can be written as $[c^{-2}\omega_{n\vec{k}}^2\varepsilon(\vec{r})+\nabla^2]E_{n\vec{k}}(\vec{r})=0$. The perturbation theory now gives [8]

$$\left(\frac{\tilde{\omega}_{n\vec{k}}}{\omega_{n\vec{k}}}\right)^2-1\approx\frac{\int[\varepsilon(\vec{r})-\tilde{\varepsilon}\ (\vec{r})]\,|E_{n\vec{k}}(\vec{r})|^2\,d\vec{r}}{\int\varepsilon(\vec{r})\,|E_{n\vec{k}}(\vec{r})|^2\,d\vec{r}}.\tag{2}$$

In the following, we show explicitly the method by using Eq. (2). The system we considered here consists of a square array of air cylinders with radii R and dielectric constant $\varepsilon_c=1$ in a background of dielectric constant $\varepsilon_b=11.4$ [7]. The calculated band structures with R=0.485*a* are plotted in Fig. 1, where *a* denotes the lattice constant. In terms of the dimensionless frequency $\nu \equiv \omega a / 2\pi c$, the first gap appears from $\nu_{1M} \cong 0.249$ to $\nu_{2X} \cong 0.314$, whereas the second gap appears from $\nu_{3X} \cong 0.450$ to $\nu_{4\Gamma} \cong 0.490$. The corresponding eigenfunctions $E_{n\bar{k}}(\bar{r})$ for the band-edge states $1M$, $2X$, $3X$, and 4Γ are plotted in Fig. 2 in a unit cell, where the corners of the unit cell correspond to the centers of air cylinders. The insertion is made by an air cylinder ($\varepsilon_i = 1$) of radius R_i at the center of each unit cell. Thus, we have $\delta \equiv \varepsilon_i^{-1} - \varepsilon_b^{-1} \cong 0.91 > 0$. For the original system, we have used the multiple-scattering method to calculate the band structures $\omega_{n\bar{k}}$, eigenfields $|E_{n\bar{k}}(\bar{r})|$, and gap positions [9,10]. After the insertion of air cylinders, we estimate the new gap positions by using Eq. (2) and plot the results as a function of the ratio $\beta \equiv R_i / R$ by dashed and solid lines in Fig. 3 for the first and second gaps, respectively. Since the function $|E_{n\bar{k}}(\bar{r})|$ has its minimum at the insertion position for states $2X$ and $3X$, the upper edge of the first gap and the lower edge of the second gap remains unaffected. However, for the states at $1M$ and 4Γ, $|E_{n\bar{k}}(\bar{r})|$ becomes a maximum at the insertion position. Thus, both the lower edge of the first gap and upper edge of the second gap increase with β. As a result, the first gap is reduced while the second gap is enlarged. For comparison, we also plot in Fig. 3 the calculated gap position obtained from the multiple-scattering approach by solid circles and triangles, respectively. The excellent agreement between the estimated and calculated results demonstrates the validity of the method and the accuracy of Eq. (2) when $\beta < 0.2$. We can also enlarge the first gap by choosing a different insertion. We observe that $|E_{n\bar{k}}(\bar{r})|$ is small for 1M state at the center of the air cylinder, but it is large for 2X state. Thus, by inserting a metallic cylinder with a negative dielectric constant at this

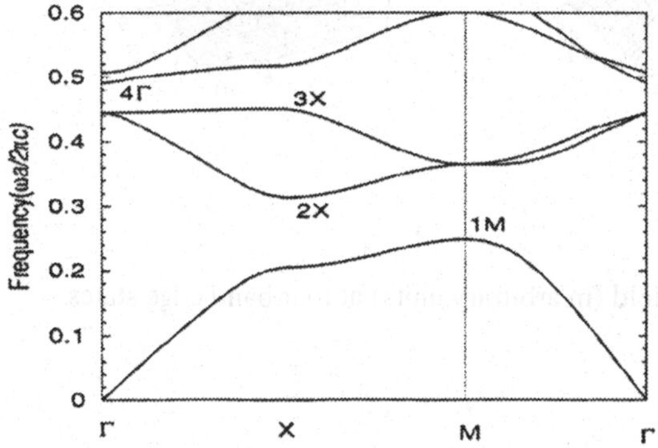

Figure 1. Calculated band structure for s waves with $\varepsilon_r = 1$, $\varepsilon_b = 11.4$ and R=0.485*a*.

position, the upper band edge should shift to higher frequency with the lower edge unchanged. The results of such metallic insertion are shown in Fig. 3 as open circles and squares for the first and second gaps, respectively. Indeed, the first gap is significantly enlarged. Similarly, the second gap is also enhanced. For the case of p waves, the magnetic field is parallel to the cylinder axis and Eq. (1) can guide us to enlarge a gap effectively. Thus, by combining Eqs. (1) and (2), we are able to enhance an absolute gap as well [8].

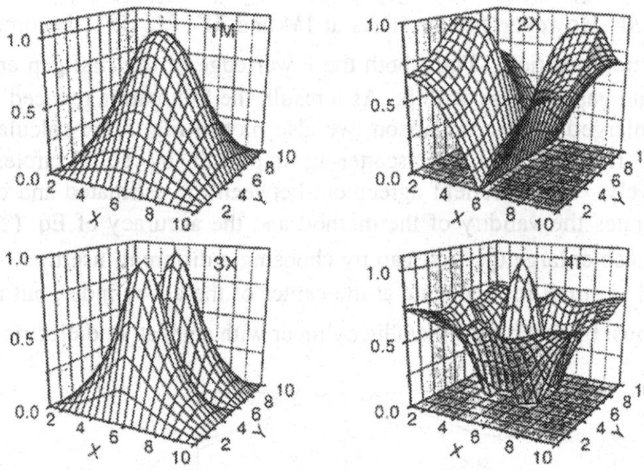

Figure 2. Distribution of electric field (in arbitrary units) at four band edge states.

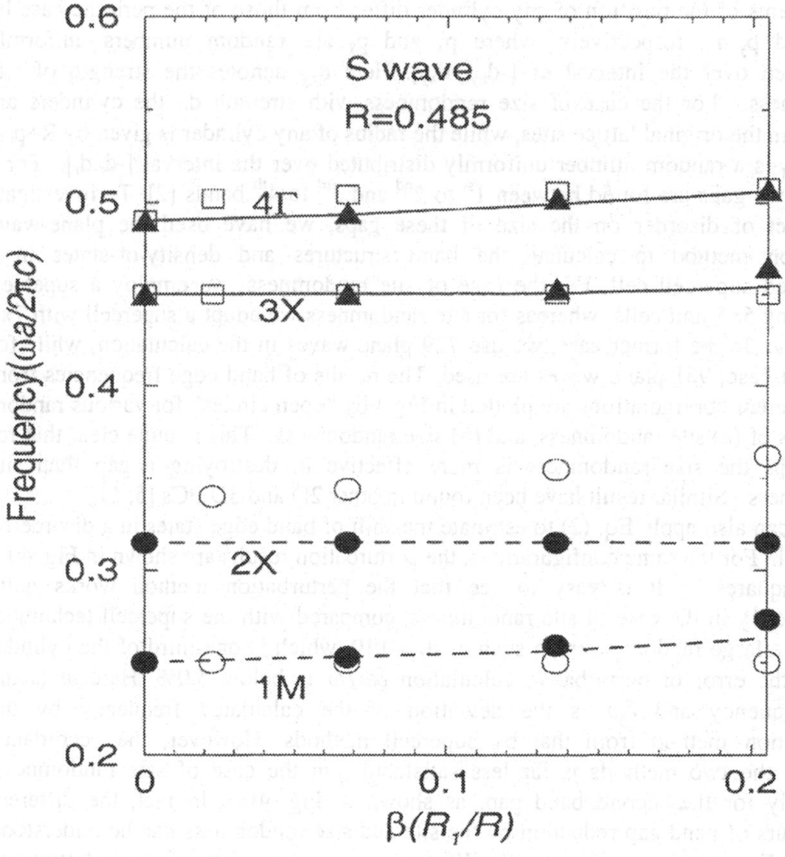

Figure 3. Band edge frequencies after the insertion of air cylinders of radii R_i. The dashed and solid lines denote the estimated results. The solid circles and triangles denote the calculated gaps. The open circles and squares are the results of inserting a metallic cylinder inside the air cylinder of the original system.

3. Disordered Photonic Crystals Understood by the Perturbation Formalism

The above perturbative analysis can also help us understand why a gap size is sensitive to one kind of disorder, while insensitive to another kind of disorder. Here we consider two kinds of randomness: site randomness and size randomness. As an example, we consider a 2D PC in a square lattice with dielectric cylinders in air ($\varepsilon_b = 1$). The cylinder has radius R=0.309*a* and dielectric constant $\varepsilon_c = 12.96$. In the case of site randomness, every cylinder has the same radius R. The x and y components of the position of any cylinder differ from those of the periodic case by $p_x\, a$ and $p_y\, a$, respectively, where p_x and p_y are random numbers uniformly distributed over the interval of $[-d_{xy}, d_{xy}]$. Here d_{xy} denotes the strength of site randomness. For the case of size randomness with strength d_r, the cylinders are arrayed in the original lattice sites, while the radius of any cylinder is given by $R+p_r a$ where p_r is a random number uniformly distributed over the interval $[-d_r, d_r]$. For s waves, two gaps are found between 1st to 2nd and 3rd to 4th bands [2]. To investigate the effect of disorder on the size of these gaps, we have used the plane-wave expansion method to calculate the band structures and density-of-states in a disordered supercell cell. For the case of site randomness, we employ a supercell containing 5x5 unit cells, whereas for site randomness we adopt a supercell with 7x7 unit cells. In the former case, we use 729 plane waves in the calculation, while for the latter case, 961 plane waves are used. The results of band edge frequencies from five different configurations are plotted in Fig.4 by "open circles" for various random strengths of (a) site randomness, and (b) size randomness. This is quite clear that for both gaps the size randomness is more effective in destroying a gap than site randomness. Similar result have been found in other 2D and 3D PCs [5, 11].

We can also apply Eq. (2) to estimate the shift of band edge states in a disordered supercell. For the same configurations, the perturbation results are shown in Fig. 4 by "open squares." It is easy to see that the perturbation method works quite satisfactorily in the case of site randomness, compared with the supercell technique. Even at a large random strength such as $d_{xy}=0.10$, which is one-third of the cylinder radius, the error of perturbative calculation $\delta\omega/\omega$ is below 5.0%. Here ω is the edge-frequency and $\delta\omega$ is the deviation of the calculated frequency by the perturbation method from that by supercell methods. However, the accordance between the two methods is far less satisfactory in the case of size randomness, especially for the second band gap, as shown in Fig. 4(b). In fact, the different behaviours of band gap reduction by the site and size randomness can be understood by using Eq. (2) in a single unit cell. When a cylinder is displaced from its lattice site, the frequency shift is

$$\left(\frac{\tilde{\omega}_{n\bar{k}}}{\omega_{n\bar{k}}}\right)^2 - 1 \approx \frac{[\varepsilon_r - 1]\{\int_{S_1} |E_{n\bar{k}}(\bar{r})|^2\, d\bar{r} + \int_{S_2} |E_{n\bar{k}}(\bar{r})|^2\, d\bar{r}\}}{\int_S \varepsilon(\bar{r})\,|E_{n\bar{k}}(\bar{r})|^2\, d\bar{r}}, \tag{3}$$

where S_1 is the region which is in the cylinder before displacement and now in the air, and S_2 is just the inverse. Notes S_1 and S_2 have the same area. Due to the continuity of the electric field at cylinder surface, the field in S_1 and S_2 does not differ much at a weak disorder. Then, the field integration in these two regions will cancel each other. Therefore, the frequency shift is small. In the case of size randomness, the frequency shift becomes

$$\left(\frac{\tilde{\omega}_{n\bar{k}}}{\omega_{n\bar{k}}}\right)^2 - 1 \approx \frac{\pm[\varepsilon_c - 1]\{\int_{S_3} |E_{n\bar{k}}(\bar{r})|^2 \, d\bar{r}\}}{\int_S \varepsilon(\bar{r}) |E_{n\bar{k}}(\bar{r})|^2 \, d\bar{r}}, \tag{4}$$

where S_3 is the region where the dielectric function changes, "+" and "-" apply when the radius of the cylinder reduces and grows, respectively. As no cancellation effect occurs, it is clear that the frequency shift by such a size fluctuation is far more significant than in the case of site randomness.

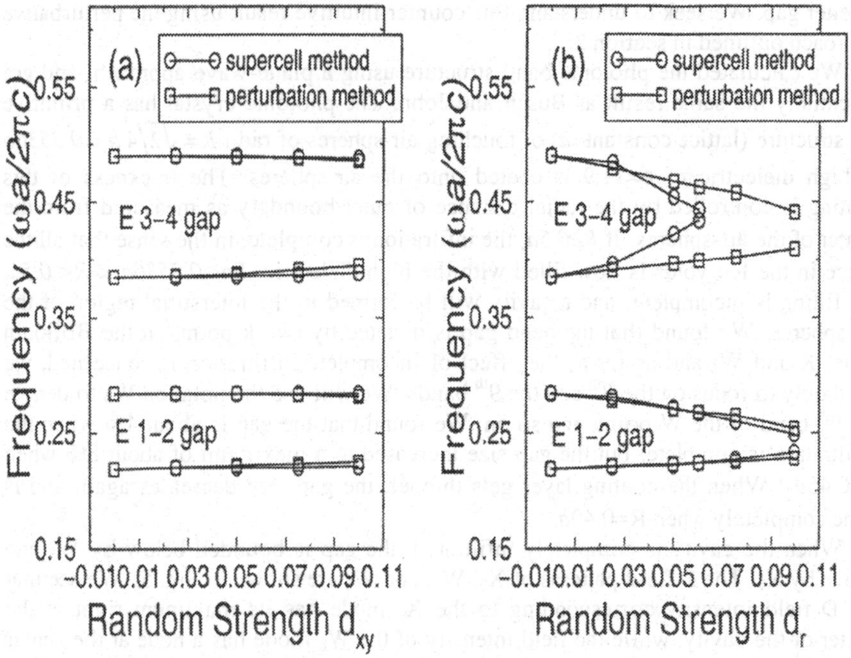

Figure 4. Band edge frequencies calculated by the supercell and perturbation methods, respectively. (a) site randomness, and (b) size randomness.

4. Incomplete Infiltration and a Large Photonic Gap in Inverse Optical Photonic Crystals

The "inverse opal" method [13] is a promising technique to fabricate photonic band gap material at optical wavelength. This method infiltrates dielectric material into the voids of an artificial opal crystal, which is usually made of an fcc packing of SiO_2 or polystyrene spheres. The silica spheres in the opal template are then removed, leaving behind an fcc array of air-spheres in a background of high dielectrics. If the infiltrated dielectric has a refractive index of 2.8 or higher, an absolute photonic band gap can form between the 8th and the 9th bands [14]. In practice, the infiltration may not be complete. The high dielectric material wets the surface of the silica spheres, but may not fill up all the space in the void, resulting in an incompletely infiltrated inverted opal. It is well known that a higher contrast between the dielectric material in the void and the air-spheres makes bigger photonic gaps. If the infiltration is incomplete, the average dielectric constant in the opal void is reduced, and we would normally expect a deterioration of the photonic band gap. Quite on the contrary, Busch and John [15] found that the photonic gap size can actually double in the case of incomplete infiltration. This is a delightful surprise, since an imperfectly infiltrated sample yields a better gap. We seek to understand this counter-intuitive result using the perturbative approach outlined in section 2.

We calculated the photonic band structure using a plane-wave approach, and got essentially the same result as Busch and John. The photonic crystal has a primitive fcc structure (lattice constant=a) of touching air-spheres of radii $R=\sqrt{2}/4\,a=0.3536a$. A high dielectric of $\varepsilon=11.9$ is coated onto the air-spheres. The thickness of this coating is controlled by the radial distance of outer boundary as measured from the center of the air-spheres. If $R\geq 0.5a$, the infilration is complete, in the sense that all-the space in the fcc voids is now filled with the high dielectric. For $0.3536a < R < 0.5a$, the filling is incomplete, and a cavity will be formed in the interstitial region of the air-spheres. We found that the band gap is dictated by two k-points in the Brillouin zone: X and W; and as far as the effect of incomplete infiltration is concerned, we need only to focus on the 8th and the 9th bands. We will use the notation W_9 to denote the 9th band of the W point, and so on. We found that the gap is about 4% when the infiltration is complete, but the gap size increased to a maximum of about 8% when $R\approx 0.45a$. When the coating layer gets thinner, the gap size decreases again and is gone completely when $R\approx 0.40a$.

When the cavity is completely infiltrated, the gap is bounded below by W_8 and above by X_9. The D field patterns of X_9, W_9, and W_8 are shown in Fig. 5. We see that the D field intensity corresponding to the X_9 mode has its maximum right at the center of the cavity; while the field intensity of the W_8 mode has a node at the center of the cavity and peaks in a ring encircling the center of the cavity. The D field of the W_9 mode is strongest on the surface of the air-spheres. According to the perturbation formula Eq. (1), a decrease in $\varepsilon(r)$ in the locality where D is strong will cause an upshift in ω. Let us start with the voids completely infiltrated ($R=0.5$). When R is reduced, a small hole will appear in the middle of the cavity (See Fig. 5, upper-left panel). In this void, $\varepsilon(r)$ will decrease from that of the dielectric material to one. When the hole is small, only the mode X_9 (which peaks at the center) will "feel" the effect since both bands at W have a node there. The consequence is that X_9 will have a higher frequency, while W_8 and W_9 is relatively untouched. This leads to an increase of the gap, reaching a maximum when $R\cong 0.45a$. However, as R is reduced further, the size of the hole gets bigger, and the effect of $\Delta\left(\frac{1}{\varepsilon}\right)$ starts to catch up with W_8 and the frequency corresponding to W_8 starts to increase too. Since the field pattern of W_9 is concentrated on the surface the air-spheres and does not feel the change of $\varepsilon(r)$, its eigenfrequency remains nearly the same, while the frequency of X_9 continues to increase. Eventually, the incomplete infiltration causes $\omega(X_9) > \omega(W_9)$ and the gap becomes "direct" and bounded between W_9 an W_8. Since the frequency of W_9 remains almost unchanged to the first order, while W_8 has started to increase in frequency, the gap will get smaller once the gap changes from indirect to direct and eventually closes.

We thus see that the counter-intuitive increase in the photonic gap due to incomplete infiltration in inverted opal is due to the fairly subtle interplay between the eigenmode field patterns and the precise location of the removal of high dielectric material. However, this can be understood by perturbation theory once the field patterns are computed.

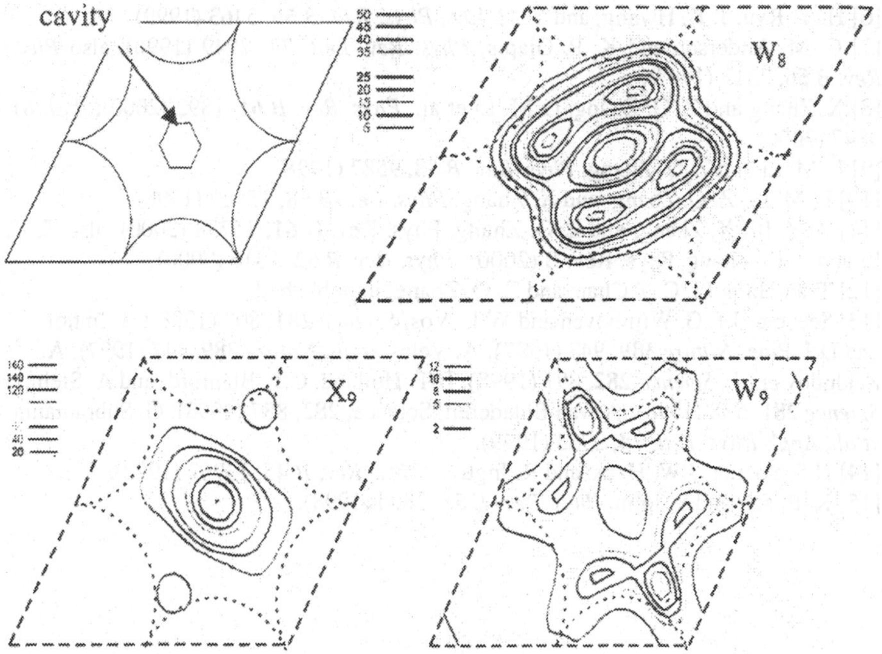

Figure 5. Upper left panel shows that a small hole forms in the interstitial region (R=0.45a) for incomplete infiltration. Other panels show the projected D-field pattern for the X_9, W_8, and W_9 modes, respectively. These 3 modes govern the size of the absolute gap.

References:

[1] *Photonic Band Gap Materials*, edited by C. M. Soukoulis (Kluwer Academic, Dordrecht, 1996); E. Yablonovitch, *Phys. Rev. Lett.* **58**, 2059 (1987); S. John, *ibid.* **58**, 2486 (1987).
[2] J. D. Joannopoulos, R. D. Meade, and J. N. Winn, *Photonic Crystal-Molding the Flow of Light* (Princeton University Press, Princeton, NJ, 1995).
[3] K. M. Leung and Y. F. Liu, *Phys. Rev. Lett.* **65**, 2646(1990); Z. Zhang and S. Satpathy, *ibid.* **65**, 2650 (1990); K. M. Ho, C. T. Chan, and C. M. Soukoulis, *ibid.* **65**, 3152 (1990); S. L. McCall *et al.*, **67**, 2017 (1991).
[4] S. Fan, P. R. Villeneuve, and J. D. Joannopoulos, *J. Appl. Phys.* **78**, 1415 (1995).
[5] M. M. Sigalas, C. M. Soukoulis, C. T. Chan *et al*, *Phys. Rev. B* **53**, 8340 (1996); *ibid.* **59,** 12767(1999); also E. Lidorikis *et al.*, *Phys. Rev. B* **61**, 13458 (2000).
[6] H. Y. Ryu, J. K. Hwang, and Y. H. Lee, *Phys. Rev. B* **59**, 5463 (1999).
[7] C. M. Anderson and K. P. Giapis, *Phys. Rev. Lett.* **77**, 2949 (1996); also *Phys. Rev. B* **56**, 7313 (1997).
[8] X. Zhang and Z. Q. Zhang, L. M. Li et al., *Phys. Rev. B* **61**, 1892 (2000); *ibid.* **61,** 9847 (2000).
[9] L. M. Li and Z. Q. Zhang, *Phys. Rev. B* **58**, 9587 (1998).
[10] L. M. Li, Z. Q. Zhang, and X. Zhang, *Phys. Rev. B* **58,** 15589 (1998).
[11] Z. Y. Li, X. Zhang, and Z. Q. Zhang, Phys. Rev. B **61,** 15738 (2000); also Z. Y. Li and Z. Q. Zhang, Phys. Rev. B (2000). *Phys. Rev. B* **62**, 1516 (2000).
[12] Tsan-Hang Li, C. T.Chan, and Z. Q. Zhang, unpublished.
[13] See, e.g. J.E.G. Wijnhoven and W.L. Vos, *Science* **281**, 802 (1998); A. Imhof and D.J. Pine, *Nature* **389**, 948 (1997); A. Velev *et al.*, *Nature* **389**, 447 (1997); A. Zakhidov *et al.*, *Science* **282**, 897 (1998); B.T. Holland, C.F. Blanford, and A. Stein, *Science* **281**, 538 (1998); A. van Blaaderen, Science, **282**, 887 (1998); G. Subramania *et al.*, *Appl. Phys. Lett.* **74**, 3933 (1999).
[14] H.S. Sozuer, J.W. Haus, and R. Inguva, *Phys. Rev. B* **45**, 13962 (1992).
[15] K. Busch and S. John, *Phys. Rev. E* **58**, 3896 (1998).

TIGHT-BINDING WANNIER FUNCTION METHOD FOR PHOTONIC BAND GAP MATERIALS

J. P. ALBERT, C. JOUANIN, D. CASSAGNE, AND D. MONGE
Groupe d'Etude des Semiconducteurs, UMR 5650 du CNRS, CC074, Université Montpellier II, Place E. Bataillon, 34095 Montpellier Cedex 05, France.

Abstract: Using the concept of generalized Wannier functions, adapted form the electronic theory of solids, we demonstrate for two-dimensional photonic crystals the existence of a localized state basis and we establish an efficient computational method allowing a tight-binding-like parameter free modelization of any dielectric structure deviating from periodicity. Examples of numerical simulations using this formalism, including modal analysis of microcavities and waveguides and calculations of the transmission coefficients are presented to prove the ability of this approach to deal accurately with large scale systems and complex structures.

1. Introduction

Over the past few years much effort has been devoted to the study of the propagation of electromagnetic (EM) waves in periodic dielectric structures. The possibility of creating, under favorable circumstances, frequency ranges for which EM wave propagation is forbidden has attracted much theoretical and experimental attention.[1–4] The study of localized or extended defects in these photonic band gap (PBG) materials is now becoming a field of growing activity owing to the potential applications of these perturbed structures in the realization of high quality waveguides or microcavities.[5] The next step will be the development of integrated photonic devices which will require new modelization techniques to deal with very large systems. From a theoretical point of view the plane wave method (PWM) has been largely used to calculate the band structures and the defect modes in photonic crystals. Much less attention has been given to the possibility of an expansion of the EM wave field on localized functions in a similar way to the tight-binding (TB) description of the electron states in solids. Since the approach uses small sets of basis functions, the computational effort is smaller than required by methods based on plane waves. It then allows consideration of complex systems with large unit cells where plane wave methods come to their limits of applicability. However, the essence of this approach and its efficiency to modelize complex systems relies on the existence of localized basis states. Unlike the

C.M. Soukoulis (ed.), Photonic Crystals and Light Localization in the 21st Century, 545–553.

electron case where the atomic orbitals localized on individual atoms constitute a natural basis, in the case of light propagating in a dielectric material only scattering extended states can be associated with the individual scattering centers. The extension of the TB method to PBG materials appears then not trivial. We will contend ourselves here to its implementation in the two-dimensional (2D) case where one can get rid of the complications arising from the vectorial nature of the wave field while keeping with the basic features of the problem. In this paper we demonstrate that a set of localized basis states associated with a periodic 2D photonic crystal exists and can be constructed. We then establish an efficient computational procedure allowing large scale simulations on complex PBG structures.

Our work is rooted to the concept of generalized Wannier functions[6] whose construction is performed for the first time in photonic crystals. This construction only requires a prior knowledge of the Bloch fields and frequencies of a periodic structure taken as reference system. The calculation strategy goes as follows. In a first stage a TB empirical parametrization of the band structure of this reference system is performed. Together with the Bloch functions already determined, it then allows the construction of the Wannier functions of the periodic lattice.[7–9] Any perturbation of the reference system can be characterized by calculating explicitly and without any additional assumption all the relevant matrix elements in this basis. The determination of the corresponding perturbed eigenmodes can then finally be obtained by employing a TB formalism coupled with a supercell method which is more competitive for large scale simulations.

Once the basis states are determined, this method can deal with any dielectric structure within a "first principles" scheme. This approach differs fundamentally from the mixed TB-plane wave empirical framework recently proposed by Lidorikis *et al.*[10] for the treatment of 2D PBG structures with high dielectric contrast. The homogeneous and localized nature of the basis states used here avoids all the complications arising from the coupling between localized and extended states. Furthermore, the non-empirical modelization of perturbations adopted here allows us to deal with a far wider class of defects such as changes in the dielectric constant in some units, where an empirical scheme appears difficult to apply.

2. Tight-binding parametrization

This photonic version of the TB method will now be presented by studying a model system.[11] It consists of a periodic array of infinitely long dielectric rods whose vertical axes are arrayed on a square lattice of lattice constant d. The rods have a dielectric constant of 11.56, a radius of $0.2d$, and are embedded in a vacuum. We will limit ourselves here to a study of the propagation of waves with electric field parallel to the rod axis (TM waves).[10,11] This working model is sufficiently standard to ensure that no conceptual nor numerical difficulties should be expected when dealing with other different 2D problems.

Considering first the fully periodic structure, which is taken as the reference system, the scalar wave equation obeyed by the electric field can be written as

$$\Delta E_n(\mathbf{k},\mathbf{r}) = -\frac{\omega_n^2(\mathbf{k})}{c^2}\varepsilon_p(\mathbf{r})\,E_n(\mathbf{k},\mathbf{r})\,, \tag{1}$$

where $\varepsilon_p(\mathbf{r})$ stands for the dielectric function of the periodic medium. A band index n and a 2D vector $\mathbf{k}$ lying in the first Brillouin zone (BZ) have been used to label the band modes $E_n(\mathbf{k},\mathbf{r})$ and their associated frequency $\omega_n(\mathbf{k})$. In order to introduce a hermitic operator, we define $\overline{E}_n(\mathbf{k},\mathbf{r}) = \sqrt{\varepsilon_p(\mathbf{r})}E_n(\mathbf{k},\mathbf{r})$. Equation (1) can be then rewritten in the following form:

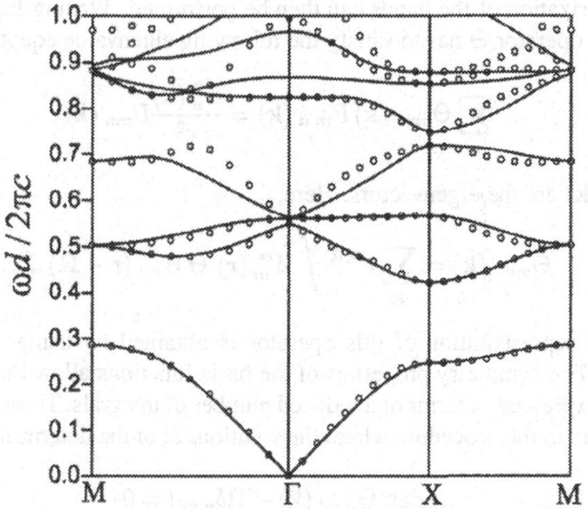

Figure 1. TM photonic band structure of a 2D square lattice (period d) of dielectric rods ($\varepsilon = 11.6$) with radius $0.2d$. Solid lines correspond to numerical results from PWM while circles correspond to TB fit. Only the lower frequency region which is relevant for the present study is shown.

$$\left(-\frac{1}{\sqrt{\varepsilon_p(\mathbf{r})}}\Delta\frac{1}{\sqrt{\varepsilon_p(\mathbf{r})}}\right)\overline{E}_n(\mathbf{k},\mathbf{r}) = \frac{\omega_n^2(\mathbf{k})}{c^2}\overline{E}_n(\mathbf{k},\mathbf{r}). \quad (2)$$

This allow us to define an hermitic operator Θ:

$$\Theta = -\frac{1}{\sqrt{\varepsilon_p(\mathbf{r})}}\Delta\frac{1}{\sqrt{\varepsilon_p(\mathbf{r})}}. \quad (3)$$

The band modes have first to be calculated by an "ab initio" method. With the PWM, 441 plane waves were amply sufficient to ensure a good convergence for the low frequency bands of interest and their associated Bloch fields. These latter are then orthonormalized on the 2D crystal surface as:

$$\int_S \overline{E}_n^*(\mathbf{k},\mathbf{r})\,\overline{E}_{n'}(\mathbf{k}',\mathbf{r})\,d^2\mathbf{r} = \delta_{nn'}\delta_{\mathbf{k}\mathbf{k}'}. \quad (4)$$

In the present work we are interested in modes whose frequencies lie in the vicinity of the first gap, between the first two bands. A convenient localized basis for their expansion is then obtained by constructing the Wannier functions associated with a group of bands situated in this frequency range. These Wannier functions can be classified according to the irreducible representations of the square group (C_{4v}). [12] We have found that eight functions per lattice site are sufficient to obtain a good description: two functions with symmetry A_1($s - type$), four functions with symmetry E (two p_x- and two p_y-type), one function with symmetry B_1($d_{x^2-y^2}$-type) and one function with symmetry B_2(d_{xy}-type). Since they are unitary transforms of the Bloch functions, the Wannier functions $W_m(\mathbf{r})$ obey the orthonormality condition:

$$\int_S W_m^*(\mathbf{r}-\mathbf{R})\,W_{m'}(\mathbf{r}-\mathbf{R}')\,d^2\mathbf{r} = \delta_{mm'}\delta_{\mathbf{R}\mathbf{R}'}. \quad (5)$$

where an index $m = 1, 8$ has been used to label the functions centered at lattice site $\mathbf{R}$. A

TB-like parametrization of the bands can then be performed. Writing Eq. (1) in this basis, it is found that the operator Θ has to satisfy the following eigenvalue equation:

$$\sum_{m'} \Theta_{mm'}(\mathbf{k})\, U_{m'n}(\mathbf{k}) = \frac{\omega_n^2(\mathbf{k})}{c^2} U_{mn}(\mathbf{k}), \tag{6}$$

where the $U_{mn}(\mathbf{k})$ are the eigenvectors. Here,

$$\Theta_{mm'}(\mathbf{k}) = \sum_{\mathbf{R}} e^{i\mathbf{kR}} \int W_m^*(\mathbf{r})\, \Theta\, W_{m'}(\mathbf{r}-\mathbf{R})\, d^2\mathbf{r}. \tag{7}$$

The matrix representation of this operator is obtained by using the standard Slater-Koster method. The symmetry properties of the basis functions allow the $\mathbf{k}$ dependent terms $\Theta_{mm'}(\mathbf{k})$ to be expressed in terms of a reduced number of integrals. These are then considered as free parameters in the procedure where the solutions Ω of the determinantal 8×8 equation:

$$\det\left|\Theta_{mm'}(\mathbf{k}) - \Omega\delta_{mm'}\right| = 0 \tag{8}$$

are fitted to the results $\omega_n^2(\mathbf{k})/c^2$ of the plane wave calculation. Taking into account only first-neighbor interactions, the fit involves the determination of 26 independent parameters.

The resulting band-structure scheme calculated along high symmetry directions in the BZ is shown in Fig. 1, together with that obtained by the PWM. The agreement between the two calculations is quite good for the lowest frequency bands. Because of our limitation to first neighbor interactions, the quality of the fit slightly decreases with increasing frequency. However it will be shown that this worsening does not seriously affect the determination of the defect modes in which we are interested.

3. Wannier functions

The basis functions involved in this TB parameterization procedure can be effectively constructed by performing two successive unitary transformations on the Bloch waves already calculated by the PWM. Generalized Bloch functions are first defined for each $\mathbf{k}$ in the BZ zone by taking linear combinations of the Bloch functions as

$$\Phi_m(\mathbf{k},\mathbf{r}) = \sum_n U_{mn}^*(\mathbf{k})\, \overline{E}_n(\mathbf{k},\mathbf{r}), \tag{9}$$

where the unitary 8×8 matrix $U_{mn}(\mathbf{k})$ is formed by the orthonormalized eigenvectors obtained in solving Eq. (8). Then the Wannier functions are obtained by Fourier transforming these generalized Bloch functions $\Phi_m(\mathbf{k},\mathbf{r})$

$$W_m(\mathbf{r}-\mathbf{R}) = \frac{1}{\sqrt{N}} \sum_{\mathbf{k}} e^{-i\mathbf{kR}}\Phi_m(\mathbf{k},\mathbf{r}), \tag{10}$$

where N is the number of unit cells in the 2D periodic lattice. Symmetry considerations allow the summation to be restricted to the irreducible wedge of the BZ. 67 $\mathbf{k}$-vectors in this reduced zone have been considered. An idea of the localization of the resulting Wannier functions can be inferred from Fig. (2) where we have plotted two functions with respective symmetry A_1 and E. These plots are made in the (10) direction, which is the direction of their slowest decrease. A strong localization of these Wannier functions about their origin, followed by small decaying oscillations around successive lattice sites, can be observed. This rapid decay of the amplitudes beyond the first-neighbor site is coherent with the limitation to

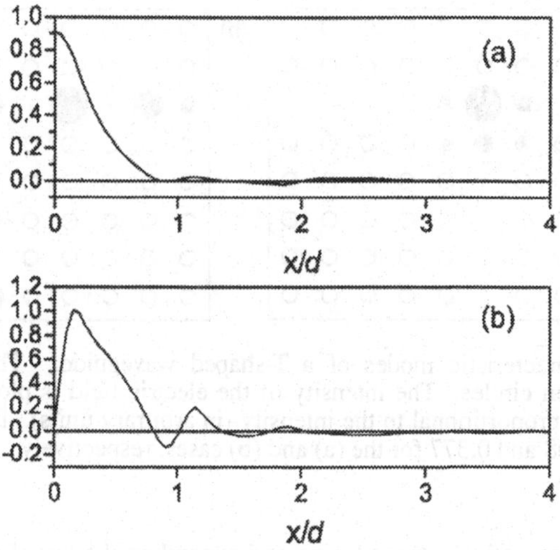

Figure 2. Wannier functions of the square lattice with A_1 (a) and E (b) symmetry plotted along the (10) direction. The integer values of x/d correspond to successive neighbors in this direction. We have plotted $W_n(\mathbf{r})/\sqrt{\varepsilon_p(\mathbf{r})}$ in order to avoid discontinuities due to $\varepsilon_p(\mathbf{r})$.

first-neighbor interactions in the parameterization procedure and gives a clear indication of the validity of this TB-like approach for the description of the periodic structure.

4. Structures with defects

We next consider structures containing defects. These perturbed structures are characterized by the local deviation $\delta\varepsilon(\mathbf{r})$ of the dielectric constant from its original periodic value, $\varepsilon_p(\mathbf{r})$, in the reference system. The wave equation in this case takes the following form:

$$\Delta E(\mathbf{r}) = -\frac{\omega^2}{c^2}\left[\varepsilon_p(\mathbf{r}) + \delta\varepsilon(\mathbf{r})\right] E(\mathbf{r}). \tag{11}$$

This can be rewritten as:

$$\left(-\frac{1}{\sqrt{\varepsilon_p(\mathbf{r})}}\Delta\frac{1}{\sqrt{\varepsilon_p(\mathbf{r})}}\right)\overline{E}(\mathbf{r}) = \frac{\omega^2}{c^2}\left[1 + \frac{\delta\varepsilon(\mathbf{r})}{\varepsilon_p(\mathbf{r})}\right]\overline{E}(\mathbf{r}) \tag{12}$$

which gives the following generalized eigenvalue equation:

$$\Theta\overline{E}(\mathbf{r}) = \frac{\omega^2}{c^2}\left[1 + \mathbf{V}\right]\overline{E}(\mathbf{r}) \text{ with } \mathbf{V} = \frac{\delta\varepsilon(\mathbf{r})}{\varepsilon_p(\mathbf{r})} \tag{13}$$

Within the TB formalism the perturbation can be completely characterized by constructing the matrix representation of V in the Wannier function basis. This is greatly facilitated by the short range properties of these functions: the only non-negligible matrix elements are those which involve functions centered in the close vicinity of the perturbed domain. These are easily obtained by 2D numerical integration.

Equation (13) can then be solved by using the TB method, coupled with the supercell approximation (TBSC approximation). Only the TB representation of the Θ operator previously determined is needed. This method is used here to study the two types of point

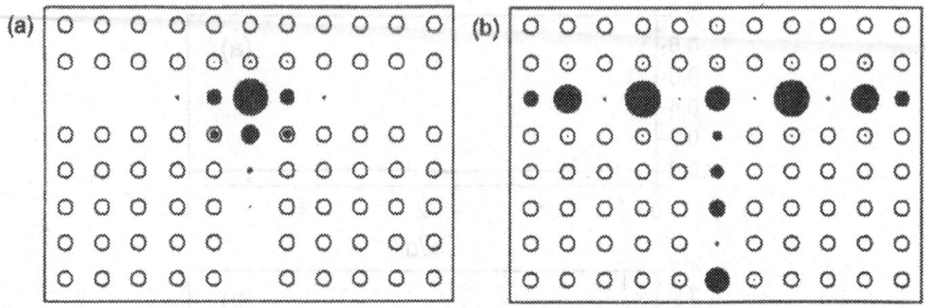

Figure 3. Two characteristic modes of a T-shaped waveguide. The dielectric rods are represented by open circles. The intensity of the electric field is plotted with gray circles whose diameter is proportionnal to the intensity (in arbitrary units). The reduced frequency of the mode is 0.308 and 0.377 for the (a) and (b) cases, respectively.

defects obtained, respectively, by reducing and expanding the initial radius of a single rod. These two calculations will allow an appreciation of the validity of the TB determination of the defect modes in the two characteristic situations where these are extracted from the bands lying above or below the gap. The specific values attributed to the radius are, respectively, zero, corresponding to the creation of a vacancy, and $0.3d$. For both cases it was found that a 3×3 supercell suffices in the TBSC approximation. In the first case a single non-degenerate A_1-type monopole defect mode appears in the gap at a reduced frequency $\omega d/2\pi c = 0.390$, while in the second case a doubly degenerate mode with E-symmetry is found at 0.384. Both values compare favorably with the PWM results, 0.380 and 0.374, respectively.[11] It is to be noted that here only nearest-neighbors have been taken into account in the TB calculations, both in the periodic and perturbed structures. Inclusion of more distant interactions should improve the accuracy of the TBSC approximation which, however, appears at this stage to be quite competitive for further investigations of perturbed structures.

The potential usefulness of this approach for modelling extended PBG structures involving microcavities and waveguides will finally be assessed here by considering the specific case of a T-shaped PBG waveguide. This structure is created by removing rods in the periodic original 2D lattice (see Fig. 3). The TBSC method allows Eq. (11) to be solved for this specific configuration, obtaining the field $E_i(\mathbf{r})$ associated with the eigenfrequency ω_i as

$$\overline{E}_i(\mathbf{r}) = \sum_{m\mathbf{R}} B^i_m(\mathbf{R})\, W_m(\mathbf{r} - \mathbf{R}). \tag{14}$$

Because of the localization of the Wannier functions around their respective centers a clear indication about the intensity variations of the wave field in the structure can then be obtained by calculating and plotting:

$$\mathrm{I}_i(\mathbf{R}) = \sum_{m} \left| B^i_m(\mathbf{R}) \right|^2 \tag{15}$$

for each site $\mathbf{R}$ in the supercell. Figure 3 plots $\mathrm{I}_i(\mathbf{R})$ for two characteristic modes. The first one at the reduced frequency $\omega_i d/2\pi c = 0.308$ constitutes a bound state whose electric field is strongly localized at the junction of the three waveguides. The second one at 0.377 is confined inside the whole waveguide. It corresponds to a guided mode. The existence of such a mode shows the ability of PBG waveguide to guide light through cross junctions.

Such types of plot made for specific patterns of line defects in periodic structures may give useful information about their associated guiding properties for EM waves.[5] Due to the method appears to be appealing because of its ability to handle extended structures with reasonable matrix sizes. For comparison a PWM calculation made on the 11×8 supercell considered here would involve at least 10^4 plane waves since more than 100 plane waves per site (as it is generally accepted) are needed to obtain well converged results. It is to be noted that, although this approach retains the simplicity and efficiency of the empirical TB method, no adjustable parameter is involved in the calculation. Instead all the necessary matrix elements characterizing any perturbation of a reference structure are explicitly calculated. Furthermore the short range properties of the basis functions reduce drastically the effective number of those which have to be calculated. The difficulties related to the evaluation [13] and the transferability of the parameters in empirical versions of the TB method[10] are then circumvented.

5. Transmission and reflection coefficients

A TB approach of the transfer matrix method.(TMM) can be derived from this formalism. The TMM allows to calculate the transmission and reflection properties of a photonic crystal with a finite size thickness. In the standard TMM proposed by Pendry *et al.*,[14] a plane wave basis is used to calculate the transmission and reflection coefficients. In the case of a square lattice of circular cylinders, a discretization mesh of approximately 10×10 points per cylinder is required. In the TB TMM, each cylinder is described using a 8 Wannier functions basis. We consider a photonic crystal infinitely periodic in the y direction and with a finite size in the x direction, as shown in Fig 4.

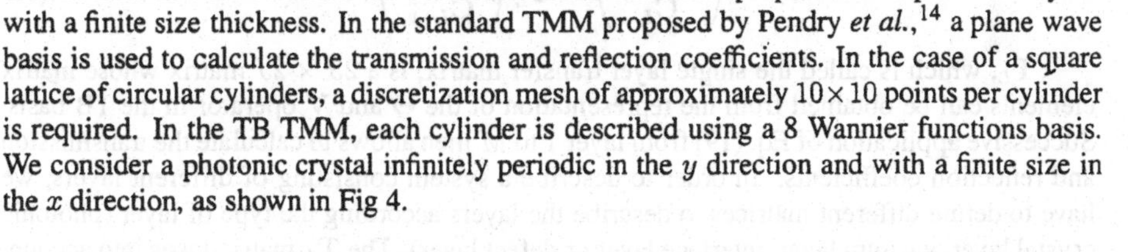

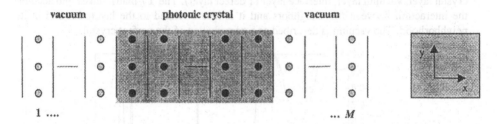

Figure 4. Typical system studied using the transfer matrix method. This system consists of vacuum layers in the front and the back of the photonic crystal. The total number of layers is M. The system is periodic in the y direction and has a finite size in the x direction.

This system consists of vacuum layers in the front and the back of the photonic crystal. The total number of layers is M. We consider a localized basis consisting of the Wannier functions already constructed and located on each site $\{W_\mu(\mathbf{r} - \mathbf{R}_i)\}$. This basis is constituted of J functions annotated with the index μ and centered on the position R_{iy} in each layer L. The system is periodic and infinite in the y direction, so it is possible to construct a Bloch sum:

$$\phi_{L\mu}(k_y, \mathbf{r}) = \frac{1}{\sqrt{N_y}} \sum_{\mathbf{R}_{i,L}} e^{ik_y R_{iy}} W_\mu(\mathbf{r} - \mathbf{R}_{i,L}), \tag{16}$$

where $\mathbf{r}$ indicates the position, k_y is the component of the $\mathbf{k}$ vector along the y direction, $\mathbf{R}_{i,L}$ indicates the position of the unit cell in the layer L, N_y is the number of unit cells in the layer. This constitutes a Bloch sum basis in the y direction, which is valid for each layer. The electric field $\overline{\mathbf{E}}_L(k_y, \mathbf{r})$ of the L layer can be expanded on this basis of planar orbitals as:

$$\overline{\mathbf{E}}_L(k_y, \mathbf{r}) = \sum_{\mu=1}^{J} C_{L\mu}\phi_{L\mu}(k_y, \mathbf{r}), \tag{17}$$

where the expansion coefficients $C_{L\mu}$ constitute a vector $\mathbf{C}_L$ of length J:

$$\mathbf{C}_L = \begin{pmatrix} C_{L1} \\ \vdots \\ C_{LJ} \end{pmatrix}. \tag{18}$$

A tight-binding adaptation of the transfer matrix method, as formulated by Ting *et al.*[15] and Schulman *et al.*,[16] can then be used to relate the coefficient pertaining to each layer with those of its adjacent layers as:

$$\begin{pmatrix} \mathbf{C}_{L-1} \\ \mathbf{C}_L \end{pmatrix} = \mathbf{T}_L \begin{pmatrix} \mathbf{C}_L \\ \mathbf{C}_{L+1} \end{pmatrix}. \tag{19}$$

$\mathbf{T}_L$, which is called the single layer transfer matrix, is a $2J \times 2J$ matrix whose matrix elements can be obtained from the representation of the Θ and $\mathbf{V}$ operator in the TB basis. Successive application of Eq. (19) from layer 1 to M then allows to calculate the transmission and reflection coefficients. In order to describe a system consisting of different layers, we have to define different matrices to describe the layers according the type of layer (photonic crystal layer, vacuum layer, interface layer or defect layer). The $\mathbf{T}_L$ matrix takes into account the interaction between first neighbors and it is hence related to the layers located in its neighborhood. The vacuum is described as a perturbation of the perfect crystal.

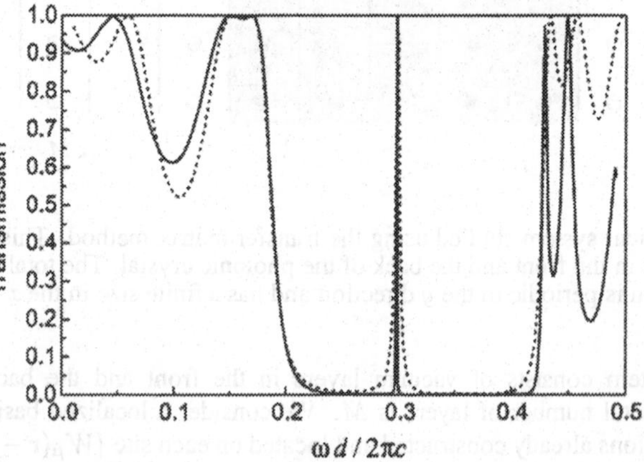

Figure 5. Transmission of a slab consisting of 5 layers of the square lattice photonic crystal described in Fig. 1 with a defect layer in its middle where all the cylinders are removed. The solid line corresponds to the transmission calculated by the TB TMM. The dotted curve indicated the standard TMM results.

In Fig. 5, we present the transmission of a slab consisting of 5 layers of the square lattice photonic crystal described in Fig. 1 with a defect layer in its middle where all the cylinders are removed. We consider normal incidence, so $k_y = 0$. A frequency range with no transmission is found in the photonic band gap region and, approximately in the middle of the gap, a 100% transmission peak appears, due to the defect layer. These results present a very good agreement with calculations by the standard TMM in the frequency range of the photonic band gap. The agreement above the gap is less good. This can be easily understood since our limitation to first neighbor interactions decreases the quality of the description of the higher bands.

Conclusion

We have shown that it is possible to calculate explicitly a localized state basis using Wannier functions in 2D photonic crystals and that a TB formalism based on these functions constitutes a very efficient tool in the description of eigenmodes associated with structures deviating from periodicity. This method offers a new promising way to study large integrated photonic devices associating microcavities and waveguides. The efficiency of such a localized representation of EM waves should become decisive in numerical simulations on disordered or quasicrystalline structures to investigate their localization properties for light. Also, an extension of this approach to the treatment of 3D structures, with vector Wannier functions[17] replacing the scalar ones obtained here, appears feasible and promising.

References

1. E. Yablonovitch, *Phys. Rev. Lett.* **58**, 2059 (1987).
2. S. John, *Phys. Rev. Lett.* **58**, 2486 (1987).
3. See for example *Photonic Band Gaps and Localization*, edited by C. M. Soukoulis (Plenum, New York, 1993); *Photonic Band Gap Materials*, edited by C. M. Soukoulis (Kluwer, Dordrecht, 1996).
4. J. Joannopoulos, R. D. Meade, and J. Winn, *Photonic Crystals*, (Princeton University, Princeton, N.J. 1995).
5. A. Mekis, J. C. Chen, I. Kurland, S. Fan, P. R. Villeneuve, and J. D. Joannopoulos, *Phys. Rev. Lett.* **77**, 3787 (1996); *Phys. Rev. B* **58**, 4809 (1998).
6. Generalized Wannier functions which are referred in the text as Wannier functions for simplicity constitute for a group of interlacing bands the equivalent of the elementary Wannier functions defined in the case of isolated bands. These site centered functions span the same space as the Bloch functions and are symmetry adapted to the point group of the crystal. For their definition and properties see Des Cloiseaux[7] and Kohn.[8]
7. J. Des Cloiseaux, *Phys. Rev.* **129**, 554 (1963); *Phys. Rev.* **135**, A698 (1964).
8. W. Kohn, *Phys. Rev. B* **7**, 4388 (1973).
9. B. Sporkmann and H. Bross, *Phys. Rev. B* **49**, 10869 (1994).
10. E. Lidorikis, M. M. Sigalas, E. N. Economou, and C. M. Soukoulis, *Phys. Rev. Lett.* **81**, 1405 (1998).
11. P. R. Villeneuve, S. Fan, and J. Joannopoulos, *Phys. Rev. B* **54**, 7837 (1996).
12. K. Sakoda, *Phys. Rev. B* **52**, 7982 (1995).
13. We refer here to the difficulties associated with the evaluation of matrix elements at the interface between two materials where, in the empirical TB method, *ad hoc* weighting rules have to be considered.
14. J. B. Pendry and A. MacKinnon, *Phys. Rev. Lett.* **69**, 2772 (1992).
15. D. Z.-Y. Ting, E. T. Yu, and T. C. McGill, *Phys. Rev. B* **45**, 3583 (1992).
16. J. N. Schulman and Y.-C. Chang, *Phys. Rev. B* **27**, 2346 (1983).
17. K. M. Leung, *J. Opt. Soc. Am. B* **10**, 303 (1993).

1, 2 AND 3 DIMENSIONAL PHOTONIC MATERIALS MADE USING ION BEAMS: FABRICATION AND OPTICAL DENSITY-OF-STATES

M.J.A. DE DOOD[1], L.H. SLOOFF[1], T.M. HENSEN[1], D.L.J. VOSSEN[1], A. MOROZ[1,3], T. ZIJLSTRA[2], E.W.J.M. VAN DER DRIFT[2], A. VAN BLAADEREN[1,3] AND A. POLMAN[1]

[1]*FOM Institute for Atomic and Molecular Physics*
Kruislaan 407
1098 SJ Amsterdam, The Netherlands
[2]*Delft Institute for Microelectronics and Submicron Technology*
P.O. Box 5053
2600 GB Delft, The Netherlands
[3]*Debye Institute, Utrecht University*
Padualaan 8
3584 CH Utrecht, The Netherlands

1. Introduction

The spontaneous emission rate of an optical probe atom is strongly dependent on its optical environment. This concept is well known in one-dimensional geometries, e.g. for an atom placed near a mirror, a dielectric interface, or in a microcavity.[1,2,3,4,5,6] With the recent development of two- and three-dimensional photonic crystals it becomes possible to tailor optical modes and the local optical density-of-states (DOS) to a much greater extent. Large effects on the spontaneous emission rate of optical probe ions are expected in these materials.

In order to study these effects, accurate and reproducable methods of optical doping must be developed. Ion implantation is a technique with which ions can be introduced at a well defined depth and concentration into any material, in a reproducible fashion. In this paper we demonstrate this concept for Cr ions implanted near the surface of an Al_2O_3 single crystal. In this one-dimensional system the DOS near the interface can be calculated from Fermi's Golden rule. It can be experimentally varied by bringing liquids with different refractive index in contact with the crystal surface, as we will show. In this way it becomes possible to determine the radiative decay rate and quantum efficiency of Cr in Al_2O_3. These well-characterized samples can then be used to study the changes in spontaneous emission in more complicated systems such as absorbing and strongly scattering materials. We also study the DOS in a one-dimensional system with two interfaces: a SiO_2 thin film on a Si substrate. Er ions are implanted in the SiO_2 thin film, and their radiative decay rate is derived from experiments in which the DOS is varied.

C.M. Soukoulis (ed.), Photonic Crystals and Light Localization in the 21st Century, 555–566.

Using these data it becomes possible to study the effect of a varying DOS in a 3-dimensional system composed of Er-doped SiO_2 colloidal particles. Large effects on the spontaneous emission rate are observed, as will be shown. Finally, we will discuss the design and fabrication of two-dimensional photonic crystals in silicon. A method to incorporate a luminescent dye in these crystals is described which may be used to study the DOS.

2. Spontaneous Emission near A dielectric interface

Experimental

Single crystal (0001) oriented α-Al_2O_3 substrates were implanted with 150 keV Cr^+ ions at room temperature to fluences of 0.6, 1.6, 2.5, 3.0 and 4.0×10^{15} at/cm^2. The samples were rotated by 7° with respect to the ion beam to avoid ion channeling along the [0001] crystal direction. After implantation, the samples were annealed at 1450 °C for 2 hours in air. PL measurements were performed using the 457.9 nm line of an Ar ion laser as an excitation source and by collecting the PL signal using a 48 cm monochromator with a spectral resolution of 3.3 cm^{-1} in combination with a GaAs photomultiplier tube. The Ar ion laser was modulated at 13 Hz using an acousto-optic-modulator. Luminescence decay traces were recorded using the photomultiplier tube in combination with a multichannel photon counting system. The overall time resolution was 400 ns.

SiO_2 layers, of 100 nm thickness, were grown on Si(100) substrates in two consecutive steps, using a solution of 10.5 ml ethanol, 0.3 ml water (29 wt.% NH_3), and 0.4 ml TEOS under continuous stirring. The layers were then implanted with 70 keV Er ions to a fluence of 3.4×10^{14} at/cm^2, resulting in a Gaussian depth profile with a peak concentration of 0.22 at.% peaking at a depth of 39 nm and a standard deviation of 11 nm. The implanted layers were annealed at 100 °C for 1h and 900 °C for 1h in a vacuum furnace.

Silica colloids with a diameter of 339 nm and a polydispersity of 5% were synthesized under similar reaction conditions as described by van Blaaderen.[7] After synthesis the colloidal particles were kept in pure ethanol. A layer of these colloidal particles was deposited on a Si substrate by drying a droplet of this suspension on the substrate. This resulted in a layer consisting of 3-4 layers of stacked spheres as determined by Rutherford backcattering spectrometry (RBS) and scanning electron microscopy (SEM) measurements. The colloids were implanted with 350 keV Er to a fluence of 1.5×10^{15} at/cm^2. The projected ion range of the 350 keV Er is 200 nm. After implantation the samples were annealed at 100 °C for 1h and 900 °C for 1h in a vacuum furnace to optically activate the Er ions.[8] Photoluminescence (PL) measurements were done by exciting the Er ions using the 488 nm line of an Ar ion laser. The PL signal was collected using a 48 cm monochromator in combination with a liquid nitrogen cooled Ge detector, using standard lock-in techniques at a modulation frequency of 13 Hz. PL decay traces were recorded and averaged at the peak of the Er luminescence at 1.536 μm using a digitizing oscilloscope. The overall time resolution was 30 μs.

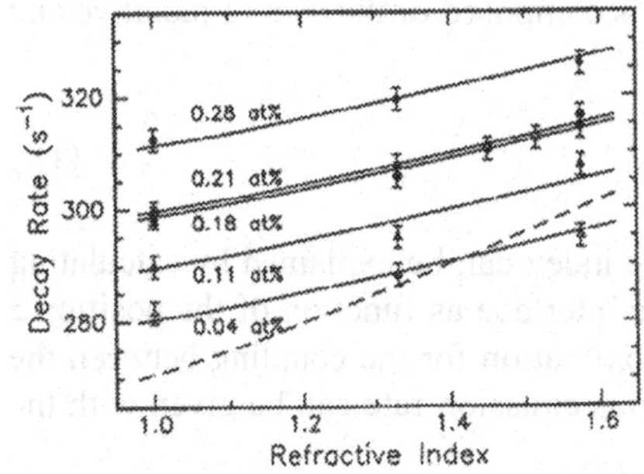

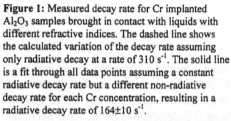

Figure 1: Measured decay rate for Cr implanted Al_2O_3 samples brought in contact with liquids with different refractive indices. The dashed line shows the calculated variation of the decay rate assuming only radiative decay at a rate of 310 s^{-1}. The solid line is a fit through all data points assuming a constant radiative decay rate but a different non-radiative decay rate for each Cr concentration, resulting in a radiative decay rate of 164±10 s^{-1}.

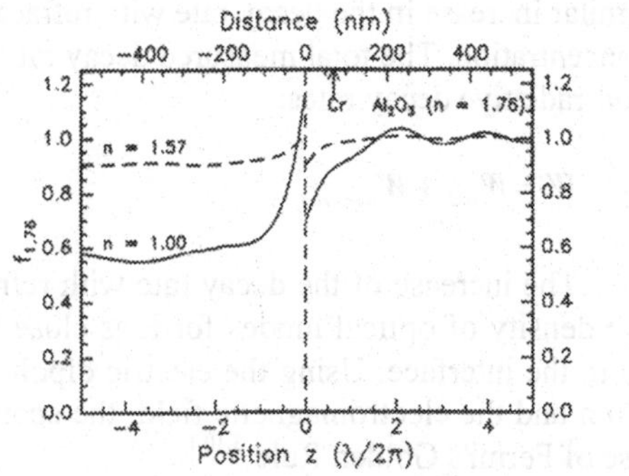

Figure 2: Polarization- and angle-averaged optical DOS $f_{1.76}$ as function of position, calculated for an Al_2O_3 sample brought in contact with air (n = 1.00) and a liquid with a refractive index of 1.57. The optical DOS was normalized to the optical DOS in bulk Al_2O_3 (n = 1.76). The arrow indicates the peak of the Cr distribution.

Various liquid films with different refractive index, ranging from n = 1.33 to n = 1.57, were brought in contact with the implanted side of both the Er implanted and Cr implanted samples. A ~1 mm thick liquid film was created by holding a liquid droplet between the sample and a fused silica slide. The luminescence signal was collected from the back. Using the same setup, the SiO_2 colloids were index matched by using a glycerol-water-mixture with a refractive index of 1.45, and photoluminescence decay traces were measured.

Results and Discussion

Characteristic luminescence, around λ = 694 nm, from Cr^{3+} doped Al_2O_3 occurs if the Cr ions are incorporated as substitutional atoms on the Al sublattice in the Al_2O_3 crystal lattice. Because the electrons involved in the transition are the outer lying 3d electrons, the transition wavelength is extremely sensitive to the local electronic environment provided by the surrounding atoms. After annealing the Cr implanted samples show the characteristic R line luminescence at wavelengths of 694.3 and 692.9 nm. It was found that the luminescence intensity of ion implanted samples increased with increasing fraction of substitutional Cr ions, as measured by RBS channeling measurements.[9]

The decay rate of the R_1 line luminescence at 694.3 nm was measured for samples brought in contact with liquids with different refractive indices. The luminescence decay can be described as a single-exponential over at least 4 orders of magnitude within experimental error. Figure 1 shows the measured decay rate as a function of the refractive index of the liquid for samples with different Cr peak concentrations. All samples show a similar increase in the decay rate with refractive index of the liquid, independent of the Cr concentration. The total measured decay rate (W) is composed of the sum of radiative and non-radiative decay rates:

$$W = W_{rad} + W_{non-rad} \, . \tag{1}$$

The increase of the decay rate with refractive index can be explained by calculating the density of optical modes for ions close to the interface as function of the position z from the interface. Using the electric dipole approximation for the coupling between the atom and the electromagnetic field, the spontaneous emission rate can be given with the use of Fermi's Golden Rule,[5,10,11]

$$W_{rad}(z) = \frac{\pi \omega}{\hbar \varepsilon(z)} |D|^2 \rho(\omega, z), \tag{2}$$

where D is the dipole matrix element of the atomic transition between the excited state and the ground state at a transition frequency ω. ρ is the polarization- and angle-averaged local density-of-states (DOS)[12] at position z from the interface and $\varepsilon(z)$ is the position dependent dielectric constant. The matrix element D is determined by the local electronic environment of the emitting ion and is not influenced by the optical properties of the interface. Note that the presence of the interface does not affect the local-field as studied in Ref. 13. Therefore, the only parameter varied in our experiment is the local DOS at a fixed frequency.

The changes in the radiative decay rate can be expressed using an optical DOS which differs by a factor ε from the local DOS defined above.[14] Using this optical DOS, the total decay rate for an ion at position z can be written as:

$$W(n, z) = f_{1.76}(n, z) W_{rad}^{1.76} + W_{non-rad} \, , \tag{3}$$

where $f_{1.76}$ denotes the optical DOS, normalized to the optical DOS for bulk Al_2O_3 with a refractive index of 1.76. $W_{rad}^{1.76}$ is the radiative decay rate in bulk Al_2O_3.

Figure 2 shows the calculated optical DOS as a function of the distance z from the interface. The solid line shows the calculation for an infinite half space of Al_2O_3 (n = 1.76) brought in contact with an infinite half-space of air (n = 1.00). The interface is positioned at $z = 0$. The dashed line shows a calculation for Al_2O_3 in contact with a medium with a refractive index of 1.57. The optical DOS is discontinuous at the interface due to the discontinuity in the contribution of the polarization component that is parallel to the interface[11]. The oscillations observed on both sides are caused by interference between incoming and reflected waves and have a periodicity of $\sim\lambda/2n$. The peak position of the Cr distribution is indicated by the arrow. As can be seen, the radiative decay rate is suppressed towards the interface and increases for increasing refractive index at the position of the Cr ions.

The effect of the optical DOS on the radiative lifetime was obtained by integrating the optical DOS over depth using the known Cr depth distribution. This calculation was repeated for refractive indices of the liquid in the range 1.0-1.76. The result of this calculation is shown by the dashed line in Fig. 1, assuming a radiative decay rate of 310 s^{-1} for Cr ions in bulk Al_2O_3 and no non-radiative decay ($W_{non\text{-}rad} = 0$). The value of 310 s^{-1} was arbitrarily chosen such that the calculated variation of the radiative decay rate can be compared to the experimental data. As can be seen by comparing the dashed line with the data, the slope in the data cannot be described by assuming radiative decay only. The data can be fitted if non-radiative decay rate is introduced as given by Eq. (3). The solid lines show a single fit to all data, assuming the same radiative rate for all Cr concentrations, but a different non-radiative rate, resulting in a radiative decay rate $W_{rad}^{1.76}$=164±10 s^{-1} for bulk Al_2O_3. The corresponding non-radiative decay rate increases linearly from 137 to 168 s^{-1} with Cr concentration. These well characterized samples will be used to measure changes in spontaneous emission induced by absorbing or strongly scattering media where theory is less well developed.

Similar experiments were performed by bringing 100 nm thick SiO_2 layers implanted with erbium in contact with a range of transparent liquids. After annealing, the Er implanted samples show clear luminescence at a wavelength of 1.536 μm, related to the transition from the $^4I_{13/2}$ first excited state to the $^4I_{15/2}$ ground state of the Er^{3+} ion. The measured decay rate for liquids with different refractive indices is shown in Fig. 3. The inset shows the experimental setup, where the Er ions are pumped from the front and the PL signal is collected from the back of the sample, through the silicon substrate. As for the Cr doped Al_2O_3 an increase of the decay rate with refractive index of the liquid is observed.

Calculations of the optical DOS for a thin film geometry involving two interfaces were done.[11] Because the refractive index of the SiO_2 layer ($n = 1.45$) is much lower than that of the Si substrate ($n = 3.44$), the structure does not support guided modes in the SiO_2 layer. It was found that for a 100 nm thick SiO_2 film on Si the optical DOS for a wavelength of 1.5 μm increases in the entire SiO_2 film, when the refractive index of the liquid is increased. No oscillations of the optical DOS in the SiO_2 film are observed because the film thickness is much smaller than the wavelength of emission. However, the optical DOS in the layer is significantly increased with respect to the bulk value due to the presence of the high index Si substrate.

The effect of the position-dependent optical DOS was integrated over the film thickness using the known Er depth distribution and the known distribution of the 488 nm pump laser light through the film. The non-radiative decay rate was assumed to be independent of the refractive index of the covering liquid. The solid line in Fig. 3 shows a best fit to the data by assuming a radiative decay rate of 69 s^{-1} and a non-radiative decay rate of 115 s^{-1}. The difference between the solid line and the dashed line shows the calculated variation of the radiative decay rate as a function of the refractive index of the covering liquid. The radiative decay rate of the Er ions in the SiO_2 layer of 69±10 s^{-1} can be converted into a radiative decay rate for Er ions in bulk SiO_2 of 48±10 s^{-1} using the known optical DOS of the layer structure. This value is lower than that for the layer, because the high refractive index Si substrate increases the optical DOS in the SiO_2 film.

Using the now known radiative decay rate of Er ions in SiO_2 prepared via a wet chemical process, changes in the Er decay rate can now be used to probe the optical DOS in systems where theory to calculate the optical DOS is less well developed. Figure 4 shows luminescence decay traces measured at a wavelength of 1.536 μm for an Er-implanted colloidal particle (340 nm diameter) in air and in contact with an index matching liquid (n = 1.45). A clear increase in the decay rate from 69 s^{-1} to 101 s^{-1} is observed when the spheres are index matched. The inset shows a SEM image, taken from the top, that shows the arrangement of the colloidal spheres on the Si substrate. Some local ordering of the spheres in a hexagonal pattern is visible.

The difference in the measured decay rates is caused by a change in the optical DOS, assuming that the non-radiative decay rate is independent of the optical surrounding. The optical DOS can be calculated for the index matched spheres, where the problem reduces to the problem of a single interface between Si (n = 3.44) and SiO_2 (n = 1.45). The result of that calculation shows that the influence of the interface is negligible (< 6%) at the position of the Er ions, so that the radiative decay rate is the same as that for bulk SiO_2. In absence of non-radiative decay, it would be concluded that the index matching liquid increases the radiative decay rate by a factor of 1.5 (from 69 to 101 s^{-1}). However, using the radiative decay rate determined from the 100 nm thick SiO_2 film of 48±10 s^{-1}, we obtain a non-radiative decay rate of 53±10 s^{-1}. Using this non-radiative decay rate the radiative decay rate will be suppressed from 48±10 s^{-1} (101-53), for the index matched sample, to 16±10 s^{-1} (69-53) for the same sample in air. This corresponds to a factor 2-4 increase of the radiative decay rate due to the presence of the liquid. Note that the extremely low radiative decay rate of Er in silica is partly due to the fact that the colloids are surrounded by air (n = 1.0).

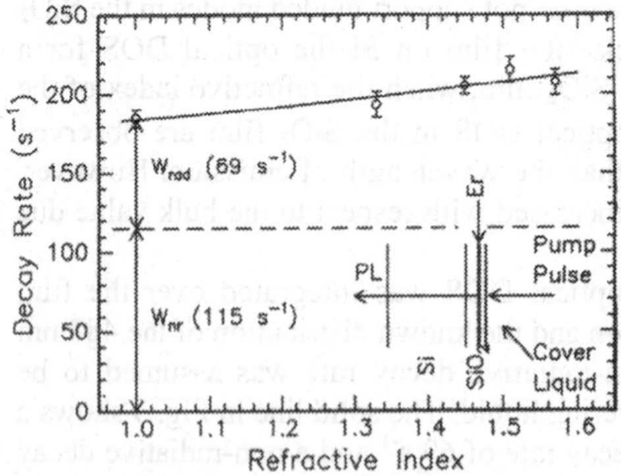

Figure 3: Measured decay rate of Er ions implanted into a 100 nm thick SiO_2 layer brought in contact with liquids with different refractive indices. The data can be fitted using the calculated optical DOS, resulting in a radiative decay rate of 69±10 s^{-1} and a non-radiative decay rate of 115±10 s^{-1}. The inset shows the experimental setup.

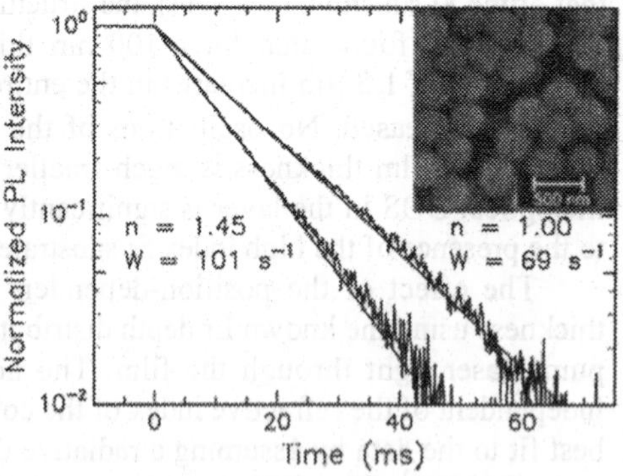

Figure 4: Luminescence decay traces for Er implanted SiO_2 colloidal spheres of 339 nm diameter. The inset shows a SEM image of the sample looking from the top. A clear increase in decay rate is observed when the spheres are index matched using a water-glycerol mixture with n = 1.45.

3. 2-D Photonic Crystals

Bandstructure Calculations

Figure 5 shows the structure of a 2-D photonic crystal of infinitely long cylinders on a square lattice. Indicated in the figure are the cylinder radius r and pitch a. The photonic bandstructure of this structure was calculated using the transfer matrix method,[15] for different dielectric constant ε of the rods and for various values of the radius-to-pitch ratio r/a. The bandstructure was calculated for transverse magnetic (TM) polarization (E field along the cylinder axis) and transverse electric (TE) polarization (E field perpendicular to the cylinder axis). The definition of TM and TE polarization is indicated in the right side of Fig. 5. For sufficiently high dielectric constant of the rods, such a structure shows photonic bandgaps for TM polarization only,[16] i.e., no waves with TM polarization can propagate in any direction perpendicular to the rods. One interesting application of the square lattice of rods is the fabrication of a 90° waveguide bend.[17,18]

Figure 6 shows the calculated bandstructure for a lattice of Si rods ($\varepsilon = 11.8$, $n = 3.44$) for $r/a = 0.18$. A photonic bandgap is observed for TM polarization extending from $\omega a/2\pi c = 0.30$ to 0.44. Bandstructure calculations repeated for different r/a and ε show that bandgaps for TM polarization exist for $\varepsilon > 3.8$ ($n > 1.95$),[19] which is just out of reach of standard polymers and glasses. Therefore, silicon seems a natural choice because of its high refractive index and because microfabrication technology is well developed for this material. The optical bandgap energy of Si is 1.1 eV, corresponding to a vacuum wavelength of ~1.1 μm, consequently Si is transparent in the near-infrared, which allows for fabrication of devices operating at the standard telecommunication windows at 1.3 and 1.5 μm.

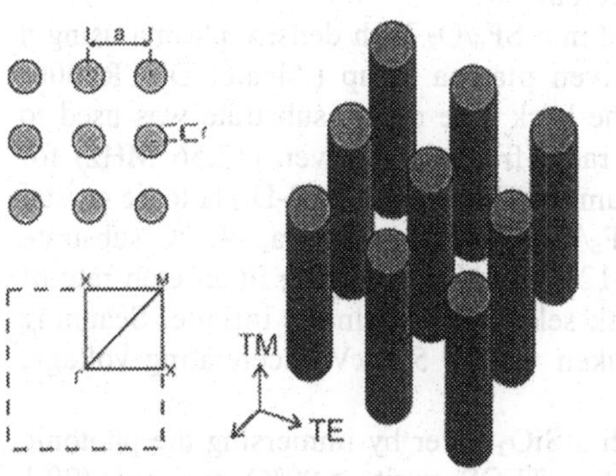

Figure 5: Square lattice of dielectric cylinders with radius r and pitch a. The Γ, X, and M points of symmetry in the square Brillouin zone are indicated in the left side of the figure. The electric field vector for transverse magnetic (TM) and transverse electric (TE) polarization are indicated in the right side of the figure.

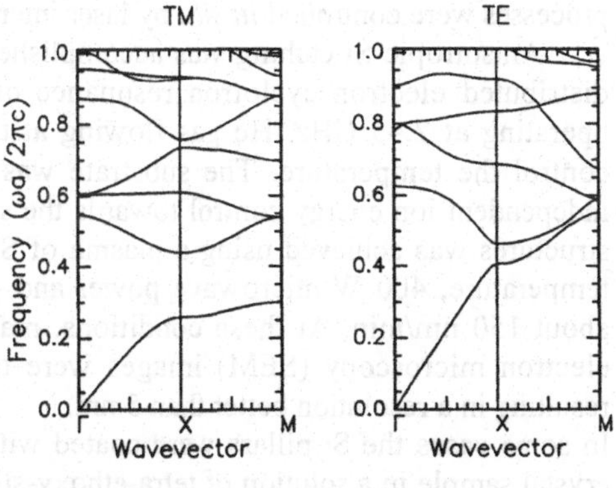

Figure 6: Calculated bandstructure along the ΓX and XM directions for a square lattice of Si cylinders ($n = 3.44$). A bandgap for TM polarization is observed from $\omega a/2\pi c = 0.30$ to 0.40. No bandgaps are observed for TE polarization

For devices operating at a wavelength of 1.5 μm, a lattice constant of 570 nm is required, with a corresponding diameter of 205 nm of the rods. For proper vertical confinement in the photonic crystal index guiding may be used. This could be achieved using amorphous Si (n = 3.74) on Si (n = 3.44).[19] Using dielectric waveguide theory to calculate the modes of such a waveguide, it is concluded that the rods need to be etched at least 5 μm deep through a 2 μm thick amorphous silicon layer to prevent light from leaking to the substrate.

Experimental

Amorphous Si (a-Si) layers on crystalline Si (c-Si) were obtained by irradiation of (100) oriented crystalline Si substrates with 4 MeV Xe ions at 77 K to a fluence of 2×10^{15} cm^{-2}. Annealing at 500 °C for 1 hr in a vacuum furnace was performed to remove point defects and to relax the a-Si network structure,[20] to reach a thermally stable state with small absorption at 1.5 μm. The irradiation resulted in a 1.93 μm thick a-Si layer as measured by variable angle spectroscopic ellipsometry in the 300-1700 nm wavelength range. Rutherford backscattering spectrometry (RBS) measurements were done with a 2 MeV He^+ beam at a scattering angle of 165°.

All samples were coated with a resist double layer consisting of a 400 nm thick bottom layer of hardbaked AZ S1813 photoresist (Shipley) with an overlying 80 nm thick silicon containing negative tone e-beam resist SNR (Toyo Soda). Mask patterns were defined using e-beam lithography. After exposure (Leica EBPG05, 100 kV, 100 μC cm^{-2}) the patterns were developed in xylene for 20 s followed by dipping in isopropyl-alcohol for 30 s to remove the unexposed areas. The pattern was then anisotropically transferred into the bottom resist layer by low pressure (0.3 Pa) oxygen reactive ion etching, using a plasma at a low rf power density of 0.07 W cm^{-2} (dc bias of -170 V). All patterning processes were controlled *in situ* by laser interferometry.

Anisotropic Si etching was accomplished in a SF_6/O_2 high density plasma using a distributed electron cyclotron resonance driven plasma setup (Alcatel DECR2000) operating at 2.45 GHz. He gas flowing at the back side of the substrate was used to control the temperature. The substrate was radio-frequency driven (13.56 MHz) for independent ion energy control towards the sample. Etching of the 2-D photonic crystal structures was achieved using a plasma of SF_6/O_2 (7.3:1.0) at 0.1 Pa, -97 °C substrate temperature, 400 W microwave power and -12 V dc bias, resulting in an etch rate of about 150 nm/min. At these conditions, mask selectivity is almost infinite. Scanning electron microscopy (SEM) images were taken with a 5.0 kV accelerating voltage, resulting in a resolution better than 5 nm.

In some cases the Si pillars were coated with a SiO_2 layer by immersing the photonic crystal sample in a solution of tetra-ethoxy-silane (TEOS, purity ≥ 99%), ammonia (29.1 wt.%), water, and ethanol. All substrates were cleaned using 2 M KOH in ethanol for 15 min and rinsed with pure ethanol prior to deposition. For incorporation of a fluorescent dye in the silica layer,[7,21] 12.52 mg eosin-5-isothiocyanate (eosin-ITC) was first reacted with 41.8 mg (3-aminopropyl)-triethoxy-silane (APS) in 2.2 g dry ethanol by stirring for 16 h. Then 0.250 g of this mixture was added to a solution of 7.641 g ethanol, 0.809 g

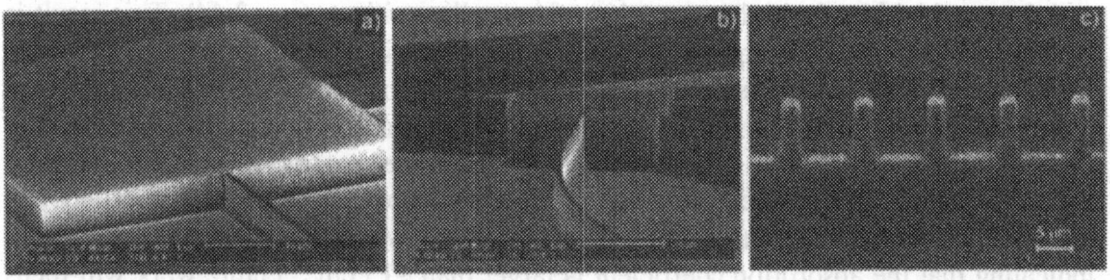

Figure 7: SEM images of a square lattice of Si cylinders of 205 nm diameter and a pitch of 570 nm, etched 5 µm deep (Figs. a) and b)). Figure a) shows a waveguide bend defined by removing a row of rods etched in crystalline Si, with input and output waveguide defined. Figure b) shows a similar bend structure etched through a 2 µm thick a-Si layer on c-Si. The waveguides serve to couple light in and out of the structure. Figure c) shows a cross-section made using confocal microscopy of a square lattice of micrometer size Si pillars, coated with a SiO_2 layer containing a luminescent dye (eosin-ITC).

water, and 0.699 g ammonia. Next 0.380 g TEOS was added to the solution. All reactions took place at room temperature under continuous stirring. Fluorescence confocal microscopy (Leica TCS NT, 100× lens with NA 1.4) at excitation wavelengths of 476 and 488 nm was used to image the eosin-ITC coated silicon pillars.

Results and Discussion

Anisotropic etching of Si in a high density SF_6/O_2 plasma, using either an electron cyclotron resonance driven[22] or inductively coupled plasma,[23] is a well understood process. The anisotropy is the result of involatile oxofluoride species. The overall etch profile is a delicate balance between etch product formation and ion-enhanced desorption. By changing the temperature, the oxygen flow and dc-bias separately at a given fluorine content, the dependence of the etching process on these parameters was optimized to great precision.[24]

Figures 7a and b show SEM images of an array of 205 nm diameter silicon rods placed on a square lattice with a pitch of 570 nm, etched 5 µm deep. Figure 7a shows a square lattice in which a waveguide bend is defined by removing a row of rods from the square lattice. The row of rods removed to form a 90° waveguide bend is clearly visible. Such a line defect serves as a waveguide that can guide light around the corner with high efficiency[17] with a bending radius that is much smaller than that of a conventional dielectric waveguide bend. Figure 7b shows an image of a similar device etched through an a-Si/c-Si stack. As can be seen the etching has proceeded continuous through the a-Si/c-Si interface, despite the fact that the etch rate of amorphous silicon is 30% lower than that of crystalline silicon. Waveguides to couple light in and out of the structure are integrated as well. They also include the 1.9 µm thick a-Si top layer that serves to confine the light in the vertical direction. The three waveguides at the right are defined to test the leakage of the bend in the straight forward and 45 degree directions.

The optical properties of the amorphous silicon guiding layer were measured by variable angle spectroscopic ellipsometry (not shown). The refractive index of a-Si is 3.73

at 1.5 μm, significantly higher than that of crystalline silicon (n = 3.44). This result is similar to that found for amorphous silicon made by ion irradiation with different ions.[25] Ellipsometry and transmission measurements on 2 μm thick a-Si layers gave no indication for measurable absorption, suggesting that the absorption coefficient is smaller than ~50 cm^{-1}. Hence, a-Si will be a suitable waveguide material in a photonic crystal with dimensions of the order of 10 μm. However, no measurable transmission was observed through the input and output waveguides, which are of order mm length, indicating that the absorption coefficient is larger than ~15 cm^{-1}. Future work will focus on reducing the absorption losses of a-Si.

Figure 7c shows a cross-section made by fluorescence confocal microscopy of Si pillars coated with a SiO_2 layer containing eosin-ITC fluorescent dye. From this image it can be seen that the full surface of the structure is covered with a fluorescent layer. Although the pillars in this image are much wider than those needed for photonic crystals operating around 1.5 μm, these results show that it is possible to coat micrometer size structures with a fluorescent layer by means of a wet chemical process at room temperature. By using other luminescent species that luminesce at wavelengths in the photonic bandgap region, the influence of a 2-D photonic crystal on spontaneous emission can be studied. For instance, similar oxide films on a stratified substrate doped with erbium ions show clear photoluminescence around 1.5 μm with a luminescence lifetime as long as 5.5 ms, and a quantum efficiency of ~38%, depending on the Er concentration.

4. Conclusions

The spontaneous emission of Cr ions implanted into Al_2O_3 and Er ions implanted in 100 nm thick SiO_2 layers on Si was influenced by covering the samples with different refractive index liquids. The measured changes in spontaneous emission rate of the atoms were compared to a calculation of the optical density-of-states. The experimental data can be fitted by assuming both radiative and non-radiative decay processes. From these fits a radiative decay rate of 164±10 s^{-1} was determined for Cr ions in Al_2O_3 independent of Cr concentration. For the Er implanted SiO_2 samples a radiative decay rate of 48±10 s^{-1} was found, which was then used to study the reduction of spontaneous emission rate in Er doped colloidal spheres with a diameter of 339 nm. The colloids surrounded by air show an Er decay rate as low as 69±10 s^{-1}. By index matching the spheres, the emission rate was found to be increased by a factor of 2-4.

Bandstructure calculations were performed for a square lattice of Si cylinders and show bandgaps for TM polarization only. For a radius-to-pitch ratio of 0.18 a bandgap was found for $\omega a/2\pi c$ = 0.30 to 0.44. Devices for a wavelength of 1.5 μm using this photonic bandgap were fabricated using deep anisotropic etching of 205 nm diameter cylinders on a square lattice with a pitch of 570 nm in a SF_6/O_2 plasma. Vertical confinement may be provided by etching 5 μm long cylinders through a 2 μm thick amorphous Si layer (n = 3.73) on crystalline Si. Coating of Si cylinders with SiO_2 layers containing a luminescent dye was achieved using a wet chemical process. Similar layers can be used to probe spontaneous emission in 2-D photonic crystals.

Acknowledgments

We would like to acknowledge Ad Lagendijk and Adriaan Tip for stimulating discussions. This work is part of the research program of the foundation for fundamental research on matter (FOM) and was made possible by financial support of the Dutch organization for scientific research (NWO).

References

[1] E.M. Purcell, Spontaneous emission probabilities at radio frequencies, *Phys. Rev.* **69**, 681 (1946).

[2] K.H. Drexhage, Influence of a dielectric interface on fluorescence decay time, *J. Lumin.* **1,2**, 693 (1970).

[3] R.G. Hulet, E.S. Hilfer, and D. Kleppner, Inhibited spontaneous emission by a Rydberg atom, *Phys. Rev. Lett.* **55**, 2137 (1985).

[4] A.M. Vredenberg, N.E.J. Hunt, E.F. Schubert, D.C. Jacobson, J.M. Poate, and G.J. Zydzik, Controlled spontaneous emission from Er^{3+} in a transparent Si/SiO_2 microcavity, *Phys. Rev. Lett.* **71**, 517 (1993).

[5] E. Snoeks, A. Lagendijk, and A. Polman, Measuring and modifying the spontaneous emission rate of erbium near an interface, *Phys. Rev. Lett.* **74**, 2459 (1995)

[6] W.L. Barnes, Topical review: Fluorescence near interfaces: the role of photonic mode density, *J. Mod. Opt.* **45**, 661 (1998).

[7] A. van Blaaderen, and A. Vrij, Synthesis and characterization of colloidal dispersions of fluorescent monodisperse silica spheres, *Langmuir* **8**, 2921 (1993).

[8] L.H. Slooff, M.J.A. de Dood, A. van Blaaderen, and A. Polman, Erbium-implanted silica colloids with 80% luminescence quantum efficiency, *Appl. Phys. Lett.* **76**, 3682 (2000).

[9] T.M. Hensen, M.J.A. de Dood, and A. Polman, Luminescence quantum efficiency and local optical density of states in thin film ruby made by ion implantation, (unpublished).

[10] H. Khosravi, and R. Loudon, Vacuum field fluctuation and spontaneous emission in the vicinity of a dielectric surface, *Proc. R. Soc. Lond. A* **433**, 337 (1991).

[11] H.P. Urbach, and G.L.J.A. Rikken, Spontaneous emission from a dielectric slab, *Phys. Rev. A* **57**, 3913 (1998).

[12] B.A. van Tiggelen, and E. Kogan, Analogies between light and electrons: Density of states and Friedel's identity, *Phys. Rev. A* **75**, 422 (1995).

[13] F.J.P. Schuurmans, D.T.N. de Lang, G.H. Wegdam, R. Sprik, and A. Lagendijk, Local-field effects on spontaneous emission in a dense supercritical gas, *Phys. Rev. Lett.* **80**, 5077 (1998).

[14] R. Sprik, B.A. van Tiggelen, and A. Lagendijk, Optical emission in periodic dielectrics, *Europhys. Lett.* **35**, 265 (1996).

[15] J.B. Pendry, and A. MacKinnon, Calculation of photon dispersion relations, *Phys. Rev. Lett.* **69**, 2772 (1992).

[16] J.D. Joannopoulos, R.D. Meade, and J.N. Winn, *Photonic Crystals: Molding the Flow of Light*, Princeton University Press (1995).

[17] A. Mekis, J.C. Chen, I. Kurland, S. Fan, and J.D. Joannopoulos, High transmission through sharp bends in photonic crystal waveguides, *Phys. Rev. Lett.* **77**, 3787 (1996).

[18] S.Y. Lin, E. Chow, and V. Hietala and P.R. Villeneuve and J.D. Joannopoulos, Experimental demonstration of guiding and bending of electromagnetic waves in a photonic crystal, *Science* **282**, 274 (1998).

[19] M.J.A. de Dood, E. Snoeks, A. Moroz, and A. Polman, Design and optimization of 2-D photonic crystal waveguides based on silicon, (unpublished).

[20] S. Roorda, W.C. Sinke, J.M. Poate, D.C. Jacobson, S. Dierker, B.S. Dennis, D.J. Eaglesham, F. Spaepen, and P. Fuoss, Structural relaxation and defect annihilation in pure amorphous silicon, *Phys. Rev. B* **44**, 3702 (1991).

[21] N.A.M. Verhaegh, and A. van Blaaderen, Dispersions of Rhodamine-labeled silica spheres - synthesis, characterization and fluorescence confocal scanning laser microscopy, *Langmuir* **10**, 1427 (1994).

[22] S. Tachi, K. Tsujimoto, S. Arai and T. Kure, Low-temperature dry etching, *J. Vac. Sci. Technol. A* **9**, 796 (1991).

[23] J.K. Bhardwaj, and H. Ashraf, Advanced silicon etching using high density plasmas, *SPIE* **2639**, 224 (1995).

[24] T. Zijlstra, E. van der Drift, M.J.A. de Dood, E. Snoeks, and A. Polman, Fabrication of two-dimensional photonic crystal waveguides at 1.5 µm in silicon by deep anisotropic etching, *J. Vac. Sci. Technol. B* **17**, 2734 (1999).

[25] C.N. Waddell, W.G. Spitzer, J.E. Fredrickson, G.K. Hubler, and T.A. Kennedy, Amorphous silicon produced by ion implantation: Effects of ion mass and thermal annealing, *J. Appl. Phys.* **55**, 4361 (1984).

PERCOLATION COMPOSITES: LOCALIZATION OF SURFACE PLASMONS AND ENHANCED OPTICAL NONLINEARITIES

V. A. Podolskiy, A. K. Sarychev, and Vladimir M. Shalaev

Department of Physics, New Mexico State University, Las Cruces, NM 88003, U.S.A.

In random metal-dielectric composites near the percolation threshold surface plasmons are localized in small nanometer-sized areas, hot spots, where the local field can exceed the applied field by several orders of magnitude. The high local fields result in dramatic enhancement of optical responses, especially, nonlinear ones. The local-field distributions and enhanced optical nonlinearities are described using the scale renormalization. A theory predicts that the local fields consist of spatially separated clusters of sharp peaks representing localized surface plasmons. Experimental observations are in good accord with theoretical predictions. The localization of plasmons maps the Anderson localization problem described by the random Hamiltonian with both on- and off-diagonal disorder. A feasibility of nonlinear surface-enhanced spectroscopy of single molecules and nanocrystals on percolation films is shown.

I. Introduction

Metal-dielectric composites attract much attention because of their unique optical properties, which are significantly different from those of constituents forming the composite.[1–3] Semicontinuous metal films can be produced by thermal evaporation or sputtering of metal onto an insulating substrate. First, in the growing process, small metallic grains are formed on the substrate. A typical size a of a metal grain is about 5 nm to 50 nm. As the film grows, the metal filling factor increases and coalescence occurs,

C.M. Soukoulis (ed.), Photonic Crystals and Light Localization in the 21st Century, 567–575.

so that irregularly shaped self-similar clusters (fractals) are formed on the substrate. The concept of scale-invariance (fractality) plays an important role in description of various properties of percolation systems.[2,4] The sizes of the fractal structures diverge in the vicinity of the percolation threshold, where an "infinite" percolation cluster of metal is eventually formed, representing a continuous conducting path between the ends of a sample. At the percolation threshold the metal-insulator transition occurs in the system. At higher surface coverage, the film is mostly metallic, with voids of irregular shape. With further coverage increase, the film becomes uniform.

In random metal-dielectric films, surface-plasmon excitations are localized in small nanometer-scale areas referred to as "hot spots".[2,5,6] As discussed below, the localization can be attributed to the Anderson localization of plasmons in semicontinuous metal films near a percolation threshold (in this case, referred to as percolation films). The electromagnetic energy is accumulated in the hot spots associated with localized plasmons, leading to the local fields that can exceed the intensity of the applied field by four to five orders of magnitude. The high local fields in the hot spots also result in dramatically enhanced *nonlinear* optical responses proportional to the local field raised to a power greater than one.

Below, we consider a simple scaling approach explaining the extremely inhomogeneous field distribution and giant optical nonlinearities of fractal composites. We also show a great potential of percolation films for surface-enhanced local spectroscopy of single molecules and nanocrystals.

II. Scaling in the local-field distribution

For the films concerned, gaps between metal grains are filled by a dielectric substrate so that a semicontinuous metal film can be thought of as a $2d$ array of metal and dielectric grains randomly distributed over the plane. The dielectric constant of a metal can be approximated by the Drude formula

$$\epsilon_m = \epsilon_b - (\omega_p/\omega)^2/(1 + i\omega_\tau/\omega), \tag{1}$$

where ϵ_b is the interband contribution, ω_p is the plasma frequency, and ω_τ is the plasmon relaxation rate ($\omega_\tau \ll \omega_p$). In the high-frequency range considered here, losses in metal grains are relatively small, $\omega_\tau \ll \omega$. Therefore, the real part ϵ'_m of the metal dielectric function ϵ_m is much larger (in modulus) than the imaginary part ϵ''_m, i.e., the loss parameter κ is small, $\kappa = \epsilon''_m/|\epsilon'_m| \cong \omega_\tau/\omega \ll 1$. We note that ϵ'_m is negative for frequencies ω less than the renormalized plasma frequency,

$$\tilde{\omega}_p = \omega_p/\sqrt{\epsilon_b}. \tag{2}$$

It is instructive to consider first the special case of $-\epsilon'_m = \epsilon_d$, where $\epsilon_m \equiv \epsilon'_m + i\epsilon''_m$ and ϵ_d are the dielectric constants of the metallic and dielectric components, respectively. The condition $-\epsilon'_m = \epsilon_d$ corresponds to the resonance of individual metal particles in a dielectric host, in the two-dimensional case. For simplicity, we also set $-\epsilon_m = \epsilon_d = 1$, which can always be done by simply renormalizing the corresponding quantities.

It can be shown that the field distribution on a percolation film at $-\epsilon_m = \epsilon_d = 1$ formally maps the Anderson metal-insulator transition problem.[2,5,6] In accord with this, the field potential representing plasmon modes of a percolation film must be characterized by the same spatial distribution as the electron wavefunction in the Anderson transition problem. Such mathematical equivalence of the two physically different problems stems from the fact that the current conservation law for a percolation film acquires (when written in the discretized form) the form of the Kirchhoff's equations, which, in turn, (when written in the matrix form) become identical to the equations describing the Anderson transition problem.[6] The corresponding Kirchhoff Hamiltonian for the field-distribution problem is given by a matrix with random elements which can be expressed in terms of the dielectric constants for metal and dielectric bonds of the lattice representing the film. In this matrix, the values $\epsilon_m = -1$ and $\epsilon_d = 1$ appear in the matrix elements with probability p and $(1-p)$, respectively (where p is the metal filling factor given at percolation by $p = p_c$, with $p_c = 1/2$ for a self-dual system). In such a form, the Kirchhoff Hamiltonian is characterized by the random matrix, similar to that in the Anderson transition problem, with both on- and off-diagonal disorder. Based on this mathematical equivalence, it was concluded in[2,5,6] that the plasmons in a percolation film can experience the Anderson-type localization within small areas, with the size given by the Anderson length ξ_A. For the most localized plasmon modes, ξ_A can be as small as the size of one grain a.

Below we develop a simple scaling approach that explains the non-trivial field distribution predicted and observed in percolation films. This scale-renormalization method supports main conclusions of a rigorous (but tedious) theory of Refs.[2,5,6] and has a virtue of being simple and clear, which is important for understanding and interpretation of future experiments.

First, we estimate the field in the hot spots for the considered case of $-\epsilon_m' = \epsilon_d$. Hereafter we use the sign * (not to be confused with complex conjugation) to indicate that the quantity concerned is given for the considered case of $-\epsilon_m'/\epsilon_d$ (with $\epsilon_d \sim 1$); for ξ_A, however, we omit this sign since this quantity always refers to the case of $-\epsilon_m'/\epsilon_d$.

Since at the optical frequencies ϵ_m' is negative, metal particles can be roughly thought of as inductor-resistor $(L-R)$ elements, whereas the dielectric gaps between the particles can be treated as capacitive (C) elements. Then, the condition $\epsilon_m' = -\epsilon_d$ means that the conductivities of the $L-R$ and C elements are equal in magnitude and opposite in sign, i.e., there is a resonance in the equivalent $L-R-C$ circuit corresponding to individual particles.

The local field in resonating particles is enhanced by the resonance quality-factor Q which is the inverse of the loss-factor, $Q = \kappa^{-1}$, so that

$$E_m^* \sim E_0 \kappa^{-1} (a/\xi_A)^2 , \tag{3}$$

where the factor $(a/\xi_A)^2$ takes into account that the resonating mode is localized within ξ_A. The resonant modes excited by a monochromatic light represent only the fraction κ of all the modes so that the average distance (referred to as the field correlation length ξ_e^*) between the field peaks is given by

$$\xi_e^* \sim a/\sqrt{\kappa} \gg \xi_A. \tag{4}$$

Note that the field peaks associated with the resonance plasmon modes represent in fact the normal modes, with the near-zero eigennumbers, of the Kirchhoff's Hamiltonian discussed above.[2,6] These modes are strongly excited by the applied field and seen as giant field fluctuations on the surface of the film.

Now we turn to the important case of the "high contrast," with $|\epsilon_m| \gg \epsilon_d$, that corresponds to the long-wavelength part of the spectrum where the local-field enhancement can be especially strong. From basic principles of Anderson localization,[2] it is clear that a higher contrast favors localization so that plasmon modes are expected to be localized in this case as well.

It is clear that at $|\epsilon_m| \gg \epsilon_d$ individual metal particles cannot resonate. We can renormalize, however, the high-contrast system to the case of $-\epsilon'_m = \epsilon_d$ considered above by formally "dividing" the film into square elements of the special resonant size

$$l_r = a\left(|\epsilon_m|/\epsilon_d\right)^{\nu/(t+s)} \quad (5)$$

and considering these squares as new renormalized elements of the film. Using the known scaling dependences[1,4] for "metal" and "dielectric" squares of size l (which, respectively, do or do not contain a metal continuous path through the square):

$$\epsilon_m(l) \sim (l/a)^{-t/\nu}\epsilon_m \quad (6)$$

and

$$\epsilon_d(l) \sim (l/a)^{s/\nu}\epsilon_d, \quad (7)$$

we obtain the dielectric constants of the renormalized elements with the size $l = l_r$, equal in magnitude and opposite in sign, i.e.,

$$-\epsilon_m(l_r) = \epsilon_d(l_r). \quad (8)$$

Thus, for these renormalized elements of the size l_r, there is a resonance similar to the resonance in the $R-L-C$ circuit describing individual metal particles in a dielectric host. In this case, however, some effective (renormalized) $R-L-C$ circuits represent the resonating square elements.

For a two-dimensional percolation film, the critical exponents are given by $t \approx s \approx \nu \approx 4/3$; they represent the percolation critical exponents for conductivity, dielectric constant, and percolation correlation length, respectively.[1,4]

In the renormalized system, the estimate obtained above for field peaks still holds. Since the electric field and eigenfunction both scale as l_r we arrive at the conclusion that in the high-contrast system (with $|\epsilon_m| \gg \epsilon_d$), the field maxima are estimated as

$$E_m \sim (l_r/a)E_m^* \sim E_0\kappa^{-1}(l_r/a)(a/\xi_A)^2 \sim E_0\kappa^{-1}\left(l_r/\xi_A\right)^2 \sim E_0(a/\xi_A)^2|\epsilon_m|^{3/2}/\left(\epsilon_d^{1/2}\epsilon''_m\right). \quad (9)$$

The light-induced eigenmodes in the high-contrast system are separated, on the average, by the distance ξ_e that exceeds the mode separation ξ_e^* at $\epsilon_m = -\epsilon_d$ by factor l_r/a,

$$\xi_e \sim (l_r/a)\xi_e^* \sim l_r/\sqrt{\kappa} \sim a|\epsilon_m|/\sqrt{\epsilon''_m\epsilon_d}. \quad (10)$$

For a Drude metal at $\omega \ll \omega_p$, the local field peaks, according to (1) and (9) are given by

$$E_m/E_0 \sim \epsilon_d^{-1/2}(a/\xi_A)^2\left(\omega_p/\omega_\tau\right), \quad (11)$$

and the distance between the excited modes (10) is estimated as

$$\xi_e \sim a\omega_p / \sqrt{\epsilon_d \omega \omega_\tau}. \tag{12}$$

Figure 1 illustrates the above described renormalization of the field peaks and their spatial separations at the transition between the reference (renormalized) system with $-\epsilon_m = \epsilon_d = 1$ and the high-contrast system of $|\epsilon_m/\epsilon_d| \gg 1$.

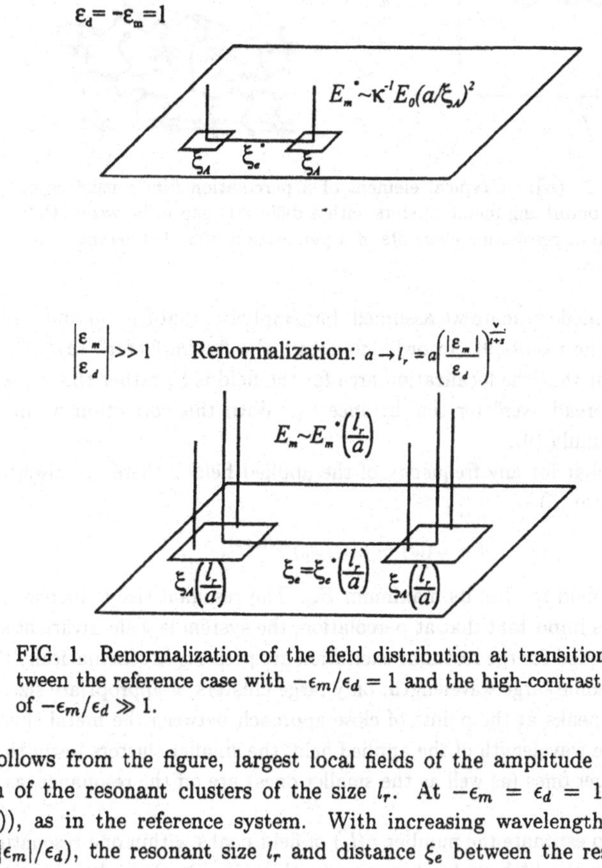

FIG. 1. Renormalization of the field distribution at transition between the reference case with $-\epsilon_m/\epsilon_d = 1$ and the high-contrast case of $-\epsilon_m/\epsilon_d \gg 1$.

As follows from the figure, largest local fields of the amplitude E_m result from excitation of the resonant clusters of the size l_r. At $-\epsilon_m = \epsilon_d = 1$, we have $l_r = a$ (see (5)), as in the reference system. With increasing wavelength (and thus the contrast $|\epsilon_m|/\epsilon_d$), the resonant size l_r and distance ξ_e between the resonating modes both increase.

The above results have a clear physical interpretation and can be also obtained from the following complementary considerations. Let us consider two metal clusters, with conductance $\Sigma_m = -i(a/4\pi)\omega\epsilon_m(l)$, separated by a dielectric gap, with the conductance $\Sigma_d = -i(a/4\pi)\omega\epsilon_d(l)$, as shown in Fig. 2a. The clusters and the gap are both of a size l, and $\epsilon_m(l)$ and $\epsilon_d(l)$ are defined in (6) and (7), respectively. The equivalent conductance Σ_e for Σ_m and Σ_d in series is given by $\Sigma_e = \Sigma_m\Sigma_d\big/(\Sigma_m + \Sigma_d)$ and the current j through the system is $j = \Sigma_e E_0 l$. The local field, however, is strongly inhomogeneous and the largest field occurs at the point of the close approach between the clusters, where the separation between clusters can be as small as a; then, the maximum field E_m is estimated as $E_m = (j/\Sigma_d)/a \sim E_0(l/a)\big/\left[1 + (l/a)^{(t+s)/\nu}\epsilon_d/\epsilon_m\right]$ (where we used Eqs. (6) and (7)). For the "resonant" size $l = l_r$, the real part of the denominator in the expression for E_m becomes zero, and the field E_m reaches its maximum, where it is estimated as $E_m/E_0 \sim \kappa^{-1}(l_r/a)$.

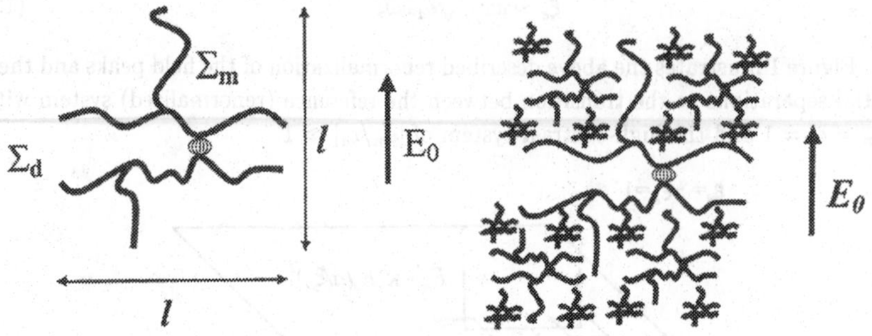

FIG. 2. **(a):** A typical element of a percolation film consisting of two conducting metal clusters with a dielectric gap in between. **(b):** Different resonating elements of a percolation film at different wavelengths.

In the obtained estimate we assumed, for simplicity, that $\xi_A \sim a$ and, in this limit, we reproduced the result (9). In order to obtain the "extra-factor" $(a/\xi_A)^2$ of (9), we take into account that the localization area for the field is ξ_A rather than a, so that the field peak is "spread over" for the distance ξ_A. With this correction we immediately arrive at the formula (9).

It is clear that for any frequency of the applied field ω there are always resonant clusters of the size (5)

$$l = l_r(\omega) \sim a(\omega/\tilde{\omega}_p)^{2\nu/(t+s)}, \tag{13}$$

where the local field reaches its maximum E_m. The resonant size l_r increases with the wavelength. It is important that at percolation, the system is scale-invariant so that all possible sizes needed for the resonant excitation are present, as schematically illustrated in Fig. 1b. At some large wavelength, only large clusters of appropriate sizes resonate leading to field peaks at the points of close approach between the metal clusters; with a decrease of the wavelength of the applied field, the smaller clusters begin to resonate, whereas the larger ones (as well as the smaller ones) are off the resonance, as shown in Fig. 1b.

We can also estimate the number $n(l_r)$ of field peaks within one resonating square of the size l_r. In the high-contrast system (with $|\epsilon_m/\epsilon_d| \gg 1$) each field maximum of the renormalized system (with $|\epsilon_m/\epsilon_d| = 1$) splits into $n(l_r)$ peaks of the E_m amplitude located along a dielectric gap in the "dielectric" square of the l_r size (see Figs. 1 and 2). The gap "area" scales as the capacitance of the dielectric gap, so must do the number of field peaks in the resonance square. Therefore, we estimate that

$$n(l_r) \propto (l_r/a)^{s/\nu_p}. \tag{14}$$

In accordance with the above considerations, the average (over the film surface) intensity of the local field is enhanced as

$$\left\langle \left|\frac{E}{E_0}\right|^2 \right\rangle \sim (E_m/E_0)^2 n(l_r)(\xi_A/\xi_e)^2 \sim (a/\xi_A)^2 \left|\epsilon_m\right|^{3/2} / (\epsilon_m'' \epsilon_d), \tag{15}$$

where we used (5), (10), and (14) and the critical exponents $t = s = \nu = 4/3$.

In Fig. 3, we also show the simulated field distribution on a silver-glass percolation film at two different wavelengths. In accordance with the consideration above, we see that the local field distribution consists of clusters of very sharp peaks with the spatial separation increasing with the wavelength. Qualitatively similar field distribution was detected in recent experiments[5] using scanning near-field optical microscopy.

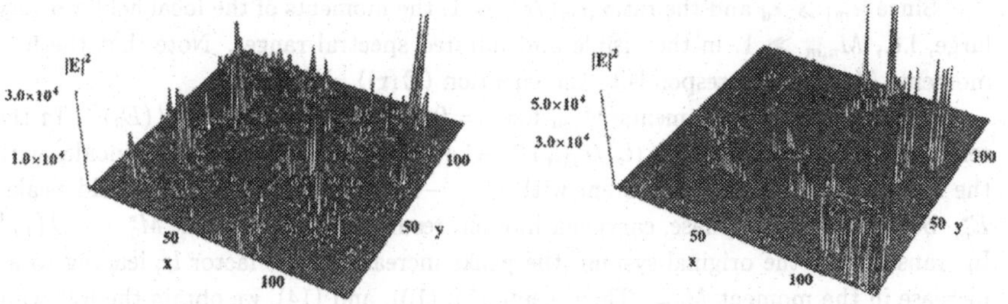

FIG. 3. Local field distribution on silver-glass percolation film at different wavelengths; **(a)**: $\lambda = 1.5\mu m$ and **(b)**: $\lambda := 10\mu m$.

Thus, using simple arguments based on the scaling dependences of $\epsilon_m(l)$ and $\epsilon_d(l)$ on l and the resonance condition $-\epsilon_m(l_r) = \epsilon_d(l_r)$, one can define the renormalization procedure that allows one to re-scale the "high-contrast" system to the renormalized one with $-\epsilon_m = \epsilon_d = 1$.

Below, we show that the enhanced local-field in the hot spots result in giant enhancement of *nonlinear* optical responses of semicontinuous films.

III. Enhanced optical nonlinearities

In general, we can define the high-order field moments as

$$M_{n,m} = \frac{1}{SE_0^m \left|E_0\right|^n} \int \left|E\left(\mathbf{r}\right)\right|^n E^m\left(\mathbf{r}\right) d\mathbf{r}, \tag{16}$$

where, as above, E_0 is the amplitude of the external field and $E(\mathbf{r})$ is the local field (note that $E^2(\mathbf{r}) \equiv \mathbf{E}(\mathbf{r}) \cdot \mathbf{E}(\mathbf{r})$). The integration is over the entire surface S of the film.

The high-order field moment $M_{2k,m} \propto E^{k+m}E^{*k}$ represents a nonlinear optical process in which, in one elementary act, $k+m$ photons are added and k photons are subtracted.[7] This is because the complex conjugated field in the general expression for the nonlinear polarization implies photon subtraction so that the corresponding frequency enters the nonlinear susceptibility with the minus sign.[7] Below, we show that the enhancement is significantly different for nonlinear processes with photon subtraction in comparison with those where all photons are entering the nonlinear susceptibility with the sign plus. Enhancement of the Kerr optical nonlinearity G_K (see below) is equal to $M_{2,2}$, second harmonic generation (SHG) and third harmonic generation (THG) enhancements are given by $|M_{0,2}|^2$ and $|M_{0,3}|^2$, respectively, and surface-enhanced Raman scattering (SERS) is represented by $M_{4,0}$.

The high-order moments of the local field in $d = 2$ percolation films can be estimated as $M_{n,m} \sim (E_m/E_0)^{n+m} n(l_r)(\xi_A/\xi_e)^2$. Using the scaling formulas (5)-(14) for the field distribution, we obtain the following estimate for the field moments

$$M_{n,m} \sim \left(\frac{E_m}{E_0}\right)^{n+m} \frac{(l_r/a)^{s/\nu}}{(\xi_e/\xi_A)^2} \sim \left(\frac{|\epsilon_m|^{3/2}}{(\xi_A/a)^2 \epsilon_d^{1/2} \epsilon_m''}\right)^{n+m-1}, \tag{17}$$

for $n + m > 1$ and $n > 0$ (where, we took into account that for two-dimensional percolation composites, the critical exponents are given by $t \cong s \cong \nu \cong 4/3$).

Since $|\epsilon_m| \gg \epsilon_d$ and the ratio $|\epsilon_m| / \epsilon_m'' \gg 1$, the moments of the local field are very large, i.e., $M_{n,m} \gg 1$, in the visible and infrared spectral ranges. Note that the first moment, $M_{0,1} \simeq 1$, corresponds to the equation $\langle \mathbf{E}(\mathbf{r}) \rangle = \mathbf{E}_0$.

Consider now the moments $M_{n,m}$ for $n = 0$, i.e., $M_{0,m} = \langle E^m(\mathbf{r}) \rangle / (E_0)^m$. In the renormalized system where $\epsilon_m(l_r)/\epsilon_d(l_r) \cong -1 + i\kappa$, the field distribution coincides with the field distribution in the system with $\epsilon_d \simeq -\epsilon_m' \sim 1$. In that system, field peaks, E_m^*, being different in phase, cancel each other, resulting in the moment $M_{0,m}^* \sim O(1)$.[6] In transition to the original system, the peaks increase by the factor l_r, leading to an increase in the moment $M_{0,m}$. Then, using (5), (10), and (14), we obtain the following equation for the moment:

$$M_{0,m} \sim M_{0,m}^*(l_r/a)^m \left(\frac{n(l_r)}{(\xi_e/a)^2}\right) \sim \kappa (l_r/a)^{m-2+s/\nu} \sim \frac{\epsilon_m'' |\epsilon_m|^{(m-3)/2}}{\epsilon_d^{(m-1)/2}}, \tag{18}$$

for $m > 1$ (where we again used the critical exponents $t \cong s \cong \nu \cong 4/3$).

For a Drude metal (1) and $\omega \ll \omega_p$, from (17) and (18), we obtain

$$M_{n,m} \sim \epsilon_d^{(1-n-m)/2} (a/\xi_A)^{2(n+m-1)} (\omega_p/\omega_\tau)^{n+m-1}, \tag{19}$$

for $n + m > 1$ and $n > 0$, and

$$M_{0,m} \sim \epsilon_d^{(1-m)/2} \left(\frac{\omega_p^{m-1}\omega_\tau}{\omega^m}\right), \tag{20}$$

for $m > 1$.

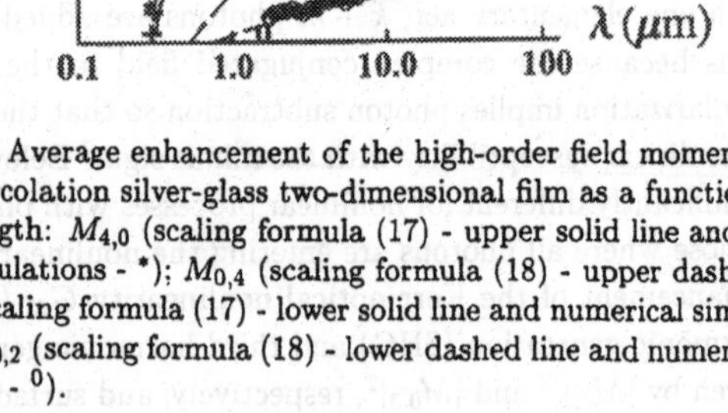

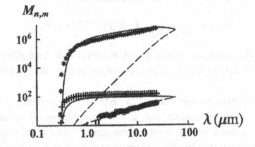

FIG. 4. Average enhancement of the high-order field moments $M_{n,m}$ in a percolation silver-glass two-dimensional film as a function of the wavelength: $M_{4,0}$ (scaling formula (17) - upper solid line and numerical simulations - *); $M_{0,4}$ (scaling formula (18) - upper dashed line); $M_{2,0}$ (scaling formula (17) - lower solid line and numerical simulations - $^+$); $M_{0,2}$ (scaling formula (18) - lower dashed line and numerical simulations - ^{0}).

Note that for all moments the maximum in (19) and (20) is approximately the same (if $\xi_A \sim a$), so that

$$M_{n,m}^{(\max)} \sim \epsilon_d^{(1-n-m)/2} \left(\frac{\omega_p}{\omega_\tau}\right)^{n+m-1} \tag{21}$$

However, in the spectral range $\omega_p \gg \omega \gg \omega_\tau$, moments $M_{0,m}$ gradually increase with the wavelength and the maximum is reached only at $\omega \sim \omega_\tau$, whereas the moments $M_{n,m}$ (with $n > 1$) reach this maximum at much shorter wavelengths (roughly, at $\omega \approx \tilde{\omega}_p/2$) and remain almost constant in the indicated spectral interval. This conclusion is supported by the numerical simulations for silver-glass percolation films shown in Fig. 4; one can see that the above scaling formulas are in good accord with the simulations.

For silver-glass percolation films, with $\omega_p = 9.1$ ev and $\omega_\tau = 0.021$ ev, we find that the average field-enhancement can be as large as $G_{RS} \sim M_{4,0} \sim 10^7$, for Raman scattering (see also Fig. 4), and as $G_{FWM} \sim |M_{2,2}|^2 \sim 10^{14}$, for degenerate four-wave mixing. According to Fig. 3, the local field intensity in the hot spots can approach the magnitude 10^5 so that the enhancement for nonlinear optical responses can be truly gigantic, up to 10^{10}, for Raman scattering, and up to 10^{20}, for four-wave mixing signals. With this level of enhancement, one can perform *nonlinear* spectroscopy of single molecules and nanocrystals. It is important that the enhancement can be obtained in the huge spectral range, from the near-UV to the far-infrared, which is a big virtue for spectroscopic studies of different molecules and nanocrystals. We also note that the field-enhancement provided by semicontinuous metal films can be used for various photo-biological and photo-chemical processes.

---

[1] D. J. Bergman and D. Stroud. In: *Solid State Physics* **46**, 147, Academic Press, Inc., New York (1992).

[2] V. M. Shalaev, *Nonlinear Optics Of Random Media: Fractal Composites and Metal-Dielectric Films* (Springer, Berlin Heidelberg, 2000).

[3] A. K. Sarychev and V. M.Shalaev, *Physics Reports* **335**, 275 (2000).

[4] D. Stauffer and A. Aharony, *Introduction to Percolation Theory*, 2 ed., Taylor and Francis, Philadelphia (1991).

[5] S. Grésillon, L. Aigouy, A.C. Boccara, J.C. Rivoal, X. Quelin, C. Desmarest, P. Gadenne, V. A. Shubin, A. K. Sarychev, and V. M. Shalaev, *Phys. Rev. Lett.* **82**, 4520 (1999).

[6] A. K. Sarychev, V. A. Shubin and V. M. Shalaev, *Phys. Rev. B* **60**, 16389 (1999); A. K. Sarychev and V. M. Shalaev, *Physica A* **266**, 115 (1999); V. M. Shalaev and A. K. Sarychev, *Phys. Rev. B* **57**, 13265 (1998); A. K. Sarychev, V. A. Shubin, and V. M. Shalaev, *Phys. Rev. E* **59**, 7239 (1999).

[7] R. W. Boyd, *Nonlinear Optics*, Academic Press Inc., New York (1992).

QUADRATIC NONLINEAR INTERACTIONS IN 1-DIMENSIONAL PHOTONIC CRYSTALS

JORDI MARTORELL, CRINA COJOCARU, MURIEL BOTEY, J. TRULL AND R. VILASECA

Departament de Física i Enginyeria Nuclear, Universitat Politècnica de Catalunya,
C/ Colom 11, 08222 Terrassa (Barcelona), Spain

1. Introduction

Photonic crystals in 1-dimension constitute a frame that may be used to modify the quadratic nonlinear interaction in much the same way as in the 3-dimensional lattices considered previously in this book. Moreover, the simplicity of a 1-dimensional structure offers several advantages such as for instance to facilitate a controlled introduction of defects, or the study of the nonlinear interaction at resonance. In fact, it was shown that light localization within a defect of a 1- dimensional multilayer periodic structure could lead to a strong enhancement or inhibition of the second order nonlinear interaction.[1] Other 1-dimensional structures have been used to obtain a doubly resonant phase matched second harmonic generation (SHG).[2] In such structures one may easily resolve the effective index of refraction dispersion and rigorously show that the phase matching mechanism is provided by the periodicity build into the material.[3] More recently, such structures have also been used to induce all-optical changes in the transmission or reflection, when the nonlinear interaction is considered in a cascading configuration.

In this paper, we will consider first the generation of second harmonic (SH) in a 1-dimensional geometry where the nonlinear material is localized in a sub-wavelength layer placed at a controllable distance from a reflecting boundary. We will see that the presence of a mirror can strongly influence the generation of second harmonic light leading to full inhibition of the SH radiation. Later we will place a similar sub-wavelength layer within a defect of a 1-dimensional photonic crystal and show that that the control over the SHG can be largely enhanced not only by the light localization but also by the modified phase relationship between the polarization and the generated SH wave is established within a periodic structure. Finally, we shall consider a similar 1-dimensional photonic crystal, where the quadratic nonlinear material is filling, the entire defect space. In that case, we will consider the nonlinear interaction in a cascaded

C.M. Soukoulis (ed.), Photonic Crystals and Light Localization in the 21st Century, 577–587.

configuration [4] and show that when an intense SH beam is simultaneously incident with a weak fundamental beam, the interaction within that truncated periodic structure introduces not only a change in the value of the effective index of refraction, but a change in the slope of this effective index of refraction dispersion curve. We will see that this last change, which can be viewed in the case of pulse propagation as a change in the group velocity, can be particularly significant when the fundamental wavelength falls within the resonant state of the 1-D truncated photonic structure.

2. Second harmonic generation in 1-dimensional structures

2.1. SH GENERATION IN FRONT OF A REFLECTING BOUNDARY

We will begin by considering one of the simplest systems consisting of a thin layer of nonlinear material in front of a reflecting boundary. Even in this simple configuration where only one surface is present, changes in the radiation pattern can lead to an almost complete inhibition if the nonlinear material is localized in a sub-wavelength region of space. Moreover, after being reflected by the mirror, the forward-radiated energy is transferred back to the fundamental wave or viceversa, in a momentum nonconserving interaction.[5] In fact, the energy stored between the nonlinear layer and the mirror is different from zero while the total SH radiated energy outside the structure vanishes.

To properly study the separate contributions to the radiated energy from the nonlinear interactions between all froward an backward propagating waves, we considered in Ref. [5] the geometry shown in Figure 1a, where only the SH light is reflected back by a single mirror placed in front of a thin planar layer of nonlinear material. It was observed that the output SH light form this type of structure was strongly dependent on the mirror position relative to the location of the layer, and could be inhibited even when the SH intensity within the structure is nonvanishing.[5] This result is in accordance with an experimental observation by Kauranen et al.[6] where SH generation was studied in a single mirror configuration almost identical to the one described above. This apparent contradiction could only be explained if one considers the interaction of the fundamental field with both the forward generated and the reflected SH fields, as well as the interaction of the same total SH field with the incident and reflected fundamental. In fact, it was seen that the major contribution to this interaction comes from the nonconserving momentum transfer of energy from the reflected SH field back to the incident fundamental. In bulk generation of SH light, the contribution of such terms would vanish, however, in generation from a sub-wavelength layer momentum is conserved due to the presence of a nearby interface between a linear and a nonlinear material.[5]

We may conclude that in order to fully describe the interaction within a layer of nonlinear material localized in a sub-wavelength region of the space in front of a reflecting boundary it is essential to consider all interactions between the fundamental and the SH fields, including non-conserving momentum terms.

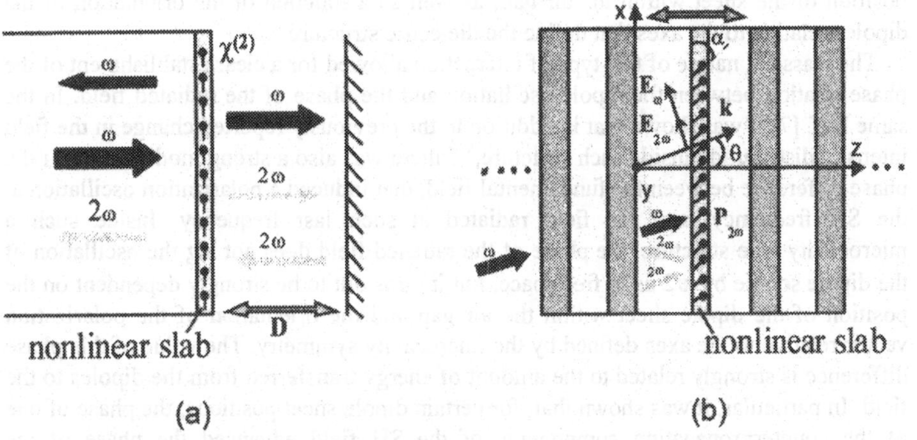

Figure 1. (a) Schematic model of a thin nonlinear material placed at a variable distance of a mirror. The forward generated SH is reflected back onto the film whereas the fundamental is transmitted through it The fields propagation direction is normal to all surfaces and also normal to the dipole orientation.
(b) Schematic diagram of a truncated 1-D periodic structure. The fields at the fundamental and SH frequency propagate in the direction of the wavevector k. The dipole orientation is defined through the angle (α).

2.2. SH GENERATION WITHIN A 1-D PHOTONIC CRYSTAL

A larger control over the second harmonic radiation can be obtained if the nonlinear layer is placed within a structure such a 1-D photonic crystal or the periodic structure with a defect considered in Figure 1b. In that event, the distribution of dielectric material surrounding the nonlinear material introduces a change in the amplitude field intensity distribution as well as a change in the relative phase between the generated SH field and the oscillation of the dipole source. Both such changes must be taken into account when considering the energy transfer from the radiation dipole to the field and viceversa, which is governed by the dot product of the field and current density vectors.

In a recent theoretical work[7] it was studied the amplitude and relative phase behaviour of a field radiated at the SH frequency through a quadratic nonlinear interaction from a thin sheet of coherent dipoles that were placed in between two identical dielectric multilayer mirrors separated by an air gap, defining the 1-D photonic structure shown in Figure 1b. The dipole layer was "forced" to oscillate by an incident beam at the fundamental frequency. This interaction was considered as a function of the position of the sheet within the air gap, as well as a function of the orientation of the dipoles relative to the axes that define the dielectric structure.

The classical nature of this type of interaction allowed for a clear establishment of the phase relation between the dipole oscillation and the phase of the radiated field. In the same Ref. [7] it was shown that in addition to the previously reported change in the field intensity distribution inside such structure,[8, 9] there was also a strong modification of the phase difference between the fundamental field, that induced a polarization oscillation at the SH frequency, and the field radiated at such last frequency. Inside such a microcavity type structure, the phase of the radiated field does not lag the oscillation of the dipole source by $\pi/2$ as in free space, but it turns out to be strongly dependent on the position of the dipole sheet within the air gap and the orientation of the polarization vector relative to the axes defined by the microcavity symmetry. The value of this phase difference is strongly related to the amount of energy transferred from the dipoles to the field. In particular, it was shown that, for certain dipole sheet positions, the phase of one of the counterpropagating components of the SH field advanced the phase of the radiation source, indicating that the energy radiated at the SH frequency was transferred back to the oscillating dipole, resulting in a strong "inhibition" of the radiation from such classical dipole source. This is the same type of "inhibition" observed from SHG of a thin dipole sheet placed in front of a single mirror considered in the section 2.1.

One should note that, in general, the results obtained, were not limited to the understanding of the quadratic nonlinear interaction, and their applicability can be extended to a wider range of cases since the SH radiation of a thin layer of dipoles "forced" by an incident beam at the fundamental frequency, is formally equivalent to the radiation of a sheet of forced classical linear dipoles.

3. Nonlinear dispersive properties of a truncated 1-dimensional photonic crystal

The last configuration that we will consider in larger detail, consists of a 1-D photonic crystal such that the first forbidden band is at resonance with the fundamental instead of the SH wave. As we shall see, the presence of the periodic distribution of dielectric material will change the relative phase relation between the fundamental and SH field leading to a nonlinear change in the transmission or reflection for the fundamental wave.

This type of phase shift induced in a cascaded quadratic nonlinear interaction has been considered in many different configurations to obtain a change in the effective index of refraction of a wave propagating through a quadratic nonlinear material.[10] Such type of change provides the possibility of a phase modulation that leads to an all-optical switching mechanism faster and more efficient than most of the mechanisms based on a third order intensity dependent modulation. To date, this cascaded nonlinear interaction has been studied mostly in configurations where the induced phase shifts result in a change of the value of the effective index of refraction. Unfortunately, if one considers a seeded SH configuration to enhance the nonlinear interaction, this interaction becomes input phase dependent, imposing a limitation on its applicability in any kind of all-optical switching or transistor device.

Here, we will show that when the cascaded quadratic nonlinear interaction is considered in a 1-dimensional photonic crystal, such as the one shown in Figure 2, it may induce a change not only in the value of the effective index of refraction of the fundamental wave, but also in the slope of its effective index of refraction dispersion curve or, in other words, the group velocity of this fundamental wave. We will also show that this last change can be particularly significant when a defect breaking the perfect periodicity of the lattice is introduced in such a 1-dimensional photonic crystal.

The combined effects of a phase and group velocity change may lead to a cascaded nonlinear interaction that can be almost input phase independent. In fact, in a recent work that considered the cascaded nonlinear interaction within a microcavity filled with a quadratic nonlinear material, it was found that large changes in the reflection or transmission of a fundamental field resonant with the cavity could be induced by a strong beam incident simultaneously at the second harmonic frequency.[11] These changes could be made almost input phase independent either when the linear reflectivity of the mirrors or the input intensity of the SH beam was increased.

In the present work, we consider a finite 1-D photonic crystal made by alternatively stacking quarter wavelength thick layers of two materials with different index of refraction.

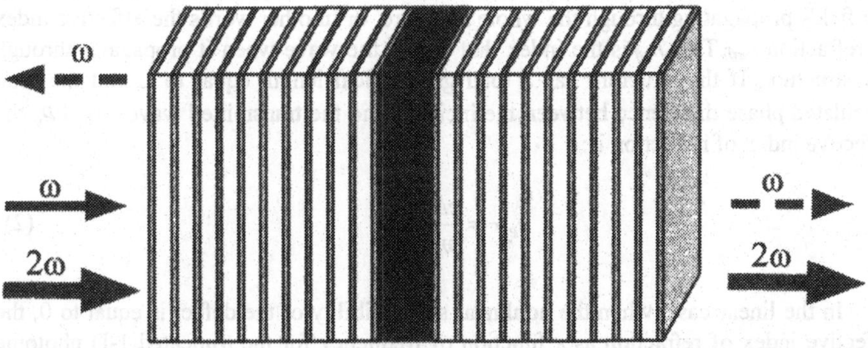

Figure 2. 1-dimensional truncated photonic crystal, resonant for the fundamental frequency.

As shown in Figure 2, a defect filled with a quadratic nonlinear material is introduced in the middle of the structure. The periodicity of the layers as well as the thickness of the defect is adjusted to have a resonance at the frequency of the fundamental field ω_0.

The propagation of the fundamental and SH waves through the nonlinear material of the truncated structure described above, can be studied starting with the coupled complex amplitude nonlinear wave equations for both fields. Assuming that both fundamental and SH are plane waves propagating in the z direction, normal incident to the structure and that the absorption of the material is neglected, the coupled equations can be written as:

$$-\frac{\partial^2}{\partial z^2}E_1(z)-n_1^2\frac{\omega_0^2}{c^2}E_1(z)=\frac{\omega_0^2}{c^2}\chi^{(2)}E_2(z)E_1^*(z) \tag{1a}$$

$$-\frac{\partial^2}{\partial z^2}E_2(z)-n_2^2\frac{4\omega_0^2}{c^2}E_2(z)=\frac{2\omega_0^2}{c^2}\chi^{(2)}E_1^2(z) \tag{1b}$$

where $E_1(z)$ and $E_2(z)$ are the complex amplitudes of the fundamental and SH wave respectively, n_1 and n_2 are the refractive indexes of the nonlinear material at the fundamental and SH frequencies, respectively, and $\chi^{(2)}$ is the second order nonlinear susceptibility. Note that we do not use the SVEA approximation and also take into account the energy transfer between the fundamental and the SH waves both in the forward and backward directions. Equations 1a and 1b are numerically integrated in steps much shorter than a wavelength, using the method of variation of constants described in detail in Refs [11] and [12]. This solution can be numerically propagated through the periodic structure using the transfer matrix method and setting the usual boundary conditions at either end of the structure that consider the fields incident from the right to be zero and the fields incident from the left having fixed amplitudes and phases. The values obtained for the amplitude and phase of both electric fields at any point within the structure can be used to determine the total phase shift accumulated by the fields propagating through the whole structure, or in other words the effective index of refraction n_{eff}. This n_{eff} is the index that "sees" the wave when it propagates through the structure. If the structure has a total geometrical length equal to L and the total calculated phase difference between the incident and the transmitted waves is $\Delta\Phi$, the effective index of refraction is:

$$n_{eff}=\frac{c\Delta\Phi}{\omega_0 L}. \tag{2}$$

In the linear case, when the nonlinear susceptibility of the defect is equal to 0, the effective index of refraction as a function of frequency for the truncated 1-D photonic crystal considered here is shown in Figure 3. For the numerical calculation we have considered a structure consisting of 20 periods of alternating layers, with high (n_h) and low (n_l) index of refraction. The thickness of the each period is equal to a quarter of fundamental wavelength, which is λ_F=1064 nm. At this wavelength the refractive indexes of the layers are n_h=1.93, n_l=1.44, and they follow a typical dispersion for these dielectric materials. The defect filled with the nonlinear material of index of refraction equal to 1.44 at the fundamental wavelength, was assumed to be 2,2 μm. The n_{eff} as a function of frequency corresponding to this truncated structure is shown as continuous lines in Figure 3. When the defect is removed and the structure becomes perfectly periodic, the corresponding n_{eff} curves are shown as dotted lines.

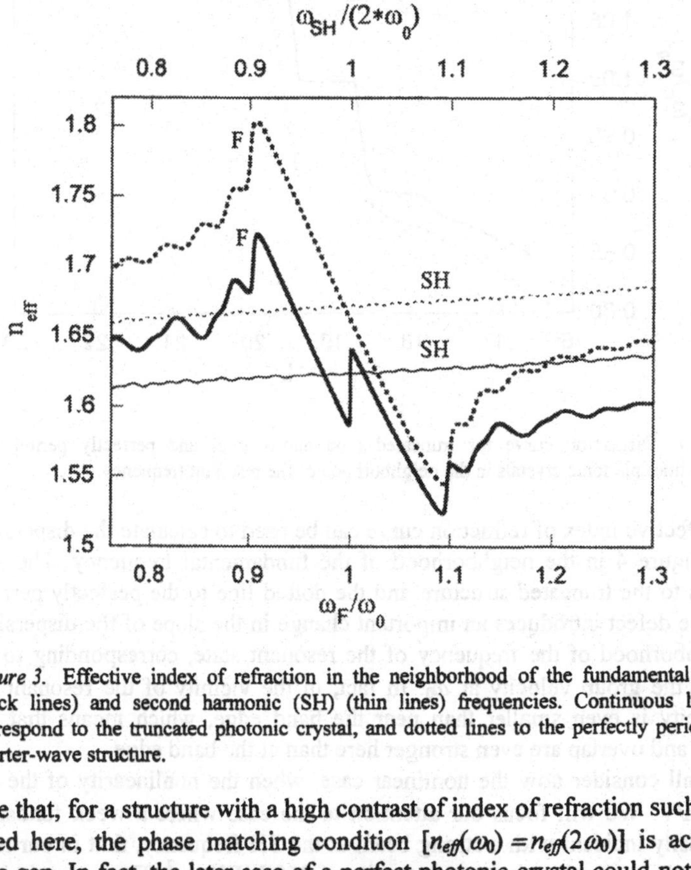

Figure 3. Effective index of refraction in the neighborhood of the fundamental (F) (thick lines) and second harmonic (SH) (thin lines) frequencies. Continuous lines correspond to the truncated photonic crystal, and dotted lines to the perfectly periodic quarter-wave structure.

Note that, for a structure with a high contrast of index of refraction such as the ones considered here, the phase matching condition $[n_{eff}(\omega_0) = n_{eff}(2\omega_0)]$ is achieved only inside the gap. In fact, the later case of a perfect photonic crystal could not be used for nonlinear interactions, since the fundamental beam would be strongly reflected out of the structure. However, when the defect is introduced as in the former case, the light at the frequency of the defect can propagates through the structure and then phase matching between the two waves is possible.

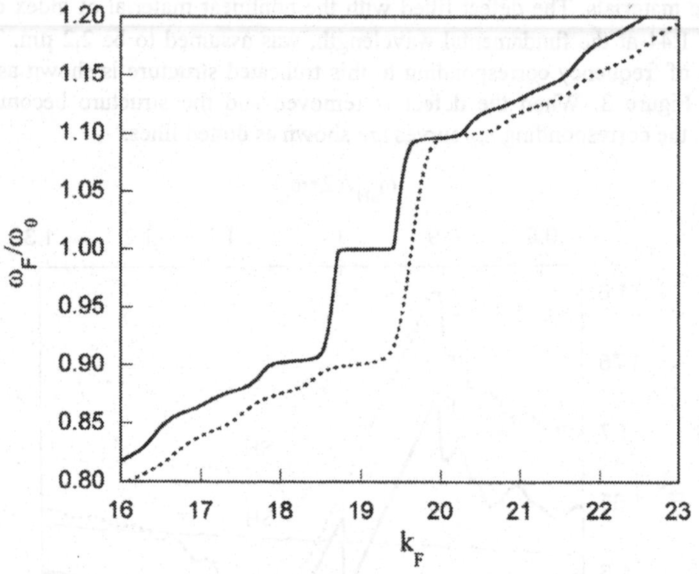

Figure 4. Dispersion curve for truncated (continuous line) and perfectly periodic (dotted line) photonic crystals in the neighborhood of the resonant frequency.

The effective index of refraction curve can be used to calculate the dispersion curve shown in Figure 4 in the neighborhood of the fundamental frequency. The solid line corresponds to the truncated structure and the dotted line to the perfectly periodic one. Note that the defect introduces an important change in the slope of the dispersion curve in the neighborhood of the frequency of the resonant state, corresponding to a strong decrease of the group velocity at ω_0. In fact, in the vicinity of the resonant state the group velocity is even smaller than near the band edge, which means that the field localization and overlap are even stronger here than at the band edge.

We shall consider now the nonlinear case, when the nonlinearity of the defect is $\chi^{(2)}$=100 pm/V. We will focus our attention to the case where a week fundamental is simultaneouslly incident with a strong beam at the SH frequency, that in our numerical calculations we assumed to have an intensity of 250 MW/ cm^2. The transmission of the fundamental through the entire structure in the vicinity of the resonant state is shown in Figure 5 as a function of frequency, for different values of the input phase difference between the fundamental and SH waves ($\Delta\phi = 2\phi(\omega_0) - \phi(2\omega_0)$, where $\phi(\omega_0)$ and $\phi(2\omega_0)$ are the phases of the fundamental and SH waves, respectively, at the end of the defect).

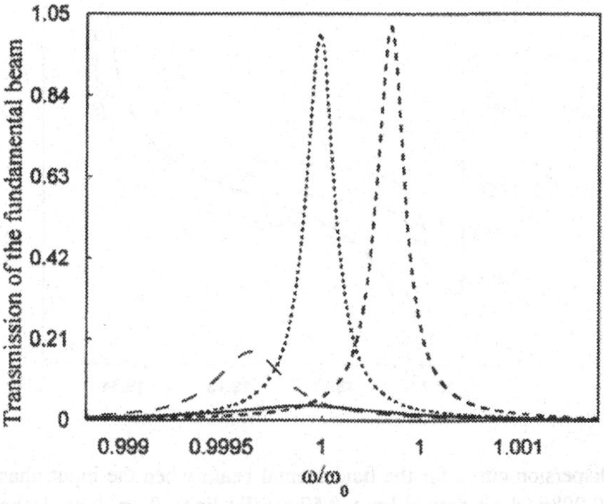

Figure 5. **Transmission of the fundamental beam as a function of frequency when the input phase difference $\Delta\Phi$ is equal to: 0.008π (short-dashed line), 0.57π (solid line), 0.9π (long-dashed line). The dotted line corresponds to the linear transmission. The quadratic nonlinear susceptibility $\chi^{(2)}$ is equal to 0 pm/V for the linear case and to 100 pm/V for all other cases and the SH intensity is 250 MW/cm^2.**

When the SH field is turned off the transmission spectra shown in Figure 5 corresponds to the resonant transmission peak of a 1-D photonic crystal with a defect. When SH field is turned on for certain values of the input phase difference this resonance is shifted to either side of the linear resonance peak. Such a shift corresponds to a change in the value of the effective index of refraction as expected from the cascaded quadratic nonlinear interaction taking place within the structure. However, in addition to this shift, we observe that, for certain values of the input phase difference, the resonance peak is barely shifted but is height is strongly reduced. Such a decrease in the amplitude of the resonance can not be explained by a mere change in the value of n_{eff}, and it requires that the cascaded nonlinear interactions within a periodic structure lead to a change on the slope of this n_{eff}, as well. Such a change in the slope of the n_{eff} is confirmed by the changes in the photon dispersion curve shown in Figure 6. In this figure, the photon dispersion curves are shown for the same values of the input phase difference as in Figure 5. In the case that the cascaded interaction leads to a change in the value of n_{eff}, the entire photon dispersion curve is shifted up and down, depending on the sign of the change, while the slope remains the same. However, when the amplitude of the resonance is largely reduced, the slope of the photon dispersion curve is largely increased.

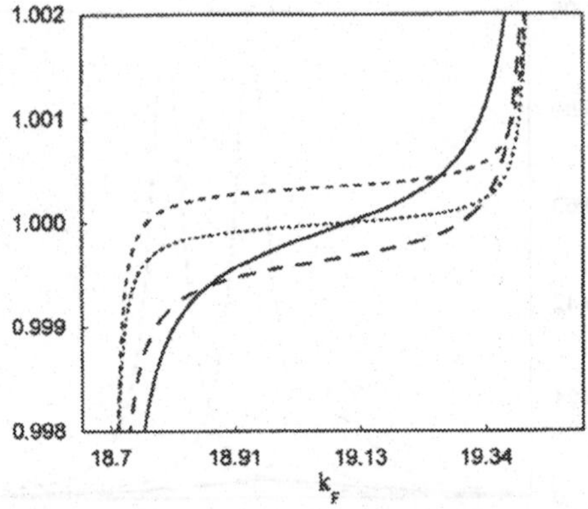

Figure 6. Dispersion curve for the fundamental beam when the input phase difference is equal to: 0.008π (short-dashed line), 0.57π (solid line), 0.9π (long-dashed line). The dotted line corresponds to the linear case. The nonlinear susceptibility $\chi^{(2)}$ and the SH intensity has the same values as in Figure 4.

4. Conclusions

We may conclude that the quadratic nonlinear interaction between a fundamental and a SH beam within a truncated 1-dimensional photonic crystal, resonant for the fundamental frequency, results in changes of both phase and group velocity for the fundamental beam. The combination of these two effects may lead to actively induced changes in the reflection and transmission of the fundamental beam, which can be almost input phase-independent. This is an important result that can be applied in the design of very fast all-optical devices (i.e. optical time division demultiplexors) with an overall length of less than 10 μm and insensitive to changing environmental conditions.

5. References

1. Trull, J., Vilaseca, R., Martorell, J. and Corbalán, R. "Second-harmonic generation in local modes of a truncated periodic structure", *Optics Lett.* **20**, 1746-1748, (1995).
2. Scalora, M., Bloemer, J.M., Manka, A.S., Dowling, J.P., Bowden, C.M., Viswanathan, R. and Haus, J.M. "Pulsed second harmonic generation in nonlinear, one-dimensional periodic structure", *Phys. Rev. A*, **56**, 3166 (1997).

3. Centini, M., Sibilia, C., Scalora, M., D'Aguanno, G., Bertolotti, M., Bloemer, M.J., Bowden, C.M. and Nefedov, I. "Dispersive properties of finite, one-dimensional photonic band gap structures: applications to nonlinear quadratic interactions", *Phys. Rew. E* **60**, 4891-4898 (1999).
4. DeSalvo, R., Hagan, D.J., Sheik-Bahae, M., Stegeman, G., Van Stryland, E.W. and Vanherzeele, H. "Self-focusing and self-defocusing by cascaded second-order effects in KTP", *Optics Lett.* **17**, 28-30 (1992).
5. Botey, M., Martorell, J., Trull, J. and Vilaseca, R. "Suppression of radiation in a momentum-nonconserving nonlinear interaction", *Optics Lett* **25**, 1177-1179 (2000).
6. Kauranen, M., Van Rompaey, Y., Maki, J.J. and Persoons, A. "Nonvanishing field between a dipole oscillator and a reflecting boundary during suppression of dipole radiation", *Phys. Rev. Lett.* **20**, 952-955 (1998).
7. Trull, J., Vilaseca, R. and Martorell, J. "Quadratic nonlinear radiation within a 1-dimensional photonic crystal", *J. Opt. B* **1**, 307-314 (1999).
8. Dowling, J.P. and Bowden, C.M. "Atomic emission rates in inhomogeneous media with applications to photonic band structures", *Phys. Rev. A* **46**, 612 (1992).
9. Lidzey, D.G., Bradley, D.D.C., Pate, M.A., David, J.P., Ficher, T.A. and Skolnik, M.S. *Appl. Phys. Lett.* **71**, 774 (1997).
10. Stegeman, G.I., Hagan, D.J. and Torner, L. "$\chi^{(2)}$ cascading phenomena and their applications to all-optical signal processing, mode-locking, pulse compression and solitons", *Optical and Quantum Electronics* **28**, 1691-1741 (1996).
11. Cojocaru, C., Martorell, J., Vilaseca, R., Trull, J. and Fazio, E. "Active reflection via a phase-insensitive quadratic nonlinear interaction within a microcavity", *Appl. Phys. Lett.* **74**, 504-506 (1999).
12. Martorell, J., Vilaseca, R. and Corbalan, R. "Pseudo-metal reflection at the interface between a linear and a nonlinear material", *Opt. Comm.* **144**, 65-69 (1997).

QUADRATIC NONLINEAR INTERACTIONS IN 3-DIMENSIONAL PHOTONIC CRYSTALS

JORDI MARTORELL

Departament de Física i Enginyeria Nuclear, Universitat Politècnica de Catalunya,
C/Colom, 11, 08222 Terrassa (Barcelona), Spain

1. Introduction

The periodic distribution of dielectric material in a photonic crystal offers an ideal frame to consider the interaction between radiation and matter. Within the lattice of the crystal this interaction can be modified in several ways, depending on the level of reflection and transmission of light at frequencies that fall within or near the corresponding Bragg stop bands.[1] In certain conditions, the strength of the interaction may be highly enhanced, an effect that can be particularly interesting when the interaction considered is nonlinear.[2,3,4] Moreover, the large amount of interfaces that are found in photonic lattices offer the possibility of a local symmetry breaking, a property that can be shown to be very useful when the nonlinear interaction considered is the second order in the dipole approximation.[5]

In this work we will present an experimental and theoretical study of the quadratic nonlinear interaction in a 3-dimensional photonic crystal and consider the specific case of second harmonic generation (SHG). In a first part of our theoretical study, we will consider linear light propagation through a set of crystalline planes that are made of spherical particles ordered in an hexagonal configuration. This study will be used to analyze the result of the first set of experiments we performed, where we considered the linear collective scattering of a set of planes from a face centered cubic (fcc) lattice made of polystyrene microspheres surrounded with water. We will show that the experimentally measured Bragg stop bands can be accurately reproduced using the lattice parameters of the actual crystals in our numerical calculations.

In a second set of experiments, we coated the spherical polystyrene particles with several nonlinear dye molecules and measured the generation of second harmonic light in reflection. To explain the results, we extended the theoretical model to include a nonlinear polarization source. In that study we assumed the nonlinear material localized at the surface of each spherical particle and solved the wave equation fully considering the 3-

C.M. Soukoulis (ed.), Photonic Crystals and Light Localization in the 21st Century, 589–599.

dimensional character of the distribution of dielectric material. Introducing again the parameters of the actual lattice into the theoretical model, we find a very good agreement with the predictions of the numerical calculations and the experimental measurements of SHG.

2. Linear reflection and transmission from a 3-D photonic crystal

A kind of photonic crystals can be made from dielectric spherical particles distributed in a 3-dimensional lattice. The collective light scattering from one set of planes of such a structure can be studied by the electric field wave equation derived from Maxwell's equations. Under the assumption of harmonic solutions, the electric field amplitude wave equation at frequency 2ω becomes

$$\nabla(\nabla\cdot\mathbf{E})-\nabla^2\mathbf{E}=\frac{(2\omega)^2}{\varepsilon_o c^2}\varepsilon(\mathbf{r})\mathbf{E}\,, \tag{1}$$

where the dielectric tensor $\varepsilon(\mathbf{r})$ has the periodicity of the lattice. Contribution to collective scattering by a given set of planes, that without loss of generality are taken to be perpendicular to the z-direction, can be accounted for by considering spheres periodically distributed on each plane, as shown in Figure 1.

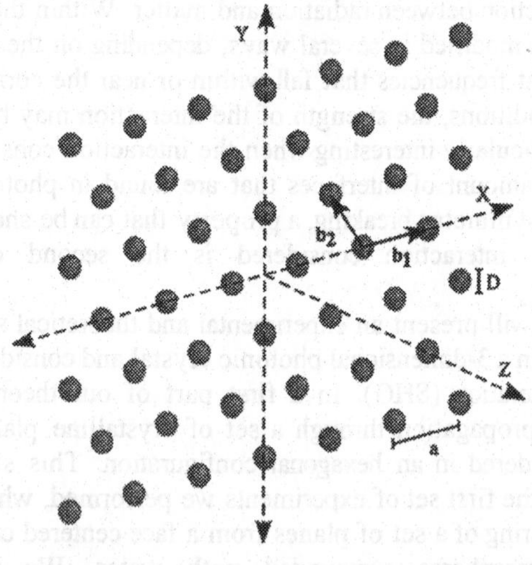

Figure 1 Spheres distributed on a plane triangular lattice corresponding to one of the (111) planes of an fcc lattice. The separation between spheres on that plane is *a* and the diameter of the spheres is *D*.

Then, we can expand the dielectric tensor into a Fourier series

$$\varepsilon(\mathbf{r}) = \sum_{\mathbf{G}} \varepsilon_{\mathbf{G}}(z) e^{i\mathbf{G}\cdot\rho}, \tag{2}$$

where ρ is a position vector contained on the xy plane of spheres and **G** runs over all reciprocal-lattice vectors lying on that same xy plane, including **G** = 0.

By expressing the electric field vector as a Fourier integral

$$\mathbf{E}(\mathbf{r}) = \int d^3k \mathbf{E}(\mathbf{k}) e^{i\mathbf{k}\mathbf{r}}, \tag{3}$$

and after substitution of Eqs. (2) and (3) in Eq. (1), we obtain for the transverse part of the electric field wave vector $E_\perp$ that

$$\int [\frac{d^2}{dz^2} E_\perp(\mathbf{k}) + (\frac{(2\omega)^2}{c^2} - \mathbf{k}_\rho^2) E_\perp(\mathbf{k}) + \frac{(2\omega)^2}{\varepsilon_o c^2} \sum_{\mathbf{G}} \varepsilon_o \varepsilon_{\mathbf{G}} E_\perp(\mathbf{k}-\mathbf{G})] e^{i\mathbf{k}_\rho \rho} e^{ik_z z} d\mathbf{k}_\rho dk_z = 0, \tag{4}$$

where $\mathbf{k}_\rho$ is a wavevector on the xy plane and k_z is the z component of the same wavevector. Equation (6) can be satisfied only when all coefficients of $e^{i\mathbf{k}_\rho \rho}$ vanish. Thus, after integration over dk_z,

$$\frac{d^2}{dz^2} E_\perp(z,\mathbf{k}_\rho) + [\frac{(2\omega)^2}{c^2} - \mathbf{k}_\rho^2] E_\perp(z,\mathbf{k}_\rho) = -\frac{(2\omega)^2}{\varepsilon_o c^2} \sum_{\mathbf{G}} \varepsilon_o \varepsilon_{\mathbf{G}} E_\perp(z,\mathbf{k}_\rho - \mathbf{G}). \tag{5}$$

If we consider propagation on the xz plane, we can determine the reflected field from a single plane of spheres by using a one dimensional Green´s function integration for the variable z (5)

$$E_\perp(z,k_x) = \int_{-\infty}^{\infty} G(z,z') R(z') dz', \tag{6}$$

where R(z') is the inhomogenous part of Eq. (5), and when z < z'

$$G(z,z') = -\frac{i}{2k_z} e^{-ik_z(z-z')}. \tag{7}$$

Integration of Eq. (6) may be performed under the Debye approximation, taking the electric field amplitude within the integral as

$$E_\perp(z,k_x\hat{\mathbf{x}} - \mathbf{G}) = E_{\perp in}(k_x\hat{\mathbf{x}} - \mathbf{G}) e^{ik_z z}. \tag{8}$$

Under this approximation, the amplitude for the reflected field parallel to the plane of incidence is

$$E_{\perp}(z,k_x) = e^{-ik_z z}\frac{8\pi}{3\sqrt{3}}\frac{(2\omega)^2}{c^2}\frac{(D/2)^3}{k_z a^2}(\varepsilon_r - 1)\sum_{\mathbf{G}} F_1(|\mathbf{g}|D/2)E_{\perp in}(k_x\hat{\mathbf{x}} - \mathbf{G}), \tag{9}$$

where $\mathbf{g} = k_z\,\hat{\mathbf{z}} + \mathbf{G}$, D is the diameter of the sphere, a is the separation between spheres, ε_r is the relative dielectric constant between the sphere and the surrounding medium, and F_1 is the form factor

$$F_1(|\mathbf{g}|D/2) = \frac{3}{(|\mathbf{g}|D/2)^3}[\sin(|\mathbf{g}|D/2) - (|\mathbf{g}|D/2)\cos(|\mathbf{g}|D/2)] \tag{10}$$

resulting from the integration of over z' of each coefficient ε_G of the dielectric tensor Fourier series expansion,

$$\frac{1}{A_c}\sum_j e^{i\mathbf{G}\rho_j}\int_{A_c}\int_{-\infty}^{\infty} dA dz' (\varepsilon_r(\mathbf{R}) - 1)e^{i\mathbf{G}\cdot\mathbf{R}}e^{i2k_z z'} \tag{11}$$

where A_c is the area of a unit cell, ρ_j is the position vector for each sphere within that unit cell, and $\mathbf{R} = \rho - \rho_j$. Once the transmitted field is determined by energy conservation from the reflected field, we can apply the transfer matrix method to numerically determine the collective reflection of the entire set of planes.

This kind of 3-dimensional photonic crystals can be fabricated from suspensions of colloidal spherical particles that at high concentrations self organize in a face centered cubic (fcc) lattice. The dimensions and separation between spheres can be chosen in such a way that light at a frequency 2ω in the visible portion of the spectrum is Bragg reflected by the set of planes with miller indexes of (111). The experimentally measured transmission at a fixed wavelength of 532 nm and as a function of the angle of incidence is shown in Figure 2. In that same figure we show the numerically calculated transmission using the actual parameters of the experimental crystalline lattice. Considering that the magnitude of the form factor F_1 decreases very rapidly as the magnitude of the reciprocal vector **G** increases; we may take under a first approximation, the sole contribution of the shortest reciprocal lattice vector. Under such approximation, we find a very good agreement between the experimental data points at or near the Bragg stop band and the numerical calculation, when no adjustable parameters are used. At larger angles, away from the stop band, the contribution from terms with a larger magnitude reciprocal lattice vector becomes more important, and it should be included to obtain a better match with the experimental data points.

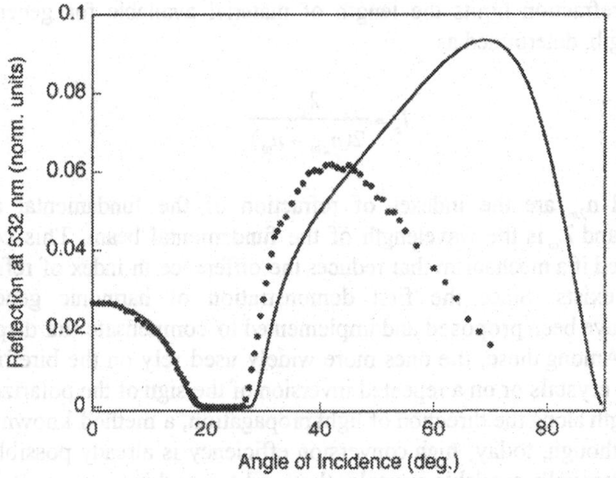

Figure 2 Transmission of light at 532 nm through a photonic crystal made of 115 μm (CV% = 4.7) in diameter polystyrene spheres (dots) and numerically determined reflection (solid line) when the parameters of the actual crystal are used. The effective absorption due to scattering losses was measured at normal incidence to be 10.6 cm^{-1}.

3. Second harmonic generation

We may establish the birth of nonlinear optics 39 years ago, when the use of a moderately high light intensity, made available at that time by the newly developed Ruby laser, lead to the experimental demonstration of light generation at the second harmonic frequency of the laser wave in a noncentrosymmetric crystal made of quartz.[7] This effect would not have been seen in materials with a center of inversion, since the second order nonlinear interaction in the dipole approximation vanishes, as can be seen after an inversion of **r** to -**r**:

$$\chi_{ijk}^{(2)} : E_j E_k = -\chi_{ijk}^{(2)} : (-E_j)(-E_k) \tag{12}$$

leading to

$$\chi_{ijk}^{(2)} = -\chi_{ijk}^{(2)} = 0 \tag{13}$$

This necessary noncentrosymmetry must be combined with a mechanism of long range of phase matching, capable of maintaining the appropriate phase difference for continuous generation of a light wave at the SH frequency from an input light wave at the fundamental frequency.[8] In principle, in any kind of material, the normal dispersion of the index of refraction limits the length of material available for generation to half a coherence length, determined as

$$l_c = \frac{\lambda_\omega}{2(n_{2\omega} - n_\omega)} \quad , \tag{14}$$

where n_ω and $n_{2\omega}$ are the indexes of refraction of the fundamental and SH waves respectively, and λ_ω is the wavelength of the fundamental beam. This coherence length can be increased if a mechanism that reduces the difference in index of refraction between both waves exists. Since the first demonstration of harmonic generation, several mechanisms have been proposed and implemented to compensate the dispersion in index of refraction. Among these, the ones more widely used rely on the birefringent character of anisotropic crystals or on a repeated inversion of the sign of the polarization after each coherence length along the direction of light propagation, a method known as quasi-phase matching.[9] Although, today, high conversion efficiency is already possible using several types of commercially available crystals, the need to combine a noncentrosymmetry and phase matching with a strong nonlinear coefficient in a single crystal reduces the versatility in the applications of SHG, as well as, increases the cost of fabrication of such materials. As we shall see below, photonic crystals might provide a solution for such requirements in an independent manner. On the one hand, the interface separating the dielectric particles from the surrounding material provides a local breaking of the noncentrosymmetry, which allows for the existence of a nonvanishing second order interaction throughout the bulk of the entire crystal. This quadratic nonlinear interaction at the interface can be enhanced by the adsorption of a highly nonlinear molecule. In addition, the periodical distribution of dielectric material leads to a bending of the photon dispersion curve near the Bragg stop band, resulting in a change of the effective index of refraction that can be used as a mechanism of phase matching.

4. Second harmonic generation within a 3-D photonic crystal

Any quadratic nonlinear process in the photonic crystal considered above can take advantage of the particular distribution of dielectric material, described in the previous section. On the one hand, the SHG requirement of a noncentrosymmetry throughout the bulk of the nonlinear material can be relaxed and within a 3-dimesnional photonic crystal we may rely on the breaking of symmetry obtained at the interface separating the spherical particles from the surrounding medium. Although as a whole the crystal remains centrosymmetric, the local breaking of the symmetry, combined with the large number of interfaces and the finite dimensions of the spherical particles, is sufficient to lead to a nonvanishing second harmonic interaction in the dipole approximation. On the other hand, as already predicted[2,10] and experimentally observed,[11,12] the bending of the photon dispersion curve near the upper edge of the Bragg stop band can lead, as shown in Figure

3, to a matching of the wavevectors for the fundamental and SH waves and consequently to the necessary phase matching mechanism for efficient generation of SH.

To date, all theoretical models developed to consider the quadratic nonlinear interaction within photonic crystals are limited to a treatment of a 1-dimensional distribution of the dielectric material. Although such models can provide accurate predictions for SHG in multilayer structures[2,13] and explain the main features of quadratic nonlinear processes in 3-dimensional crystals,[14] they lack the predictability required to ultimate a design of a 3-dimensional photonic crystal capable of efficiently generating optical harmonics.

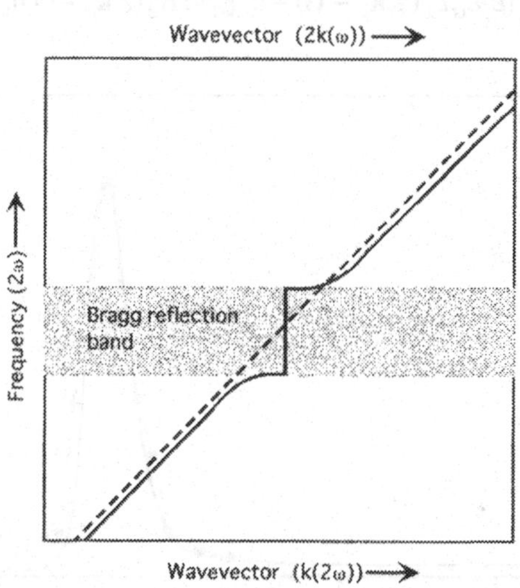

Figure 3 Photon dispersion curve in the neighborhood of the frequency of the second harmonic (solid line) and of the fundamental frequency (dashed line). The last curve has been multiplied by two.

The 3-dimensional model developed in the preceding section can be extended to include the nonlinear interaction by the inclusion in Eq. (3) of the nonlinear polarization source term

$$\mathbf{P}(\mathbf{r}) = \varepsilon_o \chi^{(2)}(\mathbf{r}) : E_\omega^2(\mathbf{r}), \tag{15}$$

where $\chi^{(2)}(\mathbf{r})$ is the periodic second order nonlinear susceptibility, and the E_ω's are the electric field components for a wave at a frequency ω. After a Fourier series expansion of the nonlinear susceptibility in terms of the same reciprocal lattice vectors from the previous section, expressing the product of the fundamental field components as a Fourier integral, and substituting into Equation (15), we get

$$\mathbf{P}(\mathbf{r}) = \varepsilon_o \sum_{\mathbf{G}} \int d\mathbf{k}' \, e^{i\mathbf{k}'\rho} e^{ikz} \chi_{\mathbf{G}}^{(2)} : E_{\omega}^2(\mathbf{k}' - \mathbf{G}) \tag{16}$$

Following the same procedure as in the previous section, the resulting wave equation for the transverse electric field is

$$\frac{d^2}{dz^2} E_{\perp}(z,\mathbf{k}_\rho) + [\frac{(2\omega)^2}{c^2} - \mathbf{k}_\rho^2] E_{\perp}(z,\mathbf{k}_\rho) = - \frac{(2\omega)^2}{\varepsilon_o c^2} \sum_{\mathbf{G}} [\varepsilon_o \varepsilon_{\mathbf{G}} E_{\perp}(z,\mathbf{k}_\rho - \mathbf{G}) + \varepsilon_o \chi_{\mathbf{G}}^{(2)} : E_{\omega}^2(z,\mathbf{k}_\rho - \mathbf{G})]. \tag{17}$$

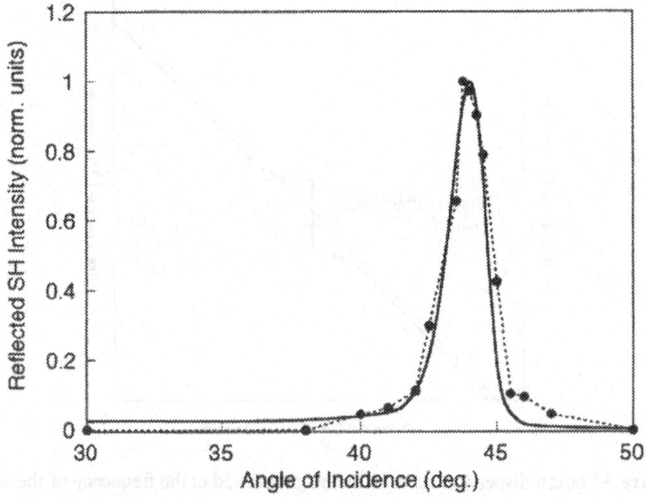

Figure 4 The dots correspond to the reflected SH intensity as a function of the angle of incidence for a photonic crystal made of 115 μm diameter spheres ordered in an fcc lattice. A layer of a triphenylmetahne dye was adsorbed on the surface of the spheres. The solid line corresponds to the reflected SH intensity was numerically determined using the actual parameters of the fabricated photonic crystal.

On the surface of a centrosymmetric material or when a layer of oriented nonlinear molecules are deposited on that surface, the dominant tensor element is $\chi_{r'r'r'}^{(2)}$, where r' is the coordinate in the direction of $\hat{\mathbf{r}}$. Note that contribution from such elements is different from zero because of the finite diameter of the spheres.[5] Then, following the same asymptotic Green's function integration as in the previous section, we can obtain, under the Debye approximation and when only the contribution from the shortest **G** is considered, the amplitude of the electric field polarized on the plane of incidence (xz plane) at the second harmonic frequency

$$E_{\perp}(z,k_x)=\frac{2\pi}{\sqrt{3}}\left(\frac{2\omega}{c}\right)^2\frac{\delta D}{k_z k_s a^2}\chi^{(2)}E_{\omega}^2 \tag{18}$$
$$\left[(-2sin\theta_i\cos\theta_r-2sin\theta_i\cos\theta_r)\cos\theta_i F_1^{SH}(k_s D/2)+2sin^2\theta_i\cos\theta_r F_2^{SH}(k_s D/2)\right]$$

where δ is the thickness of the layer, $k_s = k_z + 2k_{\omega z}$, $k_{\omega z}$ is the z-component of the fundamental wave, θ_i and θ_r are the angle of incidence and reflection, respectively, and the form factors F_1^{SH} and F_2^{SH} given in Ref. (5).

Equation (18) can be used together with the transfer matrix formalism[2] to numerically determine the intensity of the SH light generated from a 3-D structure made of dielectric spherical particles such as the one considered in the previous section. This calculation is show in Figure 4 as a function of the angle of incidence for the fundamental beam when the parameters used are the actual parameters of the photonic crystals fabricated from colloidal suspension of polystyrene microspheres of 115 μm in diameter. The experimental data points for the measured SH intensity, shown also in Figure 5, are in very good agreement with the numerical prediction. The reduced coverage of a surface with a highly nonlinear molecule, such as Malachite Green or Victoria Blue R, limits the conversion to a small fraction of the incident input power.

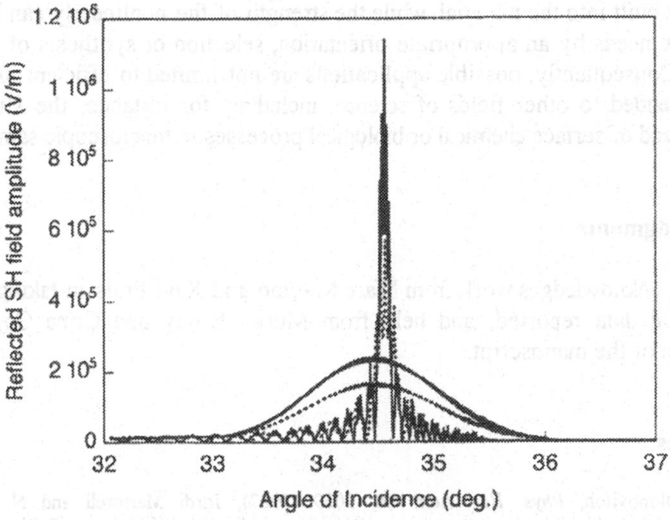

Figure 5 Reflected SHG as a function of the angle of incidence for a photonic crystal 0.5 mm long (dashed lines) and a 1 μm long (solid lines). The thin lines correspond to the case of no dispersion of the sphere diameter, while the thick lines correspond to the case of a coefficient of variation of 2% in the sphere diameter. The input power at 1064 nm was taken to be 100 MW/cm², $\chi^{(2)}$ = 100 pm/V, while the thickness of the nonlinear layer was less than 0.1 times the sphere diameter.

Calculations performed with the same numerical model, but under the assumption of a large coverage of the spherical surface of each dielectric particle, indicates that conversion of a few percent would be possible with crystal lengths shorter than 1 mm. These numerical calculations shown in Figure 5 consider generation of SH from a photonic crystal fabricated from polystyrene spheres of 170 μm in diameter ordered in an fcc lattice of 0.5 mm and 1 mm long. To consider larger conversion efficiencies either by increasing the nonlinearity or the fundamental field input intensity would require a modification of the model to include the fundamental intensity depletion.

For the longest crystal considered in figure 5, the amplitude of the SH reflected field is slightly higher than 10^6 V/m when the fundamental input field amplitude is less than 100 MW/cm^4. Such a conversion efficiency is better than most of the commercially available inorganic crystals.

5. Conclusions

We may conclude that 3-dimensional photonic crystals can be considered as a new frame to obtain not only an enhanced nonlinear interaction, but a frame, where the strength of the nonlinearity as well as the noncentrosymmetry can be considered separate from the mechanism of phase matching. This last mechanism is provided naturally by the periodicity built into the material, while the strength of the nonlinearly can be tailored to the specific needs by an appropriate orientation, selection or synthesis of the nonlinear molecule. Consequently, possible applications are not limited to efficient SHG, but they can be extended to other fields of science, including, for instance, the study of wave scattering and of surface chemical or biological processes in macroscopic samples.

Acknowledgments

The author acknowledges work from Marc Maymó and Xavi Prats in taking some of the experimental data reported, and help from Muriel Botey and Crina Cojocaru in the preparation of the manuscript.

References

1. E. Yablonovitch, *Phys. Rev. Lett.* **58**, 2059 (1987), Jordi Martorell and N. M. Lawandy, "Observation of inhibited spontaneous emission in periodic dielectric structure," *Phys. Rev. Lett.* **65**, 1877 (1990).
2. Jordi Martorell and R. Corbalán, "Enhancement of second harmonic generation in a periodic structure with a defect," *Optics Comm.* **108**, 319 (1994).
3. Michael Scalora, Jonathan P. Dowling, Charles M. Bowden, and Mark J. Bloemer, "Optical limiting and switching of ultrshort pulses in nonlinear photonic band gap materials," *Phys. Rev. Lett.* **73**, 1368 (1994).

4. Rusell J. Gehr, George L. Fischer, Robert W. Boyd, and J. E. Sipe, "Nonlinear response of layered composite materials," Phys. Rev. A **53**, 2796 (1996)
5. Jordi Martorell, R. Vilaseca, and R. Corbalán, "Scattering of second harmonic light from small spherical particles ordered in a crystalline lattice," *Phys. Rev. A.* **55**, 4520 (1997)
6. The boundary conditions for integration in that case assume that the solution is everywhere bounded.
7. P. A. Franken, A. E. Hill, C. W. Peters, and G. Weinreich, "Generation of optical harmonics," *Phys. Rev. Lett.* **7**, 118 (1961).
8. J. A. Armstrong, N. Bloembergen, J. Ducuing, and P. S. Pershan, "Interactions between light waves in a nonlinear dielectric," *Phys. Rev.* **127**, 1918 (1962).
9. Martin M. Fejer, G. A. Magel, Dieter H. Jundt, and Robert L. Bayer, "Quasi-Phase-Matched Second Harmonic Generation: Tuning and Tolerances," *IEEE JQE* **28**, 2631 (1992).
10. N. Bloembergen and A. J: Sievers, "Nonlienar optical properties of periodic laminar structures," *Appl. Phys. Lett.* **17**, 483 (1970), Amnon Yariv and Pochi Yeh, "Electromagnetic propagation in periodic stratified media. II Birefringence, phase matching, and x-ray lasers," *JOSA B* **67**, 438 (1977).
11. J. P. Van der Ziel and M. Ilegems, "Optical second harmonic generation in periodic multilayer GaAs-$Al_{0.3}Ga_{0.7}As$ structures," *Appl. Phys. Lett.* **28**, 437 (1976).
12. Jordi Martorell, R. Vilaseca, and R. Corbalán, "Second harmonic generation in a photonic crystal," *Appl. Phys. Lett.* **70**, 702 (1997), Jordi Martorell, R. Vilaseca, J. Trull, and R. Corbalán, "Second harmonic generation in a photonic crystal, " *Optics and photonics news* **8**, 34 (1997).
13. M. Scalora, M. J. Bloemer, A. S. Manka, J. P. Dowling, C. M. Bowden, R. Viswanathan, and J. W. Haus, "Pulsed second harmonic generation in nonlinear, one-dimensional, periodic structures," *Phys. Rev. A* **56**, 3166 (1997).
14. J. Trull, Jordi Martorell, and R. Vilaseca, "Angular dependence of phase matched second harmonic generation in a photonic crystal," *JOSA B* **15**, 2581 (1998).

AUTHOR INDEX

SUBJECT INDEX

9 780792 369486